Intermediate Algebra

Elayn Martin-Gay

Intermediate Algebra

Third Custom Edition for Palm Beach State College
MAT1033C
Based on Beginning & Intermediate Algebra

Taken from:
Beginning & Intermediate Algebra, Sixth Edition
by Elayn Martin-Gay

Cover Art: courtesy of Zeljko Radojko. Shutterstock.

Taken from:

Beginning & Intermediate Algebra, Sixth Edition
by Elayn Martin-Gay
Copyright © 2017, 2013, 2009 by Pearson Education, Inc.
New York, New York 10013

This special edition published in cooperation with Pearson Education, Inc.

Pearson Education, Inc., 330 Hudson Street, New York, New York 10013
A Pearson Education Company
www.pearsoned.com

Printed in the United States of America

1   17

000200010272128748

HG

MN 11.14.2018 1055

ISBN 10: 1-323-80135-9
ISBN 13: 978-1-323-80135-2

This book is dedicated to my sister—Karen Martin Callac Pasch

There's not enough space on this page to write how wonderful she was while walking this earth.

She is in a better place now; and for that, I celebrate.

Contents

Preface   xiii
Applications Index   xxiii

CHAPTER

GRAPHING   171

3.1   Reading Graphs and the Rectangular Coordinate System   172
3.2   Graphing Linear Equations   187
3.3   Intercepts   197
3.4   Slope and Rate of Change   205
     Integrated Review—Summary on Slope and Graphing Linear Equations   219
3.5   Equations of Lines   220
3.6   Functions   229
     Chapter 3 Vocabulary Check   241
     Chapter 3 Highlights   241
     Chapter 3 Review   245
     Chapter 3 Getting Ready for the Test   248
     Chapter 3 Test   249
     Chapter 3 Cumulative Review   251

CHAPTER

SOLVING SYSTEMS OF LINEAR EQUATIONS   252

4.1   Solving Systems of Linear Equations by Graphing   253
4.2   Solving Systems of Linear Equations by Substitution   261
4.3   Solving Systems of Linear Equations by Addition   268
     Integrated Review—Solving Systems of Equations   275
4.4   Solving Systems of Linear Equations in Three Variables   276
4.5   Systems of Linear Equations and Problem Solving   283
     Chapter 4 Vocabulary Check   301
     Chapter 4 Highlights   301
     Chapter 4 Review   304
     Chapter 4 Getting Ready for the Test   306
     Chapter 4 Test   307
     Chapter 4 Cumulative Review   308

CHAPTER

EXPONENTS AND POLYNOMIALS   310

5.1   Exponents   311
5.2   Polynomial Functions and Adding and Subtracting Polynomials   322
5.3   Multiplying Polynomials   334
5.4   Special Products   341
     Integrated Review—Exponents and Operations on Polynomials   348
5.5   Negative Exponents and Scientific Notation   348
5.6   Dividing Polynomials   357
5.7   Synthetic Division and the Remainder Theorem   364
     Chapter 5 Vocabulary Check   368
     Chapter 5 Highlights   369
     Chapter 5 Review   371
     Chapter 5 Getting Ready for the Test   374
     Chapter 5 Test   375
     Chapter 5 Cumulative Review   376

CHAPTER

6

FACTORING POLYNOMIALS   378

6.1   The Greatest Common Factor and Factoring by Grouping   379
6.2   Factoring Trinomials of the Form $x^2 + bx + c$ 387
6.3   Factoring Trinomials of the Form $ax^2 + bx + c$ and Perfect Square Trinomials   394
6.4   Factoring Trinomials of the Form $ax^2 + bx + c$ by Grouping   402
6.5   Factoring Binomials   407
       Integrated Review—Choosing a Factoring Strategy   414
6.6   Solving Quadratic Equations by Factoring   417
6.7   Quadratic Equations and Problem Solving   426
       Chapter 6 Vocabulary Check   435
       Chapter 6 Highlights   436
       Chapter 6 Review   439
       Chapter 6 Getting Ready for the Test   441
       Chapter 6 Test   442
       Chapter 6 Cumulative Review   442

CHAPTER

7

RATIONAL EXPRESSIONS   444

7.1   Rational Functions and Simplifying Rational Expressions   445
7.2   Multiplying and Dividing Rational Expressions   455
7.3   Adding and Subtracting Rational Expressions with Common Denominators
       and Least Common Denominator   464
7.4   Adding and Subtracting Rational Expressions with Unlike Denominators   472
7.5   Solving Equations Containing Rational Expressions   478
       Integrated Review—Summary on Rational Expressions   485
7.6   Proportion and Problem Solving with Rational Equations   486
7.7   Simplifying Complex Fractions   499
       Chapter 7 Vocabulary Check   506
       Chapter 7 Highlights   506
       Chapter 7 Review   510
       Chapter 7 Getting Ready for the Test   512
       Chapter 7 Test   513
       Chapter 7 Cumulative Review   514

CHAPTER

9

INEQUALITIES AND ABSOLUTE VALUE   559

9.1   Compound Inequalities   560
9.2   Absolute Value Equations   567
9.3   Absolute Value Inequalities   572
       Integrated Review—Solving Compound Inequalities and Absolute Value
       Equations and Inequalities   578
9.4   Graphing Linear Inequalities in Two Variables and Systems
       of Linear Inequalities   578
       Chapter 9 Vocabulary Check   587
       Chapter 9 Highlights   588
       Chapter 9 Review   590
       Chapter 9 Getting Ready for the Test   591
       Chapter 9 Test   592
       Chapter 9 Cumulative Review   592

CHAPTER

10

RATIONAL EXPONENTS, RADICALS, AND COMPLEX NUMBERS 595

10.1   Radicals and Radical Functions 596
10.2   Rational Exponents 605
10.3   Simplifying Radical Expressions 612
10.4   Adding, Subtracting, and Multiplying Radical Expressions 620
10.5   Rationalizing Denominators and Numerators of Radical Expressions 626
          Integrated Review—Radicals and Rational Exponents 632
10.6   Radical Equations and Problem Solving 633
10.7   Complex Numbers 643
          Chapter 10 Vocabulary Check 650
          Chapter 10 Highlights 650
          Chapter 10 Review 654
          Chapter 10 Getting Ready for the Test 656
          Chapter 10 Test 657
          Chapter 10 Cumulative Review 658

CHAPTER

11

QUADRATIC EQUATIONS AND FUNCTIONS 660

11.1   Solving Quadratic Equations by Completing the Square 661
11.2   Solving Quadratic Equations by the Quadratic Formula 671
11.3   Solving Equations by Using Quadratic Methods 681
          Integrated Review—Summary on Solving Quadratic Equations 690
11.4   Nonlinear Inequalities in One Variable 691
11.5   Quadratic Functions and Their Graphs 698
11.6   Further Graphing of Quadratic Functions 706
          Chapter 11 Vocabulary Check 714
          Chapter 11 Highlights 714
          Chapter 11 Review 717
          Chapter 11 Getting Ready for the Test 718
          Chapter 11 Test 719
          Chapter 11 Cumulative Review 720

Answers to Selected Exercises A8
Index I1

Preface

Beginning & Intermediate Algebra, **Sixth Edition** was written to provide a solid foundation in algebra for students who might not have previous experience in algebra. Specific care was taken to make sure students have the most up-to-date, relevant text preparation for their next mathematics course or for nonmathematical courses that require an understanding of algebraic fundamentals. I have tried to achieve this by writing a user-friendly text that is keyed to objectives and contains many worked-out examples. As suggested by AMATYC and the NCTM Standards (plus Addenda), real-life and real-data applications, data interpretation, conceptual understanding, problem solving, writing, cooperative learning, appropriate use of technology, number sense, estimation, critical thinking, and geometric concepts are emphasized and integrated throughout the book.

The many factors that contributed to the success of the previous editions have been retained. In preparing the Sixth Edition, I considered comments and suggestions of colleagues, students, and many users of the prior edition throughout the country.

What's New in the Sixth Edition?

- **New Getting Ready for the Test** can be found before each Chapter Test. These exercises help increase student success by helping students prepare for their chapter test. The purpose of these exercises is to check students' conceptual understanding of the topics in the chapter as well as common student errors. It is suggested that students complete and check these exercises before taking a practice Chapter Test. All Getting Ready for the Test exercises are either Multiple Choice or Matching, and all answers can be found in the answer section of this text.

  Video Solutions of all Getting Ready exercises can be found in MyMathLab and on the Interactive DVD Lecture Series. These video solutions contain brief explanations and reminders of material in the chapter. Where applicable, incorrect choices contain explanations.

  Getting Ready for the Test exercise numbers marked in blue indicate that the question is available in **Learning Catalytics**. `lc`

- **New Learning Catalytics** is an interactive student response tool that uses students' smartphones, tablets, or laptops to engage them in more sophisticated tasks and thinking. Generate class discussion, guide your lecture, and promote peer-to-peer learning with real-time analytics. Accessible through MyMathLab, instructors can use Learning Catalytics to:

  - Pose a variety of open-ended questions that help your students develop critical thinking skills.

  - Monitor responses to find out where students are struggling.

  - Use real-time data to adjust your instructional strategy and try other ways of engaging your students during class.

  - Manage student interactions by automatically grouping students for discussion, teamwork, and peer-to-peer learning.

  For *Beginning & Intermediate Algebra,* Sixth Edition, new Getting Ready for the Test exercises marked in blue are available in Learning Catalytics. To search for the questions in Learning Catalytics, select **Discipline: Developmental Math,** and **Book: Martin-Gay, Beginning & Intermediate Algebra, 6e;** or search the question library for **MGCOMBO6e Ch** and the chapter number. For example, search **MGCOMBO6e Ch4** for questions from Chapter 4.

- **New Student Success Tips Videos** are 3- to 5-minute video segments designed to be daily reminders to students to continue practicing and maintaining good organizational and study habits. They are organized in three categories and are available in MyMathLab and the Interactive Lecture Series. The categories are:

1. Success Tips that apply to any course in college in general, such as Time Management.

2. Success Tips that apply to any mathematics course. One example is based on understanding that mathematics is a course that requires homework to be completed in a timely fashion.

3. Section- or Content-specific Success Tips to help students avoid common mistakes or to better understand concepts that often prove challenging. One example of this type of tip is how to apply the order of operations to simplify an expression.

- **New Key Concept Activity Lab Workbook** includes Extension Exercises, Exploration Activities, Conceptual Exercises, and Group Activities. These activities are a great way to engage students in conceptual projects and exploration as well as group work.

- **The Martin-Gay MyMathLab** course has been updated and revised to provide more exercise coverage, including assignable video check questions and an expanded video program. There are section lectures videos for every section, which students can also access at the specific objective level; new Getting Ready for the Test video solutions; new Student Success Tips videos; and an increased number of watch clips at the exercise level to help students while doing homework in MathXL.

  Vocabulary, Readiness & Video Check Questions continue to be available in the text and for assignment in MyMathLab. The **Readiness** exercises center on a student's understanding of a concept that is necessary in order to continue to the exercise set. The **video check questions** are included in every section for every learning objective. These exercises are a great way to assess whether students have viewed and understood the key concepts presented in the videos.

- **Exercise Sets Revised and Updated** The text exercise sets have been carefully examined and revised. Special focus was placed on making sure that even- and odd-numbered exercises are paired and that real-life applications are updated.

Key Continuing Resources and Pedagogical Features

- **Interactive DVD Lecture Series**, featuring your text author Elayn Martin-Gay, provides students with active learning at their own pace. The videos offer the following resources and more:

  A complete lecture for each section of the text highlights key examples and exercises from the text. Pop-ups reinforce key terms, definitions, and concepts.

  An interface with menu navigation features allows students to quickly find and focus on the examples and exercises they need to review.

  Interactive Concept Check exercises measure students' understanding of key concepts and common trouble spots.

  New Student Success Tips Videos.

- **The Interactive DVD Lecture Series** also includes the following resources for test prep:

  New Getting Ready for the Chapter Test Videos

  The Chapter Test Prep Videos help students during their most teachable moment—when they are preparing for a test. This innovation provides step-by-step solutions for the exercises found in each Chapter Test. For the Sixth Edition, the chapter test prep videos are also available on YouTube™. The videos are captioned in English and Spanish.

The **Practice Final Exam Videos** help students prepare for an end-of-course final. Students can watch full video solutions to each exercise in the Practice Final Exam at the end of this text.

- **The Video Organizer** is designed to help students take notes and work practice exercises while watching the Interactive Lecture Series videos (available in MyMathLab and on DVD). All content in the Video Organizer is presented in the same order as it is presented in the videos, making it easy for students to create a course notebook and build good study habits.

  - Covers all of the video examples in order.
  - Provides ample space for students to write down key definitions and properties.
  - Includes Play and Pause button icons to prompt students to follow along with the author for some exercises while they try others on their own.

  The Video Organizer is available in a loose-leaf, notebook-ready format. It is also available for download in MyMathLab. Answers to all video questions are available to instructors in MyMathLab and the Instructor's Resource Center.

Key Pedagogical Features

The following key features have been retained and/or updated for the Sixth Edition of the text:

Problem-Solving Process   This is formally introduced in Chapter 2 with a four-step process that is integrated throughout the text. The four steps are **Understand, Translate, Solve,** and **Interpret.** The repeated use of these steps in a variety of examples shows their wide applicability. Reinforcing the steps can increase students' comfort level and confidence in tackling problems.

Exercise Sets Revised and Updated   The exercise sets have been carefully examined and extensively revised. Special focus was placed on making sure that even- and odd-numbered exercises are paired.

Examples   Detailed, step-by-step examples were added, deleted, replaced, or updated as needed. Many examples reflect real life. Additional instructional support is provided in the annotated examples.

Practice Exercises   Throughout the text, each worked-out example has a parallel Practice Exercise. These invite students to be actively involved in the learning process. Students should try each Practice Exercise after finishing the corresponding example. Learning by doing will help students grasp ideas before moving on to other concepts. Answers to the Practice Exercises are provided in the back of the text.

Helpful Hints   Helpful Hints contain practical advice on applying mathematical concepts. Strategically placed where students are most likely to need immediate reinforcement, Helpful Hints help students avoid common trouble areas and mistakes.

Concept Checks   This feature allows students to gauge their grasp of an idea as it is being presented in the text. Concept Checks stress conceptual understanding at the point of use and help suppress misconceived notions before they start. Answers appear at the bottom of the page. Exercises related to Concept Checks are included in the exercise sets.

Mixed Practice Exercises   Found in the section exercise sets, these require students to determine the problem type and strategy needed to solve it just as they would need to do on a test.

Integrated Reviews   A unique, mid-chapter exercise set that helps students assimilate new skills and concepts that they have learned separately over several sections. These reviews provide yet another opportunity for students to work with mixed exercises as they master the topics.

Vocabulary Check Provides an opportunity for students to become more familiar with the use of mathematical terms as they strengthen their verbal skills. These appear at the end of each chapter before the Chapter Highlights. Vocabulary, Readiness, and Video Check exercises provide practice at the section level.

Chapter Highlights Found at the end of every chapter, these contain key definitions and concepts with examples to help students understand and retain what they have learned and help them organize their notes and study for tests.

Chapter Review The end of every chapter contains a comprehensive review of topics introduced in the chapter. The Chapter Review offers exercises keyed to every section in the chapter, as well as Mixed Review exercises that are not keyed to sections.

Chapter Test and Chapter Test Prep Video The Chapter Test is structured to include those problems that involve common student errors. The **Chapter Test Prep Videos** give students instant author access to a step-by-step video solution of each exercise in the Chapter Test.

Cumulative Review Follows every chapter in the text (except Chapter 1). Each odd-numbered exercise contained in the Cumulative Review is an earlier worked example in the text that is referenced in the back of the book along with the answer.

Writing Exercises ╲ These exercises occur in almost every exercise set and require students to provide a written response to explain concepts or justify their thinking.

Applications Real-world and real-data applications have been thoroughly updated, and many new applications are included. These exercises occur in almost every exercise set, show the relevance of mathematics, and help students gradually and continuously develop their problem-solving skills.

Review Exercises These exercises occur in each exercise set (except in Chapter 1) and are keyed to earlier sections. They review concepts learned earlier in the text that will be needed in the next section or chapter.

Exercise Set Resource Icons Located at the opening of each exercise set, these icons remind students of the resources available for extra practice and support:

MyMathLab® ▶

See Student Resource descriptions page xvii for details on the individual resources available.

Exercise Icons These icons facilitate the assignment of specialized exercises and let students know what resources can support them.

- ▶ Video icon: exercise worked on the Interactive DVD Lecture Series and in MyMathLab.
- △ Triangle icon: identifies exercises involving geometric concepts.
- ╲ Pencil icon: indicates a written response is needed.
- ▦ Calculator icon: optional exercises intended to be solved using a scientific or graphing calculator.

Optional: Calculator Exploration Boxes and Calculator Exercises The optional Calculator Explorations provide keystrokes and exercises at appropriate points to give an opportunity for students to become familiar with these tools. Section exercises that are best completed by using a calculator are identified by ▦ for ease of assignment.

Student and Instructor Resources

STUDENT RESOURCES

Interactive DVD Lecture Series Videos Provides students with active learning at their own pace. The videos offer: • A complete lecture for each text section. The interface allows easy navigation to examples and exercises students need to review. • Interactive Concept Check exercises • Student Success Tips Videos • Practice Final Exam • Getting Ready for the Chapter Test Videos • Chapter Test Prep Videos	**Video Organizer** Designed to help students take notes and work practice exercises while watching the Interactive Lecture Series videos. • Covers all of the video examples in order. • Provides ample space for students to write down key definitions and rules. • Includes Play and Pause button icons to prompt students to follow along with the author for some exercises while they try others on their own. Available in loose-leaf, notebook-ready format and in MyMathLab.	**Student Solutions Manual** Provides completely worked-out solutions to the odd-numbered section exercises; all exercises in the Integrated Reviews, Chapter Reviews, Chapter Tests, and Cumulative Reviews. **Key Concept Activity Lab Workbook** includes Extension Exercises, Exploration Activities, Conceptual Exercises, and Group Activities.

INSTRUCTOR RESOURCES

Annotated Instructor's Edition Contains all the content found in the student edition, plus the following: • Classroom example paired to each example • Answers to exercises on the same text page • Teaching Tips throughout the text, placed at key points • Video Answer Section	**Instructor's Resource Manual with Tests and Mini-Lectures** • Mini-lectures for each text section • Additional Practice worksheets for each section • Several forms of test per chapter—free response and multiple choice • Answers to all items **Instructor's Solutions Manual** **TestGen®** (Available for download from the IRC)
Instructor-to-Instructor Videos—available in the Instructor Resources section of the MyMathLab course.	**Online Resources** **MyMathLab®** (access code required) **MathXL®** (access code required)

Get the most out of
MyMathLab®

MyMathLab is the world's leading online resource for teaching and learning mathematics. MyMathLab helps students and instructors improve results and provides engaging experiences and personalized learning for each student so learning can happen in any environment. Plus, it offers flexible and time-saving course-management features to allow instructors to easily manage their classes while remaining in complete control, regardless of course format.

Personalized Support for Students

- MyMathLab comes with many learning resources—eText, animations, videos, and more—all designed to support your students as they progress through their course.

- The Adaptive Study Plan acts as a personal tutor, updating in real time based on student performance to provide personalized recommendations on what to work on next. With the new Companion Study Plan assignments, instructors can now assign the Study Plan as a prerequisite to a test or quiz, helping to guide students through concepts they need to master.

- Personalized Homework allows instructors to create homework assignments tailored to each student's specific needs by focusing on just the topics they have not yet mastered.

Used by nearly 4 million students each year, the MyMathLab and MyStatLab family of products delivers consistent, measurable gains in student learning outcomes, retention, and subsequent course success.

Acknowledgments

Many people helped me develop this text, and I will attempt to thank some of them here. Cindy Trimble was *invaluable* for contributing to the overall accuracy of the text. Dawn Nuttall, Emily Keaton, and Suellen Robinson were *invaluable* for their many suggestions and contributions during the development and writing of this Sixth Edition. Courtney Slade, Chakira Lane, Patty Bergin, and Lauren Morse provided guidance throughout the production process.

A very special thank you goes to my editor, Mary Beckwith, for being there 24/7/365, as my students say. Last, my thanks to the staff at Pearson for all their support: Michael Hirsch, Rachel Ross, Heather Scott, Michelle Renda, Chris Hoag, and Paul Corey.

I would like to thank the following reviewers for their input and suggestions:

Rosalie Abraham, *Florida Community College—Jacksonville*
Ana Bacica, *Brazosport College*
Nelson Collins, *Joliet Junior College*
Nancy Desilet, *Carroll Community College*
Elizabeth Eagle, *University of North Carolina—Charlotte*
Dorothy French, *Community College of Philadelphia*
Sharda Gudehithla, *Wilbur Wright College*
Pauline Hall, *Iowa State University*
Debra R. Hill, *University of North Carolina—Charlotte*
Glenn Jablonski, *Triton College*
Sue Kellicut, *Seminole State College*
Jean McArthur, *Joliet Junior College*
Mary T. McMahon, *North Central College*
Owen Mertens, *Missouri State University*
Jeri Rogers, *Seminole State College*
William Stammerman, *Des Moines Area Community College*
Patrick Stevens, *Joliet Junior College*
Arnavaz Taraporevala, *New York City College of Technology*

I would also like to thank the following dedicated group of instructors who participated in our focus groups, Martin-Gay Summits, and our design review for the series. Their feedback and insights have helped to strengthen this edition of the text. These instructors include:

Billie Anderson, *Tyler Junior College*
Cedric Atkins, *Mott Community College*
Lois Beardon, *Schoolcraft College*
Laurel Berry, *Bryant & Stratton College*
John Beyers, *University of Maryland*
Bob Brown, *Community College of Baltimore County–Essex*
Lisa Brown, *Community College of Baltimore County–Essex*
NeKeith Brown, *Richland College*
Gail Burkett, *Palm Beach State College*
Cheryl Cantwell, *Seminole State College*
Ivette Chuca, *El Paso Community College*
Jackie Cohen, *Augusta State College*
Julie Dewan, *Mohawk Valley Community College*
Monette Elizalde, *Palo Alto College*
Kiel Ellis, *Delgado Community College*
Janice Ervin, *Central Piedmont Community College*
Richard Fielding, *Southwestern College*
Dena Frickey, *Delgado Community College*
Cindy Gaddis, *Tyler Junior College*
Gary Garland, *Tarrant County Community College*
Kim Ghiselin, *State College of Florida*
Nita Graham, *St. Louis Community College*

Kim Granger, *St. Louis Community College*
Pauline Hall, *Iowa State University*
Pat Hussey, *Triton College*
Dorothy Johnson, *Lorain County Community College*
Sonya Johnson, *Central Piedmont Community College*
Ann Jones, *Spartanburg Community College*
Irene Jones, *Fullerton College*
Paul Jones, *University of Cincinnati*
Mike Kirby, *Tidewater Community College*
Kathy Kopelousous, *Lewis and Clark Community College*
Tara LaFrance, *Delgado Community College*
John LaMaster, *Indiana Purdue University Fort Wayne*
Nancy Lange, *Inver Hills Community College*
Judy Langer, *Westchester Community College*
Kathy Lavelle, *Westchester Community College*
Lisa Lindloff, *McLennan Community College*
Sandy Lofstock, *St. Petersburg College*
Nicole Mabine, *North Lake College*
Jean McArthur, *Joliet Junior College*
Kevin McCandless, *Evergreen Valley College*
Ena Michael, *State College of Florida*
Armando Perez, *Laredo Community College*
Davidson Pierre, *State College of Florida*
Marilyn Platt, *Gaston College*
Chris Riola, *Moraine Valley Community College*
Carole Shapero, *Oakton Community College*
Janet Sibol, *Hillsborough Community College*
Anne Smallen, *Mohawk Valley Community College*
Barbara Stoner, *Reading Area Community College*
Jennifer Strehler, *Oakton Community College*
Ellen Stutes, *Louisiana State University Eunice*
Tanomo Taguchi, *Fullerton College*
Robyn Toman, *Anne Arundel Community College*
MaryAnn Tuerk, *Elgin Community College*
Walter Wang, *Baruch College*
Leigh Ann Wheeler, *Greenville Technical Community College*
Darlene Williams, *Delgado Community College*
Valerie Wright, *Central Piedmont Community College*

A special thank you to those students who participated in our design review: Katherine Browne, Mike Bulfin, Nancy Canipe, Ashley Carpenter, Jeff Chojnachi, Roxanne Davis, Mike Dieter, Amy Dombrowski, Kay Herring, Todd Jaycox, Kaleena Levan, Matt Montgomery, Tony Plese, Abigail Polkinghorn, Harley Price, Eli Robinson, Avery Rosen, Robyn Schott, Cynthia Thomas, and Sherry Ward.

Elayn Martin-Gay

About the Author

Elayn Martin-Gay has taught mathematics at the University of New Orleans for more than 25 years. Her numerous teaching awards include the local University Alumni Association's Award for Excellence in Teaching, and Outstanding Developmental Educator at University of New Orleans, presented by the Louisiana Association of Developmental Educators.

Prior to writing textbooks, Elayn Martin-Gay developed an acclaimed series of lecture videos to support developmental mathematics students in their quest for success. These highly successful videos originally served as the foundation material for her texts. Today, the videos are specific to each book in the Martin-Gay series. The author has also created Chapter Test Prep videos to help students during their most "teachable moment"—as they prepare for a test—along with Instructor-to-Instructor videos that provide teaching tips, hints, and suggestions for each developmental mathematics course, including basic mathematics, prealgebra, beginning algebra & intermediate algebra. Her most recent innovations are the Algebra Prep Apps for the iPhone and iPod Touch. These Apps embrace the different learning styles, schedules, and paces of students and provide them with quality math tutoring.

Elayn is the author of 12 published textbooks as well as multimedia interactive mathematics, all specializing in developmental mathematics courses. She has participated as an author across the broadest range of educational materials: textbooks, videos, tutorial software, and courseware. This offers an opportunity of various combinations for an integrated teaching and learning package offering great consistency for the student.

Applications Index

A

Academics. *See* Education
Agriculture
  bug spray mixtures, 497, 750
  combine rental fees, 857
  cranberry-producing states, 16, 137
  DDT pesticides, 750
  farm sizes in U.S., 184, 680
  farmland prices, 219
  farms, number of, 138, 307
  weed killer mixtures, 497
Animals & Insects
  bear populations, 784
  beetle species, 114
  bison populations, 751
  bug sprays, 497, 750, 848, 857
  cheetah running speeds, 461
  condor populations, 785
  crane births, 857
  cricket chirps, 116, 126, 127
  DDT pesticides, 750
  dog medicine dosages, 240, 532
  dog run width, 119
  fish tank dividers, 638
  flying fish speeds, 128
  goldfish numbers in tanks, 126
  gorilla births, 839
  grasshopper species, 114
  hyenas overtaking giraffes, 499
  insecticides, 848, 857
  mosquitoes, 747, 767, 857
  opossum deaths, 841
  otter births, 841
  owl populations, 841
  pen dimensions, 127, 679, 813
  pet types owned in U.S., 130
  pet-related expenditures, 183
  pine beetle infestations, 856
  piranha fish tank dimensions, 126
  prairie dog populations, 787, 932
  puppy weight gain, 827
  rat populations, 751
  sparrow populations, 828
  wolf populations, 778
  wood duck populations, 787
Astronomy & Space
  alignment of planets, 471
  comet distance from Earth, 355
  gamma ray conversion by Sun, 356
  Jupiter, 373
  light travel time/distance, 127–128, 356
  magnitude of stars, 16–17
  meteorite weights, 96, 114

  Milky Way, 373
  moon's light reaching Earth, 357
  moon's surface area, 640
  orbit of planets and comets, 806–807
  planet temperatures, 61
  Sun's light reaching Earth, 357
  telescope elevation above sea level, 355
  weight of objects in relation to Earth's center, 549
  weights on Earth *vs.* other planets, 495
Automobiles
  age of, 218
  bus speeds, 145, 494, 497, 498
  car speeds, 145, 493–494, 496, 497, 498, 511, 549, 640, 658
  compact cars, cost of operating, 218
  dealership discounts, 136
  driver's licenses, 195
  fatalities, 298
  fuel economy, 218
  motorcycle speeds, 498
  registered vehicles on road, 138
  sales, 228, 848
  traffic tickets, 146, 497
  used car values, 138, 181, 554
Aviation
  airplane seats, 876
  airplane speed in still air, 296, 497, 498
  airport elevations, 50
  airport traffic, 718, 870, 877
  hang glider flight rate, 128
  hypersonic flight time around Earth, 128
  jet *vs.* car distances, 497
  jet *vs.* propeller plane speeds, 145, 497
  runway length, 127
  SpaceShipOne rocket plane speed, 463
  vertical elevation changes, 50
  wind speeds, 296, 496, 497, 498

B

Business & Industry
  advertising, 220, 848
  balancing company books, 498
  book store closures, 228
  break-even point, 147, 291–292, 299
  car rental fees, 296, 587
  charity donations, 845
  Coca-Cola production, 137
  Coca-Cola sign dimensions, 124
  consulting fees, 511
  Cyber Monday, 746
  defective products, 514
  delivery service daily operating costs, 642
  depreciation of copiers, 827
  diamond production, 114, 532

Business & Industry (*continued*)
  discounts, 131, 136, 166
  downsizing, 138, 165, 168
  Dunkin' Donuts stores, 228
  employee age, 274
  employee production numbers and hourly wages, 185
  employment decline, 524, 751, 875, 876
  employment growth, 167, 228, 298, 524, 875
  faxes and fax machines, 848, 876
  food manufacturing plants, 137
  gross profit margin, 454
  group/bulk pricing, 287–288, 297
  Home Depot revenue, 195
  home prices, 524
  hourly minimum wage, 238–239, 533
  labor estimates, 491–492, 494, 496, 497, 498, 499, 511, 550, 684–685, 689, 691, 717, 720
  laundromat prices, 213
  manufacturing costs, 245, 299, 434, 450–451, 453, 510, 511, 513, 549, 713, 728, 788
  manufacturing volumes, 204, 355
  markup and new price, 166
  NASDAQ sign dimensions, 124
  net income, 43, 77
  net sales, 176
  occupations predicted to increase, 275
  online shopping, 706, 874
  original price after discount, 166
  percent increase/decrease, 136, 166, 167
  postage for large envelopes, 239
  price and demand, 670, 813
  price decrease and new price, 138, 872
  price per items purchased, 294, 296, 659
  price to sales ratio, 524
  pricing and sales relationship, 228–229, 297
  profits, 228, 454, 524, 713, 728
  proofreading rates, 497
  quantity pricing, 184, 245
  restaurant employees, 874
  restaurant sales, 213, 680
  restaurants in U.S., 228, 524
  retail sales, 706
  revenue, 195, 299, 372, 453, 728, 857
  salary after pay raise, 136
  salary growth, 832, 836, 841, 848, 856, 857
  sale prices, 137–138, 224, 752
  sales tax, 859
  sales volume, predicting, 224–225
  volume of items sold at original *vs.* reduced prices, 297
  Walmart stores, 186
  word processing, 587, 684–685
  work rates, 491–492, 494, 496, 497, 498, 499, 511, 550, 684–685, 689, 691, 717, 720
  years on market and profit relationship, 228

C

Cars. *See* Automobiles
Chemistry
  Avogadro's number, 356
  eyewash stations, 134
  freezing and boiling points of water, 15
  gas pressure and Boyle's law, 545, 555
  greenhouse gases, 746
  lotion mixtures, 139
  methane gas emissions, 713–714
  nickel, half-life of, 752
  nuclear waste, 746
  pH of liquids, 760
  radioactive material, 744, 746, 751, 760, 836, 841, 857
  solution mixtures, 133–134, 136, 138, 162, 166, 251, 290–291, 296, 297, 299, 300, 305, 307, 497, 658, 930
  sulfur dioxide emissions, 516, 523
  uranium, half-life of, 752
Communications & Technology
  area codes, 111, 168, 930
  cell phone discounts, 131
  cell phone use, 78, 166, 611
  computer assembly, 848
  computer discounts, 872
  computer rentals, 848
  computer values, 180–181
  country codes, 114
  digital media use, 298
  Dish Network subscribers, 250
  email, 874
  engineers, 193
  faxes and fax machines, 848, 876
  Google searches, 373
  households with computers, 195–196, 217
  Internet advertising, 220
  Internet crime complaints, 136
  Internet usage, 166, 172, 310, 333, 680, 877
  light bulbs, 877
  mobile devices, time spent on, 137
  music streaming, 387
  newspaper circulation figures, 228
  radio stations in U.S., 268
  security keypads, 813
  smart televisions, 787
  social media, 402, 559, 577
  software revenue, 372
  switchboard connections, 434
  television assembly, 857
  Wi-Fi enabled cell phones, 713, 864, 875, 878
  ZIP codes, 875
Construction & Home Improvement
  balsa wood stick lengths, 443, 658
  baseboard and carpeting measurements, 124
  beam lengths, 113
  beams, 113, 333, 550
  blueprint measurements, 495
  board lengths, 92, 95, 104, 108, 113, 115, 165, 477
  board pricing, 184
  building values, 554
  carpet rolls, 843
  column weight, 547–548, 550
  computer desk length, 95
  dams, 660

deck dimensions, 168, 442, 497

doors, 679

fencing, 125, 251, 300, 873

fertilizer needs, 126

gardens, 116, 119, 125, 251, 300, 435, 492, 840, 859

golden ratio, 679

grass seed, 125

housing starts *vs.* housing completions, 566

ladders, 433

lawn care, 125, 126

measurement conversions, 460–461, 463

molding lengths, 75, 333

painting houses, 511

picture frames, 125, 876

pipe length, 656

roofing pitch, 212, 217, 218

roofing time, 721

rope lengths, 93, 112

sewer pipe slope, 217

siding section lengths, 115

spotlight placement, 640

sprinklers, 689

stained glass windows, 679

steel section lengths, 112

string/wire lengths, 93, 95, 114, 115, 167, 433, 604, 640

swimming pools, 165, 321, 363, 435, 497

trees planted, 840

wall border, 125

washer circumference, 158

wire placement, 637–638, 640

D

Demographics

age groups predicted to increase on workforce, 274

bill collectors, 298

birth rate in U.S., 138

child care centers, 76

driver's licenses, 195

engineers, 193

Internet usage, 166, 172, 310, 333

joggers, 195

metropolitan populations, 869, 876

occupations predicted to increase, 275

octuplet birth weights, 74

pet types owned in U.S., 130

population growth, 748–749, 751, 784, 785, 787, 828, 834, 859, 876

population per square mile of land, 228

population size, 775, 778, 779, 787

postal carriers, 298

registered nurses, 192

water use per person, 250, 549

world population, 356

Distance. *See* Time & Distance

E

Economics & Finance. *See also* Personal Finances

coin/bill denominations, 142–143, 145, 146, 166, 294, 296, 305, 306

compound interest, 666–667, 669, 743, 747, 770, 772–773, 776, 778, 783, 784, 785, 787, 859, 860

interest rates, 36, 434, 666–667, 669, 670, 717, 743, 747, 770, 772–773, 776, 778, 783, 784, 785, 787, 859, 860

investment amounts, 143–144, 145, 146, 166, 168, 295, 514

loans, money needed to pay off, 321

money problems, 142–143

national debts, 356

shares of stock owned, 296

simple interest, 145, 146

stamp denominations, 296, 306

stock market gains and losses, 61, 73, 75, 77

stock prices, 296

Education

ACT Assessment scores, 166, 300

admission rates, 15

alumni donations, 844

associate degrees, 246, 378

bachelor's degrees, 267–268, 378

book page numbers, 114

classrooms, 96, 114, 496

college budgeting, 155

combination lock codes, 114

desired employment benefits, 138

graduate and undergraduate student enrollment, 15, 96, 527–528, 828

high school graduates, 387

hours spent studying, 184

Internet access in classrooms, 138

IQ scores, 642

learning curves, 778

president salaries, 876

students per teacher, 183

study abroad students, 746

summer school students, 751

test scores, 158, 567, 875

textbook prices, 876

tuition and fees, 132, 247

Entertainment & Recreation

allowances, 828

auditorium seats, 836, 856

card game scores, 50

casino gaming, 461

deep-sea diving, 15

diving, 15, 61

DVD sale prices, 166

Easter eggs, 158

exercise bikes, 836

Ferris wheels, 799

fund-raiser attendance, 297

gambling, 848

group rate admissions to events, 287–288

hang gliders, 128, 429

ice sculpting, 843

iTunes expenditures, 186

jogging, 195, 305, 496, 688

movie admission prices, 185, 204

movie industry revenue, 183

movie patron ages, 877

Entertainment & Recreation (*continued*)
movie theater screens, 26, 113, 133, 204
movie theater seats, 828, 857
movie ticket sales, 250
museums and art galleries, 73
music CDs, 136, 450–451
music streaming, 387
national park visits, 245, 331–332, 434
Netflix growth, 722, 742–743, 746
ping-pong tables, 363
pool, 848
poster contests, 679
pyramids formed by surfers, 841
Redbox rentals, 488–489
sail dimensions, 126, 428–429, 440, 497, 515
smart televisions, 787
snowboarding, 872
summer camp tournaments, 784
swimming, 165
tickets sold by type, 145, 287–288, 305
tourism expenditures, 217
tourist destinations, 171, 182
video games, 116
zorbing, 595, 620

F

Finance. *See* Economics & Finance; Personal Finances
Food & Nutrition
barbecues, 471
breakfast item prices, 305
calories burned while walking/bicycling, 157
calories in food items, 495, 497
candy mixtures, 300, 305
cheese consumption and production, 298, 572, 746
coffee blends, 137, 297
cook preparation time, 498
dinner cost with tip, 136
drink machines, coin denominations in, 86
fishery products, domestic and imported, 252, 260
frozen yogurt store revenue, 857
fruit companies, 228
grocery store displays, 836
liter-bottles of Pepsi, 489
nut mixtures, 137, 297, 497
nutrition labels, 139
pepper hotness (Scoville units), 139
percent decrease/increase of consumption, 138
pizza sizes, 126
rabbit food mixtures, 299
red meat and poultry consumption, 283–284
restaurant sales, 213
trail mix ingredients, 139
vitamin A and body weight, 681
yogurt production, 248

G

Geography
continent/regional percentage of Earth's land, 136
desert areas, 96, 114
earthquake magnitudes, 768–769, 772, 874
elevation, 10, 15, 42, 47, 50, 61
federally owned land, 874
Newgrange tomb, 790, 799
ponds, 494, 511, 656, 688
river length, 96
river lenth, 96
rope needed to wrap around Earth, 126
Sarsen Circle of Stonehenge, 798–799
state counties, 115
tallest buildings in U.S., 907
tornado classification, 168
volcano heights, 161
volcano surface area, 620
wildfires, 177
Geology
diamond production, 114, 532
glacier flow rates, 117–118, 128
lava flow rates, 118, 127
mixtures, 138
stalactites and stalagmites, 128
Geometry
angle measurements, 15, 50, 74, 95, 96, 109–110, 113, 114, 115, 116, 293–294, 297, 299, 300, 308, 478, 485, 649, 875, 876
area, 24, 35–36, 74, 127, 136, 138, 320, 332, 339, 340, 346, 347, 356, 363, 368, 373, 374, 376, 387, 402, 432, 433, 440, 464, 477, 510, 532, 546, 626, 641
billboard dimensions, 127, 165
boxes/cubes, 36, 122, 127, 320, 321, 339, 356, 368, 372, 532, 689
circles, 24–25, 74, 158, 320, 432, 532, 550–551
circumference, 158, 550–551
complementary angle measurements, 50, 93, 95, 115, 297, 478, 485
cones, 550, 620, 632
cylinders, 320, 546, 551
Fibonacci sequence, 824, 829
flag dimensions, 113
fraction representations in, 24–25, 74
geodesic dome measurements, 115
golden rectangles, 116
hang glider dimensions, 429
Hoberman Sphere volume, 127
parallelograms, 15, 113, 127, 138, 320, 363, 368, 432, 515
Pentagon floor space dimensions, 115, 463
pentagons, 105, 126
percent decrease/increase problems, 136, 138
perimeter, 25, 35–36, 74, 86, 104, 105, 122–123, 126–127, 157, 165, 196, 294, 299, 305, 306, 333, 363, 374, 393, 402, 407, 432, 440, 441, 471, 477, 510, 546, 604, 625–626, 812, 873, 877
polygons, 546
Pythagorean theorem, 430–431, 636–638, 914
quadrilaterals, 96, 114, 299, 300, 432, 440
radius, 432, 532, 632
rectangles, 24, 35–36, 86, 116, 122–123, 136, 157, 165, 196, 294, 320, 339, 340, 346, 373, 374, 393, 432, 433, 434, 440, 441, 464, 477, 625, 679, 873
sail dimensions, 126, 428–429, 440, 497, 515
sign dimensions, 120–121, 124, 125, 298, 877

spheres, 549, 555, 632

squares, 136, 320, 339, 346, 363, 373, 402, 432, 433, 440, 471, 670, 873

supplementary angle measurements, 50, 93, 95, 115, 297, 478, 485

surface area, 321, 334, 372, 546, 555, 620, 640

trapezoids, 432, 471, 625, 626

triangles, 15, 24, 36, 86, 96, 104, 105, 113, 114, 115, 116, 127, 138, 157, 293, 294, 298, 299, 300, 305, 306, 308, 339, 356, 374, 430–431, 432, 434, 440, 441, 442, 464, 490, 495, 498, 511, 512, 514, 604, 625, 639, 641, 649, 670, 679, 717, 824, 875, 876, 877, 913–914

Vietnam Veterans Memorial angle measurements, 109–110

volume, 36, 122, 127, 320, 321, 339, 356, 363, 368, 532, 550, 551, 632

Washington Monument height and base, 165

Government. *See* Politics & Government

H

Health & Medicine

bacterial cultures, 828, 834, 841

basal metabolic rate, 611

blinking rate of human eye, 116

body mass index, 454

body surface area of humans, 604

breast cancer pink ribbons, 127

cephalic index, 454

dog medicine dosages, 240, 532

flu epidemics, 778

fungal cultures, 841

hospital heights, 877

infectious diseases, 828

kidney transplants, 246

medication administration, 97, 453, 477

octuplet birth weights, 74

organ transplants, 219, 246

pediatric dosages, 453, 477

radiation, 784

registered nurses, 192

smoking and pulse rate, 173

treadmills, 131

virus cultures, 836

woman's height given femur bone length, 240, 532

yeast cultures, 856, 857

Home Improvement. *See* Construction & Home Improvement

I

Industry. *See* Business & Industry

Insects. *See* Animals & Insects

M

Medicine. *See* Health & Medicine

N

Nutrition. *See* Food & Nutrition

P

Personal Finances

bank account balances, 47, 295, 649–650

bankruptcy, 514

charge account balances, 50

donations, 844–845

interest rates, 36, 434, 666–667, 669, 670, 717, 743, 747, 770, 772–773, 776, 778, 783, 784, 785, 787, 859, 860

loans, money needed to pay off, 321

money problems, 142–143

retirement party budgeting, 157

salary after pay raise, 136

salary growth, 832, 836, 841, 848, 856, 857

sales needed to ensure monthly salary, 166

savings accounts, 15, 295, 848

wedding budget, 155, 157, 587

Physics

angstroms, 373

angular frequency of oscillations, 612

currents and resistance, 549

Doppler effect, 505

Earth's interior temperature, 355

force exerted by tractors, 641

Hoberman Sphere volume, 127

horsepower, 550, 551

pendulum arc, 836, 841, 846, 856, 859

pendulum period, 641

speed of waves traveling over stretched string, 612

springs stretching and Hooke's law, 543–544

velocity, 604, 658

weight of objects in relation to Earth's center, 549

wind power generated, 498

Politics & Government

Democrats *vs.* Republicans, 109

governors, 109

mayoral elections, 95

national debts, 356

representatives, 109, 251

Supreme Court decisions, 138

R

Real Estate

condominium sales and price relationships, 225

depreciation, 229

plot perimeter, 104

property values, 836

Recreation. *See* Entertainment & Recreation

S

Safety. *See* Transportation & Safety

School. *See* Education

Space. *See* Astronomy & Space

Sports

baseball earned run average, 505

baseball game admissions, 288

baseball game attendance, 260

baseball Hall of Fame admittance, 16

baseball payroll and team wins, 557

baseball runs batted in, 295

baseball slugging percentage, 454

baseball team wins, 877

basketball player heights, 157

Sports (*continued*)
  basketball points scored, 295, 299–300
  bowling average, 157
  disc throwing records, 139
  football stadiums, 876
  football yards lost/gained, 61, 77
  golf flags, 440
  golf scores, 43, 58, 167
  golf tournament participants, 749–750
  hockey payrolls, 876
  ice hockey penalty killing percentage, 477
  NASCAR grandstand seats, 876
  NASCAR speeds, 690
  Olympics, 114, 461, 877
  quarterback rating, 454
  racquetball, 856
  stock cars, 463
  Super Bowl attendance, 182
  Tour de France, 166

T

Technology. *See* Communications & Technology
Temperature & Weather
  atmospheric pressure, 747, 778
  average temperatures, 43, 51, 127, 234, 250
  changes in, 40, 42, 50, 61, 77
  Earth's interior temperature, 355
  highest and lowest temperatures, 40, 42, 50, 127, 166, 680
  inequality statements regarding, 15
  of planets, 61
  rainfall data, 300
  snowfall at distances from Equator, 184
  sunrise times, 233
  sunset times, 238
  temperature conversions, 119–120, 121, 123, 125, 127, 166, 567, 724
  thermometer readings, 38
  tornado classification, 168
  tornadoes, 168, 874
Time & Distance
  airplane speed in still air, 296, 497, 498
  bicycling speeds, 496, 688
  bicycling travel time, 140, 296
  boat speed in still water, 305, 496, 497, 511, 514
  boats traveling apart at right angles, 435
  bus speeds, 145, 494, 497, 498
  car speeds, 145, 493–494, 496, 497, 498, 511, 549, 640, 658
  catamaran auto ferry speed, 125
  comet distance from Earth, 355
  conveyor belt speeds, 496
  current speeds, 296, 305
  Daytona 500 speeds, 690
  distance saved, 675–676, 678–679, 720, 931
  distance traveled over time, 166, 717
  driving distance, 145
  driving speeds, 36, 146, 493–494, 496, 497, 498, 685–686, 688
  driving time, 125, 127

dropped/falling objects, 35, 228, 325, 331, 372, 376, 413–414, 433, 434, 440, 441, 442, 524, 557, 641, 669–670, 676–677, 679–680, 828, 836, 846, 848, 856, 857
free-fall time/distance, 427, 848, 859
hiking trails, 25, 141, 308
hyenas overtaking giraffes, 499
hypersonic flight time around Earth, 128
jet *vs.* car distances, 497
lakes/ponds, distance across, 656, 800
light intensity by distance from source, 549, 550
light travel time/distance, 127–128, 356
moon's light to reach Earth, 357
motorcycle speeds, 498
objects traveling in opposite directions, 146, 168, 288–290, 297, 308, 496, 822, 930
of images and objects to focal length, 444
pendulum swings, 836, 841, 846, 856, 859
rate and, 117–118
rope needed to wrap around Earth, 126
rowing against current, 496
rowing distance, 146
rowing rate in still water, 296
sight distance from a height, 549, 641
Sun's light to reach Earth, 357
thrown/launched objects, 393, 426, 433, 440, 697, 712–713, 717, 718, 720, 859, 931
traffic tickets, 146, 497
train travel speeds, 115, 128, 141–142, 166, 168, 496, 930
travel time, 140–141
walking/running speeds, 305, 496, 688, 691
walking/running time, 166, 296, 305
wind speeds, 296, 496, 497, 498, 550
Transportation & Safety
  bridge lengths, 95
  bridges, 220, 800, 822
  bus speeds, 145, 494, 497, 498
  car speeds, 145, 493–494, 496, 497, 498, 511, 549, 640, 658
  catamaran auto ferry speed, 125
  cell phone use while driving, 166
  cloverleaf exits, 658
  grade of roads/railroad tracks, 213, 217, 377
  interstate highway length, 96
  motorcycle speeds, 498
  parking lot dimensions, 125
  railroad tracks, 213, 217
  road sign dimensions, 120–121, 125, 298, 377, 877
  taxi cab fares, 586
  traffic tickets, 146, 497
  train fares for children and adults, 295
  wheelchair ramps, 217
  yield signs, 125

V

Vehicles. *See* Automobiles

W

Weather. *See* Temperature & Weather

3.1 Reading Graphs and the Rectangular Coordinate System

3.2 Graphing Linear Equations

3.3 Intercepts

3.4 Slope and Rate of Change

Integrated Review—Summary on Slope and Graphing Linear Equations

3.5 Equations of Lines

3.6 Functions

✓ CHECK YOUR PROGRESS

Vocabulary Check
Chapter Highlights
Chapter Review
Getting Ready for the Test
Chapter Test
Cumulative Review

In the previous chapter, we learned to solve and graph the solutions of linear equations and inequalities in one variable. Now we define and present techniques for solving and graphing linear equations and inequalities in two variables.

International Tourist Arrivals Forecast for 2020–2030 (numbers shown in millions)

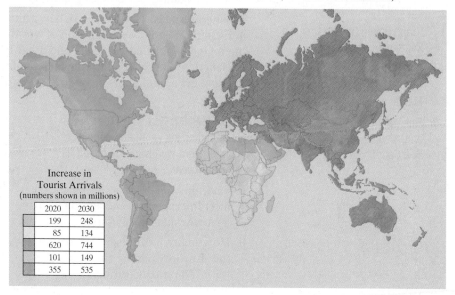

Increase in Tourist Arrivals (numbers shown in millions)

2020	2030
199	248
85	134
620	744
101	149
355	535

What Is Tourism Toward 2030?

Tourism 2020 Vision is the World Tourism Organization's long-term forecast of world tourism through 2020. *Tourism Towards 2030* is its new program title for longer-term forecasts to 2030. The broken-line graph below shows the forecast for number of tourists, which is extremely important as these numbers greatly affect a country's economy. In Section 3.1, Exercises 1 through 6, we read a bar graph showing the top tourist destinations by country.

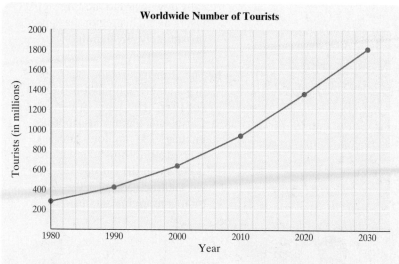

Data from World Tourism Organization (UNWTO)

3.1 | Reading Graphs and the Rectangular Coordinate System

OBJECTIVES

1 Read Bar and Line Graphs.

2 Define the Rectangular Coordinate System and Plot Ordered Pairs of Numbers.

3 Graph Paired Data to Create a Scatter Diagram.

4 Determine Whether an Ordered Pair Is a Solution of an Equation in Two Variables.

5 Find the Missing Coordinate of an Ordered Pair Solution, Given One Coordinate of the Pair.

In today's world, where the exchange of information must be fast and entertaining, graphs are becoming increasingly popular. They provide a quick way of making comparisons, drawing conclusions, and approximating quantities.

OBJECTIVE

1   Reading Bar and Line Graphs

A **bar graph** consists of a series of bars arranged vertically or horizontally. The bar graph in Example 1 shows a comparison of worldwide Internet users by region. The names of the regions are listed vertically and a bar is shown for each region. Corresponding to the length of the bar for each region is a number along a horizontal axis. These horizontal numbers are numbers of Internet users in millions.

EXAMPLE 1   The bar graph shows the estimated number of Internet users worldwide by region as of a recent year.

a. Find the region that has the most Internet users and approximate the number of users.

b. How many more users are in the Europe region than the Latin America/Caribbean region?

Solution

a. Since these bars are arranged horizontally, we look for the longest bar, which is the bar representing Asia. To approximate the number associated with this region, we move from the right edge of this bar vertically downward to the Internet Users axis. This region has approximately 1390 million Internet users.

b. The Europe region has approximately 580 million Internet users. The Latin America/Caribbean region has approximately 320 million Internet users. To find how many more users are in the Europe region, we subtract $580 - 320 = 260$ million more Internet users.

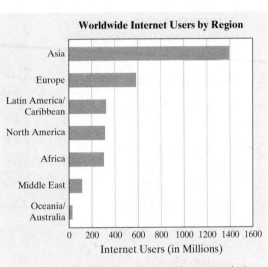

Data from Internet World Stats (www.internetworldstats.com/stats.htm)

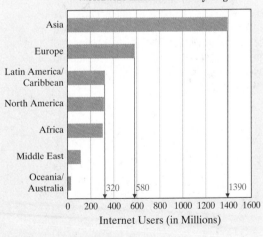

Data from Internet World Stats (www.internetworldstats.com/stats.htm)

PRACTICE

1   Use the graph from Example 1 to answer the following.

a. Find the region with the fewest Internet users and approximate the number of users.

b. How many more users are in the Middle East region than in the Oceania/Australia region?

A **line graph** consists of a series of points connected by a line. The next graph is an example of a line graph. It is also sometimes called a **broken-line graph.**

EXAMPLE 2   The line graph shows the relationship between time spent smoking a cigarette and pulse rate. Time is recorded along the horizontal axis in minutes, with 0 minutes being the moment a smoker lights a cigarette. Pulse is recorded along the vertical axis in heartbeats per minute.

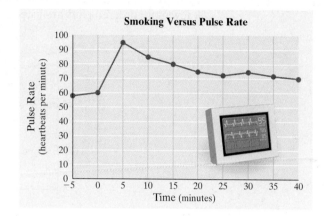

a. What is the pulse rate 15 minutes after a cigarette is lit?

b. When is the pulse rate the lowest?

c. When does the pulse rate show the greatest change?

Solution

a. We locate the number 15 along the time axis and move vertically upward until the line is reached. From this point on the line, we move horizontally to the left until the pulse rate axis is reached. Reading the number of beats per minute, we find that the pulse rate is 80 beats per minute 15 minutes after a cigarette is lit.

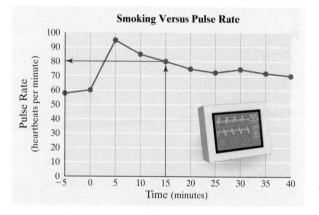

b. We find the lowest point of the line graph, which represents the lowest pulse rate. From this point, we move vertically downward to the time axis. We find that the pulse rate is the lowest at −5 minutes, which means 5 minutes *before* lighting a cigarette.

c. The pulse rate shows the greatest change during the 5 minutes between 0 and 5. Notice that the line graph is *steepest* between 0 and 5 minutes.   □

PRACTICE

2   Use the graph from Example 2 to answer the following.

a. What is the pulse rate 40 minutes after lighting a cigarette?

b. What is the pulse rate when the cigarette is being lit?

c. When is the pulse rate the highest?

OBJECTIVE

2 Defining the Rectangular Coordinate System and Plotting Ordered Pairs of Numbers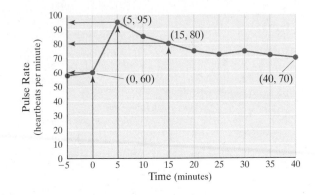

Notice in the previous graph that two numbers are associated with each point of the graph. For example, we discussed earlier that 15 minutes after lighting a cigarette, the pulse rate is 80 beats per minute. If we agree to write the time first and the pulse rate second, we can say there is a point on the graph corresponding to the **ordered pair** of numbers (15, 80). A few more ordered pairs are listed alongside their corresponding points.

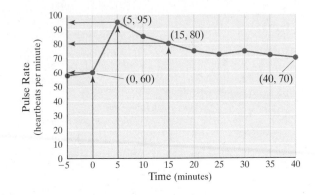

In general, we use this same ordered pair idea to describe the location of a point in a plane (such as a piece of paper). We start with a horizontal and a vertical axis. Each axis is a number line and, for the sake of consistency, we construct our axes to intersect at the 0 coordinate of both. This point of intersection is called the **origin.** Notice that these two number lines or axes divide the plane into four regions called **quadrants.** The quadrants are usually numbered with Roman numerals as shown. The axes are not considered to be in any quadrant.

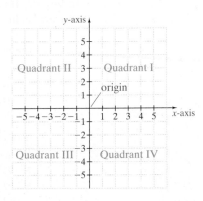

It is helpful to label axes, so we label the horizontal axis the **x-axis** and the vertical axis the **y-axis.** We call the system described above the **rectangular coordinate system.**

Just as with the pulse rate graph, we can then describe the locations of points by ordered pairs of numbers. We list the horizontal **x-axis** measurement first and the vertical **y-axis** measurement second.

To plot or graph the point corresponding to the ordered pair

$$(a, b)$$

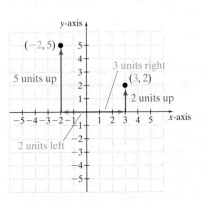

we start at the origin. We then move a units left or right (right if a is positive, left if a is negative). From there, we move b units up or down (up if b is positive, down if b is negative). For example, to plot the point corresponding to the ordered pair (3, 2), we start at the origin, move 3 units right and from there move 2 units up. (See the figure to the left.) The x-value, 3, is called the **x-coordinate** and the y-value, 2, is called the **y-coordinate.** From now on, we will call the point with coordinates (3, 2) simply the point (3, 2). The point (−2, 5) is graphed to the left also.

Does the order in which the coordinates are listed matter? Yes! Notice below that the point corresponding to the ordered pair $(2, 3)$ is in a different location than the point corresponding to $(3, 2)$. These two ordered pairs of numbers describe two different points of the plane.

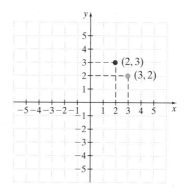

✔ **CONCEPT CHECK**

Is the graph of the point $(-5, 1)$ in the same location as the graph of the point $(1, -5)$? Explain.

Helpful Hint

Don't forget that **each ordered pair corresponds to exactly one point in the plane and that each point in the plane corresponds to exactly one ordered pair.**

EXAMPLE 3   On a single coordinate system, plot each ordered pair. State in which quadrant, if any, each point lies.

a. $(5, 3)$ **b.** $(-5, 3)$ **c.** $(-2, -4)$ **d.** $(1, -2)$ **e.** $(0, 0)$

f. $(0, 2)$ **g.** $(-5, 0)$ **h.** $\left(0, -5\frac{1}{2}\right)$ **i.** $\left(4\frac{2}{3}, -3\right)$

Solution

a. Point $(5, 3)$ lies in quadrant I.

b. Point $(-5, 3)$ lies in quadrant II.

c. Point $(-2, -4)$ lies in quadrant III.

d. Point $(1, -2)$ lies in quadrant IV.

e.–h. Points $(0, 0)$, $(0, 2)$, $(-5, 0)$, and $\left(0, -5\frac{1}{2}\right)$ lie on axes, so they are not in any quadrant.

i. Point $\left(4\frac{2}{3}, -3\right)$ lies in quadrant IV.

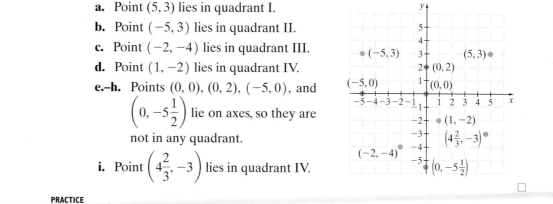

PRACTICE

3   On a single coordinate system, plot each ordered pair. State in which quadrant, if any, each point lies.

a. $(4, -3)$ **b.** $(-3, 5)$ **c.** $(0, 4)$ **d.** $(-6, 1)$

e. $(-2, 0)$ **f.** $(5, 5)$ **g.** $\left(3\frac{1}{2}, 1\frac{1}{2}\right)$ **h.** $(-4, -5)$

Answer to Concept Check:
The graph of point $(-5, 1)$ lies in quadrant II and the graph of point $(1, -5)$ lies in quadrant IV. They are *not* in the same location.

From Example 3, notice that the y-coordinate of any point on the x-axis is 0. For example, the point $(-5, 0)$ lies on the x-axis. Also, the x-coordinate of any point on the y-axis is 0. For example, the point $(0, 2)$ lies on the y-axis.

✔ **CONCEPT CHECK**

For each description of a point in the rectangular coordinate system, write an ordered pair that represents it.

a. Point *A* is located three units to the left of the *y*-axis and five units above the *x*-axis.

b. Point *B* is located six units below the origin.

OBJECTIVE

3   Graphing Paired Data ▷

Data that can be represented as an ordered pair is called **paired data.** Many types of data collected from the real world are paired data. For instance, the annual measurement of a child's height can be written as an ordered pair of the form (year, height in inches) and is paired data. The graph of paired data as points in the rectangular coordinate system is called a **scatter diagram.** Scatter diagrams can be used to look for patterns and trends in paired data.

EXAMPLE 4   The table gives the annual net sales (in billions of dollars) for Target stores for the years shown. (*Source:* Corporate.target.com)

Year	Target Net Sales (in billions of dollars)
2009	65
2010	67
2011	70
2012	73
2013	73
2014	73

a. Write this paired data as a set of ordered pairs of the form (year, sales in billions of dollars).

b. Create a scatter diagram of the paired data.

c. What trend in the paired data does the scatter diagram show?

Solution

a. The ordered pairs are (2009, 65), (2010, 67), (2011, 70), (2012, 73), (2013, 73), (2014, 73).

b. We begin by plotting the ordered pairs. Because the *x*-coordinate in each ordered pair is a year, we label the *x*-axis "Year" and mark the horizontal axis with the years given. Then we label the *y*-axis or vertical axis "Net Sales (in billions of dollars)." In this case we can mark the vertical axis in multiples of 2. Since no net sale is less than 64, we use the notation ⋛ to skip to 64, then proceed by multiples of 2.

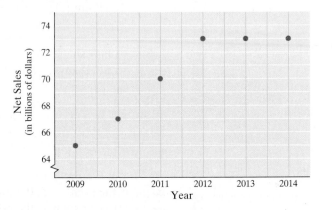

c. The scatter diagram shows that Target net sales were constant or increasing over the years 2009–2014. ☐

PRACTICE
4 The table gives the approximate annual number of wildfires (in thousands) that have occurred in the United States for the years shown. (*Source:* National Interagency Fire Center)

Year	Wildfires (in thousands)
2008	79
2009	79
2010	72
2011	73
2012	56
2013	48
2014	46

a. Write this paired data as a set of ordered pairs of the form (year, number of wild-fires in thousands).

b. Create a scatter diagram of the paired data. ■

OBJECTIVE
4 Determining Whether an Ordered Pair Is a Solution ▶

Let's see how we can use ordered pairs to record solutions of equations containing two variables. An equation in one variable such as $x + 1 = 5$ has one solution, which is 4: The number 4 is the value of the variable x that makes the equation true.

An equation in two variables, such as $2x + y = 8$, has solutions consisting of two values, one for x and one for y. For example, $x = 3$ and $y = 2$ is a solution of $2x + y = 8$ because, if x is replaced with 3 and y with 2, we get a true statement.

$$2x + y = 8$$
$$2(3) + 2 = 8$$
$$8 = 8 \quad \text{True}$$

The solution $x = 3$ and $y = 2$ can be written as $(3, 2)$, an **ordered pair** of numbers. The first number, 3, is the x-value and the second number, 2, is the y-value.

In general, an ordered pair is a **solution** of an equation in two variables if replacing the variables by the values of the ordered pair results in a true statement.

EXAMPLE 5 Determine whether each ordered pair is a solution of the equation $x - 2y = 6$.

a. $(6, 0)$ **b.** $(0, 3)$ **c.** $\left(1, -\dfrac{5}{2}\right)$

Solution

a. Let $x = 6$ and $y = 0$ in the equation $x - 2y = 6$.

$$x - 2y = 6$$
$$6 - 2(0) = 6 \quad \text{Replace } x \text{ with 6 and } y \text{ with 0.}$$
$$6 - 0 = 6 \quad \text{Simplify.}$$
$$6 = 6 \quad \text{True}$$

$(6, 0)$ is a solution, since $6 = 6$ is a true statement.

(Continued on next page)

b. Let $x = 0$ and $y = 3$.

$$x - 2y = 6$$
$$0 - 2(3) = 6 \quad \text{Replace } x \text{ with 0 and } y \text{ with 3.}$$
$$0 - 6 = 6$$
$$-6 = 6 \quad \text{False}$$

$(0, 3)$ is *not* a solution, since $-6 = 6$ is a false statement.

c. Let $x = 1$ and $y = -\dfrac{5}{2}$ in the equation.

$$x - 2y = 6$$
$$1 - 2\left(-\frac{5}{2}\right) = 6 \quad \text{Replace } x \text{ with 1 and } y \text{ with } -\frac{5}{2}.$$
$$1 + 5 = 6$$
$$6 = 6 \quad \text{True}$$

$\left(1, -\dfrac{5}{2}\right)$ is a solution, since $6 = 6$ is a true statement. □

PRACTICE

5 Determine whether each ordered pair is a solution of the equation $x + 3y = 6$.

a. $(3, 1)$ **b.** $(6, 0)$ **c.** $\left(-2, \dfrac{2}{3}\right)$ ▪

OBJECTIVE

5 Completing Ordered Pair Solutions ▷

If one value of an ordered pair solution of an equation is known, the other value can be determined. To find the unknown value, replace one variable in the equation by its known value. Doing so results in an equation with just one variable that can be solved for the variable using the methods of Chapter 2.

EXAMPLE 6 Complete the following ordered pair solutions of the equation $3x + y = 12$.

a. $(0, \quad)$ **b.** $(\quad, 6)$ **c.** $(-1, \quad)$

Solution

a. In the ordered pair $(0, \ )$, the x-value is 0. Let $x = 0$ in the equation and solve for y.

$$3x + y = 12$$
$$3(0) + y = 12 \quad \text{Replace } x \text{ with 0.}$$
$$0 + y = 12$$
$$y = 12$$

The completed ordered pair is $(0, 12)$.

b. In the ordered pair $(\ , 6)$, the y-value is 6. Let $y = 6$ in the equation and solve for x.

$$3x + y = 12$$
$$3x + 6 = 12 \quad \text{Replace } y \text{ with 6.}$$
$$3x = 6 \quad \text{Subtract 6 from both sides.}$$
$$x = 2 \quad \text{Divide both sides by 3.}$$

The ordered pair is $(2, 6)$.

c. In the ordered pair $(-1,\ )$, the x-value is -1. Let $x = -1$ in the equation and solve for y.

$$3x + y = 12$$
$$3(-1) + y = 12 \quad \text{Replace } x \text{ with } -1.$$
$$-3 + y = 12$$
$$y = 15 \quad \text{Add 3 to both sides.}$$

The ordered pair is $(-1, 15)$. □

PRACTICE

6 Complete the following ordered pair solutions of the equation $2x - y = 8$.

 a. $(0,\ )$ **b.** $(\ , 4)$ **c.** $(-3,\ )$ ■

Solutions of equations in two variables can also be recorded in a **table of values,** as shown in the next example.

EXAMPLE 7 Complete the table for the equation $y = 3x$.

	x	y
a.	-1	
b.		0
c.		-9

Solution

a. Replace x with -1 in the equation and solve for y.

$$y = 3x$$
$$y = 3(-1) \quad \text{Let } x = -1.$$
$$y = -3$$

The ordered pair is $(-1, -3)$.

b. Replace y with 0 in the equation and solve for x.

$$y = 3x$$
$$0 = 3x \quad \text{Let } y = 0.$$
$$0 = x \quad \text{Divide both sides by 3.}$$

The ordered pair is $(0, 0)$.

c. Replace y with -9 in the equation and solve for x.

$$y = 3x$$
$$-9 = 3x \quad \text{Let } y = -9.$$
$$-3 = x \quad \text{Divide both sides by 3.}$$

The ordered pair is $(-3, -9)$. The completed table is shown to the left. □

	x	y
a.	-1	-3
b.	0	0
c.	-3	-9

PRACTICE

7 Complete the table for the equation $y = -4x$.

	x	y
a.	-2	
b.		-12
c.	0	

■

EXAMPLE 8 Complete the table for the equation

$$y = \frac{1}{2}x - 5.$$

	x	y
a.	−2	
b.	0	
c.		0

Solution

a. Let $x = -2$.

$$y = \frac{1}{2}x - 5$$
$$y = \frac{1}{2}(-2) - 5$$
$$y = -1 - 5$$
$$y = -6$$

b. Let $x = 0$.

$$y = \frac{1}{2}x - 5$$
$$y = \frac{1}{2}(0) - 5$$
$$y = 0 - 5$$
$$y = -5$$

c. Let $y = 0$.

$$y = \frac{1}{2}x - 5$$
$$0 = \frac{1}{2}x - 5 \quad \text{Now, solve for } x.$$
$$5 = \frac{1}{2}x \quad \text{Add 5.}$$
$$10 = x \quad \text{Multiply by 2.}$$

Ordered pairs: **a.** $(-2, -6)$, **b.** $(0, -5)$, **c.** $(10, 0)$

The completed table is

	x	y
a.	−2	−6
b.	0	−5
c.	10	0

☐

PRACTICE
8 Complete the table for the equation $y = \frac{1}{5}x - 2$.

	x	y
a.	−10	
b.	0	
c.		0

■

EXAMPLE 9 Finding the Value of a Computer

A computer was recently purchased for a small business for $2000. The business manager predicts that the computer will be used for 5 years and the value in dollars y of the computer in x years is $y = -300x + 2000$. Complete the table.

x	0	1	2	3	4	5
y						

Solution To find the value of y when x is 0, replace x with 0 in the equation. We use this same procedure to find y when x is 1 and when x is 2.

When $x = 0$,

$$y = -300x + 2000$$
$$y = -300 \cdot 0 + 2000$$
$$y = 0 + 2000$$
$$y = 2000$$

When $x = 1$,

$$y = -300x + 2000$$
$$y = -300 \cdot 1 + 2000$$
$$y = -300 + 2000$$
$$y = 1700$$

When $x = 2$,

$$y = -300x + 2000$$
$$y = -300 \cdot 2 + 2000$$
$$y = -600 + 2000$$
$$y = 1400$$

We have the ordered pairs $(0, 2000)$, $(1, 1700)$, and $(2, 1400)$. This means that in 0 years, the value of the computer is $2000, in 1 year the value of the computer is $1700, and in

2 years the value is $1400. To complete the table of values, we continue the procedure for $x = 3$, $x = 4$, and $x = 5$.

When $x = 3$,

$y = -300x + 2000$
$y = -300 \cdot 3 + 2000$
$y = -900 + 2000$
$y = 1100$

When $x = 4$,

$y = -300x + 2000$
$y = -300 \cdot 4 + 2000$
$y = -1200 + 2000$
$y = 800$

When $x = 5$,

$y = -300x + 2000$
$y = -300 \cdot 5 + 2000$
$y = -1500 + 2000$
$y = 500$

The completed table is

x	0	1	2	3	4	5
y	2000	1700	1400	1100	800	500

PRACTICE

9   A college student purchased a used car for $12,000. The student predicted that she would need to use the car for four years and the value in dollars y of the car in x years is $y = -1800x + 12{,}000$. Complete this table.

x	0	1	2	3	4
y	12,000	10,200	8400	6600	4800

The ordered pair solutions recorded in the completed table for the example above are graphed below. Notice that the graph gives a visual picture of the decrease in value of the computer.

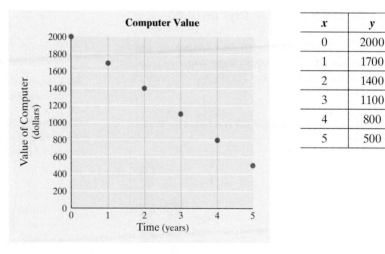

x	y
0	2000
1	1700
2	1400
3	1100
4	800
5	500

Vocabulary, Readiness & Video Check

Use the choices below to fill in each blank. The exercises below all have to do with the rectangular coordinate system.

origin	x-coordinate	x-axis	one	four
quadrants	y-coordinate	y-axis	solution	

1. The horizontal axis is called the _____ and the vertical axis is called the _____.

2. The intersection of the horizontal axis and the vertical axis is a point called the _____.

3. The axes divide the plane into regions called _____. There are _____ of these regions.

4. In the ordered pair of numbers $(-2, 5)$, the number -2 is called the _____ and the number 5 is called the _____.

5. Each ordered pair of numbers corresponds to _____ point in the plane.

6. An ordered pair is a(n) _____ of an equation in two variables if replacing the variables by the coordinates of the ordered pair results in a true statement.

Martin-Gay Interactive Videos

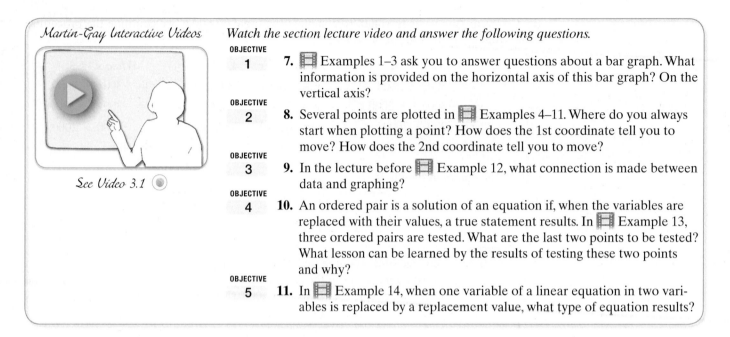

See Video 3.1 ●

Watch the section lecture video and answer the following questions.

OBJECTIVE 1

7. ▦ Examples 1–3 ask you to answer questions about a bar graph. What information is provided on the horizontal axis of this bar graph? On the vertical axis?

OBJECTIVE 2

8. Several points are plotted in ▦ Examples 4–11. Where do you always start when plotting a point? How does the 1st coordinate tell you to move? How does the 2nd coordinate tell you to move?

OBJECTIVE 3

9. In the lecture before ▦ Example 12, what connection is made between data and graphing?

OBJECTIVE 4

10. An ordered pair is a solution of an equation if, when the variables are replaced with their values, a true statement results. In ▦ Example 13, three ordered pairs are tested. What are the last two points to be tested? What lesson can be learned by the results of testing these two points and why?

OBJECTIVE 5

11. In ▦ Example 14, when one variable of a linear equation in two variables is replaced by a replacement value, what type of equation results?

3.1 Exercise Set MyMathLab® ▶

The following bar graph shows the top 10 tourist destinations and the number of tourists that visit each destination per year forecasted for 2020. Use this graph to answer Exercises 1 through 6. See Example 1.

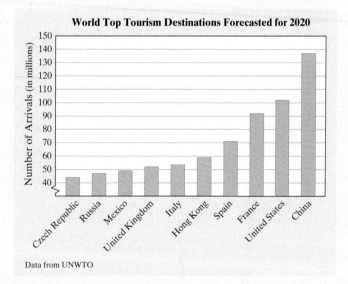

Data from UNWTO

▶ **1.** Which location shown is predicted to be the most popular tourist destination?

2. Which location shown is predicted to be the least popular tourist destination?

▶ **3.** Which locations shown are predicted to have more than 70 million tourists per year?

4. Which locations shown are predicted to have more than 100 million tourists per year?

▶ **5.** Estimate the predicted number of tourists per year whose destination is Italy.

6. Estimate the predicted number of tourists per year whose destination is Mexico.

The following line graph shows the paid attendance at each Super Bowl game from 2008 through 2014. Use this graph to answer Exercises 7 through 10. See Example 2.

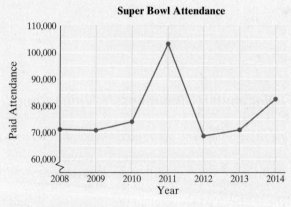

Data from National Football League

7. Estimate the Super Bowl attendance in 2014.

8. Estimate the Super Bowl attendance in 2010.

9. Find the year on the graph with the greatest Super Bowl attendance and approximate that attendance.

10. Find the year on the graph with the least Super Bowl attendance and approximate that attendance.

The line graph below shows the number of students per teacher in U.S. public elementary and secondary schools. Use this graph for Exercises 11 through 16. See Example 2.

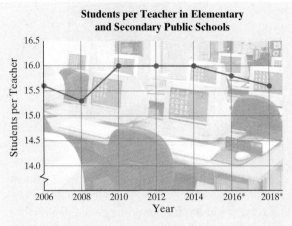

Students per Teacher in Elementary and Secondary Public Schools

Data from National Center for Education Statistics * Some years are projected.

11. Approximate the number of students per teacher predicted in 2016.

12. Approximate the number of students per teacher predicted in 2018.

13. Between what years shown did the greatest increase in number of students per teacher occur?

14. What was the first year shown that the number of students per teacher fell below 15.5?

15. During what period was the student per teacher number at 16?

16. Discuss any trends shown by this line graph.

Plot each ordered pair. State in which quadrant or on which axis each point lies. See Example 3.

17. a. $(1, 5)$ **b.** $(-5, -2)$
 c. $(-3, 0)$ **d.** $(0, -1)$
 e. $(2, -4)$ **f.** $\left(-1, 4\frac{1}{2}\right)$
 g. $(3.7, 2.2)$ **h.** $\left(\frac{1}{2}, -3\right)$

18. a. $(2, 4)$ **b.** $(0, 2)$
 c. $(-2, 1)$ **d.** $(-3, -3)$
 e. $\left(3\frac{3}{4}, 0\right)$ **f.** $(5, -4)$
 g. $(-3.4, 4.8)$ **h.** $\left(\frac{1}{3}, -5\right)$

Find the x- and y-coordinates of each labeled point. See Example 3.

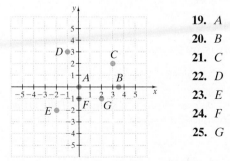

19. A
20. B
21. C
22. D
23. E
24. F
25. G

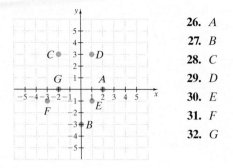

26. A
27. B
28. C
29. D
30. E
31. F
32. G

Solve. See Example 4.

33. The table shows the worldwide box office (in billions of dollars) for the movie industry during the years shown. (*Source:* Motion Picture Association of America)

Year	Box Office (in billions of dollars)
2010	21.0
2011	22.4
2012	23.9
2013	25.0
2014	28.0

a. Write this paired data as a set of ordered pairs of the form (year, box office).

b. In your own words, write the meaning of the ordered pair (2014, 28.0).

c. Create a scatter diagram of the paired data. Be sure to label the axes appropriately.

d. What trend in the paired data does the scatter diagram show?

34. The table shows the amount of money (in billions of dollars) Americans spent on their pets for the years shown. (*Source:* American Pet Products Manufacturers Association)

Year	Pet-Related Expenditures (in billions of dollars)
2011	51.0
2012	53.3
2013	55.7
2014	58.5

a. Write this paired data as a set of ordered pairs of the form (year, pet-related expenditures).

b. In your own words, write the meaning of the ordered pair (2014, 58.5).

c. Create a scatter diagram of the paired data. Be sure to label the axes appropriately.

d. What trend in the paired data does the scatter diagram show?

35. Minh, a psychology student, kept a record of how much time she spent studying for each of her 20-point psychology quizzes and her score on each quiz.

Hours Spent Studying	0.50	0.75	1.00	1.25	1.50	1.50	1.75	2.00
Quiz Score	10	12	15	16	18	19	19	20

a. Write the data as ordered pairs of the form (hours spent studying, quiz score).

b. In your own words, write the meaning of the ordered pair (1.25, 16).

c. Create a scatter diagram of the paired data. Be sure to label the axes appropriately.

d. What might Minh conclude from the scatter diagram?

36. A local lumberyard uses quantity pricing. The table shows the price per board for different amounts of lumber purchased.

Price per Board (in dollars)	Number of Boards Purchased
8.00	1
7.50	10
6.50	25
5.00	50
2.00	100

a. Write the data as ordered pairs of the form (price per board, number of boards purchased).

b. In your own words, write the meaning of the ordered pair (2.00, 100).

c. Create a scatter diagram of the paired data. Be sure to label the axes appropriately.

d. What trend in the paired data does the scatter diagram show?

37. The table shows the distance from the equator (in miles) and the average annual snowfall (in inches) for each of eight selected U.S. cities. (*Source:* National Climatic Data Center, Wake Forest University Albatross Project)

City	Distance from Equator (in miles)	Average Annual Snowfall (in inches)
1. Atlanta, GA	2313	2
2. Austin, TX	2085	1
3. Baltimore, MD	2711	21
4. Chicago, IL	2869	39
5. Detroit, MI	2920	42
6. Juneau, AK	4038	99
7. Miami, FL	1783	0
8. Winston-Salem, NC	2493	9

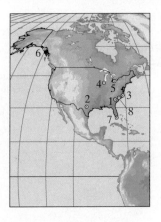

a. Write this paired data as a set of ordered pairs of the form (distance from equator, average annual snowfall).

b. Create a scatter diagram of the paired data. Be sure to label the axes appropriately.

c. What trend in the paired data does the scatter diagram show?

38. The table shows the average farm size (in acres) in the United States during the years shown. (*Source:* National Agricultural Statistics Service)

Year	Average Farm Size (in acres)
2009	418
2010	418
2011	429
2012	433
2013	435
2014	437

a. Write this paired data as a set of ordered pairs of the form (year, average farm size).

b. Create a scatter diagram of the paired data. Be sure to label the axes appropriately.

Determine whether each ordered pair is a solution of the given linear equation. See Example 5.

39. $2x + y = 7$; $(3, 1), (7, 0), (0, 7)$

40. $3x + y = 8$; $(2, 3), (0, 8), (8, 0)$

41. $x = -\frac{1}{3}y$; $(0, 0), (3, -9)$

42. $y = -\frac{1}{2}x$; $(0, 0), (4, 2)$

43. $x = 5$; $(4, 5), (5, 4), (5, 0)$

44. $y = -2$; $(-2, 2), (2, -2), (0, -2)$

Complete each ordered pair so that it is a solution of the given linear equation. See Examples 6 through 8.

45. $x - 4y = 4$; $(\quad, -2), (4, \quad)$

46. $x - 5y = -1$; $(\quad, -2), (4, \quad)$

47. $y = \dfrac{1}{4}x - 3;\ (-8,\ \ ),\ (\ ,1)$

48. $y = \dfrac{1}{5}x - 2;\ (-10,\ \ ),\ (\ ,1)$

Complete the table of ordered pairs for each linear equation. See Examples 6 through 8.

49. $y = -7x$

x	y
0	
−1	
	2

50. $y = -9x$

x	y
0	
−3	
	2

51. $y = -x + 2$

x	y
0	
	0
−3	

52. $x = -y + 4$

x	y
	0
0	
	−3

53. $y = \dfrac{1}{2}x$

x	y
0	
−6	
	1

54. $y = \dfrac{1}{3}x$

x	y
0	
−6	
	1

55. $x + 3y = 6$

x	y
0	
	0
	1

56. $2x + y = 4$

x	y
	4
2	
	2

57. $y = 2x - 12$

x	y
0	
	−2
3	

58. $y = 5x + 10$

x	y
	0
	5
0	

59. $2x + 7y = 5$

x	y
0	
	0
	1

60. $x - 6y = 3$

x	y
0	
	1
	−1

MIXED PRACTICE

Complete the table of ordered pairs for each equation. Then plot the ordered pair solutions. See Examples 1 through 7.

61. $x = -5y$

x	y
	0
	1
10	

62. $y = -3x$

x	y
	0
−2	
	9

63. $y = \dfrac{1}{3}x + 2$

x	y
0	
−3	
	0

64. $y = \dfrac{1}{2}x + 3$

x	y
0	
−4	
	0

Solve. See Example 9.

65. The cost in dollars y of producing x computer desks is given by $y = 80x + 5000$.

   a. Complete the table.

x	100	200	300
y			

   b. Find the number of computer desks that can be produced for $8600. (*Hint:* Find x when $y = 8600$.)

66. The hourly wage y of an employee at a certain production company is given by $y = 0.25x + 9$ where x is the number of units produced by the employee in an hour.

   a. Complete the table.

x	0	1	5	10
y				

   b. Find the number of units that an employee must produce each hour to earn an hourly wage of $12.25. (*Hint:* Find x when $y = 12.25$.)

67. The average annual cinema admission price y (in dollars) from 2010 through 2014 is given by $y = 0.09x + 7.85$. In this equation, x represents the number of years after 2010. (*Source:* Motion Picture Association of America)

   a. Complete the table.

x	0	2	4
y			

   b. Find the year in which the average cinema admission price was approximately $8.10.

     (*Hint:* Find x when $y = 8.10$ and round to the nearest whole number.)

   c. Use the given equation to predict when the cinema admission price might be $10.00. (Use the hint for part (b).)

   d. In your own words, write the meaning of the ordered pair $(1, 7.94)$.

68. The average amount of money y spent per person per year on music from iTunes from 2008 to 2013 can be approximated by $y = -5.74x + 38.05$. In this equation, x represents the number of years since 2008. (*Source:* billboard.com)

  a. Complete the table.

x	1	3	5
y			

  b. Find the year in which the yearly average amount spent on music in iTunes was approximately $26.00. (*Hint:* Find x when $y = 26$ and round to the nearest whole number.)

The graph below shows the number of U.S. Walmart stores for each year. Use this graph to answer Exercises 69 through 72.

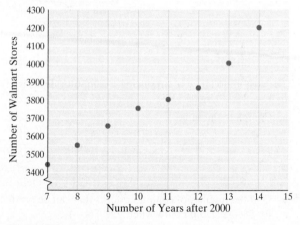

Data from Walmart

69. The ordered pair (14, 4203) is a point of the graph. Write a sentence describing the meaning of this ordered pair.

70. The ordered pair (12, 3868) is a point of the graph. Write a sentence describing the meaning of this ordered pair.

71. Estimate the increase in Walmart stores for years 8, 9, and 10.

72. Use a straightedge or ruler and this graph to predict the number of Walmart stores in the year 2018.

73. Describe what is similar about the coordinates of points whose graph lies on the x-axis.

74. Describe what is similar about the coordinates of points whose graph lies on the y-axis.

REVIEW AND PREVIEW

Solve each equation for y. See Section 2.5.

75. $x + y = 5$ **76.** $x - y = 3$

77. $2x + 4y = 5$ **78.** $5x + 2y = 7$

79. $10x = -5y$ **80.** $4y = -8x$

81. $x - 3y = 6$ **82.** $2x - 9y = -20$

CONCEPT EXTENSIONS

Answer each exercise with true or false.

83. Point $(-1, 5)$ lies in quadrant IV.

84. Point $(3, 0)$ lies on the y-axis.

85. For the point $\left(-\dfrac{1}{2}, 1.5\right)$, the first value, $-\dfrac{1}{2}$, is the x-coordinate and the second value, 1.5, is the y-coordinate.

86. The ordered pair $\left(2, \dfrac{2}{3}\right)$ is a solution of $2x - 3y = 6$.

For Exercises 87 through 91, fill in each blank with "0," "positive," or "negative." For Exercises 92 and 93, fill in each blank with "x" or "y."

	Point	Location
87.	(_____ , _____)	quadrant III
88.	(_____ , _____)	quadrant I
89.	(_____ , _____)	quadrant IV
90.	(_____ , _____)	quadrant II
91.	(_____ , _____)	origin
92.	(number, 0)	__ -axis
93.	(0, number)	__ -axis

94. Give an example of an ordered pair whose location is in (or on)

  a. quadrant I   **b.** quadrant II

  c. quadrant III   **d.** quadrant IV

  e. x-axis   **f.** y-axis

Solve. See the first Concept Check in this section.

95. Is the graph of $(3, 0)$ in the same location as the graph of $(0, 3)$? Explain why or why not.

96. Give the coordinates of a point such that if the coordinates are reversed, their location is the same.

97. In general, what points can have coordinates reversed and still have the same location?

98. In your own words, describe how to plot or graph an ordered pair of numbers.

Write an ordered pair for each point described. See the second Concept Check in this section.

99. Point C is four units to the right of the y-axis and seven units below the x-axis.

100. Point D is three units to the left of the origin.

Solve.

△ **101.** Find the perimeter of the rectangle whose vertices are the points with coordinates $(-1, 5)$, $(3, 5)$, $(3, -4)$, and $(-1, -4)$.

△ **102.** Find the area of the rectangle whose vertices are the points with coordinates $(5, 2)$, $(5, -6)$, $(0, -6)$, and $(0, 2)$.

103. Three vertices of a rectangle are $(-2, -3)$, $(-7, -3)$, and $(-7, 6)$.

  a. Find the coordinates of the fourth vertex of the rectangle.

  b. Find the perimeter of the rectangle.

  c. Find the area of the rectangle.

104. Three vertices of a square are $(-4, -1)$, $(-4, 8)$, and $(5, 8)$.

  a. Find the coordinates of the fourth vertex of the square.

  b. Find the perimeter of the square.

  c. Find the area of the square.

3.2 | Graphing Linear Equations

OBJECTIVES

1 Identify Linear Equations.

2 Graph a Linear Equation by Finding and Plotting Ordered Pair Solutions.

OBJECTIVE

1   Identifying Linear Equations

In the previous section, we found that equations in two variables may have more than one solution. For example, both $(6, 0)$ and $(2, -2)$ are solutions of the equation $x - 2y = 6$. In fact, this equation has an infinite number of solutions. Other solutions include $(0, -3)$, $(4, -1)$, and $(-2, -4)$. If we graph these solutions, notice that a pattern appears.

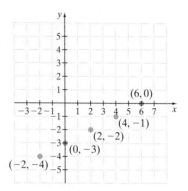

These solutions all appear to lie on the same line, which has been filled in below. It can be shown that every ordered pair solution of the equation corresponds to a point on this line, and every point on this line corresponds to an ordered pair solution. Thus, we say that this line is the **graph of the equation** $x - 2y = 6$.

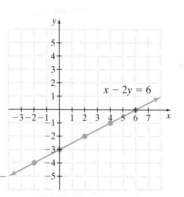

Helpful Hint

Notice that we can only show a part of a line on a graph. The arrowheads on each end of the line remind us that the line actually extends indefinitely in both directions.

The equation $x - 2y = 6$ is called a **linear equation in two variables** and **the graph of every linear equation in two variables is a line.**

Linear Equation in Two Variables

A linear equation in two variables is an equation that can be written in the form

$$Ax + By = C$$

where A, B, and C are real numbers and A and B are not both 0. **The graph of a linear equation in two variables is a straight line.**

The form $Ax + By = C$ is called **standard form**.

Helpful Hint

Notice in the form $Ax + By = C$, the understood exponent on both x and y is 1.

Examples of Linear Equations in Two Variables

$$2x + y = 8 \qquad -2x = 7y \qquad y = \frac{1}{3}x + 2 \qquad y = 7$$

(Standard Form)

Before we graph linear equations in two variables, let's practice identifying these equations.

▶ **EXAMPLE 1** Determine whether each equation is a linear equation in two variables.

a. $x - 1.5y = -1.6$ **b.** $y = -2x$ **c.** $x + y^2 = 9$ **d.** $x = 5$

Solution

a. This is a linear equation in two variables because it is written in the form $Ax + By = C$ with $A = 1$, $B = -1.5$, and $C = -1.6$.

b. This is a linear equation in two variables because it can be written in the form $Ax + By = C$.

$$y = -2x$$
$$2x + y = 0 \qquad \text{Add } 2x \text{ to both sides.}$$

c. This is *not* a linear equation in two variables because y is squared.

d. This is a linear equation in two variables because it can be written in the form $Ax + By = C$.

$$x = 5$$
$$x + 0y = 5 \qquad \text{Add } 0 \cdot y.$$

☐

PRACTICE

1 Determine whether each equation is a linear equation in two variables.

a. $3x + 2.7y = -5.3$ **b.** $x^2 + y = 8$

c. $y = 12$ **d.** $5x = -3y$

■

OBJECTIVE

2 Graphing Linear Equations by Plotting Ordered Pair Solutions ▶

From geometry, we know that a straight line is determined by just two points. Graphing a linear equation in two variables, then, requires that we find just two of its infinitely many solutions. Once we do so, we plot the solution points and draw the line connecting the points. Usually, we find a third solution as well, as a check.

EXAMPLE 2 Graph the linear equation $2x + y = 5$.

Solution Find three ordered pair solutions of $2x + y = 5$. To do this, choose a value for one variable, x or y, and solve for the other variable. For example, let $x = 1$. Then $2x + y = 5$ becomes

$$2x + y = 5$$
$$2(1) + y = 5 \qquad \text{Replace } x \text{ with 1.}$$
$$2 + y = 5 \qquad \text{Multiply.}$$
$$y = 3 \qquad \text{Subtract 2 from both sides.}$$

Since $y = 3$ when $x = 1$, the ordered pair $(1, 3)$ is a solution of $2x + y = 5$. Next, let $x = 0$.

$$2x + y = 5$$
$$2(0) + y = 5 \qquad \text{Replace } x \text{ with 0.}$$
$$0 + y = 5$$
$$y = 5$$

The ordered pair $(0, 5)$ is a second solution.

The two solutions found so far allow us to draw the straight line that is the graph of all solutions of $2x + y = 5$. However, we find a third ordered pair as a check. Let $y = -1$.

$$2x + y = 5$$
$$2x + (-1) = 5 \quad \text{Replace } y \text{ with } -1.$$
$$2x - 1 = 5$$
$$2x = 6 \quad \text{Add 1 to both sides.}$$
$$x = 3 \quad \text{Divide both sides by 2.}$$

The third solution is $(3, -1)$. These three ordered pair solutions are listed in table form as shown. The graph of $2x + y = 5$ is the line through the three points.

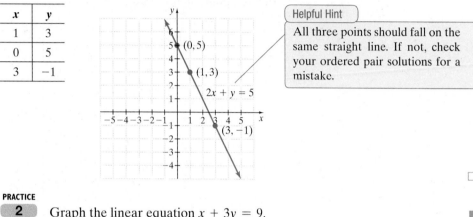

x	y
1	3
0	5
3	−1

Helpful Hint

All three points should fall on the same straight line. If not, check your ordered pair solutions for a mistake.

PRACTICE
2 Graph the linear equation $x + 3y = 9$.

EXAMPLE 3 Graph the linear equation $-5x + 3y = 15$.

Solution Find three ordered pair solutions of $-5x + 3y = 15$.

Let $x = 0$.	**Let $y = 0$.**	**Let $x = -2$.**
$-5x + 3y = 15$	$-5x + 3y = 15$	$-5x + 3y = 15$
$-5 \cdot 0 + 3y = 15$	$-5x + 3 \cdot 0 = 15$	$-5(-2) + 3y = 15$
$0 + 3y = 15$	$-5x + 0 = 15$	$10 + 3y = 15$
$3y = 15$	$-5x = 15$	$3y = 5$
$y = 5$	$x = -3$	$y = \dfrac{5}{3}$

The ordered pairs are $(0, 5)$, $(-3, 0)$, and $\left(-2, \dfrac{5}{3}\right)$. The graph of $-5x + 3y = 15$ is the line through the three points.

x	y
0	5
−3	0
−2	$\dfrac{5}{3} = 1\dfrac{2}{3}$

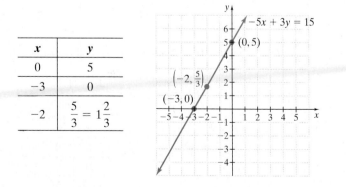

PRACTICE
3 Graph the linear equation $3x - 4y = 12$.

EXAMPLE 4 Graph the linear equation $y = 3x$.

Solution To graph this linear equation, we find three ordered pair solutions. Since this equation is solved for y, choose three x-values.

If $x = 2$, $y = 3 \cdot 2 = 6$.

If $x = 0$, $y = 3 \cdot 0 = 0$.

If $x = -1$, $y = 3 \cdot -1 = -3$.

x	y
2	6
0	0
-1	-3

Next, graph the ordered pair solutions listed in the table above and draw a line through the plotted points as shown below. The line is the graph of $y = 3x$. Every point on the graph represents an ordered pair solution of the equation and every ordered pair solution is a point on this line.

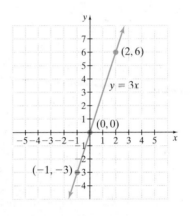

PRACTICE
4 Graph the linear equation $y = -2x$.

> **Helpful Hint**
>
> When graphing a linear equation in two variables, if it is
>
> - solved for y, it may be easier to find ordered pair solutions by choosing x-values. If it is
> - solved for x, it may be easier to find ordered pair solutions by choosing y-values.

EXAMPLE 5 Graph the linear equation $y = -\dfrac{1}{3}x + 2$.

Solution Find three ordered pair solutions, graph the solutions, and draw a line through the plotted solutions. To avoid fractions, choose x-values that are multiples of 3 to substitute in the equation. When a multiple of 3 is multiplied by $-\dfrac{1}{3}$, the result is an integer. See the calculations below used to fill in the table.

If $x = 6$, then $y = -\dfrac{1}{3} \cdot 6 + 2 = -2 + 2 = 0$

If $x = 0$, then $y = -\dfrac{1}{3} \cdot 0 + 2 = 0 + 2 = 2$

If $x = -3$, then $y = -\dfrac{1}{3} \cdot -3 + 2 = 1 + 2 = 3$

x	y
6	0
0	2
-3	3

PRACTICE
5 Graph the linear equation $y = \dfrac{1}{2}x + 3$.

Let's compare the graphs in Examples 4 and 5. The graph of $y = 3x$ tilts upward (as we follow the line from left to right) and the graph of $y = -\dfrac{1}{3}x + 2$ tilts downward (as we follow the line from left to right). We will learn more about the tilt, or slope, of a line in Section 3.4.

EXAMPLE 6   Graph the linear equation $y = -2$.

Solution The equation $y = -2$ can be written in standard form as $0x + y = -2$. No matter what value we replace x with, y is always -2.

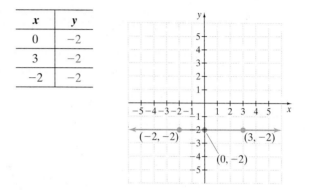

x	y
0	-2
3	-2
-2	-2

Notice that the graph of $y = -2$ is a horizontal line.

PRACTICE
6   Graph the linear equation $x = -2$.

EXAMPLE 7   Graph the linear equation $y = 3x + 6$ and compare this graph with the graph of $y = 3x$ in Example 4.

Solution Find ordered pair solutions, graph the solutions, and draw a line through the plotted solutions. We choose x-values and substitute in the equation $y = 3x + 6$.

If $x = -3$, then $y = 3(-3) + 6 = -3$.
If $x = 0$, then $y = 3(0) + 6 = 6$.
If $x = 1$, then $y = 3(1) + 6 = 9$.

x	y
-3	-3
0	6
1	9

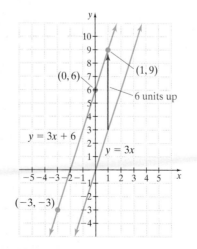

The most startling similarity is that both graphs appear to have the same upward tilt as we move from left to right. Also, the graph of $y = 3x$ crosses the y-axis at the origin, while the graph of $y = 3x + 6$ crosses the y-axis at 6. In fact, the graph of $y = 3x + 6$ is the same as the graph of $y = 3x$ moved vertically upward 6 units.

(Continued on next page)

PRACTICE
7   Graph the linear equation $y = -2x + 3$ and compare this graph with the graph of $y = -2x$ in Practice 4.   ∎

Notice that the graph of $y = 3x + 6$ crosses the y-axis at 6. This happens because when $x = 0$, $y = 3x + 6$ becomes $y = 3 \cdot 0 + 6 = 6$. The graph contains the point $(0, 6)$, which is on the y-axis.

In general, if a linear equation in two variables is solved for y, we say that it is written in the form $y = mx + b$. The graph of this equation contains the point $(0, b)$ because when $x = 0$, $y = mx + b$ is $y = m \cdot 0 + b = b$.

> The graph of $y = mx + b$ crosses the y-axis at $(0, b)$.

We will review this again in Section 3.5.

Linear equations are often used to model real data as seen in the next example.

EXAMPLE 8   **Estimating the Number of Registered Nurses**

The occupation expected to have the most employment growth in the next few years is registered nurse. The number of people y (in thousands) employed as registered nurses in the United States can be estimated by the linear equation $y = 58.1x + 2619$, where x is the number of years after the year 2008. (*Source:* U.S. Bureau of Labor Statistics)

   a. Graph the equation.

   b. Use the graph to predict the number of registered nurses in the year 2018.

Solution

   a. To graph $y = 58.1x + 2619$, choose x-values and substitute in the equation.

If $x = 0$, then $y = 58.1(0) + 2619 = 2619$.
If $x = 2$, then $y = 58.1(2) + 2619 = 2735.2$.
If $x = 5$, then $y = 58.1(5) + 2619 = 2909.5$.

x	y
0	2619
2	2735.2
5	2909.5

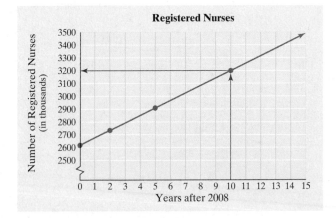

   b. To use the graph to *predict* the number of registered nurses in the year 2018, we need to find the y-coordinate that corresponds to $x = 10$. (10 years after 2008 is the year 2018.) To do so, find 10 on the x-axis. Move vertically upward to the graphed line and then horizontally to the left. We approximate the number on the y-axis to be 3200. Thus, in the year 2018, we predict that there will be 3200 thousand registered nurses. (The actual value, using 10 for x, is 3200.)   □

PRACTICE
8   One of the occupations expected to have a large growth in employment in the next few years is computer software application engineers. The number of people y (in thousands) employed as computer software application engineers in the United States can be estimated by the linear equation $y = 17.5x + 515$, where x is the number of years after 2008. (*Source:* Based on data from the Bureau of Labor Statistics)

a. Graph the equation.

b. Use the graph to predict the number of computer software application engineers in the year 2020.   ▪

> **Helpful Hint**
>
> Make sure you understand that models are mathematical approximations of the data for the known years. (For example, see the model in Example 8.) Any number of unknown factors can affect future years, so be cautious when using models to predict.

Graphing Calculator Explorations

In this section, we begin an optional study of graphing calculators and graphing software packages for computers. These graphers use the same point plotting technique that was introduced in this section. The advantage of this graphing technology is, of course, that graphing calculators and computers can find and plot ordered pair solutions much faster than we can. Note, however, that the features described in these boxes may not be available on all graphing calculators.

The rectangular screen where a portion of the rectangular coordinate system is displayed is called a **window.** We call it a **standard window** for graphing when both the x- and y-axes show coordinates between -10 and 10. This information is often displayed in the window menu on a graphing calculator as

$$Xmin = -10$$
$$Xmax = 10$$
$$Xscl = 1 \qquad \text{The scale on the } x\text{-axis is one unit per tick mark.}$$
$$Ymin = -10$$
$$Ymax = 10$$
$$Yscl = 1 \qquad \text{The scale on the } y\text{-axis is one unit per tick mark.}$$

To use a graphing calculator to graph the equation $y = 2x + 3$, press the $\boxed{Y =}$ key and enter the keystrokes $\boxed{2}\ \boxed{x}\ \boxed{+}\ \boxed{3}$. The top row should now read $Y_1 = 2x + 3$. Next press the $\boxed{\text{GRAPH}}$ key, and the display should look like this:

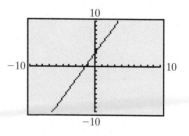

Use a standard window and graph the following linear equations. (Unless otherwise stated, use a standard window when graphing.)

1. $y = -3x + 7$ **2.** $y = -x + 5$ **3.** $y = 2.5x - 7.9$

4. $y = -1.3x + 5.2$ **5.** $y = -\dfrac{3}{10}x + \dfrac{32}{5}$ **6.** $y = \dfrac{2}{9}x - \dfrac{22}{3}$

✔ **Vocabulary, Readiness & Video Check**

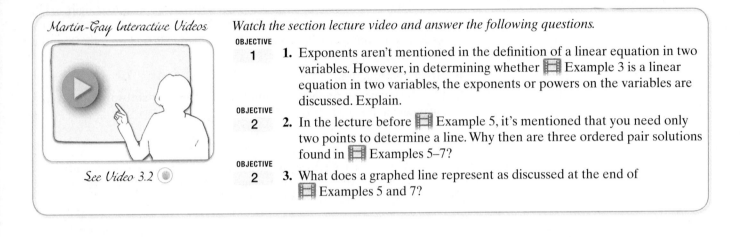

Martin-Gay Interactive Videos

See Video 3.2 🔘

Watch the section lecture video and answer the following questions.

OBJECTIVE 1

1. Exponents aren't mentioned in the definition of a linear equation in two variables. However, in determining whether 🎬 Example 3 is a linear equation in two variables, the exponents or powers on the variables are discussed. Explain.

OBJECTIVE 2

2. In the lecture before 🎬 Example 5, it's mentioned that you need only two points to determine a line. Why then are three ordered pair solutions found in 🎬 Examples 5–7?

OBJECTIVE 2

3. What does a graphed line represent as discussed at the end of 🎬 Examples 5 and 7?

3.2 Exercise Set MyMathLab® ▶

Determine whether each equation is a linear equation in two variables. See Example 1.

1. $-x = 3y + 10$

2. $y = x - 15$

3. $x = y$

4. $x = y^3$

5. $x^2 + 2y = 0$

6. $0.01x - 0.2y = 8.8$

7. $y = -1$

8. $x = 25$

For each equation, find three ordered pair solutions by completing the table. Then use the ordered pairs to graph the equation. See Examples 2 through 7.

9. $x - y = 6$

x	y
	0
4	
	-1

10. $x - y = 4$

x	y
	0
	2
	-1

11. $y = -4x$

x	y
1	
0	
-1	

12. $y = -5x$

x	y
1	
0	
-1	

13. $y = \frac{1}{3}x$

x	y
0	
6	
-3	

14. $y = \frac{1}{2}x$

x	y
0	
-4	
2	

15. $y = -4x + 3$

x	y
0	
1	
2	

16. $y = -5x + 2$

x	y
0	
1	
2	

MIXED PRACTICE

Graph each linear equation. See Examples 2 through 7.

17. $x + y = 1$

18. $x + y = 7$

19. $x - y = -2$

20. $-x + y = 6$

21. $x - 2y = 6$

22. $-x + 5y = 5$

23. $y = 6x + 3$

24. $y = -2x + 7$

25. $x = -4$

26. $y = 5$

27. $y = 3$

28. $x = -1$

29. $y = x$

30. $y = -x$

31. $x = -3y$

32. $x = -5y$

33. $x + 3y = 9$

34. $2x + y = 2$

35. $y = \frac{1}{2}x + 2$

36. $y = \frac{1}{4}x + 3$

37. $3x - 2y = 12$

38. $2x - 7y = 14$

39. $y = -3.5x + 4$

40. $y = -1.5x - 3$

Graph each pair of linear equations on the same set of axes. Discuss how the graphs are similar and how they are different. See Example 7.

41. $y = 5x; y = 5x + 4$

42. $y = 2x; y = 2x + 5$

43. $y = -2x; y = -2x - 3$

44. $y = x; y = x - 7$

45. $y = \frac{1}{2}x; y = \frac{1}{2}x + 2$

46. $y = -\frac{1}{4}x; y = -\frac{1}{4}x + 3$

The graph of $y = 5x$ is given below as well as Figures A–D. For Exercises 47 through 50, match each equation with its graph. *Hint: Recall that if an equation is written in the form $y = mx + b$, its graph crosses the y-axis at $(0, b)$.*

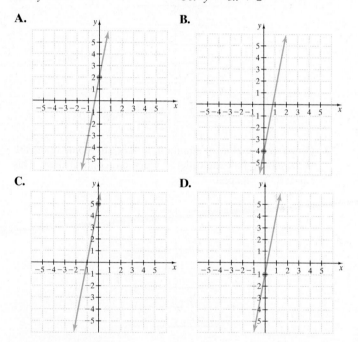

47. $y = 5x + 5$

48. $y = 5x - 4$

49. $y = 5x - 1$

50. $y = 5x + 2$

A.

B.

C.

D.

Solve. See Example 8.

51. Jogging is one of the few sports that has been consistently increasing over the past few years. The number of people jogging (in millions) from the years 2000 to 2009 is given by the equation $y = x + 23$, where x is the number of years after 2000. (*Source:* Based on data from the National Sporting Goods Association)

a. Use this equation or a graph of it to complete the ordered pair (8,   ).

b. Write a sentence explaining the meaning of the answer to part (a).

c. If this trend continues, how many joggers will there be in 2017?

52. The revenue y (in billions of dollars) for Home Depot stores during the years 2010 through 2014 is given by the equation $y = 3.2x + 65.2$, where x is the number of years after 2010. (*Source:* Based on data from Home Depot stores)

a. Use this equation or a graph of it to complete the ordered pair (3,   ).

b. Write a sentence explaining the meaning of the answer to part (a).

c. If this trend continues, predict the revenue for Home Depot stores for the year 2018.

53. One American rite of passage is a driver's license. The number of people y (in millions) who have a driver's license can be estimated by the linear equation $y = 2.2x + 190$, where x is the number of years after 2000. (*Source:* Federal Highway Administration)

a. Use this equation to complete the ordered pair (12,   ).

b. Write a sentence explaining the meaning of the ordered pair in part (a).

c. If this trend continues, predict the number of people with driver's licenses in 2020.

54. The percent of U.S. households y with at least one computer can be approximated by the linear equation $y = 2.4x + 51$, where x is the number of years since 2000. (*Source:* Pew Research)

a. Use the equation to complete the ordered pair (10,   ).

b. Write a sentence explaining the meaning of the ordered pair found in part (a).

c. If this trend continues, predict the percent of U.S. households that have at least one computer in 2018.

d. Explain any issues with your answer to part (c).

REVIEW AND PREVIEW

Solve. See Section 3.1.

△ **55.** The coordinates of three vertices of a rectangle are $(-2, 5)$, $(4, 5)$, and $(-2, -1)$. Find the coordinates of the fourth vertex.

△ **56.** The coordinates of two vertices of a square are $(-3, -1)$ and $(2, -1)$. Find the coordinates of two pairs of points possible for the third and fourth vertices.

Complete each table.

57. $x - y = -3$

x	y
0	
	0

58. $y - x = 5$

x	y
0	
	0

59. $y = 2x$

x	y
0	
	0

60. $x = -3y$

x	y
0	
	0

CONCEPT EXTENSIONS

Write each statement as an equation in two variables. Then graph the equation.

61. The y-value is 5 more than the x-value.

62. The y-value is twice the x-value.

63. Two times the x-value, added to three times the y-value is 6.

64. Five times the x-value, added to twice the y-value is -10.

Solve.

△ **65.** The perimeter of the trapezoid below is 22 centimeters. Write a linear equation in two variables for the perimeter. Find y if x is 3 cm.

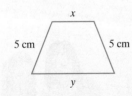

△ **66.** The perimeter of the rectangle below is 50 miles. Write a linear equation in two variables for this perimeter. Use this equation to find x when y is 20.

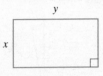

╲ **67.** Explain how to find ordered pair solutions of linear equations in two variables.

╲ **68.** If (a, b) is an ordered pair solution of $x + y = 5$, is (b, a) also a solution? Explain why or why not.

69. Graph the nonlinear equation $y = x^2$ by completing the table shown. Plot the ordered pairs and connect them with a smooth curve.

x	y
0	
1	
-1	
2	
-2	

70. Graph the nonlinear equation $y = |x|$ by completing the table shown. Plot the ordered pairs and connect them. This curve is "V" shaped.

x	y
0	
1	
-1	
2	
-2	

3.3 | Intercepts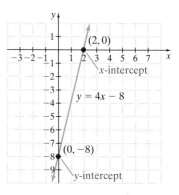

OBJECTIVES

1 Identify Intercepts of a Graph.

2 Graph a Linear Equation by Finding and Plotting Intercepts.

3 Identify and Graph Vertical and Horizontal Lines.

OBJECTIVE

1   Identifying Intercepts

In this section, we graph linear equations in two variables by identifying intercepts. For example, the graph of $y = 4x - 8$ is shown on the right. Notice that this graph crosses the y-axis at the point $(0, -8)$. This point is called the **y-intercept.** Likewise, the graph crosses the x-axis at $(2, 0)$, and this point is called the **x-intercept.**

The intercepts are $(2, 0)$ and $(0, -8)$.

Helpful Hint

If a graph crosses the x-axis at $(-3, 0)$ and the y-axis at $(0, 7)$, then

$$(-3, 0) \qquad (0, 7)$$

$$\uparrow \qquad\qquad \uparrow$$

x-intercept   y-intercept

Notice that for the y-intercept, the x-value is 0 and for the x-intercept, the y-value is 0.
Note: Sometimes in mathematics, you may see just the number -3 stated as the x-intercept, and 7 stated as the y-intercept.

EXAMPLES   Identify the *x*- and *y*-intercepts.

1.

Solution

x-intercept: $(-3, 0)$
y-intercept: $(0, 2)$

2.

Solution

x-intercepts: $(-4, 0), (-1, 0)$
y-intercept: $(0, 1)$

Helpful Hint

Notice that any time $(0, 0)$ is a point of a graph, then it is an x-intercept and a y-intercept. Why? It is the only point that lies on both axes.

3.

Solution

x-intercept: $(0, 0)$
y-intercept: $(0, 0)$

4.

Solution

x-intercept: $(2, 0)$
y-intercept: none

5.

Solution

x-intercepts:
$(-1, 0), (3, 0)$
y-intercepts:
$(0, 2), (0, -1)$

(Continued on next page)

PRACTICE

1–5   Identify the *x*- and *y*-intercepts.

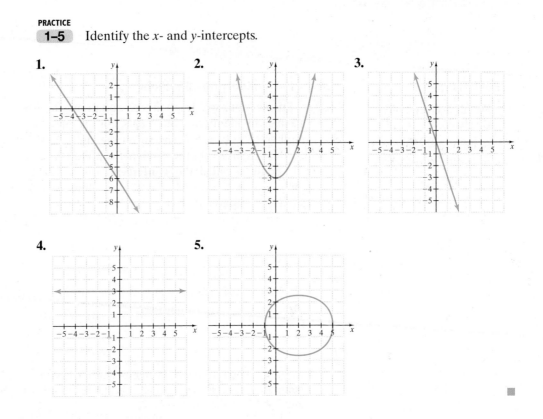

1.

2.

3.

4.

5.

OBJECTIVE

2   Using Intercepts to Graph a Linear Equation ▶

Given the equation of a line, intercepts are usually easy to find since one coordinate is 0.

One way to find the *y*-intercept of a line, given its equation, is to let $x = 0$, since a point on the *y*-axis has an *x*-coordinate of 0. To find the *x*-intercept of a line, let $y = 0$, since a point on the *x*-axis has a *y*-coordinate of 0.

Finding *x*- and *y*-intercepts

To find the *x*-intercept, let $y = 0$ and solve for *x*.

To find the *y*-intercept, let $x = 0$ and solve for *y*.

EXAMPLE 6   Graph $x - 3y = 6$ by finding and plotting intercepts.

Solution Let $y = 0$ to find the *x*-intercept and let $x = 0$ to find the *y*-intercept.

$$
\begin{array}{ll}
\text{Let } y = 0 & \text{Let } x = 0 \\
x - 3y = 6 & x - 3y = 6 \\
x - 3(0) = 6 & 0 - 3y = 6 \\
x - 0 = 6 & -3y = 6 \\
x = 6 & y = -2
\end{array}
$$

The *x*-intercept is $(6, 0)$ and the *y*-intercept is $(0, -2)$. We find a third ordered pair solution to check our work. If we let $y = -1$, then $x = 3$. Plot the points $(6, 0)$, $(0, -2)$, and $(3, -1)$. The graph of $x - 3y = 6$ is the line drawn through these points, as shown.

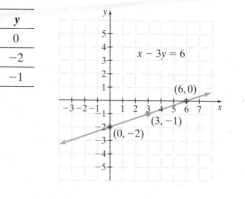

x	y
6	0
0	−2
3	−1

PRACTICE

6 Graph $x + 2y = -4$ by finding and plotting intercepts.

EXAMPLE 7 Graph $x = -2y$ by plotting intercepts.

Solution Let $y = 0$ to find the x-intercept and $x = 0$ to find the y-intercept.

Let $y = 0$ $\qquad\qquad$ Let $x = 0$

$\quad x = -2y$ $\qquad\qquad\quad x = -2y$

$\quad x = -2(0)$ $\qquad\qquad\; 0 = -2y$

$\quad x = 0$ $\qquad\qquad\qquad 0 = y$

Both the x-intercept and y-intercept are $(0, 0)$. In other words, when $x = 0$, then $y = 0$, which gives the ordered pair $(0, 0)$. Also, when $y = 0$, then $x = 0$, which gives the same ordered pair $(0, 0)$. This happens when the graph passes through the origin. Since two points are needed to determine a line, we must find at least one more ordered pair that satisfies $x = -2y$. We will let $y = -1$ to find a second ordered pair solution and let $y = 1$ as a checkpoint.

Let $y = -1$ $\qquad\qquad$ Let $y = 1$

$\quad x = -2(-1)$ $\qquad\qquad x = -2(1)$

$\quad x = 2$ $\qquad\qquad\qquad x = -2$

The ordered pairs are $(0, 0)$, $(2, -1)$, and $(-2, 1)$. Plot these points to graph $x = -2y$.

x	y
0	0
2	−1
−2	1

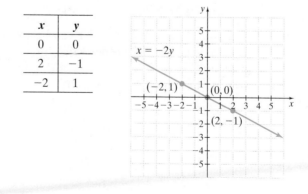

PRACTICE

7 Graph $x = 3y$ by plotting intercepts.

EXAMPLE 8   Graph: $4x = 3y - 9$

Solution Find the x- and y-intercepts, and then choose $x = 2$ to find a checkpoint.

Let $y = 0$	Let $x = 0$	Let $x = 2$
$4x = 3(0) - 9$	$4 \cdot 0 = 3y - 9$	$4(2) = 3y - 9$
$4x = -9$	$9 = 3y$	$8 = 3y - 9$
Solve for x.	Solve for y.	Solve for y.
$x = -\dfrac{9}{4}$ or $-2\dfrac{1}{4}$	$3 = y$	$17 = 3y$
		$\dfrac{17}{3} = y$ or $y = 5\dfrac{2}{3}$

The ordered pairs are $\left(-2\dfrac{1}{4}, 0\right)$, $(0, 3)$, and $\left(2, 5\dfrac{2}{3}\right)$. The equation $4x = 3y - 9$ is graphed as follows.

x	y
$-2\dfrac{1}{4}$	0
0	3
2	$5\dfrac{2}{3}$

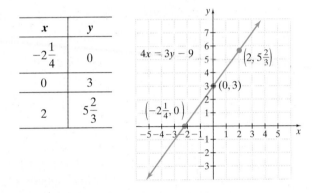

PRACTICE

8   Graph: $3x = 2y + 4$

OBJECTIVE

3   Graphing Vertical and Horizontal Lines ▶

The equation $x = c$, where c is a real number constant, is a linear equation in two variables because it can be written in the form $x + 0y = c$. The graph of this equation is a vertical line as shown in the next example.

EXAMPLE 9   Graph: $x = 2$

Solution The equation $x = 2$ can be written as $x + 0y = 2$. For any y-value chosen, notice that x is 2. No other value for x satisfies $x + 0y = 2$. Any ordered pair whose x-coordinate is 2 is a solution of $x + 0y = 2$. We will use the ordered pair solutions $(2, 3), (2, 0)$, and $(2, -3)$ to graph $x = 2$.

x	y
2	3
2	0
2	-3

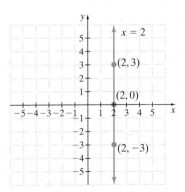

The graph is a vertical line with x-intercept $(2, 0)$. Note that this graph has no y-intercept because x is never 0.

PRACTICE
9   Graph: $x = -2$

Vertical Lines

The graph of $x = c$, where c is a real number, is a vertical line with x-intercept $(c, 0)$.

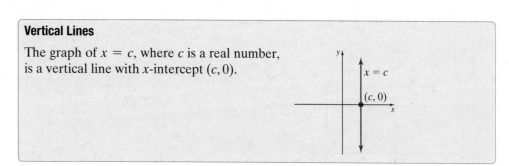

EXAMPLE 10   Graph: $y = -3$

Solution   The equation $y = -3$ can be written as $0x + y = -3$. For any x-value chosen, y is -3. If we choose 4, 1, and -2 as x-values, the ordered pair solutions are $(4, -3)$, $(1, -3)$, and $(-2, -3)$. Use these ordered pairs to graph $y = -3$. The graph is a horizontal line with y-intercept $(0, -3)$ and no x-intercept.

x	y
4	−3
1	−3
−2	−3

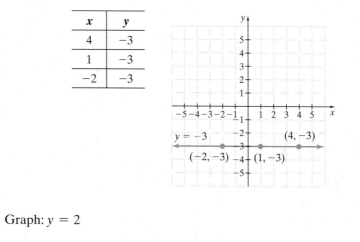

PRACTICE
10   Graph: $y = 2$

Horizontal Lines

The graph of $y = c$, where c is a real number, is a horizontal line with y-intercept $(0, c)$.

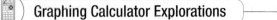

Graphing Calculator Explorations

You may have noticed that to use the $\boxed{Y=}$ key on a grapher to graph an equation, the equation must be solved for y. For example, to graph $2x + 3y = 7$, we solve this equation for y.

$$2x + 3y = 7$$

$$3y = -2x + 7 \quad \text{Subtract } 2x \text{ from both sides.}$$

$$\frac{3y}{3} = -\frac{2x}{3} + \frac{7}{3} \quad \text{Divide both sides by 3.}$$

$$y = -\frac{2}{3}x + \frac{7}{3} \quad \text{Simplify.}$$

To graph $2x + 3y = 7$ or $y = -\frac{2}{3}x + \frac{7}{3}$, press the $\boxed{Y=}$ key and enter

$$Y_1 = -\frac{2}{3}x + \frac{7}{3}$$

Graph each linear equation.

1. $x = 3.78y$

2. $-2.61y = x$

3. $3x + 7y = 21$

4. $-4x + 6y = 21$

5. $-2.2x + 6.8y = 15.5$

6. $5.9x - 0.8y = -10.4$

Vocabulary, Readiness & Video Check

Use the choices below to fill in each blank. Some choices may be used more than once. Exercises 1 and 2 come from Section 3.2.

x	vertical	x-intercept	linear
y	horizontal	y-intercept	standard

1. An equation that can be written in the form $Ax + By = C$ is called a(n) _____ equation in two variables.

2. The form $Ax + By = C$ is called _____ form.

3. The graph of the equation $y = -1$ is a _____ line.

4. The graph of the equation $x = 5$ is a _____ line.

5. A point where a graph crosses the y-axis is called a(n) _____.

6. A point where a graph crosses the x-axis is called a(n) _____.

7. Given an equation of a line, to find the x-intercept (if there is one), let _____ = 0 and solve for _____.

8. Given an equation of a line, to find the y-intercept (if there is one), let _____ = 0 and solve for _____.

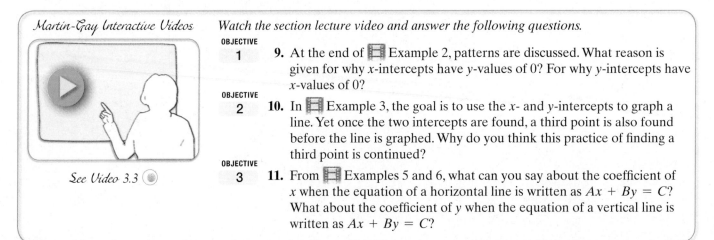

Martin-Gay Interactive Videos

See Video 3.3

Watch the section lecture video and answer the following questions.

OBJECTIVE 1

9. At the end of Example 2, patterns are discussed. What reason is given for why x-intercepts have y-values of 0? For why y-intercepts have x-values of 0?

OBJECTIVE 2

10. In Example 3, the goal is to use the x- and y-intercepts to graph a line. Yet once the two intercepts are found, a third point is also found before the line is graphed. Why do you think this practice of finding a third point is continued?

OBJECTIVE 3

11. From Examples 5 and 6, what can you say about the coefficient of x when the equation of a horizontal line is written as $Ax + By = C$? What about the coefficient of y when the equation of a vertical line is written as $Ax + By = C$?

3.3   Exercise Set   MyMathLab®

Identify the intercepts. See Examples 1 through 5.

1.   **2.**

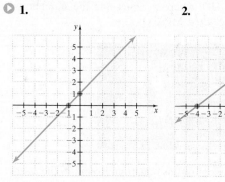

3.   **4.**

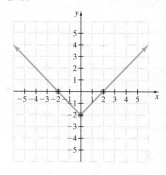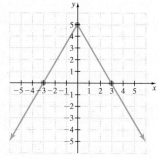

5.   **6.**

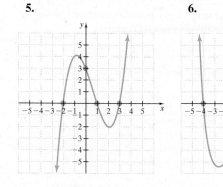

7.   **8.**

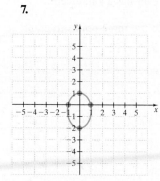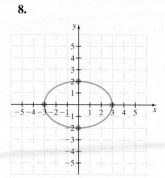

Solve. See Examples 1 through 5.

9. What is the greatest number of intercepts for a line?

10. What is the least number of intercepts for a line?

11. What is the least number of intercepts for a circle?

12. What is the greatest number of intercepts for a circle?

Graph each linear equation by finding and plotting its intercepts. See Examples 6 through 8.

13. $x - y = 3$ **14.** $x - y = -4$ **15.** $x = 5y$

16. $x = 2y$ **17.** $-x + 2y = 6$ **18.** $x - 2y = -8$

19. $2x - 4y = 8$ **20.** $2x + 3y = 6$ **21.** $y = 2x$

22. $y = -2x$ **23.** $y = 3x + 6$ **24.** $y = 2x + 10$

Graph each linear equation. See Examples 9 and 10.

25. $x = -1$ **26.** $y = 5$ **27.** $y = 0$

28. $x = 0$ **29.** $y + 7 = 0$ **30.** $x - 2 = 0$

31. $x + 3 = 0$ **32.** $y - 6 = 0$

MIXED PRACTICE

Graph each linear equation. See Examples 6 through 10.

33. $x = y$ **34.** $x = -y$

35. $x + 8y = 8$ **36.** $x + 3y = 9$

37. $5 = 6x - y$ **38.** $4 = x - 3y$

39. $-x + 10y = 11$ **40.** $-x + 9y = 10$

41. $x = -4\frac{1}{2}$ **42.** $x = -1\frac{3}{4}$

43. $y = 3\frac{1}{4}$ **44.** $y = 2\frac{1}{2}$

45. $y = -\frac{2}{3}x + 1$ **46.** $y = -\frac{3}{5}x + 3$

47. $4x - 6y + 2 = 0$ **48.** $9x - 6y + 3 = 0$

For Exercises 49 through 54, match each equation with its graph. See graphs A–F below and on the next page.

49. $y = 3$ **50.** $y = 2x + 2$

51. $x = -1$ **52.** $x = 3$

53. $y = 2x + 3$ **54.** $y = -2x$

A.   **B.**

C.   **D.**

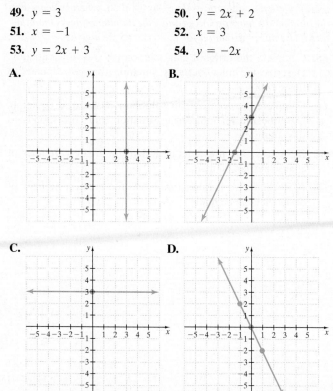

E.

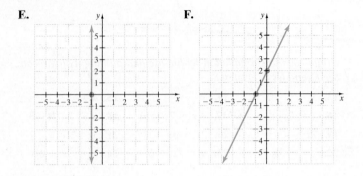

F.

REVIEW AND PREVIEW

Simplify. See Sections 1.4 through 1.7.

55. $\dfrac{-6 - 3}{2 - 8}$

56. $\dfrac{4 - 5}{-1 - 0}$

57. $\dfrac{-8 - (-2)}{-3 - (-2)}$

58. $\dfrac{12 - 3}{10 - 9}$

59. $\dfrac{0 - 6}{5 - 0}$

60. $\dfrac{2 - 2}{3 - 5}$

CONCEPT EXTENSIONS

Answer the following true or false.

61. All lines have an x-intercept *and* a y-intercept.

62. The graph of $y = 4x$ contains the point $(0, 0)$.

63. The graph of $x + y = 5$ has an x-intercept of $(5, 0)$ and a y-intercept of $(0, 5)$.

64. The graph of $y = 5x$ contains the point $(5, 1)$.

The production supervisor at Alexandra's Office Products finds that it takes 3 hours to manufacture a particular office chair and 6 hours to manufacture an office desk. A total of 1200 hours is available to produce office chairs and desks of this style. The linear equation that models this situation is $3x + 6y = 1200$, where x represents the number of chairs produced and y the number of desks manufactured. Use this information for Exercises 65 through 68.

65. Complete the ordered pair solution $(0,\ )$ of this equation. Describe the manufacturing situation that corresponds to this solution.

66. Complete the ordered pair solution $(\ , 0)$ of this equation. Describe the manufacturing situation that corresponds to this solution.

67. If 50 desks are manufactured, find the greatest number of chairs that can be made.

68. If 50 chairs are manufactured, find the greatest number of desks that can be made.

Solve.

69. Since 2009, the number of analog theater screens has been on the decline in the U.S. The number of analog movie screens y each year can be estimated by the equation $y = -7000x + 31{,}800$, where x represents the number of years since 2009. (*Source:* MPAA)

a. Find the x-intercept of this equation. Round to the nearest tenth.

b. What does this x-intercept mean?

c. Use part (b) to comment on your opinion of the limitations of using equations to model real data.

70. The price of admission to a movie theater has been steadily increasing. The price of regular admission y (in dollars) to a movie theater may be represented by the equation $y = 0.24x + 5.28$, where x is the number of years after 2000. (*Source:* Based on data from Motion Picture Association of America)

a. Find the x-intercept of this equation.

b. What does this x-intercept mean?

c. Use part (b) to comment on your opinion of the limitations of using equations to model real data.

*Two lines in the same plane that do not intersect are called **parallel lines.***

71. Draw a line parallel to the line $x = 5$ that intersects the x-axis at $(1, 0)$. What is the equation of this line?

72. Draw a line parallel to the line $y = -1$ that intersects the y-axis at $(0, -4)$. What is the equation of this line?

73. Discuss whether a vertical line ever has a y-intercept.

74. Explain why it is a good idea to use three points to graph a linear equation.

75. Discuss whether a horizontal line ever has an x-intercept.

76. Explain how to find intercepts.

3.4 Slope and Rate of Change

OBJECTIVES

1 Find the Slope of a Line Given Two Points of the Line.

2 Find the Slope of a Line Given Its Equation.

3 Find the Slopes of Horizontal and Vertical Lines.

4 Compare the Slopes of Parallel and Perpendicular Lines.

5 Interpret Slope as a Rate of Change.

OBJECTIVE

1   Finding the Slope of a Line Given Two Points of the Line

Thus far, much of this chapter has been devoted to graphing lines. You have probably noticed by now that a key feature of a line is its slant or steepness. In mathematics, the slant or steepness of a line is formally known as its **slope.** We measure the slope of a line by the ratio of vertical change to the corresponding horizontal change as we move along the line.

On the line below, for example, suppose that we begin at the point $(1, 2)$ and move to the point $(4, 6)$. The vertical change is the change in y-coordinates: $6 - 2$ or 4 units. The corresponding horizontal change is the change in x-coordinates: $4 - 1 = 3$ units. The ratio of these changes is

$$\text{slope} = \frac{\text{change in } y \,(\text{vertical change})}{\text{change in } x \,(\text{horizontal change})} = \frac{4}{3}$$

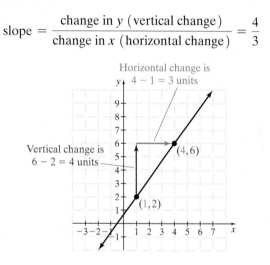

The slope of this line, then, is $\dfrac{4}{3}$. This means that for every 4 units of change in y-coordinates, there is a corresponding change of 3 units in x-coordinates.

> **Helpful Hint**
>
> It makes no difference what two points of a line are chosen to find its slope. The slope of a line is the same everywhere on the line.

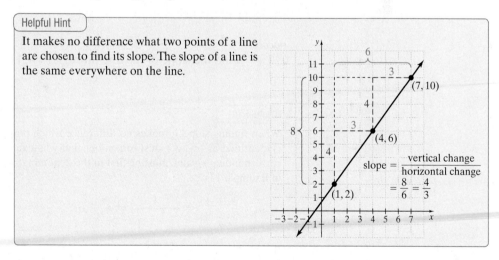

To find the slope of a line, then, choose two points of the line. Label the x-coordinates of the two points x_1 and x_2 (read "x sub one" and "x sub two"), and label the corresponding y-coordinates y_1 and y_2.

The vertical change or **rise** between these points is the difference in the y-coordinates: $y_2 - y_1$. The horizontal change or **run** between the points is the difference of the x-coordinates: $x_2 - x_1$. The slope of the line is the ratio of $y_2 - y_1$ to $x_2 - x_1$, and we traditionally use the letter m to denote slope: $m = \dfrac{y_2 - y_1}{x_2 - x_1}$.

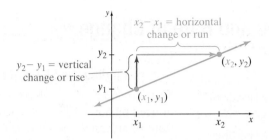

Slope of a Line

The slope m of the line containing the points (x_1, y_1) and (x_2, y_2) is given by

$$m = \frac{\text{rise}}{\text{run}} = \frac{\text{change in } y}{\text{change in } x} = \frac{y_2 - y_1}{x_2 - x_1}, \qquad \text{as long as } x_2 \neq x_1$$

EXAMPLE 1 Find the slope of the line through $(-1, 5)$ and $(2, -3)$. Graph the line.

Solution If we let (x_1, y_1) be $(-1, 5)$, then $x_1 = -1$ and $y_1 = 5$. Also, let (x_2, y_2) be $(2, -3)$ so that $x_2 = 2$ and $y_2 = -3$. Then, by the definition of slope,

$$m = \frac{y_2 - y_1}{x_2 - x_1}$$

$$= \frac{-3 - 5}{2 - (-1)}$$

$$= \frac{-8}{3} = -\frac{8}{3}$$

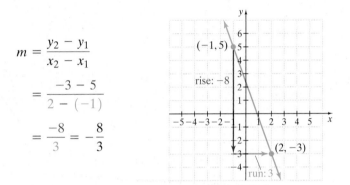

The slope of the line is $-\dfrac{8}{3}$.

PRACTICE

1 Find the slope of the line through $(-4, 11)$ and $(2, 5)$.

> **Helpful Hint**
>
> When finding slope, it makes no difference which point is identified as (x_1, y_1) and which is identified as (x_2, y_2). Just remember that whatever y-value is first in the numerator, its corresponding x-value must be first in the denominator. Another way to calculate the slope in Example 1 is:
>
> $$m = \frac{y_2 - y_1}{x_2 - x_1} = \frac{5 - (-3)}{-1 - 2} = \frac{8}{-3} \quad \text{or} \quad -\frac{8}{3} \quad \leftarrow \text{Same slope as found in Example 1.}$$

✔ **CONCEPT CHECK**

The points $(-2, -5)$, $(0, -2)$, $(4, 4)$, and $(10, 13)$ all lie on the same line. Work with a partner and verify that the slope is the same no matter which points are used to find slope.

Answer to Concept Check:

$$m = \frac{3}{2}$$

EXAMPLE 2   Find the slope of the line through $(-1, -2)$ and $(2, 4)$. Graph the line.

Solution Let (x_1, y_1) be $(2, 4)$ and (x_2, y_2) be $(-1, -2)$.

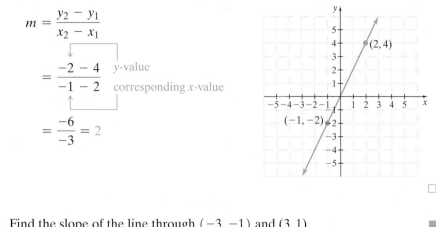

$$m = \frac{y_2 - y_1}{x_2 - x_1}$$

$$= \frac{-2 - 4}{-1 - 2} \quad \begin{array}{l} y\text{-value} \\ \text{corresponding } x\text{-value} \end{array}$$

$$= \frac{-6}{-3} = 2$$

> **Helpful Hint**
>
> The slope for Example 2 is the same if we let (x_1, y_1) be $(-1, -2)$ and (x_2, y_2) be $(2, 4)$.
>
> $$m = \frac{\overset{y\text{-value}}{4 - (-2)}}{\underset{\text{corresponding } x\text{-value}}{2 - (-1)}} = \frac{6}{3} = 2$$

PRACTICE
2   Find the slope of the line through $(-3, -1)$ and $(3, 1)$.

✔ **CONCEPT CHECK**

What is wrong with the following slope calculation for the points $(3, 5)$ and $(-2, 6)$?

$$m = \frac{5 - 6}{-2 - 3} = \frac{-1}{-5} = \frac{1}{5}$$

Notice that the slope of the line in Example 1 is negative, whereas the slope of the line in Example 2 is positive. Let your eye follow the line with negative slope from left to right and notice that the line "goes down." Following the line with positive slope from left to right, notice that the line "goes up." This is true in general.

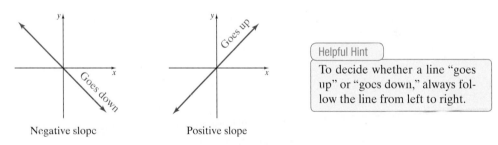

Negative slope   Positive slope

> **Helpful Hint**
>
> To decide whether a line "goes up" or "goes down," always follow the line from left to right.

OBJECTIVE
2   Finding the Slope of a Line Given Its Equation ▶

As we have seen, the slope of a line is defined by two points on the line. Thus, if we know the equation of a line, we can find its slope by finding two of its points. For example, let's find the slope of the line

$$y = 3x + 2$$

To find two points, we can choose two values for x and substitute to find corresponding y-values. If $x = 0$, for example, $y = 3 \cdot 0 + 2$ or $y = 2$. If $x = 1$, $y = 3 \cdot 1 + 2$ or $y = 5$. This gives the ordered pairs $(0, 2)$ and $(1, 5)$. Using the definition for slope, we have

$$m = \frac{5 - 2}{1 - 0} = \frac{3}{1} = 3 \quad \text{The slope is 3.}$$

Notice that the slope, 3, is the same as the coefficient of x in the equation $y = 3x + 2$.

Also, recall from Section 3.2 that the graph of an equation of the form $y = mx + b$ has y-intercept $(0, b)$.

This means that the y-intercept of the graph of $y = 3x + 2$ is $(0, 2)$. This is true in general and the form $y = mx + b$ is appropriately called the **slope-intercept form.**

$$\underset{\underset{(0,\,b)}{\text{slope } y\text{-intercept}}}{\overset{\uparrow\qquad\uparrow}{y = mx + b}}$$

> **Slope-Intercept Form**
>
> When a linear equation in two variables is written in slope-intercept form,
>
> $$y = mx + b$$
>
> m is the slope of the line and $(0, b)$ is the y-intercept of the line.

EXAMPLE 3   Find the slope and y-intercept of the line whose equation is $y = \dfrac{3}{4}x + 6$

Solution The equation is in slope-intercept form, $y = mx + b$.

$$y = \frac{3}{4}x + 6$$

The coefficient of x, $\dfrac{3}{4}$, is the slope and the constant term, 6, is the y-value of the y-intercept, $(0, 6)$. $\qquad\square$

PRACTICE

3   Find the slope and y-intercept of the line whose equation is $y = \dfrac{2}{3}x - 2$. ∎

EXAMPLE 4   Find the slope and the y-intercept of the line whose equation is $-y = 5x - 2$.

Solution Remember, the equation must be solved for y (not $-y$) in order for it to be written in slope-intercept form.

To solve for y, let's divide both sides of the equation by -1.

$$-y = 5x - 2$$
$$\frac{-y}{-1} = \frac{5x}{-1} - \frac{2}{-1} \quad \text{Divide both sides by } -1.$$
$$y = -5x + 2 \quad \text{Simplify.}$$

The coefficient of x, -5, is the slope and the constant term, 2, is the y-value of the y-intercept, $(0, 2)$. $\qquad\square$

PRACTICE

4   Find the slope and y-intercept of the line whose equation is $-y = -6x + 5$. ∎

EXAMPLE 5   Find the slope and the y-intercept of the line whose equation is $3x - 4y = 4$.

Solution Write the equation in slope-intercept form by solving for y.

$$3x - 4y = 4$$
$$-4y = -3x + 4 \quad \text{Subtract } 3x \text{ from both sides.}$$
$$\frac{-4y}{-4} = \frac{-3x}{-4} + \frac{4}{-4} \quad \text{Divide both sides by } -4.$$
$$y = \frac{3}{4}x - 1 \quad \text{Simplify.}$$

The coefficient of x, $\dfrac{3}{4}$, is the slope, and the y-intercept is $(0, -1)$. $\qquad\square$

PRACTICE
5   Find the slope and the y-intercept of the line whose equation is $5x + 2y = 8$. ■

OBJECTIVE

3   Finding Slopes of Horizontal and Vertical Lines

Recall that if a line tilts upward from left to right, its slope is positive. If a line tilts downward from left to right, its slope is negative. Let's now find the slopes of two special lines, horizontal and vertical lines.

EXAMPLE 6   Find the slope of the line $y = -1$.

Solution Recall that $y = -1$ is a horizontal line with y-intercept $(0, -1)$. To find the slope, find two ordered pair solutions of $y = -1$. Solutions of $y = -1$ must have a y-value of -1. Let's use points $(2, -1)$ and $(-3, -1)$, which are on the line.

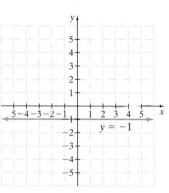

$$m = \frac{y_2 - y_1}{x_2 - x_1} = \frac{-1 - (-1)}{-3 - 2} = \frac{0}{-5} = 0$$

The slope of the line $y = -1$ is 0 and its graph is shown.   □

PRACTICE

6   Find the slope of the line $y = 3$. ■

Any two points of a horizontal line will have the same y-values. This means that the y-values will always have a difference of 0 for all horizontal lines. Thus, **all horizontal lines have a slope of 0.**

EXAMPLE 7   Find the slope of the line $x = 5$.

Solution Recall that the graph of $x = 5$ is a vertical line with x-intercept $(5, 0)$.

To find the slope, find two ordered pair solutions of $x = 5$. Solutions of $x = 5$ must have an x-value of 5. Let's use points $(5, 0)$ and $(5, 4)$, which are on the line.

$$m = \frac{y_2 - y_1}{x_2 - x_1} = \frac{4 - 0}{5 - 5} = \frac{4}{0}$$

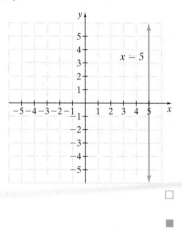

Since $\dfrac{4}{0}$ is undefined, we say the slope of the vertical line $x = 5$ is undefined, and its graph is shown.   □

PRACTICE

7   Find the slope of the line $x = -4$. ■

Any two points of a vertical line will have the same x-values. This means that the x-values will always have a difference of 0 for all vertical lines. Thus **all vertical lines have undefined slope.**

Helpful Hint
Slope of 0 and undefined slope are not the same. Vertical lines have undefined slope or no slope, while horizontal lines have a slope of 0.

Here is a general review of slope.

Summary of Slope

Slope m of the line through (x_1, y_1) and (x_2, y_2) is given by the equation $m = \dfrac{y_2 - y_1}{x_2 - x_1}$.

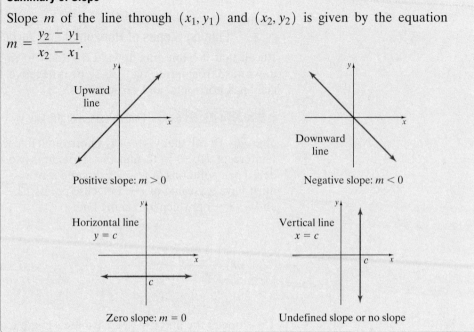

Upward line

Positive slope: $m > 0$

Downward line

Negative slope: $m < 0$

Horizontal line
$y = c$

Zero slope: $m = 0$

Vertical line
$x = c$

Undefined slope or no slope

OBJECTIVE

4 Slopes of Parallel and Perpendicular Lines

Two lines in the same plane are **parallel** if they do not intersect. Slopes of lines can help us determine whether lines are parallel. Parallel lines have the same steepness, so it follows that they have the same slope.

For example, the graphs of

$$y = -2x + 4$$

and

$$y = -2x - 3$$

are shown. These lines have the same slope, -2. They also have different y-intercepts, so the lines are distinct and parallel. (If the y-intercepts were the same also, the lines would be the same.)

Parallel Lines

Nonvertical parallel lines have the same slope and different y-intercepts.

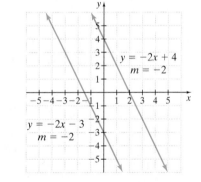

Two lines are **perpendicular** if they lie in the same plane and meet at a 90° (right) angle. How do the slopes of perpendicular lines compare? The product of the slopes of two perpendicular lines is -1.

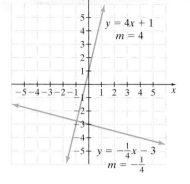

For example, the graphs of

$$y = 4x + 1$$

and

$$y = -\frac{1}{4}x - 3$$

are shown. The slopes of the lines are 4 and $-\frac{1}{4}$. Their product is $4\left(-\frac{1}{4}\right) = -1$, so the lines are perpendicular.

Perpendicular Lines

If the product of the slopes of two lines is -1, then the lines are perpendicular.

(Two nonvertical lines are perpendicular if the slope of one is the negative reciprocal of the slope of the other.)

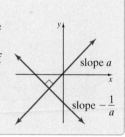

Helpful Hint

Here are examples of numbers that are negative (opposite) reciprocals.

Number	Negative Reciprocal	Their Product Is -1.
$\dfrac{2}{3}$	$-\dfrac{3}{2}$	$\dfrac{2}{3} \cdot -\dfrac{3}{2} = -\dfrac{6}{6} = -1$
-5 or $-\dfrac{5}{1}$	$\dfrac{1}{5}$	$-5 \cdot \dfrac{1}{5} = -\dfrac{5}{5} = -1$

Helpful Hint

Here are a few important facts about vertical and horizontal lines.

- Two distinct vertical lines are parallel.
- Two distinct horizontal lines are parallel.
- A horizontal line and a vertical line are always perpendicular.

△ **EXAMPLE 8**   Determine whether each pair of lines is parallel, perpendicular, or neither.

a. $y = -\dfrac{1}{5}x + 1$ **b.** $x + y = 3$ **c.** $3x + y = 5$
$2x + 10y = 3$ $-x + y = 4$ $2x + 3y = 6$

Solution

a. The slope of the line $y = -\dfrac{1}{5}x + 1$ is $-\dfrac{1}{5}$. We find the slope of the second line by solving its equation for y.

$$2x + 10y = 3$$
$$10y = -2x + 3 \qquad \text{Subtract } 2x \text{ from both sides.}$$
$$y = \frac{-2}{10}x + \frac{3}{10} \qquad \text{Divide both sides by 10.}$$
$$y = -\frac{1}{5}x + \frac{3}{10} \qquad \text{Simplify.}$$

The slope of this line is $-\dfrac{1}{5}$ also. Since the lines have the same slope and different y-intercepts, they are parallel, as shown in the margin.

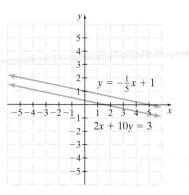

(Continued on next page)

b. To find each slope, we solve each equation for y.

$$x + y = 3 \qquad\qquad -x + y = 4$$
$$y = -x + 3 \qquad\qquad y = x + 4$$
$$\uparrow \qquad\qquad\qquad \uparrow$$
The slope is -1. $\qquad\qquad$ The slope is 1.

The slopes are not the same, so the lines are not parallel. Next we check the product of the slopes: $(-1)(1) = -1$. Since the product is -1, the lines are perpendicular, as shown in the figure.

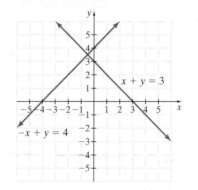

c. We solve each equation for y to find each slope. The slopes are -3 and $-\dfrac{2}{3}$.

The slopes are not the same and their product is not -1. Thus, the lines are neither parallel nor perpendicular. $\qquad\qquad \square$

PRACTICE

8   Determine whether each pair of lines is parallel, perpendicular, or neither.

a. $y = -5x + 1$ $\qquad$ **b.** $x + y = 11$ $\qquad$ **c.** $2x + 3y = 21$
$\quad\ x - 5y = 10$ $\qquad\qquad\ \ 2x + y = 11$ $\qquad\qquad\ \ 6y = -4x - 2$ $\qquad$ ∎

✔ **CONCEPT CHECK**

Consider the line $-6x + 2y = 1$.

a. Write the equations of two lines parallel to this line.
b. Write the equations of two lines perpendicular to this line.

OBJECTIVE

5   **Slope as a Rate of Change** ▶

Slope can also be interpreted as a rate of change. In other words, slope tells us how fast y is changing with respect to x. To see this, let's look at a few of the many real-world applications of slope. For example, the pitch of a roof, used by builders and architects, is its slope. The pitch of the roof on the left is $\dfrac{7}{10}\left(\dfrac{\text{rise}}{\text{run}}\right)$. This means that the roof rises vertically 7 feet for every horizontal 10 feet. The rate of change for the roof is 7 vertical feet (y) per 10 horizontal feet (x).

The grade of a road is its slope written as a percent. A 7% grade, as shown below, means that the road rises (or falls) 7 feet for every horizontal 100 feet. $\Big($ Recall that $7\% = \dfrac{7}{100}.\Big)$ Here, the slope of $\dfrac{7}{100}$ gives us the rate of change. The road rises (in our diagram) 7 vertical feet (y) for every 100 horizontal feet (x).

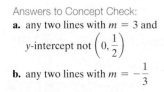

Answers to Concept Check:
a. any two lines with $m = 3$ and y-intercept not $\left(0, \dfrac{1}{2}\right)$

b. any two lines with $m = -\dfrac{1}{3}$

$\dfrac{7}{100} = 7\%$ grade $\qquad$ 7 feet

100 feet

EXAMPLE 9   **Finding the Grade of a Road**

At one part of the road to the summit of Pikes Peak, the road rises at a rate of 15 vertical feet for a horizontal distance of 250 feet. Find the grade of the road.

Solution   Recall that the grade of a road is its slope written as a percent.

$$\text{grade} = \frac{\text{rise}}{\text{run}} = \frac{15}{250} = 0.06 = 6\%$$

15 feet

250 feet

The grade is 6%.   ☐

PRACTICE

9   One part of the Mt. Washington (New Hampshire) cog railway rises about 1794 feet over a horizontal distance of 7176 feet. Find the grade of this part of the railway.   ◼

EXAMPLE 10   **Finding the Slope of a Line**

The following graph shows annual food and drink sales y (in billions of dollars) for year x.

    a. Find the slope of the line and attach the proper units for the rate of change.

    b. Then write a sentence explaining the meaning of the slope for this application.

Solution

    a. Use (2000, 377) and (2014, 685) to calculate slope.

$$m = \frac{685 - 377}{2014 - 2000} = \frac{308}{14} = \frac{22 \text{ billion dollars}}{1 \text{ year}}$$

    b. This means that the rate of change of restaurant food and drink sales increases by 22 billion dollars every 1 year, or $22 billion per year.   ☐

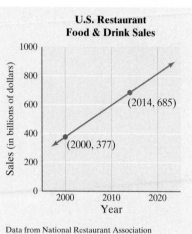

U.S. Restaurant Food & Drink Sales

Data from National Restaurant Association

PRACTICE

10   The following graph shows the cost y (in dollars) of having laundry done at the Wash-n-Fold, where x is the number of pounds of laundry.

    a. Find the slope of the line, and attach the proper units for the rate of change.

    b. Then write a sentence explaining the meaning of the slope for this application.

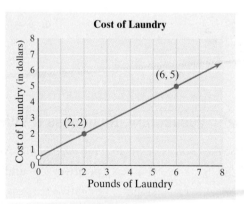

Cost of Laundry

◼

Graphing Calculator Explorations

It is possible to use a grapher to sketch the graph of more than one equation on the same set of axes. This feature can be used to confirm our findings from Section 3.2 when we learned that the graph of an equation written in the form $y = mx + b$ has a y-intercept of b. For example, graph the equations $y = \frac{2}{5}x$, $y = \frac{2}{5}x + 7$, and $y = \frac{2}{5}x - 4$

(Continued on next page)

on the same set of axes. To do so, press the $\boxed{Y=}$ key and enter the equations on the first three lines.

$$Y_1 = \left(\frac{2}{5}\right)x$$

$$Y_2 = \left(\frac{2}{5}\right)x + 7$$

$$Y_3 = \left(\frac{2}{5}\right)x - 4$$

The screen should look like:

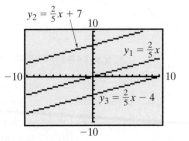

Notice that all three graphs appear to have the same positive slope. The graph of $y = \frac{2}{5}x + 7$ is the graph of $y = \frac{2}{5}x$ moved 7 units upward with a y-intercept of 7. Also, the graph of $y = \frac{2}{5}x - 4$ is the graph of $y = \frac{2}{5}x$ moved 4 units downward with a y-intercept of -4.

Graph the equations on the same set of axes. Describe the similarities and differences in their graphs. Use the standard window setting or any other convenient window setting.

1. $y = 3.8x, y = 3.8x - 3, y = 3.8x + 7$
2. $y = -4.9x, y = -4.9x + 1, y = -4.9x + 8$
3. $y = \frac{1}{4}x; y = \frac{1}{4}x + 5, y = \frac{1}{4}x - 8$
4. $y = -\frac{3}{4}x, y = -\frac{3}{4}x - 5, y = -\frac{3}{4}x + 6$

✔ Vocabulary, Readiness & Video Check

Use the choices below to fill in each blank. Not all choices will be used.

m	x	0	positive	undefined
b	y	slope	negative	

1. The measure of the steepness or tilt of a line is called _____.
2. If an equation is written in the form $y = mx + b$, the value of the letter _____ is the value of the slope of the graph.
3. The slope of a horizontal line is _____.
4. The slope of a vertical line is _____.
5. If the graph of a line moves upward from left to right, the line has _____ slope.
6. If the graph of a line moves downward from left to right, the line has _____ slope.
7. Given two points of a line, slope $= \dfrac{\text{change in } \underline{}}{\text{change in } \underline{}}$.

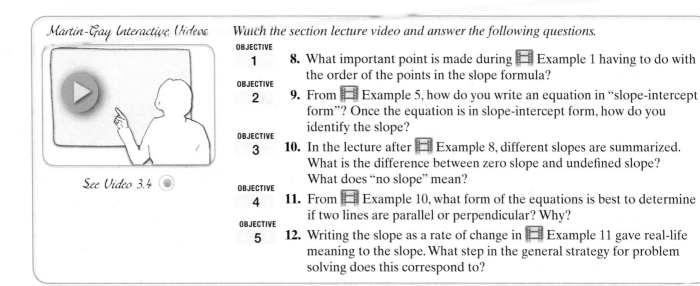

Martin-Gay Interactive Videos

See Video 3.4

Watch the section lecture video and answer the following questions.

OBJECTIVE 1

8. What important point is made during Example 1 having to do with the order of the points in the slope formula?

OBJECTIVE 2

9. From Example 5, how do you write an equation in "slope-intercept form"? Once the equation is in slope-intercept form, how do you identify the slope?

OBJECTIVE 3

10. In the lecture after Example 8, different slopes are summarized. What is the difference between zero slope and undefined slope? What does "no slope" mean?

OBJECTIVE 4

11. From Example 10, what form of the equations is best to determine if two lines are parallel or perpendicular? Why?

OBJECTIVE 5

12. Writing the slope as a rate of change in Example 11 gave real-life meaning to the slope. What step in the general strategy for problem solving does this correspond to?

3.4   Exercise Set   MyMathLab®

Find the slope of the line that passes through the given points. See Examples 1 and 2.

1. $(-1, 5)$ and $(6, -2)$

2. $(3, 1)$ and $(2, 6)$

3. $(-4, 3)$ and $(-4, 5)$

4. $(6, -6)$ and $(6, 2)$

5. $(-2, 8)$ and $(1, 6)$

6. $(4, -3)$ and $(2, 2)$

7. $(5, 1)$ and $(-2, 1)$

8. $(0, 13)$ and $(-4, 13)$

Find the slope of each line if it exists. See Examples 1 and 2.

9.

10.

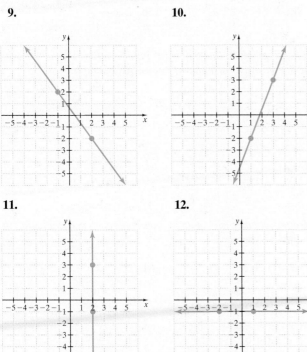

11.

12.

13.

14.

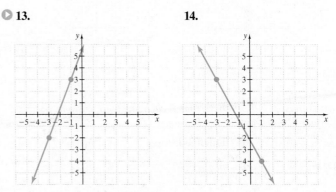

State whether the slope of the line is positive, negative, 0, or is undefined. See the top box on p. 210.

15.

16.

17.

18.

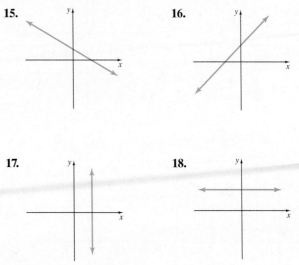

Decide whether a line with the given slope is upward, downward, horizontal, or vertical. See the top box on p. 210.

19. $m = \dfrac{7}{6}$ _____

20. $m = -3$ _____

21. $m = 0$ _____

22. m is undefined. _____

For each graph, determine which line has the greater slope. See the top box on p. 210.

23.

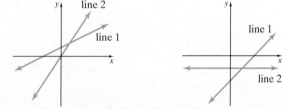

line 1

line 2

24.

line 1   line 2

25.

line 2

line 1

26.

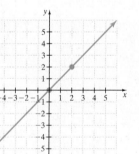

line 1

line 2

In Exercises 27 through 32, match each line with its slope. See Examples 1 and 2 and the top box on p. 210.

A. $m = 0$

B. undefined slope

C. $m = 3$

D. $m = 1$

E. $m = -\dfrac{1}{2}$

F. $m = -\dfrac{3}{4}$

27.

28.

29.

30.

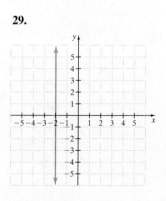

31.

32.

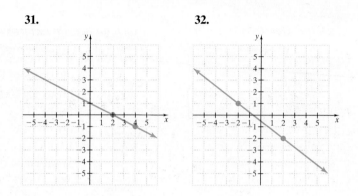

Find the slope of each line. See Examples 6 and 7.

33. $x = 6$

34. $y = 4$

35. $y = -4$

36. $x = 2$

37. $x = -3$

38. $y = -11$

39. $y = 0$

40. $x = 0$

MIXED PRACTICE

Find the slope of each line. See Examples 3 through 7.

41. $y = 5x - 2$

42. $y = -2x + 6$

43. $y = -0.3x + 2.5$

44. $y = -7.6x - 0.1$

45. $2x + y = 7$

46. $-5x + y = 10$

47. $2x - 3y = 10$

48. $3x - 5y = 1$

49. $x = 1$

50. $y = -2$

51. $x = 2y$

52. $x = -4y$

53. $y = -3$

54. $x = 5$

55. $-3x - 4y = 6$

56. $-4x - 7y = 9$

57. $20x - 5y = 1.2$

58. $24x - 3y = 5.7$

△ *Find the slope of the line that is (a) parallel and (b) perpendicular to the line through each pair of points. See Example 8.*

59. $(-3, -3)$ and $(0, 0)$

60. $(6, -2)$ and $(1, 4)$

61. $(-8, -4)$ and $(3, 5)$

62. $(6, -1)$ and $(-4, -10)$

△ *Determine whether each pair of lines is parallel, perpendicular, or neither. See Example 8.*

63. $y = \dfrac{2}{9}x + 3$

$y = -\dfrac{2}{9}x$

64. $y = \dfrac{1}{5}x + 20$

$y = -\dfrac{1}{5}x$

65. $x - 3y = -6$

$y = 3x - 9$

66. $y = 4x - 2$

$4x + y = 5$

67. $6x = 5y + 1$

$-12x + 10y = 1$

68. $-x + 2y = -2$

$2x = 4y + 3$

69. $6 + 4x = 3y$

$3x + 4y = 8$

70. $10 + 3x = 5y$

$5x + 3y = 1$

The pitch of a roof is its slope. Find the pitch of each roof shown. See Example 9. (Note: Pitch of a roof is a positive value.)

71.

72.

The grade of a road is its slope written as a percent. Find the grade of each road shown. See Example 9. (Note: Grade of a road is a positive value.)

73.

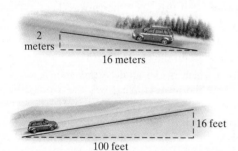

74.

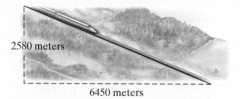

75. One of Japan's superconducting "bullet" trains is researched and tested at the Yamanashi Maglev Test Line near Otsuki City. The steepest section of the track has a rise of 2580 meters for a horizontal distance of 6450 meters. What is the grade of this section of track? (*Source:* Japan Railways Central Co.)

76. Professional plumbers suggest that a sewer pipe should rise 0.25 inch for every horizontal foot. Find the recommended slope for a sewer pipe. Round to the nearest hundredth.

77. There has been controversy over the past few years about the world's steepest street. The *Guinness Book of Records*

actually listed Baldwin Street, in Dunedin, New Zealand, as the world's steepest street, but Canton Avenue in the Pittsburgh neighborhood of Beechview may be steeper. Calculate each grade to the nearest percent.

		Grade (%)
Canton Avenue	for every 30 meters of horizontal distance, the vertical change is 11 meters	
Baldwin Street	for every 2.86 meters of horizontal distance, the vertical change is 1 meter	

78. According to federal regulations, a wheelchair ramp should rise no more than 1 foot for a horizontal distance of 12 feet. Write the slope as a grade. Round to the nearest tenth of a percent.

For Exercises 79 through 82, find the slope of each line and write a sentence explaining the meaning of the slope as a rate of change. Don't forget to attach the proper units. See Example 10.

79. This graph approximates the number of U.S. households that have computers *y* (in millions) for year *x*. (*Source:* U.S. census and statistics)

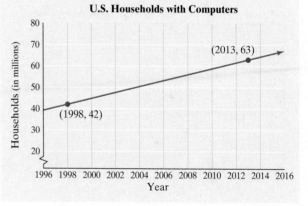

80. The graph approximates the amount of money *y* (in billions of dollars) spent worldwide on leisure travel and tourism for year *x*. (*Source:* World Travel and Tourism Council)

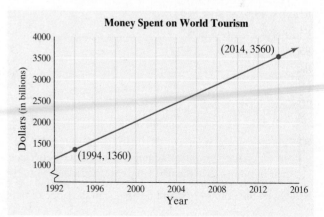

For Exercises 81 and 82, write the slope as a decimal.

81. The graph below shows the total cost y (in dollars) of owning and operating a compact car where x is the number of miles driven.

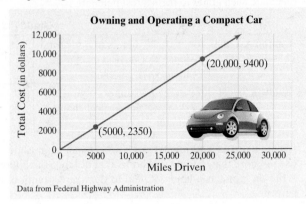

Owning and Operating a Compact Car

(20,000, 9400)

(5000, 2350)

Total Cost (in dollars) vs. Miles Driven

Data from Federal Highway Administration

82. Americans are keeping their cars longer. The graph below shows the median age y (in years) of automobiles in the United States for the years shown. (*Source:* Bureau of Transportation Statistics)

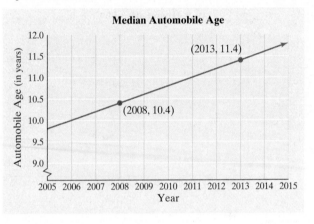

Median Automobile Age

(2013, 11.4)

(2008, 10.4)

Automobile Age (in years) vs. Year

REVIEW AND PREVIEW

Solve each equation for y. See Section 2.5.

83. $y - (-6) = 2(x - 4)$

84. $y - 7 = -9(x - 6)$

85. $y - 1 = -6(x - (-2))$

86. $y - (-3) = 4(x - (-5))$

CONCEPT EXTENSIONS

Solve. See a Concept Check in this section.

87. Verify that the points $(2, 1)$, $(0, 0)$, $(-2, -1)$ and $(-4, -2)$ are all on the same line by computing the slope between each pair of points. (See the first Concept Check.)

88. Given the points $(2, 3)$ and $(-5, 1)$, can the slope of the line through these points be calculated by $\dfrac{1 - 3}{2 - (-5)}$? Why or why not? (See the second Concept Check.)

89. Write the equations of three lines parallel to $10x - 5y = -7$. (See the third Concept Check.)

90. Write the equations of two lines perpendicular to $10x - 5y = -7$. (See the third Concept Check.)

The following line graph shows the average fuel economy (in miles per gallon) of passenger automobiles produced during each of the model years shown. Use this graph to answer Exercises 91 through 96.

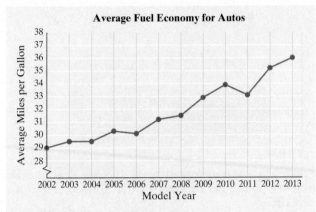

Average Fuel Economy for Autos

Average Miles per Gallon vs. Model Year

Data from U.S. Bureau of Transportation Statistics

91. Between what two years shown was there a decrease in average fuel economy for automobiles?

92. What was the average fuel economy (in miles per gallon) for automobiles produced during 2008?

93. During which of the model years shown was average fuel economy the lowest? What was the average fuel economy that year?

94. During which of the model years shown was average fuel economy the highest? What was the average fuel economy for that year?

95. Of the following line segments, which has the greatest slope: from 2008 to 2009, 2009 to 2010, or 2011 to 2012?

96. Which line segment has a slope of 0?

Solve.

97. Find x so that the pitch of the roof is $\dfrac{1}{3}$.

18 feet

98. Find x so that the pitch of the roof is $\dfrac{2}{5}$.

4 feet

99. Approximately 27,000 organ transplants were performed in the United States in 2004. In 2014, the number rose to approximately 29,500. (*Source:* Organ Procurement and Transplantation Network)

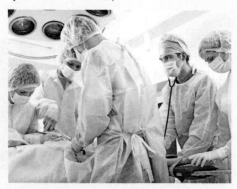

a. Write two ordered pairs of the form (year, number of organ transplants).

b. Find the slope of the line between the two points.

c. Write a sentence explaining the meaning of the slope as a rate of change.

100. The average price of an acre of midgrade Iowa farmland in 2008 was $2300. In 2012, the average price for midgrade farmland was $8300 per acre. (*Source:* National Agricultural Statistics Service)

a. Write two ordered pairs of the form (year, price of an acre).

b. Find the slope of the line through the two points.

c. Write a sentence explaining the meaning of the slope as a rate of change.

101. Show that a triangle with vertices at the points $(1, 1)$, $(-4, 4)$, and $(-3, 0)$ is a right triangle.

102. Show that the quadrilateral with vertices $(1, 3)$, $(2, 1)$, $(-4, 0)$, and $(-3, -2)$ is a parallelogram.

Find the slope of the line through the given points.

103. $(2.1, 6.7)$ and $(-8.3, 9.3)$

104. $(-3.8, 1.2)$ and $(-2.2, 4.5)$

105. $(2.3, 0.2)$ and $(7.9, 5.1)$

106. $(14.3, -10.1)$ and $(9.8, -2.9)$

107. The graph of $y = -\frac{1}{3}x + 2$ has a slope of $-\frac{1}{3}$. The graph of $y = -2x + 2$ has a slope of -2. The graph of $y = -4x + 2$ has a slope of -4. Graph all three equations on a single coordinate system. As the absolute value of the slope becomes larger, how does the steepness of the line change?

108. The graph of $y = \frac{1}{2}x$ has a slope of $\frac{1}{2}$. The graph of $y = 3x$ has a slope of 3. The graph of $y = 5x$ has a slope of 5. Graph all three equations on a single coordinate system. As slope becomes larger, how does the steepness of the line change?

Integrated Review Summary on Slope and Graphing Linear Equations

Sections 3.1–3.4

Find the slope of each line.

1.

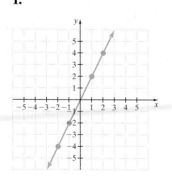

2.

3.

4.

Graph each linear equation.

5. $y = -2x$

6. $x + y = 3$

7. $x = -1$

8. $y = 4$

9. $x - 2y = 6$

10. $y = 3x + 2$

11. $5x + 3y = 15$

12. $2x - 4y = 8$

Determine whether the lines through the points are parallel, perpendicular, or neither.

13. $y = -\dfrac{1}{5}x + \dfrac{1}{3}$

$3x = -15y$

14. $x - y = \dfrac{1}{2}$

$3x - y = \dfrac{1}{2}$

15. In the years 2002 through 2013 the number of bridges on public roads (in thousands) in the United States can be modeled by the linear equation $y = 4.09x + 490$, where x is the number of years after 2002 and y is the number of bridges (in thousands). (*Source:* U.S. Dept. of Transportation)

a. Find the y-intercept of the line.

b. Write a sentence explaining the meaning of this intercept.

c. Find the slope of this line.

d. Write a sentence explaining the meaning of the slope as a rate of change.

16. Online advertising is a means of promoting products and services using the Internet. The revenue y (in billions of dollars) for online advertising for the years 2009 through 2014 is given by $y = 5.3x + 22.7$, where x is the number of years after 2009.

a. Use this equation to complete the ordered pair $(4, \quad)$.

b. Write a sentence explaining the meaning of the answer to part (a).

3.5 Equations of Lines

OBJECTIVES

1 Use the Slope-Intercept Form to Graph a Linear Equation.

2 Use the Slope-Intercept Form to Write an Equation of a Line.

3 Use the Point-Slope Form to Find an Equation of a Line Given Its Slope and a Point on the Line.

4 Use the Point-Slope Form to Find an Equation of a Line Given Two Points on the Line.

5 Find Equations of Vertical and Horizontal Lines.

6 Use the Point-Slope Form to Solve Problems.

Recall that the form $y = mx + b$ is appropriately called the *slope-intercept form* of a linear equation.

slope y-intercept is $(0, b)$

> **Slope-Intercept Form**
>
> When a linear equation in two variables is written in **slope-intercept form,**
>
> $$y = mx + b$$
>
> slope $(0, b)$, y-intercept
>
> then m is the slope of the line and $(0, b)$ is the y-intercept of the line.

OBJECTIVE

1   Using the Slope-Intercept Form to Graph an Equation

We can use the slope-intercept form of the equation of a line to graph a linear equation.

EXAMPLE 1   Use the slope-intercept form to graph the equation

$$y = \frac{3}{5}x - 2.$$

Solution   Since the equation $y = \frac{3}{5}x - 2$ is written in slope-intercept form $y = mx + b$, the slope of its graph is $\frac{3}{5}$ and the y-intercept is $(0, -2)$. To graph this equation, we begin by plotting the point $(0, -2)$. From this point, we can find another point of the graph by using the slope $\frac{3}{5}$ and recalling that slope is $\frac{\text{rise}}{\text{run}}$. We start at the y-intercept and move 3 units up since the numerator of the slope is 3; then we move 5 units to the right since the denominator of the slope is 5. We stop at the point $(5, 1)$. The line through $(0, -2)$ and $(5, 1)$ is the graph of $y = \frac{3}{5}x - 2$.   □

PRACTICE

1   Graph: $y = \frac{2}{3}x - 5$ ■

EXAMPLE 2   Use the slope-intercept form to graph the equation $4x + y = 1$.

Solution   First we write the given equation in slope-intercept form.

$$4x + y = 1$$
$$y = -4x + 1$$

The graph of this equation will have slope -4 and y-intercept $(0, 1)$. To graph this line, we first plot the point $(0, 1)$. To find another point of the graph, we use the slope -4, which can be written as $\frac{-4}{1}$ $\left(\frac{4}{-1} \text{ could also be used}\right)$. We start at the point $(0, 1)$ and move 4 units down (since the numerator of the slope is -4) and then 1 unit to the right (since the denominator of the slope is 1).

We arrive at the point $(1, -3)$. The line through $(0, 1)$ and $(1, -3)$ is the graph of $4x + y = 1$.   □

> **Helpful Hint**
> In Example 2, if we interpret the slope of -4 as $\frac{4}{-1}$, we arrive at $(-1, 5)$ for a second point. Notice that this point is also on the line.

PRACTICE

2   Use the slope-intercept form to graph the equation $3x - y = 2$.   ■

OBJECTIVE

2   Using the Slope-Intercept Form to Write an Equation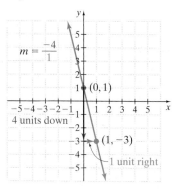

The slope-intercept form can also be used to write the equation of a line when we know its slope and y-intercept.

EXAMPLE 3   Find an equation of the line with y-intercept $(0, -3)$ and slope of $\frac{1}{4}$.

Solution   We are given the slope and the y-intercept. We let $m = \frac{1}{4}$ and $b = -3$ and write the equation in slope-intercept form, $y = mx + b$.

$$y = mx + b$$
$$y = \frac{1}{4}x + (-3) \quad \text{Let } m = \frac{1}{4} \text{ and } b = -3.$$
$$y = \frac{1}{4}x - 3 \quad \text{Simplify.}$$

□

(Continued on next page)

PRACTICE
3 Find an equation of the line with y-intercept $(0, 7)$ and slope of $\dfrac{1}{2}$. ∎

OBJECTIVE

3 Writing an Equation Given Slope and a Point ▶

Thus far, we have seen that we can write an equation of a line if we know its slope and y-intercept. We can also write an equation of a line if we know its slope and any point on the line. To see how we do this, let m represent slope and (x_1, y_1) represent the point on the line. Then if (x, y) is any other point on the line, we have that

$$\frac{y - y_1}{x - x_1} = m$$

$$y - y_1 = m(x - x_1) \quad \text{Multiply both sides by } (x - x_1).$$

slope

This is the *point-slope form* of the equation of a line.

Point-Slope Form of the Equation of a Line

The **point-slope form** of the equation of a line is

$$y - y_1 = m(x - x_1)$$

slope (x_1, y_1) point on the line

where m is the slope of the line and (x_1, y_1) is a point on the line.

EXAMPLE 4 Find an equation of the line with slope -2 that passes through $(-1, 5)$. Write the equation in slope-intercept form, $y = mx + b$, and in standard form, $Ax + By = C$.

Solution Since the slope and a point on the line are given, we use point-slope form $y - y_1 = m(x - x_1)$ to write the equation. Let $m = -2$ and $(-1, 5) = (x_1, y_1)$.

$$y - y_1 = m(x - x_1)$$
$$y - 5 = -2[x - (-1)] \quad \text{Let } m = -2 \text{ and } (x_1, y_1) = (-1, 5).$$
$$y - 5 = -2(x + 1) \quad \text{Simplify.}$$
$$y - 5 = -2x - 2 \quad \text{Use the distributive property.}$$

To write the equation in slope-intercept form, $y = mx + b$, we simply solve the equation for y. To do this, we add 5 to both sides.

$$y - 5 = -2x - 2$$
$$y = -2x + 3 \quad \text{Slope-intercept form.}$$
$$2x + y = 3 \quad \text{Add } 2x \text{ to both sides and we have standard form.} \quad \square$$

PRACTICE
4 Find an equation of the line passing through $(2, 3)$ with slope 4. Write the equation in standard form: $Ax + By = C$. ∎

OBJECTIVE

4 Writing an Equation Given Two Points ▶

We can also find an equation of a line when we are given any two points on the line.

EXAMPLE 5   Find an equation of the line through $(2, 5)$ and $(-3, 4)$. Write the equation in standard form.

Solution First, use the two given points to find the slope of the line.

$$m = \frac{4 - 5}{-3 - 2} = \frac{-1}{-5} = \frac{1}{5}$$

Next we use the slope $\frac{1}{5}$ and either one of the given points to write the equation in point-slope form. We use $(2, 5)$. Let $x_1 = 2$, $y_1 = 5$, and $m = \frac{1}{5}$.

$$y - y_1 = m(x - x_1) \qquad \text{Use point-slope form.}$$

$$y - 5 = \frac{1}{5}(x - 2) \qquad \text{Let } x_1 = 2, y_1 = 5, \text{ and } m = \frac{1}{5}.$$

$$5(y - 5) = 5 \cdot \frac{1}{5}(x - 2) \qquad \text{Multiply both sides by 5 to clear fractions.}$$

$$5y - 25 = x - 2 \qquad \text{Use the distributive property and simplify.}$$

$$-x + 5y - 25 = -2 \qquad \text{Subtract } x \text{ from both sides.}$$

$$-x + 5y = 23 \qquad \text{Add 25 to both sides.} \qquad \square$$

PRACTICE

5   Find an equation of the line through $(-1, 6)$ and $(3, 1)$. Write the equation in standard form.   ◼

> **Helpful Hint**
>
> Multiply both sides of the equation $-x + 5y = 23$ by -1, and it becomes $x - 5y = -23$. Both $-x + 5y = 23$ and $x - 5y = -23$ are in standard form, and they are equations of the same line.

OBJECTIVE

5   Finding Equations of Vertical and Horizontal Lines

Recall from Section 3.3 that:

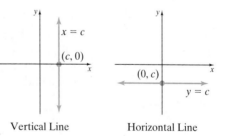

Vertical Line   Horizontal Line

EXAMPLE 6   Find an equation of the vertical line through $(-1, 5)$.

Solution The equation of a vertical line can be written in the form $x = c$, so an equation for the vertical line passing through $(-1, 5)$ is $x = -1$.

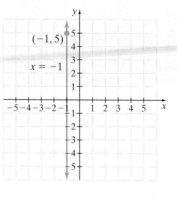

PRACTICE

6   Find an equation of the vertical line through $(3, -2)$.   ◼

⚠ **EXAMPLE 7** Find an equation of the line parallel to the line $y = 5$ and passing through $(-2, -3)$.

Solution Since the graph of $y = 5$ is a horizontal line, any line parallel to it is also horizontal. The equation of a horizontal line can be written in the form $y = c$. An equation for the horizontal line passing through

$$(-2, -3) \text{ is } y = -3.$$

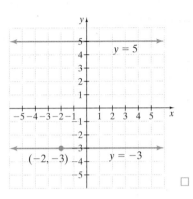

☐

PRACTICE

7 Find an equation of the line parallel to the line $y = -2$ and passing through $(4, 3)$. ■

OBJECTIVE

6 Using the Point-Slope Form to Solve Problems ▶

Problems occurring in many fields can be modeled by linear equations in two variables. The next example is from the field of marketing and shows how consumer demand of a product depends on the price of the product.

EXAMPLE 8 **Predicting the Sales of T-Shirts**

A web-based T-shirt company has learned that by pricing a clearance-sale T-shirt at $6, sales will reach 2000 T-shirts per day. Raising the price to $8 will cause the sales to fall to 1500 T-shirts per day.

a. Assume that the relationship between sales price and number of T-shirts sold is linear and write an equation describing this relationship. Write the equation in slope-intercept form.

b. Predict the daily sales of T-shirts if the price is $7.50.

Solution

a. First, use the given information and write two ordered pairs. Ordered pairs will be in the form (sales price, number sold) so that our ordered pairs are $(6, 2000)$ and $(8, 1500)$. Use the point-slope form to write an equation. To do so, we find the slope of the line that contains these points.

$$m = \frac{2000 - 1500}{6 - 8} = \frac{500}{-2} = -250$$

Next, use the slope and either one of the points to write the equation in point-slope form. We use $(6, 2000)$.

$y - y_1 = m(x - x_1)$	Use point-slope form.
$y - 2000 = -250(x - 6)$	Let $x_1 = 6$, $y_1 = 2000$, and $m = -250$.
$y - 2000 = -250x + 1500$	Use the distributive property.
$y = -250x + 3500$	Write in slope-intercept form.

b. To predict the sales if the price is $7.50, we find y when $x = 7.50$.

$$y = -250x + 3500$$
$$y = -250(7.50) + 3500 \quad \text{Let } x = 7.50.$$
$$y = -1875 + 3500$$
$$y = 1625$$

If the price is $7.50, sales will reach 1625 T-shirts per day. ☐

PRACTICE

8   The new *Camelot* condos were selling at a rate of 30 per month when they were priced at $150,000 each. Lowering the price to $120,000 caused the sales to rise to 50 condos per month.

a. Assume that the relationship between number of condos sold and price is linear, and write an equation describing this relationship. Write the equation in slope-intercept form. Use ordered pairs of the form (number sold, sales price).

b. How should the condos be priced if the developer wishes to sell 60 condos per month?   ∎

The preceding example may also be solved by using ordered pairs of the form (sales price, number sold).

Forms of Linear Equations

$Ax + By = C$	**Standard form** of a linear equation. A and B are not both 0.
$y = mx + b$	**Slope-intercept form** of a linear equation. The slope is m and the y-intercept is $(0, b)$.
$y - y_1 = m(x - x_1)$	**Point-slope form** of a linear equation. The slope is m and (x_1, y_1) is a point on the line.
$y = c$	**Horizontal line** The slope is 0 and the y-intercept is $(0, c)$.
$x = c$	**Vertical line** The slope is undefined and the x-intercept is $(c, 0)$.

Parallel and Perpendicular Lines

Nonvertical parallel lines have the same slope.

The product of the slopes of two nonvertical perpendicular lines is -1.

Graphing Calculator Explorations

A grapher is a very useful tool for discovering patterns. To discover the change in the graph of a linear equation caused by a change in slope, try the following. Use a standard window and graph a linear equation in the form $y = mx + b$. Recall that the graph of such an equation will have slope m and y-intercept b.

First, graph $y = x + 3$. To do so, press the ⌊Y =⌋ key and enter $Y_1 = x + 3$. Notice that this graph has slope 1 and that the y-intercept is 3. Next, on the same set of axes, graph $y = 2x + 3$ and $y = 3x + 3$ by pressing ⌊Y =⌋ and entering $Y_2 = 2x + 3$ and $Y_3 = 3x + 3$.

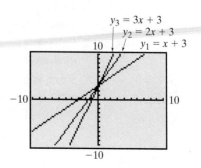

(Continued on next page)

Notice the difference in the graph of each equation as the slope changes from 1 to 2 to 3. How would the graph of $y = 5x + 3$ appear? To see the change in the graph caused by a change in negative slope, try graphing $y = -x + 3$, $y = -2x + 3$, and $y = -3x + 3$ on the same set of axes.

Use a grapher to graph the following equations. For each exercise, graph the first equation and use its graph to predict the appearance of the other equations. Then graph the other equations on the same set of axes and check your prediction.

1. $y = x$; $y = 6x$, $y = -6x$

2. $y = -x$; $y = -5x$, $y = -10x$

3. $y = \frac{1}{2}x + 2$; $y = \frac{3}{4}x + 2$, $y = x + 2$

4. $y = x + 1$; $y = \frac{5}{4}x + 1$, $y = \frac{5}{2}x + 1$

5. $y = -7x + 5$; $y = 7x + 5$

6. $y = 3x - 1$; $y = -3x - 1$

✓ Vocabulary, Readiness & Video Check

Use the choices below to fill in each blank. Some choices may be used more than once and some not at all.

b	(y_1, x_1)	point-slope	vertical	standard
m	(x_1, y_1)	slope-intercept	horizontal	

1. The form $y = mx + b$ is called _____ form. When a linear equation in two variables is written in this form, _____ is the slope of its graph and $(0,$ _____$)$ is its y-intercept.

2. The form $y - y_1 = m(x - x_1)$ is called _____ form. When a linear equation in two variables is written in this form, _____ is the slope of its graph and _____ is a point on the graph.

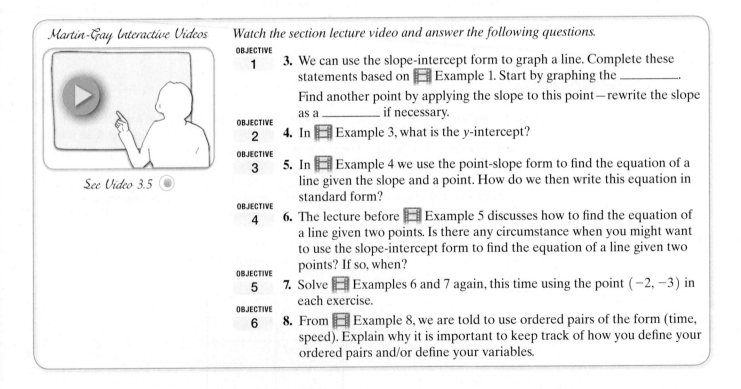

Martin-Gay Interactive Videos

See Video 3.5 ⊙

Watch the section lecture video and answer the following questions.

OBJECTIVE 1

3. We can use the slope-intercept form to graph a line. Complete these statements based on ▦ Example 1. Start by graphing the _____. Find another point by applying the slope to this point—rewrite the slope as a _____ if necessary.

OBJECTIVE 2

4. In ▦ Example 3, what is the y-intercept?

OBJECTIVE 3

5. In ▦ Example 4 we use the point-slope form to find the equation of a line given the slope and a point. How do we then write this equation in standard form?

OBJECTIVE 4

6. The lecture before ▦ Example 5 discusses how to find the equation of a line given two points. Is there any circumstance when you might want to use the slope-intercept form to find the equation of a line given two points? If so, when?

OBJECTIVE 5

7. Solve ▦ Examples 6 and 7 again, this time using the point $(-2, -3)$ in each exercise.

OBJECTIVE 6

8. From ▦ Example 8, we are told to use ordered pairs of the form (time, speed). Explain why it is important to keep track of how you define your ordered pairs and/or define your variables.

3.5 Exercise Set   MyMathLab®

Use the slope-intercept form to graph each equation. See Examples 1 and 2.

1. $y = 2x + 1$

2. $y = -4x - 1$

3. $y = \dfrac{2}{3}x + 5$

4. $y = \dfrac{1}{4}x - 3$

5. $y = -5x$

6. $y = -6x$

7. $4x + y = 6$

8. $-3x + y = 2$

9. $4x - 7y = -14$

10. $3x - 4y = 4$

11. $x = \dfrac{5}{4}y$

12. $x = \dfrac{3}{2}y$

Write an equation of the line with each given slope, m, and y-intercept, (0, b). See Example 3.

13. $m = 5, b = 3$

14. $m = -3, b = -3$

15. $m = -4, b = -\dfrac{1}{6}$

16. $m = 2, b = \dfrac{3}{4}$

17. $m = \dfrac{2}{3}, b = 0$

18. $m = -\dfrac{4}{5}, b = 0$

19. $m = 0, b = -8$

20. $m = 0, b = -2$

21. $m = -\dfrac{1}{5}, b = \dfrac{1}{9}$

22. $m = \dfrac{1}{2}, b = -\dfrac{1}{3}$

Find an equation of each line with the given slope that passes through the given point. Write the equation in the form Ax + By = C. See Example 4.

23. $m = 6;\ (2, 2)$

24. $m = 4;\ (1, 3)$

25. $m = -8;\ (-1, -5)$

26. $m = -2;\ (-11, -12)$

27. $m = \dfrac{3}{2};\ (5, -6)$

28. $m = \dfrac{2}{3};\ (-8, 9)$

29. $m = -\dfrac{1}{2};\ (-3, 0)$

30. $m = -\dfrac{1}{5};\ (4, 0)$

Find an equation of the line passing through each pair of points. Write the equation in the form Ax + By = C. See Example 5.

31. $(3, 2)$ and $(5, 6)$

32. $(6, 2)$ and $(8, 8)$

33. $(-1, 3)$ and $(-2, -5)$

34. $(-4, 0)$ and $(6, -1)$

35. $(2, 3)$ and $(-1, -1)$

36. $(7, 10)$ and $(-1, -1)$

37. $(0, 0)$ and $\left(-\dfrac{1}{8}, \dfrac{1}{13}\right)$

38. $(0, 0)$ and $\left(-\dfrac{1}{2}, \dfrac{1}{3}\right)$

Find an equation of each line. See Example 6.

39. Vertical line through $(0, 2)$

40. Horizontal line through $(1, 4)$

41. Horizontal line through $(-1, 3)$

42. Vertical line through $(-1, 3)$

43. Vertical line through $\left(-\dfrac{7}{3}, -\dfrac{2}{5}\right)$

44. Horizontal line through $\left(\dfrac{2}{7}, 0\right)$

Find an equation of each line. See Example 7.

45. Parallel to $y = 5$, through $(1, 2)$

46. Perpendicular to $y = 5$, through $(1, 2)$

47. Perpendicular to $x = -3$, through $(-2, 5)$

48. Parallel to $y = -4$, through $(0, -3)$

49. Parallel to $x = 0$, through $(6, -8)$

50. Perpendicular to $x = 7$, through $(-5, 0)$

MIXED PRACTICE

See Examples 1 through 7. Find an equation of each line described. Write each equation in slope-intercept form (solved for y), when possible.

51. With slope $-\dfrac{1}{2}$, through $\left(0, \dfrac{5}{3}\right)$

52. With slope $\dfrac{5}{7}$, through $(0, -3)$

53. Through $(10, 7)$ and $(7, 10)$

54. Through $(5, -6)$ and $(-6, 5)$

55. With undefined slope, through $\left(-\dfrac{3}{4}, 1\right)$

56. With slope 0, through $(6.7, 12.1)$

57. Slope 1, through $(-7, 9)$

58. Slope 5, through $(6, -8)$

59. Slope -5, y-intercept $(0, 7)$

60. Slope -2; y-intercept $(0, -4)$

61. Through $(6, 7)$, parallel to the x-axis

62. Through $(1, -5)$, parallel to the y-axis

63. Through $(2, 3)$ and $(0, 0)$

64. Through $(4, 7)$ and $(0, 0)$

65. Through $(-2, -3)$, perpendicular to the y-axis

66. Through $(0, 12)$, perpendicular to the x-axis

67. Slope $-\dfrac{4}{7}$, through $(-1, -2)$

68. Slope $-\dfrac{3}{5}$, through $(4, 4)$

Solve. Assume each exercise describes a linear relationship. Write the equations in slope-intercept form. See Example 8.

69. A rock is dropped from the top of a 400-foot cliff. After 1 second, the rock is traveling 32 feet per second. After 3 seconds, the rock is traveling 96 feet per second.

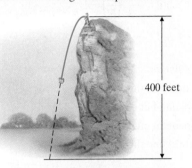

400 feet

a. Assume that the relationship between time and speed is linear and write an equation describing this relationship. Use ordered pairs of the form (time, speed).

b. Use this equation to determine the speed of the rock 4 seconds after it was dropped.

70. A Hawaiian fruit company is studying the sales of a pineapple sauce to see if this product is to be continued. At the end of its first year, profits on this product amounted to $30,000. At the end of the fourth year, profits were $66,000.

a. Assume that the relationship between years on the market and profit is linear and write an equation describing this relationship. Use ordered pairs of the form (years on the market, profit).

b. Use this equation to predict the profit at the end of 7 years.

71. Sales of automobiles worldwide continues to grow as emerging economies provide their citizens more purchasing power. In 2011, there were 66 thousand new car sales worldwide, and in 2014, this number increased to 72 thousand cars. (*Source:* statista)

a. Write an equation describing the relationship between time and the number of new automobiles sold worldwide. Use ordered pairs of the form (years past 2011, number of automobiles sold).

b. Use this equation to predict the number of new car sales worldwide in the year 2018.

72. In 2004, the restaurant industry in the United States employed about 11.9 million people. In 2014, this number increased to 13.5 million employees. (*Source:* National Restaurant Association)

a. Write an equation describing the relationship between time and the number of restaurant industry employees. Use ordered pairs of the form (years past 2004, number of restaurant employees in millions).

b. Use this equation to predict the number of restaurant industry employees in 2018. Round to the nearest tenth of a million.

73. In 2006, the U.S. population (or persons) per square mile of land area was 85. In 2014, the persons per square mile was 89.48.

a. Write an equation describing the relationship between year and persons per square mile. Use ordered pairs of the form (years past 2006, persons per square mile).

b. Use this equation to predict the persons per square mile in 2018. Round to the nearest tenth of a person.

74. Dunkin' Donuts started as a New England brand coffee and donut shop, but has expanded recently throughout the world. In 2011, there were 10,083 stores worldwide. By 2014, this had grown to 10,884. (*Source:* Dunkin' Donuts)

a. Write an equation describing the relationship between year and number of Dunkin' Donuts stores. Use ordered pairs of the form (years past 2011, number of Dunkin' Donuts stores).

b. Use this equation to predict the number of Dunkin' Donuts stores in 2018.

75. It has been said that newspapers are disappearing, replaced by various electronic media. In 2003, newspaper circulation (the number of copies distributed in a day) was about 55 million. In 2013, this had dropped to 44 million. (*Source:* Newspaper Association of America).

a. Write an equation describing the relationship between time and circulation. Use ordered pairs of the form (years past 2003, number of newspapers circulated in millions).

b. Use this equation to predict newspaper circulation in 2018.

76. A certain chain of book stores is slowly closing down stores. Suppose that in 2006 there were 3991 stores and in 2010 there were 3200 stores.

a. Write an equation describing the relationship between time and number of store locations. Use ordered pairs of the form (years past 2006, number of stores).

b. Use this equation to predict the number of stores in 2018.

77. The Pool Fun Company has learned that, by pricing a newly released Fun Noodle at $3, sales will reach 10,000 Fun Noodles per day during the summer. Raising the price to $5 will cause sales to fall to 8000 Fun Noodles per day.

a. Assume that the relationship between price and number of Fun Noodles sold is linear and write an equation describing this relationship. Use ordered pairs of the form (price, number sold).

b. Predict the daily sales of Fun Noodles if the price is $3.50.

78. The value of a building bought in 2000 may be depreciated (or decreased) as time passes for income tax purposes. Seven years after the building was bought, this value was $225,000 and 12 years after it was bought, this value was $195,000.

a. If the relationship between number of years past 2000 and the depreciated value of the building is linear, write an equation describing this relationship. Use ordered pairs of the form (years past 2000, value of building).

b. Use this equation to estimate the depreciated value of the building in 2018.

REVIEW AND PREVIEW

Find the value of $x^2 - 3x + 1$ for each given value of x. See Section 1.7.

79. 2   **80.** 5

81. −1   **82.** −3

For each graph, determine whether any x-values correspond to two or more y-values. See Section 3.1.

83.   **84.**

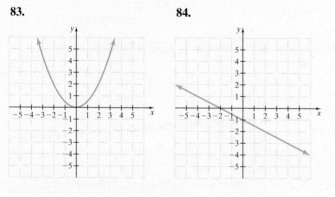

85.   **86.**

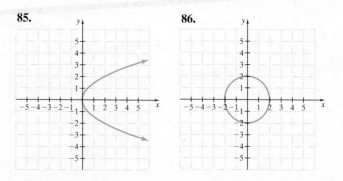

CONCEPT EXTENSIONS

For Exercises 87 through 90, identify the form that the linear equation in two variables is written in. For Exercises 91 and 92, identify the appearance of the graph of the equation.

87. $y - 7 = 4(x + 3);$ _____ form

88. $5x - 9y = 11;$ _____ form

89. $y = \dfrac{3}{4}x - \dfrac{1}{3};$ _____ form

90. $y + 2 = -\dfrac{1}{3}(x - 2);$ _____ form

91. $y = \dfrac{1}{2};$ _____ line **92.** $x = -17;$ _____ line

93. Given the equation of a nonvertical line, explain how to find the slope without finding two points on the line.

94. Given two points on a nonvertical line, explain how to use the point-slope form to find the equation of the line.

95. Write an equation in standard form of the line that contains the point $(-1, 2)$ and is

  a. parallel to the line $y = 3x - 1$.

  b. perpendicular to the line $y = 3x - 1$.

96. Write an equation in standard form of the line that contains the point $(4, 0)$ and is

  a. parallel to the line $y = -2x + 3$.

  b. perpendicular to the line $y = -2x + 3$.

97. Write an equation in standard form of the line that contains the point $(3, -5)$ and is

  a. parallel to the line $3x + 2y = 7$.

  b. perpendicular to the line $3x + 2y = 7$.

98. Write an equation in standard form of the line that contains the point $(-2, 4)$ and is

  a. parallel to the line $x + 3y = 6$.

  b. perpendicular to the line $x + 3y = 6$.

3.6 | Functions ▶

OBJECTIVES

1 Identify Relations, Domains, and Ranges. ▶

2 Identify Functions. ▶

3 Use the Vertical Line Test. ▶

4 Use Function Notation. ▶

OBJECTIVE

1 Identifying Relations, Domains, and Ranges ▶

In previous sections, we have discussed the relationships between two quantities. For example, the relationship between the length of the side of a square x and its area y is described by the equation $y = x^2$. Ordered pairs can be used to write down solutions of this equation. For example, $(2, 4)$ is a solution of $y = x^2$, and this notation tells us that the x-value 2 is related to the y-value 4 for this equation. In other words, when the length of the side of a square is 2 units, its area is 4 square units.

Examples of Relationships Between Two Quantities

Area of Square: $y = x^2$	Equation of Line: $y = x + 2$	Internet Advertising Revenue

Some Ordered Pairs		Some Ordered Pairs		Ordered Pairs	

x	y
2	4
5	25
7	49
12	144

x	y
−3	−1
0	2
2	4
9	11

Year	Billions of Dollars
2010	26
2011	31.7
2012	36.6
2013	42.8
2014	49.5

(*Source:* PricewaterhouseCoopers LLP)

A set of ordered pairs is called a **relation.** The set of all x-coordinates is called the **domain** of a relation, and the set of all y-coordinates is called the **range** of a relation. Equations such as $y = x^2$ are also called relations since equations in two variables define a set of ordered pair solutions.

EXAMPLE 1 Find the domain and the range of the relation $\{(0, 2), (3, 3), (-1, 0), (3, -2)\}$.

Solution The domain is the set of all x-values or $\{-1, 0, 3\}$, and the range is the set of all y-values, or $\{-2, 0, 2, 3\}$. □

PRACTICE
1 Find the domain and the range of the relation $\{(1, 3), (5, 0), (0, -2), (5, 4)\}$.

OBJECTIVE
2 Identifying Functions ▶
Some relations are also functions.

Function

A function is a set of ordered pairs that assigns to each x-value exactly one y-value.

In other words, a function cannot have two ordered pairs with the same x-coordinate but different y-coordinates.

EXAMPLE 2 Determine whether each relation is also a function.

a. $\{(-1, 1), (2, 3), (7, 3), (8, 6)\}$ **b.** $\{(0, -2), (1, 5), (0, 3), (7, 7)\}$

Solution

a. Although the ordered pairs $(2, 3)$ and $(7, 3)$ have the same y-value, each x-value is assigned to only one y-value, so this set of ordered pairs is a function.

b. The x-value 0 is assigned to two y-values, -2 and 3, so this set of ordered pairs is not a function. □

PRACTICE

2 Determine whether each relation is also a function.

   a. $\{(4,1),(3,-2),(8,5),(-5,3)\}$ **b.** $\{(1,2),(-4,3),(0,8),(1,4)\}$

Relations and functions can be described by a graph of their ordered pairs.

EXAMPLE 3 Determine whether each graph is the graph of a function.

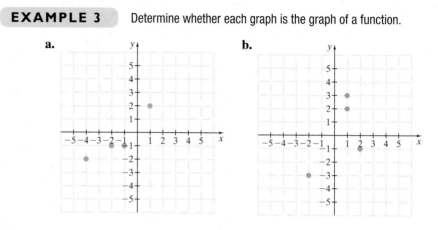

a.   **b.**

Solution

a. This is the graph of the relation $\{(-4,-2),(-2,-1),(-1,-1),(1,2)\}$. Each x-coordinate has exactly one y-coordinate, so this is the graph of a function.

b. This is the graph of the relation $\{(-2,-3),(1,2),(1,3),(2,-1)\}$. The x-coordinate 1 is paired with two y-coordinates, 2 and 3, so this is not the graph of a function.

PRACTICE

3 Determine whether each graph is the graph of a function.

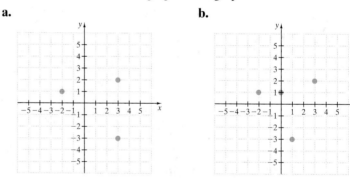

a.   **b.**

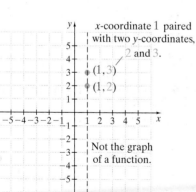

x-coordinate 1 paired with two y-coordinates, 2 and 3.

(1, 3)
(1, 2)

Not the graph of a function.

OBJECTIVE

3 Using the Vertical Line Test

The graph in Example 3(b) was not the graph of a function because the x-coordinate 1 was paired with two y-coordinates, 2 and 3. Notice that when an x-coordinate is paired with more than one y-coordinate, a vertical line can be drawn that will intersect the graph at more than one point. We can use this fact to determine whether a relation is also a function. We call this the **vertical line test.**

Vertical Line Test

If a vertical line can be drawn so that it intersects a graph more than once, the graph is not the graph of a function.

This vertical line test works for all types of graphs on the rectangular coordinate system.

EXAMPLE 4 Use the vertical line test to determine whether each graph is the graph of a function.

a. **b.** **c.** **d.**

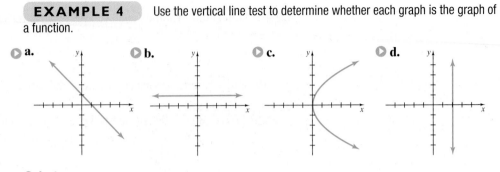

Solution

a. This graph is the graph of a function since no vertical line will intersect this graph more than once.

b. This graph is also the graph of a function; no vertical line will intersect it more than once.

c. This graph is not the graph of a function. Vertical lines can be drawn that intersect the graph in two points. An example of one is shown.

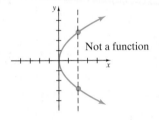

Not a function

d. This graph is not the graph of a function. A vertical line can be drawn that intersects this line at every point. □

PRACTICE

4 Use the vertical line test to determine whether each graph is the graph of a function.

a. **b.** **c.** **d.**

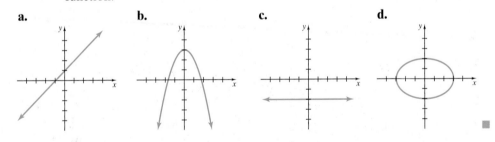

■

Recall that the graph of a linear equation is a line, and a line that is not vertical will pass the vertical line test. **Thus, all linear equations are functions except those of the form $x = c$, which are vertical lines.**

EXAMPLE 5 Decide whether the equation describes a function.

a. $y = x$ **b.** $y = 2x + 1$ **c.** $y = 5$ **d.** $x = -1$

Solution **a, b,** and **c** are functions because their graphs are nonvertical lines. **d** is not a function because its graph is a vertical line. □

PRACTICE

5 Decide whether the equation describes a function.

a. $y = 2x$ **b.** $y = -3x - 1$ **c.** $y = 8$ **d.** $x = 2$ ■

Examples of functions can often be found in magazines, newspapers, books, and other printed material in the form of tables or graphs such as that in Example 6.

EXAMPLE 6   The graph shows the sunrise time for Indianapolis, Indiana, for the year. Use this graph to answer the questions.

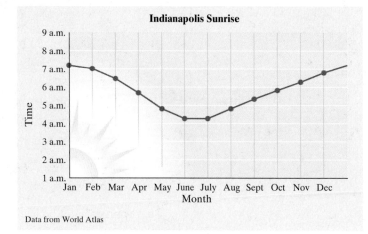

a. Approximate the time of sunrise on February 1.

b. Approximately when does the sun rise at 5 a.m.?

c. Is this the graph of a function?

Solution

a. To approximate the time of sunrise on February 1, we find the mark on the horizontal axis that corresponds to February 1. From this mark, we move vertically upward until the graph is reached. From that point on the graph, we move horizontally to the left until the vertical axis is reached. The vertical axis there reads 7 a.m.

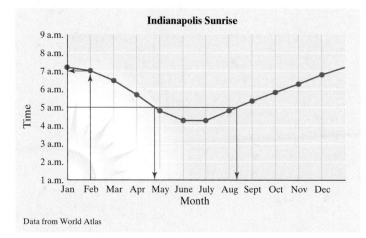

b. To approximate when the sun rises at 5 a.m., we find 5 a.m. on the time axis and move horizontally to the right. Notice that we will reach the graph twice, corresponding to two dates for which the sun rises at 5 a.m. We follow both points on the graph vertically downward until the horizontal axis is reached. The sun rises at 5 a.m. at approximately the end of the month of April and near the middle of the month of August.

c. The graph is the graph of a function since it passes the vertical line test. In other words, for every day of the year in Indianapolis, there is exactly one sunrise time.   □

(Continued on next page)

PRACTICE

6 The graph shows the average monthly temperature for Chicago, Illinois, for the year. Use this graph to answer the questions.

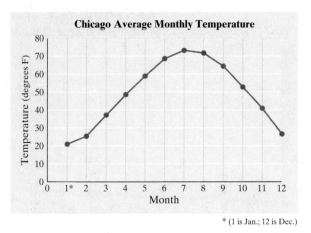

Chicago Average Monthly Temperature

* (1 is Jan.; 12 is Dec.)

a. Approximate the average monthly temperature for June.

b. For what month is the average monthly temperature 25°?

c. Is this the graph of a function?

OBJECTIVE

4 Using Function Notation ▶

The graph of the linear equation $y = 2x + 1$ passes the vertical line test, so we say that $y = 2x + 1$ is a function. In other words, $y = 2x + 1$ gives us a rule for writing ordered pairs where every x-coordinate is paired with one and only one y-coordinate.

The variable y is a function of the variable x. For each value of x, there is only one value of y. Thus, we say the variable x is the **independent variable** because any value in the domain can be assigned to x. The variable y is the **dependent variable** because its value depends on x.

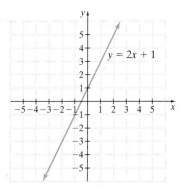

We often use letters such as f, g, and h to name functions. For example, the symbol $f(x)$ means *function of x* and is read "f of x." This notation is called **function notation.** The equation $y = 2x + 1$ can be written as $f(x) = 2x + 1$ using function notation, and these equations mean the same thing. In other words, $y = f(x)$.

The notation $f(1)$ means to replace x with 1 and find the resulting y or function value. Since

$$f(x) = 2x + 1$$

then

$$f(1) = 2(1) + 1$$
$$= 3$$

This means that, when $x = 1$, y or $f(x) = 3$, and we have the ordered pair $(1, 3)$. Now let's find $f(2), f(0)$, and $f(-1)$.

$$f(x) = 2x + 1 \qquad\qquad f(x) = 2x + 1 \qquad\qquad f(x) = 2x + 1$$
$$f(2) = 2(2) + 1 \qquad f(0) = 2(0) + 1 \qquad f(-1) = 2(-1) + 1$$
$$\qquad\quad = 4 + 1 \qquad\qquad\quad = 0 + 1 \qquad\qquad\quad = -2 + 1$$
$$\qquad\quad = 5 \qquad\qquad\qquad = 1 \qquad\qquad\qquad = -1$$

> **Helpful Hint**
>
> Note that, for example, if $f(2) = 5$, the corresponding ordered pair is $(2,5)$.

Ordered
Pair: $(2,5)$ $\qquad\qquad\qquad (0,1) \qquad\qquad\qquad (-1,-1)$

> **Helpful Hint**
>
> Note that $f(x)$ is a special symbol in mathematics used to denote a function. The symbol $f(x)$ is read "f of x." It does **not** mean $f \cdot x$ (f times x).

EXAMPLE 7   Given $g(x) = x^2 - 3$, find the following. Then write the corresponding ordered pairs generated.

   a. $g(2)$ **b.** $g(-2)$ **c.** $g(0)$

Solution

a. $g(x) = x^2 - 3$ **b.** $g(x) = x^2 - 3$ **c.** $g(x) = x^2 - 3$
$\quad g(2) = 2^2 - 3 \qquad\qquad g(-2) = (-2)^2 - 3 \qquad\quad g(0) = 0^2 - 3$
$\qquad\quad = 4 - 3 \qquad\qquad\qquad = 4 - 3 \qquad\qquad\qquad = 0 - 3$
$\qquad\quad = 1 \qquad\qquad\qquad\qquad = 1 \qquad\qquad\qquad\qquad = -3$

Ordered Pairs:	$g(2) = 1$ gives $(2,1)$	$g(-2) = 1$ gives $(-2,1)$	$g(0) = -3$ gives $(0,-3)$

PRACTICE
7   Given $h(x) = x^2 + 5$, find the following. Then write the corresponding ordered pairs generated.

   a. $h(2)$ **b.** $h(-5)$ **c.** $h(0)$

We now practice finding the domain and the range of a function. The domains of our functions will be the set of all possible real numbers that x can be replaced by. The range is the set of corresponding y-values.

EXAMPLE 8   Find the domain of each function.

   a. $g(x) = \dfrac{1}{x}$ **b.** $f(x) = 2x + 1$

Solution

   a. Recall that we cannot divide by 0, so the domain of $g(x)$ is the set of all real numbers except 0. In interval notation, we can write $(-\infty, 0) \cup (0, \infty)$.

   b. In this function, x can be any real number. The domain of $f(x)$ is the set of all real numbers, or $(-\infty, \infty)$ in interval notation.

PRACTICE
8   Find the domain of each function.

   a. $h(x) = 6x + 3$ **b.** $f(x) = \dfrac{1}{x^2}$

✔ **CONCEPT CHECK**

Suppose that the value of *f* is −7 when the function is evaluated at 2. Write this situation in function notation.

EXAMPLE 9 Find the domain and the range of each function graphed. Use interval notation.

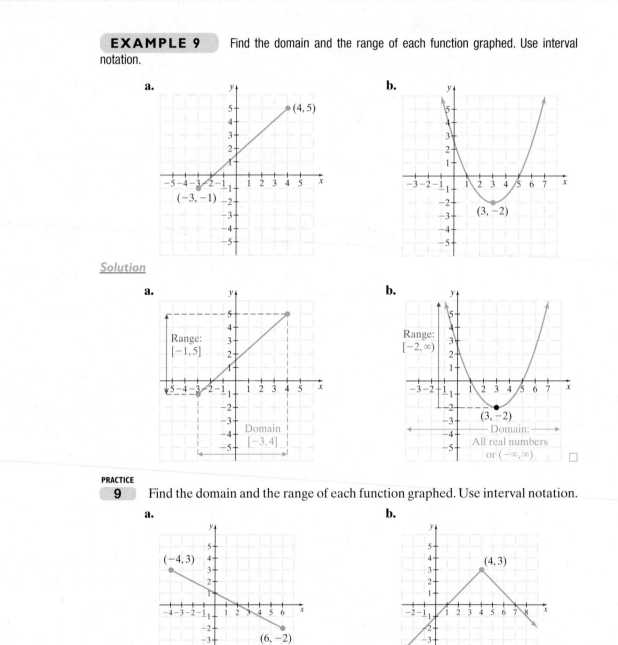

Solution

PRACTICE

9 Find the domain and the range of each function graphed. Use interval notation.

Answer to Concept Check:
$f(2) = -7$

✔ Vocabulary, Readiness & Video Check

Use the choices below to fill in each blank. Some choices may not be used.

$x = c$	horizontal	domain	relation
$y = c$	vertical	range	function

1. A set of ordered pairs is called a(n) _____.

2. A set of ordered pairs that assigns to each *x*-value exactly one *y*-value is called a(n) _____.

3. The set of all *y*-coordinates of a relation is called the _____.

4. The set of all *x*-coordinates of a relation is called the _____.

5. All linear equations are functions except those whose graphs are _____ lines.

6. All linear equations are functions except those whose equations are of the form _____.

Martin-Gay Interactive Videos

See Video 3.6 ⊙

Watch the section lecture video and answer the following questions.

OBJECTIVE 1

7. In the lecture before 🎬 Example 1, relations are discussed. Why can an equation in two variables define a relation?

OBJECTIVE 2

8. Based on 🎬 Examples 2 and 3, can a set of ordered pairs with no repeated *x*-values, but with repeated *y*-values be a function? For example: $\{(0, 4), (-3, 4), (2, 4)\}$.

OBJECTIVE 3

9. After reviewing 🎬 Example 8, explain why the vertical line test works.

OBJECTIVE 4

10. In 🎬 Example 10, three function values were found and their corresponding ordered pairs were written. For example, $f(0) = 2$ corresponds to $(0, 2)$. Write the other two function values found and their corresponding ordered pairs.

3.6 Exercise Set MyMathLab® ▶

Find the domain and the range of each relation. See Example 1.

1. $\{(2, 4), (0, 0), (-7, 10), (10, -7)\}$

2. $\{(3, -6), (1, 4), (-2, -2)\}$

▶ **3.** $\{(0, -2), (1, -2), (5, -2)\}$

4. $\{(5, 0), (5, -3), (5, 4), (5, 3)\}$

Determine whether each relation is also a function. See Example 2.

▶ **5.** $\{(1, 1), (2, 2), (-3, -3), (0, 0)\}$

6. $\{(11, 6), (-1, -2), (0, 0), (3, -2)\}$

▶ **7.** $\{(-1, 0), (-1, 6), (-1, 8)\}$

8. $\{(1, 2), (3, 2), (1, 4)\}$

MIXED PRACTICE

Determine whether each graph is the graph of a function. See Examples 3 and 4.

▶ **9.**   **10.**

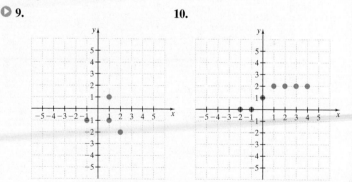

11.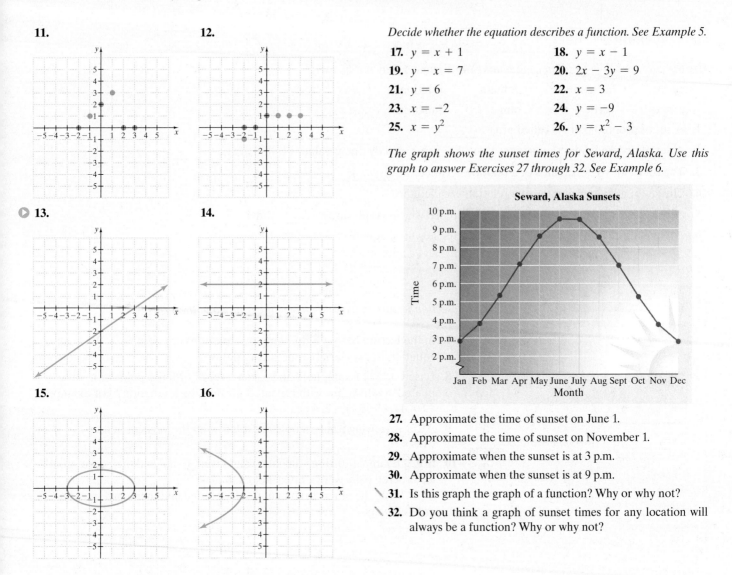

12.

13.

14.

15.

16.

Decide whether the equation describes a function. See Example 5.

17. $y = x + 1$ **18.** $y = x - 1$

19. $y - x = 7$ **20.** $2x - 3y = 9$

21. $y = 6$ **22.** $x = 3$

23. $x = -2$ **24.** $y = -9$

25. $x = y^2$ **26.** $y = x^2 - 3$

The graph shows the sunset times for Seward, Alaska. Use this graph to answer Exercises 27 through 32. See Example 6.

27. Approximate the time of sunset on June 1.

28. Approximate the time of sunset on November 1.

29. Approximate when the sunset is at 3 p.m.

30. Approximate when the sunset is at 9 p.m.

31. Is this graph the graph of a function? Why or why not?

32. Do you think a graph of sunset times for any location will always be a function? Why or why not?

This graph shows the U.S. hourly minimum wage for each year shown. Use this graph to answer Exercises 33 through 38. See Example 6.

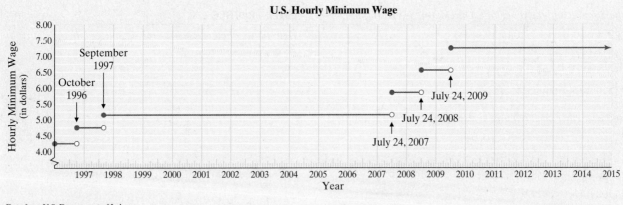

33. Approximate the minimum wage before October 1996.

34. Approximate the minimum wage in 2006.

35. Approximate the year when the minimum wage increased to over $7.00 per hour.

36. According to the graph, what hourly wage was in effect for the greatest number of years?

37. Is this graph the graph of a function? Why or why not?

38. Do you think that a similar graph of your hourly wage on January 1 of every year (whether you are working or not) will be the graph of a function? Why or why not?

This graph shows the cost of mailing a large envelope through the U.S. Postal Service by weight at this time. Use this graph to answer Exercises 39 through 44.

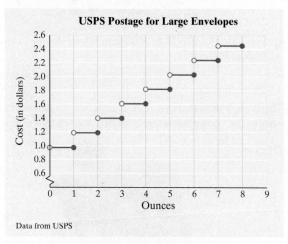

USPS Postage for Large Envelopes

Data from USPS

39. Approximate the postage to mail a large envelope weighing more than 4 ounces but not more than 5 ounces.

40. Approximate the postage to mail a large envelope weighing more than 7 ounces but not more than 8 ounces.

41. Give the weight of a large envelope that costs about $2.00 to mail.

42. If you have $1.50, what is the weight of the largest envelope you can mail for that money?

43. Is this graph a function? Why or why not?

44. Do you think that a similar graph of postage to mail a first-class letter will be the graph of a function? Why or why not?

Find $f(-2), f(0),$ and $f(3)$ for each function. See Example 7.

45. $f(x) = 2x - 5$ **46.** $f(x) = 3 - 7x$

47. $f(x) = x^2 + 2$ **48.** $f(x) = x^2 - 4$

49. $f(x) = 3x$ **50.** $f(x) = -3x$

51. $f(x) = |x|$ **52.** $f(x) = |2 - x|$

Find $h(-1), h(0),$ and $h(4)$ for each function. See Example 7.

53. $h(x) = -5x$ **54.** $h(x) = -3x$

55. $h(x) = 2x^2 + 3$ **56.** $h(x) = 3x^2$

For each given function value, write a corresponding ordered pair.

57. $f(3) = 6$ **58.** $f(7) = -2$

59. $g(0) = -\dfrac{1}{2}$ **60.** $g(0) = -\dfrac{7}{8}$

61. $h(-2) = 9$ **62.** $h(-10) = 1$

Find the domain of each function. See Example 8.

63. $f(x) = 3x - 7$ **64.** $g(x) = 5 - 2x$

65. $h(x) = \dfrac{1}{x + 5}$ **66.** $f(x) = \dfrac{1}{x - 6}$

67. $g(x) = |x + 1|$ **68.** $h(x) = |2x|$

Find the domain and the range of each relation graphed. See Example 9.

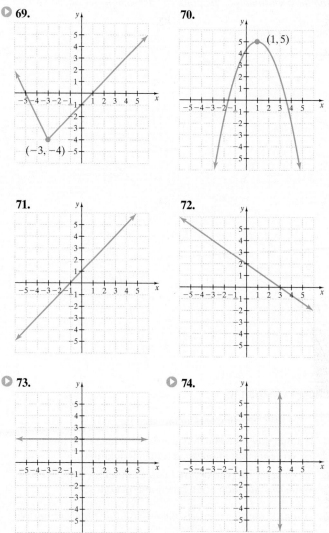

69.

70.

71.

72.

73.

74.

Use the graph of f below to answer Exercises 75 through 80.

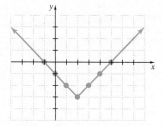

75. Complete the ordered pair solution for f. $(0, \ \ )$

76. Complete the ordered pair solution for f. $(3, \ \ )$

77. $f(0) = $ _____ ?

78. $f(3) = $ _____ ?

79. If $f(x) = 0$, find the value(s) of x.

80. If $f(x) = -1$, find the value(s) of x.

REVIEW AND PREVIEW

Find the coordinates of the point of intersection. See Section 3.1.

81.

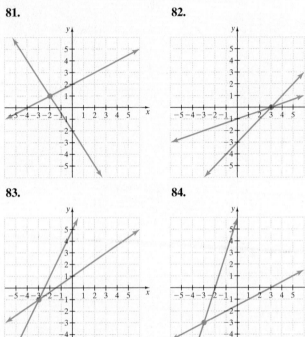

82.

83.

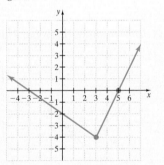

84.

CONCEPT EXTENSIONS

Solve. See the Concept Check in this section.

85. If a function *f* is evaluated at −5, the value of the function is 12. Write this situation using function notation.

86. Suppose (9, 20) is an ordered-pair solution for the function *g*. Write this situation using function notation.

The graph of the function f is below. Use this graph to answer Exercises 87 through 90.

87. Write the coordinates of the lowest point of the graph.

88. Write the answer to Exercise 87 in function notation.

89. An *x*-intercept of this graph is (5, 0). Write this using function notation.

90. Write the other *x*-intercept of this graph (see Exercise 89) using function notation.

91. Forensic scientists use the function

$$H(x) = 2.59x + 47.24$$

to estimate the height of a woman in centimeters given the length *x* of her femur bone.

a. Estimate the height of a woman whose femur measures 46 centimeters.

b. Estimate the height of a woman whose femur measures 39 centimeters.

92. The dosage in milligrams *D* of Ivermectin, a heartworm preventive for a dog who weighs *x* pounds, is given by the function

$$D(x) = \frac{136}{25}x$$

a. Find the proper dosage for a dog that weighs 35 pounds.

b. Find the proper dosage for a dog that weighs 70 pounds.

93. In your own words, define **(a)** function; **(b)** domain; **(c)** range.

94. Explain the vertical line test and how it is used.

95. Since *y* = *x* + 7 is a function, rewrite the equation using function notation.

96. Since *y* = 3 is a function, rewrite this equation using function notation.

See the example below for Exercises 97 through 100.

Example

If $f(x) = x^2 + 2x + 1$, find $f(\pi)$.

Solution:

$$f(x) = x^2 + 2x + 1$$
$$f(\pi) = \pi^2 + 2\pi + 1$$

Given the following functions, find the indicated values.

97. $f(x) = 2x + 7$

a. $f(2)$ **b.** $f(a)$

98. $g(x) = -3x + 12$

a. $g(5)$ **b.** $g(r)$

99. $h(x) = x^2 + 7$

a. $h(3)$ **b.** $h(a)$

100. $f(x) = x^2 - 12$

a. $f(12)$ **b.** $f(a)$

Chapter 3 Vocabulary Check

Fill in each blank with one of the words listed below.

relation	function	domain	range	standard	slope-intercept
y-axis	*x*-axis	solution	linear	slope	point-slope
x-intercept	*y*-intercept	*y*	*x*		

1. An ordered pair is a(n) _____ of an equation in two variables if replacing the variables by the coordinates of the ordered pair results in a true statement.
2. The vertical number line in the rectangular coordinate system is called the _____.
3. A(n) _____ equation can be written in the form $Ax + By = C$.
4. A(n) _____ is a point of the graph where the graph crosses the *x*-axis.
5. The form $Ax + By = C$ is called _____ form.
6. A(n) _____ is a point of the graph where the graph crosses the *y*-axis.
7. The equation $y = 7x - 5$ is written in _____ form.
8. The equation $y + 1 = 7(x - 2)$ is written in _____ form.
9. To find an *x*-intercept of a graph, let _____ = 0.
10. The horizontal number line in the rectangular coordinate system is called the _____.
11. To find a *y*-intercept of a graph, let _____ = 0.
12. The _____ of a line measures the steepness or tilt of a line.
13. A set of ordered pairs that assigns to each *x*-value exactly one *y*-value is called a(n) _____.
14. The set of all *x*-coordinates of a relation is called the _____ of the relation.
15. The set of all *y*-coordinates of a relation is called the _____ of the relation.
16. A set of ordered pairs is called a(n) _____.

Chapter 3 Highlights

DEFINITIONS AND CONCEPTS	EXAMPLES

Section 3.1 Reading Graphs and the Rectangular Coordinate System

The **rectangular coordinate system** consists of a plane and a vertical and a horizontal number line intersecting at their 0 coordinates. The vertical number line is called the **y-axis** and the horizontal number line is called the **x-axis.** The point of intersection of the axes is called the **origin**.

To **plot** or **graph** an ordered pair means to find its corresponding point on a rectangular coordinate system.

To plot or graph an ordered pair such as $(3, -2)$, start at the origin. Move 3 units to the right and, from there, 2 units down.

To plot or graph $(-3, 4)$, start at the origin. Move 3 units to the left and, from there, 4 units up.

(continued)

DEFINITIONS AND CONCEPTS	EXAMPLES

Section 3.1 Reading Graphs and the Rectangular Coordinate System (continued)

An ordered pair is a **solution** of an equation in two variables if replacing the variables by the coordinates of the ordered pair results in a true statement.

Determine whether $(-1, 5)$ is a solution of $2x + 3y = 13$.

$$2x + 3y = 13$$
$$2(-1) + 3 \cdot 5 = 13 \quad \text{Let } x = -1, y = 5$$
$$-2 + 15 = 13$$
$$13 = 13 \quad \text{True}$$

If one coordinate of an ordered pair solution is known, the other value can be determined by substitution.

Complete the ordered pair solution $(0, \ )$ for the equation $x - 6y = 12$.

$$x - 6y = 12$$
$$0 - 6y = 12 \quad \text{Let } x = 0.$$
$$\frac{-6y}{-6} = \frac{12}{-6} \quad \text{Divide by } -6.$$
$$y = -2$$

The ordered pair solution is $(0, -2)$.

Section 3.2 Graphing Linear Equations

A **linear equation in two variables** is an equation that can be written in the form $Ax + By = C$ where A and B are not both 0. The form $Ax + By = C$ is called **standard form.**

Linear Equations

$$3x + 2y = -6 \qquad x = -5$$
$$y = 3 \qquad y = -x + 10$$

$x + y = 10$ is in standard form.

To graph a linear equation in two variables, find three ordered pair solutions. Plot the solution points and draw the line connecting the points.

Graph $x - 2y = 5$.

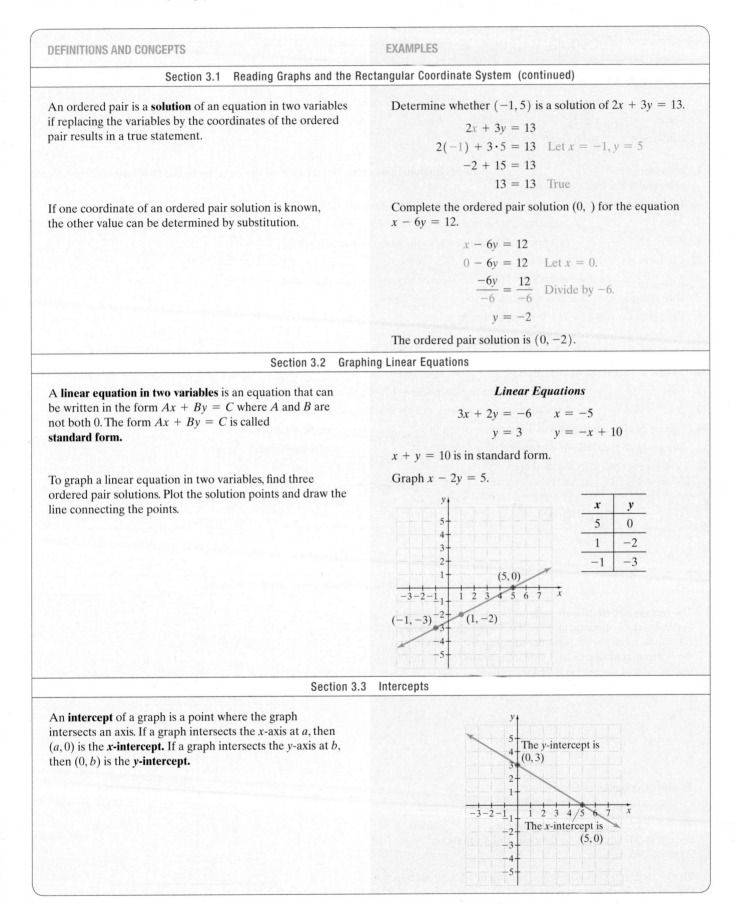

x	y
5	0
1	-2
-1	-3

Section 3.3 Intercepts

An **intercept** of a graph is a point where the graph intersects an axis. If a graph intersects the x-axis at a, then $(a, 0)$ is the **x-intercept.** If a graph intersects the y-axis at b, then $(0, b)$ is the **y-intercept.**

The y-intercept is $(0, 3)$

The x-intercept is $(5, 0)$

DEFINITIONS AND CONCEPTS	EXAMPLES

Section 3.3   Intercepts (continued)

To find the *x*-intercept, let $y = 0$ and solve for x.

To find the *y*-intercept, let $x = 0$ and solve for y.

Graph $2x - 5y = -10$ by finding intercepts.

$$\text{If } y = 0, \text{ then} \qquad\qquad \text{If } x = 0, \text{ then}$$

$$2x - 5\cdot 0 = -10 \qquad\qquad 2\cdot 0 - 5y = -10$$

$$2x = -10 \qquad\qquad\qquad -5y = -10$$

$$\frac{2x}{2} = \frac{-10}{2} \qquad\qquad \frac{-5y}{-5} = \frac{-10}{-5}$$

$$x = -5 \qquad\qquad\qquad y = 2$$

The x-intercept is $(-5, 0)$. The y-intercept is $(0, 2)$.

The graph of $x = c$ is a vertical line with x-intercept $(c, 0)$.

The graph of $y = c$ is a horizontal line with y-intercept $(0, c)$.

Section 3.4   Slope and Rate of Change

The **slope *m*** of the line through points (x_1, y_1) and (x_2, y_2) is given by

$$m = \frac{y_2 - y_1}{x_2 - x_1} \quad \text{as long as } x_2 \neq x_1$$

A horizontal line has slope 0.
The slope of a vertical line is undefined.

Nonvertical parallel lines have the same slope.

Two nonvertical lines are perpendicular if the slope of one is the negative reciprocal of the slope of the other.

The slope of the line through points $(-1, 6)$ and $(-5, 8)$ is

$$m = \frac{y_2 - y_1}{x_2 - x_1} = \frac{8 - 6}{-5 - (-1)} = \frac{2}{-4} = -\frac{1}{2}$$

The slope of the line $y = -5$ is 0.
The line $x = 3$ has undefined slope.

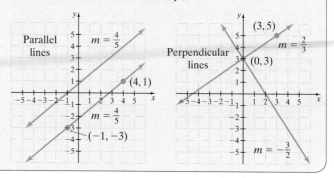

DEFINITIONS AND CONCEPTS	EXAMPLES

Section 3.5   Equations of Lines

Slope-Intercept Form

$$y = mx + b$$

m is the slope of the line.
$(0, b)$ is the y-intercept.

Find the slope and the y-intercept of the line whose equation is $2x + 3y = 6$.

Solve for y:

$$2x + 3y = 6$$
$$3y = -2x + 6 \quad \text{Subtract } 2x.$$
$$y = -\frac{2}{3}x + 2 \quad \text{Divide by 3.}$$

The slope of the line is $-\dfrac{2}{3}$ and the y-intercept is $(0, 2)$.

Find an equation of the line with slope 3 and y-intercept $(0, -1)$.

The equation is $y = 3x - 1$.

Point-Slope Form

$$y - y_1 = m(x - x_1)$$

m is the slope.
(x_1, y_1) is a point on the line.

Find an equation of the line with slope $\dfrac{3}{4}$ that contains the point $(-1, 5)$.

$$y - 5 = \frac{3}{4}[x - (-1)]$$

$$4(y - 5) = 3(x + 1) \quad \text{Multiply by 4.}$$
$$4y - 20 = 3x + 3 \quad \text{Distribute.}$$
$$-3x + 4y = 23 \quad \text{Subtract } 3x \text{ and add 20.}$$

Section 3.6   Functions

A set of ordered pairs is a **relation.** The set of all x-coordinates is called the **domain** of the relation, and the set of all y-coordinates is called the **range** of the relation.

The domain of the relation $\{(0, 5), (2, 5), (4, 5), (5, -2)\}$ is $\{0, 2, 4, 5\}$. The range is $\{-2, 5\}$.

A **function** is a set of ordered pairs that assigns to each x-value exactly one y-value.

Which are graphs of functions?

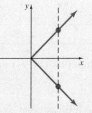
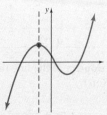

Vertical Line Test

If a vertical line can be drawn so that it intersects a graph more than once, the graph is not the graph of a function.

This graph is not the graph of a function.

This graph is the graph of a function.

The symbol $f(x)$ means **function of x.** This notation is called **function** notation.

If $f(x) = 2x^2 + 6x - 1$, find $f(3)$.

$$f(3) = 2(3)^2 + 6 \cdot 3 - 1$$
$$= 2 \cdot 9 + 18 - 1$$
$$= 18 + 18 - 1$$
$$= 35$$

Chapter 3 Review

(3.1) *Plot the following ordered pairs on a Cartesian coordinate system.*

1. $(-7, 0)$
2. $\left(0, 4\frac{4}{5}\right)$
3. $(-2, -5)$
4. $(1, -3)$
5. $(0.7, 0.7)$
6. $(-6, 4)$

7. A local office supply store uses quantity pricing. The table shows the price per box of #10 security envelopes for different numbers of envelopes in a box purchased.

Price per Box of Envelopes (in dollars)	Number of Envelopes in Box
5.00	50
8.50	100
20.00	250
27.00	500

a. Write each paired data as an ordered pair of the form (price per box of envelopes, number of envelopes in box).

b. Create a scatter diagram of the paired data. Be sure to label the axes appropriately.

8. The table shows the annual overnight stays in national parks. (*Source:* National Park Service)

Year	Overnight Stays in National Parks (in millions)
2008	13.9
2009	14.6
2010	14.6
2011	14.0
2012	14.3
2013	13.5

a. Write each paired data as an ordered pair of the form (year, number of overnight stays).

b. Create a scatter diagram of the paired data. Be sure to label the axes properly.

Determine whether each ordered pair is a solution of the given equation.

9. $7x - 8y = 56$; $(0, 56), (8, 0)$
10. $-2x + 5y = 10$; $(-5, 0), (1, 1)$
11. $x = 13$; $(13, 5), (13, 13)$
12. $y = 2$; $(7, 2), (2, 7)$

Complete the ordered pairs so that each is a solution of the given equation.

13. $-2 + y = 6x$; $(7, \quad)$
14. $y = 3x + 5$; $(\quad, -8)$

Complete the table of values for each given equation; then plot the ordered pairs. Use a single coordinate system for each exercise.

15. $9 = -3x + 4y$

x	y
	0
	3
9	

16. $x = 2y$

x	y
	0
	5
	-5

The cost in dollars of producing x compact disc holders is given by $y = 5x + 2000$. Use this equation for Exercises 17 and 18.

17. Complete the following table.

x	y
1	
100	
1000	

18. Find the number of compact disc holders that can be produced for $6430.

(3.2) *Graph each linear equation.*

19. $x - y = 1$
20. $x + y = 6$
21. $x - 3y = 12$
22. $5x - y = -8$
23. $x = 3y$
24. $y = -2x$
25. $2x - 3y = 6$
26. $4x - 3y = 12$

(3.3) *Identify the intercepts.*

27.

28.

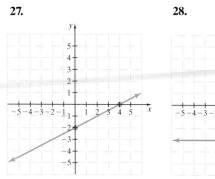

29.

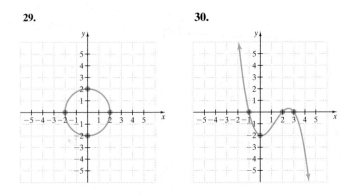

30.

Graph each linear equation by finding its intercepts.

31. $x - 3y = 12$

32. $-4x + y = 8$

33. $y = -3$

34. $x = 5$

35. $y = -3x$

36. $x = 5y$

37. $x - 2 = 0$

38. $y + 6 = 0$

(3.4) Find the slope of each line.

39.

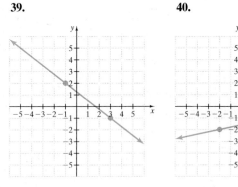

40.

For Exercises 41 through 44, match each slope with its line.

A.

B.

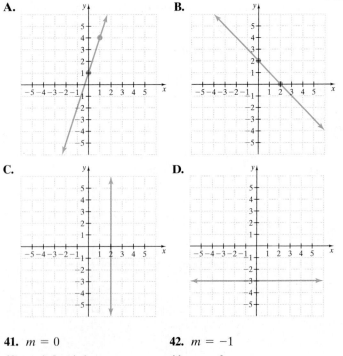

C.

D.

41. $m = 0$

42. $m = -1$

43. undefined slope

44. $m = 3$

Find the slope of the line that goes through the given points.

45. $(2, 5)$ and $(6, 8)$

46. $(4, 7)$ and $(1, 2)$

47. $(1, 3)$ and $(-2, -9)$

48. $(-4, 1)$ and $(3, -6)$

Find the slope of each line.

49. $y = 3x + 7$

50. $x - 2y = 4$

51. $y = -2$

52. $x = 0$

Determine whether each pair of lines is parallel, perpendicular, or neither.

53. $x - y = -6$
$x + y = 3$

54. $3x + y = 7$
$-3x - y = 10$

55. $y = 4x + \dfrac{1}{2}$
$4x + 2y = 1$

56. $x = 4$
$y = -2$

Find the slope of each line. Then write a sentence explaining the meaning of the slope as a rate of change. Don't forget to attach the proper units.

57. The graph below approximates the number of U.S. college students (in thousands) earning an associate's degree for each year x.

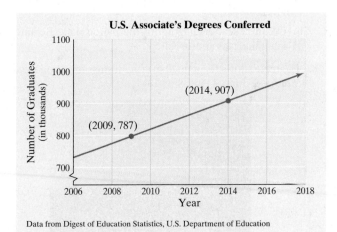

U.S. Associate's Degrees Conferred

Data from Digest of Education Statistics, U.S. Department of Education

58. The graph below approximates the number of kidney transplants y in the United States for year x.

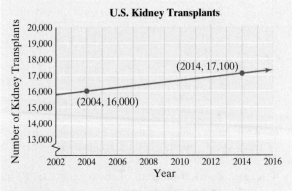

U.S. Kidney Transplants

Data from Organ Procurement and Transplantation Network, U.S. Department of Health and Human Services

(3.5) Determine the slope and the y-intercept of the graph of each equation.

59. $3x + y = 7$

60. $x - 6y = -1$

61. $y = 2$

62. $x = -5$

Use the slope-intercept form to graph each equation.

63. $y = 3x - 1$

64. $y = -3x$

65. $5x - 3y = 15$

66. $-x + 2y = 8$

Write an equation of each line in slope-intercept form.

67. slope -5; y-intercept $\left(0, \dfrac{1}{2}\right)$

68. slope $\dfrac{2}{3}$; y-intercept $(0, 6)$

For exercises 69 through 72, match each equation with its graph.

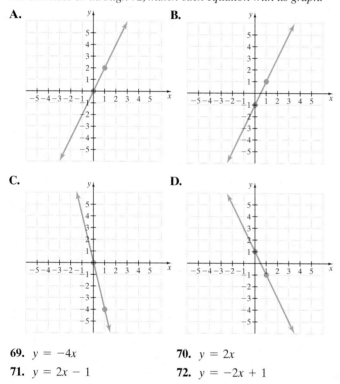

A.   **B.**

C.   **D.**

69. $y = -4x$

70. $y = 2x$

71. $y = 2x - 1$

72. $y = -2x + 1$

College is getting more expensive every year. The average cost for tuition and fees at a public two-year college y from 1995 through 2011 can be approximated by the linear equation $y = 56x + 1859$, where x is the number of years after 1995. Use this information for Exercises 73 and 74. (Source: The College Board: Trends in College Pricing 2010)

73. Find the y-intercept of this equation.

74. What does the y-intercept mean?

Write an equation of each line. Write each equation in standard form, $Ax + By = C$, or $x = c$ or $y = c$ form.

75. With slope -3, through $(0, -5)$

76. With slope $\dfrac{1}{2}$, through $\left(0, -\dfrac{7}{2}\right)$

77. With slope 0, through $(-2, -3)$

78. With slope 0, through the origin

79. With slope -6, through $(2, -1)$

80. With slope 12, through $\left(\dfrac{1}{2}, 5\right)$

81. Through $(0, 6)$ and $(6, 0)$

82. Through $(0, -4)$ and $(-8, 0)$

83. Vertical line, through $(5, 7)$

84. Horizontal line, through $(-6, 8)$

85. Through $(6, 0)$, perpendicular to $y = 8$

86. Through $(10, 12)$, perpendicular to $x = -2$

(3.6) Determine whether each of the following is a function.

87. $\{(7, 1), (7, 5), (2, 6)\}$

88. $\{(0, -1), (5, -1), (2, 2)\}$

89. $7x - 6y = 1$

90. $y = 7$

91. $x = 2$

92. $y = x^3$

93.   **94.**

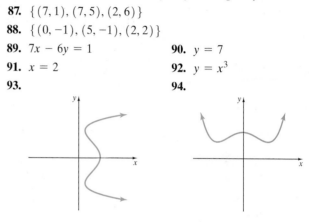

Given the following functions, find the indicated function values.

95. Given $f(x) = -2x + 6$, find

   a. $f(0)$ **b.** $f(-2)$ **c.** $f\left(\dfrac{1}{2}\right)$

96. Given $h(x) = -5 - 3x$, find

   a. $h(2)$ **b.** $h(-3)$ **c.** $h(0)$

97. Given $g(x) = x^2 + 12x$, find

   a. $g(3)$ **b.** $g(-5)$ **c.** $g(0)$

98. Given $h(x) = 6 - |x|$, find

   a. $h(-1)$ **b.** $h(1)$ **c.** $h(-4)$

Find the domain of each function.

99. $f(x) = 2x + 7$ **100.** $g(x) = \dfrac{7}{x - 2}$

Find the domain and the range of each function graphed.

101.   **102.**

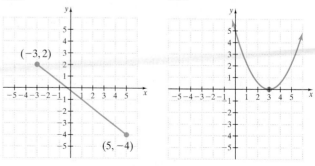

103. **104.**

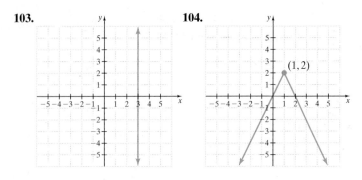

117. **118.**

Find the slope of each line.

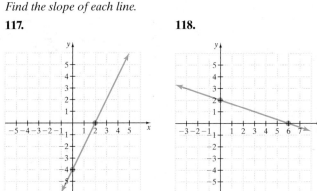

MIXED REVIEW

Complete the table of values for each given equation.

105. $2x - 5y = 9$

x	y
	1
2	
	-3

106. $x = -3y$

x	y
0	
	1
6	

Find the intercepts for each equation.

107. $2x - 3y = 6$

108. $-5x + y = 10$

Graph each linear equation.

109. $x - 5y = 10$ **110.** $x + y = 4$

111. $y = -4x$ **112.** $2x + 3y = -6$

113. $x = 3$ **114.** $y = -2$

Find the slope of the line that passes through each pair of points.

115. $(3, -5)$ and $(-4, 2)$ **116.** $(1, 3)$ and $(-6, -8)$

Determine the slope and y-intercept of the graph of each equation.

119. $-2x + 3y = -15$

120. $6x + y - 2 = 0$

Write an equation of the line with the given slope that passes through the given point. Write the equation in the form $Ax + By = C$.

121. $m = -5; (3, -7)$

122. $m = 3; (0, 6)$

Write an equation of the line passing through each pair of points. Write the equation in the form $Ax + By = C$.

123. $(-3, 9)$ and $(-2, 5)$

124. $(3, 1)$ and $(5, -9)$

Yogurt is an ever more popular food item. In 2009, American Dairy affiliates produced 3800 million pounds of yogurt. In 2012, this number rose to 4400 million pounds of yogurt. Use this information for Exercises 125 and 126.

125. Assume that the relationship between time and yogurt production is linear and write an equation describing this relationship. Use ordered pairs of the form (years past 2009, millions of pounds of yogurt produced).

126. Use this equation to predict yogurt production in the year 2018.

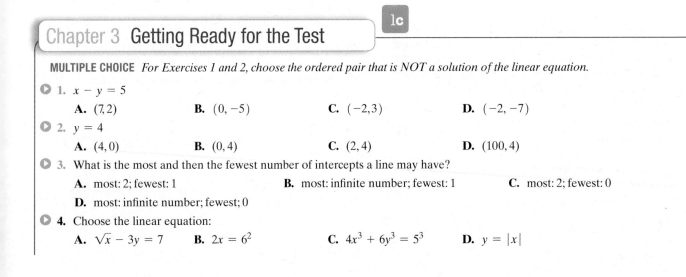

1c

Chapter 3 Getting Ready for the Test

MULTIPLE CHOICE *For Exercises 1 and 2, choose the ordered pair that is NOT a solution of the linear equation.*

▶ **1.** $x - y = 5$

    A. $(7, 2)$ **B.** $(0, -5)$ **C.** $(-2, 3)$ **D.** $(-2, -7)$

▶ **2.** $y = 4$

    A. $(4, 0)$ **B.** $(0, 4)$ **C.** $(2, 4)$ **D.** $(100, 4)$

▶ **3.** What is the most and then the fewest number of intercepts a line may have?

    A. most: 2; fewest: 1   **B.** most: infinite number; fewest: 1   **C.** most: 2; fewest: 0

    D. most: infinite number; fewest: 0

▶ **4.** Choose the linear equation:

    A. $\sqrt{x} - 3y = 7$ **B.** $2x = 6^2$ **C.** $4x^3 + 6y^3 = 5^3$ **D.** $y = |x|$

MATCHING *Match each graph in the rectangular system with its slope to the right. Each slope may be used only once.*

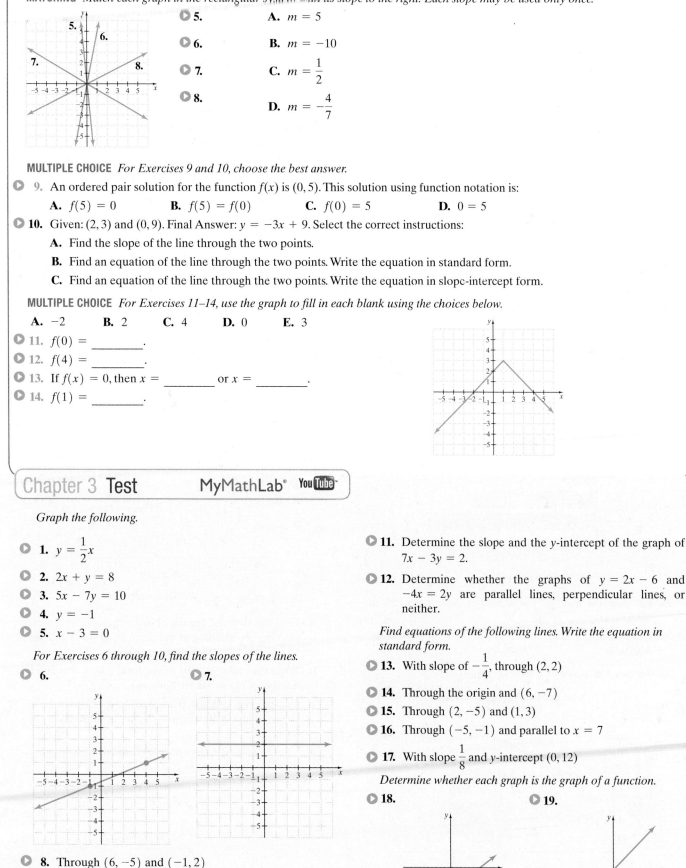

▶ **5.** **A.** $m = 5$

▶ **6.** **B.** $m = -10$

▶ **7.** **C.** $m = \dfrac{1}{2}$

▶ **8.** **D.** $m = -\dfrac{4}{7}$

MULTIPLE CHOICE *For Exercises 9 and 10, choose the best answer.*

▶ **9.** An ordered pair solution for the function $f(x)$ is $(0, 5)$. This solution using function notation is:

    A. $f(5) = 0$ **B.** $f(5) = f(0)$ **C.** $f(0) = 5$ **D.** $0 = 5$

▶ **10.** Given: $(2, 3)$ and $(0, 9)$. Final Answer: $y = -3x + 9$. Select the correct instructions:

    A. Find the slope of the line through the two points.

    B. Find an equation of the line through the two points. Write the equation in standard form.

    C. Find an equation of the line through the two points. Write the equation in slope-intercept form.

MULTIPLE CHOICE *For Exercises 11–14, use the graph to fill in each blank using the choices below.*

    A. -2 **B.** 2 **C.** 4 **D.** 0 **E.** 3

▶ **11.** $f(0) = $ _____ .

▶ **12.** $f(4) = $ _____ .

▶ **13.** If $f(x) = 0$, then $x = $ _____ or $x = $ _____ .

▶ **14.** $f(1) = $ _____ .

Chapter 3 **Test**   MyMathLab®   You Tube™

Graph the following.

▶ **1.** $y = \dfrac{1}{2}x$

▶ **2.** $2x + y = 8$

▶ **3.** $5x - 7y = 10$

▶ **4.** $y = -1$

▶ **5.** $x - 3 = 0$

For Exercises 6 through 10, find the slopes of the lines.

▶ **6.**   ▶ **7.**

▶ **8.** Through $(6, -5)$ and $(-1, 2)$

▶ **9.** $-3x + y = 5$

▶ **10.** $x = 6$

▶ **11.** Determine the slope and the y-intercept of the graph of $7x - 3y = 2$.

▶ **12.** Determine whether the graphs of $y = 2x - 6$ and $-4x = 2y$ are parallel lines, perpendicular lines, or neither.

Find equations of the following lines. Write the equation in standard form.

▶ **13.** With slope of $-\dfrac{1}{4}$, through $(2, 2)$

▶ **14.** Through the origin and $(6, -7)$

▶ **15.** Through $(2, -5)$ and $(1, 3)$

▶ **16.** Through $(-5, -1)$ and parallel to $x = 7$

▶ **17.** With slope $\dfrac{1}{8}$ and y-intercept $(0, 12)$

Determine whether each graph is the graph of a function.

▶ **18.**   ▶ **19.**

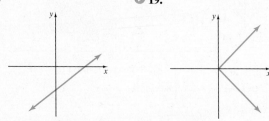

Given the following function, find the indicated function values.

20. $h(x) = x^3 - x$

    a. $h(-1)$ **b.** $h(0)$ **c.** $h(4)$

21. Find the domain of $y = \dfrac{1}{x + 1}$.

For Exercises 22 and 23, **a.** *Identify the x- and y-intercepts.* **b.** *Find the domain and the range of each function graphed.*

22.   **23.**

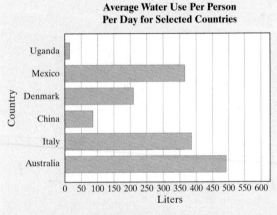

24. If $f(7) = 20$, write the corresponding ordered pair.

Use the bar graph below to answer Exercises 25 and 26.

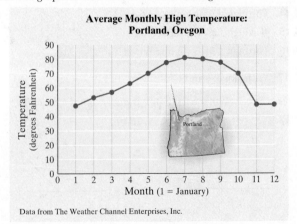

Average Water Use Per Person Per Day for Selected Countries

Data from United Nations Development Programme

25. Estimate the average water use per person per day in Denmark.

26. Estimate the average water use per person per day in Australia.

Use this graph to answer Exercises 27 through 29.

Average Monthly High Temperature: Portland, Oregon

Data from The Weather Channel Enterprises, Inc.

27. During what month is the average high temperature the greatest?

28. Approximate the average high temperature for the month of April.

29. During what month(s) is the average high temperature below 60°F?

30. The table gives the number of Dish Network subscribers (in millions) for the years shown. (*Source:* Dish Network)

Year	Dish Network Subscribers (in millions)
2008	13.68
2009	14.10
2010	14.13
2011	13.97
2012	14.06
2013	14.06
2014	13.98

  a. Write this data as a set of ordered pairs of the form (year, number of Dish Network subscribers in millions).

  b. Create a scatter diagram of the data. Be sure to label the axes properly.

31. This graph approximates the number of movie ticket sales y (in millions) for the year x.

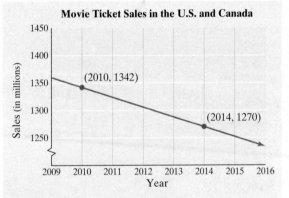

Movie Ticket Sales in the U.S. and Canada

Data from National Association of Theater Owners

  a. Find the slope of the line. Then write a sentence explaining the meaning of the slope as a rate of change. Don't forget to attach the proper units.

  b. Write two ordered pairs of the form (years past 2000, number of tickets sold in millions).

  c. Use the two ordered pairs from part (b) to write a linear equation. Write the equation in slope-intercept form.

  d. Use the equation from part (c) to predict the number of movie tickets sold in 2020.

Chapter 3 Cumulative Review

1. Insert $<$, $>$, or $=$ in the space between each pair of numbers to make each statement true.
   a. 2   3   **b.** 7   4   **c.** 72   27

2. Write the fraction $\dfrac{56}{64}$ in lowest terms.

3. Multiply $\dfrac{2}{15}$ and $\dfrac{5}{13}$. Simplify the product if possible.

4. Add: $\dfrac{10}{3} + \dfrac{5}{21}$

5. Simplify: $\dfrac{3 + |4 - 3| + 2^2}{6 - 3}$

6. Simplify: $16 - 3 \cdot 3 + 2^4$

7. Add.
   a. $-8 + (-11)$ **b.** $-5 + 35$
   c. $0.6 + (-1.1)$ **d.** $-\dfrac{7}{10} + \left(-\dfrac{1}{10}\right)$
   e. $11.4 + (-4.7)$ **f.** $-\dfrac{3}{8} + \dfrac{2}{5}$

8. Simplify: $|9 + (-20)| + |-10|$

9. Simplify each expression.
   a. $-14 - 8 + 10 - (-6)$
   b. $1.6 - (-10.3) + (-5.6)$

10. Simplify: $-9 - (3 - 8)$

11. If $x = -2$ and $y = -4$, evaluate each expression.
    a. $5x - y$ **b.** $x^4 - y^2$
    c. $\dfrac{3x}{2y}$

12. Is -20 a solution of $\dfrac{x}{-10} = 2$?

13. Simplify each expression.
    a. $10 + (x + 12)$ **b.** $-3(7x)$

14. Simplify: $(12 + x) - (4x - 7)$

15. Identify the numerical coefficient of each term.
    a. $-3y$ **b.** $22z^4$ **c.** y
    d. $-x$ **e.** $\dfrac{x}{7}$

16. Multiply: $-5(x - 7)$

17. Solve $x - 7 = 10$ for x.

18. Solve: $5(3 + z) - (8z + 9) = -4$

19. Solve: $\dfrac{5}{2}x = 15$

20. Solve: $\dfrac{x}{4} - 1 = -7$

21. If x is the first of three consecutive integers, express the sum of the three integers in terms of x. Simplify if possible.

22. Solve: $\dfrac{x}{3} - 2 = \dfrac{x}{3}$

23. Solve: $\dfrac{2(a + 3)}{3} = 6a + 2$

24. Solve: $x + 2y = 6$ for y

25. The 114th Congress began on January 3, 2015, and had a total of 435 Democratic and Republican representatives. There were 59 fewer Democratic representatives than Republican. Find the number of representatives from each party. (*Source:* congress.gov)

26. Solve $5(x + 4) \geq 4(2x + 3)$. Write the solution set in interval notation.

27. Charles Pecot can afford enough fencing to enclose a rectangular garden with a perimeter of 140 feet. If the width of his garden must be 30 feet, find the length.

28. Solve $-3 < 4x - 1 \leq 2$. Write the solution set in interval notation.

29. Solve: $y = mx + b$ for x

30. Complete the table for $y = -5x$.

x	y
0	
-1	
	-10

31. A chemist working on his doctoral degree at Massachusetts Institute of Technology needs 12 liters of a 50% acid solution for a lab experiment. The stockroom has only 40% and 70% solutions. How much of each solution should be mixed together to form 12 liters of a 50% solution?

32. Graph: $y = -3x + 5$

33. Graph: $x \geq -1$. Then write the solutions in interval notation.

34. Find the x- and y-intercepts of $2x + 4y = -8$.

35. Solve $-1 \leq 2x - 3 < 5$. Graph the solution set and write it in interval notation.

36. Graph $x = 2$ on a rectangular coordinate system.

37. Determine whether each ordered pair is a solution of the equation $x - 2y = 6$.
    a. $(6, 0)$ **b.** $(0, 3)$
    c. $\left(1, -\dfrac{5}{2}\right)$

38. Find the slope of the line through $(0, 5)$ and $(-5, 4)$.

39. Determine whether each equation is a linear equation in two variables.
    a. $x - 1.5y = -1.6$ **b.** $y = -2x$
    c. $x + y^2 = 9$ **d.** $x = 5$

40. Find the slope of the line $x = -10$.

41. Find the slope of the line $y = -1$.

42. Find the slope and y-intercept of the line whose equation is $2x - 5y = 10$.

43. Find an equation of the line with y-intercept $(0, -3)$ and slope of $\dfrac{1}{4}$.

44. Write an equation of the line through $(2, 3)$ and $(0, 0)$. Write the equation in standard form.

Solving Systems of Linear Equations

4.1 Solving Systems of Linear Equations by Graphing

4.2 Solving Systems of Linear Equations by Substitution

4.3 Solving Systems of Linear Equations by Addition

Integrated Review—Solving Systems of Equations

4.4 Solving Systems of Linear Equations in Three Variables

4.5 Systems of Linear Equations and Problem Solving

✔ CHECK YOUR PROGRESS

Vocabulary Check
Chapter Highlights
Chapter Review
Getting Ready for the Test
Chapter Test
Cumulative Review

In Chapter 3, we graphed equations containing two variables. Equations like these are often needed to represent relationships between two different values. There are also many real-life opportunities to compare and contrast two such equations, called a system of equations. This chapter presents linear systems and ways we solve these systems and apply them to real-life situations.

Do You Know That We Often Import and Export the Same Type of Item?

The economic importance of the United States' fishing industry extends well beyond the coastal communities, for which it is a vital industry. Commercial fishing operations, including seafood wholesalers, processors, and retailers, contribute billions of dollars annually to the United States economy. Recreational fishing is also a major factor in the economy of the Gulf coast and the South Atlantic states.

Depending on the supply and demand of our country's needs, we also import and export fish of the same type. In Section 4.1, Exercises 69 and 70, we will explore the exportation and importation of Pacific salmon over the years.

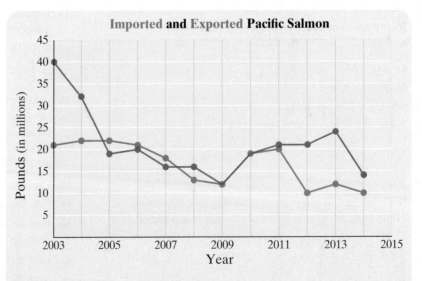

Imported and Exported Pacific Salmon

Data from USDA Economic Research Service

4.1 Solving Systems of Linear Equations by Graphing ▶

OBJECTIVES

1 Determine if an Ordered Pair Is a Solution of a System of Equations in Two Variables. ▶

2 Solve a System of Linear Equations by Graphing. ▶

3 Without Graphing, Determine the Number of Solutions of a System. ▶

A **system of linear equations** consists of two or more linear equations. In this section, we focus on solving systems of linear equations containing two equations in two variables. Examples of such linear systems are

$$\begin{cases} 3x - 3y = 0 \\ x = 2y \end{cases} \quad \begin{cases} x - y = 0 \\ 2x + y = 10 \end{cases} \quad \begin{cases} y = 7x - 1 \\ y = 4 \end{cases}$$

OBJECTIVE

1 Deciding Whether an Ordered Pair Is a Solution ▶

A **solution** of a system of two equations in two variables is an ordered pair of numbers that is a solution of both equations in the system.

EXAMPLE 1   Determine whether $(12, 6)$ is a solution of the system.

$$\begin{cases} 2x - 3y = 6 \\ x = 2y \end{cases}$$

Solution To determine whether $(12, 6)$ is a solution of the system, we replace x with 12 and y with 6 in both equations.

$2x - 3y = 6$ First equation $x = 2y$ Second equation

$2(12) - 3(6) \overset{?}{=} 6$ Let $x = 12$ and $y = 6$. $12 \overset{?}{=} 2(6)$ Let $x = 12$ and $y = 6$.

$24 - 18 \overset{?}{=} 6$ Simplify. $12 = 12$ True

$6 = 6$ True

Since $(12, 6)$ is a solution of both equations, it is a solution of the system.   □

PRACTICE

1   Determine whether $(4, 12)$ is a solution of the system.

$$\begin{cases} 4x - y = 2 \\ y = 3x \end{cases}$$

■

EXAMPLE 2   Determine whether $(-1, 2)$ is a solution of the system.

$$\begin{cases} x + 2y = 3 \\ 4x - y = 6 \end{cases}$$

Solution We replace x with -1 and y with 2 in both equations.

$x + 2y = 3$ First equation $4x - y = 6$ Second equation

$-1 + 2(2) \overset{?}{=} 3$ Let $x = -1$ and $y = 2$. $4(-1) - 2 \overset{?}{=} 6$ Let $x = -1$ and $y = 2$.

$-1 + 4 \overset{?}{=} 3$ Simplify. $-4 - 2 \overset{?}{=} 6$ Simplify.

$3 = 3$ True $-6 = 6$ False

$(-1, 2)$ is not a solution of the second equation, $4x - y = 6$, so it is not a solution of the system.   □

PRACTICE

2   Determine whether $(-4, 1)$ is a solution of the system.

$$\begin{cases} x - 3y = -7 \\ 2x + 9y = 1 \end{cases}$$

■

2 Solving Systems of Equations by Graphing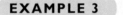

Since a solution of a system of two equations in two variables is a solution common to both equations, it is also a point common to the graphs of both equations. Let's practice finding solutions of both equations in a system—that is, solutions of a system—by graphing and identifying points of intersection.

EXAMPLE 3   Solve the system of equations by graphing.

$$\begin{cases} -x + 3y = 10 \\ x + y = 2 \end{cases}$$

Solution   On a single set of axes, graph each linear equation.

$-x + 3y = 10$

x	y
0	$\frac{10}{3}$
-4	2
2	4

$x + y = 2$

x	y
0	2
2	0
1	1

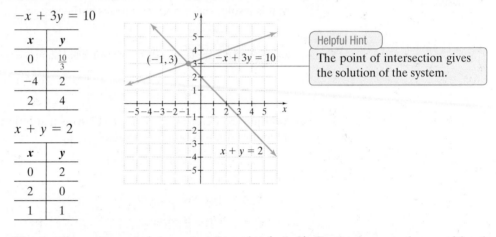

Helpful Hint

The point of intersection gives the solution of the system.

The two lines appear to intersect at the point $(-1, 3)$. To check, we replace x with -1 and y with 3 in both equations.

$-x + 3y = 10$	First equation	$x + y = 2$	Second equation
$-(-1) + 3(3) \stackrel{?}{=} 10$	Let $x = -1$ and $y = 3$.	$-1 + 3 \stackrel{?}{=} 2$	Let $x = -1$ and $y = 3$.
$1 + 9 \stackrel{?}{=} 10$	Simplify.	$2 = 2$	True
$10 = 10$	True		

$(-1, 3)$ checks, so it is the solution of the system. ☐

PRACTICE

3   Solve the system of equations by graphing.

$$\begin{cases} x - y = 3 \\ x + 2y = 18 \end{cases}$$

Helpful Hint

Neatly drawn graphs can help when you are estimating the solution of a system of linear equations by graphing.

In the example above, notice that the two lines intersected in a point. This means that the system has 1 solution.

EXAMPLE 4   Solve the system of equations by graphing.

$$\begin{cases} 2x + 3y = -2 \\ x = 2 \end{cases}$$

Solution We graph each linear equation on a single set of axes.

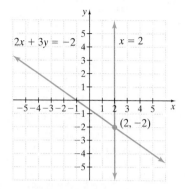

The two lines appear to intersect at the point $(2, -2)$. To determine whether $(2, -2)$ is the solution, we replace x with 2 and y with -2 in both equations.

$2x + 3y = -2$ First equation	$x = 2$ Second equation
$2(2) + 3(-2) \overset{?}{=} -2$ Let $x = 2$ and $y = -2$.	$2 \overset{?}{=} 2$ Let $x = 2$.
$4 + (-6) \overset{?}{=} -2$ Simplify.	$2 = 2$ True
$-2 = -2$ True	

Since a true statement results in both equations, $(2, -2)$ is the solution of the system. □

PRACTICE
4   Solve the system of equations by graphing.

$$\begin{cases} -4x + 3y = -3 \\ y = -5 \end{cases}$$

A system of equations that has at least one solution as in Examples 3 and 4 is said to be a **consistent system.** A system that has no solution is said to be an **inconsistent system.**

EXAMPLE 5   Solve the following system of equations by graphing.

$$\begin{cases} 2x + y = 7 \\ 2y = -4x \end{cases}$$

Solution Graph the two lines in the system.

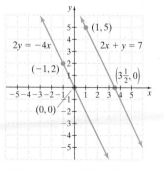

The lines **appear** to be parallel. To confirm this, write both equations in slope-intercept form by solving each equation for y.

$2x + y = 7$ First equation	$2y = -4x$ Second equation
$y = -2x + 7$ Subtract 2x from both sides.	$\dfrac{2y}{2} = \dfrac{-4x}{2}$ Divide both sides by 2.
	$y = -2x$

Recall that when an equation is written in slope-intercept form, the coefficient of x is the slope. Since both equations have the same slope, -2, but different y-intercepts, the lines are parallel and have no points in common. Thus, there is no solution of the system and the system is inconsistent. To indicate this, we can say the system has no solution or the solution set is $\{\,\}$ or $\varnothing$. □

PRACTICE

5 Solve the system of equations by graphing.

$$\begin{cases} 3y = 9x \\ 6x - 2y = 12 \end{cases}$$

In Examples 3, 4, and 5, the graphs of the two linear equations of each system are different. When this happens, we call these equations **independent equations.** If the graphs of the two equations in a system are identical, we call the equations **dependent equations.**

EXAMPLE 6 Solve the system of equations by graphing.

$$\begin{cases} x - y = 3 \\ -x + y = -3 \end{cases}$$

Solution Graph each line.

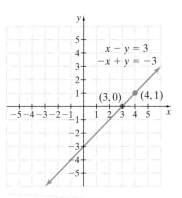

These graphs **appear** to be identical. To confirm this, write each equation in slope-intercept form.

$x - y = 3$	First equation	$-x + y = -3$	Second equation
$-y = -x + 3$	Subtract x from both sides.	$\boldsymbol{y = x - 3}$	Add x to both sides.

$$\frac{-y}{-1} = \frac{-x}{-1} + \frac{3}{-1} \qquad \text{Divide both sides by } -1.$$

$$\boldsymbol{y = x - 3}$$

The equations are identical and so must be their graphs. The lines have an infinite number of points in common. Thus, there is an infinite number of solutions of the system and this is a consistent system. The equations are dependent equations. Here, we can say that there are an infinite number of solutions or the solution set is $\{(x, y)\,|\,x - y = 3\}$ or equivalently $\{(x, y)\,|\,-x + y = -3\}$ since the equations describe identical ordered pairs. The second set is read "the set of all ordered pairs (x, y) such that $-x + y = -3$". □

PRACTICE

6 Solve the system of equations by graphing.

$$\begin{cases} x - y = 4 \\ -2x + 2y = -8 \end{cases}$$

As we have seen, three different situations can occur when graphing the two lines associated with the two equations in a linear system:

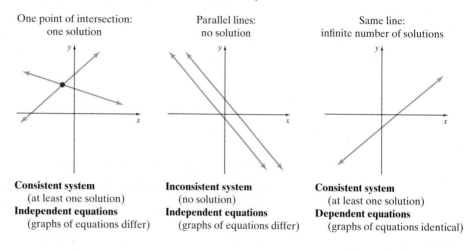

One point of intersection: one solution	Parallel lines: no solution	Same line: infinite number of solutions
Consistent system (at least one solution) **Independent equations** (graphs of equations differ)	**Inconsistent system** (no solution) **Independent equations** (graphs of equations differ)	**Consistent system** (at least one solution) **Dependent equations** (graphs of equations identical)

OBJECTIVE

3   Finding the Number of Solutions of a System without Graphing ▶

You may have suspected by now that graphing alone is not an accurate way to solve a system of linear equations. For example, a solution of $\left(\dfrac{1}{2}, \dfrac{2}{9}\right)$ is unlikely to be read correctly from a graph. The next two sections present two accurate methods of solving these systems. In the meantime, we can decide how many solutions a system has by writing each equation in the slope-intercept form.

EXAMPLE 7   Without graphing, determine the number of solutions of the system.

$$\begin{cases} \dfrac{1}{2}x - y = 2 \\ x = 2y + 5 \end{cases}$$

Solution   First write each equation in slope-intercept form.

$\dfrac{1}{2}x - y = 2$	First equation	$x = 2y + 5$	Second equation
		$x - 5 = 2y$	Subtract 5 from both sides.
$\dfrac{1}{2}x = y + 2$	Add y to both sides.	$\dfrac{x}{2} - \dfrac{5}{2} = \dfrac{2y}{2}$	Divide both sides by 2.
$\dfrac{1}{2}x - 2 = y$	Subtract 2 from both sides.	$\dfrac{1}{2}x - \dfrac{5}{2} = y$	Simplify.

The slope of each line is $\dfrac{1}{2}$, but they have different y-intercepts. This tells us that the lines representing these equations are parallel. Since the lines are parallel, the system has no solution and is inconsistent.   ☐

PRACTICE

7   Without graphing, determine the number of solutions of the system.

$$\begin{cases} 5x + 4y = 6 \\ x - y = 3 \end{cases}$$

EXAMPLE 8   Without graphing, determine the number of solutions of the system.

$$\begin{cases} 3x - y = 4 \\ x + 2y = 8 \end{cases}$$

(Continued on next page)

Solution Once again, the slope-intercept form helps determine how many solutions this system has.

$3x - y = 4$	First equation	$x + 2y = 8$	Second equation
$3x = y + 4$	Add y to both sides.	$x = -2y + 8$	Subtract $2y$ from both sides.
$3x - 4 = y$	Subtract 4 from both sides.	$x - 8 = -2y$	Subtract 8 from both sides.

$$\frac{x}{-2} - \frac{8}{-2} = \frac{-2y}{-2} \qquad \text{Divide both sides by } -2.$$

$$-\frac{1}{2}x + 4 = y \qquad \text{Simplify.}$$

The slope of the second line is $-\dfrac{1}{2}$, whereas the slope of the first line is 3. Since the slopes are not equal, the two lines are neither parallel nor identical and must intersect. Therefore, this system has one solution and is consistent. □

PRACTICE

8   Without graphing, determine the number of solutions of the system.

$$\begin{cases} -\dfrac{2}{3}x + y = 6 \\ 3y = 2x + 5 \end{cases}$$

Graphing Calculator Explorations

A graphing calculator may be used to approximate solutions of systems of equations. For example, to approximate the solution of the system

$$\begin{cases} y = -3.14x - 1.35 \\ y = 4.88x + 5.25, \end{cases}$$

first graph each equation on the same set of axes. Then use the intersect feature of your calculator to approximate the point of intersection.

The approximate point of intersection is $(-0.82, 1.23)$.

Solve each system of equations. Approximate the solutions to two decimal places.

1. $\begin{cases} y = -2.68x + 1.21 \\ y = 5.22x - 1.68 \end{cases}$ 2. $\begin{cases} y = 4.25x + 3.89 \\ y = -1.88x + 3.21 \end{cases}$

3. $\begin{cases} 4.3x - 2.9y = 5.6 \\ 8.1x + 7.6y = -14.1 \end{cases}$ 4. $\begin{cases} -3.6x - 8.6y = 10 \\ -4.5x + 9.6y = -7.7 \end{cases}$

✓ Vocabulary, Readiness & Video Check

Fill in each blank with one of the words or phrases listed below.

system of linear equations	solution	consistent
dependent	inconsistent	independent

1. In a system of linear equations in two variables, if the graphs of the equations are the same, the equations are _____ equations.

2. Two or more linear equations are called a(n) _____.

3. A system of equations that has at least one solution is called a(n) _____ system.

4. A(n) _____ of a system of two equations in two variables is an ordered pair of numbers that is a solution of both equations in the system.

5. A system of equations that has no solution is called a(n) _____ system.

6. In a system of linear equations in two variables, if the graphs of the equations are different, the equations are _____ equations.

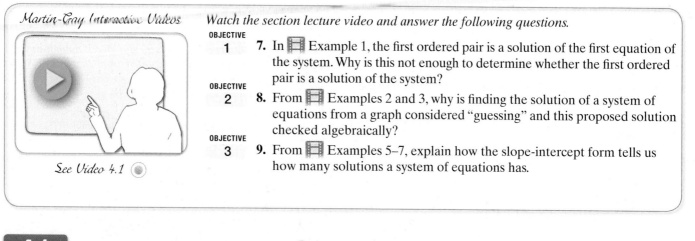

Martin-Gay Interactive Videos

See Video 4.1 ●

Watch the section lecture video and answer the following questions.

OBJECTIVE 1

7. In ▣ Example 1, the first ordered pair is a solution of the first equation of the system. Why is this not enough to determine whether the first ordered pair is a solution of the system?

OBJECTIVE 2

8. From ▣ Examples 2 and 3, why is finding the solution of a system of equations from a graph considered "guessing" and this proposed solution checked algebraically?

OBJECTIVE 3

9. From ▣ Examples 5–7, explain how the slope-intercept form tells us how many solutions a system of equations has.

4.1   **Exercise Set**   MyMathLab® ▷

Each rectangular coordinate system shows the graph of the equations in a system of equations. Use each graph to determine the number of solutions for each associated system. If the system has only one solution, give its coordinates.

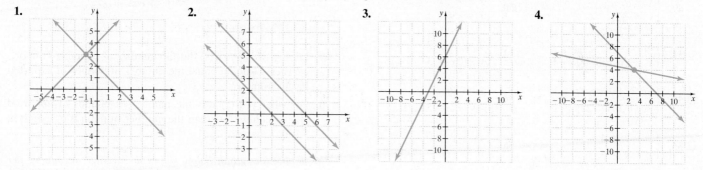

1.   **2.**   **3.**   **4.**

Determine whether each ordered pair is a solution of the system of linear equations. See Examples 1 and 2.

5. $\begin{cases} x + y = 8 \\ 3x + 2y = 21 \end{cases}$
 a. $(2, 4)$
 b. $(5, 3)$

6. $\begin{cases} 2x + y = 5 \\ x + 3y = 5 \end{cases}$
 a. $(5, 0)$
 b. $(2, 1)$

▷ 7. $\begin{cases} 3x - y = 5 \\ x + 2y = 11 \end{cases}$
 a. $(3, 4)$
 b. $(0, -5)$

8. $\begin{cases} 2x - 3y = 8 \\ x - 2y = 6 \end{cases}$
 a. $(-2, -4)$
 b. $(7, 2)$

9. $\begin{cases} 2y = 4x + 6 \\ 2x - y = -3 \end{cases}$
 a. $(-3, -3)$
 b. $(0, 3)$

10. $\begin{cases} x + 5y = -4 \\ -2x = 10y + 8 \end{cases}$
 a. $(-4, 0)$
 b. $(6, -2)$

11. $\begin{cases} -2 = x - 7y \\ 6x - y = 13 \end{cases}$
 a. $(-2, 0)$
 b. $\left(\dfrac{1}{2}, \dfrac{5}{14} \right)$

12. $\begin{cases} 4x = 1 - y \\ x - 3y = -8 \end{cases}$
 a. $(0, 1)$
 b. $\left(\dfrac{1}{6}, \dfrac{1}{3} \right)$

MIXED PRACTICE

Solve each system of linear equations by graphing. See Examples 3 through 6.

13. $\begin{cases} x + y = 4 \\ x - y = 2 \end{cases}$

14. $\begin{cases} x + y = 3 \\ x - y = 5 \end{cases}$

15. $\begin{cases} x + y = 6 \\ -x + y = -6 \end{cases}$

16. $\begin{cases} x + y = 1 \\ -x + y = -3 \end{cases}$

17. $\begin{cases} y = 2x \\ 3x - y = -2 \end{cases}$

18. $\begin{cases} y = -3x \\ 2x - y = -5 \end{cases}$

19. $\begin{cases} y = x + 1 \\ y = 2x - 1 \end{cases}$

20. $\begin{cases} y = 3x - 4 \\ y = x + 2 \end{cases}$

▷ 21. $\begin{cases} 2x + y = 0 \\ 3x + y = 1 \end{cases}$

22. $\begin{cases} 2x + y = 1 \\ 3x + y = 0 \end{cases}$

23. $\begin{cases} y = -x - 1 \\ y = 2x + 5 \end{cases}$

24. $\begin{cases} y = x - 1 \\ y = -3x - 5 \end{cases}$

▷ 25. $\begin{cases} x + y = 5 \\ x + y = 6 \end{cases}$

26. $\begin{cases} x - y = 4 \\ x - y = 1 \end{cases}$

27. $\begin{cases} 2x - y = 6 \\ y = 2 \end{cases}$

28. $\begin{cases} x + y = 5 \\ x = 4 \end{cases}$

29. $\begin{cases} x - 2y = 2 \\ 3x + 2y = -2 \end{cases}$

30. $\begin{cases} x + 3y = 7 \\ 2x - 3y = -4 \end{cases}$

31. $\begin{cases} 2x + y = 4 \\ 6x = -3y + 6 \end{cases}$

32. $\begin{cases} y + 2x = 3 \\ 4x = 2 - 2y \end{cases}$

33. $\begin{cases} y - 3x = -2 \\ 6x - 2y = 4 \end{cases}$

34. $\begin{cases} x - 2y = -6 \\ -2x + 4y = 12 \end{cases}$

35. $\begin{cases} x = 3 \\ y = -1 \end{cases}$

36. $\begin{cases} x = -5 \\ y = 3 \end{cases}$

37. $\begin{cases} y = x - 2 \\ y = 2x + 3 \end{cases}$

38. $\begin{cases} y = x + 5 \\ y = -2x - 4 \end{cases}$

39. $\begin{cases} 2x - 3y = -2 \\ -3x + 5y = 5 \end{cases}$

40. $\begin{cases} 4x - y = 7 \\ 2x - 3y = -9 \end{cases}$

41. $\begin{cases} 6x - y = 4 \\ \dfrac{1}{2}y = -2 + 3x \end{cases}$ 　　42. $\begin{cases} 3x - y = 6 \\ \dfrac{1}{3}y = -2 + x \end{cases}$

Without graphing, decide.

 a. Are the graphs of the equations identical lines, parallel lines, or lines intersecting at a single point?

 b. How many solutions does the system have? See Examples 7 and 8.

43. $\begin{cases} 4x + y = 24 \\ x + 2y = 2 \end{cases}$ 　　44. $\begin{cases} 3x + y = 1 \\ 3x + 2y = 6 \end{cases}$

45. $\begin{cases} 2x + y = 0 \\ 2y = 6 - 4x \end{cases}$ 　　46. $\begin{cases} 3x + y = 0 \\ 2y = -6x \end{cases}$

47. $\begin{cases} 6x - y = 4 \\ \dfrac{1}{2}y = -2 + 3x \end{cases}$ 　　48. $\begin{cases} 3x - y = 2 \\ \dfrac{1}{3}y = -2 + 3x \end{cases}$

49. $\begin{cases} x = 5 \\ y = -2 \end{cases}$ 　　50. $\begin{cases} y = 3 \\ x = -4 \end{cases}$

51. $\begin{cases} 3y - 2x = 3 \\ x + 2y = 9 \end{cases}$ 　　52. $\begin{cases} 2y = x + 2 \\ y + 2x = 3 \end{cases}$

53. $\begin{cases} 6y + 4x = 6 \\ 3y - 3 = -2x \end{cases}$ 　　54. $\begin{cases} 8y + 6x = 4 \\ 4y - 2 = 3x \end{cases}$

55. $\begin{cases} x + y = 4 \\ x + y = 3 \end{cases}$ 　　56. $\begin{cases} 2x + y = 0 \\ y = -2x + 1 \end{cases}$

REVIEW AND PREVIEW

Solve each equation. See Section 2.3.

57. $5(x - 3) + 3x = 1$

58. $-2x + 3(x + 6) = 17$

59. $4\left(\dfrac{y + 1}{2}\right) + 3y = 0$

60. $-y + 12\left(\dfrac{y - 1}{4}\right) = 3$

61. $8a - 2(3a - 1) = 6$

62. $3z - (4z - 2) = 9$

CONCEPT EXTENSIONS

63. Draw a graph of two linear equations whose associated system has the solution $(-1, 4)$.

64. Draw a graph of two linear equations whose associated system has the solution $(3, -2)$.

65. Draw a graph of two linear equations whose associated system has no solution.

66. Draw a graph of two linear equations whose associated system has an infinite number of solutions.

67. The ordered pair $(-2, 3)$ is a solution of all three independent equations:

$$x + y = 1$$
$$2x - y = -7$$
$$x + 3y = 7$$

Describe the graph of all three equations on the same axes.

68. Explain how to use a graph to determine the number of solutions of a system.

The double line graph below shows the number of pounds of fresh Pacific salmon imported to or exported from the United States during the given years. Use this graph to answer Exercises 69 and 70.

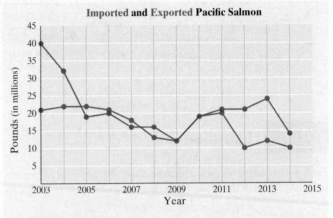

Imported and Exported Pacific Salmon

Data from USDA Economic Research Service

69. During which year(s) did the number of pounds of imported Pacific salmon equal the number of pounds of exported Pacific salmon?

70. For what year(s) was the number of pounds of imported Pacific salmon less than the number of pounds of exported Pacific salmon?

The double line graph below shows the average attendance per game for the years shown for the Minnesota Twins and the Texas Rangers baseball teams. Use this for Exercises 71 and 72.

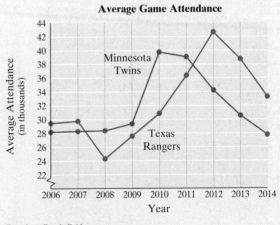

Average Game Attendance

Data from Baseball Almanac

71. In what year(s) was the average attendance per game for the Texas Rangers greater than the average attendance per game for the Minnesota Twins?

72. In what year was the average attendance per game for the Texas Rangers closest to the average attendance per game for the Minnesota Twins, 2007 or 2012?

73. Construct a system of two linear equations that has $(1, 3)$ as a solution.

74. Construct a system of two linear equations that has $(0, 7)$ as a solution.

75. Below are tables of values for two linear equations.

   a. Find a solution of the corresponding system.

   b. Graph several ordered pairs from each table and sketch the two lines.

x	y
1	3
2	5
3	7
4	9
5	11

x	y
1	6
2	7
3	8
4	9
5	10

   c. Does your graph confirm the solution from part (a)?

76. Tables of values for two linear equations are shown.

   a. Find a solution of the corresponding system.

   b. Graph several ordered pairs from each table and sketch the two lines.

x	y
-3	5
-1	1
0	-1
1	-3
2	-5

x	y
-3	7
-1	1
0	-2
1	-5
2	-8

   c. Does your graph confirm the solution from part (a)?

77. Explain how writing each equation in a linear system in slope-intercept form helps determine the number of solutions of a system.

78. Is it possible for a system of two linear equations in two variables to be inconsistent but with dependent equations? Why or why not?

4.2 Solving Systems of Linear Equations by Substitution

OBJECTIVE

1 Use the Substitution Method to Solve a System of Linear Equations.

OBJECTIVE

1 Using the Substitution Method

As we stated in the preceding section, graphing alone is not an accurate way to solve a system of linear equations. In this section, we discuss a second, more accurate method for solving systems of equations. This method is called the **substitution method** and is introduced in the next example.

EXAMPLE 1 Solve the system:

$$\begin{cases} 2x + y = 10 & \text{First equation} \\ x = y + 2 & \text{Second equation} \end{cases}$$

Solution The second equation in this system is $x = y + 2$. This tells us that x and $y + 2$ have the same value. This means that we may substitute $y + 2$ for x in the first equation.

$$2x + y = 10 \quad \text{First equation}$$

$$2(y + 2) + y = 10 \quad \text{Substitute } y + 2 \text{ for } x \text{ since } x = y + 2.$$

Notice that this equation now has one variable, y. Let's now solve this equation for y.

Helpful Hint

Don't forget the distributive property.

$$2(y + 2) + y = 10$$
$$2y + 4 + y = 10 \quad \text{Use the distributive property.}$$
$$3y + 4 = 10 \quad \text{Combine like terms.}$$
$$3y = 6 \quad \text{Subtract 4 from both sides.}$$
$$y = 2 \quad \text{Divide both sides by 3.}$$

Now we know that the y-value of the ordered pair solution of the system is 2. To find the corresponding x-value, we replace y with 2 in the equation $x = y + 2$ and solve for x.

$$x = y + 2$$
$$x = 2 + 2 \quad \text{Let } y = 2.$$
$$x = 4$$

(Continued on next page)

The solution of the system is the ordered pair $(4, 2)$. Since an ordered pair solution must satisfy both linear equations in the system, we could have chosen the equation $2x + y = 10$ to find the corresponding x-value. The resulting x-value is the same.

Check: We check to see that $(4, 2)$ satisfies both equations of the original system.

First Equation	*Second Equation*
$2x + y = 10$	$x = y + 2$
$2(4) + 2 \stackrel{?}{=} 10$	$4 \stackrel{?}{=} 2 + 2$ Let $x = 4$ and $y = 2$.
$10 = 10$ True	$4 = 4$ True

The solution of the system is $(4, 2)$.

A graph of the two equations shows the two lines intersecting at the point $(4, 2)$.

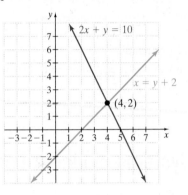

PRACTICE

1   Solve the system:

$$\begin{cases} 2x - y = 9 \\ x = y + 1 \end{cases}$$

EXAMPLE 2   Solve the system:

$$\begin{cases} 5x - y = -2 \\ y = 3x \end{cases}$$

<u>Solution</u> The second equation is solved for y in terms of x. We substitute $3x$ for y in the first equation.

$$5x - y = -2 \quad \text{First equation}$$
$$\downarrow$$
$$5x - (3x) = -2 \quad \text{Substitute } 3x \text{ for } y.$$

Now we solve for x.

$$5x - 3x = -2$$
$$2x = -2 \quad \text{Combine like terms.}$$
$$x = -1 \quad \text{Divide both sides by 2.}$$

The x-value of the ordered pair solution is -1. To find the corresponding y-value, we replace x with -1 in the second equation $y = 3x$.

$$y = 3x \quad \text{Second equation}$$
$$y = 3(-1) \quad \text{Let } x = -1.$$
$$y = -3$$

Check to see that the solution of the system is $(-1, -3)$.

PRACTICE
2 Solve the system:

$$\begin{cases} 7x - y = -15 \\ y = 2x \end{cases}$$

To solve a system of equations by substitution, we first need an equation solved for one of its variables, as in Examples 1 and 2. If neither equation in a system is solved for x or y, this will be our first step.

EXAMPLE 3 Solve the system:

$$\begin{cases} x + 2y = 7 \\ 2x + 2y = 13 \end{cases}$$

<u>Solution</u> We choose one of the equations and solve for x or y. We will solve the first equation for x by subtracting $2y$ from both sides.

$$x + 2y = 7 \qquad \text{First equation}$$
$$x = 7 - 2y \quad \text{Subtract } 2y \text{ from both sides.}$$

Since $x = 7 - 2y$, we now substitute $7 - 2y$ for x in the second equation and solve for y.

Helpful Hint
Don't forget to insert parentheses when substituting $7 - 2y$ for x.

$$2x + 2y = 13 \qquad \text{Second equation}$$
$$2(7 - 2y) + 2y = 13 \qquad \text{Let } x = 7 - 2y.$$
$$14 - 4y + 2y = 13 \qquad \text{Use the distributive property.}$$
$$14 - 2y = 13 \qquad \text{Simplify.}$$
$$-2y = -1 \qquad \text{Subtract 14 from both sides.}$$
$$y = \frac{1}{2} \qquad \text{Divide both sides by } -2.$$

To find x, we let $y = \frac{1}{2}$ in the equation $x = 7 - 2y$.

Helpful Hint
To find x, any equation in two variables equivalent to the original equations of the system may be used. We used this equation since it is solved for x.

$$x = 7 - 2y$$
$$x = 7 - 2\left(\frac{1}{2}\right) \quad \text{Let } y = \frac{1}{2}.$$
$$x = 7 - 1$$
$$x = 6$$

The solution is $\left(6, \frac{1}{2}\right)$. Check the solution in both equations of the original system. □

PRACTICE
3 Solve the system:

$$\begin{cases} x + 3y = 6 \\ 2x + 3y = 10 \end{cases}$$

The following steps may be used to solve a system of equations by the substitution method.

Solving a System of Two Linear Equations by the Substitution Method

Step 1. Solve one of the equations for one of its variables.

Step 2. Substitute the expression for the variable found in Step 1 into the other equation.

Step 3. Solve the equation from Step 2 to find the value of one variable.

Step 4. Substitute the value found in Step 3 in any equation containing both variables to find the value of the other variable.

Step 5. Check the proposed solution in the original system.

✔ **CONCEPT CHECK**

As you solve the system $\begin{cases} 2x + y = -5 \\ x - y = 5 \end{cases}$ you find that $y = -5$. Is this the solution of the system?

EXAMPLE 4 Solve the system:

$$\begin{cases} 7x - 3y = -14 \\ -3x + y = 6 \end{cases}$$

Solution To avoid introducing fractions, we will solve the second equation for y.

$$-3x + y = 6 \qquad \text{Second equation}$$
$$y = 3x + 6$$

Next, substitute $3x + 6$ for y in the first equation.

$$7x - 3y = -14 \quad \text{First equation}$$
$$7x - 3(\overbrace{3x + 6}) = -14 \quad \text{Let } y = 3x + 6.$$
$$7x - 9x - 18 = -14 \quad \text{Use the distributive property.}$$
$$-2x - 18 = -14 \quad \text{Simplify.}$$
$$-2x = 4 \quad \text{Add 18 to both sides.}$$
$$x = -2 \quad \text{Divide both sides by } -2.$$

To find the corresponding y-value, substitute -2 for x in the equation $y = 3x + 6$. Then $y = 3(-2) + 6$ or $y = 0$. The solution of the system is $(-2, 0)$. Check this solution in both equations of the system. □

PRACTICE

4 Solve the system:

$$\begin{cases} 5x + 3y = -9 \\ -2x + y = 8 \end{cases}$$

■

Helpful Hint

When solving a system of equations by the substitution method, begin by solving an equation for one of its variables. If possible, solve for a variable that has a coefficient of 1 or -1. This way, we avoid working with time-consuming fractions.

✔ **CONCEPT CHECK**

To avoid fractions, which of the equations below would you use to solve for x?
a. $3x - 4y = 15$ **b.** $14 - 3y = 8x$ **c.** $7y + x = 12$

Answer to Concept Check:
No, the solution will be an ordered pair.

Answer to Concept Check:
c

EXAMPLE 5 Solve the system:

$$\begin{cases} \dfrac{1}{2}x - y = 3 \\ x = 6 + 2y \end{cases}$$

Solution The second equation is already solved for x in terms of y. Thus we substitute $6 + 2y$ for x in the first equation and solve for y.

$$\frac{1}{2}x - y = 3 \quad \text{First equation}$$

$$\frac{1}{2}(6 + 2y) - y = 3 \quad \text{Let } x = 6 + 2y.$$

$$3 + y - y = 3 \quad \text{Use the distributive property.}$$

$$3 = 3 \quad \text{Simplify.}$$

Arriving at a true statement such as $3 = 3$ indicates that the two linear equations in the original system are equivalent. This means that their graphs are identical and there is an infinite number of solutions of the system. Any solution of one equation is also a solution of the other. For the solution, we can write "infinite number of solutions" or, in set notation, $\left\{ (x, y) \mid \frac{1}{2}x - y = 3 \right\}$ or $\{(x, y) \mid x = 6 + 2y\}$.

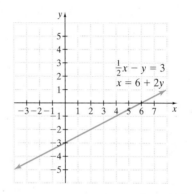

PRACTICE

5   Solve the system:

$$\begin{cases} \frac{1}{4}x - y = 2 \\ x = 4y + 8 \end{cases}$$

EXAMPLE 6   Use substitution to solve the system.

$$\begin{cases} 6x + 12y = 5 \\ -4x - 8y = 0 \end{cases}$$

Solution Choose the second equation and solve for y.

$$-4x - 8y = 0 \quad \text{Second equation}$$

$$-8y = 4x \quad \text{Add } 4x \text{ to both sides.}$$

$$\frac{-8y}{-8} = \frac{4x}{-8} \quad \text{Divide both sides by } -8.$$

$$y = -\frac{1}{2}x \quad \text{Simplify.}$$

Now replace y with $-\frac{1}{2}x$ in the first equation.

$$6x + 12y = 5 \quad \text{First equation}$$

$$6x + 12\left(-\frac{1}{2}x\right) = 5 \quad \text{Let } y = -\frac{1}{2}x.$$

$$6x + (-6x) = 5 \quad \text{Simplify.}$$

$$0 = 5 \quad \text{Combine like terms.}$$

(Continued on next page)

The false statement $0 = 5$ indicates that this system has no solution and is inconsistent. The graph of the linear equations in the system is a pair of parallel lines. For the solution, we can write "no solution" or, in set notation, write $\{\ \}$ or $\varnothing$.

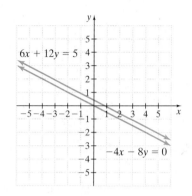

PRACTICE

6   Use substitution to solve the system.

$$\begin{cases} 4x - 3y = 12 \\ -8x + 6y = -30 \end{cases}$$

✔ **CONCEPT CHECK**

Describe how the graphs of the equations in a system appear if the system has
a. no solution
b. one solution
c. an infinite number of solutions

✔ **Vocabulary, Readiness & Video Check**

Give the solution of each system. If the system has no solution or an infinite number of solutions, say so. If the system has one solution, find it.

1. $\begin{cases} y = 4x \\ -3x + y = 1 \end{cases}$
When solving, you obtain $x = 1$.

2. $\begin{cases} 4x - y = 17 \\ -8x + 2y = 0 \end{cases}$
When solving, you obtain $0 = 34$.

3. $\begin{cases} 4x - y = 17 \\ -8x + 2y = -34 \end{cases}$
When solving, you obtain $0 = 0$.

4. $\begin{cases} 5x + 2y = 25 \\ x - y + 5 \end{cases}$
When solving, you obtain $y = 0$.

5. $\begin{cases} x + y = 0 \\ 7x - 7y = 0 \end{cases}$
When solving, you obtain $x = 0$.

6. $\begin{cases} y = -2x + 5 \\ 4x + 2y = 10 \end{cases}$
When solving, you obtain $0 = 0$.

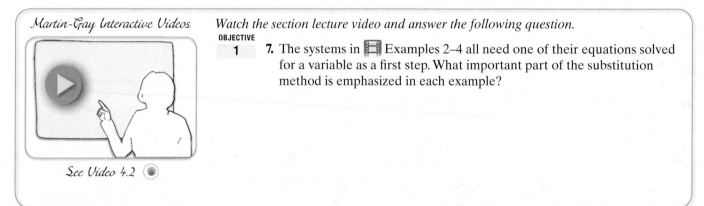

Martin-Gay Interactive Videos

See Video 4.2 ⦿

Watch the section lecture video and answer the following question.

OBJECTIVE

1   **7.** The systems in ▦ Examples 2–4 all need one of their equations solved for a variable as a first step. What important part of the substitution method is emphasized in each example?

Answers to Concept Check:
a. parallel lines
b. intersect at one point
c. identical graphs

4.2   Exercise Set   MyMathLab®

Solve each system of equations by the substitution method. See Examples 1 and 2.

1. $\begin{cases} x + y = 3 \\ x = 2y \end{cases}$

2. $\begin{cases} x + y = 20 \\ x = 3y \end{cases}$

3. $\begin{cases} x + y = 6 \\ y = -3x \end{cases}$

4. $\begin{cases} x + y = 6 \\ y = -4x \end{cases}$

5. $\begin{cases} y = 3x + 1 \\ 4y - 8x = 12 \end{cases}$

6. $\begin{cases} y = 2x + 3 \\ 5y - 7x = 18 \end{cases}$

7. $\begin{cases} y = 2x + 9 \\ y = 7x + 10 \end{cases}$

8. $\begin{cases} y = 5x - 3 \\ y = 8x + 4 \end{cases}$

MIXED PRACTICE

Solve each system of equations by the substitution method. See Examples 1 through 6.

9. $\begin{cases} 3x - 4y = 10 \\ y = x - 3 \end{cases}$

10. $\begin{cases} 4x - 3y = 10 \\ y = x - 5 \end{cases}$

11. $\begin{cases} x + 2y = 6 \\ 2x + 3y = 8 \end{cases}$

12. $\begin{cases} x + 3y = -5 \\ 2x + 2y = 6 \end{cases}$

13. $\begin{cases} 3x + 2y = 16 \\ x = 3y - 2 \end{cases}$

14. $\begin{cases} 2x + 3y = 18 \\ x = 2y - 5 \end{cases}$

15. $\begin{cases} 2x - 5y = 1 \\ 3x + y = -7 \end{cases}$

16. $\begin{cases} 3y - x = 6 \\ 4x + 12y = 0 \end{cases}$

17. $\begin{cases} 4x + 2y = 5 \\ -2x = y + 4 \end{cases}$

18. $\begin{cases} 2y = x + 2 \\ 6x - 12y = 0 \end{cases}$

19. $\begin{cases} 4x + y = 11 \\ 2x + 5y = 1 \end{cases}$

20. $\begin{cases} 3x + y = -14 \\ 4x + 3y = -22 \end{cases}$

21. $\begin{cases} x + 2y + 5 = -4 + 5y - x \\ 2x + x = y + 4 \end{cases}$

(*Hint:* First simplify each equation.)

22. $\begin{cases} 5x + 4y - 2 = -6 + 7y - 3x \\ 3x + 4x = y + 3 \end{cases}$

(*Hint:* See Exercise 21.)

23. $\begin{cases} 6x - 3y = 5 \\ x + 2y = 0 \end{cases}$

24. $\begin{cases} 10x - 5y = -21 \\ x + 3y = 0 \end{cases}$

25. $\begin{cases} 3x - y = 1 \\ 2x - 3y = 10 \end{cases}$

26. $\begin{cases} 2x - y = -7 \\ 4x - 3y = -11 \end{cases}$

27. $\begin{cases} -x + 2y = 10 \\ -2x + 3y = 18 \end{cases}$

28. $\begin{cases} -x + 3y = 18 \\ -3x + 2y = 19 \end{cases}$

29. $\begin{cases} 5x + 10y = 20 \\ 2x + 6y = 10 \end{cases}$

30. $\begin{cases} 6x + 3y = 12 \\ 9x + 6y = 15 \end{cases}$

31. $\begin{cases} 3x + 6y = 9 \\ 4x + 8y = 16 \end{cases}$

32. $\begin{cases} 2x + 4y = 6 \\ 5x + 10y = 16 \end{cases}$

33. $\begin{cases} \dfrac{1}{3}x - y = 2 \\ x - 3y = 6 \end{cases}$

34. $\begin{cases} \dfrac{1}{4}x - 2y = 1 \\ x - 8y = 4 \end{cases}$

35. $\begin{cases} x = \dfrac{3}{4}y - 1 \\ 8x - 5y = -6 \end{cases}$

36. $\begin{cases} x = \dfrac{5}{6}y - 2 \\ 12x - 5y = -9 \end{cases}$

Solve each system by the substitution method. First, simplify each equation by combining like terms.

37. $\begin{cases} -5y + 6y = 3x + 2(x - 5) - 3x + 5 \\ 4(x + y) - x + y = -12 \end{cases}$

38. $\begin{cases} 5x + 2y - 4x - 2y = 2(2y + 6) - 7 \\ 3(2x - y) - 4x = 1 + 9 \end{cases}$

REVIEW AND PREVIEW

Write equivalent equations by multiplying both sides of the given equation by the given nonzero number. See Section 2.2.

39. $3x + 2y = 6$ by -2

40. $-x + y = 10$ by 5

41. $-4x + y = 3$ by 3

42. $5a - 7b = -4$ by -4

Add the expressions by combining any like terms. See Section 2.1.

43. $\begin{array}{r} 3n + 6m \\ 2n - 6m \\ \hline \end{array}$

44. $\begin{array}{r} -2x + 5y \\ 2x + 11y \\ \hline \end{array}$

45. $\begin{array}{r} -5a - 7b \\ 5a - 8b \\ \hline \end{array}$

46. $\begin{array}{r} 9q + p \\ -9q - p \\ \hline \end{array}$

CONCEPT EXTENSIONS

47. Explain how to identify a system with no solution when using the substitution method.

48. Occasionally, when using the substitution method, we obtain the equation $0 = 0$. Explain how this result indicates that the graphs of the equations in the system are identical.

Solve. See a Concept Check in this section.

49. As you solve the system $\begin{cases} 3x - y = -6 \\ -3x + 2y = 7 \end{cases}$, you find that $y = 1$. Is this the solution of the system?

50. As you solve the system $\begin{cases} x = 5y \\ y = 2x \end{cases}$, you find that $x = 0$ and $y = 0$. What is the solution of this system?

51. To avoid fractions, which of the equations below would you use if solving for y? Explain why.

a. $\dfrac{1}{2}x - 4y = \dfrac{3}{4}$

b. $8x - 5y = 13$

c. $7x - y = 19$

52. Give the number of solutions of a system if the graphs of the equations in the system are

a. lines intersecting in one point

b. parallel lines

c. same line

53. The number of men and women receiving bachelor's degrees each year has been steadily increasing. For the years 1970 through 2014, the number of men receiving degrees (in thousands) is given by the equation $y = 3.9x + 443$, and for women the equation is $y = 14.2x + 314$, where x is the number of years after 1970. (*Source:* National Center for Education Statistics)

a. Use the substitution method to solve this system of equations. (Round your final results to the nearest whole numbers.)

b. Explain the meaning of your answer to part (a).

c. Sketch a graph of the system of equations. Write a sentence describing the trends for men and women receiving bachelor's degrees.

54. The number of Adult Contemporary Music radio stations in the United States from 2000 to 2014 is given by the equation $y = 6x + 734$, where x is the number of years after 2000. The number of Spanish radio stations is given by $y = 13x + 542$ for the same time period. (*Source:* M Street Corporation)

a. Use the substitution method to solve this system of equations. (Round your numbers to the nearest tenth.)

b. Explain the meaning of your answer to part (a).

c. Sketch a graph of the system of equations. Write a sentence describing the trends in the popularity of these two types of music formats.

Solve each system by substitution. When necessary, round answers to the nearest hundredth.

55. $\begin{cases} y = 5.1x + 14.56 \\ y = -2x - 3.9 \end{cases}$

56. $\begin{cases} y = 3.1x - 16.35 \\ y = -9.7x + 28.45 \end{cases}$

57. $\begin{cases} 3x + 2y = 14.05 \\ 5x + y = 18.5 \end{cases}$

58. $\begin{cases} x + y = -15.2 \\ -2x + 5y = -19.3 \end{cases}$

4.3 Solving Systems of Linear Equations by Addition

OBJECTIVE

1 Use the Addition Method to Solve a System of Linear Equations.

OBJECTIVE

1 Using the Addition Method

We have seen that substitution is an accurate way to solve a linear system. Another method for solving a system of equations accurately is the **addition** or **elimination method.** The addition method is based on the addition property of equality: adding equal quantities to both sides of an equation does not change the solution of the equation. In symbols,

$$\text{if } A = B \text{ and } C = D, \text{ then } A + C = B + D.$$

EXAMPLE 1 Solve the system:

$$\begin{cases} x + y = 7 \\ x - y = 5 \end{cases}$$

Solution Since the left side of each equation is equal to the right side, we add equal quantities by adding the left sides of the equations together and the right sides of the equations together. This adding eliminates the variable y and gives us an equation in one variable, x. We can then solve for x.

> **Helpful Hint**
>
> Notice in Example 1 that our goal when solving a system of equations by the addition method is to eliminate a variable when adding the equations.

$$
\begin{aligned}
x + y &= 7 \qquad \text{First equation} \\
x - y &= 5 \qquad \text{Second equation} \\
\hline
2x \phantom{{}+y} &= 12 \qquad \text{Add the equations.} \\
x &= 6 \qquad \text{Divide both sides by 2.}
\end{aligned}
$$

The x-value of the solution is 6. To find the corresponding y-value, let $x = 6$ in either equation of the system. We will use the first equation.

$$
\begin{aligned}
x + y &= 7 \qquad \text{First equation} \\
6 + y &= 7 \qquad \text{Let } x = 6. \\
y &= 7 - 6 \qquad \text{Solve for } y. \\
y &= 1 \qquad \text{Simplify.}
\end{aligned}
$$

Check: The solution is $(6, 1)$. Check this in both equations.

First Equation	***Second Equation***
$x + y = 7$	$x - y = 5$
$6 + 1 \stackrel{?}{=} 7$	$6 - 1 \stackrel{?}{=} 5$ Let $x = 6$ and $y = 1$.
$7 = 7$ True	$5 = 5$ True

Thus, the solution of the system is $(6, 1)$ and the graphs of the two equations intersect at the point $(6, 1)$ as shown next.

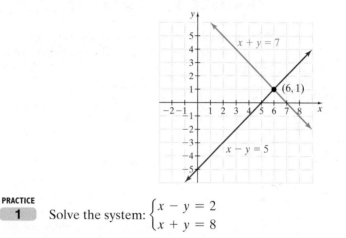

PRACTICE
1   Solve the system: $\begin{cases} x - y = 2 \\ x + y = 8 \end{cases}$

EXAMPLE 2   Solve the system: $\begin{cases} -2x + y = 2 \\ -x + 3y = -4 \end{cases}$

Solution If we simply add the two equations, the result is still an equation in two variables. However, remember from Example 1 that our goal is to eliminate one of the variables. Notice what happens if we multiply *both sides* of the first equation by -3, which we are allowed to do by the multiplication property of equality. The system

$$\begin{cases} -3(-2x + y) = -3(2) \\ -x + 3y = -4 \end{cases} \quad \text{simplifies to} \quad \begin{cases} 6x - 3y = -6 \\ -x + 3y = -4 \end{cases}$$

Now add the resulting equations and the y-variable is eliminated.

$$\begin{array}{rl} 6x - 3y = & -6 \\ \underline{-x + 3y = -4} & \\ 5x \quad\quad = & -10 \quad \text{Add.} \\ x = & -2 \quad \text{Divide both sides by 5.} \end{array}$$

To find the corresponding y-value, let $x = -2$ in any of the preceding equations containing both variables. We use the first equation of the original system.

$$\begin{array}{ll} -2x + y = 2 & \text{First equation} \\ -2(-2) + y = 2 & \text{Let } x = -2. \\ 4 + y = 2 & \\ y = -2 & \text{Subtract 4 from both sides.} \end{array}$$

The solution is $(-2, -2)$. Check this ordered pair in both equations of the original system.

PRACTICE
2   Solve the system: $\begin{cases} x - 2y = 11 \\ 3x - y = 13 \end{cases}$

Helpful Hint

When finding the second value of an ordered pair solution, any equation equivalent to one of the original equations in the system may be used.

In Example 2, the decision to multiply the first equation by -3 was no accident. **To eliminate a variable** when adding two equations, **the coefficient of the variable in one equation must be the opposite of its coefficient in the other equation.**

> **Helpful Hint**
>
> Be sure to multiply *both sides* of an equation by a chosen number when solving by the addition method. A common mistake is to multiply only the side containing the variables.

EXAMPLE 3   Solve the system: $\begin{cases} 2x - y = 7 \\ 8x - 4y = 1 \end{cases}$

Solution   Multiply both sides of the first equation by -4 and the resulting coefficient of x is -8, the opposite of 8, the coefficient of x in the second equation. The system becomes

> **Helpful Hint**
>
> Don't forget to multiply **both** sides by -4.

$$\begin{cases} -4(2x - y) = -4(7) \\ 8x - 4y = 1 \end{cases} \quad \text{simplifies to} \quad \begin{cases} -8x + 4y = -28 \\ 8x - 4y = 1 \end{cases}$$

Now add the resulting equations.

$$\begin{array}{rl} -8x + 4y = & -28 \\ \underline{8x - 4y = 1} & \text{Add the equations.} \\ 0 = & -27 \quad \text{False} \end{array}$$

When we add the equations, both variables are eliminated and we have $0 = -27$, a false statement. This means that the system has no solution. The graphs of these equations are parallel lines. For the solution, we can write "no solution" or, in set notation, $\{\ \}$ or $\varnothing$ ▫

PRACTICE
3   Solve the system: $\begin{cases} x - 3y = 5 \\ 2x - 6y = -3 \end{cases}$ ∎

EXAMPLE 4   Solve the system: $\begin{cases} 3x - 2y = 2 \\ -9x + 6y = -6 \end{cases}$

Solution   First we multiply both sides of the first equation by 3, then we add the resulting equations.

$$\begin{cases} 3(3x - 2y) = 3(2) \\ -9x + 6y = -6 \end{cases} \quad \text{simplifies to} \quad \begin{cases} 9x - 6y = 6 \\ \underline{-9x + 6y = -6} \quad \text{Add the equations.} \\ 0 = 0 \quad \text{True} \end{cases}$$

Both variables are eliminated and we have $0 = 0$, a true statement. Whenever you eliminate a variable and get the equation $0 = 0$, the system has an infinite number of solutions. The graphs of these equations are identical. The solution is "infinite number of solutions" or, in set notation, $\{(x, y)\,|\,3x - 2y = 2\}$ or $\{(x, y)\,|\,-9x + 6y = -6\}$ ▫

PRACTICE
4   Solve the system: $\begin{cases} 4x - 3y = 5 \\ -8x + 6y = -10 \end{cases}$ ∎

✔ **CONCEPT CHECK**

Suppose you are solving the system

$$\begin{cases} 3x + 8y = -5 \\ 2x - 4y = 3. \end{cases}$$

You decide to use the addition method and begin by multiplying both sides of the first equation by -2. In which of the following was the multiplication performed correctly? Explain.
a. $-6x - 16y = -5$ **b.** $-6x - 16y = 10$

EXAMPLE 5   Solve the system: $\begin{cases} 3x + 4y = 13 \\ 5x - 9y = 6 \end{cases}$

Solution We can eliminate the variable y by multiplying the first equation by 9 and the second equation by 4.

$$\begin{cases} 9(3x + 4y) = 9(13) \\ 4(5x - 9y) = 4(6) \end{cases} \text{ simplifies to } \begin{cases} 27x + 36y = 117 \\ \underline{20x - 36y = 24} \end{cases}$$

$$47x = 141 \quad \text{Add the equations.}$$
$$x = 3 \quad \text{Divide both sides by 47.}$$

To find the corresponding y-value, we let $x = 3$ in any equation in this example containing two variables. Doing so in any of these equations will give $y = 1$. The solution of this system is $(3, 1)$. Check to see that $(3, 1)$ satisfies each equation in the original system.   □

PRACTICE
5   Solve the system: $\begin{cases} 4x + 3y = 14 \\ 3x - 2y = 2 \end{cases}$ ■

If we had decided to eliminate x instead of y in Example 5, the first equation could have been multiplied by 5 and the second by -3. Try solving the original system this way to check that the solution is $(3, 1)$.

The following steps summarize how to solve a system of linear equations by the addition method.

Solving a System of Two Linear Equations by the Addition Method

Step 1. Rewrite each equation in standard form $Ax + By = C$.

Step 2. If necessary, multiply one or both equations by a nonzero number so that the coefficients of a chosen variable in the system are opposites.

Step 3. Add the equations.

Step 4. Find the value of one variable by solving the resulting equation from Step 3.

Step 5. Find the value of the second variable by substituting the value found in Step 4 into either of the original equations.

Step 6. Check the proposed solution in the original system.

✔ **CONCEPT CHECK**

Suppose you are solving the system

$$\begin{cases} -4x + 7y = 6 \\ x + 2y = 5 \end{cases}$$

by the addition method.
a. What step(s) should you take if you wish to eliminate x when adding the equations?
b. What step(s) should you take if you wish to eliminate y when adding the equations?

Answers to Concept Check:
a. multiply the second equation by 4
b. possible answer: multiply the first equation by -2 and the second equation by 7

EXAMPLE 6   Solve the system: $\begin{cases} -x - \dfrac{y}{2} = \dfrac{5}{2} \\ \dfrac{x}{6} - \dfrac{y}{2} = 0 \end{cases}$

Solution: We begin by clearing each equation of fractions. To do so, we multiply both sides of the first equation by the LCD, 2, and both sides of the second equation by the LCD, 6. Then the system

(Continued on next page)

$$\begin{cases} 2\left(-x - \dfrac{y}{2}\right) = 2\left(\dfrac{5}{2}\right) \\ 6\left(\dfrac{x}{6} - \dfrac{y}{2}\right) = 6(0) \end{cases} \qquad \text{simplifies to} \qquad \begin{cases} -2x - y = 5 \\ x - 3y = 0 \end{cases}.$$

We can now eliminate the variable x by multiplying the second equation by 2.

$$\begin{cases} -2x - y = 5 \\ 2(x - 3y) = 2(0) \end{cases} \qquad \text{simplifies to} \qquad \begin{cases} -2x - y = 5 \\ \underline{2x - 6y = 0} \end{cases}$$

$$-7y = 5 \qquad \text{Add the equations.}$$

$$y = -\frac{5}{7} \qquad \text{Solve for } y.$$

To find x, we could replace y with $-\dfrac{5}{7}$ in one of the equations with two variables.

Instead, let's go back to the simplified system and multiply by appropriate factors to eliminate the variable y and solve for x. To do this, we multiply the first equation by -3. Then the system

$$\begin{cases} -3(-2x - y) = -3(5) \\ x - 3y = 0 \end{cases} \qquad \text{simplifies to} \qquad \begin{cases} 6x + 3y = -15 \\ \underline{x - 3y = 0} \end{cases}$$

$$7x = -15 \qquad \text{Add the equations.}$$

$$x = -\frac{15}{7} \qquad \text{Solve for } x.$$

Check the ordered pair $\left(-\dfrac{15}{7}, -\dfrac{5}{7}\right)$ in both equations of the original system. The solution is $\left(-\dfrac{15}{7}, -\dfrac{5}{7}\right)$. □

PRACTICE
6 Solve the system: $\begin{cases} -2x + \dfrac{3y}{2} = 5 \\ -\dfrac{x}{2} - \dfrac{y}{4} = \dfrac{1}{2} \end{cases}$ ■

✓ Vocabulary, Readiness & Video Check

Given the system $\begin{cases} 3x - 2y = -9 \\ x + 5y = 14 \end{cases}$ *read each row (Step 1, Step 2, and Result). Then answer whether the result is true or false.*

	Step 1	Step 2	Result	True or False?
1.	Multiply 2nd equation through by −3.	Add the resulting equation to the 1st equation.	The y's are eliminated.	
2.	Multiply 2nd equation through by −3.	Add the resulting equation to the 1st equation.	The x's are eliminated.	
3.	Multiply 1st equation by 5 and 2nd equation by 2.	Add the two new equations.	The y's are eliminated.	
4.	Multiply 1st equation by 5 and 2nd equation by −2.	Add the two new equations.	The y's are eliminated.	

Martin-Gay Interactive Videos

Watch the section lecture video and answer the following question.

OBJECTIVE
1

5. For the addition/elimination methods, sometimes you need to multiply an equation through by a nonzero number so that the coefficients of a variable are opposites, as is shown in ▦ Example 2. What property allows us to do this? What important reminder is made at this step?

See Video 4.3 ◉

4.3   Exercise Set   MyMathLab® ▸

Solve each system of equations by the addition method. See Example 1.

1. $\begin{cases} 3x + y = 5 \\ 6x - y = 4 \end{cases}$

2. $\begin{cases} 4x + y = 13 \\ 2x - y = 5 \end{cases}$

3. $\begin{cases} x - 2y = 8 \\ -x + 5y = -17 \end{cases}$

4. $\begin{cases} x - 2y = -11 \\ -x + 5y = 23 \end{cases}$

Solve each system of equations by the addition method. If a system contains fractions or decimals, you may want to clear each equation of fractions or decimals first. See Examples 2 through 6.

5. $\begin{cases} 3x + y = -11 \\ 6x - 2y = -2 \end{cases}$

6. $\begin{cases} 4x + y = -13 \\ 6x - 3y = -15 \end{cases}$

7. $\begin{cases} 3x + 2y = 11 \\ 5x - 2y = 29 \end{cases}$

8. $\begin{cases} 4x + 2y = 2 \\ 3x - 2y = 12 \end{cases}$

9. $\begin{cases} x + 5y = 18 \\ 3x + 2y = -11 \end{cases}$

10. $\begin{cases} x + 4y = 14 \\ 5x + 3y = 2 \end{cases}$

11. $\begin{cases} x + y = 6 \\ x - y = 6 \end{cases}$

12. $\begin{cases} x - y = 1 \\ -x + 2y = 0 \end{cases}$

13. $\begin{cases} 2x + 3y = 0 \\ 4x + 6y = 3 \end{cases}$

14. $\begin{cases} 3x + y = 4 \\ 9x + 3y = 6 \end{cases}$

15. $\begin{cases} -x + 5y = -1 \\ 3x - 15y = 3 \end{cases}$

16. $\begin{cases} 2x + y = 6 \\ 4x + 2y = 12 \end{cases}$

17. $\begin{cases} 3x - 2y = 7 \\ 5x + 4y = 8 \end{cases}$

18. $\begin{cases} 6x - 5y = 25 \\ 4x + 15y = 13 \end{cases}$

19. $\begin{cases} 8x = -11y - 16 \\ 2x + 3y = -4 \end{cases}$

20. $\begin{cases} 10x + 3y = -12 \\ 5x = -4y - 16 \end{cases}$

21. $\begin{cases} 4x - 3y = 7 \\ 7x + 5y = 2 \end{cases}$

22. $\begin{cases} -2x + 3y = 10 \\ 3x + 4y = 2 \end{cases}$

23. $\begin{cases} 4x - 6y = 8 \\ 6x - 9y = 16 \end{cases}$

24. $\begin{cases} 9x - 3y = 12 \\ 12x - 4y = 18 \end{cases}$

25. $\begin{cases} 2x - 5y = 4 \\ 3x - 2y = 4 \end{cases}$

26. $\begin{cases} 6x - 5y = 7 \\ 4x - 6y = 7 \end{cases}$

27. $\begin{cases} \dfrac{x}{3} + \dfrac{y}{6} = 1 \\ \dfrac{x}{2} - \dfrac{y}{4} = 0 \end{cases}$

28. $\begin{cases} \dfrac{x}{2} + \dfrac{y}{8} = 3 \\ x - \dfrac{y}{4} = 0 \end{cases}$

29. $\begin{cases} \dfrac{10}{3}x + 4y = -4 \\ 5x + 6y = -6 \end{cases}$

30. $\begin{cases} \dfrac{3}{2}x + 4y = 1 \\ 9x + 24y = 5 \end{cases}$

31. $\begin{cases} x - \dfrac{y}{3} = -1 \\ -\dfrac{x}{2} + \dfrac{y}{8} = \dfrac{1}{4} \end{cases}$

32. $\begin{cases} 2x - \dfrac{3y}{4} = -3 \\ x + \dfrac{y}{9} = \dfrac{13}{3} \end{cases}$

33. $\begin{cases} -4(x + 2) = 3y \\ 2x - 2y = 3 \end{cases}$

34. $\begin{cases} -9(x + 3) = 8y \\ 3x - 3y = 8 \end{cases}$

35. $\begin{cases} \dfrac{x}{3} - y = 2 \\ -\dfrac{x}{2} + \dfrac{3y}{2} = -3 \end{cases}$

36. $\begin{cases} \dfrac{x}{2} + \dfrac{y}{4} = 1 \\ -\dfrac{x}{4} - \dfrac{y}{8} = 1 \end{cases}$

37. $\begin{cases} \dfrac{3}{5}x - y = -\dfrac{4}{5} \\ 3x + \dfrac{y}{2} = -\dfrac{9}{5} \end{cases}$

38. $\begin{cases} 3x + \dfrac{7}{2}y = \dfrac{3}{4} \\ -\dfrac{x}{2} + \dfrac{5}{3}y = -\dfrac{5}{4} \end{cases}$

39. $\begin{cases} 3.5x + 2.5y = 17 \\ -1.5x - 7.5y = -33 \end{cases}$

40. $\begin{cases} -2.5x - 6.5y = 47 \\ 0.5x - 4.5y = 37 \end{cases}$

41. $\begin{cases} 0.02x + 0.04y = 0.09 \\ -0.1x + 0.3y = 0.8 \end{cases}$

42. $\begin{cases} 0.04x - 0.05y = 0.105 \\ 0.2x - 0.6y = 1.05 \end{cases}$

MIXED PRACTICE

Solve each system by either the addition method or the substitution method.

43. $\begin{cases} 2x - 3y = -11 \\ y = 4x - 3 \end{cases}$

44. $\begin{cases} 4x - 5y = 6 \\ y = 3x - 10 \end{cases}$

45. $\begin{cases} x + 2y = 1 \\ 3x + 4y = -1 \end{cases}$

46. $\begin{cases} x + 3y = 5 \\ 5x + 6y = -2 \end{cases}$

47. $\begin{cases} 2y = x + 6 \\ 3x - 2y = -6 \end{cases}$

48. $\begin{cases} 3y = x + 14 \\ 2x - 3y = -16 \end{cases}$

49. $\begin{cases} y = 2x - 3 \\ y = 5x - 18 \end{cases}$

50. $\begin{cases} y = 6x - 5 \\ y = 4x - 11 \end{cases}$

51. $\begin{cases} x + \dfrac{1}{6}y = \dfrac{1}{2} \\ 3x + 2y = 3 \end{cases}$

52. $\begin{cases} x + \dfrac{1}{3}y = \dfrac{5}{12} \\ 8x + 3y = 4 \end{cases}$

53. $\begin{cases} \dfrac{x+2}{2} = \dfrac{y+11}{3} \\ \dfrac{x}{2} = \dfrac{2y+16}{6} \end{cases}$

54. $\begin{cases} \dfrac{x+5}{2} = \dfrac{y+14}{4} \\ \dfrac{x}{3} = \dfrac{2y+2}{6} \end{cases}$

55. $\begin{cases} 2x + 3y = 14 \\ 3x - 4y = -69.1 \end{cases}$

56. $\begin{cases} 5x - 2y = -19.8 \\ -3x + 5y = -3.7 \end{cases}$

REVIEW AND PREVIEW

Translating *Rewrite the following sentences using mathematical symbols. Do not solve the equations. See Sections 2.3 and 2.4.*

57. Twice a number, added to 6, is 3 less than the number.

58. The sum of three consecutive integers is 66.

59. Three times a number, subtracted from 20, is 2.

60. Twice the sum of 8 and a number is the difference of the number and 20.

61. The product of 4 and the sum of a number and 6 is twice the number.

62. If the quotient of twice a number and 7 is subtracted from the reciprocal of the number, the result is 2.

CONCEPT EXTENSIONS

Solve. See a Concept Check in this section.

63. To solve this system by the addition method and eliminate the variable y,

$$\begin{cases} 4x + 2y = -7 \\ 3x - y = -12 \end{cases}$$

by what value would you multiply the second equation? What do you get when you complete the multiplication?

64. Given the system of linear equations $\begin{cases} 3x - y = -8 \\ 5x + 3y = 2 \end{cases}$, use the addition method and

 a. Solve the system by eliminating x.

 b. Solve the system by eliminating y.

65. Suppose you are solving the system

$$\begin{cases} 3x + 8y = -5 \\ 2x - 4y = 3. \end{cases}$$

You decide to use the addition method by multiplying both sides of the second equation by 2. In which of the following was the multiplication performed correctly? Explain.
 a. $4x - 8y = 3$
 b. $4x - 8y = 6$

66. Suppose you are solving the system

$$\begin{cases} -2x - y = 0 \\ -2x + 3y = 6. \end{cases}$$

You decide to use the addition method by multiplying both sides of the first equation by 3, then adding the resulting equation to the second equation. Which of the following is the correct sum? Explain.

 a. $-8x = 6$

 b. $-8x = 9$

67. When solving a system of equations by the addition method, how do we know when the system has no solution?

68. Explain why the addition method might be preferred over the substitution method for solving the system $\begin{cases} 2x - 3y = 5 \\ 5x + 2y = 6. \end{cases}$

69. Use the system of linear equations below to answer the questions.

$$\begin{cases} x + y = 5 \\ 3x + 3y = b \end{cases}$$

 a. Find the value of b so that the system has an infinite number of solutions.

 b. Find a value of b so that there are no solutions to the system.

70. Use the system of linear equations below to answer the questions.

$$\begin{cases} x + y = 4 \\ 2x + by = 8 \end{cases}$$

 a. Find the value of b so that the system has an infinite number of solutions.

 b. Find a value of b so that the system has a single solution.

Solve each system by the addition method.

71. $\begin{cases} 1.2x + 3.4y = 27.6 \\ 7.2x - 1.7y = -46.56 \end{cases}$

72. $\begin{cases} 5.1x - 2.4y = 3.15 \\ -15.3x + 1.2y = 27.75 \end{cases}$

Solve.

73. According to the Bureau of Labor Statistics, the percent of workers age 20 to 24 predicted for 2012 to 2022 can be approximated by $0.36x + y = 70.9$. The percent of workers age 55 to 64 years for the same years can be approximated by $0.3x - y = -64.5$. For both equations, x is the number of years since 2012, and y is the percent of the workforce. (*Source:* Bureau of Labor Statistics)

 a. Use the addition method to solve the system:
$$\begin{cases} 0.36x + y = 70.9 \\ 0.30x - y = -64.5 \end{cases}$$

 (Eliminate y first and solve for x. Round this result to the nearest whole. Then find y and round to the nearest whole.)

 b. Use your result from part (a) and estimate the year in which both percents are the same.

 c. Use your results from parts (a) and (b) to estimate the percent of workers age 20–24 and those age 55–64 in the year that we found in part (b).

74. Two occupations predicted to greatly increase in the number of jobs are construction workers and personal care aides. The number of construction workers predicted for 2012 through 2022 can be approximated by $32.5x - y = -1284$. The number of personal care aides predicted for 2012 through 2022 can be approximated by $58x - y = -1191$. For both equations, x is the number of years since 2012, and y is the number of jobs (in thousands). (*Source:* Bureau of Labor Statistics)

a. Use the addition method to solve this system of equations:

$$\begin{cases} 32.5x - y = -1284 \\ 58x - y = -1191 \end{cases}$$

(Eliminate y first and solve for x. Round this result to the nearest whole.)

b. Interpret the solution from part (a).

c. Using the year in your answer to part (b), estimate the number of construction workers or personal care aides in that year.

Integrated Review   Solving Systems of Equations

Sections 4.1–4.3

Solve each system by either the addition method or the substitution method.

1. $\begin{cases} 2x - 3y = -11 \\ y = 4x - 3 \end{cases}$

2. $\begin{cases} 4x - 5y = 6 \\ y = 3x - 10 \end{cases}$

3. $\begin{cases} x + y = 3 \\ x - y = 7 \end{cases}$

4. $\begin{cases} x - y = 20 \\ x + y = -8 \end{cases}$

5. $\begin{cases} x + 2y = 1 \\ 3x + 4y = -1 \end{cases}$

6. $\begin{cases} x + 3y = 5 \\ 5x + 6y = -2 \end{cases}$

7. $\begin{cases} y = x + 3 \\ 3x - 2y = -6 \end{cases}$

8. $\begin{cases} y = -2x \\ 2x - 3y = -16 \end{cases}$

9. $\begin{cases} y = 2x - 3 \\ y = 5x - 18 \end{cases}$

10. $\begin{cases} y = 6x - 5 \\ y = 4x - 11 \end{cases}$

11. $\begin{cases} x + \dfrac{1}{6}y = \dfrac{1}{2} \\ 3x + 2y = 3 \end{cases}$

12. $\begin{cases} x + \dfrac{1}{3}y = \dfrac{5}{12} \\ 8x + 3y = 4 \end{cases}$

13. $\begin{cases} x - 5y = 1 \\ -2x + 10y = 3 \end{cases}$

14. $\begin{cases} -x + 2y = 3 \\ 3x - 6y = -9 \end{cases}$

15. $\begin{cases} 0.2x - 0.3y = -0.95 \\ 0.4x + 0.1y = 0.55 \end{cases}$

16. $\begin{cases} 0.08x - 0.04y = -0.11 \\ 0.02x - 0.06y = -0.09 \end{cases}$

17. $\begin{cases} x = 3y - 7 \\ 2x - 6y = -14 \end{cases}$

18. $\begin{cases} y = \dfrac{x}{2} - 3 \\ 2x - 4y = 0 \end{cases}$

19. $\begin{cases} 2x + 5y = -1 \\ 3x - 4y = 33 \end{cases}$

20. $\begin{cases} 7x - 3y = 2 \\ 6x + 5y = -21 \end{cases}$

21. Which method, substitution or addition, would you prefer to use to solve the system below? Explain your reasoning.

$$\begin{cases} 3x + 2y = -2 \\ y = -2x \end{cases}$$

22. Which method, substitution or addition, would you prefer to use to solve the system below? Explain your reasoning.

$$\begin{cases} 3x - 2y = -3 \\ 6x + 2y = 12 \end{cases}$$

4.4 Solving Systems of Linear Equations in Three Variables ▷

OBJECTIVE

1 Solve a System of Three Linear Equations in Three Variables. ▷

In this section, the algebraic methods of solving systems of two linear equations in two variables are extended to systems of three linear equations in three variables. We call the equation $3x - y + z = -15$, for example, a **linear equation in three variables** since there are three variables and each variable is raised only to the power 1. A solution of this equation is an **ordered triple (x, y, z)** that makes the equation a true statement. For example, the ordered triple $(2, 0, -21)$ is a solution of $3x - y + z = -15$ since replacing x with 2, y with 0, and z with -21 yields the true statement $3(2) - 0 + (-21) = -15$. The graph of this equation is a plane in three-dimensional space, just as the graph of a linear equation in two variables is a line in two-dimensional space.

Although we will not discuss the techniques for graphing equations in three variables, visualizing the possible patterns of intersecting planes gives us insight into the possible patterns of solutions of a system of three three-variable linear equations. There are four possible patterns.

1. Three planes have a single point in common. This point represents the single solution of the system. This system is **consistent.**

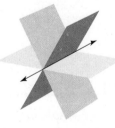

2. Three planes intersect at no point common to all three. This system has no solution. A few ways that this can occur are shown. This system is **inconsistent.**

3. Three planes intersect at all the points of a single line. The system has infinitely many solutions. This system is **consistent.**

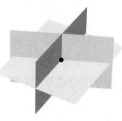

4. Three planes coincide at all points on the plane. The system is consistent, and the equations are **dependent.**

OBJECTIVE

1   Solving a System of Three Linear Equations in Three Variables ▶

Just as with systems of two equations in two variables, we can use the elimination or substitution method to solve a system of three equations in three variables. To use the elimination method, we eliminate a variable and obtain a system of two equations in two variables. Then we use the methods we learned in the previous section to solve the system of two equations.

EXAMPLE 1   Solve the system:

$$\begin{cases} 3x - y + z = -15 & \text{Equation (1)} \\ x + 2y - z = 1 & \text{Equation (2)} \\ 2x + 3y - 2z = 0 & \text{Equation (3)} \end{cases}$$

Solution Add equations (1) and (2) to eliminate z.

$$\begin{array}{r} 3x - y + z = -15 \\ x + 2y - z = 1 \\ \hline 4x + y \quad\quad = -14 \quad \text{Equation (4)} \end{array}$$

Next, add two _other_ equations and _eliminate z again._ To do so, multiply both sides of equation (1) by 2 and add this resulting equation to equation (3). Then

$$\begin{cases} 2(3x - y + z) = 2(-15) \\ 2x + 3y - 2z = 0 \end{cases} \text{ simplifies to } \begin{array}{r} 6x - 2y + 2z = -30 \\ 2x + 3y - 2z = 0 \\ \hline 8x + y \quad\quad = -30 \quad \text{Equation (5)} \end{array}$$

> **Helpful Hint**
>
> Don't forget to add two other equations besides equations (1) and (2) _and_ to **eliminate the same variable.**

Now solve equations (4) and (5) for x and y. To solve by elimination, multiply both sides of equation (4) by -1 and add this resulting equation to equation (5). Then

$$\begin{cases} -1(4x + y) = -1(-14) \\ 8x + y = -30 \end{cases} \text{ simplifies to } \begin{array}{r} -4x - y = 14 \\ 8x + y = -30 \\ \hline 4x \quad\quad = -16 \quad \text{Add the equations.} \\ x = -4 \quad \text{Solve for } x. \end{array}$$

Replace x with -4 in equation (4) or (5).

$$\begin{array}{rl} 4x + y = -14 & \text{Equation (4)} \\ 4(-4) + y = -14 & \text{Let } x = -4. \\ y = 2 & \text{Solve for } y. \end{array}$$

Finally, replace x with -4 and y with 2 in equation (1), (2), or (3).

$$\begin{array}{rl} x + 2y - z = 1 & \text{Equation (2)} \\ -4 + 2(2) - z = 1 & \text{Let } x = -4 \text{ and } y = 2. \\ -4 + 4 - z = 1 & \\ -z = 1 & \\ z = -1 & \end{array}$$

The solution is $(-4, 2, -1)$. To check, let $x = -4$, $y = 2$, and $z = -1$ in all three original equations of the system.

Equation (1)	_Equation (2)_	_Equation (3)_
$3x - y + z = -15$	$x + 2y - z = 1$	$2x + 3y - 2z = 0$
$3(-4) - 2 + (-1) \stackrel{?}{=} -15$	$-4 + 2(2) - (-1) \stackrel{?}{=} 1$	$2(-4) + 3(2) - 2(-1) \stackrel{?}{=} 0$
$-12 - 2 - 1 \stackrel{?}{=} -15$	$-4 + 4 + 1 \stackrel{?}{=} 1$	$-8 + 6 + 2 \stackrel{?}{=} 0$
$-15 = -15$ True	$1 = 1$ True	$0 = 0$ True

(Continued on next page)

All three statements are true, so the solution is $(-4, 2, -1)$. □

PRACTICE
1   Solve the system: $\begin{cases} 3x + 2y - z = 0 \\ x - y + 5z = 2 \\ 2x + 3y + 3z = 7 \end{cases}$

EXAMPLE 2   Solve the system:

$$\begin{cases} 2x - 4y + 8z = 2 & (1) \\ -x - 3y + z = 11 & (2) \\ x - 2y + 4z = 0 & (3) \end{cases}$$

Solution   Add equations (2) and (3) to eliminate x, and the new equation is

$$-5y + 5z = 11 \quad (4)$$

To eliminate x again, multiply both sides of equation (2) by 2 and add the resulting equation to equation (1). Then

$$\begin{cases} 2x - 4y + 8z = 2 \\ 2(-x - 3y + z) = 2(11) \end{cases} \quad \begin{array}{c} \text{simplifies} \\ \text{to} \end{array} \quad \begin{cases} 2x - 4y + 8z = 2 \\ \underline{-2x - 6y + 2z = 22} \\ -10y + 10z = 24 \quad (5) \end{cases}$$

Next, solve for y and z using equations (4) and (5). Multiply both sides of equation (4) by -2 and add the resulting equation to equation (5).

$$\begin{cases} -2(-5y + 5z) = -2(11) \\ -10y + 10z = 24 \end{cases} \quad \begin{array}{c} \text{simplifies} \\ \text{to} \end{array} \quad \begin{cases} 10y - 10z = -22 \\ \underline{-10y + 10z = 24} \\ 0 = 2 \quad \text{False} \end{cases}$$

Since the statement is false, this system is inconsistent and has no solution. The solution set is the empty set $\{\ \}$ or $\varnothing$. □

PRACTICE
2   Solve the system: $\begin{cases} 6x - 3y + 12z - 4 \\ -6x + 4y - 2z = 7 \\ -2x + y - 4z = 3 \end{cases}$

The elimination method is summarized next.

Solving a System of Three Linear Equations by the Elimination Method

Step 1. Write each equation in standard form $Ax + By + Cz = D$.

Step 2. Choose a pair of equations and use the equations to eliminate a variable.

Step 3. Choose any **other** pair of equations and eliminate the **same variable** as in Step 2.

Step 4. Two equations in two variables should be obtained from Step 2 and Step 3. Use methods from Sections 4.1 through 4.3 to solve this system for both variables.

Step 5. To solve for the third variable, substitute the values of the variables found in Step 4 into any of the original equations containing the third variable.

Step 6. Check the ordered triple solution in *all three* original equations.

Helpful Hint

Make sure you read closely and follow Step 3.

✔ **CONCEPT CHECK**

In the system

$$\begin{cases} x + y + z = 6 & \text{Equation (1)} \\ 2x - y + z = 3 & \text{Equation (2)} \\ x + 2y + 3z = 14 & \text{Equation (3)} \end{cases}$$

equations (1) and (2) are used to eliminate y. Which action could best be used to finish solving? Why?

a. Use (1) and (2) to eliminate z.   **b.** Use (2) and (3) to eliminate y.

c. Use (1) and (3) to eliminate x.

EXAMPLE 3   Solve the system:

$$\begin{cases} 2x + 4y \quad\;\; = 1 & (1) \\ 4x \quad\;\; - 4z = -1 & (2) \\ \quad\;\; y - 4z = -3 & (3) \end{cases}$$

Solution Notice that equation (2) has no term containing the variable y. Let us eliminate y using equations (1) and (3). Multiply both sides of equation (3) by -4 and add the resulting equation to equation (1). Then

$$\begin{cases} 2x + 4y \quad\;\; = 1 \\ -4(y - 4z) = -4(-3) \end{cases} \text{simplifies to} \begin{cases} 2x + 4y \quad\;\;\;\;\; = 1 \\ \underline{-4y + 16z = 12} \\ 2x \quad\;\; + 16z = 13 \quad (4) \end{cases}$$

Next, solve for z using equations (4) and (2). Multiply both sides of equation (4) by -2 and add the resulting equation to equation (2).

$$\begin{cases} -2(2x + 16z) = -2(13) \\ 4x - 4z = -1 \end{cases} \text{simplifies to} \begin{cases} -4x - 32z = -26 \\ \underline{4x - 4z = -1} \\ -36z = -27 \\ z = \dfrac{3}{4} \end{cases}$$

Replace z with $\dfrac{3}{4}$ in equation (3) and solve for y.

$$y - 4\left(\dfrac{3}{4}\right) = -3 \quad \text{Let } z = \dfrac{3}{4} \text{ in equation (3).}$$

$$y - 3 = -3$$

$$y = 0$$

Replace y with 0 in equation (1) and solve for x.

$$2x + 4(0) = 1$$

$$2x = 1$$

$$x = \dfrac{1}{2}$$

The solution is $\left(\dfrac{1}{2}, 0, \dfrac{3}{4}\right)$. Check to see that this solution satisfies all three equations of the system.   □

PRACTICE

3   Solve the system: $\begin{cases} 3x + 4y \quad\;\; = 0 \\ 9x \quad\;\; - 4z = 6 \\ \quad\; -2y + 7z = 1 \end{cases}$

EXAMPLE 4   Solve the system:

$$\begin{cases} x - 5y - 2z = 6 & (1) \\ -2x + 10y + 4z = -12 & (2) \\ \dfrac{1}{2}x - \dfrac{5}{2}y - z = 3 & (3) \end{cases}$$

Solution Multiply both sides of equation (3) by 2 to eliminate fractions and multiply both sides of equation (2) by $-\dfrac{1}{2}$ so that the coefficient of x is 1. The resulting system is then

$$\begin{cases} x - 5y - 2z = 6 & (1) \\ x - 5y - 2z = 6 & \text{Multiply (2) by } -\dfrac{1}{2}. \\ x - 5y - 2z = 6 & \text{Multiply (3) by 2.} \end{cases}$$

All three equations are identical, and therefore equations (1), (2), and (3) are all equivalent. There are infinitely many solutions of this system. The equations are dependent. The solution set can be written as $\{(x, y, z) \mid x - 5y - 2z = 6\}$.   □

PRACTICE
4   Solve the system: $\begin{cases} 2x + y - 3z = 6 \\ x + \dfrac{1}{2}y - \dfrac{3}{2}z = 3 \\ -4x - 2y + 6z = -12 \end{cases}$ ■

As mentioned earlier, we can also use the substitution method to solve a system of linear equations in three variables.

EXAMPLE 5   Solve the system:

$$\begin{cases} x - 4y - 5z = 35 & (1) \\ x - 3y = 0 & (2) \\ -y + z = -55 & (3) \end{cases}$$

Solution Notice in equations (2) and (3) that a variable is missing. Also notice that both equations contain the variable y. Let's use the substitution method by solving equation (2) for x and equation (3) for z and substituting the results in equation (1).

$$x - 3y = 0 \qquad (2)$$
$$x = 3y \qquad \text{Solve equation (2) for } x.$$
$$-y + z = -55 \qquad (3)$$
$$z = y - 55 \qquad \text{Solve equation (3) for } z.$$

Now substitute $3y$ for x and $y - 55$ for z in equation (1).

$$x - 4y - 5z = 35 \qquad (1)$$

> **Helpful Hint**
> Do not forget to distribute.

$$3y - 4y - 5(y - 55) = 35 \qquad \text{Let } x = 3y \text{ and } z = y - 55.$$
$$3y - 4y - 5y + 275 = 35 \qquad \text{Use the distributive law and multiply.}$$
$$-6y + 275 = 35 \qquad \text{Combine like terms.}$$
$$-6y = -240 \qquad \text{Subtract 275 from both sides.}$$
$$y = 40 \qquad \text{Solve.}$$

To find x, recall that $x = 3y$ and substitute 40 for y. Then $x = 3y$ becomes $x = 3 \cdot 40 = 120$. To find z, recall that $z = y - 55$ and substitute 40 for y, also. Then $z = y - 55$ becomes $z = 40 - 55 = -15$. The solution is $(120, 40, -15)$.   □

PRACTICE
5   Solve the system: $\begin{cases} x + 2y + 4z = 16 \\ x + 2z = -4 \\ y - 3z = 30 \end{cases}$ ■

✔ **Vocabulary, Readiness & Video Check**

Solve.

1. Choose the equation(s) that has $(-1, 3, 1)$ as a solution.
   a. $x + y + z = 3$ **b.** $-x + y + z = 5$ **c.** $-x + y + 2z = 0$ **d.** $x + 2y - 3z = 2$

2. Choose the equation(s) that has $(2, 1, -4)$ as a solution.
   a. $x + y + z = -1$ **b.** $x - y - z = -3$ **c.** $2x - y + z = -1$ **d.** $-x - 3y - z = -1$

3. Use the result of Exercise 1 to determine whether $(-1, 3, 1)$ is a solution of the system below. Explain your answer.
$$\begin{cases} x + y + z = 3 \\ -x + y + z = 5 \\ x + 2y - 3z = 2 \end{cases}$$

4. Use the result of Exercise 2 to determine whether $(2, 1, -4)$ is a solution of the system below. Explain your answer.
$$\begin{cases} x + y + z = -1 \\ x - y - z = -3 \\ 2x - y + z = -1 \end{cases}$$

Martin-Gay Interactive Videos

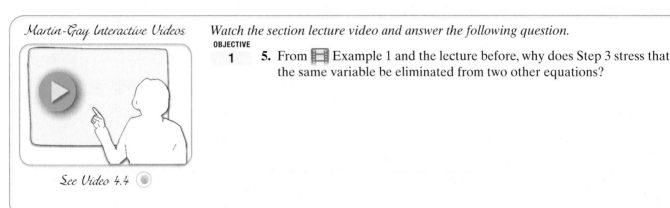

Watch the section lecture video and answer the following question.

OBJECTIVE
1

5. From ▥ Example 1 and the lecture before, why does Step 3 stress that the same variable be eliminated from two other equations?

See Video 4.4 ◉

4.4   Exercise Set   MyMathLab ▷

Solve each system. See Examples 1 through 5.

1. $\begin{cases} x - y + z = -4 \\ 3x + 2y - z = 5 \\ -2x + 3y - z = 15 \end{cases}$

2. $\begin{cases} x + y - z = -1 \\ -4x - y + 2z = -7 \\ 2x - 2y - 5z = 7 \end{cases}$

9. $\begin{cases} 4x - y + 2z = 5 \\ 2y + z = 4 \\ 4x + y + 3z = 10 \end{cases}$

10. $\begin{cases} 5y - 7z = 14 \\ 2x + y + 4z = 10 \\ 2x + 6y - 3z = 30 \end{cases}$

3. $\begin{cases} x + y = 3 \\ 2y = 10 \\ 3x + 2y - 3z = 1 \end{cases}$

4. $\begin{cases} 5x = 5 \\ 2x + y = 4 \\ 3x + y - 4z = -15 \end{cases}$

11. $\begin{cases} x + 5z = 0 \\ 5x + y = 0 \\ y - 3z = 0 \end{cases}$

12. $\begin{cases} x - 5y = 0 \\ x - z = 0 \\ -x + 5z = 0 \end{cases}$

5. $\begin{cases} 2x + 2y + z = 1 \\ -x + y + 2z = 3 \\ x + 2y + 4z = 0 \end{cases}$

6. $\begin{cases} 2x - 3y + z = 5 \\ x + y + z = 0 \\ 4x + 2y + 4z = 4 \end{cases}$

13. $\begin{cases} 6x - 5z = 17 \\ 5x - y + 3z = -1 \\ 2x + y = -41 \end{cases}$

14. $\begin{cases} x + 2y = 6 \\ 7x + 3y + z = -33 \\ x - z = 16 \end{cases}$

7. $\begin{cases} x - 2y + z = -5 \\ -3x + 6y - 3z = 15 \\ 2x - 4y + 2z = -10 \end{cases}$

8. $\begin{cases} 3x + y - 2z = 2 \\ -6x - 2y + 4z = -4 \\ 9x + 3y - 6z = 6 \end{cases}$

15. $\begin{cases} x + y + z = 8 \\ 2x - y - z = 10 \\ x - 2y - 3z = 22 \end{cases}$

16. $\begin{cases} 5x + y + 3z = 1 \\ x - y + 3z = -7 \\ -x + y = 1 \end{cases}$

17. $\begin{cases} x + 2y - z = 5 \\ 6x + y + z = 7 \\ 2x + 4y - 2z = 5 \end{cases}$ **18.** $\begin{cases} 4x - y + 3z = 10 \\ x + y - z = 5 \\ 8x - 2y + 6z = 10 \end{cases}$

▶ **19.** $\begin{cases} 2x - 3y + z = 2 \\ x - 5y + 5z = 3 \\ 3x + y - 3z = 5 \end{cases}$ **20.** $\begin{cases} 4x + y - z = 8 \\ x - y + 2z = 3 \\ 3x - y + z = 6 \end{cases}$

21. $\begin{cases} -2x - 4y + 6z = -8 \\ x + 2y - 3z = 4 \\ 4x + 8y - 12z = 16 \end{cases}$ **22.** $\begin{cases} -6x + 12y + 3z = -6 \\ 2x - 4y - z = 2 \\ -x + 2y + \dfrac{z}{2} = -1 \end{cases}$

23. $\begin{cases} 2x + 2y - 3z = 1 \\ y + 2z = -14 \\ 3x - 2y = -1 \end{cases}$ **24.** $\begin{cases} 7x + 4y = 10 \\ x - 4y + 2z = 6 \\ y - 2z = -1 \end{cases}$

25. $\begin{cases} x + 2y - z = 5 \\ -3x - 2y - 3z = 11 \\ 4x + 4y + 5z = -18 \end{cases}$ **26.** $\begin{cases} 3x - 3y + z = -1 \\ 3x - y - z = 3 \\ -6x + 4y + 3z = -8 \end{cases}$

27. $\begin{cases} \dfrac{3}{4}x - \dfrac{1}{3}y + \dfrac{1}{2}z = 9 \\ \dfrac{1}{6}x + \dfrac{1}{3}y - \dfrac{1}{2}z = 2 \\ \dfrac{1}{2}x - y + \dfrac{1}{2}z = 2 \end{cases}$ **28.** $\begin{cases} \dfrac{1}{3}x - \dfrac{1}{4}y + z = -9 \\ \dfrac{1}{2}x - \dfrac{1}{3}y - \dfrac{1}{4}z = -6 \\ x - \dfrac{1}{2}y - z = -8 \end{cases}$

REVIEW AND PREVIEW

Translating Solve. See Section 2.4.

29. The sum of two numbers is 45 and one number is twice the other. Find the numbers.

30. The difference of two numbers is 5. Twice the smaller number added to five times the larger number is 53. Find the numbers.

Solve. See Section 2.3.

31. $2(x - 1) - 3x = x - 12$

32. $7(2x - 1) + 4 = 11(3x - 2)$

33. $-y - 5(y + 5) = 3y - 10$

34. $z - 3(z + 7) = 6(2z + 1)$

CONCEPT EXTENSIONS

35. Write a single linear equation in three variables that has $(-1, 2, -4)$ as a solution. (There are many possibilities.) Explain the process you used to write an equation.

36. Write a system of three linear equations in three variables that has $(2, 1, 5)$ as a solution. (There are many possibilities.) Explain the process you used to write an equation.

37. Write a system of linear equations in three variables that has the solution $(-1, 2, -4)$. Explain the process you used to write your system.

38. When solving a system of three equations in three unknowns, explain how to determine that a system has no solution.

39. The fraction $\dfrac{1}{24}$ can be written as the following sum:

$$\frac{1}{24} = \frac{x}{8} + \frac{y}{4} + \frac{z}{3}$$

where the numbers x, y, and z are solutions of

$$\begin{cases} x + y + z = 1 \\ 2x - y + z = 0 \\ -x + 2y + 2z = -1 \end{cases}$$

Solve the system and see that the sum of the fractions is $\dfrac{1}{24}$.

40. The fraction $\dfrac{1}{18}$ can be written as the following sum:

$$\frac{1}{18} = \frac{x}{2} + \frac{y}{3} + \frac{z}{9}$$

where the numbers x, y, and z are solutions of

$$\begin{cases} x + 3y + z = -3 \\ -x + y + 2z = -14 \\ 3x + 2y - z = 12 \end{cases}$$

Solve the system and see that the sum of the fractions is $\dfrac{1}{18}$.

Solving systems involving more than three variables can be accomplished with methods similar to those encountered in this section. Apply what you already know to solve each system of equations in four variables.

41. $\begin{cases} x + y - w = 0 \\ y + 2z + w = 3 \\ x - z = 1 \\ 2x - y - w = -1 \end{cases}$

42. $\begin{cases} 5x + 4y = 29 \\ y + z - w = -2 \\ 5x + z = 23 \\ y - z + w = 4 \end{cases}$

43. $\begin{cases} x + y + z + w = 5 \\ 2x + y + z + w = 6 \\ x + y + z = 2 \\ x + y = 0 \end{cases}$

44. $\begin{cases} 2x - z = -1 \\ y + z + w = 9 \\ y - 2w = -6 \\ x + y = 3 \end{cases}$

45. Write a system of three linear equations in three variables that are dependent equations.

46. How many solutions are there to the system in Exercise 45?

4.5 | Systems of Linear Equations and Problem Solving

OBJECTIVES

1 Solve Problems That Can Be Modeled by a System of Two Linear Equations.

2 Solve Problems with Cost and Revenue Functions.

3 Solve Problems That Can Be Modeled by a System of Three Linear Equations.

OBJECTIVE

1 Solving Problems Modeled by Systems of Two Equations

Thus far, we have solved problems by writing one-variable equations and solving for the variable. Some of these problems can be solved, perhaps more easily, by writing a system of equations, as illustrated in this section.

EXAMPLE 1 **Predicting Equal Consumption of Red Meat and Poultry**

America's consumption of red meat has decreased most years since 2005, while consumption of poultry has decreased also, but by a much smaller amount. The function $y = -2.03x + 119.05$ approximates the annual pounds of red meat consumed per capita, where x is the number of years since 2005. The function $y = -0.41x + 103.21$ approximates the annual pounds of poultry consumed per capita, where x is also the number of years since 2005. Based on this trend, determine the year when the annual consumption of red meat and poultry is equal. (*Source:* USDA: Economic Research Service)

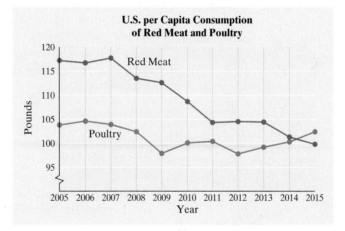

Solution

1. UNDERSTAND. Read and reread the problem and guess a year. Without using the graph for assistance, guess the year 2025. This year is 20 years since 2005, so $x = 20$. Now let $x = 20$ in each given function.

   Red meat: $y = -2.03x + 119.05 = -2.03(20) + 119.05 = 78.45$ pounds

   Poultry: $y = -0.41x + 103.21 = -0.41(20) + 103.21 = 95.01$ pounds

   Since the projected pounds in 2025 for red meat and poultry are not the same, we guessed incorrectly, but we do have a better understanding of the problem. We know that the year is earlier than 2025. Why? Because consumption of red meat for 2025 is less than consumption of poultry.

2. TRANSLATE. We are already given the system of equations.

3. SOLVE. We want to know the year x in which pounds y are the same, so we solve the system

$$\begin{cases} y = -2.03x + 119.05 \\ y = -0.41x + 103.21 \end{cases}$$

   Since both equations are solved for y, one way to solve is to use the substitution method.

(Continued on next page)

$$y = -0.41x + 103.21 \quad \text{Second equation}$$

$$-2.03x + 119.05 = -0.41x + 103.21 \quad \text{Let } y = -2.03x + 119.05.$$
$$-1.62x = -15.84$$
$$x = \frac{-15.84}{-1.62} \approx 9.78$$

4. INTERPRET. Since we are only asked to find the year, we need only solve for x.

Check: To check, see whether $x \approx 9.78$ gives approximately the same number of pounds of red meat and poultry.

Red meat: $y = -2.03x + 119.05 = -2.03(9.78) + 119.05 = 99.1966$ pounds
Poultry: $y = -0.41x + 103.21 = -0.41(9.78) + 103.21 = 99.2002$ pounds

Since we rounded the number of years, the numbers of pounds do differ slightly. They differ only by 0.0036, so we can assume we solved correctly.

State: The consumption of red meat and poultry will be the same about 9.78 years after 2005, or 2014.78. Thus, in the year 2014, we calculate the consumption is the same. □

PRACTICE

1 Read Example 1. If we use the years 2012, 2013, 2014, and 2015 only to write functions approximating the consumption of red meat and poultry, we have the following:

Red meat: $y = -0.91x + 110.45$
Poultry: $y = 0.11x + 98.6$

where x is the number of years since 2005 and y is the pounds per year per capita consumed.

a. Assuming this trend continues, predict the year when consumption of red meat and poultry will be the same. Round to the nearest year.

b. Does your answer differ from the answer to Example 1? Why or why not?

For Example 1, the equations in the system were given to us. Let's now practice writing our own system of equations that we will use to solve an application.

Many of the applications solved earlier using one-variable equations can also be solved using two equations in **two** variables. We use the same problem-solving steps that have been used throughout this text. The only difference is that two variables are assigned to represent the two unknown quantities and that the stated problem is translated into **two** equations.

Problem-Solving Steps

Step 1. UNDERSTAND the problem. During this step, become comfortable with the problem. Some ways of doing this are to

Read and reread the problem.

Choose two variables to represent the two unknowns.

Construct a drawing if possible.

Propose a solution and check. Pay careful attention to how you check your proposed solution. This will help when writing equations to model the problem.

Step 2. TRANSLATE the problem into two equations.

Step 3. SOLVE the system of equations.

Step 4. INTERPRET the results: **Check** the proposed solution in the stated problem and **state** your conclusion.

EXAMPLE 2 Finding Unknown Numbers

Find two numbers whose sum is 37 and whose difference is 21.

Solution

1. UNDERSTAND. Read and reread the problem. Suppose that one number is 20. If their sum is 37, the other number is 17 because $20 + 17 = 37$. Is their difference 21? No; $20 - 17 = 3$. Our proposed solution is incorrect, but we now have a better understanding of the problem.

   Since we are looking for two numbers, we let

   $$x = \text{first number}$$
   $$y = \text{second number}$$

2. TRANSLATE. Since we have assigned two variables to this problem, we translate our problem into two equations.

In words:	two numbers whose sum	is	37
	$\downarrow$	$\downarrow$	$\downarrow$
Translate:	$x + y$	$=$	37

In words:	two numbers whose difference	is	21
	$\downarrow$	$\downarrow$	$\downarrow$
Translate:	$x - y$	$=$	21

3. SOLVE. Now we solve the system

   $$\begin{cases} x + y = 37 \\ x - y = 21 \end{cases}$$

   Notice that the coefficients of the variable y are opposites. Let's then solve by the addition method and begin by adding the equations.

   $$\begin{aligned} x + y &= 37 \\ \underline{x - y} &= \underline{21} \\ 2x &= 58 \qquad \text{Add the equations.} \\ x &= \frac{58}{2} = 29 \quad \text{Divide both sides by 2.} \end{aligned}$$

   Now we let $x = 29$ in the first equation to find y.

   $$\begin{aligned} x + y &= 37 \qquad \text{First equation} \\ 29 + y &= 37 \\ y &= 8 \qquad \text{Subtract 29 from both sides.} \end{aligned}$$

4. INTERPRET. The solution of the system is $(29, 8)$.

   Check: Notice that the sum of 29 and 8 is $29 + 8 = 37$, the required sum. Their difference is $29 - 8 = 21$, the required difference.

   State: The numbers are 29 and 8. □

PRACTICE

2 Find two numbers whose sum is 30 and whose difference is 6. ■

EXAMPLE 3 Finding Unknown Numbers

A first number is 4 less than a second number. Four times the first number is 6 more than twice the second. Find the numbers.

(Continued on next page)

Solution

1. **UNDERSTAND.** Read and reread the problem and guess a solution. If a first number is 10 and this is 4 less than a second number, the second number is 14. Four times the first number is 4(10), or 40. This is not equal to 6 more than twice the second number, which is 2(14) + 6 or 34. Although we guessed incorrectly, we now have a better understanding of the problem.

   Since we are looking for two numbers, we will let

   $$x = \text{first number}$$
   $$y = \text{second number}$$

2. **TRANSLATE.** Since we have assigned two variables to this problem, we will translate the given facts into two equations. For the first statement we have

In words:	the first number	is	4 less than the second number
	↓	↓	↓
Translate:	x	$=$	$y - 4$

   Next we translate the second statement into an equation.

In words:	four times the first number	is	6 more than twice the second number
	↓	↓	↓
Translate:	$4x$	$=$	$2y + 6$

3. **SOLVE.** Here we solve the system

   $$\begin{cases} x = y - 4 \\ 4x = 2y + 6 \end{cases}$$

   Since the first equation expresses x in terms of y, we will use substitution. We substitute $y - 4$ for x in the second equation and solve for y.

   $$4x = 2y + 6 \quad \text{Second equation}$$
   $$4(y - 4) = 2y + 6 \quad \text{Let } x = y - 4.$$
   $$4y - 16 = 2y + 6$$
   $$2y = 22$$
   $$y = 11$$

   Now we replace y with 11 in the equation $x = y - 4$ and solve for x. Then $x = y - 4$ becomes $x = 11 - 4 = 7$. The ordered pair solution of the system is (7, 11).

4. **INTERPRET.** Since the solution of the system is (7, 11), then the first number we are looking for is 7 and the second number is 11.

   Check: Notice that 7 _is_ 4 less than 11, and 4 times 7 _is_ 6 more than twice 11. The proposed numbers, 7 and 11, are correct.

   State: The numbers are 7 and 11. ☐

PRACTICE
3 A first number is 5 more than a second number. Twice the first number is 2 less than 3 times the second number. Find the numbers. ∎

EXAMPLE 4   **Solving a Problem about Prices**

The Cirque du Soleil show Varekai is performing locally. Matinee admission for 4 adults and 2 children is $374, while admission for 2 adults and 3 children is $285.

a. What is the price of an adult's ticket?

b. What is the price of a child's ticket?

c. Suppose that a special rate of $1000 is offered for groups of 20 persons. Should a group of 4 adults and 16 children use the group rate? Why or why not?

Solution

1. UNDERSTAND. Read and reread the problem and guess a solution. Let's suppose that the price of an adult's ticket is $50 and the price of a child's ticket is $40. To check our proposed solution, let's see if admission for 4 adults and 2 children is $374. Admission for 4 adults is 4($50) or $200 and admission for 2 children is 2($40) or $80. This gives a total admission of $200 + $80 = $280, not the required $374. Again, though, we have accomplished the purpose of this process: We have a better understanding of the problem. To continue, we let

$$A = \text{the price of an adult's ticket}$$
$$C = \text{the price of a child's ticket}$$

2. TRANSLATE. We translate the problem into two equations using both variables.

In words:	admission for 4 adults	and	admission for 2 children	is	$374
	↓	↓	↓	↓	↓
Translate:	$4A$	$+$	$2C$	$=$	374

In words:	admission for 2 adults	and	admission for 3 children	is	$285
	↓	↓	↓	↓	↓
Translate:	$2A$	$+$	$3C$	$=$	285

3. SOLVE. We solve the system.

$$\begin{cases} 4A + 2C = 374 \\ 2A + 3C = 285 \end{cases}$$

Since both equations are written in standard form, we solve by the addition method. First we multiply the second equation by -2 so that when we add the equations, we eliminate the variable A. Then the system

$$\begin{cases} 4A + 2C = 374 \\ -2(2A + 3C) = -2(285) \end{cases}$$ simplifies to $\begin{cases} 4A + 2C = 374 \\ -4A - 6C = -570 \end{cases}$

Add the equations.

$$\overline{-4C = -196}$$
$$C = 49 \text{ or } \$49, \text{ the child's ticket price}$$

(Continued on next page)

To find A, we replace C with 49 in the first equation.

$$4A + 2C = 374 \quad \text{First equation}$$
$$4A + 2(49) = 374 \quad \text{Let } C = 49$$
$$4A + 98 = 374$$
$$4A = 276$$
$$A = 69 \text{ or } \$69, \text{ the adult's ticket price}$$

4. INTERPRET.

Check: Notice that 4 adults and 2 children will pay

$4(\$69) + 2(\$49) = \$276 + \$98 = \$374$, the required amount. Also, the price for 2 adults and 3 children is $2(\$69) + 3(\$49) = \$138 + \$147 = \$285$, the required amount.

State: Answer the three original questions.

a. Since $A = 69$, the price of an adult's ticket is $69.

b. Since $C = 49$, the price of a child's ticket is $49.

c. The regular admission price for 4 adults and 16 children is

$$4(\$69) + 16(\$49) = \$276 + \$784$$
$$= \$1060$$

This is $60 more than the special group rate of $1000, so they should request the group rate. □

PRACTICE

4 It is considered a premium game when the Red Sox or the Yankees come to Texas to play the Rangers. Admission for one of these games for three adults and three children under 14 is $75, while admission for two adults and four children is $62. (*Source:* MLB.com, Texas Rangers)

a. What is the price of an adult's admission?

b. What is the price of a child's admission?

c. Suppose that a special rate of $200 is offered for groups of 20 persons. Should a group of 5 adults and 15 children use the group rate? Why or why not? ■

EXAMPLE 5 **Finding the Rate of Speed**

Two cars leave Indianapolis, one traveling east and the other west. After 3 hours, they are 297 miles apart. If one car is traveling 5 mph faster than the other, what is the speed of each?

Solution

1. UNDERSTAND. Read and reread the problem. Let's guess a solution and use the formula $d = rt$ (distance = rate · time) to check. Suppose that one car is traveling at a rate of 55 miles per hour. This means that the other car is traveling at a rate of 50 miles per hour since we are told that one car is traveling 5 mph faster than the other. To find the distance apart after 3 hours, we will first find the distance traveled by each car. One car's distance is rate · time = $55(3) = 165$ miles. The other car's distance is rate · time = $50(3) = 150$ miles. Since one car is traveling east and the other west, their distance apart is the sum of their distances, or 165 miles + 150 miles = 315 miles. Although this distance apart is not the required distance of 297 miles, we now have a better understanding of the problem.

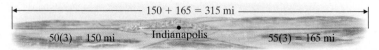

Let's model the problem with a system of equations. We will let

$$x = \text{speed of one car}$$
$$y = \text{speed of the other car}$$

We summarize the information on the following chart. Both cars have traveled 3 hours. Since distance = rate · time, their distances are $3x$ and $3y$ miles, respectively.

	Rate	· *Time*	= *Distance*
One Car	x	3	$3x$
Other Car	y	3	$3y$

2. TRANSLATE. We can now translate the stated conditions into two equations.

In words:	one car's distance	added to	the other car's distance	is	297
	↓	↓	↓	↓	↓
Translate:	$3x$	$+$	$3y$	$=$	297

In words:	one car's speed	is	5 mph faster than the other
	↓	↓	↓
Translate:	x	$=$	$y + 5$

3. SOLVE. Here we solve the system

$$\begin{cases} 3x + 3y = 297 \\ x = y + 5 \end{cases}$$

Again, the substitution method is appropriate. We replace x with $y + 5$ in the first equation and solve for y.

$$3x + 3y = 297 \quad \text{First equation}$$
$$3(y + 5) + 3y = 297 \quad \text{Let } x = y + 5.$$
$$3y + 15 + 3y = 297$$
$$6y = 282$$
$$y = 47$$

To find x, we replace y with 47 in the equation $x = y + 5$. Then $x = 47 + 5 = 52$. The ordered pair solution of the system is $(52, 47)$.

4. INTERPRET. The solution $(52, 47)$ means that the cars are traveling at 52 mph and 47 mph, respectively.

Check: Notice that one car is traveling 5 mph faster than the other. Also, if one car travels 52 mph for 3 hours, the distance is $3(52) = 156$ miles. The other car traveling for 3 hours at 47 mph travels a distance of $3(47) = 141$ miles. The sum of the distances $156 + 141$ is 297 miles, the required distance.

> **Helpful Hint**
> Don't forget to attach units if appropriate.

State: The cars are traveling at 52 mph and 47 mph. □

PRACTICE

5 In 2007, the French train TGV V150 became the fastest conventional rail train in the world. It broke the 1990 record of the next fastest conventional rail train, the French TGV Atlantique. Assume the V150 and the Atlantique left the same station in Paris, with one heading west and one heading east. After 2 hours, they were 2150 kilometers apart. If the V150 is 75 kph faster than the Atlantique, what is the speed of each?

EXAMPLE 6 **Mixing Solutions**

Lynn Pike, a pharmacist, needs 70 liters of a 50% alcohol solution. She has available a 30% alcohol solution and an 80% alcohol solution. How many liters of each solution should she mix to obtain 70 liters of a 50% alcohol solution?

Solution

1. UNDERSTAND. Read and reread the problem. Next, guess the solution. Suppose that we need 20 liters of the 30% solution. Then we need $70 - 20 = 50$ liters of the 80% solution. To see if this gives us 70 liters of a 50% alcohol solution, let's find the amount of pure alcohol in each solution.

$$
\begin{array}{ccccc}
\text{number} & \times & \text{alcohol} & = & \text{amount of} \\
\text{of liters} & & \text{strength} & & \text{pure alcohol} \\
\downarrow & & \downarrow & & \downarrow \\
20 \text{ liters} & \times & 0.30 & = & 6 \text{ liters} \\
50 \text{ liters} & \times & 0.80 & = & 40 \text{ liters} \\
70 \text{ liters} & \times & 0.50 & = & 35 \text{ liters}
\end{array}
$$

Since 6 liters + 40 liters = 46 liters and not 35 liters, our guess is incorrect, but we have gained some insight as to how to model and check this problem.

We will let

$$x = \text{amount of 30\% solution, in liters}$$
$$y = \text{amount of 80\% solution, in liters}$$

and use a table to organize the given data.

	Number of Liters	Alcohol Strength	Amount of Pure Alcohol
30% Solution	x	30%	$0.30x$
80% Solution	y	80%	$0.80y$
50% Solution Needed	70	50%	$(0.50)(70)$

2. TRANSLATE. We translate the stated conditions into two equations.

$$
\begin{array}{ccccc}
\text{In words:} & \text{amount of} & + & \text{amount of} & = & 70 \\
& \text{30\% solution} & & \text{80\% solution} & & \\
& \downarrow & & \downarrow & & \downarrow \\
\text{Translate:} & x & + & y & = & 70
\end{array}
$$

$$
\begin{array}{ccccc}
\text{In words:} & \text{amount of pure} & + & \text{amount of pure} & = & \text{amount of pure} \\
& \text{alcohol in 30\%} & & \text{alcohol in 80\%} & & \text{alcohol in 50\%} \\
& \text{solution} & & \text{solution} & & \text{solution} \\
& \downarrow & & \downarrow & & \downarrow \\
\text{Translate:} & 0.30x & + & 0.80y & = & (0.50)(70)
\end{array}
$$

3. SOLVE. Here we solve the system

$$
\begin{cases}
x + y = 70 \\
0.30x + 0.80y = (0.50)(70)
\end{cases}
$$

To solve this system, we use the elimination method. We multiply both sides of the first equation by -3 and both sides of the second equation by 10. Then

$$\begin{cases} -3(x+y) = -3(70) \\ 10(0.30x + 0.80y) = 10(0.50)(70) \end{cases} \quad \begin{matrix} \text{simplifies} \\ \text{to} \end{matrix} \quad \begin{cases} -3x - 3y = -210 \\ \underline{3x + 8y = 350} \\ \qquad 5y = 140 \\ \qquad y = 28 \end{cases}$$

Now we replace y with 28 in the equation $x + y = 70$ and find that $x + 28 = 70$, or $x = 42$.

The ordered pair solution of the system is $(42, 28)$.

4. INTERPRET.

Check: Check the solution in the same way that we checked our guess.

State: The pharmacist needs to mix 42 liters of 30% solution and 28 liters of 80% solution to obtain 70 liters of 50% solution. □

PRACTICE

6 Keith Robinson is a chemistry teacher who needs 1 liter of a solution of 5% hydrochloric acid (HCl) to carry out an experiment. If he only has a stock solution of 99% HCl, how much water (0% acid) and how much stock solution (99%) of HCl must he mix to get 1 liter of 5% solution? Round answers to the nearest hundredth of a liter. ∎

✔ **CONCEPT CHECK**

Suppose you mix an amount of 25% acid solution with an amount of 60% acid solution. You then calculate the acid strength of the resulting acid mixture. For which of the following results should you suspect an error in your calculation? Why?

a. 14% **b.** 32% **c.** 55%

OBJECTIVE

2 Solving Problems with Cost and Revenue Functions ▶

Recall that businesses are often computing cost and revenue functions or equations to predict sales, to determine whether prices need to be adjusted, and to see whether the company is making or losing money. Recall also that the value at which revenue equals cost is called the break-even point. When revenue is less than cost, the company is losing money; when revenue is greater than cost, the company is making money.

EXAMPLE 7 Finding a Break-Even Point

A manufacturing company recently purchased $3000 worth of new equipment to offer new personalized stationery to its customers. The cost of producing a package of personalized stationery is $3.00, and it is sold for $5.50. Find the number of packages that must be sold for the company to break even.

(Continued on next page)

Solution

1. **UNDERSTAND.** Read and reread the problem. Notice that the cost to the company will include a one-time cost of $3000 for the equipment and then $3.00 per package produced. The revenue will be $5.50 per package sold. To model this problem, we will let

$$x = \text{number of packages of personalized stationery}$$
$$C(x) = \text{total cost of producing } x \text{ packages of stationery}$$
$$R(x) = \text{total revenue from selling } x \text{ packages of stationery}$$

2. **TRANSLATE.** The revenue equation is

In words:	revenue for selling x packages of stationery	=	price per package	·	number of packages
Translate:	$R(x)$	=	5.5	·	x

The cost equation is

In words:	cost for producing x packages of stationery	=	cost per package	·	number of packages	+	cost for equipment
Translate:	$C(x)$	=	3	·	x	+	3000

Since the break-even point is when $R(x) = C(x)$, we solve the equation

$$5.5x = 3x + 3000$$

3. **SOLVE.**

$$5.5x = 3x + 3000$$
$$2.5x = 3000 \qquad \text{Subtract } 3x \text{ from both sides.}$$
$$x = 1200 \qquad \text{Divide both sides by 2.5.}$$

4. **INTERPRET.**

Check: To see whether the break-even point occurs when 1200 packages are produced and sold, see if revenue equals cost when $x = 1200$. When $x = 1200$, $R(x) = 5.5x = 5.5(1200) = 6600$ and $C(x) = 3x + 3000 = 3(1200) + 3000 = 6600$. Since $R(1200) = C(1200) = 6600$, the break-even point is 1200.

State: The company must sell 1200 packages of stationery to break even. The graph of this system is shown.

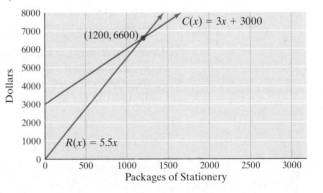

PRACTICE

7 An online-only electronics firm recently purchased $3000 worth of new equipment to create shock-proof packaging for its products. The cost of producing one shock-proof package is $2.50, and the firm charges the customer $4.50 for the packaging. Find the number of packages that must be sold for the company to break even.

OBJECTIVE

3   Solving Problems Modeled by Systems of Three Equations ▷

To introduce problem solving by writing a system of three linear equations in three variables, we solve a problem about triangles.

EXAMPLE 8   Finding Angle Measures

The measure of the largest angle of a triangle is 80° more than the measure of the smallest angle, and the measure of the remaining angle is 10° more than the measure of the smallest angle. Find the measure of each angle.

Solution

1. UNDERSTAND. Read and reread the problem. Recall that the sum of the measures of the angles of a triangle is 180°. Then guess a solution. If the smallest angle measures 20°, the measure of the largest angle is 80° more, or 20° + 80° = 100°. The measure of the remaining angle is 10° more than the measure of the smallest angle, or 20° + 10° = 30°. The sum of these three angles is 20° + 100° + 30° = 150°, not the required 180°. We now know that the measure of the smallest angle is greater than 20°.

   To model this problem, we will let

   x = degree measure of the smallest angle

   y = degree measure of the largest angle

   z = degree measure of the remaining angle

2. TRANSLATE. We translate the given information into three equations.

   In words: the sum of the measures   =   180

   Translate: $x + y + z$ =   180

   In words: the largest angle   is   80 more than the smallest angle

   Translate: y = $x + 80$

   In words: the remaining angle   is   10 more than the smallest angle

   Translate: z = $x + 10$

3. SOLVE. We solve the system

$$\begin{cases} x + y + z = 180 \\ y = x + 80 \\ z = x + 10 \end{cases}$$

Since y and z are both expressed in terms of x, we will solve using the substitution method. We substitute $y = x + 80$ and $z = x + 10$ in the first equation. Then

$$x + y + z = 180 \quad \text{First equation}$$

$$x + (x + 80) + (x + 10) = 180 \quad \text{Let } y = x + 80 \text{ and } z = x + 10.$$

$$3x + 90 = 180$$

$$3x = 90$$

$$x = 30$$

Then $y = x + 80 = 30 + 80 = 110$, and $z = x + 10 = 30 + 10 = 40$. The ordered triple solution is $(30, 110, 40)$.

(Continued on next page)

4. INTERPRET.

Check: Notice that $30° + 40° + 110° = 180°$. Also, the measure of the largest angle, $110°$, is $80°$ more than the measure of the smallest angle, $30°$. The measure of the remaining angle, $40°$, is $10°$ more than the measure of the smallest angle, $30°$. □

PRACTICE
8   The measure of the largest angle of a triangle is $40°$ more than the measure of the smallest angle, and the measure of the remaining angle is $20°$ more than the measure of the smallest angle. Find the measure of each angle.   ■

✓ | **Vocabulary, Readiness & Video Check**

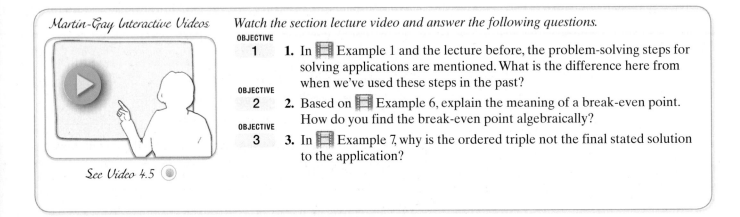

Martin-Gay Interactive Videos

See Video 4.5 ●

Watch the section lecture video and answer the following questions.

OBJECTIVE 1

1. In ▣ Example 1 and the lecture before, the problem-solving steps for solving applications are mentioned. What is the difference here from when we've used these steps in the past?

OBJECTIVE 2

2. Based on ▣ Example 6, explain the meaning of a break-even point. How do you find the break-even point algebraically?

OBJECTIVE 3

3. In ▣ Example 7, why is the ordered triple not the final stated solution to the application?

4.5 **Exercise Set** MyMathLab® ▶

Without actually solving each problem, choose each correct solution by deciding which choice satisfies the given conditions.

△ **1.** The length of a rectangle is 3 feet longer than the width. The perimeter is 30 feet. Find the dimensions of the rectangle.
 a. length = 8 feet; width = 5 feet
 b. length = 8 feet; width = 7 feet
 c. length = 9 feet; width = 6 feet

△ **2.** An isosceles triangle, a triangle with two sides of equal length, has a perimeter of 20 inches. Each of the equal sides is one inch longer than the third side. Find the lengths of the three sides.
 a. 6 inches, 6 inches, and 7 inches
 b. 7 inches, 7 inches, and 6 inches
 c. 6 inches, 7 inches, and 8 inches

3. Two computer disks and three notebooks cost $17. However, five computer disks and four notebooks cost $32. Find the price of each.
 a. notebook = $4; computer disk = $3
 b. notebook = $3; computer disk = $4
 c. notebook = $5; computer disk = $2

4. Two music CDs and four music cassette tapes cost a total of $40. However, three music CDs and five cassette tapes cost $55. Find the price of each.
 a. CD = $12; cassette = $4
 b. CD = $15; cassette = $2
 c. CD = $10; cassette = $5

5. Kesha has a total of 100 coins, all of which are either dimes or quarters. The total value of the coins is $13.00. Find the number of each type of coin.
 a. 80 dimes; 20 quarters
 b. 20 dimes; 44 quarters
 c. 60 dimes; 40 quarters

6. Samuel has 28 gallons of saline solution available in two large containers at his pharmacy. One container holds three times as much as the other container. Find the capacity of each container.
 a. 15 gallons; 5 gallons
 b. 20 gallons; 8 gallons
 c. 21 gallons; 7 gallons

TRANSLATING

Write a system of equations in x and y describing each situation. Do not solve the system. See Example 2.

7. A smaller number and a larger number add up to 15 and have a difference of 7. (Let x be the larger number.)

8. The total of two numbers is 16. The first number plus 2 more than 3 times the second equals 18. (Let x be the first number.)

9. Keiko has a total of $6500, which she has invested in two accounts. The larger account is $800 greater than the smaller account. (Let x be the amount of money in the larger account.)

10. Dominique has four times as much money in his savings account as in his checking account. The total amount is $2300. (Let x be the amount of money in his checking account.)

MIXED PRACTICE

Solve. See Examples 1 through 6. For Exercises 13 and 14, the solutions have been started for you.

11. Two numbers total 83 and have a difference of 17. Find the two numbers.

12. The sum of two numbers is 76 and their difference is 52. Find the two numbers.

13. One number is two more than a second number. Twice the first is 4 less than 3 times the second. Find the numbers.

Start the solution:

1. UNDERSTAND the problem. Since we are looking for two numbers, let

$$x = \text{one number}$$
$$y = \text{second number}$$

2. TRANSLATE. Since we have assigned two variables, we will translate the facts into two equations. (Fill in the blanks.)

First equation:

In words: | One number | is | two | more than | second number

Translate: x = ___ ___ ___

Second equation:

In words: | Twice the first number | is | 4 | less than | 3 times the second number

Translate: $2x$ = ___ ___ ___

3. SOLVE the system and

4. INTERPRET the results.

14. Three times one number minus a second is 8, and the sum of the numbers is 12. Find the numbers.

Start the solution:

1. UNDERSTAND the problem. Since we are looking for two numbers, let

$$x = \text{one number}$$
$$y = \text{second number}$$

2. TRANSLATE. Since we have assigned two variables, we will translate the facts into two equations. (Fill in the blanks.)

First equation:

In words: | Three times one number | minus | a second number | is | 8

Translate: $3x$ ___ ___ = 8

Second equation:

In words: | The sum of the numbers | is | 12

Translate: x + ___ ___ 12

Finish with:

3. SOLVE the system and

4. INTERPRET the results.

15. A first number plus twice a second number is 8. Twice the first number, plus the second totals 25. Find the numbers.

16. One number is 4 more than twice the second number. Their total is 25. Find the numbers.

17. Adrian Gonzalez of the Los Angeles Dodgers led Major League Baseball in runs batted in for the 2014 regular season. Mike Trout of the Los Angeles Angels of Anaheim, who came in second to Gonzalez, had 5 fewer runs batted in for the 2014 regular season. Together, these players brought home 227 runs during the regular 2014 season. How many runs batted in was accounted for by each player? (*Source:* MLB)

18. The highest scorer during the 2013 WNBA regular season was Angel McCoughtry of the Atlanta Dream. Over the season, McCoughtry scored 60 more points than the second-highest scorer, Diana Taurasi of the Phoenix Mercury. Together, McCoughtry and Taurasi scored 1362 points during the 2013 regular season. How many points did each player score over the course of the season? (*Source:* WNBA)

19. Ann Marie Jones has been pricing Amtrak train fares for a group trip to New York. Three adults and four children must pay $159. Two adults and three children must pay $112. Find the price of an adult's ticket and find the price of a child's ticket.

20. Last month, Jerry Papa purchased two DVDs and five CDs at Wall-to-Wall Sound for $65. This month, he bought four DVDs and three CDs for $81. Find the price of each DVD and find the price of each CD.

21. Johnston and Betsy Waring have a jar containing 80 coins, all of which are either quarters or nickels. The total value of the coins is $14.60. How many of each type of coin do they have?

22. Keith and Sarah Robinson purchased 40 stamps, a mixture of 49¢ and 34¢ stamps. Find the number of each type of stamp if they spent $17.35.

23. Norman and Suzanne Scarpulla own 35 shares of McDonald's stock and 69 shares of The Ohio Art Company stock (makers of Etch A Sketch and other toys). On a particular day in 2015, their stock portfolio consisting of these two stocks was worth $4000. The McDonald's stock was $92 more per share than The Ohio Art Company stock. What was the price of each stock on that day? (*Source:* Yahoo Finance)

24. Katy Biagini has investments in Google and Nintendo stock. During a particular day in 2015, Google stock was at $528 per share, and Nintendo stock was at $13 per share. Katy's portfolio made up of these two stocks was worth $19,809 at that time. If Katy owns 16 more shares of Google stock than she owns of Nintendo stock, how many shares of each type of stock does she own? (*Source:* Yahoo Finance)

25. Twice last month, Judy Carter rented a car from Enterprise in Fresno, California, and traveled around the Southwest on business. Enterprise rents this car for a daily fee plus an additional charge per mile driven. Judy recalls that her first trip lasted 4 days, she drove 450 miles, and the rental cost her $240.50. On her second business trip, she drove the same model of car a distance of 200 miles in 3 days and paid $146.00 for the rental. Find the daily fee and the mileage charge.

26. Joan Gundersen rented the same car model twice from Hertz, which rents this car model for a daily fee plus an additional charge per mile driven. Joan recalls that the car rented for 5 days and driven for 300 miles cost her $178, while the same model car rented for 4 days and driven for 500 miles cost $197. Find the daily fee and find the mileage charge.

27. Pratap Puri rowed 18 miles down the Delaware River in 2 hours, but the return trip took him $4\frac{1}{2}$ hours. Find the rate Pratap can row in still water and find the rate of the current. Let x = rate Pratap can row in still water
y = rate of the current

$d =$	r	$\cdot$	t
Downstream	$x + y$		
Upstream	$x - y$		

28. The Jonathan Schultz family took a canoe 10 miles down the Allegheny River in $1\frac{1}{4}$ hours. After lunch, it took them 4 hours to return. Find the rate of the current.

Let x = rate the family can row in still water
y = rate of the current

$d =$	r	$\cdot$	t
Downstream	$x + y$		
Upstream	$x - y$		

29. Dave and Sandy Hartranft are frequent flyers with Delta Airlines. They often fly from Philadelphia to Chicago, a distance of 780 miles. On one particular trip, they fly into the wind, and the flight takes 2 hours. The return trip, with the wind behind them, only takes $1\frac{1}{2}$ hours. If the wind speed is the same on each trip, find the speed of the wind and find the speed of the plane in still air.

30. With a strong wind behind it, a United Airlines jet flies 2400 miles from Los Angeles to Orlando in $4\frac{3}{4}$ hours. The return trip takes 6 hours because the plane flies into the wind. If the wind speed is the same on each trip, find the speed of the plane in still air and find the wind speed to the nearest tenth of a mile per hour.

31. Kevin Briley began a 114-mile bicycle trip to build up stamina for a triathlete competition. Unfortunately, his bicycle chain broke, so he finished the trip walking. The whole trip took 6 hours. If Kevin walks at a rate of 4 miles per hour and rides at 24 miles per hour, find the amount of time he spent on the bicycle.

32. In Canada, eastbound and westbound trains travel along the same track, with sidings to pull onto to avoid accidents. Two trains are now 150 miles apart, with the westbound train traveling twice as fast as the eastbound train. A warning must be issued to pull one train onto a siding or else the trains will crash in $1\frac{1}{4}$ hours. Find the speed of the eastbound train and the speed of the westbound train.

33. Doreen Schmidt is a chemist with Gemco Pharmaceutical. She needs to prepare 12 liters of a 9% hydrochloric acid solution. Find the amount of a 4% solution and the amount of a 12% solution she should mix to get this solution.

Concentration Rate	Liters of Solution	Liters of Pure Acid
0.04	x	0.04x
0.12	y	?
0.09	12	?

34. Elise Everly is preparing 15 liters of a 25% saline solution. Elise has two other saline solutions, with strengths of 40% and 10%. Find the amount of 40% solution and the amount of 10% solution she should mix to get 15 liters of a 25% solution.

Concentration Rate	Liters of Solution	Liters of Pure Salt
0.40	x	$0.40x$
0.10	y	?
0.25	15	?

35. Wayne Osby blends coffee for a local coffee café. He needs to prepare 200 pounds of blended coffee beans selling for $3.95 per pound. He intends to do this by blending together a high-quality bean costing $4.95 per pound and a cheaper bean costing $2.65 per pound. To the nearest pound, find how much high-quality coffee bean and how much cheaper coffee bean he should blend.

36. Macadamia nuts cost an astounding $16.50 per pound, but research by an independent firm says that mixed nuts sell better if macadamias are included. The standard mix costs $9.25 per pound. Find how many pounds of macadamias and how many pounds of the standard mix should be combined to produce 40 pounds that will cost $10 per pound. Find the amounts to the nearest tenth of a pound.

37. Recall that two angles are complementary if the sum of their measures is 90°. Find the measures of two complementary angles if one angle is twice the other.

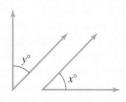

38. Recall that two angles are supplementary if the sum of their measures is 180°. Find the measures of two supplementary angles if one angle is 20° more than four times the other. (See art at top of next column.)

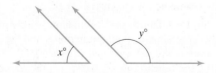

39. Find the measures of two complementary angles if one angle is 10° more than three times the other.

40. Find the measures of two supplementary angles if one angle is 18° more than twice the other.

41. Kathi and Robert Hawn had a pottery stand at the annual Skippack Craft Fair. They sold some of their pottery at the original price of $9.50 each but later decreased the price of each by $2. If they sold all 90 pieces and took in $721, find how many they sold at the original price and how many they sold at the reduced price.

42. A charity fund-raiser consisted of a spaghetti supper where a total of 387 people were fed. They charged $6.80 for adults and half price for children. If they took in $2444.60, find how many adults and how many children attended the supper.

43. The length of the Santa Fe National Historic Trail is approximately 1200 miles between Old Franklin, Missouri, and Santa Fe, New Mexico. Suppose that two groups of hikers, one from each town, start walking the trail toward each other. They meet after a total hiking time of 240 hours. If one group travels $\frac{1}{2}$ mile per hour slower than the other group, find the rate of each group. (*Source:* National Park Service)

44. California 1 is a historic highway that stretches 123 miles along the coast from Monterey to Morro Bay. Suppose that two antique cars start driving this highway, one from each town. They meet after 3 hours. Find the rate of each car if one car travels 1 mile per hour faster than the other car. (*Source:* National Geographic)

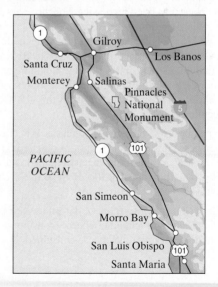

45. A 30% solution of fertilizer is to be mixed with a 60% solution of fertilizer to get 150 gallons of a 50% solution. How many gallons of the 30% solution and 60% solution should be mixed?

46. A 10% acid solution is to be mixed with a 50% acid solution to get 120 ounces of a 20% acid solution. How many ounces of the 10% solution and 50% solution should be mixed?

47. Traffic signs are regulated by the *Manual on Uniform Traffic Control Devices* (MUTCD). According to this manual, if the sign below is placed on a freeway, its perimeter must be 144 inches. Also, its length is 12 inches longer than its width. Find the dimensions of this sign.

48. According to the MUTCD (see Exercise 47), this sign must have a perimeter of 60 inches. Also, its length must be 6 inches longer than its width. Find the dimensions of this sign.

49. The annual U.S. consumption of cheddar cheese has been decreasing in recent years, while the consumption of mozzarella cheese has been increasing. For the years 2008 through 2013, the function $y = -0.24x + 10.6$ approximates the annual U.S. per capita consumption of cheddar cheese in pounds, and the function $y = 0.21x + 10.5$ approximates the annual U.S. per capita consumption of mozzarella cheese in pounds. For both functions, x is the number of years after 2008. (*Source:* Based on data from the U.S. Department of Agriculture)

a. Explain how the given function for cheddar cheese verifies that the consumption of cheddar cheese has decreased, while the given function for mozzarella verifies that the consumption of mozzarella cheese has increased.

b. Based on this information, determine the year in which the pounds of cheddar cheese consumed equaled the pounds of mozzarella cheese consumed.

50. Two of the major jobs defined by the U.S. Department of Labor are postal carrier and bill collector. The number of postal carriers is predicted to decline over the next ten years, while the number of bill collectors is predicted to increase. For the years 2012 to 2022, the function $y = -13,910x + 491,600$ approximates the number of postal carriers in the United States, while the function $y = 5820x + 397,400$ approximates the number of bill collectors. For both functions, x is the number of years after 2012. (*Source:* Based on data from the Bureau of Labor Statistics)

a. Explain how the decrease in postal carrier jobs can be verified by the given function, and the increase in bill collector jobs can be verified by the given function.

b. Based on this information, determine the year in which the number of postal carriers and the number of bill collectors in the United States is the same.

51. The average American adult is spending ever more time on digital media (online or mobile device) than watching television. From 2010 to 2014, the function $y = 0.04x + 4.27$ can be used to estimate the average number of hours per day that an adult spends watching television, and the function $y = 0.67x + 3.01$ can be used to estimate the average number of hours per day that an adult spends using digital media. For both functions, x is the number of years after 2010. (*Source:* eMarketer)

a. Based on this information, determine the year in which the hours of television viewing is the same as the hours of digital media use.

b. Use these functions to predict how many hours the average American adult spends on television viewing and on digital media for the current year.

52. The rate for fatalities per 100 million vehicle-miles has been slowly decreasing for both automobiles and light trucks (pickups, sport utility vehicles, and minivans). For the years 2007 to 2012, the function $y = -0.08x + 1.08$ can be used to estimate the rate of fatalities per 100 million vehicle-miles for light trucks during this period, and the function $y = -0.03x + 1.01$ can be used to estimate the rate of fatalities per 100 million vehicle-miles for automobiles during this period. For both functions, x is the number of years since 2007. (*Source:* Bureau of Transportation Statistics, U.S. Department of Transportation)

a. Based on this data, estimate the year in which the fatality rate for light trucks equaled the fatality rate for automobiles.

b. Use these equations to predict the fatality rate per 100 million vehicle-miles for light trucks and automobiles in the current year.

△ **53.** In the figure, line *l* and line *m* are parallel lines cut by transversal *t*. Find the values of *x* and *y*.

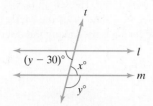

△ **54.** Find the values of *x* and *y* in the following isosceles triangle.

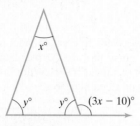

Given the cost function C(x) and the revenue function R(x), find the number of units x that must be sold to break even. See Example 7.

55. $C(x) = 30x + 10,000 \ R(x) = 46x$

56. $C(x) = 12x + 15,000 \ R(x) = 32x$

57. $C(x) = 1.2x + 1500 \ R(x) = 1.7x$

58. $C(x) = 0.8x + 900 \ R(x) = 2x$

59. $C(x) = 75x + 16,000 \ R(x) = 200x$

60. $C(x) = 105x + 70,000 \ R(x) = 245x$

▶ **61.** The planning department of Abstract Office Supplies has been asked to determine whether the company should introduce a new computer desk next year. The department estimates that $6000 of new manufacturing equipment will need to be purchased and that the cost of constructing each desk will be $200. The department also estimates that the revenue from each desk will be $450.

  a. Determine the revenue function $R(x)$ from the sale of *x* desks.

  b. Determine the cost function $C(x)$ for manufacturing *x* desks.

  c. Find the break-even point.

62. Baskets, Inc., is planning to introduce a new woven basket. The company estimates that $500 worth of new equipment will be needed to manufacture this new type of basket and that it will cost $15 per basket to manufacture. The company also estimates that the revenue from each basket will be $31.

  a. Determine the revenue function $R(x)$ from the sale of *x* baskets.

  b. Determine the cost function $C(x)$ for manufacturing *x* baskets.

  c. Find the break-even point. Round up to the next whole basket.

Solve. See Example 6.

63. Rabbits in a lab are to be kept on a strict daily diet that includes 30 grams of protein, 16 grams of fat, and 24 grams of carbohydrates. The scientist has only three food mixes available with the following grams of nutrients per unit.

	Protein	*Fat*	*Carbohydrate*
Mix A	4	6	3
Mix B	6	1	2
Mix C	4	1	12

Find how many units of each mix are needed daily to meet each rabbit's dietary need.

64. Gerry Gundersen mixes different solutions with concentrations of 25%, 40%, and 50% to get 200 liters of a 32% solution. If he uses twice as much of the 25% solution as of the 40% solution, find how many liters of each kind he uses.

△ **65.** The perimeter of a quadrilateral (four-sided polygon) is 29 inches. The longest side is twice as long as the shortest side. The other two sides are equally long and are 2 inches longer than the shortest side. Find the lengths of all four sides.

△ **66.** The measure of the largest angle of a triangle is 90° more than the measure of the smallest angle, and the measure of the remaining angle is 30° more than the measure of the smallest angle. Find the measure of each angle.

67. The sum of three numbers is 40. The first number is five more than the second number. It is also twice the third. Find the numbers.

68. The sum of the digits of a three-digit number is 15. The tens-place digit is twice the hundreds-place digit, and the ones-place digit is 1 less than the hundreds-place digit. Find the three-digit number.

69. During the 2014 regular NBA season, the top-scoring player was Kevin Durant of the Oklahoma City Thunder. Durant scored a total of 2593 points during the regular season. The number of free throws (each worth one point) he made was 127 more than 3 times the number of three-point field goals he made. The number of two-point field goals he made was 46 less than the number of free throws he made. How many free throws, two-point field goals, and three-point field goals did Kevin Durant make during the 2013–2014 NBA season? (*Source:* National Basketball Association)

70. For 2014, the WNBA's top scorer was Maya Moore of the Minnesota Lynx. She scored a total of 812 points during the regular season. The number of two-point field goals that Moore made was 15 less than 4 times the number of three-point field goals she made. The number of free throws (each worth one point) was 73 fewer than the number of two-point field goals she made. Find how many free throws, two-point field goals, and three-point field goals Maya Moore made during the 2014 regular season. (*Source:* Women's National Basketball Association)

△ **71.** Find the values of x, y, and z in the following triangle.

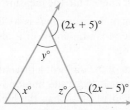

△ **72.** The sum of the measures of the angles of a quadrilateral is $360°$. Find the values of x, y, and z in the following quadrilateral.

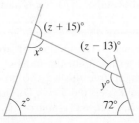

REVIEW AND PREVIEW

Solve each linear inequality. Write your solution in interval notation. See Section 2.8.

73. $-3x < -9$

74. $2x - 7 \le 5x + 11$

75. $4(2x - 1) \ge 0$

76. $\frac{2}{3}x < \frac{1}{3}$

CONCEPT EXTENSIONS

Solve. See the Concept Check in this section.

77. Suppose you mix an amount of candy costing $0.49 a pound with candy costing $0.65 a pound. Which of the following costs per pound could result?

   a. $0.58   **b.** $0.72   **c.** $0.29

78. Suppose you mix a 50% acid solution with pure acid (100%). Which of the following acid strengths are possible for the resulting acid mixture?

   a. 25%   **b.** 150%

   c. 62%   **d.** 90%

79. Dale and Sharon Mahnke have decided to fence off a garden plot behind their house, using their house as the "fence" along one side of the garden. The length (which runs parallel to the house) is 3 feet less than twice the width. Find the dimensions if 33 feet of fencing is used along the three sides requiring it.

80. Judy McElroy plans to erect 152 feet of fencing around her rectangular horse pasture. A river bank serves as one side length of the rectangle. If each width is 4 feet longer than half the length, find the dimensions.

81. Find the values of a, b, and c such that the equation $y = ax^2 + bx + c$ has ordered pair solutions $(1, 6)$, $(-1, -2)$, and $(0, -1)$. To do so, substitute each ordered pair solution into the equation. Each time, the result is an equation in three unknowns: a, b, and c. Then solve the resulting system of three linear equations in three unknowns, a, b, and c.

82. Find the values of a, b, and c such that the equation $y = ax^2 + bx + c$ has ordered pair solutions $(1, 2)$, $(2, 3)$, and $(-1, 6)$. (*Hint:* See Exercise 81.)

83. Data (x, y) for the total number (in thousands) of college-bound students who took the ACT assessment in the year x are approximately $(3, 927)$, $(11, 1179)$, and $(19, 1495)$, where $x = 3$ represents 1993 and $x = 11$ represents 2001. Find the values a, b, and c such that the equation $y = ax^2 + bx + c$ models these data. According to your model, how many students will take the ACT in 2015? (*Source:* ACT, Inc.)

84. Monthly normal rainfall data (x, y) for Portland, Oregon, are $(4, 2.47)$, $(7, 0.58)$, and $(8, 1.07)$, where x represents the month (with $x = 1$ representing January) and y represents rainfall in inches. Find the values of a, b, and c rounded to 2 decimal places such that the equation $y = ax^2 + bx + c$ models this data. According to your model, how much rain should Portland expect during September? (*Source:* National Climatic Data Center)

The function $f(x) = 0.42x + 8.4$ represents the U.S. annual bottled water consumption (in billions of gallons) and the function $f(x) = -0.17x + 14.2$ represents the U.S. annual soda consumption (in billions of gallons). For both functions, x is the number of years since 2009, and these functions are good for the years 2009–2013.

85. Solve the system formed by these functions. Round each coordinate to the nearest whole number.

86. Use your answer to Exercise 85 to predict the year in which the bottled water and soda consumption will be the same.

Chapter 4 Vocabulary Check

Fill in each blank with one of the words or phrases listed below.

system of linear equations	solution	consistent	independent
dependent	inconsistent	substitution	addition

1. In a system of linear equations in two variables, if the graphs of the equations are the same, the equations are _____ equations.
2. Two or more linear equations are called a(n) _____ .
3. A system of equations that has at least one solution is called a(n) _____ system.
4. A(n) _____ of a system of two equations in two variables is an ordered pair of numbers that is a solution of both equations in the system.
5. Two algebraic methods for solving systems of equations are _____ and _____ .
6. A system of equations that has no solution is called a(n) _____ system.
7. In a system of linear equations in two variables, if the graphs of the equations are different, the equations are _____ equations.

Chapter 4 Highlights

DEFINITIONS AND CONCEPTS	EXAMPLES

Section 4.1   Solving Systems of Linear Equations by Graphing

A **solution** of a system of two equations in two variables is an ordered pair of numbers that is a solution of both equations in the system.

Determine whether $(-1, 3)$ is a solution of the system:
$$\begin{cases} 2x - y = -5 \\ x = 3y - 10 \end{cases}$$

Replace x with -1 and y with 3 in both equations.

$$2x - y = -5 \qquad\qquad x = 3y - 10$$
$$2(-1) - 3 \stackrel{?}{=} -5 \qquad -1 \stackrel{?}{=} 3 \cdot 3 - 10$$
$$-5 = -5 \ \text{True} \qquad -1 = -1 \ \text{True}$$

$(-1, 3)$ is a solution of the system.

Graphically, a solution of a system is a point common to the graphs of both equations.

Solve by graphing. $\begin{cases} 3x - 2y = -3 \\ x + y = 4 \end{cases}$

A system of equations with at least one solution is a **consistent system**. A system that has no solution is an **inconsistent system**.

If the graphs of two linear equations are identical, the equations are **dependent**. If their graphs are different, the equations are **independent**.

Consistent and independent

Consistent and dependent

Inconsistent and independent

DEFINITIONS AND CONCEPTS	EXAMPLES

Section 4.2   Solving Systems of Linear Equations by Substitution

To solve a system of linear equations by the substitution method:

Step 1. Solve one equation for a variable.

Step 2. Substitute the expression for the variable into the other equation.

Step 3. Solve the equation from Step 2 to find the value of one variable.

Step 4. Substitute the value from Step 3 in either original equation to find the value of the other variable.

Step 5. Check the solution in both equations.

Solve by substitution.

$$\begin{cases} 3x + 2y = 1 \\ x = y - 3 \end{cases}$$

Substitute $y - 3$ for x in the first equation.

$$3x + 2y = 1$$
$$3(y - 3) + 2y = 1$$
$$3y - 9 + 2y = 1$$
$$5y = 10$$
$$y = 2 \quad \text{Divide by 5.}$$

To find x, substitute 2 for y in $x = y - 3$ so that $x = 2 - 3$ or -1. The solution $(-1, 2)$ checks.

Section 4.3   Solving Systems of Linear Equations by Addition

To solve a system of linear equations by the addition method:

Step 1. Rewrite each equation in standard form $Ax + By = C$.

Step 2. If necessary, multiply one or both equations by a nonzero number so that the coefficients of a variable are opposites.

Step 3. Add the equations.

Step 4. Find the value of one variable by solving the resulting equation.

Step 5. Substitute the value from Step 4 into either original equation to find the value of the other variable.

Step 6. Check the solution in both equations.

If solving a system of linear equations by substitution or addition yields a true statement such as $-2 = -2$, then the graphs of the equations in the system are identical and there is an infinite number of solutions of the system.

Solve by addition.

$$\begin{cases} x - 2y = 8 \\ 3x + y = -4 \end{cases}$$

Multiply both sides of the first equation by -3.

$$\begin{cases} -3x + 6y = -24 \\ \underline{3x + y = -4} \end{cases}$$
$$7y = -28 \quad \text{Add.}$$
$$y = -4 \quad \text{Divide by 7.}$$

To find x, let $y = -4$ in an original equation.

$$x - 2(-4) = 8 \quad \text{First equation}$$
$$x + 8 = 8$$
$$x = 0$$

The solution $(0, -4)$ checks.

Solve: $\begin{cases} 2x - 6y = -2 \\ x = 3y - 1 \end{cases}$

Substitute $3y - 1$ for x in the first equation.

$$2(3y - 1) - 6y = -2$$
$$6y - 2 - 6y = -2$$
$$-2 = -2 \quad \text{True}$$

The system has an infinite number of solutions. In set notation, we write $\{(x, y)\,|\,2x - 6y = -2\}$ or $\{(x, y)\,|\,x = 3y - 1\}$.

Section 4.4   Solving Systems of Linear Equations in Three Variables

A **solution** of an equation in three variables x, y, and z is an **ordered triple** (x, y, z) that makes the equation a true statement.

Verify that $(-2, 1, 3)$ is a solution of $2x + 3y - 2z = -7$. Replace x with -2, y with 1, and z with 3.

$$2(-2) + 3(1) - 2(3) \stackrel{?}{=} -7$$
$$-4 + 3 - 6 \stackrel{?}{=} -7$$
$$-7 = -7 \quad \text{True}$$

$(-2, 1, 3)$ is a solution.

DEFINITIONS AND CONCEPTS	EXAMPLES

Section 4.4 Solving Systems of Linear Equations in Three Variables (Continued)

Solving a System of Three Linear Equations by the Elimination Method

Step 1. Write each equation in standard form, $Ax + By + Cz = D$.

Step 2. Choose a pair of equations and use them to eliminate a variable.

Step 3. Choose any other pair of equations and eliminate the same variable.

Step 4. Solve the system of two equations in two variables from Steps 2 and 3.

Step 5. Solve for the third variable by substituting the values of the variables from Step 4 into any of the original equations.

Step 6. Check the solution in all three original equations.

Solve.

$$\begin{cases} 2x + y - z = 0 & (1) \\ x - y - 2z = -6 & (2) \\ -3x - 2y + 3z = -22 & (3) \end{cases}$$

1. Each equation is written in standard form.

2.
$$\begin{array}{rl} 2x + y - z = 0 & (1) \\ \underline{x - y - 2z = -6} & (2) \\ 3x \quad\ - 3z = -6 & (4) \quad \text{Add.} \end{array}$$

3. Eliminate y from equations (1) and (3) also.

$$\begin{array}{rll} 4x + 2y - 2z = 0 & & \text{Multiply equation} \\ \underline{-3x - 2y + 3z = -22} & (3) & \text{(1) by 2} \\ x \quad\quad + z = -22 & (5) & \text{Add.} \end{array}$$

4. Solve:
$$\begin{cases} 3x - 3z = -6 & (4) \\ x + z = -22 & (5) \end{cases}$$

$$\begin{array}{rl} x - z = -2 & \text{Divide equation (4) by 3.} \\ \underline{x + z = -22} & \\ 2x \quad\ = -24 & \text{Add.} \\ x = -12 & \end{array}$$

To find z, use equation (5).

$$\begin{array}{r} x + z = -22 \\ -12 + z = -22 \\ z = -10 \end{array}$$

5. To find y, use equation (1).

$$\begin{array}{r} 2x + y - z = 0 \\ 2(-12) + y - (-10) = 0 \\ -24 + y + 10 = 0 \\ y = 14 \end{array}$$

6. The solution $(-12, 14, -10)$ checks.

Section 4.5 Systems of Linear Equations and Problem Solving

Problem-solving steps

1. UNDERSTAND. Read and reread the problem.

Two angles are supplementary if their sum is 180°.

The larger of two supplementary angles is three times the smaller, decreased by twelve. Find the measure of each angle. Let

$$x = \text{measure of smaller angle}$$
$$y = \text{measure of larger angle}$$

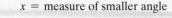

(continued)

DEFINITIONS AND CONCEPTS	EXAMPLES

Section 4.5 Systems of Linear Equations and Problem Solving (Continued)

2. TRANSLATE.

In words:

the sum of supplementary angles	is	180°
↓	↓	↓

Translate: $x + y$ $=$ 180

In words:

larger angle	is	3 times smaller	decreased by	12
↓	↓	↓	↓	↓

Translate: y $=$ $3x$ $-$ 12

3. SOLVE.

Solve the system:

$$\begin{cases} x + y = 180 \\ y = 3x - 12 \end{cases}$$

Use the substitution method and replace y with $3x - 12$ in the first equation.

$$x + y = 180$$
$$x + (3x - 12) = 180$$
$$4x = 192$$
$$x = 48$$

Since $y = 3x - 12$, $y = 3 \cdot 48 - 12$ or 132.

4. INTERPRET.

The solution checks. The smaller angle measures 48° and the larger angle measures 132°.

Chapter 4 Review

(4.1) *Determine whether each of the following ordered pairs satisfies the system of linear equations.*

1. $\begin{cases} 2x - 3y = 12 \\ 3x + 4y = 1 \end{cases}$

   a. $(12, 4)$ **b.** $(3, -2)$ **c.** $(-3, 6)$

2. $\begin{cases} 4x + y = 0 \\ -8x - 5y = 9 \end{cases}$

   a. $\left(\dfrac{3}{4}, -3\right)$ **b.** $(-2, 8)$ **c.** $\left(\dfrac{1}{2}, -2\right)$

3. $\begin{cases} 5x - 6y = 18 \\ 2y - x = -4 \end{cases}$

   a. $(-6, -8)$ **b.** $\left(3, \dfrac{5}{2}\right)$ **c.** $\left(3, -\dfrac{1}{2}\right)$

4. $\begin{cases} 2x + 3y = 1 \\ 3y - x = 4 \end{cases}$

   a. $(2, 2)$ **b.** $(-1, 1)$ **c.** $(2, -1)$

Solve each system of equations by graphing.

5. $\begin{cases} x + y = 5 \\ x - y = 1 \end{cases}$ **6.** $\begin{cases} x + y = 3 \\ x - y = -1 \end{cases}$

7. $\begin{cases} x = 5 \\ y = -1 \end{cases}$ **8.** $\begin{cases} x = -3 \\ y = 2 \end{cases}$

9. $\begin{cases} 2x + y = 5 \\ x = -3y \end{cases}$ **10.** $\begin{cases} 3x + y = -2 \\ y = -5x \end{cases}$

11. $\begin{cases} y = 3x \\ -6x + 2y = 6 \end{cases}$ **12.** $\begin{cases} x - 2y = 2 \\ -2x + 4y = -4 \end{cases}$

(4.2) *Solve each system of equations by the substitution method.*

13. $\begin{cases} y = 2x + 6 \\ 3x - 2y = -11 \end{cases}$ **14.** $\begin{cases} y = 3x - 7 \\ 2x - 3y = 7 \end{cases}$

15. $\begin{cases} x + 3y = -3 \\ 2x + y = 4 \end{cases}$ **16.** $\begin{cases} 3x + y = 11 \\ x + 2y = 12 \end{cases}$

17. $\begin{cases} 4y = 2x + 6 \\ x - 2y = -3 \end{cases}$ **18.** $\begin{cases} 9x = 6y + 3 \\ 6x - 4y = 2 \end{cases}$

19. $\begin{cases} x + y = 6 \\ y = -x - 4 \end{cases}$

20. $\begin{cases} -3x + y = 6 \\ y = 3x + 2 \end{cases}$

(4.3) *Solve each system of equations by the addition method.*

21. $\begin{cases} 2x + 3y = -6 \\ x - 3y = -12 \end{cases}$

22. $\begin{cases} 4x + y = 15 \\ -4x + 3y = -19 \end{cases}$

23. $\begin{cases} 2x - 3y = -15 \\ x + 4y = 31 \end{cases}$

24. $\begin{cases} x - 5y = -22 \\ 4x + 3y = 4 \end{cases}$

25. $\begin{cases} 2x - 6y = -1 \\ -x + 3y = \dfrac{1}{2} \end{cases}$

26. $\begin{cases} 0.6x - 0.3y = -1.5 \\ 0.04x - 0.02y = -0.1 \end{cases}$

27. $\begin{cases} \dfrac{3}{4}x + \dfrac{2}{3}y = 2 \\ x + \dfrac{y}{3} = 6 \end{cases}$

28. $\begin{cases} 10x + 2y = 0 \\ 3x + 5y = 33 \end{cases}$

(4.4) *Solve each system of equations in three variables.*

29. $\begin{cases} x \quad\ + z = 4 \\ 2x - y \quad\ - 4 \\ x + y - z = 0 \end{cases}$

30. $\begin{cases} 2x + 5y \quad\ = 4 \\ x - 5y + z = -1 \\ 4x \quad\ - z = 11 \end{cases}$

31. $\begin{cases} 4y + 2z = 5 \\ 2x + 8y \quad\ = 5 \\ 6x + \quad\ 4z = 1 \end{cases}$

32. $\begin{cases} 5x + 7y \quad\ = 9 \\ 14y - z = 28 \\ 4x \quad\ + 2z = -4 \end{cases}$

33. $\begin{cases} 3x - 2y + 2z = 5 \\ -x + 6y + z = 4 \\ 3x + 14y + 7z = 20 \end{cases}$

34. $\begin{cases} x + 2y + 3z = 11 \\ y + 2z = 3 \\ 2x \quad\ + 2z = 10 \end{cases}$

35. $\begin{cases} 7x - 3y + 2z = 0 \\ 4x - 4y - z = 2 \\ 5x + 2y + 3z = 1 \end{cases}$

36. $\begin{cases} x - 3y - 5z = -5 \\ 4x - 2y + 3z = 13 \\ 5x + 3y + 4z = 22 \end{cases}$

(4.5) *Solve each problem by writing and solving a system of linear equations.*

37. The sum of two numbers is 16. Three times the larger number decreased by the smaller number is 72. Find the two numbers.

38. The Forrest Theater can seat a total of 360 people. They take in $15,150 when every seat is sold. If orchestra section tickets cost $45 and balcony tickets cost $35, find the number of seats in the orchestra section and the number of seats in the balcony.

39. A riverboat can head 340 miles upriver in 19 hours, but the return trip takes only 14 hours. Find the current of the river and

find the speed of the riverboat in still water to the nearest tenth of a mile.

	d	$=$	r	$\cdot$	t
Upriver	340		$x - y$		19
Downriver	340		$x + y$		14

40. Find the amount of a 6% acid solution and the amount of a 14% acid solution Pat Mayfield should combine to prepare 50 cc (cubic centimeters) of a 12% solution.

41. A deli charges $3.80 for a breakfast of three eggs and four strips of bacon. The charge is $2.75 for two eggs and three strips of bacon. Find the cost of each egg and the cost of each strip of bacon.

42. An exercise enthusiast alternates between jogging and walking. He traveled 15 miles during the past 3 hours. He jogs at a rate of 7.5 miles per hour and walks at a rate of 4 miles per hour. Find how much time, to the nearest hundredth of an hour, he actually spent jogging and how much time he spent walking.

43. Chris Kringler has $2.77 in her coin jar—all in pennies, nickels, and dimes. If she has 53 coins in all and four more nickels than dimes, find how many of each type of coin she has.

44. An employee at See's Candy Store needs a special mixture of candy. She has creme-filled chocolates that sell for $3.00 per pound, chocolate-covered nuts that sell for $2.70 per pound, and chocolate-covered raisins that sell for $2.25 per pound. She wants to have twice as many pounds of raisins as pounds of nuts in the mixture. Find how many pounds of each she should use to make 45 pounds worth $2.80 per pound.

45. The perimeter of an isosceles (two sides equal) triangle is 73 centimeters. If the unequal side is 7 centimeters longer than the two equal sides, find the lengths of the three sides.

46. The sum of three numbers is 295. One number is five more than a second and twice the third. Find the numbers.

MIXED REVIEW

Solve each system of equations by graphing.

47. $\begin{cases} x - 2y = 1 \\ 2x + 3y = -12 \end{cases}$

48. $\begin{cases} 3x - y = -4 \\ 6x - 2y = -8 \end{cases}$

Solve each system of equations.

49. $\begin{cases} x + 4y = 11 \\ 5x - 9y = -3 \end{cases}$

50. $\begin{cases} x + 9y = 16 \\ 3x - 8y = 13 \end{cases}$

51. $\begin{cases} y = -2x \\ 4x + 7y = -15 \end{cases}$

52. $\begin{cases} 3y = 2x + 15 \\ -2x + 3y = 21 \end{cases}$

53. $\begin{cases} 3x - y = 4 \\ 4y = 12x - 16 \end{cases}$

54. $\begin{cases} x + y = 19 \\ x - y = -3 \end{cases}$

55. $\begin{cases} x - 3y = -11 \\ 4x + 5y = -10 \end{cases}$ **56.** $\begin{cases} -x - 15y = 44 \\ 2x + 3y = 20 \end{cases}$

57. $\begin{cases} x - 3y + 2z = 0 \\ 9y - z = 22 \\ 5x + 3z = 10 \end{cases}$

58. $\begin{cases} x - 4y = 4 \\ \dfrac{1}{8}x - \dfrac{1}{2}y = 3 \end{cases}$

Solve each problem by writing and solving a system of linear equations.

59. The sum of two numbers is 12. Three times the smaller number increased by the larger number is 20. Find the numbers.

60. The difference of two numbers is -18 Twice the smaller decreased by the larger is -23 Find the two numbers.

61. Emma Hodges has a jar containing 65 coins, all of which are either nickels or dimes. The total value of the coins is $5.30. How many of each type does she have?

62. Sarah and Owen Hebert purchased 26 stamps, a mixture of 49¢ and 34¢ stamps. Find the number of each type of stamp if they spent $11.39.

63. The perimeter of a triangle is 126 units. The length of one side is twice the length of the shortest side. The length of the third side is fourteen more than the length of the shortest side. Find the length of the sides of the triangle.

Chapter 4 Getting Ready for the Test

1. MULTIPLE CHOICE *The ordered pair* $(-1, 2)$ *is a solution of which system?*

A. $\begin{cases} 5x - y = -7 \\ x - y = 3 \end{cases}$ **B.** $\begin{cases} 3x - y = -5 \\ x + y = 1 \end{cases}$

C. $\begin{cases} x = 2 \\ x + y = 1 \end{cases}$ **D.** $\begin{cases} y = -1 \\ x + y = -3 \end{cases}$

2. MULTIPLE CHOICE *When solving a system of two linear equations in two variables, all variables subtract out and the resulting equation is* $0 = 5$. *What does this mean?*

A. the solution is $(0, 5)$ **B.** the system has an infinite number of solutions   **C.** the system has no solution

MATCHING *Match each system with its solution. Letter choices may be used more than once or not at all.*

3. $\begin{cases} y = 5x + 2 \\ y = -5x + 2 \end{cases}$ **4.** $\begin{cases} y = \dfrac{1}{2}x - 3 \\ y = \dfrac{1}{2}x + 7 \end{cases}$

A. no solution
B. one solution
C. two solutions
D. an infinite number of solutions

5. $\begin{cases} y = 4x + 2 \\ 8x - 2y = -4 \end{cases}$ **6.** $\begin{cases} y = 6x \\ y = -\dfrac{1}{6}x \end{cases}$

MULTIPLE CHOICE *Choose the correct choice for Exercises 7 and 8. The system for these exercises is:*

$$\begin{cases} 5x - y = -8 \\ 2x + 3y = 1 \end{cases}$$

7. When solving, if we decide to multiply the first equation above by 3, the result of the first equation is:

A. $15x - 3y = -8$ **B.** $6x + 9y = 1$ **C.** $6x + 9y = 3$ **D.** $15x - 3y = -24$

8. When solving, if we decide to multiply the second equation above by -5, the result of the second equation is:

A. $-10x - 15y = 1$ **B.** $-25x + 5y = 40$ **C.** $-10x - 15y = -5$ **D.** $-25x + 5y = -8$

9. The ordered triple $(1, 0, -2)$ is a solution of which system?

A. $\begin{cases} 5x - y - z = -7 \\ x + y + z = -1 \\ y + z = -1 \end{cases}$ **B.** $\begin{cases} 3x - y - 2z = 7 \\ x + y + z = -1 \\ 5x + z = 3 \end{cases}$ **C.** $\begin{cases} x = -2 \\ x + y + z = -1 \\ x + z = 1 \end{cases}$ **D.** $\begin{cases} y = 1 \\ x + y + z = -1 \\ x + y = -1 \end{cases}$

MULTIPLE CHOICE *Select the correct choice. The system for Exercises 10–12 is:*

$$\begin{cases} 3x - y + 2z = 3 & \text{Equation (1)} \\ 4x + y - z = 5 & \text{Equation (2)} \\ -x + 5y + 3z = 12 & \text{Equation (3)} \end{cases}$$

The choices for Exercises 10–12 are:

A. $[\text{Equation}(1)] + [\text{Equation}(2)]$

B. $[\text{Equation}(1)] + 3\cdot[\text{Equation}(3)]$

C. $[\text{Equation}(1)] + 2\cdot[\text{Equation}(2)]$

D. $[\text{Equation}(1)] + [\text{Equation}(3)]$

10. Which choice eliminates the variable x?

11. Which choice eliminates the variable y?

12. Which choice eliminates the variable z?

Chapter 4 Test · MyMathLab° You Tube

Answer each question true or false.

1. A system of two linear equations in two variables can have exactly two solutions.

2. Although $(1,4)$ is not a solution of $x + 2y = 6$, it can still be a solution of the system $\begin{cases} x + 2y = 6 \\ x + y = 5 \end{cases}$.

3. If the two equations in a system of linear equations are added and the result is $3 = 0$, the system has no solution.

4. If the two equations in a system of linear equations are added and the result is $3x = 0$, the system has no solution.

Is the ordered pair a solution of the given linear system?

5. $\begin{cases} 2x - 3y = 5 \\ 6x + y = 1 \end{cases}$; $(1, -1)$

6. $\begin{cases} 4x - 3y = 24 \\ 4x + 5y = -8 \end{cases}$; $(3, -4)$

7. Use graphing to find the solutions of the system $\begin{cases} y - x = 6 \\ y + 2x = -6 \end{cases}$

8. Use the substitution method to solve the system $\begin{cases} 3x - 2y = -14 \\ x + 3y = -1 \end{cases}$

9. Use the substitution method to solve the system $\begin{cases} \frac{1}{2}x + 2y = -\frac{15}{4} \\ 4x = -y \end{cases}$

10. Use the addition method to solve the system $\begin{cases} 3x + 5y = 2 \\ 2x - 3y = 14 \end{cases}$

11. Use the addition method to solve the system $\begin{cases} 4x - 6y = 7 \\ -2x + 3y = 0 \end{cases}$

Solve each system using the substitution method or the addition method.

12. $\begin{cases} 3x + y = 7 \\ 4x + 3y = 1 \end{cases}$

13. $\begin{cases} 3(2x + y) = 4x + 20 \\ x - 2y = 3 \end{cases}$

14. $\begin{cases} \dfrac{x - 3}{2} = \dfrac{2 - y}{4} \\ \dfrac{7 - 2x}{3} = \dfrac{y}{2} \end{cases}$

Solve each problem by writing and using a system of linear equations.

15. Two numbers have a sum of 124 and a difference of 32. Find the numbers.

16. Find the amount of a 12% saline solution a lab assistant should add to 80 cc (cubic centimeters) of a 22% saline solution to have a 16% solution.

17. Texas and Missouri are the states with the most farms. Texas has 140 thousand more farms than Missouri and the total number of farms for these two states is 356 thousand. Find the number of farms for each state.

▶ **18.** Two hikers start at opposite ends of the St. Tammany Trail and walk toward each other. The trail is 36 miles long and they meet in 4 hours. If one hiker walks twice as fast as the other, find both hiking speeds.

▶ **19.** $\begin{cases} 2x - 3y & = 4 \\ 3y + 2z = 2 \\ x \quad - z = -5 \end{cases}$ **20.** $\begin{cases} 3x - 2y - z = -1 \\ 2x - 2y \quad = 4 \\ 2x \quad - 2z = -12 \end{cases}$

▶ **21.** The measure of the largest angle of a triangle is three less than 5 times the measure of the smallest angle. The measure of the remaining angle is 1 less than twice the measure of the smallest angle. Find the measure of each angle.

Chapter 4 Cumulative Review

1. Insert $<, >$, or $=$ in the appropriate space between the paired numbers to make each statement true.

   a. $-1 \quad 0$ **b.** $7 \quad \dfrac{14}{2}$ **c.** $-5 \quad -6$

2. Evaluate.
   a. 5^2 **b.** 2^5

3. Name the property or properties illustrated by each true statement.

   a. $3 \cdot y = y \cdot 3$

   b. $(x + 7) + 9 = x + (7 + 9)$

   c. $(b + 0) + 3 = b + 3$

   d. $0.2 \cdot (z \cdot 5) = 0.2 \cdot (5 \cdot z)$

   e. $-2 \cdot \left(-\dfrac{1}{2}\right) = 1$

   f. $-2 + 2 = 0$

   g. $-6 \cdot (y \cdot 2) = (-6 \cdot 2) \cdot y$

4. Evaluate $y^2 - 3x$ for $x - 8$ and $y = 5$.

5. Write the phrase as an algebraic expression, then simplify if possible: Subtract $4x - 2$ from $2x - 3$.

6. Simplify: $7 - 12 + (-5) - 2 + (-2)$

7. Solve: $7 = -5(2a - 1) - (-11a + 6)$

8. Evaluate $2y^2 - x^2$ for $x = -7$ and $y = -3$.

9. Solve: $\dfrac{5}{2}x = 15$

10. Simplify: $0.4y - 6.7 + y - 0.3 - 2.6y$

11. Solve: $\dfrac{x}{2} - 1 = \dfrac{2}{3}x - 3$

12. Solve: $7(x - 2) - 6(x + 1) = 20$

13. Twice the sum of a number and 4 is the same as four times the number, decreased by 12. Find the number.

14. Solve: $5(y - 5) = 5y + 10$

15. Solve $y = mx + b$ for x.

16. Five times the sum of a number and -1 is the same as 6 times the number. Find the number.

17. Solve $-2x \le -4$ Write the solution set in interval notation.

18. Solve $P = a + b + c$ for b.

19. Graph $x = -2y$ by finding and plotting intercepts.

20. Solve $3x + 7 \ge x - 9$. Write the solution set in interval notation.

21. Find the slope of the line through $(-1, 5)$ and $(2, -3)$.

22. Complete the table of values for $x - 3y = 3$.

x	y
	-1
3	
	2

23. Find the slope and y-intercept of the line whose equation is $y = \dfrac{3}{4}x + 6$.

24. Find the slope of a line parallel to the line passing through $(-1, 3)$ and $(2, -8)$.

25. Find the slope and the y-intercept of the line whose equation is $3x - 4y = 4$.

26. Find the slope and y-intercept of the line whose equation is $y = 7x$.

27. Find an equation of the line passing through $(-1, 5)$ with slope -2. Write the equation in slope-intercept form, $y = mx + b$, and in standard form, $Ax + By = C$.

28. Determine whether the lines are parallel, perpendicular, or neither.

$$y = 4x - 5$$
$$-4x + y = 7$$

29. Find an equation of the vertical line through $(-1, 5)$.

30. Write an equation of the line with slope -5, through $(-2, 3)$.

31. Find the domain and the range of the relation $\{(0, 2), (3, 3), (-1, 0), (3, -2)\}$.

32. If $f(x) = 5x^2 - 6$, find $f(0)$ and $f(-2)$.

33. Determine whether each relation is also a function.
   a. $\{(-1, 1), (2, 3), (7, 3), (8, 6)\}$
   b. $\{(0, -2), (1, 5), (0, 3), (7, 7)\}$

34. Determine whether each graph is also the graph of a function.

a.   **b.**   **c.**

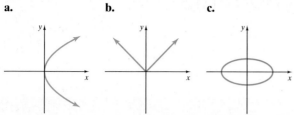

35. Determine the number of solutions of the system.
$$\begin{cases} 3x - y = 4 \\ x + 2y = 8 \end{cases}$$

36. Determine whether each ordered pair is a solution of the given system.
$$\begin{cases} 2x - y = 6 \\ 3x + 2y = -5 \end{cases}$$

a. $(1, -4)$ **b.** $(0, 6)$ **c.** $(3, 0)$

Solve each system.

37. $\begin{cases} x + 2y = 7 \\ 2x + 2y = 13 \end{cases}$

38. $\begin{cases} 3x - 4y = 10 \\ \quad\quad y = 2x \end{cases}$

39. $\begin{cases} x + y = 7 \\ x - y = 5 \end{cases}$

40. $\begin{cases} x = 5y - 3 \\ x = 8y + 4 \end{cases}$

41. Solve the system.
$$\begin{cases} 3x - y + z = -15 \\ x + 2y - z = 1 \\ 2x + 3y - 2z = 0 \end{cases}$$

42. Solve the system.
$$\begin{cases} x - 2y + z = 0 \\ 3x - y - 2z = -15 \\ 2x - 3y + 3z = 7 \end{cases}$$

43. A first number is 4 less than a second number. Four times the first number is 6 more than twice the second. Find the numbers.

44. Find two numbers whose sum is 37 and whose difference is 21.

Exponents and Polynomials

5.1 Exponents

5.2 Polynomial Functions and Adding and Subtracting Polynomials

5.3 Multiplying Polynomials

5.4 Special Products

Integrated Review—Exponents and Operations on Polynomials

5.5 Negative Exponents and Scientific Notation

5.6 Dividing Polynomials

5.7 Synthetic Division and the Remainder Theorem

✔ **CHECK YOUR PROGRESS**

Vocabulary Check

Chapter Highlights

Chapter Review

Getting Ready for the Test

Chapter Test

Cumulative Review

Recall from Chapter 1 that an exponent is a shorthand notation for repeated factors. This chapter explores additional concepts about exponents and exponential expressions. An especially useful type of exponential expression is a polynomial. Polynomials model many real-world phenomena. In this chapter, we focus on polynomials and operations on polynomials.

Can You Imagine a World Without the Internet?

In 1995, less than 1% of the world population was connected to the Internet. By 2015, that number had increased to 40%. Technology changes so fast that, if this trend continues, by the time you read this, far more than 40% of the world population will be connected to the Internet. The circle graph below shows Internet users by region of the world in 2015. In Section 5.2, Exercises 99 and 100, we explore more about the growth of Internet users.

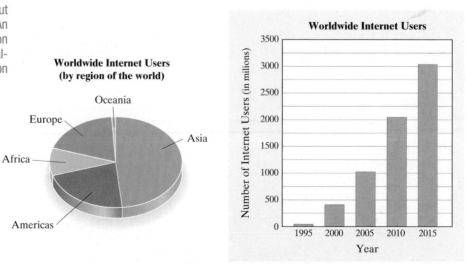

Data from International Telecommunication Union and United Nations Population Division

5.1 Exponents

OBJECTIVES

1 Evaluate Exponential Expressions.

2 Use the Product Rule for Exponents.

3 Use the Power Rule for Exponents.

4 Use the Power Rules for Products and Quotients.

5 Use the Quotient Rule for Exponents, and Define a Number Raised to the 0 Power.

6 Decide Which Rule(s) to Use to Simplify an Expression.

OBJECTIVE

1 Evaluating Exponential Expressions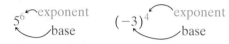

As we reviewed in Section 1.4, an exponent is a shorthand notation for repeated factors. For example, $2 \cdot 2 \cdot 2 \cdot 2 \cdot 2$ can be written as 2^5. The expression 2^5 is called an **exponential expression**. It is also called the fifth **power** of 2, or we say that 2 is **raised** to the fifth power.

$$5^6 = \underbrace{5 \cdot 5 \cdot 5 \cdot 5 \cdot 5 \cdot 5}_{6 \text{ factors; each factor is } 5} \qquad \text{and} \qquad (-3)^4 = \underbrace{(-3) \cdot (-3) \cdot (-3) \cdot (-3)}_{4 \text{ factors; each factor is } -3}$$

The **base** of an exponential expression is the repeated factor. The **exponent** is the number of times that the base is used as a factor.

$$5^6 \overset{\curvearrowleft \text{exponent}}{\underset{\curvearrowright \text{base}}{}} \qquad (-3)^4 \overset{\curvearrowleft \text{exponent}}{\underset{\curvearrowright \text{base}}{}}$$

EXAMPLE 1 Evaluate each expression.

a. 2^3 **b.** 3^1 **c.** $(-4)^2$ **d.** -4^2 **e.** $\left(\dfrac{1}{2}\right)^4$ **f.** $(0.5)^3$ **g.** $4 \cdot 3^2$

Solution

a. $2^3 = 2 \cdot 2 \cdot 2 = 8$

b. To raise 3 to the first power means to use 3 as a factor only once. Therefore, $3^1 = 3$. Also, when no exponent is shown, the exponent is assumed to be 1.

c. $(-4)^2 = (-4)(-4) = 16$ **d.** $-4^2 = -(4 \cdot 4) = -16$

e. $\left(\dfrac{1}{2}\right)^4 = \dfrac{1}{2} \cdot \dfrac{1}{2} \cdot \dfrac{1}{2} \cdot \dfrac{1}{2} = \dfrac{1}{16}$ **f.** $(0.5)^3 = (0.5)(0.5)(0.5) = 0.125$

g. $4 \cdot 3^2 = 4 \cdot 9 = 36$ □

PRACTICE

1 Evaluate each expression.

a. 3^3 **b.** 4^1 **c.** $(-8)^2$ **d.** -8^2

e. $\left(\dfrac{3}{4}\right)^3$ **f.** $(0.3)^4$ **g.** $3 \cdot 5^2$ ■

Notice how similar -4^2 is to $(-4)^2$ in the example above. The difference between the two is the parentheses. In $(-4)^2$, the parentheses tell us that the base, or repeated factor, is -4. In -4^2, only 4 is the base.

> **Helpful Hint**
>
> Be careful when identifying the base of an exponential expression. Pay close attention to the use of parentheses.
>
> $(-3)^2$ -3^2 $2 \cdot 3^2$
>
> The base is -3.   The base is 3.   The base is 3.
>
> $(-3)^2 = (-3)(-3) = 9$ $-3^2 = -(3 \cdot 3) = -9$ $2 \cdot 3^2 = 2 \cdot 3 \cdot 3 = 18$

An exponent has the same meaning whether the base is a number or a variable. If x is a real number and n is a positive integer, then x^n is the product of n factors, each of which is x.

$$x^n = \underbrace{x \cdot x \cdot x \cdot x \cdot x \cdot \ldots \cdot x}_{n \text{ factors of } x}$$

EXAMPLE 2 Evaluate each expression for the given value of x.

    a. $2x^3$; x is 5 **b.** $\dfrac{9}{x^2}$; x is -3

Solution   **a.** If x is 5, $2x^3 = 2 \cdot (5)^3$ **b.** If x is -3, $\dfrac{9}{x^2} = \dfrac{9}{(-3)^2}$

$$= 2 \cdot (5 \cdot 5 \cdot 5)$$
$$= 2 \cdot 125$$
$$= 250$$

$$= \dfrac{9}{(-3)(-3)}$$
$$= \dfrac{9}{9}$$
$$= 1 \qquad \square$$

PRACTICE

2   Evaluate each expression for the given value of x.

    a. $3x^4$; x is 3 **b.** $\dfrac{6}{x^2}$; x is -4 ■

OBJECTIVE

2   **Using the Product Rule** ▶

Exponential expressions can be multiplied, divided, added, subtracted, and themselves raised to powers. By our definition of an exponent,

$$5^4 \cdot 5^3 = \underbrace{(5 \cdot 5 \cdot 5 \cdot 5)}_{\text{4 factors of 5}} \cdot \underbrace{(5 \cdot 5 \cdot 5)}_{\text{3 factors of 5}}$$

$$= \underbrace{5 \cdot 5 \cdot 5 \cdot 5 \cdot 5 \cdot 5 \cdot 5}_{\text{7 factors of 5}}$$

$$= 5^7$$

Also,

$$x^2 \cdot x^3 = (x \cdot x) \cdot (x \cdot x \cdot x)$$
$$= x \cdot x \cdot x \cdot x \cdot x$$
$$= x^5$$

In both cases, notice that the result is exactly the same if the exponents are added.

$$5^4 \cdot 5^3 = 5^{4+3} = 5^7 \quad \text{and} \quad x^2 \cdot x^3 = x^{2+3} = x^5$$

This suggests the following rule.

Product Rule for Exponents

If m and n are positive integers and a is a real number, then

$$a^m \cdot a^n = a^{m+n} \leftarrow \text{Add exponents.}$$
       ↑——— Keep common base.

For example, $3^5 \cdot 3^7 = 3^{5+7} = 3^{12} \leftarrow$ Add exponents.
           ↑——— Keep common base.

Helpful Hint

Don't forget that

$$3^5 \cdot 3^7 \neq 9^{12} \leftarrow \text{Add exponents.}$$
       ↑——— **Common base *not* kept.**

$$3^5 \cdot 3^7 = \underbrace{3 \cdot 3 \cdot 3 \cdot 3 \cdot 3}_{\text{5 factors of 3}} \cdot \underbrace{3 \cdot 3 \cdot 3 \cdot 3 \cdot 3 \cdot 3 \cdot 3}_{\text{7 factors of 3}}$$

$$= 3^{12} \quad \text{12 factors of 3, } not \text{ 9}$$

In other words, to multiply two exponential expressions with the **same base,** we keep the base and add the exponents. We call this **simplifying** the exponential expression.

EXAMPLE 3 Use the product rule to simplify.

   a. $4^2 \cdot 4^5$ **b.** $x^4 \cdot x^6$ **c.** $y^3 \cdot y$

   ▶ **d.** $y^3 \cdot y^2 \cdot y^7$ ▶ **e.** $(-5)^7 \cdot (-5)^8$ **f.** $a^2 \cdot b^2$

Solution

   a. $4^2 \cdot 4^5 = 4^{2+5} = 4^7$ ← Add exponents.
                                    └── **Keep** common base.

   b. $x^4 \cdot x^6 = x^{4+6} = x^{10}$

   c. $y^3 \cdot y = y^3 \cdot y^1$

   $\quad = y^{3+1}$

   $\quad = y^4$

> **Helpful Hint**
> Don't forget that if no exponent is written, it is assumed to be 1.

   d. $y^3 \cdot y^2 \cdot y^7 = y^{3+2+7} = y^{12}$

   e. $(-5)^7 \cdot (-5)^8 = (-5)^{7+8} = (-5)^{15}$

   f. $a^2 \cdot b^2$ Cannot be simplified because a and b are different bases.   □

PRACTICE
3   Use the product rule to simplify.

   a. $3^4 \cdot 3^6$ **b.** $y^3 \cdot y^2$

   c. $z \cdot z^4$ **d.** $x^3 \cdot x^2 \cdot x^6$

   e. $(-2)^5 \cdot (-2)^3$ **f.** $b^3 \cdot t^5$ ▪

✔ **CONCEPT CHECK**

Where possible, use the product rule to simplify the expression.

a. $z^2 \cdot z^{14}$ **b.** $x^2 \cdot y^{14}$ **c.** $9^8 \cdot 9^3$ **d.** $9^8 \cdot 2^7$

EXAMPLE 4 Use the product rule to simplify $(2x^2)(-3x^5)$.

Solution Recall that $2x^2$ means $2 \cdot x^2$ and $-3x^5$ means $-3 \cdot x^5$.

   $(2x^2)(-3x^5) = 2 \cdot x^2 \cdot -3 \cdot x^5$ Remove parentheses.

   $\ = 2 \cdot -3 \cdot x^2 \cdot x^5$ Group factors with common bases.

   $\ = -6x^7$ Simplify.   □

PRACTICE
4   Use the product rule to simplify $(-5y^3)(-3y^4)$.   ▪

EXAMPLE 5 Simplify.

   a. $(x^2y)(x^3y^2)$ **b.** $(-a^7b^4)(3ab^9)$

Solution

   a. $(x^2y)(x^3y^2) = (x^2 \cdot x^3) \cdot (y^1 \cdot y^2)$ Group like bases and write y as y^1.

   $\ = x^5 \cdot y^3$ or x^5y^3 Multiply.

   b. $(-a^7b^4)(3ab^9) = (-1 \cdot 3) \cdot (a^7 \cdot a^1) \cdot (b^4 \cdot b^9)$

   $\ = -3a^8b^{13}$ □

PRACTICE
5   Simplify.

   a. $(y^7z^3)(y^5z)$ **b.** $(-m^4n^4)(7mn^{10})$ ▪

> **Helpful Hint**
>
> These examples will remind you of the difference between adding and multiplying terms.
>
> **Addition**
>
> $$5x^3 + 3x^3 = (5 + 3)x^3 = 8x^3 \quad \text{By the distributive property.}$$
> $$7x + 4x^2 = 7x + 4x^2 \qquad\qquad \text{Cannot be combined.}$$
>
> **Multiplication**
>
> $$(5x^3)(3x^3) = 5 \cdot 3 \cdot x^3 \cdot x^3 = 15x^{3+3} = 15x^6 \quad \text{By the product rule.}$$
> $$(7x)(4x^2) = 7 \cdot 4 \cdot x \cdot x^2 = 28x^{1+2} = 28x^3 \quad \text{By the product rule.}$$

OBJECTIVE

3 Using the Power Rule ▶

Exponential expressions can themselves be raised to powers. Let's try to discover a rule that simplifies an expression like $(x^2)^3$. By definition,

$$(x^2)^3 = \underbrace{(x^2)(x^2)(x^2)}_{3 \text{ factors of } x^2}$$

which can be simplified by the product rule for exponents.

$$(x^2)^3 = (x^2)(x^2)(x^2) = x^{2+2+2} = x^6$$

Notice that the result is exactly the same if we multiply the exponents.

$$(x^2)^3 = x^{2 \cdot 3} = x^6$$

The following property states this result.

> **Power Rule for Exponents**
>
> If m and n are positive integers and a is a real number, then
>
> $$(a^m)^n = a^{mn} \leftarrow \text{Multiply exponents.}$$
> $$\uparrow\text{—— Keep common base.}$$

For example, $(7^2)^5 = 7^{2 \cdot 5} = 7^{10} \leftarrow$ Multiply exponents.
$\quad$ —— Keep common base.

To raise a power to a power, keep the base and multiply the exponents.

EXAMPLE 6   Use the power rule to simplify.

     a. $(y^8)^2$ **b.** $(8^4)^5$ ▶ **c.** $[(-5)^3]^7$

Solution

     a. $(y^8)^2 = y^{8 \cdot 2} = y^{16}$ **b.** $(8^4)^5 = 8^{4 \cdot 5} = 8^{20}$ **c.** $[(-5)^3]^7 = (-5)^{21}$ □

PRACTICE

6   Use the power rule to simplify.

     a. $(z^3)^7$ **b.** $(4^9)^2$ **c.** $[(-2)^3]^5$ ■

> **Helpful Hint**
>
> Take a moment to make sure that you understand when to apply the product rule and when to apply the power rule.
>
> | _Product Rule_ → _Add Exponents_ | _Power Rule_ → _Multiply Exponents_ |
> |---|---|
> | $x^5 \cdot x^7 = x^{5+7} = x^{12}$ | $(x^5)^7 = x^{5 \cdot 7} = x^{35}$ |
> | $y^6 \cdot y^2 = y^{6+2} = y^8$ | $(y^6)^2 = y^{6 \cdot 2} = y^{12}$ |

OBJECTIVE

4   Using the Power Rules for Products and Quotients ▷

When the base of an exponential expression is a product, the definition of x^n still applies. To simplify $(xy)^3$, for example,

$$(xy)^3 = (xy)(xy)(xy) \quad \text{$(xy)^3$ means 3 factors of (xy).}$$
$$= x \cdot x \cdot x \cdot y \cdot y \cdot y \quad \text{Group factors with common bases.}$$
$$= x^3 y^3 \quad \text{Simplify.}$$

Notice that to simplify the expression $(xy)^3$, we raise each factor within the parentheses to a power of 3.

$$(xy)^3 = x^3 y^3$$

In general, we have the following rule.

Power of a Product Rule

If n is a positive integer and a and b are real numbers, then

$$(ab)^n = a^n b^n$$

For example, $(3x)^5 = 3^5 x^5$.

In other words, to raise a product to a power, we raise each factor to the power.

EXAMPLE 7   Simplify each expression.

a. $(st)^4$ b. $(2a)^3$ c. $\left(\dfrac{1}{3}mn^3\right)^2$ d. $(-5x^2y^3z)^2$

Solution

a. $(st)^4 = s^4 \cdot t^4 = s^4 t^4$ Use the power of a product rule.

b. $(2a)^3 = 2^3 \cdot a^3 = 8a^3$ Use the power of a product rule.

c. $\left(\dfrac{1}{3}mn^3\right)^2 = \left(\dfrac{1}{3}\right)^2 \cdot (m)^2 \cdot (n^3)^2 = \dfrac{1}{9}m^2 n^6$ Use the power of a product rule.

d. $(-5x^2y^3z)^2 = (-5)^2 \cdot (x^2)^2 \cdot (y^3)^2 \cdot (z^1)^2$ Use the power of a product rule.
   $= 25x^4 y^6 z^2$ Use the power rule for exponents. □

PRACTICE

7   Simplify each expression.

a. $(pr)^5$ b. $(6b)^2$ c. $\left(\dfrac{1}{4}x^2y\right)^3$ d. $(-3a^3b^4c)^4$ ◼

Let's see what happens when we raise a quotient to a power. To simplify $\left(\dfrac{x}{y}\right)^3$, for example,

$$\left(\dfrac{x}{y}\right)^3 = \left(\dfrac{x}{y}\right)\left(\dfrac{x}{y}\right)\left(\dfrac{x}{y}\right) \quad \text{$\left(\dfrac{x}{y}\right)^3$ means 3 factors of $\left(\dfrac{x}{y}\right)$}$$
$$= \dfrac{x \cdot x \cdot x}{y \cdot y \cdot y} \quad \text{Multiply fractions.}$$
$$= \dfrac{x^3}{y^3} \quad \text{Simplify.}$$

Notice that to simplify the expression $\left(\dfrac{x}{y}\right)^3$, we raise both the numerator and the denominator to a power of 3.

$$\left(\dfrac{x}{y}\right)^3 = \dfrac{x^3}{y^3}$$

In general, we have the following.

Power of a Quotient Rule

If n is a positive integer and a and c are real numbers, then

$$\left(\frac{a}{c}\right)^n = \frac{a^n}{c^n}, \quad c \neq 0$$

For example, $\left(\dfrac{y}{7}\right)^4 = \dfrac{y^4}{7^4}$.

In other words, to raise a quotient to a power, we raise both the numerator and the denominator to the power.

EXAMPLE 8 Simplify each expression.

a. $\left(\dfrac{m}{n}\right)^7$ **b.** $\left(\dfrac{x^3}{3y^5}\right)^4$

Solution

a. $\left(\dfrac{m}{n}\right)^7 = \dfrac{m^7}{n^7}, n \neq 0$ Use the power of a quotient rule.

b. $\left(\dfrac{x^3}{3y^5}\right)^4 = \dfrac{(x^3)^4}{3^4 \cdot (y^5)^4}, y \neq 0$ Use the power of a product or quotient rule.

$\phantom{\left(\dfrac{x^3}{3y^5}\right)^4} = \dfrac{x^{12}}{81y^{20}}$ Use the power rule for exponents.   □

PRACTICE
8   Simplify each expression.

a. $\left(\dfrac{x}{y^2}\right)^5$ **b.** $\left(\dfrac{2a^4}{b^3}\right)^5$ ■

OBJECTIVE
5   **Using the Quotient Rule and Defining the Zero Exponent**

Another pattern for simplifying exponential expressions involves quotients.

To simplify an expression like $\dfrac{x^5}{x^3}$, in which the numerator and the denominator have a common base, we can apply the fundamental principle of fractions and divide the numerator and the denominator by the common base factors. Assume for the remainder of this section that denominators are not 0.

$$\frac{x^5}{x^3} = \frac{x \cdot x \cdot x \cdot x \cdot x}{x \cdot x \cdot x}$$

$$= \frac{x \cdot x \cdot x \cdot x \cdot x}{x \cdot x \cdot x}$$

$$= x \cdot x$$

$$= x^2$$

Notice that the result is exactly the same if we subtract exponents of the common bases.

$$\frac{x^5}{x^3} = x^{5-3} = x^2$$

The quotient rule for exponents states this result in a general way.

> **Quotient Rule for Exponents**
>
> If m and n are positive integers and a is a real number, then
>
> $$\frac{a^m}{a^n} = a^{m-n}$$
>
> as long as a is not 0.

For example, $\dfrac{x^6}{x^2} = x^{6-2} = x^4$.

In other words, to divide one exponential expression by another with a common base, keep the base and subtract exponents.

EXAMPLE 9 Simplify each quotient.

▶ **a.** $\dfrac{x^5}{x^2}$ **b.** $\dfrac{4^7}{4^3}$ **c.** $\dfrac{(-3)^5}{(-3)^2}$ **d.** $\dfrac{s^2}{t^3}$ **e.** $\dfrac{2x^5y^2}{xy}$

Solution

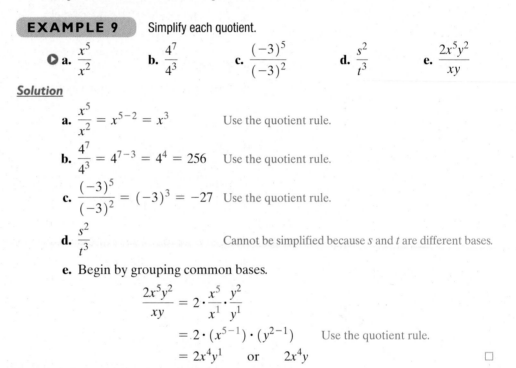

a. $\dfrac{x^5}{x^2} = x^{5-2} = x^3$ Use the quotient rule.

b. $\dfrac{4^7}{4^3} = 4^{7-3} = 4^4 = 256$ Use the quotient rule.

c. $\dfrac{(-3)^5}{(-3)^2} = (-3)^3 = -27$ Use the quotient rule.

d. $\dfrac{s^2}{t^3}$ Cannot be simplified because s and t are different bases.

e. Begin by grouping common bases.

$$\frac{2x^5y^2}{xy} = 2 \cdot \frac{x^5}{x^1} \cdot \frac{y^2}{y^1}$$

$$= 2 \cdot (x^{5-1}) \cdot (y^{2-1}) \quad \text{Use the quotient rule.}$$

$$= 2x^4y^1 \quad \text{or} \quad 2x^4y$$

PRACTICE

9 Simplify each quotient.

a. $\dfrac{z^8}{z^4}$ **b.** $\dfrac{(-5)^5}{(-5)^3}$ **c.** $\dfrac{8^8}{8^6}$ **d.** $\dfrac{q^5}{t^2}$ **e.** $\dfrac{6x^3y^7}{xy^5}$

✔ **CONCEPT CHECK**

Suppose you are simplifying each expression. Tell whether you would *add* the exponents, *subtract* the exponents, *multiply* the exponents, *divide* the exponents, or *none of these*.

a. $(x^{63})^{21}$ **b.** $\dfrac{y^{15}}{y^3}$ **c.** $z^{16} + z^8$ **d.** $w^{45} \cdot w^9$

Let's now give meaning to an expression such as x^0. To do so, we will simplify $\dfrac{x^3}{x^3}$ in two ways and compare the results.

$$\frac{x^3}{x^3} = x^{3-3} = x^0 \quad \text{Apply the quotient rule.}$$

$$\frac{x^3}{x^3} = \frac{x \cdot x \cdot x}{x \cdot x \cdot x} = 1 \quad \text{Apply the fundamental principle for fractions.}$$

Answers to Concept Check:
a. multiply   **b.** subtract
c. none of these   **d.** add

Since $\dfrac{x^3}{x^3} = x^0$ and $\dfrac{x^3}{x^3} = 1$, we define that $x^0 = 1$ as long as x is not 0.

Zero Exponent

$a^0 = 1$, as long as a is not 0.

In other words, any base raised to the 0 power is 1 as long as the base is not 0.

EXAMPLE 10 Simplify each expression.

a. 3^0 **b.** $(5x^3y^2)^0$ **c.** $(-5)^0$ **d.** -5^0 **e.** $\left(\dfrac{3}{100}\right)^0$ **f.** $4x^0$

Solution

a. $3^0 = 1$

b. Assume that neither x nor y is zero.
$$(5x^3y^2)^0 = 1$$

c. $(-5)^0 = 1$

d. $-5^0 = -1 \cdot 5^0 = -1 \cdot 1 = -1$

e. $\left(\dfrac{3}{100}\right)^0 = 1$

f. $4x^0 = 4 \cdot x^0 = 4 \cdot 1 = 4$

PRACTICE
10 Simplify the following expressions.

a. -3^0 **b.** $(-3)^0$ **c.** 8^0 **d.** $(0.2)^0$

e. $(7a^2y^4)^0$ **f.** $7y^0$

OBJECTIVE

6 Deciding Which Rule to Use ▶

Let's practice deciding which rule(s) to use to simplify. We will continue this discussion with more examples in Section 5.5.

EXAMPLE 11 Simplify each expression.

a. $x^7 \cdot x^4$ **b.** $\left(\dfrac{t}{2}\right)^4$ **c.** $(9y^5)^2$

Solution

a. Here we have a product, so we use the product rule to simplify.
$$x^7 \cdot x^4 = x^{7+4} = x^{11}$$

b. This is a quotient raised to a power, so we use the power of a quotient rule.
$$\left(\dfrac{t}{2}\right)^4 = \dfrac{t^4}{2^4} = \dfrac{t^4}{16}$$

c. This is a product raised to a power, so we use the power of a product rule.
$$(9y^5)^2 = 9^2(y^5)^2 = 81y^{10}$$

PRACTICE
11   **a.** $\left(\dfrac{z}{12}\right)^2$ **b.** $(4x^6)^3$ **c.** $y^{10} \cdot y^3$

EXAMPLE 12   Simplify each expression.

a. $4^2 - 4^0$ b. $(x^0)^3 + (2^0)^5$ c. $\left(\dfrac{3y^7}{6x^5}\right)^2$ d. $\dfrac{(2a^3b^4)^3}{-8a^9b^2}$

Solution

a. $4^2 - 4^0 = 16 - 1 = 15$ Remember that $4^0 = 1$.

b. $(x^0)^3 + (2^0)^5 = 1^3 + 1^5 = 1 + 1 = 2$

c. $\left(\dfrac{3y^7}{6x^5}\right)^2 = \dfrac{3^2(y^7)^2}{6^2(x^5)^2} = \dfrac{9 \cdot y^{14}}{36 \cdot x^{10}} = \dfrac{y^{14}}{4x^{10}}$

d. $\dfrac{(2a^3b^4)^3}{-8a^9b^2} = \dfrac{2^3(a^3)^3(b^4)^3}{-8a^9b^2} = \dfrac{8a^9b^{12}}{-8a^9b^2} = -1 \cdot (a^{9-9}) \cdot (b^{12-2})$

$= -1 \cdot a^0 \cdot b^{10} = -1 \cdot 1 \cdot b^{10} = -b^{10}$ □

PRACTICE
12   Simplify each expression.

a. $8^2 - 8^0$ b. $(z^0)^6 + (4^0)^5$ c. $\left(\dfrac{5x^3}{15y^4}\right)^2$ d. $\dfrac{(2z^8x^5)^4}{-16z^2x^{20}}$

✓ Vocabulary, Readiness & Video Check

Use the choices below to fill in each blank. Some choices may be used more than once.

0	base	add
1	exponent	multiply

1. Repeated multiplication of the same factor can be written using a(n) _____.
2. In 5^2, the 2 is called the _____ and the 5 is called the _____.
3. To simplify $x^2 \cdot x^7$, keep the base and _____ the exponents.
4. To simplify $(x^3)^6$, keep the base and _____ the exponents.
5. The understood exponent on the term y is _____.
6. If $x^{\square} = 1$, the exponent is _____.

Martin-Gay Interactive Videos

See Video 5.1 ●

Watch the section lecture video and answer the following questions.

OBJECTIVE 1

7. ▣ Examples 3 and 4 illustrate how to find the base of an exponential expression both with and without parentheses. Explain how identifying the base of ▣ Example 7 is similar to identifying the base of ▣ Example 4.

OBJECTIVE 2

8. Why were the commutative and associative properties applied in ▣ Example 12? Were these properties used in another example?

OBJECTIVE 3

9. What point is made at the end of ▣ Example 15?

OBJECTIVE 4

10. Although it's not especially emphasized in ▣ Example 20, what is helpful to remind yourself about the -2 in the problem?

OBJECTIVE 5

11. In ▣ Example 24, which exponent rule is used to show that any non-zero base raised to zero is 1?

OBJECTIVE 6

12. When simplifying an exponential expression that's a fraction, will you always use the quotient rule? Refer to ▣ Example 30 for this objective to support your answer.

5.1 Exercise Set MyMathLab®

For each of the following expressions, state the exponent shown and its corresponding base.

1. 3^2

2. $(-3)^6$

3. -4^2

4. $5 \cdot 3^4$

5. $5x^2$

6. $(5x)^2$

Evaluate each expression. See Example 1.

7. 7^2

8. -3^2

9. $(-5)^1$

10. $(-3)^2$

11. -2^4

12. -4^3

13. $(-2)^4$

14. $(-4)^3$

15. $(0.1)^5$

16. $(0.2)^5$

17. $\left(\dfrac{1}{3}\right)^4$

18. $\left(-\dfrac{1}{9}\right)^2$

19. $7 \cdot 2^5$

20. $9 \cdot 1^7$

21. $-2 \cdot 5^3$

22. $-4 \cdot 3^3$

Evaluate each expression for the replacement values given. See Example 2.

23. $x^2; x = -2$

24. $x^3; x = -2$

25. $5x^3; x = 3$

26. $4x^2; x = -1$

27. $2xy^2; x = 3 \text{ and } y = 5$

28. $-4x^2y^3; x = 2 \text{ and } y = -1$

29. $\dfrac{2z^4}{5}; z = -2$

30. $\dfrac{10}{3y^3}; y = 5$

Use the product rule to simplify each expression. Write the results using exponents. See Examples 3 through 5

31. $x^2 \cdot x^5$

32. $y^2 \cdot y$

33. $(-3)^3 \cdot (-3)^9$

34. $(-5)^7 \cdot (-5)^6$

35. $(5y^4)(3y)$

36. $(-2z^3)(-2z^2)$

37. $(x^9y)(x^{10}y^5)$

38. $(a^2b)(a^{13}b^{17})$

39. $(-8mn^6)(9m^2n^2)$

40. $(-7a^3b^3)(7a^{19}b)$

41. $(4z^{10})(-6z^7)(z^3)$

42. $(12x^5)(-x^6)(x^4)$

△ **43.** The rectangle below has width $4x^2$ feet and length $5x^3$ feet. Find its area as an expression in x. ($A = l \cdot w$)

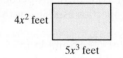

4x² feet

5x³ feet

△ **44.** The parallelogram below has base length $9y^7$ meters and height $2y^{10}$ meters. Find its area as an expression in y. ($A = b \cdot h$)

2y¹⁰ meters

9y⁷ meters

MIXED PRACTICE

Use the power rule and the power of a product or quotient rule to simplify each expression. See Examples 6 through 8.

45. $(x^9)^4$

46. $(y^7)^5$

47. $(pq)^8$

48. $(ab)^6$

49. $(2a^5)^3$

50. $(4x^6)^2$

51. $(x^2y^3)^5$

52. $(a^4b)^7$

53. $(-7a^2b^5c)^2$

54. $(-3x^7yz^2)^3$

55. $\left(\dfrac{r}{s}\right)^9$

56. $\left(\dfrac{q}{t}\right)^{11}$

57. $\left(\dfrac{mp}{n}\right)^5$

58. $\left(\dfrac{xy}{7}\right)^2$

59. $\left(\dfrac{-2xz}{y^5}\right)^2$

60. $\left(\dfrac{xy^4}{-3z^3}\right)^3$

△ **61.** The square shown has sides of length $8z^5$ decimeters. Find its area. ($A = s^2$)

8z⁵
decimeters

△ **62.** Given the circle below with radius $5y$ centimeters, find its area. Do not approximate π. ($A = \pi r^2$)

5y cm

△ **63.** The vault below is in the shape of a cube. If each side is $3y^4$ feet, find its volume. ($V = s^3$)

3y⁴ feet

3y⁴ feet

3y⁴ feet

△ **64.** The silo shown is in the shape of a cylinder. If its radius is $4x$ meters and its height is $5x^3$ meters, find its volume. Do not approximate π. ($V = \pi r^2h$)

4x meters

5x³
meters

Use the quotient rule and simplify each expression. See Example 9.

65. $\dfrac{x^3}{x}$

66. $\dfrac{y^{10}}{y^9}$

▶ **67.** $\dfrac{(-4)^6}{(-4)^3}$

68. $\dfrac{(-6)^{13}}{(-6)^{11}}$

69. $\dfrac{p^7 q^{20}}{pq^{15}}$

70. $\dfrac{x^8 y^6}{xy^5}$

71. $\dfrac{7x^2 y^6}{14x^2 y^3}$

▶ **72.** $\dfrac{9a^4 b^7}{27ab^2}$

Simplify each expression. See Example 10.

73. 7^0

74. 23^0

▶ **75.** $(2x)^0$

76. $(4y)^0$

▶ **77.** $-7x^0$

78. $-2x^0$

▶ **79.** $5^0 + y^0$

80. $-3^0 + 4^0$

MIXED PRACTICE

Simplify each expression. See Examples 1 through 12.

81. -9^2

82. $(-9)^2$

83. $\left(\dfrac{1}{4}\right)^3$

84. $\left(\dfrac{2}{3}\right)^3$

85. $b^4 b^2$

86. $y^4 y$

87. $a^2 a^3 a^4$

88. $x^2 x^{15} x^9$

▶ **89.** $(2x^3)(-8x^4)$

90. $(3y^4)(-5y)$

91. $(a^7 b^{12})(a^4 b^8)$

92. $(y^2 z^2)(y^{15} z^{13})$

93. $(-2mn^6)(-13m^8 n)$

94. $(-3s^5 t)(-7st^{10})$

95. $(z^4)^{10}$

96. $(t^5)^{11}$

97. $(4ab)^3$

98. $(2ab)^4$

99. $(-6xyz^3)^2$

100. $(-3xy^2 a^3)^3$

▶ **101.** $\dfrac{3x^5}{x^4}$

102. $\dfrac{5x^9}{x^3}$

103. $(9xy)^2$

104. $(2ab)^5$

105. $2^3 + 2^0$

106. $7^2 - 7^0$

▶ **107.** $\left(\dfrac{3y^5}{6x^4}\right)^3$

108. $\left(\dfrac{2ab}{6yz}\right)^4$

109. $\dfrac{2x^3 y^2 z}{xyz}$

110. $\dfrac{x^{12} y^{13}}{x^5 y^7}$

111. $(5^0)^3 + (y^0)^7$

112. $(9^0)^4 + (z^0)^5$

113. $\left(\dfrac{5x^9}{10y^{11}}\right)^2$

114. $\left(\dfrac{3a^4}{9b^5}\right)^2$

115. $\dfrac{(2a^5 b^3)^4}{-16a^{20} b^7}$

116. $\dfrac{(2x^6 y^2)^5}{-32x^{20} y^{10}}$

REVIEW AND PREVIEW

Simplify each expression by combining any like terms. Use the distributive property to remove any parentheses. See Section 2.1.

117. $y - 10 + y$

118. $-6z + 20 - 3z$

119. $7x + 2 - 8x - 6$

120. $10y - 14 - y - 14$

121. $2(x - 5) + 3(5 - x)$

122. $-3(w + 7) + 5(w + 1)$

CONCEPT EXTENSIONS

Solve. See the Concept Checks in this section. For Exercises 123 through 126, match the expression with the operation needed to simplify each. A letter may be used more than once and a letter may not be used at all.

123. $(x^{14})^{23}$ **A.** Add the exponents

124. $x^{14} \cdot x^{23}$ **B.** Subtract the exponents

125. $x^{14} + x^{23}$ **C.** Multiply the exponents

126. $\dfrac{x^{35}}{x^{17}}$ **D.** Divide the exponents

E. None of these

Fill in the boxes so that each statement is true. (More than one answer is possible for each exercise.)

127. $x^{\square} \cdot x^{\square} = x^{12}$

128. $(x^{\square})^{\square} = x^{20}$

129. $\dfrac{y^{\square}}{y^{\square}} = y^7$

130. $(y^{\square})^{\square} \cdot (y^{\square})^{\square} = y^{30}$

△ **131.** The formula $V = x^3$ can be used to find the volume V of a cube with side length x. Find the volume of a cube with side length 7 meters. (Volume is measured in cubic units.)

x

△ **132.** The formula $S = 6x^2$ can be used to find the surface area S of a cube with side length x. Find the surface area of a cube with side length 5 meters. (Surface area is measured in square units.)

△ **133.** To find the amount of water that a swimming pool in the shape of a cube can hold, do we use the formula for volume of the cube or surface area of the cube? (See Exercises 131 and 132.)

△ **134.** To find the amount of material needed to cover an ottoman in the shape of a cube, do we use the formula for volume of the cube or surface area of the cube? (See Exercises 131 and 132.)

✎ **135.** Explain why $(-5)^4 = 625$, while $-5^4 = -625$.

✎ **136.** Explain why $5 \cdot 4^2 = 80$, while $(5 \cdot 4)^2 = 400$.

✎ **137.** In your own words, explain why $5^0 = 1$.

✎ **138.** In your own words, explain when $(-3)^n$ is positive and when it is negative.

Simplify each expression. Assume that variables represent positive integers.

139. $x^{5a} x^{4a}$ **140.** $b^{9a} b^{4a}$ **141.** $(a^b)^5$

142. $(2a^{4b})^4$ **143.** $\dfrac{x^{9a}}{x^{4a}}$ **144.** $\dfrac{y^{15b}}{y^{6b}}$

Solve. Round money amounts to 2 decimal places.

145. Suppose you borrow money for 6 months. If the interest is compounded monthly, the formula $A = P\left(1 + \dfrac{r}{12}\right)^6$ gives the total amount A to be repaid at the end of 6 months. For a loan of $P = \$1000$ and interest rate of 9% $(r = 0.09)$, how much money is needed to pay off the loan?

146. Suppose you borrow money for 3 years. If the interest is compounded quarterly, the formula $A = P\left(1 + \dfrac{r}{4}\right)^{12}$ gives the total amount A to be repaid at the end of 3 years. For a loan of $10,000 and interest rate of 8% $(r = 0.08)$, how much money is needed to pay off the loan in 3 years?

5.2 Polynomial Functions and Adding and Subtracting Polynomials

OBJECTIVES

1 Define Polynomial, Monomial, Binomial, Trinomial, and Degree.

2 Define Polynomial Functions.

3 Simplify a Polynomial by Combining Like Terms.

4 Add and Subtract Polynomials.

OBJECTIVE

1 Defining Polynomial, Monomial, Binomial, Trinomial, and Degree

In this section, we introduce a special algebraic expression called a polynomial. Let's first review some definitions presented in Section 2.1.

Recall that a **term** is a number or the product of a number and variables raised to powers. The terms of the expression $4x^2 + 3x$ are $4x^2$ and $3x$.

The terms of the expression $9x^4 - 7x - 1$ are $9x^4$, $-7x$, and -1.

Expression	*Terms*
$4x^2 + 3x$	$4x^2, 3x$
$9x^4 - 7x - 1$	$9x^4, -7x, -1$
$7y^3$	$7y^3$
5	5

The **numerical coefficient** of a term, or simply the **coefficient**, is the numerical factor of each term. If no numerical factor appears in the term, then the coefficient is understood to be 1. If the term is a number only, it is called a **constant term** or simply a **constant**.

Term	*Coefficient*
x^5	1
$3x^2$	3
$-4x$	-4
$-x^2y$	-1
3 (constant)	3

Now we are ready to define a polynomial.

Polynomial

A **polynomial in x** is a finite sum of terms of the form ax^n, where a is a real number and n is a whole number.

For example,

$$x^5 - 3x^3 + 2x^2 - 5x + 1$$

is a polynomial. Notice that this polynomial is written in **descending powers** of x because the powers of x decrease from left to right. (Recall that the term 1 can be thought of as $1x^0$.)

On the other hand,

$$x^{-5} + 2x - 3$$

is **not** a polynomial because it contains an exponent, -5, that is not a whole number. (We study negative exponents in Section 5.5 of this chapter.)

Some polynomials are given special names.

Types of Polynomials

A **monomial** is a polynomial with exactly one term.

A **binomial** is a polynomial with exactly two terms.

A **trinomial** is a polynomial with exactly three terms.

The following are examples of monomials, binomials, and trinomials. Each of these examples is also a polynomial.

POLYNOMIALS

Monomials	Binomials	Trinomials	More than Three Terms
ax^2	$x + y$	$x^2 + 4xy + y^2$	$5x^3 - 6x^2 + 3x - 6$
$-3z$	$3p + 2$	$x^5 + 7x^2 - x$	$-y^5 + y^4 - 3y^3 - y^2 + y$
4	$4x^2 - 7$	$-q^4 + q^3 - 2q$	$x^6 + x^4 - x^3 + 1$

Each term of a polynomial has a **degree.**

Degree of a Term

The degree of a term is the sum of the exponents on the variables contained in the term.

EXAMPLE 1   Find the degree of each term.

a. $3x^2$ b. -2^3x^5 c. y d. $12x^2yz^3$ e. 5

Solution

a. The exponent on x is 2, so the degree of the term is 2.
b. The exponent on x is 5, so the degree of the term is 5. (Recall that the degree is the sum of the exponents on only the *variables*.)
c. The degree of y, or y^1, is 1.
d. The degree is the sum of the exponents on the variables, or $2 + 1 + 3 = 6$.
e. The degree of 5, which can be written as $5x^0$, is 0.   □

PRACTICE
1   Find the degree of each term.

a. $5y^3$ b. $10xy$ c. z d. $-3a^2b^5c$ e. 8 ■

From the preceding, we can say that **the degree of a constant is 0.**
Each polynomial also has a degree.

Degree of a Polynomial

The degree of a polynomial is the greatest degree of any term of the polynomial.

EXAMPLE 2   Find the degree of each polynomial and tell whether the polynomial is a monomial, binomial, trinomial, or none of these.

a. $-2t^2 + 3t + 6$ b. $15x - 10$ c. $7x + 3x^3 + 2x^2 - 1$

Solution

a. The degree of the trinomial $-2t^2 + 3t + 6$ is 2, the greatest degree of any of its terms.
b. The degree of the binomial $15x - 10$ or $15x^1 - 10$ is 1.
c. The degree of the polynomial $7x + 3x^3 + 2x^2 - 1$ is 3.   □

PRACTICE
2   Find the degree of each polynomial and tell whether the polynomial is a monomial, binomial, trinomial, or none of these.

a. $5b^2 - 3b + 7$ b. $7t + 3$
c. $5x^2 + 3x - 6x^3 + 4$ ■

EXAMPLE 3 Complete the table for the polynomial

$$7x^2y - 6xy + x^2 - 3y + 7$$

Use the table to give the degree of the polynomial.

Solution

Term	Numerical Coefficient	Degree of Term
$7x^2y$	7	3
$-6xy$	-6	2
x^2	1	2
$-3y$	-3	1
7	7	0

The degree of the polynomial is 3. ◻

PRACTICE
3 Complete the table for the polynomial $-3x^3y^2 + 4xy^2 - y^2 + 3x - 2$.

Term	Numerical Coefficient	Degree of Term
$-3x^3y^2$		
$4xy^2$		
$-y^2$		
$3x$		
-2		

■

OBJECTIVE

2 Defining Polynomial Functions ▶

At times, it is convenient to use function notation to represent polynomials. For example, we may write $P(x)$ to represent the polynomial $3x^2 - 2x - 5$. In symbols, this is

$$P(x) = 3x^2 - 2x - 5$$

This function is called a **polynomial function** because the expression $3x^2 - 2x - 5$ is a polynomial.

> **Helpful Hint**
>
> Recall that the symbol $P(x)$ **does not mean** P times x. It is a special symbol used to denote a function.

EXAMPLE 4 If $P(x) = 3x^2 - 2x - 5$, find the following.

a. $P(1)$ **b.** $P(-2)$

Solution

    a. Substitute 1 for x in $P(x) = 3x^2 - 2x - 5$ and simplify.

$$P(x) = 3x^2 - 2x - 5$$
$$P(1) = 3(1)^2 - 2(1) - 5 = -4$$

b. Substitute -2 for x in $P(x) = 3x^2 - 2x - 5$ and simplify.

$$P(x) = 3x^2 - 2x - 5$$
$$P(-2) = 3(-2)^2 - 2(-2) - 5 = 11$$

PRACTICE
4   If $P(x) = -2x^2 - x + 7$, find

a. $P(1)$ **b.** $P(-4)$

Many real-world phenomena are modeled by polynomial functions. If the polynomial function model is given, we can often find the solution of a problem by evaluating the function at a certain value.

EXAMPLE 5   **Finding the Height of a Dropped Object**

The Swiss Re Building, in London, is a unique building. Londoners often refer to it as the "pickle building." The building is 592.1 feet tall. An object is dropped from the highest point of this building. Neglecting air resistance, the height in feet of the object above ground at time t seconds is given by the polynomial function $P(t) = -16t^2 + 592.1$. Find the height of the object when $t = 1$ second, and when $t = 6$ seconds.

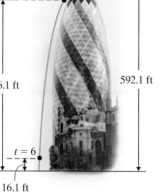

576.1 ft

592.1 ft

16.1 ft

Solution   To find each height, we find $P(1)$ and $P(6)$.

$$P(t) = -16t^2 + 592.1$$
$$P(1) = -16(1)^2 + 592.1 \quad \text{Replace } t \text{ with 1.}$$
$$P(1) = -16 + 592.1$$
$$P(1) = 576.1$$

The height of the object at 1 second is 576.1 feet.

$$P(t) = -16t^2 + 592.1$$
$$P(6) = -16(6)^2 + 592.1 \quad \text{Replace } t \text{ with 6.}$$
$$P(6) = -576 + 592.1$$
$$P(6) = 16.1$$

The height of the object at 6 seconds is 16.1 feet.

PRACTICE
5   The cliff divers of Acapulco dive 130 feet into La Quebrada several times a day for the entertainment of the tourists. If a tourist is standing near the diving platform and drops his camera off the cliff, the height of the camera above the water at time t seconds is given by the polynomial function $P(t) = -16t^2 + 130$. Find the height of the camera when $t = 1$ second and when $t = 2$ seconds.

OBJECTIVE
3   Simplifying Polynomials by Combining Like Terms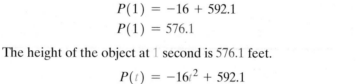

Polynomials with like terms can be simplified by combining the like terms. Recall that like terms are terms that contain exactly the same variables raised to exactly the same powers.

Like Terms	Unlike Terms
$5x^2, -7x^2$	$3x, 3y$
$y, 2y$	$-2x^2, -5x$
$\frac{1}{2}a^2b, -a^2b$	$6st^2, 4s^2t$

Only like terms can be combined. We combine like terms by applying the distributive property.

EXAMPLE 6 Simplify each polynomial by combining any like terms.

    a. $-3x + 7x$

    b. $x + 3x^2$

    c. $9x^3 + x^3$

    d. $11x^2 + 5 + 2x^2 - 7$

    e. $\dfrac{2}{5}x^4 + \dfrac{2}{3}x^3 - x^2 + \dfrac{1}{10}x^4 - \dfrac{1}{6}x^3$

Solution

    a. $-3x + 7x = (-3 + 7)x = 4x$

    b. $x + 3x^2$ These terms cannot be combined because x and $3x^2$ are not like terms.

    c. $9x^3 + x^3 = 9x^3 + 1x^3 = 10x^3$

    d. $11x^2 + 5 + 2x^2 - 7 = 11x^2 + 2x^2 + 5 - 7$

                           $= 13x^2 - 2$ Combine like terms.

    e. $\dfrac{2}{5}x^4 + \dfrac{2}{3}x^3 - x^2 + \dfrac{1}{10}x^4 - \dfrac{1}{6}x^3$

$$= \left(\frac{2}{5} + \frac{1}{10}\right)x^4 + \left(\frac{2}{3} - \frac{1}{6}\right)x^3 - x^2$$

$$= \left(\frac{4}{10} + \frac{1}{10}\right)x^4 + \left(\frac{4}{6} - \frac{1}{6}\right)x^3 - x^2$$

$$= \frac{5}{10}x^4 + \frac{3}{6}x^3 - x^2$$

$$= \frac{1}{2}x^4 + \frac{1}{2}x^3 - x^2$$

PRACTICE
6 Simplify each polynomial by combining any like terms.

    a. $-4y + 2y$

    b. $z + 5z^3$

    c. $15x^3 - x^3$

    d. $7a^2 - 5 - 3a^2 - 7$

    e. $\dfrac{3}{8}x^3 - x^2 + \dfrac{5}{6}x^4 + \dfrac{1}{12}x^3 - \dfrac{1}{2}x^4$

✔ **CONCEPT CHECK**

When combining like terms in the expression $5x - 8x^2 - 8x$, which of the following is the proper result?

    a. $-11x^2$ **b.** $-8x^2 - 3x$ **c.** $-11x$ **d.** $-11x^4$

EXAMPLE 7 Combine like terms to simplify.

$$-9x^2 + 3xy - 5y^2 + 7yx$$

Solution

$$-9x^2 + 3xy - 5y^2 + 7yx = -9x^2 + (3 + 7)xy - 5y^2$$

$$= -9x^2 + 10xy - 5y^2$$

Helpful Hint
This term can be written as $7yx$ or $7xy$.

PRACTICE
7 Combine like terms to simplify: $9xy - 3x^2 - 4yx + 5y^2$.

EXAMPLE 8 Write a polynomial that describes the total area of the squares and rectangles shown on page 327. Then simplify the polynomial.

Solution

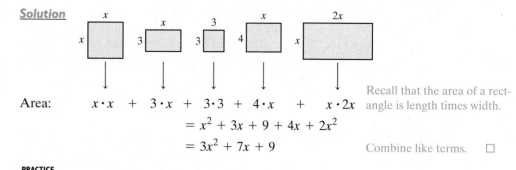

Area: $x \cdot x$ + $3 \cdot x$ + $3 \cdot 3$ + $4 \cdot x$ + $x \cdot 2x$ Recall that the area of a rect-angle is length times width.

$$= x^2 + 3x + 9 + 4x + 2x^2$$

$$= 3x^2 + 7x + 9 \qquad \text{Combine like terms.} \quad \square$$

PRACTICE

8   Write a polynomial that describes the total area of the squares and rectangles shown below. Then simplify the polynomial.

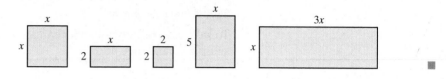

OBJECTIVE

4   **Adding and Subtracting Polynomials**

We now practice adding and subtracting polynomials.

> **Adding Polynomials**
>
> To add polynomials, combine all like terms.

EXAMPLE 9   Add.

a. $(7x^3y - xy^3 + 11) + (6x^3y - 4)$
b. $(3a^3 - b + 2a - 5) + (a + b + 5)$

Solution

a. To add, remove the parentheses and group like terms.

$$(7x^3y - xy^3 + 11) + (6x^3y - 4)$$
$$= 7x^3y - xy^3 + 11 + 6x^3y - 4$$
$$= 7x^3y + 6x^3y - xy^3 + 11 - 4 \qquad \text{Group like terms.}$$
$$= 13x^2y - xy^3 + 7 \qquad \text{Combine like terms.}$$

b. $\qquad (3a^3 - b + 2a - 5) + (a + b + 5)$
$$= 3a^3 - b + 2a - 5 + a + b + 5$$
$$= 3a^3 - b + b + 2a + a - 5 + 5 \qquad \text{Group like terms.}$$
$$= 3a^3 + 3a \qquad \text{Combine like terms.} \quad \square$$

PRACTICE

9   Add.

a. $(4y^2 + x - 3y - 7) + (x + y^2 - 2)$
b. $(-8a^2b - ab^2 + 10) + (-2ab^2 - 10)$

EXAMPLE 10   Add $(11x^3 - 12x^2 + x - 3)$ and $(x^3 - 10x + 5)$.

Solution

$$(11x^3 - 12x^2 + x - 3) + (x^3 - 10x + 5)$$
$$= 11x^3 + x^3 - 12x^2 + x - 10x - 3 + 5 \qquad \text{Group like terms.}$$
$$= 12x^3 - 12x^2 - 9x + 2 \qquad \text{Combine like terms.} \quad \square$$

PRACTICE

10   Add $(3x^2 - 9x + 11)$ and $(-3x^2 + 7x^3 + 3x - 4)$

Sometimes it is more convenient to add polynomials vertically. To do this, line up like terms beneath one another and add like terms.

The definition of subtraction of real numbers can be extended to apply to polynomials. To subtract a number, we add its opposite.

$$a - b = a + (-b)$$

Likewise, to subtract a polynomial, we add its opposite. In other words, if P and Q are polynomials, then

$$P - Q = P + (-Q)$$

The polynomial $-Q$ is the **opposite,** or **additive inverse,** of the polynomial Q. We can find $-Q$ by writing the opposite of each term of Q.

Subtracting Polynomials

To subtract two polynomials, change the signs of the terms of the polynomial being subtracted and then add.

✔ **CONCEPT CHECK**

Which polynomial is the opposite of $16x^3 - 5x + 7$?
a. $-16x^3 - 5x + 7$ **b.** $-16x^3 + 5x - 7$ **c.** $16x^3 + 5x + 7$ **d.** $-16x^3 + 5x + 7$

EXAMPLE 11   Subtract: $(2x^3 + 8x^2 - 6x) - (2x^3 - x^2 + 1)$

Solution First, change the sign of each term of the second polynomial and then add.

> **Helpful Hint**
> Notice the sign of each term is changed.

$$(2x^3 + 8x^2 - 6x) - (2x^3 - x^2 + 1) = (2x^3 + 8x^2 - 6x) + (-2x^3 + x^2 - 1)$$
$$= 2x^3 - 2x^3 + 8x^2 + x^2 - 6x - 1$$
$$= 9x^2 - 6x - 1 \quad \text{Combine like terms.} \quad \square$$

PRACTICE
11   Subtract: $(3x^3 - 5x^2 + 4x) - (x^3 - x^2 + 6)$ $2x^3 - 4x^2 + 4x - 6$ ■

EXAMPLE 12   Subtract $(5z - 7)$ from the sum of $(8z + 11)$ and $(9z - 2)$.

Solution Notice that $(5z - 7)$ is to be subtracted **from** a sum. The translation is

$$[(8z + 11) + (9z - 2)] - (5z - 7)$$
$$= 8z + 11 + 9z - 2 - 5z + 7 \quad \text{Remove grouping symbols.}$$
$$= 8z + 9z - 5z + 11 - 2 + 7 \quad \text{Group like terms.}$$
$$= 12z + 16 \quad\quad\quad\quad\quad \text{Combine like terms.} \quad \square$$

PRACTICE
12   Subtract $(3x + 5)$ from the sum of $(8x - 11)$ and $(2x + 5)$.   ■

EXAMPLE 13   Add or subtract as indicated.
     a. $(3x^2 - 6xy + 5y^2) + (-2x^2 + 8xy - y^2)$
     b. $(9a^2b^2 + 6ab - 3ab^2) - (5b^2a + 2ab - 3 - 9b^2)$

Solution
     a. $(3x^2 - 6xy + 5y^2) + (-2x^2 + 8xy - y^2)$
             $= 3x^2 - 6xy + 5y^2 - 2x^2 + 8xy - y^2$
             $= x^2 + 2xy + 4y^2$ Combine like terms.

b. $(9a^2b^2 + 6ab - 3ab^2) - (5b^2a + 2ab - 3 - 9b^2)$

$= 9a^2b^2 + 6ab - 3ab^2 - 5b^2a - 2ab + 3 + 9b^2$ Change the sign of each term of the polynomial being subtracted.

$= 9a^2b^2 + 4ab - 8ab^2 + 3 + 9b^2$ Combine like terms.   ☐

PRACTICE
13   Add or subtract as indicated.

a. $(3a^2 - 4ab + 7b^2) + (-8a^2 + 3ab - b^2)$
b. $(5x^2y^2 - 6xy - 4xy^2) - (2x^2y^2 + 4xy - 5 + 6y^2)$ ■

✔ **CONCEPT CHECK**

If possible, simplify each expression by performing the indicated operation.
a. $2y + y$ **b.** $2y \cdot y$ **c.** $-2y - y$ **d.** $(-2y)(-y)$ **e.** $2x + y$

To add or subtract polynomials vertically, just remember to line up like terms. For example, perform the subtraction $(10x^3y^2 - 7x^2y^2) - (4x^3y^2 - 3x^2y^2 + 2y^2)$ vertically.

Add the opposite of the second polynomial.

$$\begin{array}{r} 10x^3y^2 - 7x^2y^2 \\ -(4x^3y^2 - 3x^2y^2 + 2y^2) \end{array} \quad \text{is equivalent to} \quad \begin{array}{r} 10x^3y^2 - 7x^2y^2 \\ -4x^3y^2 + 3x^2y^2 - 2y^2 \\ \hline 6x^3y^2 - 4x^2y^2 - 2y^2 \end{array}$$

✔ **CONCEPT CHECK**

Why is the following subtraction incorrect?

$$(7z - 5) - (3z - 4)$$
$$= 7z - 5 - 3z - 4$$
$$= 4z - 9$$

Polynomial functions, like polynomials, can be added, subtracted, multiplied, and divided. For example, if

$$P(x) = x^2 + x + 1$$

then

$$2P(x) = 2(x^2 + x + 1) = 2x^2 + 2x + 2 \quad \text{Use the distributive property.}$$

Also, if $Q(x) = 5x^2 - 1$, then $P(x) + Q(x) = (x^2 + x + 1) + (5x^2 - 1)$
$$= 6x^2 + x.$$

A useful business and economics application of subtracting polynomial functions is finding the profit function $P(x)$ when given a revenue function $R(x)$ and a cost function $C(x)$. In business, it is true that

$$\text{profit} = \text{revenue} - \text{cost, or}$$
$$P(x) = R(x) - C(x)$$

For example, if the revenue function is $R(x) = 7x$ and the cost function is $C(x) = 2x + 5000$, then the profit function is

$$P(x) = R(x) - C(x)$$

or

$$P(x) = 7x - (2x + 5000) \quad \text{Substitute } R(x) = 7x$$
$$P(x) = 5x - 5000 \quad \text{and } C(x) = 2x + 5000.$$

Graphing Calculator Explorations

A graphing calculator may be used to visualize addition and subtraction of polynomials in one variable. For example, to visualize the following polynomial subtraction statement

$$(3x^2 - 6x + 9) - (x^2 - 5x + 6) = 2x^2 - x + 3$$

graph both

$$Y_1 = (3x^2 - 6x + 9) - (x^2 - 5x + 6) \quad \text{Left side of equation}$$

and

$$Y_2 = 2x^2 - x + 3 \quad \text{Right side of equation}$$

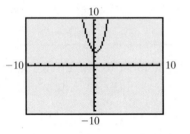

on the same screen and see that their graphs coincide. (*Note:* If the graphs do not coincide, we can be sure that a mistake has been made in combining polynomials or in calculator keystrokes. If the graphs appear to coincide, we cannot be sure that our work is correct. This is because it is possible for the graphs to differ so slightly that we do not notice it.)

The graphs of Y_1 and Y_2 are shown. The graphs appear to coincide, so the subtraction statement

$$(3x^2 - 6x + 9) - (x^2 - 5x + 6) = 2x^2 - x + 3$$

appears to be correct.

Perform the indicated operations. Then visualize by using the procedure described above.

1. $(2x^2 + 7x + 6) + (x^3 - 6x^2 - 14)$

2. $(-14x^3 - x + 2) + (-x^3 + 3x^2 + 4x)$

3. $(1.8x^2 - 6.8x - 1.7) - (3.9x^2 - 3.6x)$

4. $(-4.8x^2 + 12.5x - 7.8) - (3.1x^2 - 7.8x)$

5. $(1.29x - 5.68) + (7.69x^2 - 2.55x + 10.98)$

6. $(-0.98x^2 - 1.56x + 5.57) + (4.36x - 3.71)$

Vocabulary, Readiness & Video Check

Use the choices below to fill in each blank. Not all choices will be used.

least	monomial	trinomial	coefficient
greatest	binomial	constant	

1. A _____ is a polynomial with exactly 2 terms.

2. A _____ is a polynomial with exactly one term.

3. A _____ is a polynomial with exactly three terms.

4. The numerical factor of a term is called the _____.

5. A number term is also called a _____.

6. The degree of a polynomial is the _____ degree of any term of the polynomial.

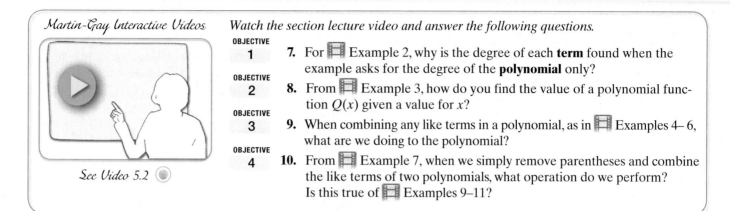

Martin-Gay Interactive Videos

See Video 5.2

Watch the section lecture video and answer the following questions.

OBJECTIVE 1

7. For ▦ Example 2, why is the degree of each **term** found when the example asks for the degree of the **polynomial** only?

OBJECTIVE 2

8. From ▦ Example 3, how do you find the value of a polynomial function $Q(x)$ given a value for x?

OBJECTIVE 3

9. When combining any like terms in a polynomial, as in ▦ Examples 4–6, what are we doing to the polynomial?

OBJECTIVE 4

10. From ▦ Example 7, when we simply remove parentheses and combine the like terms of two polynomials, what operation do we perform? Is this true of ▦ Examples 9–11?

5.2 Exercise Set MyMathLab®

Find the degree of each of the following polynomials and determine whether it is a monomial, binomial, trinomial, or none of these. See Examples 1 through 3.

1. $x + 2$

2. $-6y^2 + 4$

3. $9m^3 - 5m^2 + 4m - 8$

4. $a + 5a^2 + 3a^3 - 4a^4$

▶ **5.** $12x^4y - x^2y^2 - 12x^2y^4$

6. $7r^2s^2 + 2rs - 3rs^5$

7. $3 - 5x^8$

8. $5y^7 + 2$

In the second column, write the degree of the polynomial in the first column. See Examples 1 through 3.

Polynomial	Degree
9. $3xy^2 - 4$	
10. $8x^2y^2$	
11. $5a^2 - 2a + 1$	
12. $4z^6 + 3z^2$	

if $P(x) = x^2 + x + 1$ and $Q(x) = 5x^2 - 1$, find the following. See Examples 4 and 5.

13. $P(7)$

14. $Q(4)$

▶ **15.** $Q(-10)$

16. $P(-4)$

17. $P(0)$

18. $Q(0)$

19. $Q\left(\dfrac{1}{4}\right)$

20. $P\left(\dfrac{1}{2}\right)$

The CN Tower in Toronto, Ontario, is 1821 feet tall and is the world's tallest self-supporting structure. An object is dropped from the Skypod of the Tower, which is at 1150 feet. Neglecting air resistance, the height of the object at time t seconds is given by the polynomial function $P(t) = -16t^2 + 1150$. Find the height of the object at the given times.

	Time, t (in seconds)	Height $P(t) = -16t^2 + 1150$
21.	1	
22.	7	
23.	3	
24.	6	

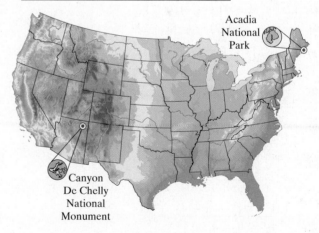

Acadia National Park

Canyon De Chelly National Monument

25. The polynomial $-7.5x^2 + 103x + 2000$ models the yearly number of visitors (in thousands) x years after 2006 at Acadia National Park in Maine. Use this polynomial to estimate the number of visitors to the park in 2016.

26. The polynomial $-0.13x^2 + x + 827$ models the yearly number of visitors (in thousands) x years after 2006 at Canyon De Chelly National Monument in Arizona. Use this polynomial to estimate the number of visitors to the park in 2010.

Simplify each of the following by combining like terms. See Examples 6 and 7.

▶ 27. $14x^2 + 9x^2$

28. $18x^3 - 4x^3$

▶ 29. $15x^2 - 3x^2 - y$

30. $12k^3 - 9k^3 + 11$

31. $8s - 5s + 4s$

32. $5y + 7y - 6y$

▶ 33. $0.1y^2 - 1.2y^2 + 6.7 - 1.9$

34. $7.6y + 3.2y^2 - 8y - 2.5y^2$

35. $\frac{2}{5}x^2 - \frac{1}{3}x^3 + x^2 - \frac{1}{4}x^3 + 6$

36. $\frac{1}{6}x^4 - \frac{1}{7}x^2 + 5 - \frac{1}{2}x^4 - \frac{3}{7}x^2 + \frac{1}{3}$

37. $6a^2 - 4ab + 7b^2 - a^2 - 5ab + 9b^2$

38. $x^2y + xy - y + 10x^2y - 2y + xy$

Perform the indicated operations. See Examples 9 through 13.

▶ 39. $(-7x + 5) + (-3x^2 + 7x + 5)$

40. $(3x - 8) + (4x^2 - 3x + 3)$

▶ 41. $(2x^2 + 5) - (3x^2 - 9)$

42. $(5x^2 + 4) - (-2y^2 + 4)$

43. $3x - (5x - 9)$

44. $4 - (-y - 4)$

45. $(2x^2 + 3x - 9) - (-4x + 7)$

46. $(-7x^2 + 4x + 7) - (-8x + 2)$

▶ 47. $\begin{array}{r} 3t^2 + 4 \\ +5t^2 - 8 \\ \hline \end{array}$

48. $\begin{array}{r} 7x^3 + 3 \\ +2x^3 - 1 \\ \hline \end{array}$

49. $\begin{array}{r} 4z^2 - 8z + 3 \\ -(6z^2 + 8z - 3) \\ \hline \end{array}$

50. $\begin{array}{r} 5u^5 - 4u^2 + 3u - 7 \\ -(3u^5 + 6u^2 - 8u + 2) \\ \hline \end{array}$

▶ 51. $\begin{array}{r} 5x^3 - 4x^2 + 6x - 2 \\ -(3x^3 - 2x^2 - x - 4) \\ \hline \end{array}$

52. $\begin{array}{r} 7a^2 - 9a + 6 \\ -(11a^2 - 4a + 2) \\ \hline \end{array}$

MIXED PRACTICE

Perform the indicated operations.

53. $(-3y^2 - 4y) + (2y^2 + y - 1)$

54. $(7x^2 + 2x - 9) + (-3x^2 + 5)$

55. $(5x + 8) - (-2x^2 - 6x + 8)$

56. $(-6y^2 + 3y - 4) - (9y^2 - 3y)$

57. $(-8x^4 + 7x) + (-8x^4 + x + 9)$

58. $(6y^5 - 6y^3 + 4) + (-2y^5 - 8y^3 - 7)$

59. $(3x^2 + 5x - 8) + (5x^2 + 9x + 12) - (x^2 - 14)$

60. $(-a^2 + 1) - (a^2 - 3) + (5a^2 - 6a + 7)$

TRANSLATING

Perform each indicated operation.

61. Subtract $4x$ from $(7x - 3)$.

62. Subtract y from $(y^2 - 4y + 1)$.

63. Add $(4x^2 - 6x + 1)$ and $(3x^2 + 2x + 1)$.

64. Add $(-3x^2 - 5x + 2)$ and $(x^2 - 6x + 9)$.

▶ 65. Subtract $(19x^2 + 5)$ from $(81x^2 + 10)$.

66. Subtract $(2x + xy)$ from $(3x - 9xy)$.

67. Subtract $(5x + 7)$ from $(7x^2 + 3x + 9)$.

68. Subtract $(5y^2 + 8y + 2)$ from $(7y^2 + 9x - 8)$.

69. Subtract $(2x + 2)$ from the sum of $(8x + 1)$ and $(6x + 3)$.

70. Subtract $(-12x - 3)$ from the sum of $(-5x - 7)$ and $(12x + 3)$.

71. Subtract $(4y^2 - 6y - 3)$ from the sum of $(8y^2 + 7)$ and $(6y + 9)$.

72. Subtract $(4x^2 - 2x + 2)$ from the sum of $(x^2 + 7x + 1)$ and $(7x + 5)$.

Find the area of each figure. Write a polynomial that describes the total area of the rectangles and squares shown in Exercises 73–74. Then simplify the polynomial. See Example 8.

△ 73.

△ 74.

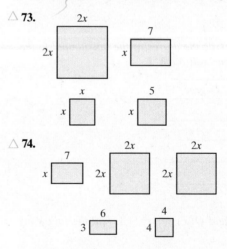

Add or subtract as indicated. See Examples 9 through 13.

75. $(9a + 6b - 5) + (-11a - 7b + 6)$

76. $(3x - 2 + 6y) + (7x - 2 - y)$

77. $(4x^2 + y^2 + 3) - (x^2 + y^2 - 2)$

78. $(7a^2 - 3b^2 + 10) - (-2a^2 + b^2 - 12)$

79. $(x^2 + 2xy - y^2) + (5x^2 - 4xy + 20y^2)$

80. $(a^2 - ab + 4b^2) + (6a^2 + 8ab - b^2)$

81. $(11r^2s + 16rs - 3 - 2r^2s^2) - (3sr^2 + 5 - 9r^2s^2)$

82. $(3x^2y - 6xy + x^2y^2 - 5) - (11x^2y^2 - 1 + 5yx^2)$

Simplify each polynomial by combining like terms.

83. $7.75x + 9.16x^2 - 1.27 - 14.58x^2 - 18.34$

84. $1.85x^2 - 3.76x + 9.25x^2 + 10.76 - 4.21x$

Perform each indicated operation.

85. $[(7.9y^4 - 6.8y^3 + 3.3y) + (6.1y^3 - 5)]$
$- (4.2y^4 + 1.1y - 1)$

86. $[(1.2x^2 - 3x + 9.1) - (7.8x^2 - 3.1 + 8)] + (1.2x - 6)$

REVIEW AND PREVIEW

Multiply. See Section 5.1.

87. $3x(2x)$

88. $-7x(x)$

89. $(12x^3)(-x^5)$

90. $6r^3(7r^{10})$

91. $10x^2(20xy^2)$

92. $-z^2y(11zy)$

CONCEPT EXTENSIONS

Recall that the perimeter of a figure is the sum of the lengths of its sides. For Exercises 93 through 96, find the perimeter of each polynomial.

△ **93.**

△ **94.**

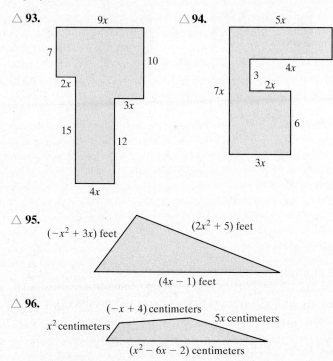

△ **95.**

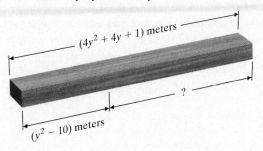

△ **96.**

△ **97.** A wooden beam is $(4y^2 + 4y + 1)$ meters long. If a piece $(y^2 - 10)$ meters is cut, express the length of the remaining piece of beam as a polynomial in y.

△ **98.** A piece of quarter-round molding is $(13x - 7)$ inches long. If a piece $(2x + 2)$ inches is removed, express the length of the remaining piece of molding as a polynomial in x.

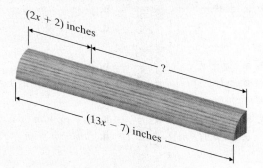

The number of worldwide Internet users (in millions) x years after the year 2000 is given by the polynomial $4.8x^2 + 104x + 431$ for the years 1995 through 2015. Use this polynomial for Exercises 99 and 100.

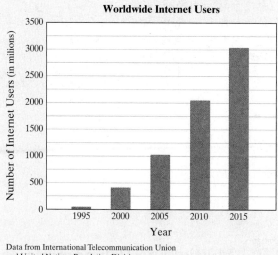

Data from International Telecommunication Union
and United Nations Population Division

99. Estimate the number of Internet users in the world in 2015.

100. Use the given polynomial to predict the number of Internet users in the world in 2020.

101. Describe how to find the degree of a term.

102. Describe how to find the degree of a polynomial.

103. Explain why xyz is a monomial while $x + y + z$ is a trinomial.

104. Explain why the degree of the term $5y^3$ is 3 and the degree of the polynomial $2y + y + 2y$ is 1.

Match each expression on the left with its simplification on the right. Not all letters on the right must be used, and a letter may be used more than once.

105. $10y - 6y^2 - y$ **A.** $3y$

106. $5x + 5x$ **B.** $9y - 6y^2$

107. $(5x - 3) + (5x - 3)$ **C.** $10x$

108. $(15x - 3) - (5x - 3)$ **D.** $25x^2$

     E. $10x - 6$

     F. none of these

Simplify each expression by performing the indicated operation. Explain how you arrived at each answer. See the third Concept Check in this section.

109. a. $z + 3z$ **b.** $z \cdot 3z$

     c. $-z - 3z$ **d.** $(-z)(-3z)$

110. a. $2y + y$ **b.** $2y \cdot y$

     c. $-2y - y$ **d.** $(-2y)(-y)$

111. a. $m \cdot m \cdot m$ **b.** $m + m + m$

     c. $(-m)(-m)(-m)$ **d.** $-m - m - m$

112. a. $x + x$ **b.** $x \cdot x$

     c. $-x - x$ **d.** $(-x)(-x)$

Perform the indicated operations.

113. $(4x^{2a} - 3x^a + 0.5) - (x^{2a} - 5x^a - 0.2)$

114. $(9y^{5a} - 4y^{3a} + 1.5y) - (6y^{5a} - y^{3a} + 4.7y)$

115. $(8x^{2y} - 7x^y + 3) + (-4x^{2y} + 9x^y - 14)$

116. $(14z^{5x} + 3z^{2x} + z) - (2z^{5x} - 10z^{2x} + 3z)$

If $P(x) = 3x + 3, Q(x) = 4x^2 - 6x + 3$, and $R(x) = 5x^2 - 7$, find the following.

117. $P(x) + Q(x)$

118. $R(x) + P(x)$

119. $Q(x) - R(x)$

120. $P(x) - Q(x)$

121. $2[Q(x)] - R(x)$

122. $-5[P(x)] - Q(x)$

*If $P(x)$ is the polynomial given, find **a.** $P(a)$, **b.** $P(-x)$, and **c.** $P(x + h)$.*

123. $P(x) = 2x - 3$

124. $P(x) = 8x + 3$

125. $P(x) = 4x$

126. $P(x) = -4x$

Fill in the squares so that each is a true statement.

127. $3x^\square + 4x^2 = 7x^\square$

128. $9y^7 + 3y^\square = 12y^7$

129. $2x^\square + 3x^\square - 5x^\square + 4x^\square = 6x^4 - 2x^3$

130. $3y^\square + 7y^\square - 2y^\square - y^\square = 10y^5 - 3y^2$

Write a polynomial that describes the surface area of each figure. (Recall that the surface area of a solid is the sum of the areas of the faces or sides of the solid.)

△ **131.**

△ **132.**

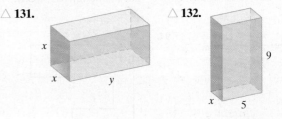

$$\boxed{5.3} \quad \textbf{Multiplying Polynomials} \; \blacktriangleright$$

OBJECTIVES

1 Multiply Monomials. ▶

2 Use the Distributive Property to Multiply Polynomials. ▶

3 Multiply Polynomials Vertically. ▶

OBJECTIVE

1 Multiplying Monomials ▶

Recall from Section 5.1 that to multiply two monomials such as $(-5x^3)$ and $(-2x^4)$, we use the associative and commutative properties and regroup. Remember, also, that to multiply exponential expressions with a common base, we use the product rule for exponents and add exponents.

$$(-5x^3)(-2x^4) = (-5)(-2)(x^3)(x^4) = 10x^7$$

EXAMPLES   Multiply.

1. $6x \cdot 4x = (6 \cdot 4)(x \cdot x)$ Use the commutative and associative properties.

$$= 24x^2 \qquad \text{Multiply.}$$

2. $-7x^2 \cdot 0.2x^5 = (-7 \cdot 0.2)(x^2 \cdot x^5)$

$$= -1.4x^7$$

3. $\left(-\frac{1}{3}x^5\right)\left(-\frac{2}{9}x\right) = \left(-\frac{1}{3} \cdot -\frac{2}{9}\right) \cdot (x^5 \cdot x)$

$$= \frac{2}{27}x^6$$

PRACTICE
1–3   Multiply.

1. $5y \cdot 2y$

2. $(5z^3) \cdot (-0.4z^5)$

3. $\left(-\frac{1}{9}b^6\right)\left(-\frac{7}{8}b^3\right)$ ■

✔ **CONCEPT CHECK**

Simplify.

a. $3x \cdot 2x$ **b.** $3x + 2x$

OBJECTIVE

2   Using the Distributive Property to Multiply Polynomials ▶

To multiply polynomials that are not monomials, use the distributive property.

EXAMPLE 4   Use the distributive property to find each product.

a. $5x(2x^3 + 6)$ **b.** $-3x^2(5x^2 + 6x - 1)$

Solution

a. $5x(2x^3 + 6) = 5x(2x^3) + 5x(6)$ Use the distributive property.

$\qquad\qquad\qquad = 10x^4 + 30x$ Multiply.

b. $-3x^2(5x^2 + 6x - 1)$

$\qquad = (-3x^2)(5x^2) + (-3x^2)(6x) + (-3x^2)(-1)$ Use the distributive property.

$\qquad = -15x^4 - 18x^3 + 3x^2$ Multiply.   □

PRACTICE
4   Use the distributive property to find each product.

a. $3x(9x^5 + 11)$ **b.** $-6x^3(2x^2 - 9x + 2)$ ■

We also use the distributive property to multiply two binomials. To multiply $(x + 3)$ by $(x + 1)$, distribute the factor $(x + 3)$ first.

$(x + 3)(x + 1) = x(x + 1) + 3(x + 1)$ Distribute $(x + 3)$.

$\qquad\qquad = x(x) + x(1) + 3(x) + 3(1)$ Apply the distributive property a second time.

$\qquad\qquad = x^2 + x + 3x + 3$ Multiply.

$\qquad\qquad = x^2 + 4x + 3$ Combine like terms.

This idea can be expanded so that we can multiply any two polynomials.

To Multiply Two Polynomials

Multiply each term of the first polynomial by each term of the second polynomial and then combine like terms.

Answers to Concept Check:

a. $6x^2$ **b.** $5x$

EXAMPLE 5   Multiply: $(3x + 2)(2x - 5)$

Solution Multiply each term of the first binomial by each term of the second.

$$(3x + 2)(2x - 5) = 3x(2x) + 3x(-5) + 2(2x) + 2(-5)$$
$$= 6x^2 - 15x + 4x - 10 \qquad \text{Multiply.}$$
$$= 6x^2 - 11x - 10 \qquad \text{Combine like terms.} \quad \square$$

PRACTICE
5   Multiply: $(5x - 2)(2x + 3)$

EXAMPLE 6   Multiply: $(2x - y)^2$

Solution Recall that $a^2 = a \cdot a$, so $(2x - y)^2 = (2x - y)(2x - y)$. Multiply each term of the first polynomial by each term of the second.

$$(2x - y)(2x - y) = 2x(2x) + 2x(-y) + (-y)(2x) + (-y)(-y)$$
$$= 4x^2 - 2xy - 2xy + y^2 \qquad \text{Multiply.}$$
$$= 4x^2 - 4xy + y^2 \qquad \text{Combine like terms.} \quad \square$$

PRACTICE
6   Multiply: $(5x - 3y)^2$

✔ **CONCEPT CHECK**
Square where indicated. Simplify if possible.
a. $(4a)^2 + (3b)^2$ **b.** $(4a + 3b)^2$

EXAMPLE 7   Multiply $(t + 2)$ by $(3t^2 - 4t + 2)$.

Solution Multiply each term of the first polynomial by each term of the second.

$$(t + 2)(3t^2 - 4t + 2) = t(3t^2) + t(-4t) + t(2) + 2(3t^2) + 2(-4t) + 2(2)$$
$$= 3t^3 - 4t^2 + 2t + 6t^2 - 8t + 4$$
$$= 3t^3 + 2t^2 - 6t + 4 \quad \text{Combine like terms.} \quad \square$$

PRACTICE
7   Multiply $(y + 4)$ by $(2y^2 - 3y + 5)$.

EXAMPLE 8   Multiply: $(3a + b)^3$

Solution Write $(3a + b)^3$ as $(3a + b)(3a + b)(3a + b)$.

$$(3a + b)(3a + b)(3a + b) = (9a^2 + 3ab + 3ab + b^2)(3a + b)$$
$$= (9a^2 + 6ab + b^2)(3a + b)$$
$$= 9a^2(3a + b) + 6ab(3a + b) + b^2(3a + b)$$
$$= 27a^3 + 9a^2b + 18a^2b + 6ab^2 + 3ab^2 + b^3$$
$$= 27a^3 + 27a^2b + 9ab^2 + b^3 \quad \square$$

Answers to Concept Check:
a. $16a^2 + 9b^2$
b. $16a^2 + 24ab + 9b^2$

PRACTICE
8   Multiply: $(s + 2t)^3$

OBJECTIVE

3   Multiplying Polynomials Vertically ▶

Another convenient method for multiplying polynomials is to use a vertical format similar to the format used to multiply real numbers. We demonstrate this method by multiplying $(3y^2 - 4y + 1)$ by $(y + 2)$.

EXAMPLE 9   Multiply $(3y^2 - 4y + 1)$ by $(y + 2)$. Use a vertical format.

Solution

$$
\begin{array}{r}
3y^2 - 4y + 1 \\
\times \qquad y + 2 \\
\hline
6y^2 - 8y + 2 \\
3y^3 - 4y^2 + \ y \\
\hline
3y^3 + 2y^2 - 7y + 2
\end{array}
$$

Helpful Hint
Make sure like terms are lined up.

1st, multiply $3y^2 - 4y + 1$ by 2.
2nd, multiply $3y^2 - 4y + 1$ by y.
Line up like terms.
3rd, combine like terms.

Thus, $(3y^2 - 4y + 1)(y + 2) = 3y^3 + 2y^2 - 7y + 2$.   ☐

PRACTICE

9   Multiply $(5x^2 - 3x + 5)$ by $(x - 4)$. Use a vertical format.   ■

When multiplying vertically, be careful if a power is missing; you may want to leave space in the partial products and take care that like terms are lined up.

EXAMPLE 10   Multiply $(2x^3 - 3x + 4)$ by $(x^2 + 1)$. Use a vertical format.

Solution

$$
\begin{array}{r}
2x^3 - 3x + 4 \\
\times \qquad x^2 + 1 \\
\hline
2x^3 \qquad - 3x + 4 \\
2x^5 - 3x^3 + 4x^2 \\
\hline
2x^5 - \ x^3 + 4x^2 - 3x + 4
\end{array}
$$

Leave space for missing powers of x.
← Line up like terms.
Combine like terms.   ☐

PRACTICE

10   Multiply $(x^3 - 2x^2 + 1)$ by $(x^2 + 2)$ using a vertical format.   ■

EXAMPLE 11   Find the product of $(2x^2 - 3x + 4)$ and $(x^2 + 5x - 2)$ using a vertical format.

Solution   First, we arrange the polynomials in a vertical format. Then we multiply each term of the second polynomial by each term of the first polynomial.

$$
\begin{array}{r}
2x^2 - \ 3x + 4 \\
\times \qquad x^2 + \ 5x - 2 \\
\hline
-4x^2 + \ 6x - 8 \\
10x^3 - 15x^2 + 20x \\
2x^4 - \ 3x^3 + \ 4x^2 \\
\hline
2x^4 + \ 7x^3 - 15x^2 + 26x - 8
\end{array}
$$

Multiply $2x^2 - 3x + 4$ by -2.
Multiply $2x^2 - 3x + 4$ by $5x$.
Multiply $2x^2 - 3x + 4$ by x^2.
Combine like terms.   ☐

PRACTICE

11   Find the product of $(5x^2 + 2x - 2)$ and $(x^2 - x + 3)$ using a vertical format.   ■

✔ Vocabulary, Readiness & Video Check

Fill in each blank with the correct choice.

1. The expression $5x(3x + 2)$ equals $5x \cdot 3x + 5x \cdot 2$ by the _____ property.

   a. commutative   **b.** associative   **c.** distributive

2. The expression $(x + 4)(7x - 1)$ equals $x(7x - 1) + 4(7x - 1)$ by the _____ property.

   a. commutative   **b.** associative   **c.** distributive

3. The expression $(5y - 1)^2$ equals _____.

   a. $2(5y - 1)$ **b.** $(5y - 1)(5y + 1)$ **c.** $(5y - 1)(5y - 1)$

4. The expression $9x \cdot 3x$ equals _____.

   a. $27x$ **b.** $27x^2$ **c.** $12x$ **d.** $12x^2$

Martin-Gay Interactive Videos

See Video 5.3 ◉

Watch the section lecture video and answer the following questions.

OBJECTIVE 1

5. For ▦ Example 1, we use the product property to multiply the monomials. Is it possible to add the same two monomials? Why or why not?

OBJECTIVE 2

6. What property and what exponent rule is used in ▦ Examples 2–6?

OBJECTIVE 3

7. Would you say the vertical format used in ▦ Example 7 also applies the distributive property? Explain.

5.3 Exercise Set   MyMathLab® ▶

Multiply. See Examples 1 through 3.

1. $-4n^3 \cdot 7n^7$
2. $9t^6(-3t^5)$
3. $(-3.1x^3)(4x^9)$
4. $(-5.2x^4)(3x^4)$
5. $\left(-\frac{1}{3}y^2\right)\left(\frac{2}{5}y\right)$
6. $\left(-\frac{3}{4}y^7\right)\left(\frac{1}{7}y^4\right)$
7. $(2x)(-3x^2)(4x^5)$
8. $(x)(5x^4)(-6x^7)$

Multiply. See Example 4.

9. $3x(2x + 5)$
10. $2x(6x + 3)$
11. $-2a(a + 4)$
12. $-3a(2a + 7)$
13. $3x(2x^2 - 3x + 4)$
14. $4x(5x^2 - 6x - 10)$
15. $-2a^2(3a^2 - 2a + 3)$
16. $-4b^2(3b^3 - 12b^2 - 6)$
17. $-y(4x^3 - 7x^2y + xy^2 + 3y^3)$
18. $-x(6y^3 - 5xy^2 + x^2y - 5x^3)$
19. $\frac{1}{2}x^2(8x^2 - 6x + 1)$
20. $\frac{1}{3}y^2(9y^2 - 6y + 1)$

Multiply. See Examples 5 and 6.

21. $(x + 4)(x + 3)$
22. $(x + 2)(x + 9)$
23. $(a + 7)(a - 2)$
24. $(y - 10)(y + 11)$
25. $\left(x + \frac{2}{3}\right)\left(x - \frac{1}{3}\right)$
26. $\left(x + \frac{3}{5}\right)\left(x - \frac{2}{5}\right)$
27. $(3x^2 + 1)(4x^2 + 7)$
28. $(5x^2 + 2)(6x^2 + 2)$
29. $(2y - 4)^2$
30. $(6x - 7)^2$
31. $(4x - 3)(3x - 5)$
32. $(8x - 3)(2x - 4)$
33. $(3x^2 + 1)^2$
34. $(x^2 + 4)^2$
35. Perform the indicated operations.

   a. $4y^2(-y^2)$

   b. $4y^2 - y^2$

   c. Explain the difference between the two expressions.

36. Perform the indicated operations.

   a. $9x^2(-10x^2)$

   b. $9x^2 - 10x^2$

   c. Explain the difference between the two expressions.

Multiply. See Example 7.

37. $(x - 2)(x^2 - 3x + 7)$

38. $(x + 3)(x^2 + 5x - 8)$

▶ **39.** $(x + 5)(x^3 - 3x + 4)$

40. $(a + 2)(a^3 - 3a^2 + 7)$

41. $(2a - 3)(5a^2 - 6a + 4)$

42. $(3 + b)(2 - 5b - 3b^2)$

Multiply. See Example 8.

43. $(x + 2)^3$

44. $(y - 1)^3$

45. $(2y - 3)^3$

46. $(3x + 4)^3$

Multiply vertically. See Examples 9 through 11.

47. $(2x - 11)(6x + 1)$

48. $(4x - 7)(5x + 1)$

▶ **49.** $(5x + 1)(2x^2 + 4x - 1)$

50. $(4x - 5)(8x^2 + 2x - 4)$

51. $(x^2 + 5x - 7)(2x^2 - 7x - 9)$

52. $(3x^2 - x + 2)(x^2 + 2x + 1)$

MIXED PRACTICE

Multiply. See Examples 1 through 11.

53. $-1.2y(-7y^6)$

54. $-4.2x(-2x^5)$

55. $-3x(x^2 + 2x - 8)$

56. $-5x(x^2 - 3x + 10)$

57. $(x + 19)(2x + 1)$

58. $(3y + 4)(y + 11)$

59. $\left(x + \dfrac{1}{7}\right)\left(x - \dfrac{3}{7}\right)$

60. $\left(m + \dfrac{2}{9}\right)\left(m - \dfrac{1}{9}\right)$

61. $(3y + 5)^2$

62. $(7y + 2)^2$

63. $(a + 4)(a^2 - 6a + 6)$

64. $(t + 3)(t^2 - 5t + 5)$

65. $(2x - 5)^3$

66. $(3y - 1)^3$

67. $(4x + 5)(8x^2 + 2x - 4)$

68. $(5x + 4)(x^2 - x + 4)$

69. $(3x^2 + 2x - 4)(2x^2 - 4x + 3)$

70. $(a^2 + 3a - 2)(2a^2 - 5a - 1)$

Express as the product of polynomials. Then multiply.

△ **71.** Find the area of the rectangle.

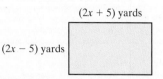

$(2x + 5)$ yards

$(2x - 5)$ yards

△ **72.** Find the area of the square field.

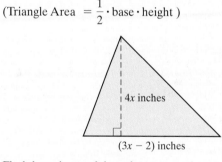

$(x + 4)$ feet

△ **73.** Find the area of the triangle.

$$\left(\text{Triangle Area } = \frac{1}{2} \cdot \text{base} \cdot \text{height}\right)$$

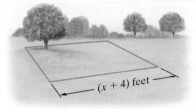

$4x$ inches

$(3x - 2)$ inches

△ **74.** Find the volume of the cube.

$$(\text{Volume} = \text{length} \cdot \text{width} \cdot \text{height})$$

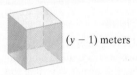

$(y - 1)$ meters

REVIEW AND PREVIEW

In this section, we review operations on monomials. Study the table below, then proceed. See Sections 2.1, 5.1, and 5.2. (Continued on next page)

Operations on Monomials	
Multiply	Review the product rule for exponents.
Divide	Review the quotient rule for exponents.
Add or Subtract	Remember, we may only combine like terms.

Perform the operations on the monomials if possible. The first two rows have been completed for you.

Monomials	Add	Subtract	Multiply	Divide
$6x, 3x$	$6x + 3x = 9x$	$6x - 3x = 3x$	$6x \cdot 3x = 18x^2$	$\dfrac{6x}{3x} = 2$
$-12x^2, 2x$	$-12x^2 + 2x$, can't be simplified	$-12x^2 - 2x$, can't be simplified	$-12x^2 \cdot 2x = -24x^3$	$\dfrac{-12x^2}{2x} = -6x$
75. $5a, 15a$				
76. $4y^7, 4y^3$				
77. $-3y^5, 9y^{\,4}$				
78. $-14x^2, 2x^{\,2}$				

CONCEPT EXTENSIONS

79. Perform each indicated operation. Explain the difference between the two expressions.

   a. $(3x + 5) + (3x + 7)$

   b. $(3x + 5)(3x + 7)$

80. Perform each indicated operation. Explain the difference between the two expressions.

   a. $(8x - 3) - (5x - 2)$

   b. $(8x - 3)(5x - 2)$

MIXED PRACTICE

Perform the indicated operations. See Sections 5.2 and 5.3.

81. $(3x - 1) + (10x - 6)$

82. $(2x - 1) + (10x - 7)$

83. $(3x - 1)(10x - 6)$

84. $(2x - 1)(10x - 7)$

85. $(3x - 1) - (10x - 6)$

86. $(2x - 1) - (10x - 7)$

CONCEPT EXTENSIONS

87. The area of the larger rectangle on the right is $x(x + 3)$. Find another expression for this area by finding the sum of the areas of the two smaller rectangles.

88. Write an expression for the area of the larger rectangle on the right in two different ways.

89. The area of the figure on the right is $(x + 2)(x + 3)$. Find another expression for this area by finding the sum of the areas of the four smaller rectangles.

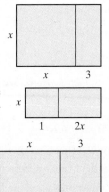

90. Write an expression for the area of the figure in two different ways.

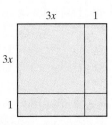

Simplify. See the Concept Checks in this section.

91. $5a + 6a$ **92.** $5a \cdot 6a$

Square where indicated. Simplify if possible.

93. $(5x)^2 + (2y)^2$ **94.** $(5x + 2y)^2$

95. Multiply each of the following polynomials.

   a. $(a + b)(a - b)$

   b. $(2x + 3y)(2x - 3y)$

   c. $(4x + 7)(4x - 7)$

   d. Can you make a general statement about all products of the form $(x + y)(x - y)$?

96. Evaluate each of the following.

   a. $(2 + 3)^2; 2^2 + 3^2$

   b. $(8 + 10)^2; 8^2 + 10^2$

   c. Does $(a + b)^2 = a^2 + b^2$ no matter what the values of a and b are? Why or why not?

97. Write a polynomial that describes the area of the shaded region. (Find the area of the larger square minus the area of the smaller square.)

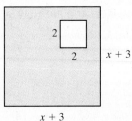

98. Write a polynomial that describes the area of the shaded region. (See Exercise 97.)

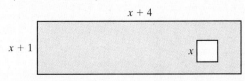

5.4   Special Products ▷

OBJECTIVES

1 Multiply Two Binomials Using the FOIL Method. ▷

2 Square a Binomial. ▷

3 Multiply the Sum and Difference of Two Terms. ▷

4 Use Special Products to Multiply Binomials. ▷

OBJECTIVE

1   Using the FOIL Method ▷

In this section, we multiply binomials using special products. First, a special order for multiplying binomials called the FOIL order or method is introduced. This method is demonstrated by multiplying $(3x + 1)$ by $(2x + 5)$ as shown below.

The FOIL Method

F stands for the product of the **First** terms. $(3x + 1)(2x + 5)$

$$(3x)(2x) = 6x^2 \quad \textbf{F}$$

O stands for the product of the **Outer** terms. $(3x + 1)(2x + 5)$

$$(3x)(5) = 15x \quad \textbf{O}$$

I stands for the product of the **Inner** terms. $(3x + 1)(2x + 5)$

$$(1)(2x) = 2x \quad \textbf{I}$$

L stands for the product of the **Last** terms. $(3x + 1)(2x + 5)$

$$(1)(5) = 5 \quad \textbf{L}$$

$$\begin{array}{cccc} \text{F} & \text{O} & \text{I} & \text{L} \end{array}$$

$$(3x + 1)(2x + 5) = 6x^2 + 15x + 2x + 5$$
$$= 6x^2 + 17x + 5 \qquad \text{Combine like terms.}$$

✔ **CONCEPT CHECK**

Multiply $(3x + 1)(2x + 5)$ using methods from the last section. Show that the product is still $6x^2 + 17x + 5$.

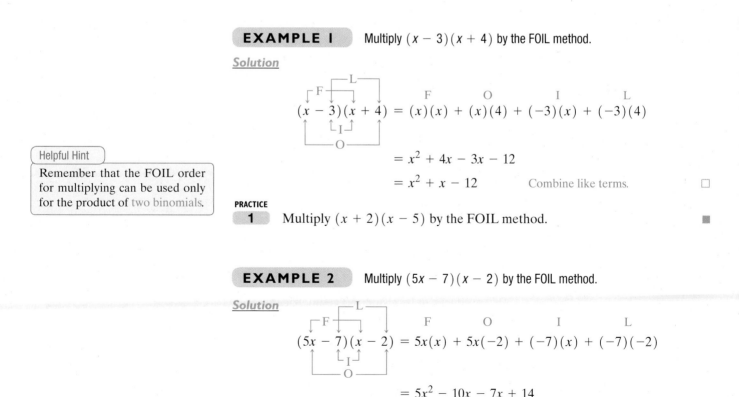

EXAMPLE 1   Multiply $(x - 3)(x + 4)$ by the FOIL method.

Solution

$$(x - 3)(x + 4) = \overset{\text{F}}{(x)(x)} + \overset{\text{O}}{(x)(4)} + \overset{\text{I}}{(-3)(x)} + \overset{\text{L}}{(-3)(4)}$$

$$= x^2 + 4x - 3x - 12$$
$$= x^2 + x - 12 \qquad \text{Combine like terms.} \qquad \square$$

Helpful Hint

Remember that the FOIL order for multiplying can be used only for the product of two binomials.

PRACTICE
1   Multiply $(x + 2)(x - 5)$ by the FOIL method.   ■

EXAMPLE 2   Multiply $(5x - 7)(x - 2)$ by the FOIL method.

Solution

$$(5x - 7)(x - 2) = \overset{\text{F}}{5x(x)} + \overset{\text{O}}{5x(-2)} + \overset{\text{I}}{(-7)(x)} + \overset{\text{L}}{(-7)(-2)}$$

$$= 5x^2 - 10x - 7x + 14$$
$$= 5x^2 - 17x + 14 \qquad \text{Combine like terms.} \qquad \square$$

Answer to Concept Check:
Multiply and simplify.
$3x(2x + 5) + 1(2x + 5)$

PRACTICE
2   Multiply $(4x - 9)(x - 1)$ by the FOIL method.   ■

EXAMPLE 3   Multiply: $2(y + 6)(2y - 1)$

Solution $2(y + 6)(2y - 1) = 2(\overset{F}{2y^2} - \overset{O}{1y} + \overset{I}{12y} - \overset{L}{6})$

$\qquad\qquad\qquad\quad = 2(2y^2 + 11y - 6)$ Simplify inside parentheses.

$\qquad\qquad\qquad\quad = 4y^2 + 22y - 12$ Now use the distributive property.   □

PRACTICE
3   Multiply: $3(x + 5)(3x - 1)$ ■

OBJECTIVE
2   Squaring Binomials   ▶

Now, try squaring a binomial using the FOIL method.

EXAMPLE 4   Multiply: $(3y + 1)^2$

Solution $(3y + 1)^2 = (3y + 1)(3y + 1)$

$\qquad\qquad\qquad = \overset{F}{(3y)(3y)} + \overset{O}{(3y)(1)} + \overset{I}{1(3y)} + \overset{L}{1(1)}$

$\qquad\qquad\qquad = 9y^2 + 3y + 3y + 1$

$\qquad\qquad\qquad = 9y^2 + 6y + 1$ □

PRACTICE
4   Multiply: $(4x - 1)^2$ ■

Notice the pattern that appears in Example 4.

$(3y + 1)^2 = 9y^2 + 6y + 1$

$9y^2$ is the first term of the binomial squared. $(3y)^2 = 9y^2$.

$6y$ is 2 times the product of both terms of the binomial. $(2)(3y)(1) = 6y$.

1 is the second term of the binomial squared. $(1)^2 = 1$.

This pattern leads to the following, which can be used when squaring a binomial. We call these **special products.**

Squaring a Binomial

A binomial squared is equal to the square of the first term plus or minus twice the product of both terms plus the square of the second term.

$$(a + b)^2 = a^2 + 2ab + b^2$$
$$(a - b)^2 = a^2 - 2ab + b^2$$

This product can be visualized geometrically.

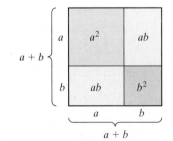

The area of the large square is side · side.

$$\text{Area} = (a + b)(a + b) = (a + b)^2$$

The area of the large square is also the sum of the areas of the smaller rectangles.

$$\text{Area} = a^2 + ab + ab + b^2 = a^2 + 2ab + b^2$$

Thus, $(a + b)^2 = a^2 + 2ab + b^2$.

EXAMPLE 5   Use a special product to square each binomial.

a. $(t + 2)^2$ **b.** $(p - q)^2$ **c.** $(2x + 5)^2$ **d.** $(x^2 - 7y)^2$

Solution

first term squared	plus or minus	twice the product of the terms	plus	second term squared

a. $(t + 2)^2 = t^2 + 2(t)(2) + 2^2 = t^2 + 4t + 4$

b. $(p - q)^2 = p^2 - 2(p)(q) + q^2 = p^2 - 2pq + q^2$

c. $(2x + 5)^2 = (2x)^2 + 2(2x)(5) + 5^2 = 4x^2 + 20x + 25$

d. $(x^2 - 7y)^2 = (x^2)^2 - 2(x^2)(7y) + (7y^2) = x^4 - 14x^2y + 49y^2$

□

PRACTICE

5   Use a special product to square each binomial.

a. $(b + 3)^2$ **b.** $(x - y)^2$

c. $(3y + 2)^2$ **d.** $(a^2 - 5b)^2$ ∎

Helpful Hint

Notice that

$$(a + b)^2 \neq a^2 + b^2 \quad \text{The middle term } 2ab \text{ is missing.}$$
$$(a + b)^2 = (a + b)(a + b) = a^2 + 2ab + b^2$$

Likewise,

$$(a - b)^2 \neq a^2 - b^2$$
$$(a - b)^2 = (a - b)(a - b) = a^2 - 2ab + b^2$$

OBJECTIVE

3   Multiplying the Sum and Difference of Two Terms ▶

Another special product is the product of the sum and difference of the same two terms, such as $(x + y)(x - y)$. Finding this product by the FOIL method, we see a pattern emerge.

$$(x + y)(x - y) = x^2 - xy + xy - y^2$$

$$= x^2 - y^2$$

Notice that the middle two terms subtract out. This is because the **O**uter product is the opposite of the **I**nner product. Only the **difference of squares** remains.

Multiplying the Sum and Difference of Two Terms

The product of the sum and difference of two terms is the square of the first term minus the square of the second term.

$$(a + b)(a - b) = a^2 - b^2$$

EXAMPLE 6   Use a special product to multiply.

a. $4(x+4)(x-4)$ b. $(6t+7)(6t-7)$ c. $\left(x-\dfrac{1}{4}\right)\left(x+\dfrac{1}{4}\right)$

d. $(2p-q)(2p+q)$ e. $(3x^2-5y)(3x^2+5y)$

Solution

first term squared	minus	second term squared
↓	↓	↙

a. $4(x+4)(x-4) = 4(x^2 \quad - \quad 4^2) = 4(x^2-16) = 4x^2-64$

b. $(6t+7)(6t-7) = (6t)^2 \quad - \quad 7^2 = 36t^2-49$

c. $\left(x-\dfrac{1}{4}\right)\left(x+\dfrac{1}{4}\right) = x^2 - \left(\dfrac{1}{4}\right)^2 = x^2 - \dfrac{1}{16}$

d. $(2p-q)(2p+q) = (2p)^2 - q^2 = 4p^2-q^2$

e. $(3x^2-5y)(3x^2+5y) = (3x^2)^2 - (5y)^2 = 9x^4-25y^2$ □

PRACTICE
6   Use a special product to multiply.

a. $3(x+5)(x-5)$ b. $(4b-3)(4b+3)$

c. $\left(x+\dfrac{2}{3}\right)\left(x-\dfrac{2}{3}\right)$ d. $(5s+t)(5s-t)$

e. $(2y-3z^2)(2y+3z^2)$ ■

✔ **CONCEPT CHECK**

Match expression number 1 and number 2 to the equivalent expression or expressions in the list below.

1. $(a+b)^2$ **2.** $(a+b)(a-b)$

A. $(a+b)(a+b)$ **B.** a^2-b^2 **C.** a^2+b^2 **D.** $a^2-2ab+b^2$ **E.** $a^2+2ab+b^2$

OBJECTIVE
4   Using Special Products ▶

Let's now practice multiplying polynomials in general. If possible, use a special product.

EXAMPLE 7   Use a special product to multiply, if possible.

a. $(x-5)(3x+4)$ b. $(7x+4)^2$ c. $(y-0.6)(y+0.6)$

d. $\left(y^4+\dfrac{2}{5}\right)\left(3y^2-\dfrac{1}{5}\right)$ e. $(a-3)(a^2+2a-1)$

Solution

a. $(x-5)(3x+4) = 3x^2+4x-15x-20$ FOIL.
$\qquad\qquad\qquad = 3x^2-11x-20$

b. $(7x+4)^2 = (7x)^2 + 2(7x)(4) + 4^2$ Squaring a binomial.
$\qquad\qquad = 49x^2+56x+16$

c. $(y-0.6)(y+0.6) = y^2-(0.6)^2 = y^2-0.36$ Multiplying the sum and difference of 2 terms.

d. $\left(y^4+\dfrac{2}{5}\right)\left(3y^2-\dfrac{1}{5}\right) = 3y^6 - \dfrac{1}{5}y^4 + \dfrac{6}{5}y^2 - \dfrac{2}{25}$ FOIL.

e. I've inserted this product as a reminder that since it is not a binomial times a binomial, the FOIL order may not be used.

$$(a - 3)(a^2 + 2a - 1) = a(a^2 + 2a - 1) - 3(a^2 + 2a - 1)$$

Multiplying each term of the binomial by each term of the trinomial.

$$= a^3 + 2a^2 - a - 3a^2 - 6a + 3$$

$$= a^3 - a^2 - 7a + 3 \qquad \square$$

PRACTICE

7   Use a special product to multiply, if possible.

a. $(4x + 3)(x - 6)$

b. $(7b - 2)^2$

c. $(x + 0.4)(x - 0.4)$

d. $\left(x^2 - \dfrac{3}{7}\right)\left(3x^4 + \dfrac{2}{7}\right)$

e. $(x + 1)(x^2 + 5x - 2)$

Helpful Hint

- When multiplying two binomials, you may always use the FOIL order or method.
- When multiplying any two polynomials, you may always use the distributive property to find the product.

✔ Vocabulary, Readiness & Video Check

Answer each exercise true or false.

1. $(x + 4)^2 = x^2 + 16$

2. For $(x + 6)(2x - 1)$ the product of the first terms is $2x^2$.

3. $(x + 4)(x - 4) = x^2 + 16$

4. The product $(x - 1)(x^3 + 3x - 1)$ is a polynomial of degree 5.

Martin-Gay Interactive Videos

See Video 5.4 ⦿

Watch the section lecture video and answer the following questions.

OBJECTIVE 1

5. From ▤ Examples 1–3, for what type of multiplication problem is the FOIL order of multiplication used?

OBJECTIVE 2

6. Name at least one other method you can use to multiply ▤ Example 4.

OBJECTIVE 3

7. From ▤ Example 5, why does multiplying the sum and difference of the same two terms always give you a binomial answer?

OBJECTIVE 4

8. Why was the FOIL method not used for ▤ Example 10?

5.4   Exercise Set   MyMathLab® ▶

Multiply using the FOIL method. See Examples 1 through 3.

▶ **1.** $(x + 3)(x + 4)$

2. $(x + 5)(x - 1)$

3. $(x - 5)(x + 10)$

4. $(y - 12)(y + 4)$

5. $(5x - 6)(x + 2)$

6. $(3y - 5)(2y - 7)$

7. $5(y - 6)(4y - 1)$

8. $2(x - 11)(2x - 9)$

9. $(2x + 5)(3x - 1)$

10. $(6x + 2)(x - 2)$

11. $\left(x - \dfrac{1}{3}\right)\left(x + \dfrac{2}{3}\right)$

12. $\left(x - \dfrac{2}{5}\right)\left(x + \dfrac{1}{5}\right)$

Multiply. See Examples 4 and 5.

13. $(x + 2)^2$

14. $(x + 7)^2$

▶ **15.** $(2x - 1)^2$

16. $(7x - 3)^2$

17. $(3a - 5)^2$

18. $(5a + 2)^2$

▶ **19.** $(5x + 9)^2$

20. $(6s - 2)^2$

Multiply. See Example 6.

21. $(a - 7)(a + 7)$

22. $(b + 3)(b - 3)$

23. $(3x - 1)(3x + 1)$

24. $(4x - 5)(4x + 5)$

25. $\left(3x - \dfrac{1}{2}\right)\left(3x + \dfrac{1}{2}\right)$

26. $\left(10x + \dfrac{2}{7}\right)\left(10x - \dfrac{2}{7}\right)$

27. $(9x + y)(9x - y)$

28. $(2x - y)(2x + y)$

29. $(2x + 0.1)(2x - 0.1)$

30. $(5x - 1.3)(5x + 1.3)$

MIXED PRACTICE

Multiply. See Example 7.

31. $(a + 5)(a + 4)$

32. $(a - 5)(a - 7)$

33. $(a + 7)^2$

34. $(b - 2)^2$

35. $(4a + 1)(3a - 1)$

36. $(6a + 7)(6a + 5)$

37. $(x + 2)(x - 2)$

38. $(x - 10)(x + 10)$

39. $(3a + 1)^2$

40. $(4a - 2)^2$

41. $(x^2 + y)(4x - y^4)$

42. $(x^3 - 2)(5x + y)$

43. $(x + 3)(x^2 - 6x + 1)$

44. $(x - 2)(x^2 - 4x + 2)$

45. $(2a - 3)^2$

46. $(5b - 4x)^2$

47. $(5x - 6z)(5x + 6z)$

48. $(11x - 7y)(11x + 7y)$

49. $(x^5 - 3)(x^5 - 5)$

50. $(a^4 + 5)(a^4 + 6)$

51. $(x + 0.8)(x - 0.8)$

52. $(y - 0.9)(y + 0.9)$

53. $(a^3 + 11)(a^4 - 3)$

54. $(x^5 + 5)(x^2 - 8)$

55. $3(x - 2)^2$

56. $2(3b + 7)^2$

57. $(3b + 7)(2b - 5)$

58. $(3y - 13)(y - 3)$

59. $(7p - 8)(7p + 8)$

60. $(3s - 4)(3s + 4)$

61. $\left(\dfrac{1}{3}a^2 - 7\right)\left(\dfrac{1}{3}a^2 + 7\right)$

62. $\left(\dfrac{2}{3}a - b^2\right)\left(\dfrac{2}{3}a + b^2\right)$

63. $5x^2(3x^2 - x + 2)$

64. $4x^3(2x^2 + 5x - 1)$

65. $(2r - 3s)(2r + 3s)$

66. $(6r - 2x)(6r + 2x)$

67. $(3x - 7y)^2$

68. $(4s - 2y)^2$

69. $(4x + 5)(4x - 5)$

70. $(3x + 5)(3x - 5)$

71. $(8x + 4)^2$

72. $(3x + 2)^2$

73. $\left(a - \dfrac{1}{2}y\right)\left(a + \dfrac{1}{2}y\right)$

74. $\left(\dfrac{a}{2} + 4y\right)\left(\dfrac{a}{2} - 4y\right)$

75. $\left(\dfrac{1}{5}x - y\right)\left(\dfrac{1}{5}x + y\right)$

76. $\left(\dfrac{y}{6} - 8\right)\left(\dfrac{y}{6} + 8\right)$

77. $(a + 1)(3a^2 - a + 1)$

78. $(b + 3)(2b^2 + b - 3)$

Express each as a product of polynomials in x. Then multiply and simplify.

79. Find the area of the square rug shown if its side is $(2x + 1)$ feet.

$(2x + 1)$ feet

$(2x + 1)$ feet

80. Find the area of the rectangular canvas if its length is $(3x - 2)$ inches and its width is $(x - 4)$ inches.

$(x - 4)$ inches

$(3x - 2)$ inches

REVIEW AND PREVIEW

Simplify each expression. See Section 5.1.

81. $\dfrac{50b^{10}}{70b^5}$

82. $\dfrac{x^3y^6}{xy^2}$

83. $\dfrac{8a^{17}b^{15}}{-4a^7b^{10}}$

84. $\dfrac{-6a^8y}{3a^4y}$

85. $\dfrac{2x^4y^{12}}{3x^4y^4}$

86. $\dfrac{-48ab^6}{32ab^3}$

Find the slope of each line. See Section 3.4.

87.

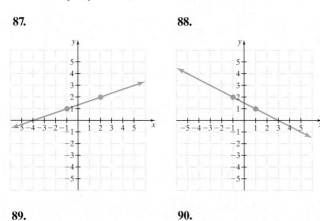

88.

89.

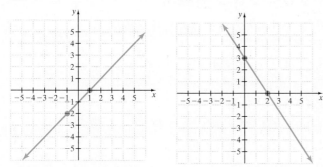

90.

99.

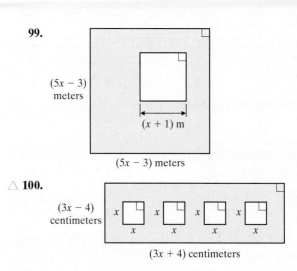

$(5x - 3)$ meters

$(x + 1)$ m

$(5x - 3)$ meters

△ **100.**

$(3x - 4)$ centimeters

x x x x

x x x x

$(3x + 4)$ centimeters

For Exercises 101 and 102, find the area of the shaded figure.

△ **101.**

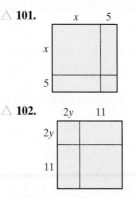

x 5

x

5

△ **102.**

$2y$ 11

$2y$

11

CONCEPT EXTENSIONS

Match each expression on the left to the equivalent expression on the right. See the second Concept Check in this section.

91. $(a - b)^2$ **A.** $a^2 - b^2$

92. $(a - b)(a + b)$ **B.** $a^2 + b^2$

93. $(a + b)^2$ **C.** $a^2 - 2ab + b^2$

94. $(a + b)^2(a - b)^2$ **D.** $a^2 + 2ab + b^2$

E. none of these

Fill in the squares so that a true statement forms.

95. $(x^\square + 7)(x^\square + 3) = x^4 + 10x^2 + 21$

96. $(5x^\square - 2)^2 = 25x^6 - 20x^3 + 4$

Find the area of the shaded figure. To do so, subtract the area of the smaller square(s) from the area of the larger geometric figure.

△ **97.**

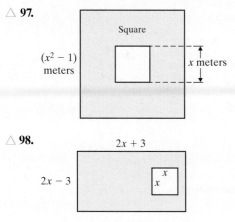

Square

$(x^2 - 1)$ meters

x meters

△ **98.**

$2x + 3$

$2x - 3$

x

x

103. In your own words, describe the different methods that can be used to find the product $(2x - 5)(3x + 1)$.

104. In your own words, describe the different methods that can be used to find the product $(5x + 1)^2$.

105. Suppose that a classmate asked you why $(2x + 1)^2$ is **not** $(4x^2 + 1)$. Write down your response to this classmate.

106. Suppose that a classmate asked you why $(2x + 1)^2$ **is** $(4x^2 + 4x + 1)$. Write down your response to this classmate.

107. Using your own words, explain how to square a binomial such as $(a + b)^2$.

108. Explain how to find the product of two binomials using the FOIL method.

Find each product. For example,

$$[(a + b) - 2][(a + b) + 2] = (a + b)^2 - 2^2$$
$$= a^2 + 2ab + b^2 - 4$$

109. $[(x + y) - 3][(x + y) + 3]$

110. $[(a + c) - 5][(a + c) + 5]$

111. $[(a - 3) + b][(a - 3) - b]$

112. $[(x - 2) + y][(x - 2) - y]$

Integrated Review — Exponents and Operations on Polynomials

Sections 5.1–5.4

Perform the indicated operations and simplify.

1. $(5x^2)(7x^3)$

2. $(4y^2)(8y^7)$

3. -4^2

4. $(-4)^2$

5. $(x - 5)(2x + 1)$

6. $(3x - 2)(x + 5)$

7. $(x - 5) + (2x + 1)$

8. $(3x - 2) + (x + 5)$

9. $\dfrac{7x^9y^{12}}{x^3y^{10}}$

10. $\dfrac{20a^2b^8}{14a^2b^2}$

11. $(12m^7n^6)^2$

12. $(4y^9z^{10})^3$

13. $3(4y - 3)(4y + 3)$

14. $2(7x - 1)(7x + 1)$

15. $(x^7y^5)^9$

16. $(3^1x^9)^3$

17. $(7x^2 - 2x + 3) - (5x^2 + 9)$

18. $(10x^2 + 7x - 9) - (4x^2 - 6x + 2)$

19. $0.7y^2 - 1.2 + 1.8y^2 - 6y + 1$

20. $7.8x^2 - 6.8x + 3.3 + 0.6x^2 - 9$

21. $(x + 4y)^2$

22. $(y - 9z)^2$

23. $(x + 4y) + (x + 4y)$

24. $(y - 9z) + (y - 9z)$

25. $7x^2 - 6xy + 4(y^2 - xy)$

26. $5a^2 - 3ab + 6(b^2 - a^2)$

27. $(x - 3)(x^2 + 5x - 1)$

28. $(x + 1)(x^2 - 3x - 2)$

29. $(2x^3 - 7)(3x^2 + 10)$

30. $(5x^3 - 1)(4x^4 + 5)$

31. $(2x - 7)(x^2 - 6x + 1)$

32. $(5x - 1)(x^2 + 2x - 3)$

Perform the indicated operations and simplify if possible.

33. $5x^3 + 5y^3$

34. $(5x^3)(5y^3)$

35. $(5x^3)^3$

36. $\dfrac{5x^3}{5y^3}$

37. $x + x$

38. $x \cdot x$

5.5 Negative Exponents and Scientific Notation ▶

OBJECTIVES

1 Simplify Expressions Containing Negative Exponents. ▶

2 Use All the Rules and Definitions for Exponents to Simplify Exponential Expressions. ▶

3 Write Numbers in Scientific Notation. ▶

4 Convert Numbers from Scientific Notation to Standard Form. ▶

5 Perform Operations on Numbers Written in Scientific Notation. ▶

OBJECTIVE

1 Simplifying Expressions Containing Negative Exponents ▶

Our work with exponential expressions so far has been limited to exponents that are positive integers or 0. Here we expand to give meaning to an expression like x^{-3}.

Suppose that we wish to simplify the expression $\dfrac{x^2}{x^5}$. If we use the quotient rule for exponents, we subtract exponents:

$$\frac{x^2}{x^5} = x^{2-5} = x^{-3}, \quad x \neq 0$$

But what does x^{-3} mean? Let's simplify $\dfrac{x^2}{x^5}$ using the definition of x^n.

$$\frac{x^2}{x^5} = \frac{x \cdot x}{x \cdot x \cdot x \cdot x \cdot x}$$

$$= \frac{\overset{1}{\cancel{x}} \cdot \overset{1}{\cancel{x}}}{\underset{1}{\cancel{x}} \cdot \underset{1}{\cancel{x}} \cdot x \cdot x \cdot x}$$

Divide numerator and denominator by common factors by applying the fundamental principle for fractions.

$$= \frac{1}{x^3}$$

If the quotient rule is to hold true for negative exponents, then x^{-3} must equal $\dfrac{1}{x^3}$.

From this example, we state the definition for negative exponents.

Negative Exponents

If a is a real number other than 0 and n is an integer, then

$$a^{-n} = \frac{1}{a^n}$$

For example, $x^{-3} = \frac{1}{x^3}$.

In other words, another way to write a^{-n} is to take its reciprocal and change the sign of its exponent.

EXAMPLE 1   Simplify by writing each expression with positive exponents only.

a. 3^{-2} **b.** $2x^{-3}$ **c.** $2^{-1} + 4^{-1}$ **d.** $(-2)^{-4}$ **e.** y^{-4}

Solution

a. $3^{-2} = \dfrac{1}{3^2} = \dfrac{1}{9}$ Use the definition of negative exponents.

b. $2x^{-3} = 2 \cdot \dfrac{1}{x^3} = \dfrac{2}{x^3}$ Use the definition of negative exponents.

c. $2^{-1} + 4^{-1} = \dfrac{1}{2} + \dfrac{1}{4} = \dfrac{2}{4} + \dfrac{1}{4} = \dfrac{3}{4}$

d. $(-2)^{-4} = \dfrac{1}{(-2)^4} = \dfrac{1}{(-2)(-2)(-2)(-2)} = \dfrac{1}{16}$

e. $y^{-4} = \dfrac{1}{y^4}$

Helpful Hint
Don't forget that since there are no parentheses, only x is the base for the exponent -3.

PRACTICE

1   Simplify by writing each expression with positive exponents only.

a. 5^{-3} **b.** $3y^{-4}$ **c.** $3^{-1} + 2^{-1}$ **d.** $(-5)^{-2}$ **e.** x^{-5}

Helpful Hint
A negative exponent _does not affect_ the sign of its base. Remember: Another way to write a^{-n} is to take its reciprocal and change the sign of its exponent: $a^{-n} = \dfrac{1}{a^n}$. For example, $$x^{-2} = \frac{1}{x^2}, \qquad 2^{-3} = \frac{1}{2^3} \text{ or } \frac{1}{8}$$ $$\frac{1}{y^{-4}} = \frac{1}{\frac{1}{y^4}} = y^4, \qquad \frac{1}{5^{-2}} = 5^2 \text{ or } 25$$

From the preceding Helpful Hint, we know that $x^{-2} = \dfrac{1}{x^2}$ and $\dfrac{1}{y^{-4}} = y^4$. We can use this to include another statement in our definition of negative exponents.

Negative Exponents

If a is a real number other than 0 and n is an integer, then

$$a^{-n} = \frac{1}{a^n} \quad \text{and} \quad \frac{1}{a^{-n}} = a^n$$

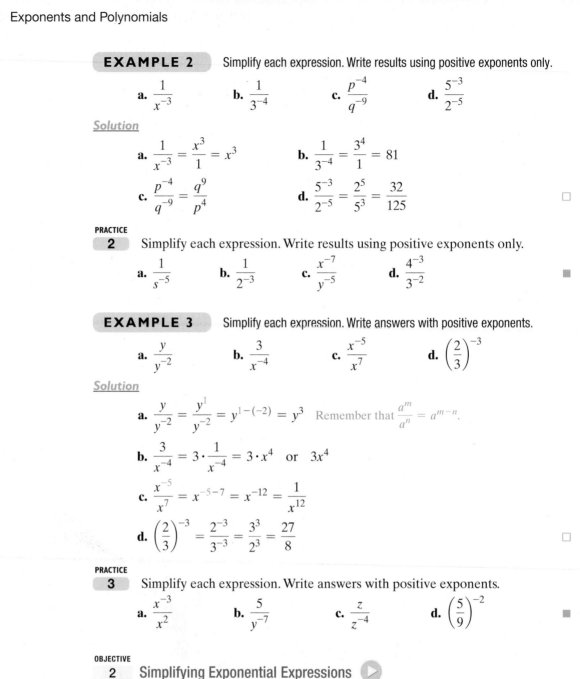

EXAMPLE 2 Simplify each expression. Write results using positive exponents only.

a. $\dfrac{1}{x^{-3}}$ **b.** $\dfrac{1}{3^{-4}}$ **c.** $\dfrac{p^{-4}}{q^{-9}}$ **d.** $\dfrac{5^{-3}}{2^{-5}}$

Solution

a. $\dfrac{1}{x^{-3}} = \dfrac{x^3}{1} = x^3$ **b.** $\dfrac{1}{3^{-4}} = \dfrac{3^4}{1} = 81$

c. $\dfrac{p^{-4}}{q^{-9}} = \dfrac{q^9}{p^4}$ **d.** $\dfrac{5^{-3}}{2^{-5}} = \dfrac{2^5}{5^3} = \dfrac{32}{125}$

PRACTICE
2 Simplify each expression. Write results using positive exponents only.

a. $\dfrac{1}{s^{-5}}$ **b.** $\dfrac{1}{2^{-3}}$ **c.** $\dfrac{x^{-7}}{y^{-5}}$ **d.** $\dfrac{4^{-3}}{3^{-2}}$

EXAMPLE 3 Simplify each expression. Write answers with positive exponents.

a. $\dfrac{y}{y^{-2}}$ **b.** $\dfrac{3}{x^{-4}}$ **c.** $\dfrac{x^{-5}}{x^7}$ **d.** $\left(\dfrac{2}{3}\right)^{-3}$

Solution

a. $\dfrac{y}{y^{-2}} = \dfrac{y^1}{y^{-2}} = y^{1-(-2)} = y^3$ Remember that $\dfrac{a^m}{a^n} = a^{m-n}$.

b. $\dfrac{3}{x^{-4}} = 3 \cdot \dfrac{1}{x^{-4}} = 3 \cdot x^4$ or $3x^4$

c. $\dfrac{x^{-5}}{x^7} = x^{-5-7} = x^{-12} = \dfrac{1}{x^{12}}$

d. $\left(\dfrac{2}{3}\right)^{-3} = \dfrac{2^{-3}}{3^{-3}} = \dfrac{3^3}{2^3} = \dfrac{27}{8}$

PRACTICE
3 Simplify each expression. Write answers with positive exponents.

a. $\dfrac{x^{-3}}{x^2}$ **b.** $\dfrac{5}{y^{-7}}$ **c.** $\dfrac{z}{z^{-4}}$ **d.** $\left(\dfrac{5}{9}\right)^{-2}$

OBJECTIVE

2 Simplifying Exponential Expressions ▶

All the previously stated rules for exponents apply for negative exponents also. Here is a summary of the rules and definitions for exponents.

Summary of Exponent Rules

If m and n are integers and a, b, and c are real numbers, then:

Product rule for exponents: $a^m \cdot a^n = a^{m+n}$

Power rule for exponents: $(a^m)^n = a^{m \cdot n}$

Power of a product: $(ab)^n = a^n b^n$

Power of a quotient: $\left(\dfrac{a}{c}\right)^n = \dfrac{a^n}{c^n},\quad c \neq 0$

Quotient rule for exponents: $\dfrac{a^m}{a^n} = a^{m-n},\quad a \neq 0$

Zero exponent: $a^0 = 1,\quad a \neq 0$

Negative exponent: $a^{-n} = \dfrac{1}{a^n},\quad a \neq 0$

EXAMPLE 4   Simplify the following expressions. Write each result using positive exponents only.

a. $(y^{-3}z^6)^{-6}$ **b.** $\dfrac{(2x^3)^4 x}{x^7}$ **c.** $\left(\dfrac{3a^2}{b}\right)^{-3}$ **d.** $\dfrac{4^{-1}x^{-3}y}{4^{-3}x^2 y^{-6}}$ **e.** $\left(\dfrac{-2x^3 y}{xy^{-1}}\right)^3$

Solution

a. $(y^{-3}z^6)^{-6} = y^{18} \cdot z^{-36} = \dfrac{y^{18}}{z^{36}}$

b. $\dfrac{(2x^3)^4 x}{x^7} = \dfrac{2^4 \cdot x^{12} \cdot x}{x^7} = \dfrac{16 \cdot x^{12+1}}{x^7} = \dfrac{16x^{13}}{x^7} = 16x^{13-7} = 16x^6$ Use the power rule.

c. $\left(\dfrac{3a^2}{b}\right)^{-3} = \dfrac{3^{-3}(a^2)^{-3}}{b^{-3}}$ Raise each factor in the numerator and the denominator to the -3 power.

$= \dfrac{3^{-3}a^{-6}}{b^{-3}}$ Use the power rule.

$= \dfrac{b^3}{3^3 a^6}$ Use the negative exponent rule.

$= \dfrac{b^3}{27a^6}$ Write 3^3 as 27.

d. $\dfrac{4^{-1}x^{-3}y}{4^{-3}x^2 y^{-6}} = 4^{-1-(-3)}x^{-3-2}y^{1-(-6)} = 4^2 x^{-5}y^7 = \dfrac{4^2 y^7}{x^5} = \dfrac{16y^7}{x^5}$

e. $\left(\dfrac{-2x^3 y}{xy^{-1}}\right)^3 = \dfrac{(-2)^3 x^9 y^3}{x^3 y^{-3}} = \dfrac{-8x^9 y^3}{x^3 y^{-3}} = -8x^{9-3}y^{3-(-3)} = -8x^6 y^6$ □

PRACTICE
4   Simplify the following expressions. Write each result using positive exponents only.

a. $(a^4 b^{-3})^{-5}$ **b.** $\dfrac{x^2(x^5)^3}{x^7}$ **c.** $\left(\dfrac{5p^8}{q}\right)^{-2}$

d. $\dfrac{6^{-2}x^{-4}y^{-7}}{6^{-3}x^3 y^{-9}}$ **e.** $\left(\dfrac{-3x^4 y}{x^2 y^{-2}}\right)^3$ ■

OBJECTIVE
3   Writing Numbers in Scientific Notation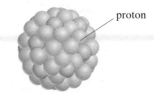

Both very large and very small numbers frequently occur in many fields of science. For example, the distance between the Sun and the dwarf planet Pluto is approximately 5,906,000,000 kilometers, and the mass of a proton is approximately 0.000000000000000000000000165 gram. It can be tedious to write these numbers in this standard decimal notation, so **scientific notation** is used as a convenient shorthand for expressing very large and very small numbers.

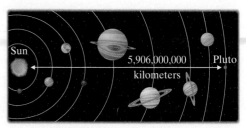

proton

Mass of proton is approximately
0.000 000 000 000 000 000 000 001 65 gram

Sun   5,906,000,000   Pluto
kilometers

Scientific Notation

A positive number is written in scientific notation if it is written as the product of a number a, where $1 \le a < 10$, and an integer power r of 10:

$$a \times 10^r$$

The numbers below are written in scientific notation. The $\times$ sign for multiplication is used as part of the notation.

$$2.03 \times 10^2 \qquad 7.362 \times 10^7 \qquad 5.906 \times 10^9 \qquad \text{(Distance between the Sun and Pluto)}$$
$$1 \times 10^{-3} \qquad 8.1 \times 10^{-5} \qquad 1.65 \times 10^{-24} \qquad \text{(Mass of a proton)}$$

The following steps are useful when writing numbers in scientific notation.

To Write a Number in Scientific Notation

Step 1. Move the decimal point in the original number to the left or right so that the new number has a value between 1 and 10 (including 1).

Step 2. Count the number of decimal places the decimal point is moved in Step 1. If the original number is 10 or greater, the count is positive. If the original number is less than 1, the count is negative.

Step 3. Multiply the new number in Step 1 by 10 raised to an exponent equal to the count found in Step 2.

EXAMPLE 5 Write each number in scientific notation.

    a. 367,000,000   **b.** 0.000003   **c.** 20,520,000,000   **d.** 0.00085

Solution

    a. Step 1. Move the decimal point until the number is between 1 and 10.

        367,000,000.
               8 places

    Step 2. The decimal point is moved 8 places, and the original number is 10 or greater, so the count is positive 8.

    Step 3. $367,000,000 = 3.67 \times 10^8$.

    b. Step 1. Move the decimal point until the number is between 1 and 10.

        0.000003
            6 places

    Step 2. The decimal point is moved 6 places, and the original number is less than 1, so the count is -6.

    Step 3. $0.000003 = 3.0 \times 10^{-6}$

    c. $20,520,000,000 = 2.052 \times 10^{10}$

    d. $0.00085 = 8.5 \times 10^{-4}$ ☐

PRACTICE
5   Write each number in scientific notation.

    a. 0.000007   **b.** 20,700,000

    c. 0.0043   **d.** 812,000,000   ■

OBJECTIVE
4   **Converting Numbers to Standard Form** ▶

A number written in scientific notation can be rewritten in standard form. For example, to write 8.63×10^3 in standard form, recall that $10^3 = 1000$.

$$8.63 \times 10^3 = 8.63(1000) = 8630$$

Notice that the exponent on the 10 is positive 3, and we moved the decimal point 3 places to the right.

To write 7.29×10^{-3} in standard form, recall that $10^{-3} = \dfrac{1}{10^3} = \dfrac{1}{1000}$.

$$7.29 \times 10^{-3} = 7.29\left(\dfrac{1}{1000}\right) = \dfrac{7.29}{1000} = 0.00729$$

The exponent on the 10 is negative 3, and we moved the decimal to the left 3 places.

In general, **to write a scientific notation number in standard form,** move the decimal point the same number of places as the exponent on 10. If the exponent is positive, move the decimal point to the right; if the exponent is negative, move the decimal point to the left.

EXAMPLE 6   Write each number in standard notation, without exponents.

a. 1.02×10^5 **b.** 7.358×10^{-3} **c.** 8.4×10^7 **d.** 3.007×10^{-5}

Solution

a. Move the decimal point 5 places to the right.

$$1.02 \times 10^5 = 102,000.$$

b. Move the decimal point 3 places to the left.

$$7.358 \times 10^{-3} = 0.007358$$

c. $8.4 \times 10^7 = 84,000,000.$ 7 places to the right

d. $3.007 \times 10^{-5} = 0.00003007$ 5 places to the left

PRACTICE

6   Write each number in standard notation, without exponents.

a. 3.67×10^{-4} **b.** 8.954×10^6

c. 2.009×10^{-5} **d.** 4.054×10^3

✔ **CONCEPT CHECK**

Which number in each pair is larger?

a. 7.8×10^3 or 2.1×10^5 **b.** 9.2×10^{-2} or 2.7×10^4 **c.** 5.6×10^{-4} or 6.3×10^{-5}

OBJECTIVE

5   **Performing Operations with Scientific Notation** ▷

Performing operations on numbers written in scientific notation uses the rules and definitions for exponents.

EXAMPLE 7   Perform each indicated operation. Write each result in standard decimal notation.

a. $(8 \times 10^{-6})(7 \times 10^3)$ **b.** $\dfrac{12 \times 10^2}{6 \times 10^{-3}}$

Solution

a. $(8 \times 10^{-6})(7 \times 10^3) = (8 \cdot 7) \times (10^{-6} \cdot 10^3)$

$$= 56 \times 10^{-3}$$

$$= 0.056$$

b. $\dfrac{12 \times 10^2}{6 \times 10^{-3}} = \dfrac{12}{6} \times 10^{2-(-3)} = 2 \times 10^5 = 200,000$

PRACTICE

7   Perform each indicated operation. Write each result in standard decimal notation.

a. $(5 \times 10^{-4})(8 \times 10^6)$ **b.** $\dfrac{64 \times 10^3}{32 \times 10^{-7}}$

Answers to Concept Check:
a. 2.1×10^5 **b.** 2.7×10^4
c. 5.6×10^{-4}

Calculator Explorations

Scientific Notation

To enter a number written in scientific notation on a scientific calculator, locate the scientific notation key, which may be marked $\boxed{EE}$ or $\boxed{EXP}$. To enter 3.1×10^7, press $\boxed{3.1}$ $\boxed{EE}$ $\boxed{7}$. The display should read $\boxed{3.1 \quad 07}$.

Enter each number written in scientific notation on your calculator.

1. 5.31×10^3 **2.** -4.8×10^{14}

3. 6.6×10^{-9} **4.** -9.9811×10^{-2}

Multiply each of the following on your calculator. Notice the form of the result.

5. $3,000,000 \times 5,000,000$

6. $230,000 \times 1000$

Multiply each of the following on your calculator. Write the product in scientific notation.

7. $(3.26 \times 10^6)(2.5 \times 10^{13})$

8. $(8.76 \times 10^{-4})(1.237 \times 10^9)$

Vocabulary, Readiness & Video Check

Fill in each blank with the correct choice.

1. The expression x^{-3} equals _____ .

   a. $-x^3$ **b.** $\dfrac{1}{x^3}$ **c.** $\dfrac{-1}{x^3}$ **d.** $\dfrac{1}{x^{-3}}$

2. The expression 5^{-4} equals _____ .

   a. -20 **b.** -625 **c.** $\dfrac{1}{20}$ **d.** $\dfrac{1}{625}$

3. The number 3.021×10^{-3} is written in _____ .

   a. standard form   **b.** expanded form

   c. scientific notation

4. The number 0.0261 is written in _____ .

   a. standard form   **b.** expanded form

   c. scientific notation

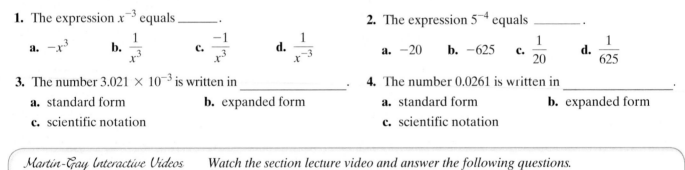

Martin-Gay Interactive Videos

See Video 5.5

Watch the section lecture video and answer the following questions.

OBJECTIVE 1 **5.** What important reminder is made at the end of ▦ Example 1?

OBJECTIVE 2 **6.** Name all the rules and definitions used to simplify ▦ Example 8.

OBJECTIVE 3 **7.** From ▦ Examples 9 and 10, explain how the movement of the decimal point in step 1 suggests the sign of the exponent on the number 10.

OBJECTIVE 4 **8.** From ▦ Example 11, what part of a number written in scientific notation is key in telling you how to write the number in standard form?

OBJECTIVE 5 **9.** For ▦ Example 13, what exponent rules were needed to evaluate?

5.5   Exercise Set   MyMathLab®

Simplify each expression. Write each result using positive exponents only. See Examples 1 through 3.

1. 4^{-3} **2.** 6^{-2} **3.** $(-3)^{-4}$

4. $(-3)^{-5}$ **5.** $7x^{-3}$ **6.** $(7x)^{-3}$

7. $\left(\dfrac{1}{2}\right)^{-5}$ **8.** $\left(\dfrac{1}{8}\right)^{-2}$ **9.** $\left(-\dfrac{1}{4}\right)^{-3}$

10. $\left(-\dfrac{1}{8}\right)^{-2}$ **11.** $3^{-1} + 5^{-1}$ **12.** $4^{-1} + 4^{-2}$

13. $\dfrac{1}{p^{-3}}$ **14.** $\dfrac{1}{q^{-5}}$ **15.** $\dfrac{p^{-5}}{q^{-4}}$

16. $\dfrac{r^{-5}}{s^{-2}}$ **17.** $\dfrac{x^{-2}}{x}$ **18.** $\dfrac{y}{y^{-3}}$

19. $\dfrac{z^{-4}}{z^{-7}}$ **20.** $\dfrac{x^{-4}}{x^{-1}}$ **21.** $3^{-2} + 3^{-1}$

22. $4^{-2} - 4^{-3}$ **23.** $\dfrac{-1}{p^{-4}}$ **24.** $\dfrac{-1}{y^{-6}}$

25. $-2^0 - 3^0$ **26.** $5^0 + (-5)^0$

MIXED PRACTICE

Simplify each expression. Write each result using positive exponents only. See Examples 1 through 4.

27. $\dfrac{x^2 x^5}{x^3}$ **28.** $\dfrac{y^4 y^5}{y^6}$ **29.** $\dfrac{p^2 p}{p^{-1}}$

30. $\dfrac{y^3 y}{y^{-2}}$ **31.** $\dfrac{(m^5)^4 m}{m^{10}}$ **32.** $\dfrac{(x^2)^8 x}{x^9}$

33. $\dfrac{r}{r^{-3} r^{-2}}$ **34.** $\dfrac{p}{p^{-3} q^{-5}}$ **35.** $(x^5 y^3)^{-3}$

36. $(z^5 x^5)^{-3}$ **37.** $\dfrac{(x^2)^3}{x^{10}}$ **38.** $\dfrac{(y^4)^2}{y^{12}}$

39. $\dfrac{(a^5)^2}{(a^3)^4}$ **40.** $\dfrac{(x^2)^5}{(x^4)^3}$ **41.** $\dfrac{8k^4}{2k}$

42. $\dfrac{27r^4}{3r^6}$ **43.** $\dfrac{-6m^4}{-2m^3}$

44. $\dfrac{15a^4}{-15a^5}$ **45.** $\dfrac{-24a^6 b}{6ab^2}$

46. $\dfrac{-5x^4 y^5}{15x^4 y^2}$ **47.** $(-2x^3 y^{-4})(3x^{-1} y)$

48. $(-5a^4 b^{-7})(-a^{-4} b^3)$ **49.** $(a^{-5} b^2)^{-6}$

50. $(4^{-1} x^5)^{-2}$ **51.** $\left(\dfrac{x^{-2} y^4}{x^3 y^7}\right)^2$

52. $\left(\dfrac{a^5 b}{a^7 b^{-2}}\right)^{-3}$ **53.** $\dfrac{4^2 z^{-3}}{4^3 z^{-5}}$

54. $\dfrac{3^{-1} x^4}{3^3 x^{-7}}$ **55.** $\dfrac{2^{-3} x^{-4}}{2^2 x}$

56. $\dfrac{5^{-1} z^7}{5^{-2} z^9}$ **57.** $\dfrac{7ab^{-4}}{7^{-1} a^{-3} b^2}$

58. $\dfrac{6^{-5} x^{-1} y^2}{6^{-2} x^{-4} y^4}$ **59.** $\left(\dfrac{a^{-5} b}{ab^3}\right)^{-4}$

60. $\left(\dfrac{r^{-2} s^{-3}}{r^{-4} s^{-3}}\right)^{-3}$ **61.** $\dfrac{(xy^3)^5}{(xy)^{-4}}$

62. $\dfrac{(rs)^{-3}}{(r^2 s^3)^2}$ **63.** $\dfrac{(-2xy^{-3})^{-3}}{(xy^{-1})^{-1}}$

64. $\dfrac{(-3x^2 y^2)^{-2}}{(xyz)^{-2}}$ **65.** $\dfrac{6x^2 y^3}{-7xy^5}$

66. $\dfrac{-8xa^2 b}{-5xa^5 b}$ **67.** $\dfrac{(a^4 b^{-7})^{-5}}{(5a^2 b^{-1})^{-2}}$

68. $\dfrac{(a^6 b^{-2})^4}{(4a^{-3} b^{-3})^3}$

Write each number in scientific notation. See Example 5.

69. 78,000   **70.** 9,300,000,000

71. 0.00000167   **72.** 0.00000017

73. 0.00635   **74.** 0.00194

75. 1,160,000   **76.** 700,000

77. More than 2,000,000,000 pencils are manufactured in the United States annually. Write this number in scientific notation. (*Source*: AbsoluteTrivia.com)

78. The temperature at the interior of the Earth is 20,000,000 degrees Celsius. Write 20,000,000 in scientific notation.

79. As of this writing, the world's largest optical telescope is the Gran Telescopio Canaris, located in La Palma, Canary Islands, Spain. The elevation of this telescope is 2400 meters above sea level. Write 2400 in scientific notation.

80. In March 2004, the European Space Agency launched the Rosetta spacecraft, whose mission was to deliver the Philae lander to explore comet 67P/Churyumov-Gerasimenko. The lander finally arrived on the comet in late 2014. This comet is currently more than 320,000,000 miles from Earth. Write 320,000,000 in scientific notation. (*Source:* European Space Agency)

Write each number in standard notation. See Example 6.

81. 8.673×10^{-10}

82. 9.056×10^{-4}

83. 3.3×10^{-2}

84. 4.8×10^{-6}

▶ **85.** 2.032×10^4

86. 9.07×10^{10}

87. Each second, the Sun converts 7.0×10^8 tons of hydrogen into helium and energy in the form of gamma rays. Write this number in standard notation. (*Source:* Students for the Exploration and Development of Space)

88. In chemistry, Avogadro's number is the number of atoms in one mole of an element. Avogadro's number is $6.02214199 \times 10^{23}$. Write this number in standard notation. (*Source:* National Institute of Standards and Technology)

89. The distance light travels in 1 year is 9.46×10^{12} kilometers. Write this number in standard notation.

90. The population of the world is 7.3×10^9. Write this number in standard notation. (*Source:* UN World Population Clock)

MIXED PRACTICE

See Examples 5 and 6. Below are some interesting facts about selected countries' external debts at a certain time. These are public and private debts owed to nonresidents of that country. If a number is written in standard form, write it in scientific notation. If a number is written in scientific notation, write it in standard form. (Source: CIA World Factbook)

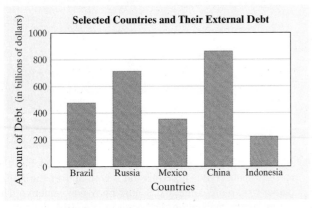

91. The external debt of Russia at a certain time was $714,000,000,000.

92. The amount by which Russia's debt was greater than Mexico's debt was $359,000,000,000.

93. At a certain time, China's external debt was 8.63×10^{11}.

94. At a certain time, the external debt of the United States was 1.5×10^{13}.

95. At a certain time, the estimated per person share of the United States external debt was 4.7×10^4.

96. The bar graph shows the external debt of five countries. Estimate the height of the tallest bar and the shortest bar in standard notation. Then write each number in scientific notation.

Evaluate each expression using exponential rules. Write each result in standard notation. See Example 7.

97. $(1.2 \times 10^{-3})(3 \times 10^{-2})$

98. $(2.5 \times 10^6)(2 \times 10^{-6})$

99. $(4 \times 10^{-10})(7 \times 10^{-9})$

100. $(5 \times 10^6)(4 \times 10^{-8})$

101. $\dfrac{8 \times 10^{-1}}{16 \times 10^5}$

102. $\dfrac{25 \times 10^{-4}}{5 \times 10^{-9}}$

▶ **103.** $\dfrac{1.4 \times 10^{-2}}{7 \times 10^{-8}}$

104. $\dfrac{0.4 \times 10^5}{0.2 \times 10^{11}}$

REVIEW AND PREVIEW

Simplify the following. See Section 5.1.

105. $\dfrac{5x^7}{3x^4}$

106. $\dfrac{27y^{14}}{3y^7}$

107. $\dfrac{15z^4y^3}{21zy}$

108. $\dfrac{18a^7b^{17}}{30a^7b}$

Use the distributive property and multiply. See Sections 5.3 and 5.5.

109. $\dfrac{1}{y}(5y^2 - 6y + 5)$

110. $\dfrac{2}{x}(3x^5 + x^4 - 2)$

CONCEPT EXTENSIONS

△ **111.** Find the volume of the cube.

$\dfrac{3x^{-2}}{z}$ inches

△ **112.** Find the area of the triangle.

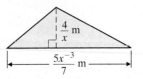

$\dfrac{4}{x}$ m

$\dfrac{5x^{-3}}{7}$ m

Simplify.

113. $(2a^3)^3a^4 + a^5a^8$

114. $(2a^3)^3a^{-3} + a^{11}a^{-5}$

Fill in the boxes so that each statement is true. (More than one answer may be possible for these exercises.)

115. $x^\square = \dfrac{1}{x^5}$

116. $7^\square = \dfrac{1}{49}$

117. $z^\square \cdot z^\square = z^{-10}$

118. $(x^\square)^\square = x^{-15}$

119. Which is larger? See the Concept Check in this section.
   a. 9.7×10^{-2} or 1.3×10^1
   b. 8.6×10^5 or 4.4×10^7
   c. 6.1×10^{-2} or 5.6×10^{-4}

120. Determine whether each statement is true or false.
   a. $5^{-1} < 5^{-2}$
   b. $\left(\dfrac{1}{5}\right)^{-1} < \left(\dfrac{1}{5}\right)^{-2}$
   c. $a^{-1} < a^{-2}$ for all nonzero numbers.

121. It was stated earlier that for an integer n,

$$x^{-n} = \frac{1}{x^n}, \quad x \neq 0$$

Explain why x may not equal 0.

122. The quotient rule states that

$$\frac{a^m}{a^n} = a^{m-n}, a \neq 0.$$

Explain why a may not equal 0.

Simplify each expression. Assume that variables represent positive integers.

123. $a^{-4m} \cdot a^{5m}$

124. $(x^{-3s})^3$

125. $(3y^{2z})^3$

126. $a^{4m+1} \cdot a^4$

Simplify each expression. Write each result in standard notation.

127. $(2.63 \times 10^{12})(-1.5 \times 10^{-10})$

128. $(6.785 \times 10^{-4})(4.68 \times 10^{10})$

Light travels at a rate of 1.86×10^5 miles per second. Use this information and the distance formula $d = r \cdot t$ to answer Exercises 129 and 130.

129. If the distance from the moon to Earth is 238,857 miles, find how long it takes the reflected light of the moon to reach Earth. (Round to the nearest tenth of a second.)

130. If the distance from the Sun to Earth is 93,000,000 miles, find how long it takes the light of the Sun to reach Earth.

5.6 Dividing Polynomials

OBJECTIVES

1 Divide a Polynomial by a Monomial.

2 Use Long Division to Divide a Polynomial by Another Polynomial.

OBJECTIVE

1 Dividing by a Monomial

Now that we know how to add, subtract, and multiply polynomials, we practice dividing polynomials.

To divide a polynomial by a monomial, recall addition of fractions. Fractions that have a common denominator are added by adding the numerators:

$$\frac{a}{c} + \frac{b}{c} = \frac{a + b}{c}$$

If we read this equation from right to left and let a, b, and c be monomials, $c \neq 0$, we have the following:

Dividing a Polynomial by a Monomial

Divide each term of the polynomial by the monomial.

$$\frac{a + b}{c} = \frac{a}{c} + \frac{b}{c}, \quad c \neq 0$$

Throughout this section, we assume that denominators are not 0.

EXAMPLE 1 Divide $6m^2 + 2m$ by $2m$.

Solution We begin by writing the quotient in fraction form. Then we divide each term of the polynomial $6m^2 + 2m$ by the monomial $2m$.

$$\frac{6m^2 + 2m}{2m} = \frac{6m^2}{2m} + \frac{2m}{2m}$$

$$= 3m + 1 \quad \text{Simplify.}$$

Check: We know that if $\dfrac{6m^2 + 2m}{2m} = 3m + 1$, then $2m \cdot (3m + 1)$ must equal $6m^2 + 2m$. Thus, to check, we multiply.

$$2m(3m + 1) = 2m(3m) + 2m(1) = 6m^2 + 2m$$

The quotient $3m + 1$ checks.

PRACTICE

1 Divide $8t^3 + 4t^2$ by $4t^2$

EXAMPLE 2 Divide: $\dfrac{9x^5 - 12x^2 + 3x}{3x^2}$

Solution $\dfrac{9x^5 - 12x^2 + 3x}{3x^2} = \dfrac{9x^5}{3x^2} - \dfrac{12x^2}{3x^2} + \dfrac{3x}{3x^2}$ Divide each term by $3x^2$.

$$= 3x^3 - 4 + \dfrac{1}{x} \qquad \text{Simplify.}$$

Notice that the quotient is not a polynomial because of the term $\dfrac{1}{x}$. This expression is called a rational expression—we will study rational expressions further in Chapter 7. Although the quotient of two polynomials is not always a polynomial, we may still check by multiplying.

Check: $3x^2\left(3x^3 - 4 + \dfrac{1}{x}\right) = 3x^2(3x^3) - 3x^2(4) + 3x^2\left(\dfrac{1}{x}\right)$

$$= 9x^5 - 12x^2 + 3x \qquad \square$$

PRACTICE
2 Divide: $\dfrac{16x^6 + 20x^3 - 12x}{4x^2}$ ■

EXAMPLE 3 Divide: $\dfrac{8x^2y^2 - 16xy + 2x}{4xy}$

Solution $\dfrac{8x^2y^2 - 16xy + 2x}{4xy} = \dfrac{8x^2y^2}{4xy} - \dfrac{16xy}{4xy} + \dfrac{2x}{4xy}$ Divide each term by $4xy$.

$$= 2xy - 4 + \dfrac{1}{2y} \qquad \text{Simplify.}$$

Check: $4xy\left(2xy - 4 + \dfrac{1}{2y}\right) = 4xy(2xy) - 4xy(4) + 4xy\left(\dfrac{1}{2y}\right)$

$$= 8x^2y^2 - 16xy + 2x \qquad \square$$

PRACTICE
3 Divide: $\dfrac{15x^4y^4 - 10xy + y}{5xy}$ ■

✔ **CONCEPT CHECK**

In which of the following is $\dfrac{x + 5}{5}$ simplified correctly?

a. $\dfrac{x}{5} + 1$ b. x c. $x + 1$

OBJECTIVE
2 Using Long Division to Divide by a Polynomial ▶

To divide a polynomial by a polynomial other than a monomial, we use a process known as long division. Polynomial long division is similar to number long division, so we review long division by dividing 13 into 3660.

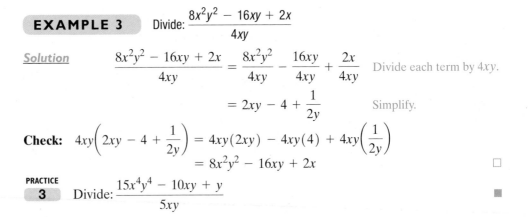

The quotient is $281\,R7$, which can be written as $281\dfrac{7}{13}$. $\leftarrow$ remainder
$\leftarrow$ divisor

Recall that division can be checked by multiplication. To check a division problem such as this one, we see that

$$13 \cdot 281 + 7 = 3660$$

Now we demonstrate long division of polynomials.

EXAMPLE 4   Divide $x^2 + 7x + 12$ by $x + 3$ using long division.

Solution

To subtract, change the signs of these terms and add.

$$\begin{array}{r} x \\ x+3\overline{\smash{)}x^2 + 7x + 12} \\ \underline{\rightarrow x^2 \mp 3x} \downarrow \\ 4x + 12 \end{array}$$

How many times does x divide x^2? $\dfrac{x^2}{x} = x.$
Multiply: $x(x+3)$
Subtract and bring down the next term.

Now we repeat this process.

To subtract, change the signs of these terms and add.

$$\begin{array}{r} x + 4 \\ x+3\overline{\smash{)}x^2 + 7x + 12} \\ \underline{x^2 \mp 3x} \\ 4x + 12 \\ \underline{\rightarrow 4x \mp 12} \\ 0 \end{array}$$

How many times does x divide $4x$? $\dfrac{4x}{x} = 4.$
Multiply: $4(x+3)$
Subtract. The remainder is 0.

The quotient is $x + 4$.

Check: We check by multiplying.

divisor	·	quotient	+	remainder	=	dividend
↓		↓		↓		↓
$(x+3)$	·	$(x+4)$	+	0	=	$x^2 + 7x + 12$

The quotient checks. □

PRACTICE
4   Divide $x^2 + 5x + 6$ by $x + 2$ using long division.

EXAMPLE 5   Divide $6x^2 + 10x - 5$ by $3x - 1$ using long division.

Solution

$$\begin{array}{r} 2x + 4 \\ 3x-1\overline{\smash{)}6x^2 + 10x - 5} \\ \underline{6x^2 \mp 2x} \downarrow \\ 12x - 5 \\ \underline{12x \mp 4} \\ -1 \end{array}$$

$\dfrac{6x^2}{3x} = 2x$, so $2x$ is a term of the quotient.
Multiply $2x(3x - 1)$.
Subtract and bring down the next term.
$\dfrac{12x}{3x} = 4$, multiply $4(3x - 1)$
Subtract. The remainder is -1.

Thus $(6x^2 + 10x - 5)$ divided by $(3x - 1)$ is $(2x + 4)$ with a remainder of -1. This can be written as

$$\frac{6x^2 + 10x - 5}{3x - 1} = 2x + 4 + \frac{-1}{3x - 1} \quad \begin{array}{l}\leftarrow \text{remainder} \\ \leftarrow \text{divisor}\end{array}$$

Check: To check, we multiply $(3x - 1)(2x + 4)$. Then we add the remainder, -1, to this product.

$$(3x - 1)(2x + 4) + (-1) = (6x^2 + 12x - 2x - 4) - 1$$
$$= 6x^2 + 10x - 5$$

The quotient checks. □

PRACTICE
5   Divide $4x^2 + 8x - 7$ by $2x + 1$ using long division.

In Example 5, the degree of the divisor, $3x - 1$, is 1 and the degree of the remainder, -1, is 0. The division process is continued until the degree of the remainder polynomial is less than the degree of the divisor polynomial.

Writing the dividend and divisor in a form with descending order of powers and with no missing terms is helpful when dividing polynomials.

EXAMPLE 6   Divide: $\dfrac{4x^2 + 7 + 8x^3}{2x + 3}$

Solution Before we begin the division process, we rewrite

$$4x^2 + 7 + 8x^3 \quad \text{as} \quad 8x^3 + 4x^2 + 0x + 7$$

Notice that we have written the polynomial in descending order and have represented the missing x^1-term by $0x$.

$$
\begin{array}{r}
4x^2 - 4x + 6 \\
2x + 3 \overline{\smash{)}8x^3 + 4x^2 + 0x + 7} \\
\underline{8x^3 + 12x^2} \\
-8x^2 + 0x \\
\underline{+8x^2 + 12x} \\
12x + 7 \\
\underline{12x + 18} \\
-11 \quad \text{Remainder}
\end{array}
$$

Thus, $\dfrac{4x^2 + 7 + 8x^3}{2x + 3} = 4x^2 - 4x + 6 + \dfrac{-11}{2x + 3}$.   ☐

PRACTICE
6   Divide: $\dfrac{11x - 3 + 9x^3}{3x + 2}$ ■

EXAMPLE 7   Divide: $\dfrac{2x^4 - x^3 + 3x^2 + x - 1}{x^2 + 1}$

Solution Before dividing, rewrite the divisor polynomial

$$x^2 + 1 \quad \text{as} \quad x^2 + 0x + 1$$

The $0x$ term represents the missing x^1-term in the divisor.

$$
\begin{array}{r}
2x^2 - x + 1 \\
x^2 + 0x + 1 \overline{\smash{)}2x^4 - x^3 + 3x^2 + x - 1} \\
\underline{2x^4 + 0x^3 + 2x^2} \\
-x^3 + x^2 + x \\
\underline{+x^3 + 0x^2 + x} \\
x^2 + 2x - 1 \\
\underline{x^2 + 0x + 1} \\
2x - 2 \quad \text{Remainder}
\end{array}
$$

Thus, $\dfrac{2x^4 - x^3 + 3x^2 + x - 1}{x^2 + 1} = 2x^2 - x + 1 + \dfrac{2x - 2}{x^2 + 1}$.   ☐

PRACTICE
7   Divide: $\dfrac{3x^4 - 2x^3 - 3x^2 + x + 4}{x^2 + 2}$ ■

EXAMPLE 8 Divide $x^3 - 8$ by $x - 2$.

<u>Solution:</u> Notice that the polynomial $x^3 - 8$ is missing an x^2-term and an x-term. We'll represent these terms by inserting $0x^2$ and $0x$.

$$
\begin{array}{r}
x^2 + 2x + 4 \\
x - 2{\overline{\smash{\big)}\,x^3 + 0x^2 + 0x - 8}} \\
\underline{-x^3 \mp 2x^2} \\
2x^2 + 0x \\
\underline{-2x^2 \mp 4x} \\
4x - 8 \\
\underline{-4x \mp 8} \\
0
\end{array}
$$

Thus, $\dfrac{x^3 - 8}{x - 2} = x^2 + 2x + 4$.

Check: To check, see that $(x^2 + 2x + 4)(x - 2) = x^3 - 8$. ☐

PRACTICE
8 Divide $x^3 + 27$ by $x + 3$. ■

✔ | **Vocabulary, Readiness & Video Check**

Use the choices below to fill in each blank. Choices may be used more than once.

  dividend   divisor   quotient

1. In $\dfrac{3}{6\overline{)18}}$, the 18 is the _____, the 3 is the _____, and the 6 is the _____.

2. In $\dfrac{x + 2}{x + 1\overline{)x^2 + 3x + 2}}$, the $x + 1$ is the _____, the $x^2 + 3x + 2$ is the _____, and the $x + 2$ is the _____.

Simplify each expression mentally.

3. $\dfrac{a^6}{a^4}$ **4.** $\dfrac{p^8}{p^3}$ **5.** $\dfrac{y^2}{y}$ **6.** $\dfrac{a^3}{a}$

Martin-Gay Interactive Videos

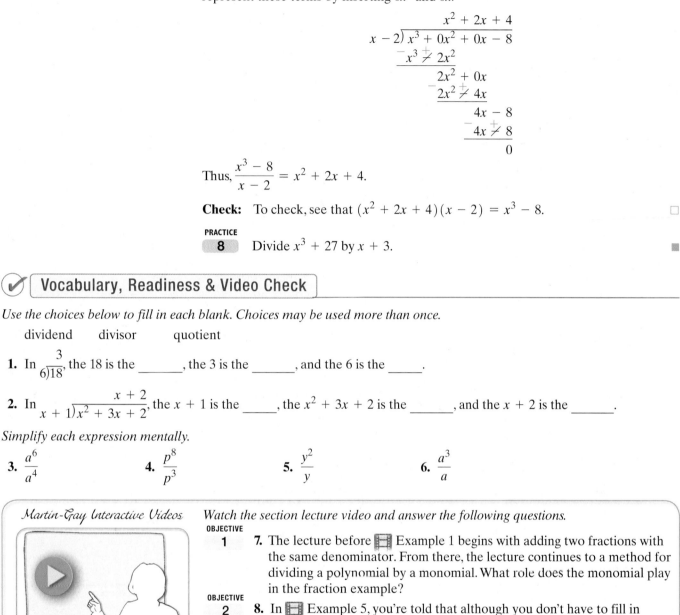

See Video 5.6 ⦾

Watch the section lecture video and answer the following questions.

OBJECTIVE 1
7. The lecture before ▦ Example 1 begins with adding two fractions with the same denominator. From there, the lecture continues to a method for dividing a polynomial by a monomial. What role does the monomial play in the fraction example?

OBJECTIVE 2
8. In ▦ Example 5, you're told that although you don't have to fill in missing powers in the divisor and the dividend, it really is a good idea to do so. Why?

5.6 **Exercise Set** MyMathLab® ▶

Perform each division. See Examples 1 through 3.

▶ **1.** $\dfrac{12x^4 + 3x^2}{x}$

2. $\dfrac{15x^2 - 9x^5}{x}$

3. $\dfrac{20x^3 - 30x^2 + 5x + 5}{5}$

4. $\dfrac{8x^3 - 4x^2 + 6x + 2}{2}$

5. $\dfrac{15p^3 + 18p^2}{3p}$

6. $\dfrac{14m^2 - 27m^3}{7m}$

7. $\dfrac{-9x^4 + 18x^5}{6x^5}$

8. $\dfrac{6x^5 + 3x^4}{3x^4}$

▶ 9. $\dfrac{-9x^5 + 3x^4 - 12}{3x^3}$

10. $\dfrac{6a^2 - 4a + 12}{-2a^2}$

11. $\dfrac{4x^4 - 6x^3 + 7}{-4x^4}$

12. $\dfrac{-12a^3 + 36a - 15}{3a}$

Find each quotient using long division. See Examples 4 and 5.

▶ 13. $\dfrac{x^2 + 4x + 3}{x + 3}$

14. $\dfrac{x^2 + 7x + 10}{x + 5}$

15. $\dfrac{2x^2 + 13x + 15}{x + 5}$

16. $\dfrac{3x^2 + 8x + 4}{x + 2}$

17. $\dfrac{2x^2 - 7x + 3}{x - 4}$

18. $\dfrac{3x^2 - x - 4}{x - 1}$

19. $\dfrac{9a^3 - 3a^2 - 3a + 4}{3a + 2}$

20. $\dfrac{4x^3 + 12x^2 + x - 14}{2x + 3}$

21. $\dfrac{8x^2 + 10x + 1}{2x + 1}$

22. $\dfrac{3x^2 + 17x + 7}{3x + 2}$

23. $\dfrac{2x^3 + 2x^2 - 17x + 8}{x - 2}$

24. $\dfrac{4x^3 + 11x^2 - 8x - 10}{x + 3}$

Find each quotient using long division. Don't forget to write the polynomials in descending order and fill in any missing terms. See Examples 6 through 8.

25. $\dfrac{x^2 - 36}{x - 6}$

26. $\dfrac{a^2 - 49}{a - 7}$

▶ 27. $\dfrac{x^3 - 27}{x - 3}$

28. $\dfrac{x^3 + 64}{x + 4}$

29. $\dfrac{1 - 3x^2}{x + 2}$

30. $\dfrac{7 - 5x^2}{x + 3}$

31. $\dfrac{-4b + 4b^2 - 5}{2b - 1}$

32. $\dfrac{-3y + 2y^2 - 15}{2y + 5}$

MIXED PRACTICE

Divide. If the divisor contains 2 or more terms, use long division. See Examples 1 through 8.

33. $\dfrac{a^2b^2 - ab^3}{ab}$

34. $\dfrac{m^3n^2 - mn^4}{mn}$

35. $\dfrac{8x^2 + 6x - 27}{2x - 3}$

36. $\dfrac{18w^2 + 18w - 8}{3w + 4}$

37. $\dfrac{2x^2y + 8x^2y^2 - xy^2}{2xy}$

38. $\dfrac{11x^3y^3 - 33xy + x^2y^2}{11xy}$

▶ 39. $\dfrac{2b^3 + 9b^2 + 6b - 4}{b + 4}$

40. $\dfrac{2x^3 + 3x^2 - 3x + 4}{x + 2}$

41. $\dfrac{5x^2 + 28x - 10}{x + 6}$

42. $\dfrac{2x^2 + x - 15}{x + 3}$

43. $\dfrac{10x^3 - 24x^2 - 10x}{10x}$

44. $\dfrac{2x^3 + 12x^2 + 16}{4x^2}$

45. $\dfrac{6x^2 + 17x - 4}{x + 3}$

46. $\dfrac{2x^2 - 9x + 15}{x - 6}$

47. $\dfrac{30x^2 - 17x + 2}{5x - 2}$

48. $\dfrac{4x^2 - 13x - 12}{4x + 3}$

49. $\dfrac{3x^4 - 9x^3 + 12}{-3x}$

50. $\dfrac{8y^6 - 3y^2 - 4y}{4y}$

51. $\dfrac{x^3 + 6x^2 + 18x + 27}{x + 3}$

52. $\dfrac{x^3 - 8x^2 + 32x - 64}{x - 4}$

53. $\dfrac{y^3 + 3y^2 + 4}{y - 2}$

54. $\dfrac{3x^3 + 11x + 12}{x + 4}$

55. $\dfrac{5 - 6x^2}{x - 2}$

56. $\dfrac{3 - 7x^2}{x - 3}$

Divide.

57. $\dfrac{x^5 + x^2}{x^2 + x}$

58. $\dfrac{x^6 - x^4}{x^3 + 1}$

REVIEW AND PREVIEW

Multiply each expression. See Section 5.3.

59. $2a(a^2 + 1)$

60. $-4a(3a^2 - 4)$

61. $2x(x^2 + 7x - 5)$

62. $4y(y^2 - 8y - 4)$

63. $-3xy(xy^2 + 7x^2y + 8)$

64. $-9xy(4xyz + 7xy^2z + 2)$

65. $9ab(ab^2c + 4bc - 8)$

66. $-7sr(6s^2r + 9sr^2 + 9rs + 8)$

CONCEPT EXTENSIONS

67. The perimeter of a square is $(12x^3 + 4x - 16)$ feet. Find the length of its side.

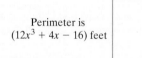

Perimeter is
$(12x^3 + 4x - 16)$ feet

△ **68.** The volume of the swimming pool shown is $(36x^5 - 12x^3 + 6x^2)$ cubic feet. If its height is $2x$ feet and its width is $3x$ feet, find its length.

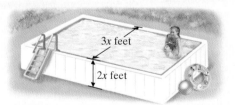

3x feet

2x feet

69. In which of the following is $\dfrac{a + 7}{7}$ simplified correctly? See the Concept Check in this section.

   a. $a + 1$ **b.** a **c.** $\dfrac{a}{7} + 1$

70. In which of the following is $\dfrac{5x + 15}{5}$ simplified correctly? See the Concept Check in this section.

   a. $x + 15$ **b.** $x + 3$ **c.** $x + 1$

71. Explain how to check a polynomial long division result when the remainder is 0.

72. Explain how to check a polynomial long division result when the remainder is not 0.

△ **73.** The area of the following parallelogram is $(10x^2 + 31x + 15)$ square meters. If its base is $(5x + 3)$ meters, find its height.

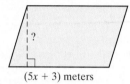

$(5x + 3)$ meters

△ **74.** The area of the top of the Ping-Pong table is $(49x^2 + 70x - 200)$ square inches. If its length is $(7x + 20)$ inches, find its width.

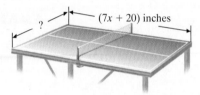

$(7x + 20)$ inches

75. $(18x^{10a} - 12x^{8a} + 14x^{5a} - 2x^{3a}) \div 2x^{3a}$

76. $(25y^{11b} + 5y^{6b} - 20y^{3b} + 100y^b) \div 5y^b$

5.7 Synthetic Division and the Remainder Theorem

OBJECTIVES

1 Use Synthetic Division to Divide a Polynomial by a Binomial.

2 Use the Remainder Theorem to Evaluate Polynomials.

OBJECTIVE

1   Using Synthetic Division

When a polynomial is to be divided by a binomial of the form $x - c$, a shortcut process called **synthetic division** may be used. On the left is an example of long division, and on the right, the same example showing the coefficients of the variables only.

$$
\begin{array}{r}
2x^2 + 5x + 2 \\
x - 3 \overline{)2x^3 - x^2 - 13x + 1} \\
\underline{2x^3 - 6x^2} \\
5x^2 - 13x \\
\underline{5x^2 - 15x} \\
2x + 1 \\
\underline{2x - 6} \\
7
\end{array}
\qquad
\begin{array}{r}
2 \quad 5 \quad 2 \\
1 - 3 \overline{)2 - 1 - 13 + 1} \\
\underline{2 - 6} \\
5 - 13 \\
\underline{5 - 15} \\
2 + 1 \\
\underline{2 - 6} \\
7
\end{array}
$$

Notice that as long as we keep coefficients of powers of x in the same column, we can perform division of polynomials by performing algebraic operations on the coefficients only. This shortcut process of dividing with coefficients only in a special format is called synthetic division. To find $(2x^3 - x^2 - 13x + 1) \div (x - 3)$ by synthetic division, follow the next example.

EXAMPLE I   Use synthetic division to divide $2x^3 - x^2 - 13x + 1$ by $x - 3$.

Solution   To use synthetic division, the divisor must be in the form $x - c$. Since we are dividing by $x - 3$, c is 3. Write down 3 and the coefficients of the dividend.

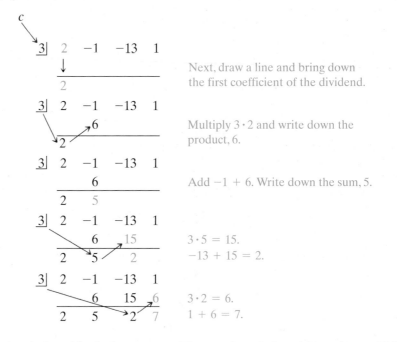

Next, draw a line and bring down the first coefficient of the dividend.

Multiply $3 \cdot 2$ and write down the product, 6.

Add $-1 + 6$. Write down the sum, 5.

$3 \cdot 5 = 15$.
$-13 + 15 = 2$.

$3 \cdot 2 = 6$.
$1 + 6 = 7$.

The quotient is found in the bottom row. The numbers 2, 5, and 2 are the coefficients of the quotient polynomial, and the number 7 is the remainder. The degree of the quotient polynomial is one less than the degree of the dividend. In our example, the degree of the dividend is 3, so the degree of the quotient polynomial is 2. As we found when we performed the long division, the quotient is

$$2x^2 + 5x + 2, \quad \text{remainder } 7$$

or

$$2x^2 + 5x + 2 + \frac{7}{x - 3}. \qquad \square$$

PRACTICE

1   Use synthetic division to divide $4x^3 - 3x^2 + 6x + 5$ by $x - 1$ ■

EXAMPLE 2   Use synthetic division to divide $x^4 - 2x^3 - 11x^2 + 5x + 34$ by $x + 2$.

Solution   The divisor is $x + 2$, which we write in the form $x - c$ as $x - (-2)$. Thus, c is -2. The dividend coefficients are $1, -2, -11, 5,$ and 34.

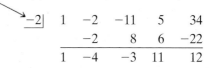

$$
\begin{array}{r|rrrrr}
-2 & 1 & -2 & -11 & 5 & 34 \\
   &   & -2 & 8 & 6 & -22 \\
\hline
   & 1 & -4 & -3 & 11 & 12
\end{array}
$$

The dividend is a fourth-degree polynomial, so the quotient polynomial is a third-degree polynomial. The quotient is $x^3 - 4x^2 - 3x + 11$ with a remainder of 12. Thus,

$$\frac{x^4 - 2x^3 - 11x^2 + 5x + 34}{x + 2} = x^3 - 4x^2 - 3x + 11 + \frac{12}{x + 2}. \qquad \square$$

PRACTICE

2   Use synthetic division to divide $x^4 + 3x^3 - 5x^2 + 6x + 12$ by $x + 3$.   ■

✔ **CONCEPT CHECK**

Which division problems are candidates for the synthetic division process?
a. $(3x^2 + 5) \div (x + 4)$ **b.** $(x^3 - x^2 + 2) \div (3x^3 - 2)$ **c.** $(y^4 + y - 3) \div (x^2 + 1)$ **d.** $x^5 \div (x - 5)$

Helpful Hint

Before dividing by synthetic division, write the dividend in descending order of variable exponents. Any "missing powers" of the variable should be represented by 0 times the variable raised to the missing power.

EXAMPLE 3   If $P(x) = 2x^3 - 4x^2 + 5$

a. Find $P(2)$ by substitution.

b. Use synthetic division to find the remainder when $P(x)$ is divided by $x - 2$.

Solution

a. $P(x) = 2x^3 - 4x^2 + 5$

$P(2) = 2(2)^3 - 4(2)^2 + 5$

$\qquad = 2(8) - 4(4) + 5 = 16 - 16 + 5 = 5$

Thus, $P(2) = 5$.

Answer to Concept Check:
a and d

(Continued on next page)

b. The coefficients of $P(x)$ are 2, -4, 0, and 5. The number 0 is the coefficient of the missing power of x^1. The divisor is $x - 2$, so c is 2.

$$\overset{c}{\searrow}\begin{array}{r|rrrr} 2 & 2 & -4 & 0 & 5 \\ & & 4 & 0 & 0 \\ \hline & 2 & 0 & 0 & 5 \end{array} \text{ remainder}$$

The remainder when $P(x)$ is divided by $x - 2$ is 5.   □

PRACTICE

3   If $P(x) = x^3 - 5x - 2$,

a. Find $P(2)$ by substitution.

b. Use synthetic division to find the remainder when $P(x)$ is divided by $x - 2$.   ■

OBJECTIVE

2   Using the Remainder Theorem ▶

Notice in the preceding example that $P(2) = 5$ and that the remainder when $P(x)$ is divided by $x - 2$ is 5. This is no accident. This illustrates the **remainder theorem.**

Remainder Theorem

If a polynomial $P(x)$ is divided by $x - c$, then the remainder is $P(c)$.

EXAMPLE 4   Use the remainder theorem and synthetic division to find $P(4)$ if

$$P(x) = 4x^6 - 25x^5 + 35x^4 + 17x^2.$$

Solution To find $P(4)$ by the remainder theorem, we divide $P(x)$ by $x - 4$. The coefficients of $P(x)$ are 4, -25, 35, 0, 17, 0, and 0. Also, c is 4.

$$\overset{c}{\searrow}\begin{array}{r|rrrrrrr} 4 & 4 & -25 & 35 & 0 & 17 & 0 & 0 \\ & & 16 & -36 & -4 & -16 & 4 & 16 \\ \hline & 4 & -9 & -1 & -4 & 1 & 4 & 16 \end{array} \text{ remainder}$$

Thus, $P(4) = 16$, the remainder.   □

PRACTICE

4   Use the remainder theorem and synthetic division to find $P(3)$ if $P(x) = 2x^5 - 18x^4 + 90x^2 + 59x$.   ■

✓ Vocabulary, Readiness & Video Check

Martin-Gay Interactive Videos

See Video 5.7 ⊚

Watch the section lecture video and answer the following questions.

OBJECTIVE
1   **1.** From 🎞 Example 1, once you've completed the synthetic division, what does the bottom row of numbers mean? What is the degree of the quotient?

OBJECTIVE
2   **2.** From 🎞 Example 4, given a polynomial function $P(x)$, under what circumstances might it be easier/faster to use the remainder theorem to find $P(c)$ rather than substituting the value c for x and then simplifying?

5.7   Exercise Set   MyMathLab® ▶

Use synthetic division to divide. See Examples 1 and 2.

1. $(x^2 + 3x - 40) \div (x - 5)$

2. $(x^2 - 14x + 24) \div (x - 2)$

3. $(x^2 + 5x - 6) \div (x + 6)$

4. $(x^2 + 12x + 32) \div (x + 4)$

▶ **5.** $(x^3 - 7x^2 - 13x + 5) \div (x - 2)$

6. $(x^3 + 6x^2 + 4x - 7) \div (x + 5)$

7. $(4x^2 - 9) \div (x - 2)$

8. $(3x^2 - 4) \div (x - 1)$

For the given polynomial P(x) and the given c, find P(c) by **(a)** *direct substitution and* **(b)** *the remainder theorem. See Examples 3 and 4.*

9. $P(x) = 3x^2 - 4x - 1; P(2)$

▶ **10.** $P(x) = x^2 - x + 3; P(5)$

11. $P(x) = 4x^4 + 7x^2 + 9x - 1; P(-2)$

12. $P(x) = 8x^5 + 7x + 4; P(-3)$

13. $P(x) = x^5 + 3x^4 + 3x - 7; P(-1)$

14. $P(x) = 5x^4 - 4x^3 + 2x - 1; P(-1)$

MIXED PRACTICE

Use synthetic division to divide.

15. $(x^3 - 3x^2 + 2) \div (x - 3)$

16. $(x^2 + 12) \div (x + 2)$

17. $(6x^2 + 13x + 8) \div (x + 1)$

18. $(x^3 - 5x^2 + 7x - 4) \div (x - 3)$

19. $(2x^4 - 13x^3 + 16x^2 - 9x + 20) \div (x - 5)$

20. $(3x^4 + 5x^3 - x^2 + x - 2) \div (x + 2)$

21. $(3x^2 - 15) \div (x + 3)$

22. $(3x^2 + 7x - 6) \div (x + 4)$

23. $(3x^3 - 6x^2 + 4x + 5) \div \left(x - \dfrac{1}{2} \right)$

24. $(8x^3 - 6x^2 - 5x + 3) \div \left(x + \dfrac{3}{4} \right)$

25. $(3x^3 + 2x^2 - 4x + 1) \div \left(x - \dfrac{1}{3} \right)$

26. $(9y^3 + 9y^2 - y + 2) \div \left(y + \dfrac{2}{3} \right)$

▶ **27.** $(7x^2 - 4x + 12 + 3x^3) \div (x + 1)$

28. $(x^4 + 4x^3 - x^2 - 16x - 4) \div (x - 2)$

29. $(x^3 - 1) \div (x - 1)$

30. $(y^3 - 8) \div (y - 2)$

31. $(2x^3 + 12x^2 - 3x - 20) \div (x + 6)$

32. $(4x^3 + 12x^2 + x - 12) \div (x + 3)$

For the given polynomial P(x) and the given c, use the remainder theorem to find P(c).

33. $P(x) = x^3 + 3x^2 - 7x + 4; 1$

34. $P(x) = x^3 + 5x^2 - 4x - 6; 2$

35. $P(x) = 3x^3 - 7x^2 - 2x + 5; -3$

36. $P(x) = 4x^3 + 5x^2 - 6x - 4; -2$

▶ **37.** $P(x) = 4x^4 + x^2 - 2; -1$

38. $P(x) = x^4 - 3x^2 - 2x + 5; -2$

39. $P(x) = 2x^4 - 3x^2 - 2; \dfrac{1}{3}$

40. $P(x) = 4x^4 - 2x^3 + x^2 - x - 4; \dfrac{1}{2}$

41. $P(x) = x^5 + x^4 - x^3 + 3; \dfrac{1}{2}$

42. $P(x) = x^5 - 2x^3 + 4x^2 - 5x + 6; \dfrac{2}{3}$

✎ **43.** Explain an advantage of using the remainder theorem instead of direct substitution.

✎ **44.** Explain an advantage of using synthetic division instead of long division.

REVIEW AND PREVIEW

Solve each equation for x. See Section 2.3.

45. $7x + 2 = x - 3$

46. $4 - 2x = 17 - 5x$

47. $\dfrac{x}{3} - 5 = 13$

48. $\dfrac{2x}{9} + 1 = \dfrac{7}{9}$

Evaluate. See Section 5.1.

49. 2^3

50. 3^4

51. $(-2)^5$

52. -2^5

53. $3 \cdot 4^2$

54. $4 \cdot 3^3$

Evaluate each expression for the given replacement value. See Section 5.1.

55. x^2 if x is -5

56. x^3 if x is -5

57. $2x^3$ if x is -1

58. $3x^2$ if x is -1

CONCEPT EXTENSIONS

Determine whether each division problem is a candidate for the synthetic division process. See the Concept Check in this section.

59. $(5x^2 - 3x + 2) \div (x + 2)$

60. $(x^4 - 6) \div (x^3 + 3x - 1)$

61. $(x^7 - 2) \div (x^5 + 1)$

62. $(3x^2 + 7x - 1) \div \left(x - \dfrac{1}{3} \right)$

△ **63.** If the area of a parallelogram is $(x^4 - 23x^2 + 9x - 5)$ square centimeters and its base is $(x + 5)$ centimeters, find its height.

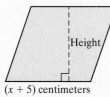

(x + 5) centimeters

△ **64.** If the volume of a box is $(x^4 + 6x^3 - 7x^2)$ cubic meters, its height is x^2 meters, and its length is $(x + 7)$ meters, find its width.

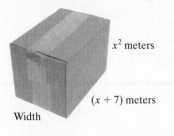

x^2 meters

(x + 7) meters

Width

Divide.

65. $\left(x^4 + \dfrac{2}{3}x^3 + x\right) \div (x - 1)$

66. $\left(2x^3 + \dfrac{9}{2}x^2 - 4x - 10\right) \div (x + 2)$

We say that 2 is a factor of 8 because 2 divides 8 evenly, or with a remainder of 0. In the same manner, the polynomial $x - 2$ is a factor of the polynomial $x^3 - 14x^2 + 24x$ because the remainder is 0 when $x^3 - 14x^2 + 24x$ is divided by $x - 2$. Use this information for Exercises 67 through 69.

67. Use synthetic division to show that $x + 3$ is a factor of $x^3 + 3x^2 + 4x + 12$.

68. Use synthetic division to show that $x - 2$ is a factor of $x^3 - 2x^2 - 3x + 6$.

69. From the remainder theorem, the polynomial $x - c$ is a factor of a polynomial function $P(x)$ if $P(c)$ is what value?

70. If a polynomial is divided by $x - 5$, the quotient is $2x^2 + 5x - 6$ and the remainder is 3. Find the original polynomial.

71. If a polynomial is divided by $x + 3$, the quotient is $x^2 - x + 10$ and the remainder is -2. Find the original polynomial.

Chapter 5 Vocabulary Check

Fill in each blank with one of the words or phrases listed below.

term   coefficient   monomial   binomial   trinomial

polynomials   degree of a term   distributive   FOIL   degree of a polynomial

1. A _____ is a number or the product of numbers and variables raised to powers.

2. The _____ method may be used when multiplying two binomials.

3. A polynomial with exactly three terms is called a _____.

4. The _____ is the greatest degree of any term of the polynomial.

5. A polynomial with exactly two terms is called a _____.

6. The _____ of a term is its numerical factor.

7. The _____ is the sum of the exponents on the variables in the term.

8. A polynomial with exactly one term is called a _____.

9. Monomials, binomials, and trinomials are all examples of _____.

10. The _____ property is used to multiply $2x(x - 4)$.

Chapter 5   Highlights

DEFINITIONS AND CONCEPTS	EXAMPLES

Section 5.1   Exponents

a^n means the product of n factors, each of which is a.

$$3^2 = 3 \cdot 3 = 9$$
$$(-5)^3 = (-5)(-5)(-5) = -125$$
$$\left(\frac{1}{2}\right)^4 = \frac{1}{2} \cdot \frac{1}{2} \cdot \frac{1}{2} \cdot \frac{1}{2} = \frac{1}{16}$$

If m and n are integers and no denominators are 0,

Product Rule: $a^m \cdot a^n = a^{m+n}$

$$x^2 \cdot x^7 = x^{2+7} = x^9$$

Power Rule: $(a^m)^n = a^{mn}$

$$(5^3)^8 = 5^{3 \cdot 8} = 5^{24}$$

Power of a Product Rule: $(ab)^n = a^n b^n$

$$(7y)^4 = 7^4 y^4$$

Power of a Quotient Rule: $\left(\dfrac{a}{b}\right)^n = \dfrac{a^n}{b^n}$

$$\left(\frac{x}{8}\right)^3 = \frac{x^3}{8^3}$$

Quotient Rule: $\dfrac{a^m}{a^n} = a^{m-n}$

$$\frac{x^9}{x^4} = x^{9-4} = x^5$$

Zero Exponent: $a^0 = 1, a \neq 0$.

$$5^0 = 1, \quad x^0 = 1, x \neq 0$$

Section 5.2   Polynomial Functions and Adding and Subtracting Polynomials

A **term** is a number or the product of numbers and variables raised to powers.

Terms

$$-5x, 7a^2 b, \frac{1}{4}y^4, 0.2$$

The **numerical coefficient** or **coefficient** of a term is its numerical factor.

Term	***Coefficient***
$7x^2$	7
y	1
$-a^2 b$	-1

A **polynomial** is a finite sum of terms in which all variables have exponents that are nonnegative integers and no variables appear in the denominator.

Polynomials

$$1.3x^2 \quad \text{(monomial)}$$
$$-\frac{1}{3}y + 5 \quad \text{(binomial)}$$
$$6z^2 - 5z + 7 \quad \text{(trinomial)}$$

A function P is a **polynomial function** if $P(x)$ is a polynomial.

For the polynomial function

$$P(x) = -x^2 + 6x - 12, \text{find } P(-2)$$
$$P(-2) = -(-2)^2 + 6(-2) - 12 = -28.$$

The **degree of a term** is the sum of the exponents on the variables in the term.

Term	***Degree***
$-5x^3$	3
3 (or $3x^0$)	0
$2a^2 b^2 c$	$2 + 2 + 1 = 5$

The **degree of a polynomial** is the greatest degree of any term of the polynomial.

Polynomial	***Degree***
$5x^2 - 3x + 2$	2
$7y + 8y^2 z^3 - 12$	$2 + 3 = 5$

(continued)

DEFINITIONS AND CONCEPTS	EXAMPLES

Section 5.2   Polynomial Functions and Adding and Subtracting Polynomials (continued)

To add polynomials, add or combine like terms.

Add:

$$(7x^2 - 3x + 2) + (-5x - 6) = 7x^2 - 3x + 2 - 5x - 6$$
$$= 7x^2 - 8x - 4$$

To subtract two polynomials, change the signs of the terms of the second polynomial, then add.

Subtract:

$$(17y^2 - 2y + 1) - (-3y^3 + 5y - 6)$$
$$= (17y^2 - 2y + 1) + (3y^3 - 5y + 6)$$
$$= 17y^2 - 2y + 1 + 3y^3 - 5y + 6$$
$$= 3y^3 + 17y^2 - 7y + 7$$

Section 5.3   Multiplying Polynomials

To multiply two polynomials, multiply each term of one polynomial by each term of the other polynomial and then combine like terms.

Multiply:

$$(2x + 1)(5x^2 - 6x + 2)$$

$$= 2x(5x^2 - 6x + 2) + 1(5x^2 - 6x + 2)$$
$$= 10x^3 - 12x^2 + 4x + 5x^2 - 6x + 2$$
$$= 10x^3 - 7x^2 - 2x + 2$$

Section 5.4   Special Products

The **FOIL method** may be used when multiplying two binomials.

Multiply: $(5x - 3)(2x + 3)$

$$(5x - 3)(2x + 3) = (5x)(2x) + (5x)(3) + (-3)(2x) + (-3)(3)$$
$$= 10x^2 + 15x - 6x - 9$$
$$= 10x^2 + 9x - 9$$

Squaring a Binomial

$$(a + b)^2 = a^2 + 2ab + b^2$$

$$(a - b)^2 = a^2 - 2ab + b^2$$

Square each binomial.

$$(x + 5)^2 = x^2 + 2(x)(5) + 5^2$$
$$= x^2 + 10x + 25$$
$$(3x - 2y)^2 = (3x)^2 - 2(3x)(2y) + (2y)^2$$
$$= 9x^2 - 12xy + 4y^2$$

Multiplying the Sum and Difference of Two Terms

$$(a + b)(a - b) = a^2 - b^2$$

Multiply:

$$(6y + 5)(6y - 5) = (6y)^2 - 5^2$$
$$= 36y^2 - 25$$

Section 5.5   Negative Exponents and Scientific Notation

If $a \neq 0$ and n is an integer,

$$a^{-n} = \frac{1}{a^n}$$

Rules for exponents are true for positive and negative integers.

$$3^{-2} = \frac{1}{3^2} = \frac{1}{9}; 5x^{-2} = \frac{5}{x^2}$$

Simplify: $\left(\dfrac{x^{-2}y}{x^5}\right)^{-2} = \dfrac{x^4 y^{-2}}{x^{-10}}$

$$= x^{4-(-10)}y^{-2}$$
$$= \frac{x^{14}}{y^2}$$

DEFINITIONS AND CONCEPTS	EXAMPLES

Section 5.5   Negative Exponents and Scientific Notation (continued)

A positive number is written in scientific notation if it is written as the product of a number a, $1 \le a < 10$, and an integer power r of 10.

$$a \times 10^r$$

Write each number in scientific notation.

$$12{,}000 = 1.2 \times 10^4$$

$$0.00000568 = 5.68 \times 10^{-6}$$

Section 5.6   Dividing Polynomials

To divide a polynomial by a monomial:

$$\frac{a+b}{c} = \frac{a}{c} + \frac{b}{c}$$

Divide:

$$\frac{15x^5 - 10x^3 + 5x^2 - 2x}{5x^2} = \frac{15x^5}{5x^2} - \frac{10x^3}{5x^2} + \frac{5x^2}{5x^2} - \frac{2x}{5x^2}$$

$$= 3x^3 - 2x + 1 - \frac{2}{5x}$$

To divide a polynomial by a polynomial other than a monomial, use long division.

$$
\begin{array}{r}
5x - 1 + \dfrac{-4}{2x+3} \\
2x + 3\overline{)10x^2 + 13x - 7} \\
\underline{10x^2 + 15x} \\
-2x - 7 \\
\underline{-2x - 3} \\
-4
\end{array}
$$

Section 5.7   Synthetic Division and the Remainder Theorem

A shortcut method called **synthetic division** may be used to divide a polynomial by a binomial of the form $x - c$.

Use synthetic division to divide $2x^3 - x^2 - 8x - 1$ by $x - 2$.

$$
\begin{array}{r|rrrr}
2 & 2 & -1 & -8 & -1 \\
  &   & 4 & 6 & -4 \\
\hline
  & 2 & 3 & -2 & -5
\end{array}
$$

The quotient is $2x^2 + 3x - 2 - \dfrac{5}{x-2}$.

Chapter 5 Review

(5.1) *State the base and the exponent for each expression.*

1. 7^9
2. $(-5)^4$
3. -5^4
4. x^6

Evaluate each expression.

5. 8^3
6. $(-6)^2$
7. -6^2
8. $-4^3 - 4^0$
9. $(3b)^0$
10. $\dfrac{8b}{8b}$

Simplify each expression.

11. $y^2 \cdot y^7$
12. $x^9 \cdot x^5$
13. $(2x^5)(-3x^6)$
14. $(-5y^3)(4y^4)$
15. $(x^4)^2$
16. $(y^3)^5$
17. $(3y^6)^4$
18. $(2x^3)^3$

19. $\dfrac{x^9}{x^4}$
20. $\dfrac{z^{12}}{z^5}$
21. $\dfrac{a^5 b^4}{ab}$
22. $\dfrac{x^4 y^6}{xy}$
23. $\dfrac{3x^4 y^{10}}{12xy^6}$
24. $\dfrac{2x^7 y^8}{8xy^2}$
25. $5a^7(2a^4)^3$
26. $(2x)^2(9x)$
27. $(-5a)^0 + 7^0 + 8^0$
28. $8x^0 + 9^0$

Simplify the given expression and choose the correct result.

29. $\left(\dfrac{3x^4}{4y}\right)^3$

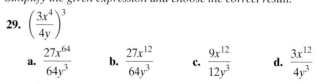

a. $\dfrac{27x^{64}}{64y^3}$
b. $\dfrac{27x^{12}}{64y^3}$
c. $\dfrac{9x^{12}}{12y^3}$
d. $\dfrac{3x^{12}}{4y^3}$

30. $\left(\dfrac{5a^6}{b^3}\right)^2$

  a. $\dfrac{10a^{12}}{b^6}$ **b.** $\dfrac{25a^{36}}{b^9}$ **c.** $\dfrac{25a^{12}}{b^6}$ **d.** $25a^{12}b^6$

(5.2) Find the degree of each term.

31. $-5x^4y^3$ **32.** $10x^3y^2z$

33. $35a^5bc^2$ **34.** $95xyz$

Find the degree of each polynomial.

35. $y^5 + 7x - 8x^4$

36. $9y^2 + 30y + 25$

37. $-14x^2y - 28x^2y^3 - 42x^2y^2$

38. $6x^2y^2z^2 + 5x^2y^3 - 12xyz$

39. The Glass Bridge Skywalk is suspended 4000 feet over the Colorado River at the very edge of the Grand Canyon. Neglecting air resistance, the height of an object dropped from the Skywalk at time *t* seconds is given by the polynomial function $P(t) = -16t^2 + 4000$. Find the height of the object at the given times.

t	0 seconds	1 second	3 seconds	5 seconds
$P(t) = -16t^2 + 4000$				

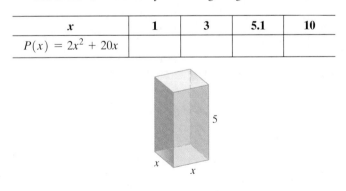

△ **40.** The surface area of a box with a square base and a height of 5 units is given by the polynomial function $P(x) = 2x^2 + 20x$. Fill in the table below by evaluating the given values of *x*.

x	1	3	5.1	10
$P(x) = 2x^2 + 20x$				

Combine like terms in each expression.

41. $6a^2 + 4a + 9a^2$

42. $21x^2 + 3x + x^2 + 6$

43. $4a^2b - 3b^2 - 8q^2 - 10a^2b + 7q^2$

44. $2s^{14} + 3s^{13} + 12s^{12} - s^{10}$

Add or subtract as indicated.

45. $(3x^2 + 2x + 6) + (5x^2 + x)$

46. $(2x^5 + 3x^4 + 4x^3 + 5x^2) + (4x^2 + 7x + 6)$

47. $(-5y^2 + 3) - (2y^2 + 4)$

48. $(3x^2 - 7xy + 7y^2) - (4x^2 - xy + 9y^2)$

TRANSLATING

Perform the indicated operations.

49. Subtract $(3x - y)$ from $(7x - 14y)$.

50. Subtract $(4x^2 + 8x - 7)$ from the sum of $(x^2 + 7x + 9)$ and $(x^2 + 4)$.

If $P(x) = 9x^2 - 7x + 8$, find the following.

51. $P(6)$ **52.** $P(-2)$

53. Find the perimeter of the rectangle.

$x^2y + 5$ cm

$2x^2y - 6x + 1$ cm

54. With the ownership of computers growing rapidly, the market for new software is also increasing. The revenue for software publishers (in millions of dollars) in the United States from 2001 to 2006 can be represented by the polynomial function $f(x) = 754x^2 - 228x + 80{,}134$ where *x* is the number of years since 2001. Use this model to find the revenues from software sales in 2009. (*Source:* Software & Information Industry Association)

(5.3) Multiply each expression.

55. $4(2a + 7)$

56. $9(6a - 3)$

57. $-7x(x^2 + 5)$

58. $-8y(4y^2 - 6)$

59. $(3a^3 - 4a + 1)(-2a)$

60. $(6b^3 - 4b + 2)(7b)$

61. $(2x + 2)(x - 7)$

62. $(2x - 5)(3x + 2)$

63. $(x - 9)^2$

64. $(x - 12)^2$

65. $(4a - 1)(a + 7)$

66. $(6a - 1)(7a + 3)$

67. $(5x + 2)^2$

68. $(3x + 5)^2$

69. $(x + 7)(x^3 + 4x - 5)$

70. $(x + 2)(x^5 + x + 1)$

71. $(x^2 + 2x + 4)(x^2 + 2x - 4)$

72. $(x^3 + 4x + 4)(x^3 + 4x - 4)$

73. $(x + 7)^3$

74. $(2x - 5)^3$

(5.4) Use special products to multiply each of the following.

75. $(x + 7)^2$

76. $(x - 5)^2$

77. $(3x - 7)^2$

78. $(4x + 2)^2$

79. $(5x - 9)^2$

80. $(5x + 1)(5x - 1)$

81. $(7x + 4)(7x - 4)$

82. $(a + 2b)(a - 2b)$

83. $(2x - 6)(2x + 6)$

84. $(4a^2 - 2b)(4a^2 + 2b)$

Express each as a product of polynomials in x. Then multiply and simplify.

△ **85.** Find the area of the square if its side is $(3x - 1)$ meters.

$(3x - 1)$ meters

△ **86.** Find the area of the rectangle.

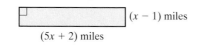

$(x - 1)$ miles

$(5x + 2)$ miles

(5.5) Simplify each expression.

87. 7^{-2}

88. -7^{-2}

89. $2x^{-4}$

90. $(2x)^{-4}$

91. $\left(\dfrac{1}{5}\right)^{-3}$

92. $\left(\dfrac{-2}{3}\right)^{-2}$

93. $2^0 + 2^{-4}$

94. $6^{-1} - 7^{-1}$

Simplify each expression. Write each answer using positive exponents only.

95. $\dfrac{x^5}{x^{-3}}$

96. $\dfrac{z^4}{z^{-4}}$

97. $\dfrac{r^{-3}}{r^{-4}}$

98. $\dfrac{y^{-2}}{y^{-5}}$

99. $\left(\dfrac{bc^{-2}}{bc^{-3}}\right)^4$

100. $\left(\dfrac{x^{-3}y^{-4}}{x^{-2}y^{-5}}\right)^{-3}$

101. $\dfrac{x^{-4}y^{-6}}{x^2y^7}$

102. $\dfrac{a^5b^{-5}}{a^{-5}b^5}$

103. $a^{6m}a^{5m}$

104. $\dfrac{(x^{5+h})^3}{x^5}$

105. $(3xy^{2z})^3$

106. $a^{m+2}a^{m+3}$

Write each number in scientific notation.

107. 0.00027

108. 0.8868

109. 80,800,000

110. 868,000

111. Google.com is an Internet search engine that handles 2,500,000,000 searches every day. Write 2,500,000,000 in scientific notation. (*Source:* Google, Inc.)

112. The approximate diameter of the Milky Way galaxy is 150,000 light years. Write this number in scientific notation. (*Source:* NASA IMAGE/POETRY Education and Public Outreach Program)

150,000 light years

Write each number in standard notation.

113. 8.67×10^5

114. 3.86×10^{-3}

115. 8.6×10^{-4}

116. 8.936×10^5

117. The volume of the planet Jupiter is 1.43128×10^{15} cubic kilometers. Write this number in standard notation. (*Source:* National Space Science Data Center)

118. An angstrom is a unit of measure, equal to 1×10^{-10} meter, used for measuring wavelengths or the diameters of atoms. Write this number in standard notation. (*Source:* National Institute of Standards and Technology)

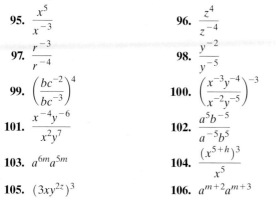

Simplify. Express each result in standard form.

119. $(8 \times 10^4)(2 \times 10^{-7})$

120. $\dfrac{8 \times 10^4}{2 \times 10^{-7}}$

(5.6) Divide.

121. $\dfrac{x^2 + 21x + 49}{7x^2}$

122. $\dfrac{5a^3b - 15ab^2 + 20ab}{-5ab}$

123. $(a^2 - a + 4) \div (a - 2)$

124. $(4x^2 + 20x + 7) \div (x + 5)$

125. $\dfrac{a^3 + a^2 + 2a + 6}{a - 2}$

126. $\dfrac{9b^3 - 18b^2 + 8b - 1}{3b - 2}$

127. $\dfrac{4x^4 - 4x^3 + x^2 + 4x - 3}{2x - 1}$

128. $\dfrac{-10x^2 - x^3 - 21x + 18}{x - 6}$

△ **129.** The area of the rectangle below is $(15x^3 - 3x^2 + 60)$ square feet. If its length is $3x^2$ feet, find its width.

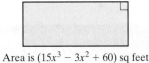

Area is $(15x^3 - 3x^2 + 60)$ sq feet

△ **130.** The perimeter of the equilateral triangle below is $(21a^3b^6 + 3a - 3)$ units. Find the length of a side.

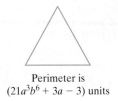

Perimeter is
$(21a^3b^6 + 3a - 3)$ units

(5.7) *Use synthetic division to find each quotient.*

131. $(3x^3 + 12x - 4) \div (x - 2)$

132. $(3x^3 + 2x^2 - 4x - 1) \div \left(x + \dfrac{3}{2}\right)$

133. $(x^5 - 1) \div (x + 1)$

134. $(x^3 - 81) \div (x - 3)$

135. $(x^3 - x^2 + 3x^4 - 2) \div (x - 4)$

136. $(3x^4 - 2x^2 + 10) \div (x + 2)$

If $P(x) = 3x^5 - 9x + 7$, use the remainder theorem to find the following.

137. $P(4)$ **138.** $P(-5)$

MIXED REVIEW

Evaluate.

139. $\left(-\dfrac{1}{2}\right)^3$

Simplify each expression. Write each answer using positive exponents only.

140. $(4xy^2)(x^3y^5)$ **141.** $\dfrac{18x^9}{27x^3}$

142. $\left(\dfrac{3a^4}{b^2}\right)^3$ **143.** $(2x^{-4}y^3)^{-4}$

144. $\dfrac{a^{-3}b^6}{9^{-1}a^{-5}b^{-2}}$

Perform the indicated operations and simplify.

145. $(6x + 2) + (5x - 7)$

146. $(-y^2 - 4) + (3y^2 - 6)$

147. $(8y^2 - 3y + 1) - (3y^2 + 2)$

148. $(5x^2 + 2x - 6) - (-x - 4)$

149. $4x(7x^2 + 3)$

150. $(2x + 5)(3x - 2)$

151. $(x - 3)(x^2 + 4x - 6)$

152. $(7x - 2)(4x - 9)$

Use special products to multiply.

153. $(5x + 4)^2$

154. $(6x + 3)(6x - 3)$

Divide.

155. $\dfrac{8a^4 - 2a^3 + 4a - 5}{2a^3}$

156. $\dfrac{x^2 + 2x + 10}{x + 5}$

157. $\dfrac{4x^3 + 8x^2 - 11x + 4}{2x - 3}$

1c

Chapter 5 Getting Ready for the Test

MATCHING *Match the expression with the exponent operation needed to simplify. Letters may be used more than once or not at all.*

▶ **1.** $x^2 \cdot x^5$ **A.** multiply the exponents

▶ **2.** $(x^2)^5$ **B.** divide the exponents

▶ **3.** $x^2 + x^5$ **C.** add the exponents

▶ **4.** $\dfrac{x^5}{x^2}$

D. subtract the exponents

E. this expression will not simplify

MATCHING *Match the operation with the result when the operation is performed on the given terms. Letters may be used more than once or not at all.*

Given Terms: 20y and 4y

5. Add the terms   **A.** $80y$ **E.** $80y^2$

6. Subtract the terms   **B.** $24y^2$ **F.** $24y$

7. Multiply the terms   **C.** $16y$ **G.** $16y^2$

8. Divide the terms.   **D.** 16 **H.** $5y$

                                        I. 5

MULTIPLE CHOICE *The expression 5^{-1} is equivalent to*

9. **A.** -5 **B.** 4 **C.** $\dfrac{1}{5}$ **D.** $-\dfrac{1}{5}$

MULTIPLE CHOICE *The expression 2^{-3} is equivalent to*

10. **A.** -6 **B.** -1 **C.** $-\dfrac{1}{6}$ **D.** $\dfrac{1}{8}$

MATCHING *Match each expression with its simplified form. Letters may be used more than once or not at all.*

11. $y + y + y$ **A.** $3y^3$ **E.** $-3y^3$

12. $y \cdot y \cdot y$ **B.** y^3 **F.** $-y^3$

13. $(-y)(-y)(-y)$ **C.** $3y$

14. $-y - y - y$ **D.** $-3y$

MULTIPLE CHOICE *Choose the division exercise that can be performed using the synthetic division process.*

15. **A.** $(x^3 - 5x + 15) \div (x^2 - 5)$ **B.** $(y^4 - y^3 + y^2 - 2) \div (y^3 + 1)$

       C. $(2x^3 - 5x^2 + 7) \div \left(x - \dfrac{1}{2}\right)$ **D.** $(z^5 - 4) \div (z^4 + 2z - 2)$

Chapter 5 Test   MyMathLab®   You Tube

Evaluate each expression.

1. 2^5

2. $(-3)^4$

3. -3^4

4. 4^{-3}

Simplify each exponential expression. Write the result using only positive exponents.

5. $(3x^2)(-5x^9)$

6. $\dfrac{y^7}{y^2}$

7. $\dfrac{r^{-8}}{r^{-3}}$

8. $\left(\dfrac{x^2 y^3}{x^3 y^{-4}}\right)^2$

9. $\dfrac{6^2 x^{-4} y^{-1}}{6^3 x^{-3} y^7}$

Express each number in scientific notation.

10. 563,000

11. 0.0000863

Write each number in standard notation.

12. 1.5×10^{-3}

13. 6.23×10^4

14. Simplify. Write the answer in standard notation.

$$(1.2 \times 10^5)(3 \times 10^{-7})$$

15. **a.** Complete the table for the polynomial $4xy^2 + 7xyz + x^3y - 2$.

Term	Numerical Coefficient	Degree of Term
$4xy^2$		
$7xyz$		
x^3y		
-2		

     b. What is the degree of the polynomial?

16. Simplify by combining like terms.

$$5x^2 + 4xy - 7x^2 + 11 + 8xy$$

Perform each indicated operation.

17. $(8x^3 + 7x^2 + 4x - 7) + (8x^3 - 7x - 6)$

18. $5x^3 + x^2 + 5x - 2 - (8x^3 - 4x^2 + x - 7)$

19. Subtract $(4x + 2)$ from the sum of $(8x^2 + 7x + 5)$ and $(x^3 - 8)$.

Multiply.

20. $(3x + 7)(x^2 + 5x + 2)$

21. $3x^2(2x^2 - 3x + 7)$

22. $(x + 7)(3x - 5)$

23. $\left(3x - \dfrac{1}{5}\right)\left(3x + \dfrac{1}{5}\right)$

24. $(4x - 2)^2$

25. $(8x + 3)^2$

26. $(x^2 - 9b)(x^2 + 9b)$

Solve.

27. The height of the Bank of China in Hong Kong is 1001 feet. Neglecting air resistance, the height of an object dropped from this building at time t seconds is given by the polynomial function $P(t) = -16t^2 + 1001$. Find the height of the object at the given times below.

t	0 seconds	1 second	3 seconds	5 seconds
$P(t) = -16t^2 + 1001$				

28. Find the area of the top of the table. Express the area as a product, then multiply and simplify.

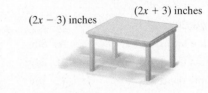

$(2x + 3)$ inches

$(2x - 3)$ inches

Divide.

29. $\dfrac{4x^2 + 24xy - 7x}{8xy}$

30. $(x^2 + 7x + 10) \div (x + 5)$

31. $\dfrac{27x^3 - 8}{3x + 2}$

32. A pebble is hurled upward from the top of the Canada Trust Tower, which is 880 feet tall, with an initial velocity of 96 feet per second. Neglecting air resistance, the height $h(t)$ of the pebble after t seconds is given by the polynomial function

$$h(t) = -16t^2 + 96t + 880$$

  a. Find the height of the pebble when $t = 1$.

  b. Find the height of the pebble when $t = 5.1$.

33. Use synthetic division to divide $(4x^4 - 3x^3 - x - 1)$ by $(x + 3)$.

34. If $P(x) = 4x^4 + 7x^2 - 2x - 5$, use the remainder theorem to find $P(-2)$.

Chapter 5 Cumulative Review

1. Tell whether each statement is true or false.

  a. $8 \geq 8$ **b.** $8 \leq 8$

  c. $23 \leq 0$ **d.** $23 \geq 0$

2. Find the absolute value of each number.

  a. $|-7.2|$ **b.** $|0|$ **c.** $\left|-\dfrac{1}{2}\right|$

3. Divide. Simplify all quotients if possible.

  a. $\dfrac{4}{5} \div \dfrac{5}{16}$ **b.** $\dfrac{7}{10} \div 14$ **c.** $\dfrac{3}{8} \div \dfrac{3}{10}$

4. Multiply. Write products in lowest terms.

  a. $\dfrac{3}{4} \cdot \dfrac{7}{21}$ **b.** $\dfrac{1}{2} \cdot 4\dfrac{5}{6}$

5. Evaluate the following.

  a. 3^2 **b.** 5^3 **c.** 2^4

  d. 7^1 **e.** $\left(\dfrac{3}{7}\right)^2$

6. Evaluate $\dfrac{2x - 7y}{x^2}$ for $x = 5$ and $y = 1$.

7. Add.

  a. $-3 + (-7)$ **b.** $-1 + (-20)$

  c. $-2 + (-10)$

8. Simplify: $8 + 3(2 \cdot 6 - 1)$

9. Subtract 8 from -4.

10. Is $x = 1$ a solution of $5x^2 + 2 = x - 8$?

11. Find the reciprocal of each number.

  a. 22   **b.** $\dfrac{3}{16}$

  c. -10 **d.** $-\dfrac{9}{13}$

12. Subtract.

  a. $7 - 40$ **b.** $-5 - (-10)$

13. Use an associative property to complete each statement.

  a. $5 + (4 + 6) =$ _____

  b. $(-1 \cdot 2) \cdot 5 =$ _____

14. Simplify: $\dfrac{4(-3) + (-8)}{5 + (-5)}$

15. Simplify each expression.

  a. $10 + (x + 12)$

  b. $-3(7x)$

16. Use the distributive property to write $-2(x + 3y - z)$ without parentheses.

17. Find each product by using the distributive property to remove parentheses.

  a. $5(3x + 2)$

  b. $-2(y + 0.3z - 1)$

  c. $-(9x + y - 2z + 6)$

18. Simplify: $2(6x - 1) - (x - 7)$

19. Solve $x - 7 = 10$ for x.

20. Write the phrase as an algebraic expression: double a number, subtracted from the sum of the number and seven

21. Solve: $\dfrac{5}{2}x = 15$

22. Solve: $2x + \dfrac{1}{8} = x - \dfrac{3}{8}$

23. Twice a number, added to seven, is the same as three subtracted from the number. Find the number.

24. Solve: $10 = 5j - 2$

25. Twice the sum of a number and 4 is the same as four times the number, decreased by 12. Find the number.

26. Solve: $\dfrac{7x + 5}{3} = x + 3$

27. The length of a rectangular road sign is 2 feet less than three times its width. Find the dimensions if the perimeter is 28 feet.

28. Graph $x < 5$ and write the solutions in interval notation.

29. Solve $F = \dfrac{9}{5}C + 32$ for C.

30. Find the slope of each line.
   a. $x = -1$
   b. $y = 7$

31. Graph: $2 < x \le 4$

32. Recall that the grade of a road is its slope written as a percent. Find the grade of the road shown.

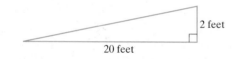

2 feet

20 feet

33. Complete the following ordered pair solutions for the equation $3x + y = 12$.
   a. $(0, \ )$
   b. $(\ , 6)$
   c. $(-1, \ )$

34. Solve the system: $\begin{cases} 3x + 2y = -8 \\ 2x - 6y = -9 \end{cases}$

35. Graph the linear equation: $2x + y = 5$

36. Solve the system: $\begin{cases} x = -3y + 3 \\ 2x + 9y = 5 \end{cases}$

37. Graph: $x = 2$

38. Evaluate.
   a. $(-5)^2$
   b. -5^2
   c. $2 \cdot 5^2$

39. Find the slope of the line $x = 5$.

40. Simplify: $\dfrac{(z^2)^3 \cdot z^7}{z^9}$

41. Subtract: $(2x^3 + 8x^2 - 6x) - (2x^3 - x^2 + 1)$

42. Subtract: $(5y^2 - 6) - (y^2 + 2)$

43. Use the product rule to simplify $(2x^2)(-3x^5)$.

44. Find the value of $-x^2$ when
   a. $x = 2$
   b. $x = -2$

45. Add $(11x^3 - 12x^2 + x - 3)$ and $(x^3 - 10x + 5)$.

46. Multiply: $(10x^2 - 3)(10x^2 + 3)$

47. Multiply: $(2x - y)^2$

48. Multiply: $(10x^2 + 3)^2$

49. Divide $6m^2 + 2m$ by $2m$.

50. Evaluate.
   a. 5^{-1}
   b. 7^{-2}

Factoring Polynomials

6.1 The Greatest Common Factor and Factoring by Grouping

6.2 Factoring Trinomials of the Form $x^2 + bx + c$

6.3 Factoring Trinomials of the Form $ax^2 + bx + c$ and Perfect Square Trinomials

6.4 Factoring Trinomials of the Form $ax^2 + bx + c$ by Grouping

6.5 Factoring Binomials

Integrated Review—Choosing a Factoring Strategy

6.6 Solving Quadratic Equations by Factoring

6.7 Quadratic Equations and Problem Solving

✓ CHECK YOUR PROGRESS

Vocabulary Check

Chapter Highlights

Chapter Review

Getting Ready for the Test

Chapter Test

Cumulative Review

In Chapter 5, we learned how to multiply polynomials. This chapter deals with an operation that is the reverse process of multiplying, called *factoring*. Factoring is an important algebraic skill because this process allows us to write a sum as a product.

At the end of this chapter, we use factoring to help us solve equations other than linear equations, and in Chapter 7, we use factoring to simplify and perform arithmetic operations on rational expressions.

Why Are You in College?

There are probably as many answers as there are students. It may help you to know that college graduates have higher earnings and lower rates of unemployment. The double line graph below shows the increasing number of associate and bachelor degrees awarded over the years. It is also enlightening to know that an increasing number of high school graduates are looking to higher education.

In Exercise 110 of Section 6.1, we will explore how many students graduate from U.S. high schools each year, and how many of those may expect to go to college.

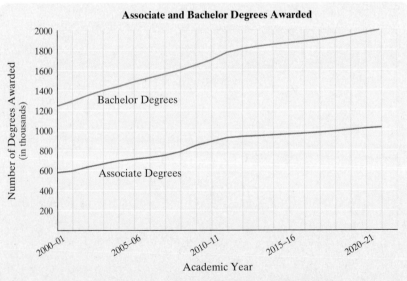

Associate and Bachelor Degrees Awarded

Source: National Center for Education Statistics (http://nces.ed.gov); U.S. Department of Education

Note: Some years are projected.

6.1 | The Greatest Common Factor and Factoring by Grouping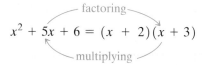

OBJECTIVES

1 Find the Greatest Common Factor of a List of Integers.

2 Find the Greatest Common Factor of a List of Terms.

3 Factor Out the Greatest Common Factor from a Polynomial.

4 Factor a Polynomial by Grouping.

In the product $2 \cdot 3 = 6$, the numbers 2 and 3 are called **factors** of 6 and $2 \cdot 3$ is a **factored form** of 6. This is true of polynomials also. Since $(x + 2)(x + 3) = x^2 + 5x + 6$, $(x + 2)$ and $(x + 3)$ are factors of $x^2 + 5x + 6$, and $(x + 2)(x + 3)$ is a factored form of the polynomial.

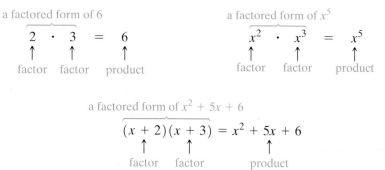

a factored form of 6

$$\underset{\text{factor}}{2} \cdot \underset{\text{factor}}{3} = \underset{\text{product}}{6}$$

a factored form of x^5

$$\underset{\text{factor}}{x^2} \cdot \underset{\text{factor}}{x^3} = \underset{\text{product}}{x^5}$$

a factored form of $x^2 + 5x + 6$

$$\underset{\text{factor}}{(x + 2)} \underset{\text{factor}}{(x + 3)} = \underset{\text{product}}{x^2 + 5x + 6}$$

> The process of writing a polynomial as a product is called **factoring** the polynomial.

Do you see that factoring is the reverse process of multiplying?

$$x^2 + 5x + 6 = (x + 2)(x + 3)$$

factoring

multiplying

✔ **CONCEPT CHECK**

Multiply: $2(x - 4)$

What do you think the result of factoring $2x - 8$ would be? Why?

OBJECTIVE

1   Finding the Greatest Common Factor of a List of Integers

The first step in factoring a polynomial is to see whether the terms of the polynomial have a common factor. If there is one, we can write the polynomial as a product by **factoring out** the common factor. We will usually factor out the **greatest common factor (GCF).**

The GCF of a list of integers is the largest integer that is a factor of all the integers in the list. For example, the GCF of 12 and 20 is 4 because 4 is the largest integer that is a factor of both 12 and 20. With large integers, the GCF may not be found easily by inspection. When this happens, use the following steps.

> **Finding the GCF of a List of Integers**
>
> **Step 1.** Write each number as a product of prime numbers.
>
> **Step 2.** Identify the common prime factors.
>
> **Step 3.** The product of all common prime factors found in Step 2 is the greatest common factor. If there are no common prime factors, the greatest common factor is 1.

Recall from Section 1.3 that a prime number is a whole number other than 1 whose only factors are 1 and itself.

EXAMPLE 1 Find the GCF of each list of numbers.

    a. 28 and 40   **b.** 55 and 21   **c.** 15, 18, and 66

Solution

    a. Write each number as a product of primes.

$$28 = 2 \cdot 2 \cdot 7 = 2^2 \cdot 7$$
$$40 = 2 \cdot 2 \cdot 2 \cdot 5 = 2^3 \cdot 5$$

There are two common factors, each of which is 2, so the GCF is

$$\text{GCF} = 2 \cdot 2 = 4$$

    b. $55 = 5 \cdot 11$

        $21 = 3 \cdot 7$

There are no common prime factors; thus, the GCF is 1.

    c. $15 = 3 \cdot 5$

        $18 = 2 \cdot 3 \cdot 3 = 2 \cdot 3^2$

        $66 = 2 \cdot 3 \cdot 11$

The only prime factor common to all three numbers is 3, so the GCF is

$$\text{GCF} = 3 \qquad \square$$

PRACTICE

1   Find the GCF of each list of numbers.

    a. 36 and 42   **b.** 35 and 44   **c.** 12, 16, and 40   ■

OBJECTIVE

2   **Finding the Greatest Common Factor of a List of Terms** ▶

The greatest common factor of a list of variables raised to powers is found in a similar way. For example, the GCF of x^2, x^3, and x^5 is x^2 because each term contains a factor of x^2 and no higher power of x is a factor of each term.

$$x^2 = x \cdot x$$
$$x^3 = x \cdot x \cdot x$$
$$x^5 = x \cdot x \cdot x \cdot x \cdot x$$

There are two common factors, each of which is x, so the GCF $= x \cdot x$ or x^2.

    From this example, we see that **the GCF of a list of common variables raised to powers is the variable raised to the smallest exponent in the list.**

EXAMPLE 2 Find the GCF of each list of terms.

    a. x^3, x^7, and x^5 **b.** y, y^4, and y^7

Solution

    a. The GCF is x^3, since 3 is the smallest exponent to which x is raised.

    b. The GCF is y^1 or y, since 1 is the smallest exponent on y.   □

PRACTICE

2   Find the GCF of each list of terms.

    a. y^7, y^4, and y^6 **b.** x, x^4, and x^2 ■

    In general, the **greatest common factor (GCF) of a list of terms** is the product of the GCF of the numerical coefficients and the GCF of the variable factors.

$$20x^2y^2 = 2 \cdot 2 \cdot 5 \cdot x \cdot x \cdot y \cdot y$$
$$6xy^3 = 2 \cdot 3 \cdot x \cdot y \cdot y \cdot y$$
$$GCF = 2 \cdot x \cdot y \cdot y = 2xy^2$$

Helpful Hint

Remember that the GCF of a list of terms contains the smallest exponent on each common variable.

The GCF of x^5y^6, x^2y^7, and x^3y^4 is x^2y^4. $\quad$ Smallest exponent on x
$\qquad\qquad\qquad\qquad\qquad\qquad\qquad\qquad\qquad\qquad$ Smallest exponent on y

EXAMPLE 3   Find the GCF of each list of terms.

  a. $6x^2$, $10x^3$, and $-8x$ **b.** $-18y^2$, $-63y^3$, and $27y^4$ **c.** a^3b^2, a^5b, and a^6b^2

Solution

a. $6x^2 = 2 \cdot 3 \cdot x^2$
$\quad 10x^3 = 2 \cdot 5 \cdot x^3$ $\quad\Big\}\rightarrow$ The GCF of x^2, x^3, and x^1 is x^1 or x.
$\quad -8x = -1 \cdot 2 \cdot 2 \cdot 2 \cdot x^1$
$\quad$ GCF $= 2 \cdot x^1$ or $2x$

b. $-18y^2 = -1 \cdot 2 \cdot 3 \cdot 3 \cdot y^2$
$\quad -63y^3 = -1 \cdot 3 \cdot 3 \cdot 7 \cdot y^3$ $\quad\Big\}\rightarrow$ The GCF of y^2, y^3, and y^4 is y^2.
$\quad 27y^4 = 3 \cdot 3 \cdot 3 \cdot y^4$
$\quad$ GCF $= 3 \cdot 3 \cdot y^2$ or $9y^2$

c. The GCF of a^3, a^5, and a^6 is a^3.
The GCF of b^2, b, and b^2 is b. Thus,
the GCF of a^3b^2, a^5b, and a^6b^2 is a^3b. $\qquad\qquad\qquad\qquad\qquad$ □

PRACTICE

3   Find the GCF of each list of terms.

  a. $5y^4$, $15y^2$, and $-20y^3$ **b.** $4x^2$, x^3, and $3x^8$ **c.** a^4b^2, a^3b^5, and a^2b^3 ■

OBJECTIVE

3   Factoring Out the Greatest Common Factor ▶

The first step in factoring a polynomial is to find the GCF of its terms. Once we do so, we can write the polynomial as a product by **factoring out** the GCF.

The polynomial $8x + 14$, for example, contains two terms: $8x$ and 14. The GCF of these terms is 2. We factor out 2 from each term by writing each term as a product of 2 and the term's remaining factors.

$$8x + 14 = 2 \cdot 4x + 2 \cdot 7$$

Using the distributive property, we can write

$$8x + 14 = 2 \cdot 4x + 2 \cdot 7$$
$$= 2(4x + 7)$$

Thus, a factored form of $8x + 14$ is $2(4x + 7)$. We can check by multiplying:

$$2(4x + 7) = 2 \cdot 4x + 2 \cdot 7 = 8x + 14.$$

Helpful Hint

A factored form of $8x + 14$ is *not*

$$2 \cdot 4x + 2 \cdot 7$$

Although the *terms* have been factored (written as products), the *polynomial* $8x + 14$ has not been factored (written as a product).

A factored form of $8x + 14$ is the *product* $2(4x + 7)$.

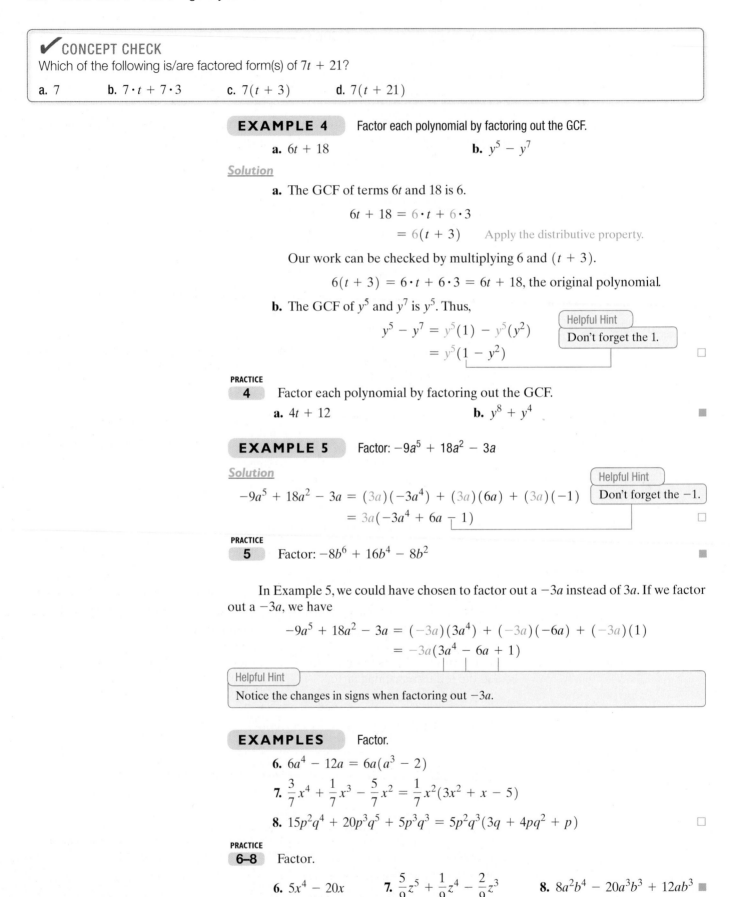

✔ CONCEPT CHECK

Which of the following is/are factored form(s) of $7t + 21$?

a. 7 b. $7 \cdot t + 7 \cdot 3$ c. $7(t + 3)$ d. $7(t + 21)$

EXAMPLE 4   Factor each polynomial by factoring out the GCF.

a. $6t + 18$ b. $y^5 - y^7$

Solution

a. The GCF of terms $6t$ and 18 is 6.

$$6t + 18 = 6 \cdot t + 6 \cdot 3$$
$$= 6(t + 3) \quad \text{Apply the distributive property.}$$

Our work can be checked by multiplying 6 and $(t + 3)$.

$$6(t + 3) = 6 \cdot t + 6 \cdot 3 = 6t + 18, \text{ the original polynomial.}$$

b. The GCF of y^5 and y^7 is y^5. Thus,

$$y^5 - y^7 = y^5(1) - y^5(y^2)$$
$$= y^5(1 - y^2)$$

> **Helpful Hint**
> Don't forget the 1.

PRACTICE
4   Factor each polynomial by factoring out the GCF.

a. $4t + 12$ b. $y^8 + y^4$

EXAMPLE 5   Factor: $-9a^5 + 18a^2 - 3a$

Solution

$$-9a^5 + 18a^2 - 3a = (3a)(-3a^4) + (3a)(6a) + (3a)(-1)$$
$$= 3a(-3a^4 + 6a - 1)$$

> **Helpful Hint**
> Don't forget the −1.

PRACTICE
5   Factor: $-8b^6 + 16b^4 - 8b^2$

In Example 5, we could have chosen to factor out a $-3a$ instead of $3a$. If we factor out a $-3a$, we have

$$-9a^5 + 18a^2 - 3a = (-3a)(3a^4) + (-3a)(-6a) + (-3a)(1)$$
$$= -3a(3a^4 - 6a + 1)$$

> **Helpful Hint**
> Notice the changes in signs when factoring out $-3a$.

EXAMPLES   Factor.

6. $6a^4 - 12a = 6a(a^3 - 2)$

7. $\dfrac{3}{7}x^4 + \dfrac{1}{7}x^3 - \dfrac{5}{7}x^2 = \dfrac{1}{7}x^2(3x^2 + x - 5)$

8. $15p^2q^4 + 20p^3q^5 + 5p^3q^3 = 5p^2q^3(3q + 4pq^2 + p)$

PRACTICE
6–8   Factor.

6. $5x^4 - 20x$ 7. $\dfrac{5}{9}z^5 + \dfrac{1}{9}z^4 - \dfrac{2}{9}z^3$ 8. $8a^2b^4 - 20a^3b^3 + 12ab^3$

EXAMPLE 9   Factor: $5(x + 3) + y(x + 3)$

Solution The binomial $(x + 3)$ is the greatest common factor. Use the distributive property to factor out $(x + 3)$.

$$5(x + 3) + y(x + 3) = (x + 3)(5 + y)$$ □

PRACTICE
9   Factor: $8(y - 2) + x(y - 2)$ ∎

EXAMPLE 10   Factor: $3m^2n(a + b) - (a + b)$

Solution The greatest common factor is $(a + b)$.

$$3m^2n(a + b) - 1(a + b) = (a + b)(3m^2n - 1)$$ □

PRACTICE
10   Factor: $7xy^3(p + q) - (p + q)$ ∎

OBJECTIVE
4   Factoring by Grouping ▶

Once the GCF is factored out, we can often continue to factor the polynomial, using a variety of techniques. We discuss here a technique for factoring polynomials called **factoring by grouping.**

EXAMPLE 11   Factor $xy + 2x + 3y + 6$ by grouping. Check by multiplying.

Solution The GCF of the first two terms is x, and the GCF of the last two terms is 3.

$$xy + 2x + 3y + 6 = (xy + 2x) + (3y + 6) \quad \text{Group terms.}$$
$$= x(y + 2) + 3(y + 2) \quad \text{Factor out GCF from each grouping.}$$

> **Helpful Hint**
> Notice that this form, $x(y + 2) + 3(y + 2)$, is _not_ a factored form of the original polynomial. It is a sum, not a product.

Next we factor out the common binomial factor, $(y + 2)$.

$$x(y + 2) + 3(y + 2) = (y + 2)(x + 3)$$

Now the result is a factored form because it is a product. We were able to write the polynomial as a product because of the common binomial factor, $(y + 2)$, that appeared. If this does not happen, try rearranging the terms of the original polynomial.

Check: Multiply: $(y + 2)$ by $(x + 3)$

$$(y + 2)(x + 3) = xy + 2x + 3y + 6,$$

the original polynomial.

Thus, a factored form of $xy + 2x + 3y + 6$ is the product $(y + 2)(x + 3)$.   □

PRACTICE
11   Factor $xy + 3y + 4x + 12$ by grouping. Check by multiplying.   ∎

You may want to try these steps when factoring by grouping.

To Factor a Four-Term Polynomial by Grouping

Step 1. Group the terms in two groups of two terms so that each group has a common factor.

Step 2. Factor out the GCF from each group.

Step 3. If there is now a common binomial factor in the groups, factor it out.

Step 4. If not, rearrange the terms and try these steps again.

EXAMPLES   Factor by grouping.

12. $15x^3 - 10x^2 + 6x - 4$

$= (15x^3 - 10x^2) + (6x - 4)$ Group the terms.

$= 5x^2(3x - 2) + 2(3x - 2)$ Factor each group.

$= (3x - 2)(5x^2 + 2)$ Factor out the common factor, $(3x - 2)$.

13. $3x^2 + 4xy - 3x - 4y$

$= (3x^2 + 4xy) + (-3x - 4y)$

$= x(3x + 4y) - 1(3x + 4y)$ Factor each group. A -1 is factored from the second pair of terms so that there is a common factor, $(3x + 4y)$.

$= (3x + 4y)(x - 1)$ Factor out the common factor, $(3x + 4y)$.

14. $2a^2 + 5ab + 2a + 5b$

$= (2a^2 + 5ab) + (2a + 5b)$

$= a(2a + 5b) + 1(2a + 5b)$ Factor each group. An understood 1 is written before $(2a + 5b)$ to help remember that $(2a + 5b)$ is $1(2a + 5b)$.

$= (2a + 5b)(a + 1)$ Factor out the common factor, $(2a + 5b)$. □

> **Helpful Hint**
> Notice the factor of 1 is written when $(2a + 5b)$ is factored out.

PRACTICE
12–14

12. Factor $40x^3 - 24x^2 + 15x - 9$ by grouping.

13. Factor $2xy + 3y^2 - 2x - 3y$ by grouping.

14. Factor $7a^3 + 5a^2 + 7a + 5$ by grouping. ■

EXAMPLES   Factor by grouping.

15. $3xy + 2 - 3x - 2y$

Notice that the first two terms have no common factor other than 1. However, if we rearrange these terms, a grouping emerges that does lead to a common factor.

$3xy + 2 - 3x - 2y$

$= (3xy - 3x) + (-2y + 2)$

$= 3x(y - 1) - 2(y - 1)$ Factor -2 from the second group so that there is a common factor, $(y - 1)$.

$= (y - 1)(3x - 2)$ Factor out the common factor, $(y - 1)$.

16. $5x - 10 + x^3 - x^2 = 5(x - 2) + x^2(x - 1)$

There is no common binomial factor that can now be factored out. No matter how we rearrange the terms, no grouping will lead to a common factor. Thus, this polynomial is not factorable by grouping. □

PRACTICE
15–16

15. Factor $4xy + 15 - 12x - 5y$ by grouping.

16. Factor $9y - 18 + y^3 - 4y^2$ by grouping. ■

> **Helpful Hint**
> One more reminder: When **factoring** a polynomial, make sure the polynomial is written as a **product**. For example, it is true that
> $$3x^2 + 4xy - 3x - 4y = \underline{x(3x + 4y) - 1(3x + 4y)},$$
> $$\text{but is not a } \textbf{factored form}$$
> since it is a **sum (difference)**, not a **product**. A factored form of $3x^2 + 4xy - 3x - 4y$ is the product $(3x + 4y)(x - 1)$.

Factoring out a greatest common factor first makes factoring by any method easier, as we see in the next example.

EXAMPLE 17   Factor: $4ax - 4ab - 2bx + 2b^2$

Solution   First, factor out the common factor 2 from all four terms.

$$4ax - 4ab - 2bx + 2b^2$$

$$= 2(2ax - 2ab - bx + b^2) \qquad \text{Factor out 2 from all four terms.}$$

$$= 2[2a(x - b) - b(x - b)] \qquad \text{Factor each pair of terms. A ``}{-b}\text{'' is factored from the}$$
$$\qquad\qquad\qquad\qquad\qquad\qquad\qquad \text{second pair so that there is a common factor, } x - b.$$

$$= 2(x - b)(2a - b) \qquad\qquad \text{Factor out the common binomial.}$$

> **Helpful Hint**
>
> Throughout this chapter, we will be factoring polynomials. Even when the instructions do not so state, it is always a good idea to check your answers by multiplying.

PRACTICE
17   Factor: $3xy - 3ay - 6ax + 6a^2$

✔ Vocabulary, Readiness & Video Check

Use the choices below to fill in each blank. Some choices may be used more than once and some may not be used at all.

| greatest common factor | factors | factoring | true | false | least | greatest |

1. Since $5 \cdot 4 = 20$, the numbers 5 and 4 are called _____ of 20.

2. The _____ of a list of integers is the largest integer that is a factor of all the integers in the list.

3. The greatest common factor of a list of common variables raised to powers is the variable raised to the _____ exponent in the list.

4. The process of writing a polynomial as a product is called _____.

5. True or false: A factored form of $7x + 21 + xy + 3y$ is $7(x + 3) + y(x + 3)$. _____

6. True or false: A factored form of $3x^3 + 6x + x^2 + 2$ is $3x(x^2 + 2)$. _____

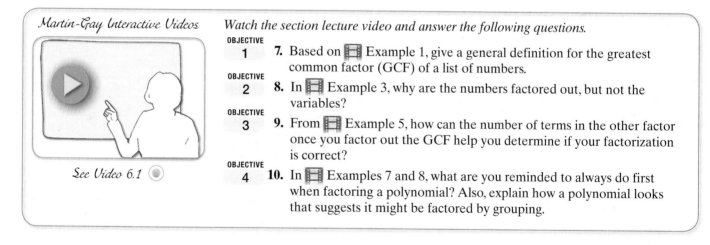

Martin-Gay Interactive Videos

See Video 6.1 ◉

Watch the section lecture video and answer the following questions.

OBJECTIVE 1   **7.** Based on ▦ Example 1, give a general definition for the greatest common factor (GCF) of a list of numbers.

OBJECTIVE 2   **8.** In ▦ Example 3, why are the numbers factored out, but not the variables?

OBJECTIVE 3   **9.** From ▦ Example 5, how can the number of terms in the other factor once you factor out the GCF help you determine if your factorization is correct?

OBJECTIVE 4   **10.** In ▦ Examples 7 and 8, what are you reminded to always do first when factoring a polynomial? Also, explain how a polynomial looks that suggests it might be factored by grouping.

6.1   Exercise Set   MyMathLab® ▶

Find the GCF for each list. See Examples 1 through 3.

1. 32, 36

2. 36, 90

3. 18, 42, 84

4. 30, 75, 135

5. 24, 14, 21

6. 15, 25, 27

7. y^2, y^4, y^7

8. x^3, x^2, x^5

9. z^7, z^9, z^{11}

10. y^8, y^{10}, y^{12}

11. $x^{10}y^2, xy^2, x^3y^3$

12. p^7q, p^8q^2, p^9q^3

13. $14x, 21$

14. $20y, 15$

15. $12y^4, 20y^3$

16. $32x^5, 18x^2$

17. $-10x^2, 15x^3$

18. $-21x^3, 14x$

19. $12x^3, -6x^4, 3x^5$

20. $15y^2, 5y^7, -20y^3$

21. $-18x^2y, 9x^3y^3, 36x^3y$

22. $7x^3y^3, -21x^2y^2, 14xy^4$

23. $20a^6b^2c^8, 50a^7b$

24. $40x^7y^2z, 64x^9y$

Factor out the GCF from each polynomial. See Examples 4 through 10.

25. $3a + 6$

26. $18a + 12$

27. $30x - 15$

28. $42x - 7$

29. $x^3 + 5x^2$

30. $y^5 + 6y^4$

31. $6y^4 + 2y^3$

32. $5x^2 + 10x^6$

33. $4x - 8y + 4$

34. $7x + 21y - 7$

35. $6x^3 - 9x^2 + 12x$

36. $12x^3 + 16x^2 - 8x$

37. $a^7b^6 - a^3b^2 + a^2b^5 - a^2b^2$

38. $x^9y^6 + x^3y^5 - x^4y^3 + x^3y^3$

39. $8x^5 + 16x^4 - 20x^3 + 12$

40. $9y^6 - 27y^4 + 18y^2 + 6$

41. $\frac{1}{3}x^4 + \frac{2}{3}x^3 - \frac{4}{3}x^5 + \frac{1}{3}x$

42. $\frac{2}{5}y^7 - \frac{4}{5}y^5 + \frac{3}{5}y^2 - \frac{2}{5}y$

43. $y(x^2 + 2) + 3(x^2 + 2)$

44. $x(y^2 + 1) - 3(y^2 + 1)$

45. $z(y + 4) - 3(y + 4)$

46. $8(x + 2) - y(x + 2)$

47. $r(z^2 - 6) + (z^2 - 6)$

48. $q(b^3 - 5) + (b^3 - 5)$

Factor a negative number or a GCF with a negative coefficient from each polynomial. See Example 5.

49. $-2x - 14$

50. $-7y - 21$

51. $-2x^5 + x^7$

52. $-5y^3 + y^6$

53. $-3a^4 + 9a^3 - 3a^2$

54. $-5m^6 + 10m^5 - 5m^3$

Factor each four-term polynomial by grouping. If this is not possible, write "not factorable by grouping." See Examples 11 through 17.

55. $x^3 + 2x^2 + 5x + 10$

56. $x^3 + 4x^2 + 3x + 12$

57. $5x + 15 + xy + 3y$

58. $xy + y + 2x + 2$

59. $6x^3 - 4x^2 + 15x - 10$

60. $16x^3 - 28x^2 + 12x - 21$

61. $5m^3 + 6mn + 5m^2 + 6n$

62. $8w^2 + 7wv + 8w + 7v$

63. $2y - 8 + xy - 4x$

64. $6x - 42 + xy - 7y$

65. $2x^3 - x^2 + 8x - 4$

66. $2x^3 - x^2 - 10x + 5$

67. $3x - 3 + x^3 - 4x^2$

68. $7x - 21 + x^3 - 2x^2$

69. $4x^2 - 8xy - 3x + 6y$

70. $5xy - 15x - 6y + 18$

71. $5q^2 - 4pq - 5q + 4p$

72. $6m^2 - 5mn - 6m + 5n$

73. $2x^4 + 5x^3 + 2x^2 + 5x$

74. $4y^4 + y^2 + 20y^3 + 5y$

75. $12x^2y - 42x^2 - 4y + 14$

76. $90 + 15y^2 - 18x - 3xy^2$

MIXED PRACTICE

Factor. See Examples 4 through 17.

77. $32xy - 18x^2$

78. $10xy - 15x^2$

79. $y(x + 2) - 3(x + 2)$

80. $z(y - 4) + 3(y - 4)$

81. $14x^3y + 7x^2y - 7xy$

82. $5x^3y - 15x^2y + 10xy$

83. $28x^3 - 7x^2 + 12x - 3$

84. $15x^3 + 5x^2 - 6x - 2$

85. $-40x^8y^6 - 16x^9y^5$

86. $-21x^3y - 49x^2y^2$

87. $6a^2 + 9ab^2 + 6ab + 9b^3$

88. $16x^2 + 4xy^2 + 8xy + 2y^3$

REVIEW AND PREVIEW

Multiply. See Sections 5.3 and 5.4.

89. $(x + 2)(x + 5)$

90. $(y + 3)(y + 6)$

91. $(b + 1)(b - 4)$

92. $(x - 5)(x + 10)$

Fill in the chart by finding two numbers that have the given product and sum. The first column is filled in for you.

	93.	94.	95.	96.	97.	98.
Two Numbers	4, 7					
Their Product	28	12	20	8	16	−10	−24
Their Sum	11	8	9	−9	−10	3	−5

CONCEPT EXTENSIONS

See the Concept Checks in this section.

99. Which of the following is/are factored form(s) of $8a - 24$?

a. $8 \cdot a - 24$

b. $8(a - 3)$

c. $4(2a - 12)$

d. $8 \cdot a - 2 \cdot 12$

100. Which of the following is/are factored form(s) of $-2x + 14$?

a. $-2(x + 7)$

b. $-2 \cdot x + 14$

c. $-2(x - 14)$

d. $-2(x - 7)$

Determine whether the following expressions are factored.

101. $(a + 6)(a + 2)$

102. $(x + 5)(x + y)$

103. $5(2y + z) - b(2y + z)$

104. $3x(a + 2b) + 2(a + 2b)$

105. Construct a binomial whose greatest common factor is $5a^3$. (*Hint:* Multiply $5a^3$ by a binomial whose terms contain no common factor other than 1. $5a^3(\square + \square)$.)

106. Construct a trinomial whose greatest common factor is $2x^2$. See the hint for Exercise 105.

107. Explain how you can tell whether a polynomial is written in factored form.

108. Construct a four-term polynomial that can be factored by grouping.

109. The percent of total music industry revenues from streaming in the United States each year during 2007 through 2014 can be modeled by the polynomial $0.6x^2 - 0.6x + 3.6$, where x is the number of years since 2007. (*Source:* Recording Industry Association of America)

   a. Find the percent of music industry revenue derived from streaming in 2013. To do so, let $x = 6$ and evaluate $0.6x^2 - 0.6x + 3.6$. Round to the nearest percent.

   b. Use this expression to predict the percent revenue derived from streaming in 2018. Round to the nearest percent.

   c. Factor the polynomial $0.6x^2 - 0.6x + 3.6$ by factoring 0.6 from each term.

110. The number (in thousands) of students who graduated from U.S. high schools, both public and private, each year during 2000 through 2013 can be modeled by $-3x^2 + 78x + 2904$, where x is the number of years since 2000. (*Source:* National Center for Educational Statistics)

   a. Find the number of students who graduated from U.S. high schools in 2010. To do so, let $x = 10$ and evaluate $-3x^2 + 78x + 2904$.

   b. Use this expression to predict the number of students who will graduate from U.S. high schools in 2018.

   c. Factor the polynomial $-3x^2 + 78x + 2904$ by factoring -3 from each term.

   d. For the year 2010, the National Center for Higher Education determined that 62.5% of U.S. high school graduates went on to higher education. Using your answer from part **a**, determine how many of those graduating in 2010 pursued higher education.

Write an expression for the area of each shaded region. Then write the expression as a factored polynomial.

△ **111.** △ **112.**

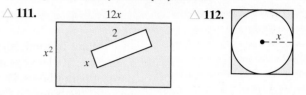

*Write an expression for the length of each rectangle. (**Hint:** Factor the area binomial and recall that Area = width · length.)*

△ **113.** △ **114.**

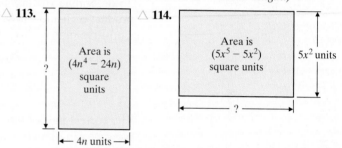

Factor each polynomial by grouping.

115. $x^{2n} + 2x^n + 3x^n + 6$
   (*Hint:* Don't forget that $x^{2n} = x^n \cdot x^n$.)

116. $x^{2n} + 6x^n + 10x^n + 60$

117. $3x^{2n} + 21x^n - 5x^n - 35$

118. $12x^{2n} - 10x^n - 30x^n + 25$

6.2 | Factoring Trinomials of the Form $x^2 + bx + c$ ▷

OBJECTIVES

1 Factor Trinomials of the Form $x^2 + bx + c$. ▷

2 Factor Out the Greatest Common Factor and Then Factor a Trinomial of the Form $x^2 + bx + c$. ▷

OBJECTIVE

1 Factoring Trinomials of the Form $x^2 + bx + c$ ▷

In this section, we factor trinomials of the form $x^2 + bx + c$, such as

$$x^2 + 4x + 3, \quad x^2 - 8x + 15, \quad x^2 + 4x - 12, \quad r^2 - r - 42$$

Notice that for these trinomials, the coefficient of the squared variable is 1.

Recall that factoring means to write as a product and that factoring and multiplying are reverse processes. Using the FOIL method of multiplying binomials, we have that

$$\overset{F\quad O\quad I\quad L}{(x + 3)(x + 1) = x^2 + 1x + 3x + 3}$$
$$= x^2 + 4x + 3$$

Thus, a factored form of $x^2 + 4x + 3$ is $(x + 3)(x + 1)$.

Notice that the product of the first terms of the binomials is $x \cdot x = x^2$, the first term of the trinomial. Also, the product of the last two terms of the binomials is $3 \cdot 1 = 3$, the third term of the trinomial. The sum of these same terms is $3 + 1 = 4$, the coefficient of the middle term, x, of the trinomial.

The product of these numbers is 3.

$$x^2 + 4x + 3 = (x + 3)(x + 1)$$

The sum of these numbers is 4.

Many trinomials, such as the one above, factor into two binomials. To factor $x^2 + 7x + 10$, let's assume that it factors into two binomials and begin by writing two pairs of parentheses. The first term of the trinomial is x^2, so we use x and x as the first terms of the binomial factors.

$$x^2 + 7x + 10 = (x + \square)(x + \square)$$

To determine the last term of each binomial factor, we look for two integers whose product is 10 and whose sum is 7. Since our numbers must have a positive product and a positive sum, we list pairs of positive integer factors of 10 only.

Positive Factors of 10	*Sum of Factors*
1, 10	$1 + 10 = 11$
2, 5	$2 + 5 = 7$

The correct pair of numbers is 2 and 5 because their product is 10 and their sum is 7. Now we can fill in the last terms of the binomial factors.

$$x^2 + 7x + 10 = (x + 2)(x + 5)$$

Check: To see if we have factored correctly, multiply.

$$(x + 2)(x + 5) = x^2 + 5x + 2x + 10$$
$$= x^2 + 7x + 10 \qquad \text{Combine like terms.}$$

> **Helpful Hint**
>
> Since multiplication is commutative, the factored form of $x^2 + 7x + 10$ can be written as either $(x + 2)(x + 5)$ or $(x + 5)(x + 2)$.

Factoring a Trinomial of the Form $x^2 + bx + c$

The factored form of $x^2 + bx + c$ is

The product of these numbers is c.

$$x^2 + bx + c = (x + \square)(x + \square)$$

The sum of these numbers is b.

EXAMPLE 1   Factor: $x^2 + 7x + 12$

Solution We begin by writing the first terms of the binomial factors.

$$(x + \square)(x + \square)$$

Next we look for two numbers whose product is 12 and whose sum is 7. Since our numbers must have a positive product and a positive sum, we look at pairs of positive factors of 12 only.

Positive Factors of 12	Sum of Factors
1, 12	13
2, 6	8
3, 4	7

Correct sum, so the numbers are 3 and 4.

Thus, $x^2 + 7x + 12 = (x + 3)(x + 4)$

Check: $(x + 3)(x + 4) = x^2 + 4x + 3x + 12 = x^2 + 7x + 12.$

PRACTICE

1   Factor: $x^2 + 5x + 6$

EXAMPLE 2   Factor: $x^2 - 12x + 35$

Solution   Again, we begin by writing the first terms of the binomials.

$$(x + \square)(x + \square)$$

Now we look for two numbers whose product is 35 and whose sum is -12. Since our numbers must have a positive product and a negative sum, we look at pairs of negative factors of 35 only.

Negative Factors of 35	Sum of Factors
$-1, -35$	-36
$-5, -7$	-12

Correct sum, so the numbers are -5 and -7.

Thus, $x^2 - 12x + 35 = (x - 5)(x - 7)$

Check: To check, multiply $(x - 5)(x - 7)$.

PRACTICE

2   Factor: $x^2 - 17x + 70$

EXAMPLE 3   Factor: $x^2 + 4x - 12$

Solution $x^2 + 4x - 12 = (x + \square)(x + \square)$

We look for two numbers whose product is -12 and whose sum is 4. Since our numbers must have a negative product, we look at pairs of factors with opposite signs.

Factors of -12	Sum of Factors
$-1, 12$	11
$1, -12$	-11
$-2, 6$	4
$2, -6$	-4
$-3, 4$	1
$3, -4$	-1

Correct sum, so the numbers are -2 and 6.

Thus, $x^2 + 4x - 12 = (x - 2)(x + 6)$

PRACTICE

3   Factor: $x^2 + 5x - 14$

EXAMPLE 4 Factor: $r^2 - r - 42$

Solution Because the variable in this trinomial is r, the first term of each binomial factor is r.

$$r^2 - r - 42 = (r + \square)(r + \square)$$

Now we look for two numbers whose product is -42 and whose sum is -1, the numerical coefficient of r. The numbers are 6 and -7. Therefore,

$$r^2 - r - 42 = (r + 6)(r - 7)$$

□

PRACTICE

4 Factor: $p^2 - 2p - 63$

■

EXAMPLE 5 Factor: $a^2 + 2a + 10$

Solution Look for two numbers whose product is 10 and whose sum is 2. Neither 1 and 10 nor 2 and 5 give the required sum, 2. We conclude that $a^2 + 2a + 10$ is not factorable with integers. A polynomial such as $a^2 + 2a + 10$ is called a **prime polynomial.**

□

PRACTICE

5 Factor: $b^2 + 5b + 1$

■

EXAMPLE 6 Factor: $x^2 + 7xy + 6y^2$

Solution

$$x^2 + 7xy + 6y^2 = (x + \square)(x + \square)$$

Recall that the middle term $7xy$ is the same as $7yx$. Thus, we can see that $7y$ is the "coefficient" of x. We then look for two terms whose product is $6y^2$ and whose sum is $7y$. The terms are $6y$ and $1y$ or $6y$ and y because $6y \cdot y = 6y^2$ and $6y + y = 7y$. Therefore,

$$x^2 + 7xy + 6y^2 = (x + 6y)(x + y)$$

□

PRACTICE

6 Factor: $x^2 + 7xy + 12y^2$

■

EXAMPLE 7 Factor: $x^4 + 5x^2 + 6$

Solution As usual, we begin by writing the first terms of the binomials. Since the greatest power of x in this polynomial is x^4, we write

$$(x^2 + \square)(x^2 + \square) \quad \text{since } x^2 \cdot x^2 = x^4$$

Now we look for two factors of 6 whose sum is 5. The numbers are 2 and 3. Thus,

$$x^4 + 5x^2 + 6 = (x^2 + 2)(x^2 + 3)$$

□

PRACTICE

7 Factor: $x^4 + 13x^2 + 12$

■

If the terms of a polynomial are not written in descending powers of the variable, you may want to do so before factoring.

EXAMPLE 8 Factor: $40 - 13t + t^2$

Solution First, we rearrange terms so that the trinomial is written in descending powers of t.

$$40 - 13t + t^2 = t^2 - 13t + 40$$

Next, try to factor.

$$t^2 - 13t + 40 = (t + \square)(t + \square)$$

Now we look for two factors of 40 whose sum is -13. The numbers are -8 and -5. Thus,

$$t^2 - 13t + 40 = (t - 8)(t - 5) \qquad \square$$

PRACTICE
8   Factor: $48 - 14x + x^2$ ■

The following sign patterns may be useful when factoring trinomials.

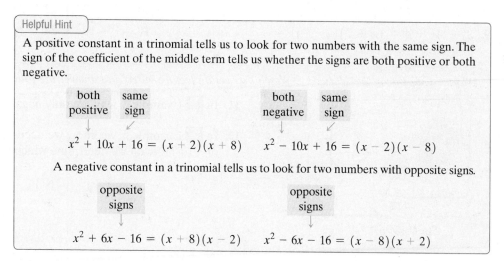

> **Helpful Hint**
>
> A positive constant in a trinomial tells us to look for two numbers with the same sign. The sign of the coefficient of the middle term tells us whether the signs are both positive or both negative.
>
> both   same
> positive   sign
>
> both   same
> negative   sign
>
> $$x^2 + 10x + 16 = (x + 2)(x + 8) \qquad x^2 - 10x + 16 = (x - 2)(x - 8)$$
>
> A negative constant in a trinomial tells us to look for two numbers with opposite signs.
>
> opposite
> signs
>
> opposite
> signs
>
> $$x^2 + 6x - 16 = (x + 8)(x - 2) \qquad x^2 - 6x - 16 = (x - 8)(x + 2)$$

OBJECTIVE
2   Factoring Out the Greatest Common Factor ▶

Remember that the first step in factoring any polynomial is to factor out the greatest common factor (if there is one other than 1 or -1).

EXAMPLE 9   Factor: $3m^2 - 24m - 60$

Solution First we factor out the greatest common factor, 3, from each term.

$$3m^2 - 24m - 60 = 3(m^2 - 8m - 20)$$

Now we factor $m^2 - 8m - 20$ by looking for two factors of -20 whose sum is -8. The factors are -10 and 2. Therefore, the complete factored form is

$$3m^2 - 24m - 60 = 3(m + 2)(m - 10) \qquad \square$$

> **Helpful Hint**
>
> Remember to write the common factor 3 as part of the factored form.

PRACTICE
9   Factor: $4x^2 - 24x + 36$ ■

EXAMPLE 10   Factor: $2x^4 - 26x^3 + 84x^2$

Solution

$$2x^4 - 26x^3 + 84x^2 = 2x^2(x^2 - 13x + 42) \qquad \text{Factor out common factor, } 2x^2.$$
$$= 2x^2(x - 6)(x - 7) \qquad \text{Factor } x^2 - 13x + 42. \qquad \square$$

PRACTICE
10   Factor: $3y^4 - 18y^3 - 21y^2$ ■

✓ Vocabulary, Readiness & Video Check

Fill in each blank with "true" or "false."

1. To factor $x^2 + 7x + 6$, we look for two numbers whose product is 6 and whose sum is 7. _____

2. We can write the factorization $(y + 2)(y + 4)$ also as $(y + 4)(y + 2)$. _____

3. The factorization $(4x - 12)(x - 5)$ is completely factored. _____

4. The factorization $(x + 2y)(x + y)$ may also be written as $(x + 2y)^2$. _____

Complete each factored form.

5. $x^2 + 9x + 20 = (x + 4)(x \quad)$

6. $x^2 + 12x + 35 = (x + 5)(x \quad)$

7. $x^2 - 7x + 12 = (x - 4)(x \quad)$

8. $x^2 - 13x + 22 = (x - 2)(x \quad)$

9. $x^2 + 4x + 4 = (x + 2)(x \quad)$

10. $x^2 + 10x + 24 = (x + 6)(x \quad)$

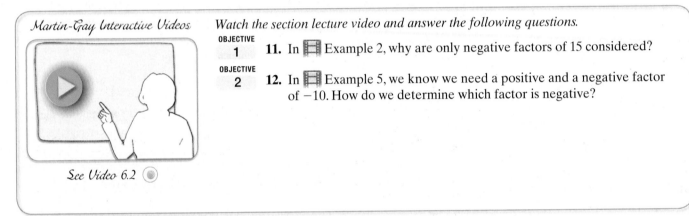

Martin-Gay Interactive Videos

Watch the section lecture video and answer the following questions.

OBJECTIVE 1

11. In ▥ Example 2, why are only negative factors of 15 considered?

OBJECTIVE 2

12. In ▥ Example 5, we know we need a positive and a negative factor of −10. How do we determine which factor is negative?

See Video 6.2 ⊙

6.2 Exercise Set   MyMathLab® ▶

Factor each trinomial completely. If a polynomial can't be factored, write "prime." See Examples 1 through 8.

▶1. $x^2 + 7x + 6$

2. $x^2 + 6x + 8$

3. $y^2 - 10y + 9$

4. $y^2 - 12y + 11$

5. $x^2 - 6x + 9$

6. $x^2 - 10x + 25$

▶7. $x^2 - 3x - 18$

8. $x^2 - x - 30$

9. $x^2 + 3x - 70$

10. $x^2 + 4x - 32$

11. $x^2 + 5x + 2$

12. $x^2 - 7x + 5$

13. $x^2 + 8xy + 15y^2$

14. $x^2 + 6xy + 8y^2$

15. $a^4 - 2a^2 - 15$

16. $y^4 - 3y^2 - 70$

17. $13 + 14m + m^2$

18. $17 + 18n + n^2$

19. $10t - 24 + t^2$

20. $6q - 27 + q^2$

21. $a^2 - 10ab + 16b^2$

22. $a^2 - 9ab + 18b^2$

MIXED PRACTICE

Factor each trinomial completely. Some of these trinomials contain a greatest common factor (other than 1). Don't forget to factor out the GCF first. See Examples 1 through 10.

23. $2z^2 + 20z + 32$

24. $3x^2 + 30x + 63$

25. $2x^3 - 18x^2 + 40x$

26. $3x^3 - 12x^2 - 36x$

▶27. $x^2 - 3xy - 4y^2$

28. $x^2 - 4xy - 77y^2$

29. $x^2 + 15x + 36$

30. $x^2 + 19x + 60$

31. $x^2 - x - 2$

32. $x^2 - 5x - 14$

33. $r^2 - 16r + 48$

34. $r^2 - 10r + 21$

35. $x^2 + xy - 2y^2$

36. $x^2 - xy - 6y^2$

▶37. $3x^2 + 9x - 30$

38. $4x^2 - 4x - 48$

39. $3x^2 \quad 60x + 108$

40. $2x^2 - 24x + 70$

41. $x^2 - 18x - 144$

42. $x^2 + x - 42$

43. $r^2 - 3r + 6$

44. $x^2 + 4x - 10$

45. $x^2 - 8x + 15$

46. $x^2 - 9x + 14$

47. $6x^3 + 54x^2 + 120x$

48. $3x^3 + 3x^2 - 126x$

49. $4x^2y + 4xy - 12y$

50. $3x^2y - 9xy + 45y$

51. $x^2 - 4x - 21$

52. $x^2 - 4x - 32$

53. $x^2 + 7xy + 10y^2$

54. $x^2 - 2xy - 15y^2$

55. $64 + 24t + 2t^2$

56. $50 + 20t + 2t^2$

57. $x^3 - 2x^2 - 24x$

58. $x^3 - 3x^2 - 28x$

59. $2t^5 - 14t^4 + 24t^3$

60. $3x^6 + 30x^5 + 72x^4$

61. $5x^3y - 25x^2y^2 - 120xy^3$

62. $7a^3b - 35a^2b^2 + 42ab^3$

63. $162 - 45m + 3m^2$

64. $48 - 20n + 2n^2$

65. $-x^2 + 12x - 11$ (Factor out -1 first.)

66. $-x^2 + 8x - 7$ (Factor out -1 first.)

67. $\dfrac{1}{2}y^2 - \dfrac{9}{2}y - 11$ (Factor out $\dfrac{1}{2}$ first.)

68. $\dfrac{1}{3}y^2 - \dfrac{5}{3}y - 8$ (Factor out $\dfrac{1}{3}$ first.)

69. $x^3y^2 + x^2y - 20x$

70. $a^2b^3 + ab^2 - 30b$

REVIEW AND PREVIEW

Multiply. See Sections 5.3 and 5.4.

71. $(2x + 1)(x + 5)$

72. $(3x + 2)(x + 4)$

73. $(5y - 4)(3y - 1)$

74. $(4z - 7)(7z - 1)$

75. $(a + 3b)(9a - 4b)$

76. $(y - 5x)(6y + 5x)$

CONCEPT EXTENSIONS

77. Write a polynomial that factors as $(x - 3)(x + 8)$.

78. To factor $x^2 + 13x + 42$, think of two numbers whose _____ is 42 and whose _____ is 13.

Complete each sentence in your own words.

79. If $x^2 + bx + c$ is factorable and c is negative, then the signs of the last-term factors of the binomials are opposite because…

80. If $x^2 + bx + c$ is factorable and c is positive, then the signs of the last-term factors of the binomials are the same because…

Remember that perimeter means distance around. Write the perimeter of each rectangle as a simplified polynomial. Then factor the polynomial.

△ **81.**

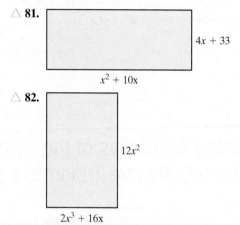

$4x + 33$

$x^2 + 10x$

△ **82.**

$12x^2$

$2x^3 + 16x$

83. An object is thrown upward from the top of an 80-foot building with an initial velocity of 64 feet per second. Neglecting air resistance, the height of the object after t seconds is given by $-16t^2 + 64t + 80$. Factor this polynomial.

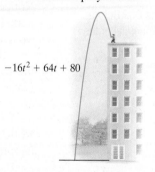

$-16t^2 + 64t + 80$

84. An object is thrown upward from the top of a 112-foot building with an initial velocity of 96 feet per second. Neglecting air resistance, the height of the object after t seconds is given by $-16t^2 + 96t + 112$. Factor this polynomial.

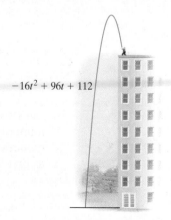

$-16t^2 + 96t + 112$

Factor each trinomial completely.

85. $x^2 + \dfrac{1}{2}x + \dfrac{1}{16}$

86. $x^2 + x + \dfrac{1}{4}$

87. $z^2(x + 1) - 3z(x + 1) - 70(x + 1)$

88. $y^2(x + 1) - 2y(x + 1) - 15(x + 1)$

*Factor each trinomial. (**Hint:** Notice that $x^{2n} + 4x^n + 3$ factors as $(x^n + 1)(x^n + 3)$. **Remember:** $x^n \cdot x^n = x^{n+n}$ or x^{2n}.)*

89. $x^{2n} + 8x^n - 20$

90. $x^{2n} + 5x^n + 6$

Find a positive value of c so that each trinomial is factorable.

91. $x^2 + 6x + c$

92. $t^2 + 8t + c$

93. $y^2 - 4y + c$

94. $n^2 - 16n + c$

Find a positive value of b so that each trinomial is factorable.

95. $x^2 + bx + 15$

96. $y^2 + by + 20$

97. $m^2 + bm - 27$

98. $x^2 + bx - 14$

6.3 Factoring Trinomials of the Form $ax^2 + bx + c$ and Perfect Square Trinomials ▷

OBJECTIVES

1 Factor Trinomials of the Form $ax^2 + bx + c$, Where $a \neq 1$. ▷

2 Factor Out the GCF Before Factoring a Trinomial of the Form $ax^2 + bx + c$. ▷

3 Factor Perfect Square Trinomials. ▷

OBJECTIVE

1 Factoring Trinomials of the Form $ax^2 + bx + c$ ▷

In this section, we factor trinomials of the form $ax^2 + bx + c$, such as

$$3x^2 + 11x + 6, \qquad 8x^2 - 22x + 5, \qquad \text{and} \qquad 2x^2 + 13x - 7$$

Notice that the coefficient of the squared variable in these trinomials is a number other than 1. We will factor these trinomials using a trial-and-check method based on our work in the last section.

To begin, let's review the relationship between the numerical coefficients of the trinomial and the numerical coefficients of its factored form. For example, since $(2x + 1)(x + 6) = 2x^2 + 13x + 6$,

a factored form of $2x^2 + 13x + 6$ is $(2x + 1)(x + 6)$

Notice that $2x$ and x are factors of $2x^2$, the first term of the trinomial. Also, 6 and 1 are factors of 6, the last term of the trinomial, as shown:

$$2x^2 + 13x + 6 = (2x + 1)(x + 6)$$

Also notice that $13x$, the middle term, is the sum of the following products:

$$2x^2 + 13x + 6 = (2x + 1)(x + 6)$$

$1x$

$+12x$

$13x$ Middle term

Let's use this pattern to factor $5x^2 + 7x + 2$. First, we find factors of $5x^2$. Since all numerical coefficients in this trinomial are positive, we will use factors with positive numerical coefficients only. Thus, the factors of $5x^2$ are $5x$ and x. Let's try these factors as first terms of the binomials. Thus far, we have

$$5x^2 + 7x + 2 = (5x + \square)(x + \square)$$

Next, we need to find positive factors of 2. Positive factors of 2 are 1 and 2. Now we try possible combinations of these factors as second terms of the binomials until we obtain a middle term of $7x$.

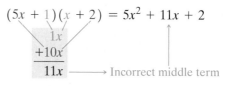

Let's try switching factors 2 and 1.

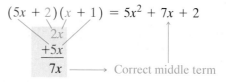

Thus the factored form of $5x^2 + 7x + 2$ is $(5x + 2)(x + 1)$. To check, we multiply $(5x + 2)$ and $(x + 1)$. The product is $5x^2 + 7x + 2$.

> **EXAMPLE 1** Factor: $3x^2 + 11x + 6$

Solution Since all numerical coefficients are positive, we use factors with positive numerical coefficients. We first find factors of $3x^2$.

$$\text{Factors of } 3x^2: \quad 3x^2 = 3x \cdot x$$

If factorable, the trinomial will be of the form

$$3x^2 + 11x + 6 = (3x + \square)(x + \square)$$

Next we factor 6.

$$\text{Factors of 6:} \quad 6 = 1 \cdot 6, \quad 6 = 2 \cdot 3$$

Now we try combinations of factors of 6 until a middle term of $11x$ is obtained. Let's try 1 and 6 first.

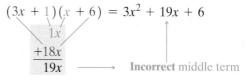

Now let's next try 6 and 1.

$$(3x + 6)(x + 1)$$

Before multiplying, notice that the terms of the factor $3x + 6$ have a common factor of 3. The terms of the original trinomial $3x^2 + 11x + 6$ have no common factor other than 1, so the terms of its factors will also contain no common factor other than 1. This means that $(3x + 6)(x + 1)$ is not a factored form.

Next let's try 2 and 3 as last terms.

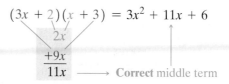

Thus a factored form of $3x^2 + 11x + 6$ is $(3x + 2)(x + 3)$. □

PRACTICE

> **1** Factor: $2x^2 + 11x + 15$

> **Helpful Hint**
> If the terms of a trinomial have no common factor (other than 1), then the terms of neither of its binomial factors will contain a common factor (other than 1).

✔ **CONCEPT CHECK**

Do the terms of $3x^2 + 29x + 18$ have a common factor? Without multiplying, decide which of the following factored forms could not be a factored form of $3x^2 + 29x + 18$.

a. $(3x + 18)(x + 1)$ **b.** $(3x + 2)(x + 9)$ **c.** $(3x + 6)(x + 3)$ **d.** $(3x + 9)(x + 2)$

EXAMPLE 2 Factor: $8x^2 - 22x + 5$

Solution Factors of $8x^2$: $\quad 8x^2 = 8x \cdot x, \quad 8x^2 = 4x \cdot 2x$

We'll try $8x$ and x.

$$8x^2 - 22x + 5 = (8x + \square)(x + \square)$$

Since the middle term, $-22x$, has a negative numerical coefficient, we factor 5 into negative factors.

$$\text{Factors of 5:} \quad 5 = -1 \cdot -5$$

Let's try -1 and -5.

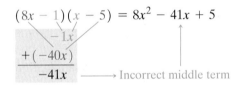

Now let's try -5 and -1.

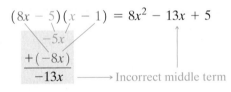

Don't give up yet! We can still try other factors of $8x^2$. Let's try $4x$ and $2x$ with -1 and -5.

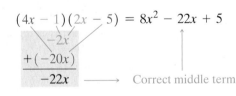

A factored form of $8x^2 - 22x + 5$ is $(4x - 1)(2x - 5)$. □

PRACTICE

2 Factor: $15x^2 - 22x + 8$ ◼

EXAMPLE 3 Factor: $2x^2 + 13x - 7$

Solution Factors of $2x^2$: $\quad 2x^2 = 2x \cdot x$

$\qquad$ Factors of -7: $\quad -7 = -1 \cdot 7, \quad -7 = 1 \cdot -7$

We try possible combinations of these factors:

$$(2x + 1)(x - 7) = 2x^2 - 13x - 7 \quad \text{Incorrect middle term}$$
$$(2x - 1)(x + 7) = 2x^2 + 13x - 7 \quad \text{Correct middle term}$$

A factored form of $2x^2 + 13x - 7$ is $(2x - 1)(x + 7)$. □

PRACTICE

3 Factor: $4x^2 + 11x - 3$ ■

EXAMPLE 4 Factor: $10x^2 - 13xy - 3y^2$

Solution Factors of $10x^2$: $10x^2 = 10x \cdot x, \quad 10x^2 = 2x \cdot 5x$

Factors of $-3y^2$: $-3y^2 = -3y \cdot y, \quad -3y^2 = 3y \cdot -y$

We try some combinations of these factors:

$$\begin{array}{c} \qquad\qquad\qquad \text{Correct} \qquad \text{Correct} \\ \qquad\qquad\qquad \downarrow \qquad\qquad \downarrow \\ (10x - 3y)(x + y) = 10x^2 + 7xy - 3y^2 \\ (x + 3y)(10x - y) = 10x^2 + 29xy - 3y^2 \\ (5x + 3y)(2x - y) = 10x^2 + xy - 3y^2 \\ (2x - 3y)(5x + y) = 10x^2 - 13xy - 3y^2 \quad \text{Correct middle term} \end{array}$$

A factored form of $10x^2 - 13xy - 3y^2$ is $(2x - 3y)(5x + y)$. □

PRACTICE

4 Factor: $21x^2 + 11xy - 2y^2$ ■

EXAMPLE 5 Factor: $3x^4 - 5x^2 - 8$

Solution Factors of $3x^4$: $3x^4 = 3x^2 \cdot x^2$

Factors of -8: $-8 = -2 \cdot 4, \ -8 = 2 \cdot -4, \ -8 = -1 \cdot 8, \ -8 = 1 \cdot -8$

Try combinations of these factors:

$$\begin{array}{c} \qquad\qquad\qquad \text{Correct} \qquad \text{Correct} \\ \qquad\qquad\qquad \downarrow \qquad\qquad \downarrow \\ (3x^2 - 2)(x^2 + 4) = 3x^4 + 10x^2 - 8 \\ (3x^2 + 4)(x^2 - 2) = 3x^4 - 2x^2 - 8 \\ (3x^2 + 8)(x^2 - 1) = 3x^4 + 5x^2 - 8 \\ (3x^2 - 8)(x^2 + 1) = 3x^4 - 5x^2 - 8 \end{array}$$

Incorrect sign on middle term, so switch signs in binomial factors.
Correct middle term.

A factored form of $3x^4 - 5x^2 - 8$ is $(3x^2 - 8)(x^2 + 1)$. □

PRACTICE

5 Factor: $2x^4 - 5x^2 - 7$ ■

Helpful Hint

Study the last two lines of Example 5. If a factoring attempt gives you a middle term whose numerical coefficient is the opposite of the desired numerical coefficient, try switching the signs of the last terms in the binomials.

$$\text{Switched signs} \begin{cases} (3x^2 + 8)(x^2 - 1) = 3x^4 + 5x^2 - 8 \quad \text{Middle term: } +5x^2 \\ (3x^2 - 8)(x^2 + 1) = 3x^4 - 5x^2 - 8 \quad \text{Middle term: } -5x^2 \end{cases}$$

OBJECTIVE

2   Factoring out the Greatest Common Factor ▶

Don't forget that the first step in factoring any polynomial is to look for a greatest common factor to factor out.

EXAMPLE 6   Factor: $24x^4 + 40x^3 + 6x^2$

Solution Notice that all three terms have a greatest common factor of $2x^2$. Thus we factor out $2x^2$ from all three terms first.

$$24x^4 + 40x^3 + 6x^2 = 2x^2(12x^2 + 20x + 3)$$

Next we factor $12x^2 + 20x + 3$.

Factors of $12x^2$: $12x^2 = 4x \cdot 3x$, $12x^2 = 12x \cdot x$, $12x^2 = 6x \cdot 2x$

Since all terms in the trinomial have positive numerical coefficients, we factor 3 using positive factors only.

Factors of 3: $3 = 1 \cdot 3$

We try some combinations of the factors.

$$2x^2(4x + 3)(3x + 1) = 2x^2(12x^2 + 13x + 3)$$
$$2x^2(12x + 1)(x + 3) = 2x^2(12x^2 + 37x + 3)$$
$$2x^2(2x + 3)(6x + 1) = 2x^2(12x^2 + 20x + 3)   \text{ Correct middle term}$$

A factored form of $24x^4 + 40x^3 + 6x^2$ is $2x^2(2x + 3)(6x + 1)$.   □

> **Helpful Hint**
>
> Don't forget to include the greatest common factor in the factored form.

PRACTICE

6   Factor: $3x^3 + 17x^2 + 10x$ ◼

When the term containing the squared variable has a negative coefficient, you may want to first factor out a common factor of -1.

EXAMPLE 7   Factor: $-6x^2 - 13x + 5$

Solution We begin by factoring out a common factor of -1.

$$-6x^2 - 13x + 5 = -1(6x^2 + 13x - 5)   \text{ Factor out } -1.$$
$$= -1(3x - 1)(2x + 5)   \text{ Factor } 6x^2 + 13x - 5.   □$$

PRACTICE

7   Factor: $-8x^2 + 2x + 3$ ◼

OBJECTIVE

3   Factoring Perfect Square Trinomials ▶

A trinomial that is the square of a binomial is called a **perfect square trinomial.** For example,

$$(x + 3)^2 = (x + 3)(x + 3)$$
$$= x^2 + 6x + 9$$

Thus $x^2 + 6x + 9$ is a perfect square trinomial.

In Chapter 5, we discovered special product formulas for squaring binomials.

$$(a + b)^2 = a^2 + 2ab + b^2   \text{ and }   (a - b)^2 = a^2 - 2ab + b^2$$

Because multiplication and factoring are reverse processes, we can now use these special products to help us factor perfect square trinomials. If we reverse these equations, we have the following.

Factoring Perfect Square Trinomials

$$a^2 + 2ab + b^2 = (a + b)^2$$
$$a^2 - 2ab + b^2 = (a - b)^2$$

Helpful Hint

Notice that for both given forms of a perfect square trinomial, the last term is positive. This is because the last term is a square.

To use these equations to help us factor, we must first be able to recognize a perfect square trinomial. A trinomial is a perfect square when

1. two terms, a^2 and b^2, are squares and
2. the remaining term is $2 \cdot a \cdot b$ or $-2 \cdot a \cdot b$. That is, this term is twice the product of a and b, or its opposite.

When a trinomial fits this description, its factored form is $(a + b)^2$ or $(a - b)^2$.

EXAMPLE 8   Factor: $x^2 + 12x + 36$

Solution   First, is this a perfect square trinomial?

$$x^2 + 12x + 36$$

1. $x^2 = (x)^2$ and $36 = 6^2$.
2. Is the middle term $2 \cdot x \cdot 6$? Yes, $2 \cdot x \cdot 6 = 12x$, the middle term.

Thus, $x^2 + 12x + 36$ factors as $(x + 6)^2$.   □

PRACTICE
8   Factor: $x^2 + 14x + 49$

EXAMPLE 9   Factor: $25x^2 + 25xy + 4y^2$

Solution   Is this a perfect square trinomial?

$$25x^2 + 25xy + 4y^2$$

1. $25x^2 = (5x)^2$ and $4y^2 = (2y)^2$.
2. Is the middle term $2 \cdot 5x \cdot 2y$? **No**, $2 \cdot 5x \cdot 2y = 20xy$, **not the middle term** $25xy$.

Helpful Hint

A perfect square trinomial can also be factored by other methods.

Therefore, $25x^2 + 25xy + 4y^2$ is not a perfect square trinomial. It is factorable, though. Using earlier techniques, we find that $25x^2 + 25xy + 4y^2$ factors as $(5x + 4y)(5x + y)$.   □

PRACTICE
9   Factor: $4x^2 + 20xy + 9y^2$

EXAMPLE 10   Factor: $4m^4 - 4m^2 + 1$

Solution   Is this a perfect square trinomial?

$$4m^4 - 4m^2 + 1$$

1. $4m^4 = (2m^2)^2$ and $1 = 1^2$.
2. Is the middle term $2 \cdot 2m^2 \cdot 1$ or $-2 \cdot 2m^2 \cdot 1$? Yes, $-2 \cdot 2m^2 \cdot 1 = -4m^2$, the middle term.

Thus, $4m^4 - 4m^2 + 1$ factors as $(2m^2 - 1)^2$.   □

PRACTICE
10   Factor: $36n^4 - 12n^2 + 1$

EXAMPLE 11   Factor: $162x^3 - 144x^2 + 32x$

Solution Don't forget to look first for a common factor. There is a greatest common factor of $2x$ in this trinomial.

$$162x^3 - 144x^2 + 32x = 2x(81x^2 - 72x + 16)$$
$$= 2x[(9x)^2 - 2 \cdot 9x \cdot 4 + 4^2]$$
$$= 2x(9x - 4)^2 \qquad \square$$

PRACTICE
11   Factor: $12x^3 - 84x^2 + 147x$ ∎

✔ Vocabulary, Readiness & Video Check

Use the choices below to fill in each blank. Some choices will be used more than once and some not used at all.

$5y^2$	$(x + 5y)^2$
$(5y)^2$	$(x - 5y)^2$

perfect square trinomial
perfect square binomial

1. A _____ is a trinomial that is the square of a binomial.
2. The term $25y^2$ written as a square is _____.
3. The expression $x^2 + 10xy + 25y^2$ is called a _____.
4. The factorization $(x + 5y)(x + 5y)$ may also be written as _____.

Complete each factorization.

5. $2x^2 + 5x + 3$ factors as $(2x + 3)(\ ?\ )$.
     a. $(x + 3)$ **b.** $(2x + 1)$ **c.** $(3x + 4)$ **d.** $(x + 1)$

6. $7x^2 + 9x + 2$ factors as $(7x + 2)(\ ?\ )$.
     a. $(3x + 1)$ **b.** $(x + 1)$ **c.** $(x + 2)$ **d.** $(7x + 1)$

Martin-Gay Interactive Videos

See Video 6.3 ⊙

Watch the section lecture video and answer the following questions.

OBJECTIVE 1
7. From ▦ Example 1, explain in general terms how you would go about factoring a trinomial with a first-term coefficient $\neq 1$.

OBJECTIVE 2
8. From ▦ Examples 3 and 5, how can factoring the GCF from a trinomial help you save time when trying to factor the remaining trinomial?

OBJECTIVE 3
9. Describe in words the special patterns that the trinomials in ▦ Examples 7 and 8 have that identify them as perfect square trinomials.

6.3   Exercise Set   MyMathLab® ▶

Complete each factored form. See Examples 1 through 5, and 8 through 10.

1. $5x^2 + 22x + 8 = (5x + 2)$
2. $2y^2 + 27y + 25 = (2y + 25)$
3. $50x^2 + 15x - 2 = (5x + 2)$
4. $6y^2 + 11y - 10 = (2y + 5)$
5. $25x^2 - 20x + 4 = (5x - 2)$
6. $4y^2 - 20y + 25 = (2y - 5)$

Factor completely. See Examples 1 through 5.

7. $2x^2 + 13x + 15$
8. $3x^2 + 8x + 4$
9. $8y^2 - 17y + 9$
10. $21x^2 - 31x + 10$
11. $2x^2 - 9x - 5$
12. $36r^2 - 5r - 24$
13. $20r^2 + 27r - 8$

14. $3x^2 + 20x - 63$

▶ **15.** $10x^2 + 31x + 3$

16. $12x^2 + 17x + 5$

17. $2m^2 + 17m + 10$

18. $3n^2 + 20n + 5$

19. $6x^2 - 13xy + 5y^2$

20. $8x^2 - 14xy + 3y^2$

21. $15m^2 - 16m - 15$

22. $25n^2 - 5n - 6$

Factor completely. See Examples 1 through 7.

23. $12x^3 + 11x^2 + 2x$

24. $8a^3 + 14a^2 + 3a$

25. $21b^2 - 48b - 45$

26. $12x^2 - 14x - 10$

27. $7z + 12z^2 - 12$

28. $16t + 15t^2 - 15$

29. $6x^2y^2 - 2xy^2 - 60y^2$

30. $8x^2y + 34xy - 84y$

▶ **31.** $4x^2 - 8x - 21$

32. $6x^2 - 11x - 10$

33. $-x^2 + 2x + 24$

34. $-x^2 + 4x + 21$

▶ **35.** $4x^3 - 9x^2 - 9x$

36. $6x^3 - 31x^2 + 5x$

37. $24x^2 - 58x + 9$

38. $36x^2 + 55x - 14$

Factor each perfect square trinomial completely. See Examples 8 through 11.

▶ **39.** $x^2 + 22x + 121$

40. $x^2 + 18x + 81$

41. $x^2 - 16x + 64$

42. $x^2 - 12x + 36$

43. $16a^2 - 24a + 9$

44. $25x^2 - 20x + 4$

45. $x^4 + 4x^2 + 4$

46. $m^4 + 10m^2 + 25$

47. $2n^2 - 28n + 98$

48. $3y^2 - 6y + 3$

49. $16y^2 + 40y + 25$

50. $9y^2 + 48y + 64$

MIXED PRACTICE

Factor each trinomial completely. See Examples 1 through 11 and Section 6.2.

51. $2x^2 - 7x - 99$

52. $2x^2 + 7x - 72$

53. $24x^2 + 41x + 12$

54. $24x^2 - 49x + 15$

55. $3a^2 + 10ab + 3b^2$

56. $2a^2 + 11ab + 5b^2$

57. $-9x + 20 + x^2$

58. $-7x + 12 + x^2$

59. $p^2 + 12pq + 36q^2$

60. $m^2 + 20mn + 100n^2$

61. $x^2y^2 - 10xy + 25$

62. $x^2y^2 - 14xy + 49$

63. $40a^2b + 9ab - 9b$

64. $24y^2x + 7yx - 5x$

▶ **65.** $30x^3 + 38x^2 + 12x$

66. $6x^3 - 28x^2 + 16x$

67. $6y^3 - 8y^2 - 30y$

68. $12x^3 - 34x^2 + 24x$

69. $10x^4 + 25x^3y - 15x^2y^2$

70. $42x^4 - 99x^3y - 15x^2y^2$

▶ **71.** $-14x^2 + 39x - 10$

72. $-15x^2 + 26x - 8$

73. $16p^4 - 40p^3 + 25p^2$

74. $9q^4 - 42q^3 + 49q^2$

75. $x + 3x^2 - 2$

76. $y + 8y^2 - 9$

77. $8x^2 + 6xy - 27y^2$

78. $54a^2 + 39ab - 8b^2$

79. $1 + 6x^2 + x^4$

80. $1 + 16x^2 + x^4$

▶ **81.** $9x^2 - 24xy + 16y^2$

82. $25x^2 - 60xy + 36y^2$

83. $18x^2 - 9x - 14$

84. $42a^2 - 43a + 6$

85. $-27t + 7t^2 - 4$

86. $-3t + 4t^2 - 7$

87. $49p^2 - 7p - 2$

88. $3r^2 + 10r - 8$

89. $m^3 + 18m^2 + 81m$

90. $y^3 + 12y^2 + 36y$

91. $5x^2y^2 + 20xy + 1$

92. $3a^2b^2 + 12ab + 1$

93. $6a^5 + 37a^3b^2 + 6ab^4$

94. $5m^5 + 26m^3h^2 + 5mh^4$

REVIEW AND PREVIEW

Multiply the following. See Sections 5.3 and 5.4.

95. $(x - 2)(x + 2)$

96. $(y^2 + 3)(y^2 - 3)$

97. $(a + 3)(a^2 - 3a + 9)$

98. $(z - 2)(z^2 + 2z + 4)$

The following graph shows the percent of online adults who participate in various social media sites. See Section 3.1.

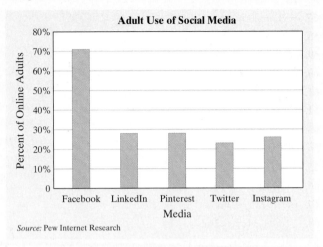

Adult Use of Social Media

Source: Pew Internet Research

99. Which social medium has the highest percent of online adult users?

100. Which social medium has the lowest percent of online adult users?

101. Describe any trend you see.

102. Why don't the percents shown in the graph add up to 100%?

CONCEPT EXTENSIONS

See the Concept Check in this section.

103. Do the terms of $4x^2 + 19x + 12$ have a common factor (other than 1)?

104. Without multiplying, decide which of the following factored forms is not a factored form of $4x^2 + 19x + 12$.

   a. $(2x + 4)(2x + 3)$ **b.** $(4x + 4)(x + 3)$

   c. $(4x + 3)(x + 4)$ **d.** $(2x + 2)(2x + 6)$

105. Describe a perfect square trinomial.

106. Write the perfect square trinomial that factors as $(x + 3y)^2$.

Write the perimeter of each figure as a simplified polynomial. Then factor the polynomial.

107.

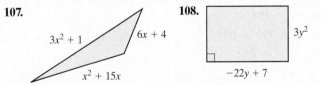

$3x^2 + 1$ $6x + 4$ $x^2 + 15x$

108.

$3y^2$ $-22y + 7$

Factor each trinomial completely.

109. $4x^2 + 2x + \dfrac{1}{4}$

110. $27x^2 + 2x - \dfrac{1}{9}$

111. $4x^2(y - 1)^2 + 10x(y - 1)^2 + 25(y - 1)^2$

112. $3x^2(a + 3)^3 - 10x(a + 3)^3 + 25(a + 3)^3$

113. Fill in the blank so that $x^2 + $ _____ $x + 16$ is a perfect square trinomial.

114. Fill in the blank so that $9x^2 + $ _____ $x + 25$ is a perfect square trinomial.

The area of the largest square in the figure is $(a + b)^2$. Use this figure to answer Exercises 115 and 116.

△ **115.** Write the area of the largest square as the sum of the areas of the smaller squares and rectangles.

△ **116.** What factoring formula from this section is visually represented by this square?

Find a positive value of b so that each trinomial is factorable.

117. $3x^2 + bx - 5$ **118.** $2y^2 + by + 3$

Find a positive value of c so that each trinomial is factorable.

119. $5x^2 + 7x + c$ **120.** $11y^2 - 40y + c$

Factor completely. Don't forget to first factor out the greatest common factor.

121. $-12x^3y^2 + 3x^2y^2 + 15xy^2$

122. $-12r^3x^2 + 38r^2x^2 + 14rx^2$

123. $4x^2(y - 1)^2 + 20x(y - 1)^2 + 25(y - 1)^2$

124. $3x^2(a + 3)^3 - 28x(a + 3)^3 + 25(a + 3)^3$

Factor.

125. $3x^{2n} + 17x^n + 10$

126. $2x^{2n} + 5x^n - 12$

127. In your own words, describe the steps you will use to factor a trinomial.

6.4   Factoring Trinomials of the Form $ax^2 + bx + c$ by Grouping

OBJECTIVE

1 Use the Grouping Method to Factor Trinomials of the Form $ax^2 + bx + c$.

OBJECTIVE

1   Using the Grouping Method

There is an alternative method that can be used to factor trinomials of the form $ax^2 + bx + c, a \neq 1$. This method is called the **grouping method** because it uses factoring by grouping as we learned in Section 6.1.

To see how this method works, recall from Section 6.2 that to factor a trinomial such as $x^2 + 11x + 30$, we find two numbers such that

Product is 30

$$x^2 + 11x + 30$$

Sum is 11.

To factor a trinomial such as $2x^2 + 11x + 12$ by grouping, we use an extension of the method in Section 6.2. Here we look for two numbers such that

Product is $2 \cdot 12 = 24$

$$2x^2 + 11x + 12$$

Sum is 11.

This time, we use the two numbers to write

$$2x^2 + 11x + 12 \text{ as}$$
$$= 2x^2 + \square x + \square x + 12$$

Then we factor by grouping. Since we want a positive product, 24, and a positive sum, 11, we consider pairs of positive factors of 24 only.

Factors of 24	Sum of Factors	
1, 24	25	
2, 12	14	
3, 8	11	Correct sum

The factors are 3 and 8. Now we use these factors to write the middle term $11x$ as $3x + 8x$ (or $8x + 3x$). We replace $11x$ with $3x + 8x$ in the original trinomial and then we can factor by grouping.

$$
\begin{aligned}
2x^2 + 11x + 12 &= 2x^2 + 3x + 8x + 12 \\
&= (2x^2 + 3x) + (8x + 12) && \text{Group the terms.} \\
&= x(2x + 3) + 4(2x + 3) && \text{Factor each group.} \\
&= (2x + 3)(x + 4) && \text{Factor out } (2x + 3).
\end{aligned}
$$

In general, we have the following procedure.

To Factor Trinomials by Grouping

Step 1. Factor out the greatest common factor if there is one other than 1.

Step 2. For the resulting trinomial $ax^2 + bx + c$, find two numbers whose product is $a \cdot c$ and whose sum is b.

Step 3. Write the middle term, bx, using the factors found in Step 2.

Step 4. Factor by grouping.

EXAMPLE 1   Factor $3x^2 + 31x + 10$ by grouping.

Solution

Step 1. The terms of this trinomial contain no greatest common factor other than 1 (or -1).

Step 2. In $3x^2 + 31x + 10$, $a = 3$, $b = 31$, and $c = 10$.

(Continued on the next page)

Let's find two numbers whose product is $a \cdot c$ or $3(10) = 30$ and whose sum is b or 31. The numbers are 1 and 30, as shown in the table below.

Factors of 30	Sum of Factors	
5, 6	11	
3, 10	13	
2, 15	17	
1, 30	31	Correct sum

Step 3. Write $31x$ as $1x + 30x$ so that $3x^2 + 31x + 10 = 3x^2 + 1x + 30x + 10$.

Step 4. Factor by grouping.

$$3x^2 + 1x + 30x + 10 = x(3x + 1) + 10(3x + 1)$$
$$= (3x + 1)(x + 10) \qquad \square$$

PRACTICE

1 Factor $5x^2 + 61x + 12$ by grouping. ■

EXAMPLE 2 Factor $8x^2 - 14x + 5$ by grouping.

Solution

Step 1. The terms of this trinomial contain no greatest common factor other than 1.

Step 2. This trinomial is of the form $ax^2 + bx + c$ with $a = 8$, $b = -14$, and $c = 5$. Find two numbers whose product is $a \cdot c$ or $8 \cdot 5 = 40$, and whose sum is b or -14.
The numbers are -4 and -10, as shown in the table below.

Factors of 40	Sum of Factors	
−40, −1	−41	
−20, −2	−22	
−10, −4	−14	Correct sum

Step 3. Write $-14x$ as $-4x - 10x$ so that

$$8x^2 - 14x + 5 = 8x^2 - 4x - 10x + 5$$

Step 4. Factor by grouping.

$$8x^2 - 4x - 10x + 5 = 4x(2x - 1) - 5(2x - 1)$$
$$= (2x - 1)(4x - 5) \qquad \square$$

PRACTICE

2 Factor $12x^2 - 19x + 5$ by grouping. ■

EXAMPLE 3 Factor $6x^2 - 2x - 20$ by grouping.

Solution

Step 1. First factor out the greatest common factor, 2.

$$6x^2 - 2x - 20 = 2(3x^2 - x - 10)$$

Step 2. Next, notice that $a = 3$, $b = -1$, and $c = -10$ in the resulting trinomial. Find two numbers whose product is $a \cdot c$ or $3(-10) = -30$ and whose sum is b, -1. The numbers are -6 and 5.

Step 3. $3x^2 - x - 10 = 3x^2 - 6x + 5x - 10$

Step 4. $3x^2 - 6x + 5x - 10 = 3x(x - 2) + 5(x - 2)$
$$= (x - 2)(3x + 5)$$

The factored form of $6x^2 - 2x - 20 = 2(x - 2)(3x + 5)$.

$\llcorner$ Don't forget to include the GCF, 2.   □

PRACTICE
3   Factor $30x^2 - 14x - 4$ by grouping.   ■

EXAMPLE 4   Factor $18y^4 + 21y^3 - 60y^2$ by grouping.

Solution

Step 1. First factor out the greatest common factor, $3y^2$.
$$18y^4 + 21y^3 - 60y^2 = 3y^2(6y^2 + 7y - 20)$$

Step 2. Notice that $a = 6, b = 7$, and $c = -20$ in the resulting trinomial. Find two numbers whose product is $a \cdot c$ or $6(-20) = -120$ and whose sum is 7. It may help to factor -120 as a product of primes and -1.
$$-120 = 2 \cdot 2 \cdot 2 \cdot 3 \cdot 5 \cdot (-1)$$

Then choose pairings of factors until you have a pairing whose sum is 7.

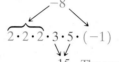

15   The numbers are -8 and 15.

Step 3. $6y^2 + 7y - 20 = 6y^2 - 8y + 15y - 20$
Step 4. $6y^2 - 8y + 15y - 20 = 2y(3y - 4) + 5(3y - 4)$
$$= (3y - 4)(2y + 5)$$

The factored form of $18y^4 + 21y^3 - 60y^2$ is $3y^2(3y - 4)(2y + 5)$.

$\llcorner$ Don't forget to include the GCF, $3y^2$
from **Step 1**.   □

PRACTICE
4   Factor $40m^4 + 5m^3 - 35m^2$ by grouping.   ■

EXAMPLE 5   Factor $4x^2 + 20x + 25$ by grouping.

Solution

Step 1. The terms of this trinomial contain no greatest common factor other than 1 (or -1).
Step 2. In $4x^2 + 20x + 25, a = 4, b = 20$, and $c = 25$. Find two numbers whose product is $a \cdot c$ or $4 \cdot 25 = 100$ and whose sum is 20. The numbers are 10 and 10.
Step 3. Write $20x$ as $10x + 10x$ so that
$$4x^2 + 20x + 25 = 4x^2 + 10x + 10x + 25$$

Step 4. Factor by grouping.
$$4x^2 + 10x + 10x + 25 = 2x(2x + 5) + 5(2x + 5)$$
$$= (2x + 5)(2x + 5)$$

The factored form of $4x^2 + 20x + 25$ is $(2x + 5)(2x + 5)$ or $(2x + 5)^2$.   □

PRACTICE
5   Factor $16x^2 + 24x + 9$ by grouping.   ■

A trinomial that is the square of a binomial, such as the trinomial in Example 5, is called a **perfect square trinomial.** From Chapter 5, there are special product formulas we can use to help us recognize and factor these trinomials. To study these formulas further, see Section 6.3, Objective 3.

> **Helpful Hint**
>
> **Remember:** A perfect square trinomial, such as the one in Example 5, may be factored by special product formulas or by other methods of factoring trinomials, such as by grouping.

✔ Vocabulary, Readiness & Video Check

For each trinomial $ax^2 + bx + c$, choose two numbers whose product is $a \cdot c$ and whose sum is b.

1. $x^2 + 6x + 8$
    a. 4, 2   **b.** 7, 1   **c.** 6, 2   **d.** 6, 8

2. $x^2 + 11x + 24$
    a. 6, 4   **b.** 24, 1   **c.** 8, 3   **d.** 2, 12

3. $2x^2 + 13x + 6$
    a. 2, 6   **b.** 12, 1   **c.** 13, 1   **d.** 3, 4

4. $4x^2 + 8x + 3$
    a. 4, 3   **b.** 4, 4   **c.** 12, 1   **d.** 2, 6

Martin-Gay Interactive Videos

Watch the section lecture video and answer the following question.

OBJECTIVE
1

5. In the lecture following ▥ Example 1, why does writing a term as the sum or difference of two terms suggest we'd then try to factor by grouping?

See Video 6.4 ◉

6.4 Exercise Set MyMathLab® ▷

Factor each polynomial by grouping. Notice that Step 3 has already been done in these exercises. See Examples 1 through 5.

▶ **1.** $x^2 + 3x + 2x + 6$

2. $x^2 + 5x + 3x + 15$

3. $y^2 + 8y - 2y - 16$

4. $z^2 + 10z - 7z - 70$

5. $8x^2 - 5x - 24x + 15$

6. $4x^2 - 9x - 32x + 72$

7. $5x^4 - 3x^2 + 25x^2 - 15$

8. $2y^4 - 10y^2 + 7y^2 - 35$

MIXED PRACTICE

Factor each trinomial by grouping. Exercises 9–12 are broken into parts to help you get started. See Examples 1 through 5.

9. $6x^2 + 11x + 3$

    a. Find two numbers whose product is $6 \cdot 3 = 18$ and whose sum is 11.

    b. Write $11x$ using the factors from part **a.**

    c. Factor by grouping.

10. $8x^2 + 14x + 3$

    a. Find two numbers whose product is $8 \cdot 3 = 24$ and whose sum is 14.

    b. Write $14x$ using the factors from part **a.**

    c. Factor by grouping.

11. $15x^2 - 23x + 4$

    a. Find two numbers whose product is $15 \cdot 4 = 60$ and whose sum is -23.

    b. Write $-23x$ using the factors from part **a.**

    c. Factor by grouping.

12. $6x^2 - 13x + 5$

    a. Find two numbers whose product is $6 \cdot 5 = 30$ and whose sum is -13.

    b. Write $-13x$ using the factors from part **a.**

    c. Factor by grouping.

13. $21y^2 + 17y + 2$

14. $15x^2 + 11x + 2$

15. $7x^2 - 4x - 11$

16. $8x^2 - x - 9$

17. $10x^2 - 9x + 2$

18. $30x^2 - 23x + 3$

19. $2x^2 - 7x + 5$

20. $2x^2 - 7x + 3$

21. $12x + 4x^2 + 9$

22. $20x + 25x^2 + 4$

23. $4x^2 - 8x - 21$

24. $6x^2 - 11x - 10$

25. $10x^2 - 23x + 12$

26. $21x^2 - 13x + 2$

27. $2x^3 + 13x^2 + 15x$

28. $3x^3 + 8x^2 + 4x$

29. $16y^2 - 34y + 18$

30. $4y^2 - 2y - 12$

31. $-13x + 6 + 6x^2$

32. $-25x + 12 + 12x^2$

33. $54a^2 - 9a - 30$

34. $30a^2 + 38a - 20$

35. $20a^3 + 37a^2 + 8a$

36. $10a^3 + 17a^2 + 3a$

37. $12x^3 - 27x^2 - 27x$

38. $30x^3 - 155x^2 + 25x$

39. $3x^2y + 4xy^2 + y^3$

40. $6r^2t + 7rt^2 + t^3$

41. $20z^2 + 7z + 1$

42. $36z^2 + 6z + 1$

43. $5x^2 + 50xy + 125y^2$

44. $3x^2 + 42xy + 147y^2$

45. $24a^2 - 6ab - 30b^2$

46. $30a^2 + 5ab - 25b^2$

47. $15p^4 + 31p^3q + 2p^2q^2$

48. $20s^4 + 61s^3t + 3s^2t^2$

49. $162a^4 - 72a^2 + 8$

50. $32n^4 - 112n^2 + 98$

51. $35 + 12x + x^2$

52. $33 + 14x + x^2$

53. $6 - 11x + 5x^2$

54. $5 - 12x + 7x^2$

REVIEW AND PREVIEW

Multiply. See Sections 5.3 and 5.4.

55. $(x - 2)(x + 2)$

56. $(y - 5)(y + 5)$

57. $(y + 4)(y + 4)$

58. $(x + 7)(x + 7)$

59. $(9z + 5)(9z - 5)$

60. $(8y + 9)(8y - 9)$

61. $(x - 3)(x^2 + 3x + 9)$

62. $(2z - 1)(4z^2 + 2z + 1)$

CONCEPT EXTENSIONS

Write the perimeter of each figure as a simplified polynomial. Then factor the polynomial.

63.

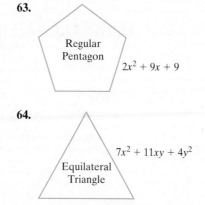

Regular Pentagon $2x^2 + 9x + 9$

64.

Equilateral Triangle $7x^2 + 11xy + 4y^2$

Factor each polynomial by grouping.

65. $x^{2n} + 2x^n + 3x^n + 6$

(*Hint:* Don't forget that $x^{2n} = x^n \cdot x^n$.)

66. $x^{2n} + 6x^n + 10x^n + 60$

67. $3x^{2n} + 16x^n - 35$

68. $12x^{2n} - 40x^n + 25$

69. In your own words, explain how to factor a trinomial by grouping.

6.5   Factoring Binomials

OBJECTIVES

1 Factor the Difference of Two Squares.

2 Factor the Sum or Difference of Two Cubes.

OBJECTIVE

1   Factoring the Difference of Two Squares

When learning to multiply binomials in Chapter 5, we studied a special product, the product of the sum and difference of two terms, a and b:

$$(a + b)(a - b) = a^2 - b^2$$

For example, the product of $x + 3$ and $x - 3$ is

$$(x + 3)(x - 3) = x^2 - 9$$

The binomial $x^2 - 9$ is called a **difference of squares**. In this section, we reverse the pattern for the product of a sum and difference to factor the binomial difference of squares.

> **Factoring the Difference of Two Squares**
>
> $$a^2 - b^2 = (a + b)(a - b)$$

> **Helpful Hint**
>
> Since multiplication is commutative, remember that the order of factors does not matter. In other words,
>
> $$a^2 - b^2 = (a + b)(a - b) \text{ or } (a - b)(a + b)$$

EXAMPLE 1 Factor: $x^2 - 25$

Solution $x^2 - 25$ is the difference of two squares since $x^2 - 25 = x^2 - 5^2$. Therefore,

$$x^2 - 25 = x^2 - 5^2 = (x + 5)(x - 5)$$

Multiply to check. □

PRACTICE
1 Factor: $x^2 - 81$ ■

EXAMPLE 2 Factor each difference of squares.

    a. $4x^2 - 1$ **b.** $25a^2 - 9b^2$ **c.** $y^2 - \dfrac{4}{9}$

Solution

    a. $4x^2 - 1 = (2x)^2 - 1^2 = (2x + 1)(2x - 1)$

    b. $25a^2 - 9b^2 = (5a)^2 - (3b)^2 = (5a + 3b)(5a - 3b)$

    c. $y^2 - \dfrac{4}{9} = y^2 - \left(\dfrac{2}{3}\right)^2 = \left(y + \dfrac{2}{3}\right)\left(y - \dfrac{2}{3}\right)$ □

PRACTICE
2 Factor each difference of squares.

    a. $9x^2 - 1$ **b.** $36a^2 - 49b^2$ **c.** $p^2 - \dfrac{25}{36}$ ■

EXAMPLE 3 Factor: $x^4 - y^6$

Solution This is a difference of squares since $x^4 = (x^2)^2$ and $y^6 = (y^3)^2$. Thus,

$$x^4 - y^6 = (x^2)^2 - (y^3)^2 = (x^2 + y^3)(x^2 - y^3)$$ □

PRACTICE
3 Factor: $p^4 - q^{10}$ ■

EXAMPLE 4 Factor each binomial.

    a. $y^4 - 16$ **b.** $x^2 + 4$

Solution

    a. $y^4 - 16 = (y^2)^2 - 4^2$

              $= (y^2 + 4)\underbrace{(y^2 - 4)}$ Factor the difference of two squares.

                                              This binomial can be factored further since it is the difference of two squares.

              $= (y^2 + 4)(y + 2)(y - 2)$ Factor the difference of two squares.

b. $x^2 + 4$

Note that the binomial $x^2 + 4$ is the *sum* of two squares since we can write $x^2 + 4$ as $x^2 + 2^2$. We might try to factor using $(x + 2)(x + 2)$ or $(x - 2)(x - 2)$. But when we multiply to check, we find that neither factoring is correct.

$$(x + 2)(x + 2) = x^2 + 4x + 4$$

$$(x - 2)(x - 2) = x^2 - 4x + 4$$

In both cases, the product is a trinomial, not the required binomial. In fact, $x^2 + 4$ is a prime polynomial.   □

PRACTICE
4   Factor each binomial.

a. $z^4 - 81$ **b.** $m^2 + 49$ ■

Helpful Hint

When factoring, don't forget:

- See whether the terms have a greatest common factor (GCF) (other than 1) that can be factored out.
- Other than the GCF, the **sum** of two squares cannot be factored using real numbers.
- Factor completely. Always check to see whether any factors can be factored further.

EXAMPLES   Factor each binomial.

5. $4x^3 - 49x = x(4x^2 - 49)$ Factor out the GCF, x.

$\qquad\qquad\quad = x[(2x)^2 - 7^2]$

$\qquad\qquad\quad = x(2x + 7)(2x - 7)$ Factor the difference of two squares.

6. $162x^4 - 2 = 2(81x^4 - 1)$ Factor out the GCF, 2.

$\qquad\qquad\quad = 2(9x^2 + 1)(9x^2 - 1)$ Factor the difference of two squares.

$\qquad\qquad\quad = 2(9x^2 + 1)(3x + 1)(3x - 1)$ Factor the difference of two squares.   □

PRACTICE
5–6   Factor each binomial.

5. $36y^3 - 25y$ **6.** $80y^4 - 5$ ■

EXAMPLE 7   Factor: $-49x^2 + 16$

Solution Factor as is, or, if you like, rearrange terms.

Factor as is: $-49x^2 + 16 = -1(49x^2 - 16)$ Factor out -1.

$\qquad\qquad\qquad\qquad = -1(7x + 4)(7x - 4)$ Factor the difference of two squares.

Helpful Hint
When rearranging terms, keep in mind that the sign of a term is in front of the term.

Rewrite binomial: $-49x^2 + 16 = 16 - 49x^2 = 4^2 - (7x)^2$

$\qquad\qquad\qquad\qquad\qquad = (4 + 7x)(4 - 7x)$

Both factorizations are correct and are equal. To see this, factor -1 from $(4 - 7x)$ in the second factorization.   □

PRACTICE
7   Factor: $-9x^2 + 100$ ■

OBJECTIVE

2 Factoring the Sum or Difference of Two Cubes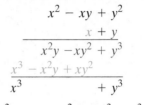

Although the sum of two squares usually does not factor, the sum or difference of two cubes can be factored and reveals factoring patterns. The pattern for the sum of cubes is illustrated by multiplying the binomial $x + y$ and the trinomial $x^2 - xy + y^2$.

$$
\begin{array}{r}
x^2 - xy + y^2 \\
\underline{x + y} \\
x^2y - xy^2 + y^3 \\
\underline{x^3 - x^2y + xy^2 \qquad} \\
x^3 \qquad\qquad + y^3
\end{array}
$$

Thus, $(x + y)(x^2 - xy + y^2) = x^3 + y^3$ Sum of cubes

The pattern for the difference of two cubes is illustrated by multiplying the binomial $x - y$ by the trinomial $x^2 + xy + y^2$. The result is

$$(x - y)(x^2 + xy + y^2) = x^3 - y^3 \quad \text{Difference of cubes}$$

Factoring the Sum or Difference of Two Cubes

$$a^3 + b^3 = (a + b)(a^2 - ab + b^2)$$
$$a^3 - b^3 = (a - b)(a^2 + ab + b^2)$$

Recall that "factor" means "to write as a product." Above are patterns for writing sums and differences as products.

EXAMPLE 8   Factor: $x^3 + 8$

Solution First, write the binomial in the form $a^3 + b^3$.

$$x^3 + 8 = x^3 + 2^3 \quad \text{Write in the form } a^3 + b^3.$$

If we replace a with x and b with 2 in the formula above, we have

$$
\begin{aligned}
x^3 + 2^3 &= (x + 2)[x^2 - (x)(2) + 2^2] \\
&= (x + 2)(x^2 - 2x + 4)
\end{aligned}
$$

PRACTICE

8   Factor: $x^3 + 64$

Helpful Hint

When factoring sums or differences of cubes, notice the sign patterns.

$$
\underbrace{x^3 + y^3 = (x + y)(x^2 - xy + y^2)}_{}
$$

same sign / opposite signs / always positive

$$
\underbrace{x^3 - y^3 = (x - y)(x^2 + xy + y^2)}_{}
$$

same sign / opposite signs / always positive

EXAMPLE 9   Factor: $y^3 - 27$

Solution
$$
\begin{aligned}
y^3 - 27 &= y^3 - 3^3 \qquad\qquad\qquad \text{Write in the form } a^3 - b^3. \\
&= (y - 3)[y^2 + (y)(3) + 3^2] \\
&= (y - 3)(y^2 + 3y + 9)
\end{aligned}
$$

PRACTICE

9   Factor: $x^3 - 125$

EXAMPLE 10 Factor: $64x^3 + 1$

Solution
$$64x^3 + 1 = (4x)^3 + 1^3$$
$$= (4x + 1)[(4x)^2 - (4x)(1) + 1^2]$$
$$= (4x + 1)(16x^2 - 4x + 1)$$

PRACTICE
10 Factor: $27y^3 + 1$

EXAMPLE 11 Factor: $54a^3 - 16b^3$

Solution Remember to factor out the greatest common factor first before using other factoring methods.

$$54a^3 - 16b^3 = 2(27a^3 - 8b^3) \qquad \text{Factor out the GCF, 2.}$$
$$= 2[(3a)^3 - (2b)^3] \quad \text{Difference of two cubes}$$
$$= 2(3a - 2b)[(3a)^2 + (3a)(2b) + (2b)^2]$$
$$= 2(3a - 2b)(9a^2 + 6ab + 4b^2)$$

PRACTICE
11 Factor: $32x^3 - 500y^3$

Graphing Calculator Explorations

Graphing

A graphing calculator is a convenient tool for evaluating an expression at a given replacement value. For example, let's evaluate $x^2 - 6x$ when $x = 2$. To do so, store the value 2 in the variable x and then enter and evaluate the algebraic expression.

```
2→X
                    2
X²-6X
                   -8
```

The value of $x^2 - 6x$ when $x = 2$ is -8. You may want to use this method for evaluating expressions as you explore the following.

We can use a graphing calculator to explore factoring patterns numerically. Use your calculator to evaluate $x^2 - 2x + 1$, $x^2 - 2x - 1$, and $(x - 1)^2$ for each value of x given in the table. What do you observe?

	$x^2 - 2x + 1$	$x^2 - 2x - 1$	$(x - 1)^2$
$x = 5$			
$x = -3$			
$x = 2.7$			
$x = -12.1$			
$x = 0$			

Notice in each case that $x^2 - 2x - 1 \neq (x - 1)^2$. Because for each x in the table the value of $x^2 - 2x + 1$ and the value of $(x - 1)^2$ are the same, we might guess that $x^2 - 2x + 1 = (x - 1)^2$. We can verify our guess algebraically with multiplication:

$$(x - 1)(x - 1) = x^2 - x - x + 1 = x^2 - 2x + 1$$

✓ Vocabulary, Readiness & Video Check

Use the choices below to fill in each blank. Some choices may be used more than once and some choices may not be used at all.

true	difference of two squares	sum of two cubes
false	difference of two cubes	

1. The expression $x^3 - 27$ is called a _____.

2. The expression $x^2 - 49$ is called a _____.

3. The expression $z^3 + 1$ is called a _____.

4. True or false: The binomial $y^2 + 9$ factors as $(y + 3)^2$. _____

Write each term as a square.

5. $49x^2$ **6.** $25y^4$

Write each term as a cube.

7. $8y^3$ **8.** x^6

Martin-Gay Interactive Videos

See Video 6.5 ⦿

Watch the section lecture video and answer the following questions.

OBJECTIVE 1

9. In ▦ Examples 1 and 2, what are two reasons the original binomial is rewritten so that each term is a square?

OBJECTIVE 1

10. From ▦ Example 3, what is a prime polynomial?

OBJECTIVE 2

11. In ▦ Examples 6–8, what tips are given to remember how to factor the sum or difference of two cubes rather than memorizing the formulas?

6.5 Exercise Set   MyMathLab® ▶

Factor each binomial completely. See Examples 1 through 7.

▶ **1.** $x^2 - 4$

2. $x^2 - 36$

3. $81p^2 - 1$

4. $49m^2 - 1$

5. $25y^2 - 9$

6. $49a^2 - 16$

▶ **7.** $121m^2 - 100n^2$

8. $169a^2 - 49b^2$

9. $x^2y^2 - 1$

10. $a^2b^2 - 16$

11. $x^2 - \dfrac{1}{4}$

12. $y^2 - \dfrac{1}{16}$

13. $-4r^2 + 1$

14. $-9t^2 + 1$

▶ **15.** $16r^2 + 1$

16. $49y^2 + 1$

17. $-36 + x^2$

18. $-1 + y^2$

19. $m^4 - 1$

20. $n^4 - 16$

21. $m^4 - n^{18}$

22. $n^4 - r^6$

Factor the sum or difference of two cubes. See Examples 8 through 11.

▶ **23.** $x^3 + 125$

24. $p^3 + 1$

25. $8a^3 - 1$

26. $27y^3 - 1$

27. $m^3 + 27n^3$

28. $y^3 + 64z^3$

29. $5k^3 + 40$

30. $6r^3 + 162$

▶ **31.** $x^3y^3 - 64$

32. $a^3b^3 - 8$

33. $250r^3 - 128t^3$

34. $24x^3 - 81y^3$

MIXED PRACTICE

Factor each binomial completely. See Examples 1 through 11.

35. $r^2 - 64$

36. $q^2 - 121$

37. $x^2 - 169y^2$

38. $x^2 - 225y^2$

39. $27 - t^3$

40. $125 - r^3$

41. $18r^2 - 8$

42. $32t^2 - 50$

43. $9xy^2 - 4x$

44. $36x^2y - 25y$

▶ 45. $8m^3 + 64$

46. $2x^3 + 54$

▶ 47. $xy^3 - 9xyz^2$

48. $x^3y - 4xy^3$

49. $36x^2 - 64y^2$

50. $225a^2 - 81b^2$

51. $144 - 81x^2$

52. $12x^2 - 27$

53. $x^3y^3 - z^6$

54. $a^3b^3 - c^9$

▶ 55. $49 - \dfrac{9}{25}m^2$

56. $100 - \dfrac{4}{81}n^2$

57. $t^3 + 343$

58. $s^3 + 216$

59. $n^3 + 49n$

60. $y^3 + 64y$

61. $x^6 - 81x^2$

62. $n^9 - n^5$

63. $64p^3q - 81pq^3$

64. $100x^3y - 49xy^3$

65. $27x^2y^3 + xy^2$

66. $8x^3y^3 + x^3y$

67. $125a^4 - 64ab^3$

68. $64m^4 - 27mn^3$

69. $16x^4 - 64x^2$

70. $25y^4 - 100y^2$

REVIEW AND PREVIEW

Solve each equation. See Section 2.2.

71. $x - 6 = 0$

72. $y + 5 = 0$

73. $2m + 4 = 0$

74. $3x - 9 = 0$

75. $5z - 1 = 0$

76. $4a + 2 = 0$

CONCEPT EXTENSIONS

Factor each expression completely.

77. $(x + 2)^2 - y^2$

78. $(y - 6)^2 - z^2$

79. $a^2(b - 4) - 16(b - 4)$

80. $m^2(n + 8) - 9(n + 8)$

81. $(x^2 + 6x + 9) - 4y^2$ (*Hint:* Factor the trinomial in parentheses first.)

82. $(x^2 + 2x + 1) - 36y^2$

83. $x^{2n} - 100$

84. $x^{2n} - 81$

85. What binomial multiplied by $(x - 6)$ gives the difference of two squares?

86. What binomial multiplied by $(5 + y)$ gives the difference of two squares?

87. In your own words, explain how to tell whether a binomial is a difference of squares. Then explain how to factor a difference of squares.

88. In your own words, explain how to tell whether a binomial is a sum of cubes. Then explain how to factor a sum of cubes.

89. The Toroweap Overlook, on the North Rim of the Grand Canyon, lies 3000 vertical feet above the Colorado River. The view is spectacular, and the sheer drop is dramatic. A film crew creating a documentary about the Grand Canyon has built a camera platform 136 feet above the Overlook. A camera filter comes loose and falls to the river below. The height of the filter above the river after t seconds is given by the expression $3136 - 16t^2$.

   a. Find the height of the filter above the river after 3 seconds.

   b. Find the height of the filter above the river after 10 seconds.

   c. To the nearest whole second, estimate when the filter lands in the river.

   d. Factor $3136 - 16t^2$.

90. An object is dropped from the top of Pittsburgh's USX Tower, which is 841 feet tall. (*Source: World Almanac* research) The height of the object after t seconds is given by the expression $841 - 16t^2$.

   a. Find the height of the object after 2 seconds.

   b. Find the height of the object after 5 seconds.

   c. To the nearest whole second, estimate when the object hits the ground.

   d. Factor $841 - 16t^2$.

841 feet

91. At this writing, the tallest completed building in the world is the Burj Khalifa, in Dubai, measuring a height of 2717 feet. (*Source:* Council on Tall Buildings and Urban Habitat) Suppose an action picture is being filmed there and a stunt man is making his way to the top of the spire. He sways in the wind and drops a clip from the height of 2704 feet. The height of the clip after t seconds is given by the expression $2704 - 16t^2$.

a. Find the height of the clip after 3 seconds.

b. Find the height of the clip after 7 seconds.

c. To the nearest whole second, estimate when the clip will hit the ground.

d. Factor $2704 - 16t^2$.

92. A performer with the Moscow Circus is planning a stunt involving a free fall from the top of the Moscow State University building, which is 784 feet tall. (*Source:* Council on Tall Buildings and Urban Habitat) Neglecting air resistance, the performer's height above gigantic cushions positioned at ground level after t seconds is given by the expression $784 - 16t^2$.

a. Find the performer's height after 2 seconds.

b. Find the performer's height after 5 seconds.

c. To the nearest whole second, estimate when the performer reaches the cushions positioned at ground level.

d. Factor $784 - 16t^2$.

Integrated Review — Choosing a Factoring Strategy

Sections 6.1–6.5

The following steps may be helpful when factoring polynomials.

Factoring a Polynomial

Step 1. Are there any common factors? If so, factor out the GCF.

Step 2. How many terms arc in the polynomial?

    a. If there are **two** terms, decide if one of the following can be applied.

        i. Difference of two squares: $a^2 - b^2 = (a + b)(a - b)$.

        ii. Difference of two cubes: $a^3 - b^3 = (a - b)(a^2 + ab + b^2)$.

        iii. Sum of two cubes: $a^3 + b^3 = (a + b)(a^2 - ab + b^2)$.

    b. If there are **three** terms, try one of the following.

        i. Perfect square trinomial: $a^2 + 2ab + b^2 = (a + b)^2$
$$a^2 - 2ab + b^2 = (a - b)^2.$$

        ii. If not a perfect square trinomial, factor using the methods presented in Sections 6.2 through 6.4.

    c. If there are **four** or more terms, try factoring by grouping.

Step 3. See if any factors in the factored polynomial can be factored further.

Step 4. Check by multiplying.

Study the next five examples to help you use the steps above.

EXAMPLE 1   Factor: $10t^2 - 17t + 3$

Solution

Step 1. The terms of this polynomial have no common factor (other than 1).

Step 2. There are three terms, so this polynomial is a trinomial. This trinomial is not a perfect square trinomial, so factor using methods from earlier sections.

Factors of $10t^2$: $10t^2 = 2t \cdot 5t$, $10t^2 = t \cdot 10t$

Since the middle term, $-17t$, has a negative numerical coefficient, find negative factors of 3.

$$\text{Factors of 3:} \quad 3 = -1 \cdot -3$$

Try different combinations of these factors. The correct combination is

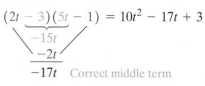

$$(2t - 3)(5t - 1) = 10t^2 - 17t + 3$$

Step 3. No factor can be factored further, so we have factored completely.

Step 4. To check, multiply $2t - 3$ and $5t - 1$.

$$(2t - 3)(5t - 1) = 10t^2 - 2t - 15t + 3 = 10t^2 - 17t + 3$$

The factored form of $10t^2 - 17t + 3$ is $(2t - 3)(5t - 1)$. □

PRACTICE

1 Factor: $6x^2 - 11x + 3$ ■

EXAMPLE 2 Factor: $2x^3 + 3x^2 - 2x - 3$

Solution

Step 1. There are no factors common to all terms.

Step 2. Try factoring by grouping since this polynomial has four terms.

$$2x^3 + 3x^2 - 2x - 3 = x^2(2x + 3) - 1(2x + 3) \quad \text{Factor out the greatest common factor for each pair of terms.}$$

$$= (2x + 3)(x^2 - 1) \quad \text{Factor out } 2x + 3.$$

Step 3. The binomial $x^2 - 1$ can be factored further. It is the difference of two squares.

$$= (2x + 3)(x + 1)(x - 1) \quad \text{Factor } x^2 - 1 \text{ as a difference of squares.}$$

Step 4. Check by finding the product of the three binomials. The polynomial factored completely is $(2x + 3)(x + 1)(x - 1)$. □

PRACTICE

2 Factor: $3x^3 + x^2 - 12x - 4$ ■

EXAMPLE 3 Factor: $12m^2 - 3n^2$

Solution

Step 1. The terms of this binomial contain a greatest common factor of 3.

$$12m^2 - 3n^2 = 3(4m^2 - n^2) \quad \text{Factor out the greatest common factor.}$$

Step 2. The binomial $4m^2 - n^2$ is a difference of squares.

$$= 3(2m + n)(2m - n) \quad \text{Factor the difference of squares.}$$

Step 3. No factor can be factored further.

Step 4. We check by multiplying.

$$3(2m + n)(2m - n) = 3(4m^2 - n^2) = 12m^2 - 3n^2$$

The factored form of $12m^2 - 3n^2$ is $3(2m + n)(2m - n)$. □

PRACTICE

3 Factor: $27x^2 - 3y^2$ ■

EXAMPLE 4 Factor: $x^3 + 27y^3$

Solution

Step 1. The terms of this binomial contain no common factor (other than 1).

Step 2. This binomial is the sum of two cubes.

$$x^3 + 27y^3 = (x)^3 + (3y)^3$$
$$= (x + 3y)[x^2 - x(3y) + (3y)^2]$$
$$= (x + 3y)(x^2 - 3xy + 9y^2)$$

Step 3. No factor can be factored further.

Step 4. We check by multiplying.

$$(x + 3y)(x^2 - 3xy + 9y^2) = x(x^2 - 3xy + 9y^2) + 3y(x^2 - 3xy + 9y^2)$$
$$= x^3 - 3x^2y + 9xy^2 + 3x^2y - 9xy^2 + 27y^3$$
$$= x^3 + 27y^3$$

Thus, $x^3 + 27y^3$ factored completely is $(x + 3y)(x^2 - 3xy + 9y^2)$. □

PRACTICE
4 Factor: $8a^3 + b^3$ ■

EXAMPLE 5 Factor: $30a^2b^3 + 55a^2b^2 - 35a^2b$

Solution

Step 1. $30a^2b^3 + 55a^2b^2 - 35a^2b = 5a^2b(6b^2 + 11b - 7)$ Factor out the GCF.

Step 2. $= 5a^2b(2b - 1)(3b + 7)$ Factor the resulting trinomial.

Step 3. No factor can be factored further.

Step 4. Check by multiplying.

The trinomial factored completely is $5a^2b(2b - 1)(3b + 7)$. □

PRACTICE
5 Factor: $60x^3y^2 - 66x^2y^2 - 36xy^2$ ■

Factor the following completely.

1. $x^2 + 2xy + y^2$
2. $x^2 - 2xy + y^2$
3. $a^2 + 11a - 12$
4. $a^2 - 11a + 10$
5. $a^2 - a - 6$
6. $a^2 - 2a + 1$
7. $x^2 + 2x + 1$
8. $x^2 + x - 2$
9. $x^2 + 4x + 3$
10. $x^2 + x - 6$
11. $x^2 + 7x + 12$
12. $x^2 + x - 12$
13. $x^2 + 3x - 4$
14. $x^2 - 7x + 10$
15. $x^2 + 2x - 15$
16. $x^2 + 11x + 30$
17. $x^2 - x - 30$
18. $x^2 + 11x + 24$
19. $2x^2 - 98$
20. $3x^2 - 75$
21. $x^2 + 3x + xy + 3y$
22. $3y - 21 + xy - 7x$
23. $x^2 + 6x - 16$
24. $x^2 - 3x - 28$
25. $4x^3 + 20x^2 - 56x$
26. $6x^3 - 6x^2 - 120x$
27. $12x^2 + 34x + 24$
28. $8a^2 + 6ab - 5b^2$
29. $4a^2 - b^2$
30. $28 - 13x - 6x^2$
31. $20 - 3x - 2x^2$
32. $x^2 - 2x + 4$
33. $a^2 + a - 3$
34. $6y^2 + y - 15$
35. $4x^2 - x - 5$
36. $x^2y - y^3$
37. $4t^2 + 36$
38. $x^2 + x + xy + y$
39. $ax + 2x + a + 2$
40. $18x^3 - 63x^2 + 9x$
41. $12a^3 - 24a^2 + 4a$
42. $x^2 + 14x - 32$
43. $x^2 - 14x - 48$
44. $16a^2 - 56ab + 49b^2$
45. $25p^2 - 70pq + 49q^2$
46. $7x^2 + 24xy + 9y^2$
47. $125 - 8y^3$
48. $64x^3 + 27$

49. $-x^2 - x + 30$

50. $-x^2 + 6x - 8$

51. $14 + 5x - x^2$

52. $3 - 2x - x^2$

53. $3x^4y + 6x^3y - 72x^2y$

54. $2x^3y + 8x^2y^2 - 10xy^3$

55. $5x^3y^2 - 40x^2y^3 + 35xy^4$

56. $4x^4y - 8x^3y - 60x^2y$

57. $12x^3y + 243xy$

58. $6x^3y^2 + 8xy^2$

59. $4 - x^2$

60. $9 - y^2$

61. $3rs - s + 12r - 4$

62. $x^3 - 2x^2 + 3x - 6$

▶ **63.** $4x^2 - 8xy - 3x + 6y$

64. $4x^2 - 2xy - 7yz + 14xz$

65. $6x^2 + 18xy + 12y^2$

66. $12x^2 + 46xy - 8y^2$

67. $xy^2 - 4x + 3y^2 - 12$

68. $x^2y^2 - 9x^2 + 3y^2 - 27$

69. $5(x + y) + x(x + y)$

70. $7(x - y) + y(x - y)$

71. $14t^2 - 9t + 1$

72. $3t^2 - 5t + 1$

73. $3x^2 + 2x - 5$

74. $7x^2 + 19x - 6$

75. $x^2 + 9xy - 36y^2$

76. $3x^2 + 10xy - 8y^2$

77. $1 - 8ab - 20a^2b^2$

78. $1 - 7ab - 60a^2b^2$

79. $9 - 10x^2 + x^4$

80. $36 - 13x^2 + x^4$

81. $x^4 - 14x^2 - 32$

82. $x^4 - 22x^2 - 75$

83. $x^2 - 23x + 120$

84. $y^2 + 22y + 96$

85. $6x^3 - 28x^2 + 16x$

86. $6y^3 - 8y^2 - 30y$

87. $27x^3 - 125y^3$

88. $216y^3 - z^3$

89. $x^3y^3 + 8z^3$

90. $27a^3b^3 + 8$

▶ **91.** $2xy - 72x^3y$

92. $2x^3 - 18x$

93. $x^3 + 6x^2 - 4x - 24$

94. $x^3 - 2x^2 - 36x + 72$

95. $6a^3 + 10a^2$

96. $4n^2 - 6n$

97. $a^2(a + 2) + 2(a + 2)$

98. $a - b + x(a - b)$

99. $x^3 - 28 + 7x^2 - 4x$

100. $a^3 - 45 - 9a + 5a^2$

CONCEPT EXTENSIONS

Factor.

101. $(x - y)^2 - z^2$

102. $(x + 2y)^2 - 9$

103. $81 - (5x + 1)^2$

104. $b^2 - (4a + c)^2$

105. Explain why it makes good sense to factor out the GCF first, before using other methods of factoring.

106. The sum of two squares usually does not factor. Is the sum of two squares $9x^2 + 81y^2$ factorable?

107. Which of the following are equivalent to $(x + 10)(x - 7)$?

    a. $(x - 7)(x + 10)$ **b.** $-1(x + 10)(x - 7)$

    c. $-1(x + 10)(7 - x)$ **d.** $-1(-x - 10)(7 - x)$

108. Which of the following are equivalent to $(x - 2)(x - 5)$?

    a. $-1(x + 2)(x + 5)$ **b.** $(x - 5)(x - 2)$

    c. $(5 - x)(2 - x)$ **d.** $-1(x + 2)(x - 5)$

6.6 Solving Quadratic Equations by Factoring ▶

OBJECTIVES

1 Solve Quadratic Equations by Factoring. ▶

2 Solve Equations with Degree Greater than 2 by Factoring. ▶

3 Find the *x*-Intercepts of the Graph of a Quadratic Equation in Two Variables. ▶

In this section, we introduce a new type of equation—the **quadratic equation**.

Quadratic Equation

A quadratic equation is one that can be written in the form

$$ax^2 + bx + c = 0$$

where a, b, and c are real numbers and $a \neq 0$.

Some examples of quadratic equations are shown below.

$$x^2 - 9x - 22 = 0 \qquad 4x^2 - 28 = -49 \qquad x(2x - 7) = 4$$

The form $ax^2 + bx + c = 0$ is called the **standard form** of a quadratic equation. The quadratic equation $x^2 - 9x - 22 = 0$ is the only equation above that is in standard form.

144 feet

Quadratic equations model many real-life situations. For example, let's suppose we want to know how long before a person diving from a 144-foot cliff reaches the ocean. The answer to this question is found by solving the quadratic equation $-16t^2 + 144 = 0$. (See Example 1 in Section 6.7.)

OBJECTIVE

1 Solving Quadratic Equations by Factoring ▶

Some quadratic equations can be solved by making use of factoring and the **zero factor property**.

> **Zero Factor Property**
>
> If a and b are real numbers and if $ab = 0$, then $a = 0$ or $b = 0$.

This property states that if the product of two numbers is 0 then at least one of the numbers must be 0.

EXAMPLE 1 Solve: $(x - 3)(x + 1) = 0$

Solution If this equation is to be a true statement, then either the factor $x - 3$ must be 0 or the factor $x + 1$ must be 0. In other words, either

$$x - 3 = 0 \quad \text{or} \quad x + 1 = 0$$

If we solve these two linear equations, we have

$$x = 3 \quad \text{or} \quad x = -1$$

Thus, 3 and -1 are both solutions of the equation $(x - 3)(x + 1) = 0$. To check, we replace x with 3 in the original equation. Then we replace x with -1 in the original equation.

Check: Let $x = 3$.

$(x - 3)(x + 1) = 0$

$(3 - 3)(3 + 1) \stackrel{?}{=} 0$ Replace x with 3.

$0(4) = 0$ True

Let $x = -1$.

$(x - 3)(x + 1) = 0$

$(-1 - 3)(-1 + 1) \stackrel{?}{=} 0$ Replace x with -1.

$(-4)(0) = 0$ True

The solutions are 3 and -1, or we say that the solution set is $\{-1, 3\}$.   □

PRACTICE

1 Solve: $(x + 4)(x - 5) = 0$

> **Helpful Hint**
>
> The zero factor property says that *if a product is 0, then a factor is 0.*
>
> If $a \cdot b = 0$, then $a = 0$ or $b = 0$.
>
> If $x(x + 5) = 0$, then $x = 0$ or $x + 5 = 0$.
>
> If $(x + 7)(2x - 3) = 0$, then $x + 7 = 0$ or $2x - 3 = 0$.
>
> Use this property only when the product is 0.
> For example, if $a \cdot b = 8$, we do not know the value of a or b. The values may be $a = 2, b = 4$ or $a = 8, b = 1$, or any other two numbers whose product is 8.

EXAMPLE 2 Solve: $(x - 5)(2x + 7) = 0$

Solution: The product is 0. By the zero factor property, this is true only when a factor is 0. To solve, we set each factor equal to 0 and solve the resulting linear equations.

$$(x - 5)(2x + 7) = 0$$
$$x - 5 = 0 \quad \text{or} \quad 2x + 7 = 0$$
$$x = 5 \quad \text{or} \quad 2x = -7$$
$$x = -\frac{7}{2}$$

Check: Let $x = 5$.

$$(x - 5)(2x + 7) = 0$$
$$(5 - 5)(2 \cdot 5 + 7) \stackrel{?}{=} 0 \quad \text{Replace } x \text{ with 5.}$$
$$0 \cdot 17 \stackrel{?}{=} 0$$
$$0 = 0 \quad \text{True}$$

Let $x = -\dfrac{7}{2}$.

$$(x - 5)(2x + 7) = 0$$
$$\left(-\frac{7}{2} - 5\right)\left(2\left(-\frac{7}{2}\right) + 7\right) \stackrel{?}{=} 0 \quad \text{Replace } x \text{ with } -\frac{7}{2}.$$
$$\left(-\frac{17}{2}\right)(-7 + 7) \stackrel{?}{=} 0$$
$$\left(-\frac{17}{2}\right) \cdot 0 \stackrel{?}{=} 0$$
$$0 = 0 \quad \text{True}$$

The solutions are 5 and $-\dfrac{7}{2}$.

☐

PRACTICE

> **2**   Solve: $(x - 12)(4x + 3) = 0$

■

EXAMPLE 3   Solve: $x(5x - 2) = 0$

Solution
$$x(5x - 2) = 0$$
$$x = 0 \quad \text{or} \quad 5x - 2 = 0 \quad \text{Use the zero factor property.}$$
$$5x = 2$$
$$x = \frac{2}{5}$$

Check: Let $x = 0$.

$$x(5x - 2) = 0$$
$$0(5 \cdot 0 - 2) \stackrel{?}{=} 0 \quad \text{Replace } x \text{ with 0.}$$
$$0(-2) \stackrel{?}{=} 0$$
$$0 = 0 \quad \text{True}$$

Let $x = \dfrac{2}{5}$.

$$x(5x - 2) = 0$$
$$\frac{2}{5}\left(5 \cdot \frac{2}{5} - 2\right) \stackrel{?}{=} 0 \quad \text{Replace } x \text{ with } \frac{2}{5}.$$
$$\frac{2}{5}(2 - 2) \stackrel{?}{=} 0$$
$$\frac{2}{5}(0) \stackrel{?}{=} 0$$
$$0 = 0 \quad \text{True}$$

The solutions are 0 and $\dfrac{2}{5}$.

☐

PRACTICE

> **3**   Solve: $x(7x - 6) = 0$

■

EXAMPLE 4   Solve: $x^2 - 9x - 22 = 0$

Solution   One side of the equation is 0. However, to use the zero factor property, one side of the equation must be 0 *and* the other side must be written as a product (must be factored). Thus, we must first factor this polynomial.

$$x^2 - 9x - 22 = 0$$
$$(x - 11)(x + 2) = 0 \quad \text{Factor.}$$

(Continued on the next page)

Now we can apply the zero factor property.

$$x - 11 = 0 \quad \text{or} \quad x + 2 = 0$$
$$x = 11 \text{ or} \qquad x = -2$$

Check: Let $x = 11$.   Let $x = -2$.

$$x^2 - 9x - 22 = 0 \qquad\qquad\qquad x^2 - 9x - 22 = 0$$
$$11^2 - 9 \cdot 11 - 22 \stackrel{?}{=} 0 \qquad\qquad (-2)^2 - 9(-2) - 22 \stackrel{?}{=} 0$$
$$121 - 99 - 22 \stackrel{?}{=} 0 \qquad\qquad\qquad 4 + 18 - 22 \stackrel{?}{=} 0$$
$$22 - 22 \stackrel{?}{=} 0 \qquad\qquad\qquad\qquad 22 - 22 \stackrel{?}{=} 0$$
$$0 = 0 \quad \text{True} \qquad\qquad\qquad\qquad 0 = 0 \quad \text{True}$$

The solutions are 11 and -2.   □

PRACTICE

4   Solve: $x^2 - 8x - 48 = 0$ ■

EXAMPLE 5   Solve: $4x^2 - 28x = -49$

Solution First we rewrite the equation in standard form so that one side is 0. Then we factor the polynomial.

$$4x^2 - 28x = -49$$
$$4x^2 - 28x + 49 = 0 \qquad \text{Write in standard form by adding 49 to both sides.}$$
$$(2x - 7)(2x - 7) = 0 \qquad \text{Factor.}$$

Next we use the zero factor property and set each factor equal to 0. Since the factors are the same, the related equations will give the same solution.

$$2x - 7 = 0 \quad \text{or} \quad 2x - 7 = 0 \quad \text{Set each factor equal to 0.}$$
$$2x = 7 \quad \text{or} \qquad 2x = 7 \quad \text{Solve.}$$
$$x = \frac{7}{2} \quad \text{or} \qquad x = \frac{7}{2}$$

Check: Although $\frac{7}{2}$ occurs twice, there is a single solution. Check this solution in the original equation. The solution is $\frac{7}{2}$.   □

PRACTICE

5   Solve: $9x^2 - 24x = -16$ ■

The following steps may be used to solve a quadratic equation by factoring.

To Solve Quadratic Equations by Factoring

Step 1. Write the equation in standard form so that one side of the equation is 0.

Step 2. Factor the quadratic expression completely.

Step 3. Set each factor containing a variable equal to 0.

Step 4. Solve the resulting equations.

Step 5. Check each solution in the original equation.

Since it is not always possible to factor a quadratic polynomial, not all quadratic equations can be solved by factoring. Other methods of solving quadratic equations are presented in Chapter 9.

EXAMPLE 6   Solve: $x(2x - 7) = 4$

Solution   First we write the equation in standard form; then we factor.

$$x(2x - 7) = 4$$
$$2x^2 - 7x = 4 \qquad \text{Multiply.}$$
$$2x^2 - 7x - 4 = 0 \qquad \text{Write in standard form.}$$
$$(2x + 1)(x - 4) = 0 \qquad \text{Factor.}$$
$$2x + 1 = 0 \quad \text{or} \quad x - 4 = 0 \qquad \text{Set each factor equal to zero.}$$
$$2x = -1 \quad \text{or} \qquad x = 4 \qquad \text{Solve.}$$
$$x = -\frac{1}{2}$$

Check the solutions in the original equation. The solutions are $-\dfrac{1}{2}$ and 4.

> **Helpful Hint**
>
> To solve the equation $x(2x - 7) = 4$, do **not** set each factor equal to 4. Remember that to apply the zero factor property, one side of the equation must be 0 and the other side of the equation must be in factored form.

PRACTICE

6   Solve: $x(3x + 7) = 6$

✔ **CONCEPT CHECK**

Explain the error and solve the equation correctly.

$$(x - 3)(x + 1) = 5$$
$$x - 3 = 5 \quad \text{or} \quad x + 1 = 5$$
$$x = 8 \quad \text{or} \qquad x = 4$$

EXAMPLE 7   Solve: $-2x^2 - 4x + 30 = 0$

Solution   The equation is in standard form, so we begin by factoring out the greatest common factor, -2.

$$-2x^2 - 4x + 30 = 0$$
$$-2(x^2 + 2x - 15) = 0 \qquad \text{Factor out } -2.$$
$$-2(x + 5)(x - 3) = 0 \qquad \text{Factor the quadratic.}$$

Next, set each factor **containing a variable** equal to 0.

$$x + 5 = 0 \qquad \text{or} \qquad x - 3 = 0 \qquad \text{Set each factor containing a variable equal to 0.}$$
$$x = -5 \qquad \text{or} \qquad x = 3 \qquad \text{Solve.}$$

Note: The factor -2 is a constant term containing no variables and can never equal 0. The solutions are -5 and 3.

PRACTICE

7   Solve: $-3x^2 - 6x + 72 = 0$

Answer to Concept Check:
To use the zero factor property, one side of the equation must be 0, not 5. Correctly, $(x - 3)(x + 1) = 5$, $x^2 - 2x - 3 = 5$, $x^2 - 2x - 8 = 0$, $(x - 4)(x + 2) = 0$, $x - 4 = 0$ or $x + 2 = 0$, $x = 4$ or $x = -2$.

OBJECTIVE

2   **Solving Equations with Degree Greater than Two by Factoring** ▷

Some equations involving polynomials of degree higher than 2 may also be solved by factoring and then applying the zero factor property.

EXAMPLE 8 Solve: $3x^3 - 12x = 0$

Solution Factor the left side of the equation. Begin by factoring out the greatest common factor, $3x$.

$$3x^3 - 12x = 0$$
$$3x(x^2 - 4) = 0 \quad \text{Factor out the GCF, } 3x.$$
$$3x(x + 2)(x - 2) = 0 \quad \text{Factor } x^2 - 4, \text{ a difference of squares.}$$
$$3x = 0 \quad \text{or} \quad x + 2 = 0 \quad \text{or} \quad x - 2 = 0 \quad \text{Set each factor equal to 0.}$$
$$x = 0 \quad \text{or} \quad x = -2 \quad \text{or} \quad x = 2 \quad \text{Solve.}$$

Thus, the equation $3x^3 - 12x = 0$ has three solutions: $0, -2$, and 2. To check, replace x with each solution in the original equation.

Let x = 0.	*Let x = -2.*	*Let x = 2.*
$3(0)^3 - 12(0) \stackrel{?}{=} 0$	$3(-2)^3 - 12(-2) \stackrel{?}{=} 0$	$3(2)^3 - 12(2) \stackrel{?}{=} 0$
$0 = 0$	$3(-8) + 24 \stackrel{?}{=} 0$	$3(8) - 24 \stackrel{?}{=} 0$
	$0 = 0$	$0 = 0$

Substituting $0, -2$, or 2 into the original equation results each time in a true equation. The solutions are $0, -2$, and 2. □

PRACTICE
8 Solve: $7x^3 - 63x = 0$ ■

EXAMPLE 9 Solve: $(5x - 1)(2x^2 + 15x + 18) = 0$

Solution

$$(5x - 1)(2x^2 + 15x + 18) = 0$$
$$(5x - 1)(2x + 3)(x + 6) = 0 \quad \text{Factor the trinomial.}$$
$$5x - 1 = 0 \quad \text{or} \quad 2x + 3 = 0 \quad \text{or} \quad x + 6 = 0 \quad \text{Set each factor equal to 0.}$$
$$5x = 1 \quad \text{or} \quad 2x = -3 \quad \text{or} \quad x = -6 \quad \text{Solve.}$$
$$x = \frac{1}{5} \quad \text{or} \quad x = -\frac{3}{2}$$

The solutions are $\frac{1}{5}, -\frac{3}{2}$, and -6. Check by replacing x with each solution in the original equation. The solutions are $-6, -\frac{3}{2}$, and $\frac{1}{5}$. □

PRACTICE
9 Solve: $(3x - 2)(2x^2 - 13x + 15) = 0$ ■

EXAMPLE 10 Solve: $2x^3 - 4x^2 - 30x = 0$

Solution Begin by factoring out the GCF, $2x$.

$$2x^3 - 4x^2 - 30x = 0$$
$$2x(x^2 - 2x - 15) = 0 \quad \text{Factor out the GCF, } 2x.$$
$$2x(x - 5)(x + 3) = 0 \quad \text{Factor the quadratic.}$$
$$2x = 0 \quad \text{or} \quad x - 5 = 0 \quad \text{or} \quad x + 3 = 0 \quad \text{Set each factor containing a variable equal to 0.}$$
$$x = 0 \quad \text{or} \quad x = 5 \quad \text{or} \quad x = -3 \quad \text{Solve.}$$

Check by replacing x with each solution in the cubic equation. The solutions are $-3, 0$, and 5. □

PRACTICE
10 Solve: $5x^3 + 5x^2 - 30x = 0$ ■

OBJECTIVE

3   Finding *x*-Intercepts of the Graph of a Quadratic Equation

In Chapter 3, we graphed linear equations in two variables, such as $y = 5x - 6$. Recall that to find the *x*-intercept of the graph of a linear equation, let $y = 0$ and solve for *x*. This is also how to find the *x*-intercepts of the graph of a **quadratic equation in two variables,** such as $y = x^2 - 5x + 4$.

EXAMPLE 11   Find the *x*-intercepts of the graph of $y = x^2 - 5x + 4$.

Solution   Let $y = 0$ and solve for *x*.

$$y = x^2 - 5x + 4$$
$$0 = x^2 - 5x + 4 \qquad \text{Let } y = 0.$$
$$0 = (x - 1)(x - 4) \qquad \text{Factor.}$$
$$x - 1 = 0 \quad \text{or} \quad x - 4 = 0 \quad \text{Set each factor equal to 0.}$$
$$x = 1 \quad \text{or} \quad x = 4 \quad \text{Solve.}$$

The *x*-intercepts of the graph of $y = x^2 - 5x + 4$ are $(1, 0)$ and $(4, 0)$.
The graph of $y = x^2 - 5x + 4$ is shown in the margin.

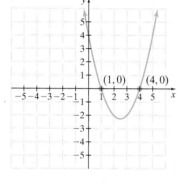

PRACTICE

11   Find the *x*-intercepts of the graph of $y = x^2 - 6x + 8$.

In general, a quadratic equation in two variables is one that can be written in the form $y = ax^2 + bx + c$ where $a \neq 0$. The graph of such an equation is called a **parabola** and will open up or down depending on the sign of *a*.

Notice that the *x*-intercepts of the graph of $y = ax^2 + bx + c$ are the real number solutions of $0 = ax^2 + bx + c$. Also, the real number solutions of $0 = ax^2 + bx + c$ are the *x*-intercepts of the graph of $y = ax^2 + bx + c$. We study more about graphs of quadratic equations in two variables in Chapter 9.

Graph of $y = ax^2 + bx + c$
x-intercepts are solutions of $0 = ax^2 + bx + c$

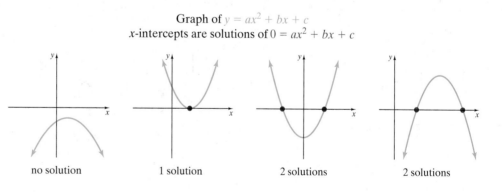

no solution   1 solution   2 solutions   2 solutions

Graphing Calculator Explorations

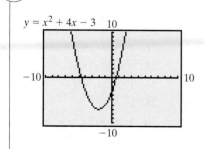

$y = x^2 + 4x - 3$

A grapher may be used to find solutions of a quadratic equation whether the related quadratic polynomial is factorable or not. For example, let's use a grapher to approximate the solutions of $0 = x^2 + 4x - 3$. To do so, graph $y_1 = x^2 + 4x - 3$. Recall that the *x*-intercepts of this graph are the solutions of $0 = x^2 + 4x - 3$.

Notice that the graph appears to have an *x*-intercept between -5 and -4 and one between 0 and 1. Many graphers contain a TRACE feature. This feature activates a graph cursor that can be used to *trace* along a graph while the corresponding *x*- and *y*-coordinates are shown on the screen. Use the TRACE feature to confirm that *x*-intercepts lie between -5 and -4 and between 0 and 1. To approximate the *x*-intercepts to the nearest tenth, use a ROOT or a ZOOM feature on your grapher or redefine the viewing window. (A ROOT feature calculates the *x*-intercept. A ZOOM feature magnifies the viewing window around a specific location such as

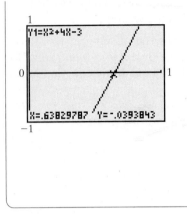

the graph cursor.) If we redefine the window to $[0, 1]$ on the x-axis and $[-1, 1]$ on the y-axis, the graph to the left is generated.

By using the TRACE feature, we can conclude that one x-intercept is approximately 0.6 to the nearest tenth. By repeating these steps for the other x-intercept, we find that it is approximately -4.6.

Use a grapher to approximate the real number solutions to the nearest tenth. If an equation has no real number solution, state so.

1. $3x^2 - 4x - 6 = 0$ **2.** $x^2 - x - 9 = 0$

3. $2x^2 + x + 2 = 0$ **4.** $-4x^2 - 5x - 4 = 0$

5. $-x^2 + x + 5 = 0$ **6.** $10x^2 + 6x - 3 = 0$

✔ Vocabulary, Readiness & Video Check

Use the choices below to fill in each blank. Not all choices will be used.

$-3, 5$	$a = 0$ or $b = 0$	0	linear
$3, -5$	quadratic	1	

1. An equation that can be written in the form $ax^2 + bx + c = 0$, with $a \neq 0$, is called a _____ equation.

2. If the product of two numbers is 0, then at least one of the numbers must be _____.

3. The solutions to $(x - 3)(x + 5) = 0$ are _____.

4. If $a \cdot b = 0$, then _____.

Martin-Gay Interactive Videos

Watch the section lecture video and answer the following questions.

OBJECTIVE 1
5. As shown in ▦ Examples 1–3, what two things have to be true in order to use the zero factor property?

OBJECTIVE 2
6. ▦ Example 4 implies that the zero factor property can be used with any number of factors on one side of the equation so long as the other side of the equation is zero. Why do you think this is true?

OBJECTIVE 3
7. From ▦ Example 5, how does finding the x-intercepts of the graph of a quadratic equation in two variables lead to solving a quadratic equation?

See Video 6.6 ⦿

6.6 Exercise Set MyMathLab▸

Solve each equation. See Examples 1 through 3.

1. $(x - 6)(x - 7) = 0$
2. $(x - 10)(x - 5) = 0$
3. $(x - 2)(x + 1) = 0$
4. $(x + 4)(x - 10) = 0$
5. $(x + 9)(x + 17) = 0$
6. $(x + 11)(x + 1) = 0$
7. $x(x + 6) = 0$
8. $x(x - 7) = 0$
9. $3x(x - 8) = 0$
10. $2x(x + 12) = 0$
▸**11.** $(2x + 3)(4x - 5) = 0$
12. $(3x - 2)(5x + 1) = 0$
13. $(2x - 7)(7x + 2) = 0$
14. $(9x + 1)(4x - 3) = 0$
15. $\left(x - \dfrac{1}{2}\right)\left(x + \dfrac{1}{3}\right) = 0$
16. $\left(x + \dfrac{2}{9}\right)\left(x - \dfrac{1}{4}\right) = 0$
17. $(x + 0.2)(x + 1.5) = 0$
18. $(x + 1.7)(x + 2.3) = 0$

Solve. See Examples 4 through 7.

19. $x^2 - 13x + 36 = 0$
20. $x^2 + 2x - 63 = 0$
▸**21.** $x^2 + 2x - 8 = 0$
22. $x^2 - 5x + 6 = 0$
23. $x^2 - 7x = 0$
24. $x^2 - 3x = 0$
25. $x^2 - 4x = 32$
26. $x^2 - 5x = 24$
27. $x^2 = 16$
28. $x^2 = 9$
29. $(x + 4)(x - 9) = 4x$
30. $(x + 3)(x + 8) = x$
▸**31.** $x(3x - 1) = 14$
32. $x(4x - 11) = 3$
33. $-3x^2 + 75 = 0$
34. $-2y^2 + 72 = 0$
35. $24x^2 + 44x = 8$
36. $6x^2 + 57x = 30$

Solve each equation. See Examples 8 through 10.

37. $x^3 - 12x^2 + 32x = 0$

38. $x^3 - 14x^2 + 49x = 0$

39. $(4x - 3)(16x^2 - 24x + 9) = 0$

40. $(2x + 5)(4x^2 + 20x + 25) = 0$

41. $4x^3 - x = 0$ **42.** $4y^3 - 36y = 0$

43. $32x^3 - 4x^2 - 6x = 0$ **44.** $15x^3 + 24x^2 - 63x = 0$

MIXED PRACTICE

Solve each equation. See Examples 1 through 10. (A few exercises are linear equations.)

45. $(x + 3)(x - 2) = 0$ **46.** $(x - 6)(x + 7) = 0$

47. $x^2 + 20x = 0$ **48.** $x^2 + 15x = 0$

49. $4(x - 7) = 6$ **50.** $5(3 - 4x) = 9$

51. $4y^2 - 1 = 0$ **52.** $4y^2 - 81 = 0$

53. $(2x + 3)(2x^2 - 5x - 3) = 0$

54. $(2x - 9)(x^2 + 5x - 36) = 0$

55. $x^2 - 15 = -2x$ **56.** $x^2 - 26 = -11x$

57. $30x^2 - 11x - 30 = 0$ **58.** $12x^2 + 7x - 12 = 0$

59. $5x^2 - 6x - 8 = 0$ **60.** $9x^2 + 7x = 2$

61. $6y^2 - 22y - 40 = 0$ **62.** $3x^2 - 6x - 9 = 0$

63. $(y - 2)(y + 3) = 6$ **64.** $(y - 5)(y - 2) = 28$

65. $3x^3 + 19x^2 - 72x = 0$

66. $36x^3 + x^2 - 21x = 0$

67. $x^2 + 14x + 49 = 0$

68. $x^2 + 22x + 121 = 0$

69. $12y = 8y^2$

70. $9y = 6y^2$

71. $7x^3 - 7x = 0$

72. $3x^3 - 27x = 0$

73. $3x^2 + 8x - 11 = 13 - 6x$

74. $2x^2 + 12x - 1 = 4 + 3x$

75. $3x^2 - 20x = -4x^2 - 7x - 6$

76. $4x^2 - 20x = -5x^2 - 6x - 5$

Find the x-intercepts of the graph of each equation. See Example 11.

77. $y = (3x + 4)(x - 1)$

78. $y = (5x - 3)(x - 4)$

79. $y = x^2 - 3x - 10$

80. $y = x^2 + 7x + 6$

81. $y = 2x^2 + 11x - 6$

82. $y = 4x^2 + 11x + 6$

For Exercises 83 through 88, match each equation with its graph. See Example 11.

83. $y = (x + 2)(x - 1)$ **84.** $y = (x - 5)(x + 2)$

85. $y = x(x + 3)$ **86.** $y = x(x - 4)$

87. $y = 2x^2 - 8$ **88.** $y = 2x^2 - 2$

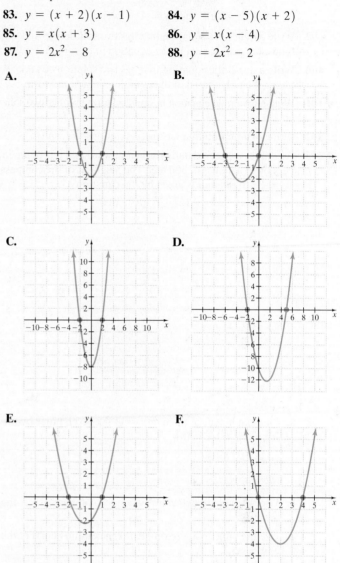

REVIEW AND PREVIEW

Perform the following operations. Write all results in lowest terms. See Section 1.3.

89. $\dfrac{3}{5} + \dfrac{4}{9}$ **90.** $\dfrac{2}{3} + \dfrac{3}{7}$

91. $\dfrac{7}{10} - \dfrac{5}{12}$ **92.** $\dfrac{5}{9} - \dfrac{5}{12}$

93. $\dfrac{7}{8} \div \dfrac{7}{15}$ **94.** $\dfrac{5}{12} - \dfrac{3}{10}$

95. $\dfrac{4}{5} \cdot \dfrac{7}{8}$ **96.** $\dfrac{3}{7} \cdot \dfrac{12}{17}$

CONCEPT EXTENSIONS

For Exercises 97 and 98, see the Concept Check in this section.

97. Explain the error and solve correctly:

$$x(x - 2) = 8$$
$$x = 8 \quad \text{or} \quad x - 2 = 8$$
$$x = 10$$

98. Explain the error and solve correctly:

$$(x - 4)(x + 2) = 0$$
$$x = -4 \quad \text{or} \quad x = 2$$

99. Write a quadratic equation that has two solutions, 6 and −1. Leave the polynomial in the equation in factored form.

100. Write a quadratic equation that has two solutions, 0 and −2. Leave the polynomial in the equation in factored form.

101. Write a quadratic equation in standard form that has two solutions, 5 and 7.

102. Write an equation that has three solutions, 0, 1, and 2.

103. A compass is accidentally thrown upward and out of an air balloon at a height of 300 feet. The height, y, of the compass at time x in seconds is given by the equation

$$y = -16x^2 + 20x + 300$$

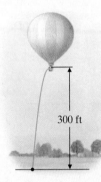

300 ft

a. Find the height of the compass at the given times by filling in the table below.

time, x	0	1	2	3	4	5	6
height, y							

b. Use the table to determine when the compass strikes the ground.

c. Use the table to approximate the maximum height of the compass.

d. Plot the points (x, y) on a rectangular coordinate system and connect them with a smooth curve. Explain your results.

104. A rocket is fired upward from the ground with an initial velocity of 100 feet per second. The height, y, of the rocket at any time x is given by the equation

$$y = -16x^2 + 100x$$

a. Find the height of the rocket at the given times by filling in the table below.

time, x	0	1	2	3	4	5	6	7
height, y								

b. Use the table to approximate when the rocket strikes the ground to the nearest second.

c. Use the table to approximate the maximum height of the rocket.

d. Plot the points (x, y) on a rectangular coordinate system and connect them with a smooth curve. Explain your results.

Solve each equation. First, multiply the binomials.

To solve $(x - 6)(2x - 3) = (x + 2)(x + 9)$, see below.

$$(x - 6)(2x - 3) = (x + 2)(x + 9)$$
$$2x^2 - 15x + 18 = x^2 + 11x + 18$$
$$x^2 - 26x = 0$$
$$x(x - 26) = 0$$
$$x = 0 \quad \text{or} \quad x - 26 = 0$$
$$x = 26$$

105. $(x - 3)(3x + 4) = (x + 2)(x - 6)$

106. $(2x - 3)(x + 6) = (x - 9)(x + 2)$

107. $(2x - 3)(x + 8) = (x - 6)(x + 4)$

108. $(x + 6)(x - 6) = (2x - 9)(x + 4)$

6.7 Quadratic Equations and Problem Solving ▷

OBJECTIVE

1 Solve Problems That Can Be Modeled by Quadratic Equations. ▷

OBJECTIVE

1 Solving Problems Modeled by Quadratic Equations ▷

Some problems may be modeled by quadratic equations. To solve these problems, we use the same problem-solving steps that were introduced in Section 2.4. When solving these problems, keep in mind that a solution of an equation that models a problem may not be a solution of the problem. For example, a person's age or the length of a rectangle is always a positive number. Discard solutions that do not make sense as solutions of the problem.

EXAMPLE 1   **Finding Free-Fall Time**

Since the 1940s, one of the top tourist attractions in Acapulco, Mexico, is watching the La Quebrada cliff divers. The divers' platform is about 144 feet above the sea. These divers must time their descent just right, since they land in the crashing Pacific in an inlet that is at most $9\frac{1}{2}$ feet deep. Neglecting air resistance, the height h in feet of a cliff diver above the ocean after t seconds is given by the quadratic equation $h = -16t^2 + 144$.

Find how long it takes the diver to reach the ocean.

Solution

1. UNDERSTAND. Read and reread the problem. Then draw a picture of the problem.

   The equation $h = -16t^2 + 144$ models the height of the falling diver at time t. Familiarize yourself with this equation by finding the height of the diver at time $t = 1$ second and $t = 2$ seconds.

   When $t = 1$ second, the height of the diver is $h = -16(1)^2 + 144 = 128$ feet.

   When $t = 2$ seconds, the height of the diver is $h = -16(2)^2 + 144 = 80$ feet.

2. TRANSLATE. To find how long it takes the diver to reach the ocean, we want to know the value of t for which $h = 0$.

3. SOLVE.

   $$0 = -16t^2 + 144$$
   $$0 = -16(t^2 - 9) \quad \text{Factor out } -16.$$
   $$0 = -16(t - 3)(t + 3) \quad \text{Factor completely.}$$
   $$t - 3 = 0 \quad \text{or} \quad t + 3 = 0 \quad \text{Set each factor containing a variable equal to 0.}$$
   $$t = 3 \quad \text{or} \quad t = -3 \quad \text{Solve.}$$

4. INTERPRET.   Since the time t cannot be negative, the proposed solution is 3 seconds.

   Check: Verify that the height of the diver when t is 3 seconds is 0.

   When $t = 3$ seconds, $h = -16(3)^2 + 144 = -144 + 144 = 0$.

   State: It takes the diver 3 seconds to reach the ocean.   ☐

PRACTICE

1   Cliff divers also frequent the falls at Waimea Falls Park in Oahu, Hawaii. One of the popular diving spots is 64 feet high. Neglecting air resistance, the height of a diver above the pool after t seconds is $h = -16t^2 + 64$. Find how long it takes a diver to reach the pool.   ■

EXAMPLE 2   **Finding an Unknown Number**

The square of a number plus three times the number is 70. Find the number.

Solution

1. UNDERSTAND. Read and reread the problem. Suppose that the number is 5. The square of 5 is 5^2 or 25. Three times 5 is 15. Then $25 + 15 = 40$, not 70, so the number is not 5. Remember, the purpose of proposing a number, such as 5, is to understand the problem better. Now that we do, we will let $x =$ the number.

(Continued on the next page)

2. TRANSLATE.

the square of a number	plus	three times the number	is	70
↓	↓	↓	↓	↓
x^2	$+$	$3x$	$=$	70

3. SOLVE.

$$x^2 + 3x = 70$$

$$x^2 + 3x - 70 = 0 \qquad \text{Subtract 70 from both sides.}$$

$$(x + 10)(x - 7) = 0 \qquad \text{Factor.}$$

$$x + 10 = 0 \quad \text{or} \quad x - 7 = 0 \qquad \text{Set each factor equal to 0.}$$

$$x = -10 \qquad\qquad x = 7 \qquad \text{Solve.}$$

4. INTERPRET.

Check: The square of -10 is $(-10)^2$, or 100. Three times -10 is $3(-10)$ or -30. Then $100 + (-30) = 70$, the correct sum, so -10 checks.

The square of 7 is 7^2 or 49. Three times 7 is $3(7)$, or 21. Then $49 + 21 = 70$, the correct sum, so 7 checks.

State: There are two numbers. They are -10 and 7. □

PRACTICE

2 The square of a number minus eight times the number is equal to forty-eight. Find the number. ■

△ **EXAMPLE 3** Finding the Dimensions of a Sail

The height of a triangular sail is 2 meters less than twice the length of the base. If the sail has an area of 30 square meters, find the length of its base and the height.

Solution

1. UNDERSTAND. Read and reread the problem. Since we are finding the length of the base and the height, we let

$$x = \text{the length of the base}$$

and since the height is 2 meters less than twice the base,

$$2x - 2 = \text{the height.}$$

An illustration is shown to the right.

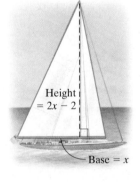

Height = $2x - 2$

Base = x

2. TRANSLATE. We are given that the area of the triangle is 30 square meters, so we use the formula for area of a triangle.

area of triangle	$=$	$\dfrac{1}{2}$	$\cdot$	base	$\cdot$	height
↓		↓		↓		↓
30	$=$	$\dfrac{1}{2}$	$\cdot$	x	$\cdot$	$(2x - 2)$

3. SOLVE. Now we solve the quadratic equation.

$$30 = \frac{1}{2}x(2x - 2)$$

$$30 = x^2 - x \qquad \text{Multiply.}$$

$$x^2 - x - 30 = 0 \qquad \text{Write in standard form.}$$

$$(x - 6)(x + 5) = 0 \qquad \text{Factor.}$$

$$x - 6 = 0 \quad \text{or} \quad x + 5 = 0 \qquad \text{Set each factor equal to 0.}$$

$$x = 6 \qquad\qquad x = -5$$

4. INTERPRET. Since x represents the length of the base, we discard the solution -5. The base of a triangle cannot be negative. The base is then 6 meters and the height is $2(6) - 2 = 10$ meters.

Check: To check this problem, we recall that $\frac{1}{2}$base $\cdot$ height $=$ area, or

$$\frac{1}{2}(6)(10) = 30. \quad \text{The required area}$$

State: The base of the triangular sail is 6 meters and the height is 10 meters. □

PRACTICE

3   An engineering team from Georgia Tech earned second place in a flight competition, with their triangular shaped paper hang glider. The base of their prize-winning entry was 1 foot less than three times the height. If the area of the triangular glider wing was 210 square feet, find the dimensions of the wing. (*Source: The Technique* [Georgia Tech's newspaper], April 18, 2003) ■

Study the following diagrams for a review of consecutive integers.

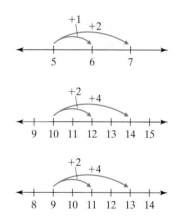

Examples

If x is the first integer, then consecutive integers are
$x, x + 1, x + 2, \ldots$

If x is the first even integer, then consecutive even integers are
$x, x + 2, x + 4, \ldots$

If x is the first odd integer, then consecutive odd integers are
$x, x + 2, x + 4, \ldots$

EXAMPLE 4   **Finding Consecutive Even Integers**

Find two consecutive even integers whose product is 34 more than their sum.

Solution

1. UNDERSTAND. Read and reread the problem. Let's just choose two consecutive even integers to help us better understand the problem. Let's choose 10 and 12. Their product is $10(12) = 120$ and their sum is $10 + 12 = 22$. The product is $120 - 22$, or 98, greater than the sum. Thus our guess is incorrect, but we have a better understanding of this example.

Let's let x and $x + 2$ be the consecutive even integers.

(Continued on the next page)

2. TRANSLATE.

Product of integers	is	34	more than	sum of integers
↓	↓	↓	↓	↓
$x(x + 2)$	$=$	34	$+$	$x + (x + 2)$

3. SOLVE. Now we solve the equation.

$$x(x + 2) = 34 + x + (x + 2)$$
$$x^2 + 2x = 34 + x + x + 2 \qquad \text{Multiply.}$$
$$x^2 + 2x = 2x + 36 \qquad \text{Combine like terms.}$$
$$x^2 - 36 = 0 \qquad \text{Write in standard form.}$$
$$(x + 6)(x - 6) = 0 \qquad \text{Factor.}$$
$$x + 6 = 0 \quad \text{or} \quad x - 6 = 0 \qquad \text{Set each factor equal to 0.}$$
$$x = -6 \qquad x = 6 \qquad \text{Solve.}$$

4. INTERPRET. If $x = -6$, then $x + 2 = -6 + 2$, or -4.
If $x = 6$, then $x + 2 = 6 + 2$, or 8.

Check: $-6, -4$ $6, 8$

$$-6(-4) \stackrel{?}{=} 34 + (-6) + (-4) \qquad\qquad 6(8) \stackrel{?}{=} 34 + 6 + 8$$
$$24 \stackrel{?}{=} 34 + (-10) \qquad\qquad\qquad\qquad 48 \stackrel{?}{=} 34 + 14$$
$$24 = 24 \qquad\qquad \text{True} \qquad\qquad 48 = 48 \qquad\qquad \text{True}$$

State: The two consecutive even integers are -6 and -4 or 6 and 8. ☐

PRACTICE
4 Find two consecutive integers whose product is 41 more than their sum. ■

The next example uses the **Pythagorean theorem** and consecutive integers. Before we review this theorem, recall that a **right triangle** is a triangle that contains a 90° or right angle. The **hypotenuse** of a right triangle is the side opposite the right angle and is the longest side of the triangle. The **legs** of a right triangle are the other sides of the triangle.

Helpful Hint

If you use this formula, don't forget that c represents the length of the hypotenuse.

Pythagorean Theorem

In a right triangle, the sum of the squares of the lengths of the two legs is equal to the square of the length of the hypotenuse.

$$(\text{leg})^2 + (\text{leg})^2 = (\text{hypotenuse})^2 \qquad \text{or} \qquad a^2 + b^2 = c^2$$

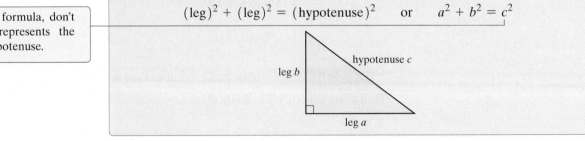

⚠ **EXAMPLE 5**   Finding the Dimensions of a Triangle

Find the lengths of the sides of a right triangle if the lengths can be expressed as three consecutive even integers.

Solution

1. **UNDERSTAND.** Read and reread the problem. Let's suppose that the length of one leg of the right triangle is 4 units. Then the other leg is the next even integer, or 6 units, and the hypotenuse of the triangle is the next even integer, or 8 units. Remember that the hypotenuse is the longest side. Let's see if a triangle with sides of these lengths forms a right triangle. To do this, we check to see whether the Pythagorean theorem holds true.

$$4^2 + 6^2 \stackrel{?}{=} 8^2$$

$$16 + 36 \stackrel{?}{=} 64$$

$$52 = 64 \quad \text{False}$$

Our proposed numbers do not check, but we now have a better understanding of the problem.

We let x, $x + 2$, and $x + 4$ be three consecutive even integers. Since these integers represent lengths of the sides of a right triangle, we have the following.

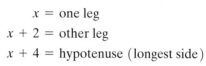

$$x = \text{one leg}$$

$$x + 2 = \text{other leg}$$

$$x + 4 = \text{hypotenuse (longest side)}$$

2. **TRANSLATE.** By the Pythagorean theorem, we have that

$$(\text{leg})^2 + (\text{leg})^2 = (\text{hypotenuse})^2$$

$$(x)^2 + (x + 2)^2 = (x + 4)^2$$

3. **SOLVE.** Now we solve the equation.

$$x^2 + (x + 2)^2 = (x + 4)^2$$

$$x^2 + x^2 + 4x + 4 = x^2 + 8x + 16 \qquad \text{Multiply.}$$

$$2x^2 + 4x + 4 = x^2 + 8x + 16 \qquad \text{Combine like terms.}$$

$$x^2 - 4x - 12 = 0 \qquad \text{Write in standard form.}$$

$$(x - 6)(x + 2) = 0 \qquad \text{Factor.}$$

$$x - 6 = 0 \quad \text{or} \quad x + 2 = 0 \qquad \text{Set each factor equal to 0.}$$

$$x = 6 \qquad\qquad x = -2$$

4. **INTERPRET.** We discard $x = -2$ since length cannot be negative. If $x = 6$, then $x + 2 = 8$ and $x + 4 = 10$.

Check: Verify that

$$(\text{leg})^2 + (\text{leg})^2 = (\text{hypotenuse})^2$$

$$6^2 + 8^2 \stackrel{?}{=} 10^2$$

$$36 + 64 \stackrel{?}{=} 100$$

$$100 = 100 \qquad \text{True}$$

State: The sides of the right triangle have lengths 6 units, 8 units, and 10 units.

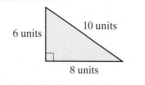

PRACTICE

5 Find the dimensions of a right triangle where the second leg is 1 unit less than double the first leg, and the hypotenuse is 1 unit more than double the length of the first leg.

✓ Vocabulary, Readiness & Video Check

Martin-Gay Interactive Videos

Watch the section lecture video and answer the following question.

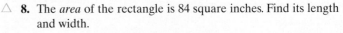

OBJECTIVE 1

1. In each of 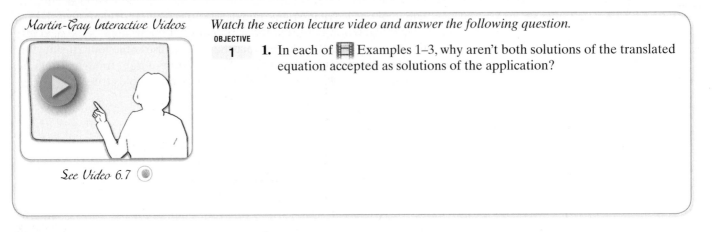 Examples 1–3, why aren't both solutions of the translated equation accepted as solutions of the application?

See Video 6.7 ●

6.7 Exercise Set MyMathLab® ▷

MIXED PRACTICE

See Examples 1 through 5 for all exercises.

TRANSLATING

For Exercises 1 through 6, represent each given condition using a single variable, x.

△ **1.** The length and width of a rectangle whose length is 4 centimeters more than its width

x ☐

△ **2.** The length and width of a rectangle whose length is twice its width

x ☐

3. Two consecutive odd integers

4. Two consecutive even integers

△ **5.** The base and height of a triangle whose height is one more than four times its base

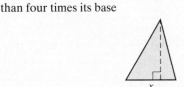

x

△ **6.** The base and height of a trapezoid whose base is three less than five times its height

base

Use the information given to find the dimensions of each figure.

△ **7.** The *area* of the square is 121 square units. Find the length of its sides.

x

△ **8.** The *area* of the rectangle is 84 square inches. Find its length and width.

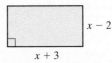

$x - 2$

$x + 3$

△ **9.** The *perimeter* of the quadrilateral is 120 centimeters. Find the lengths of the sides.

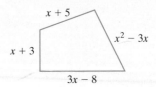

$x + 5$

$x^2 - 3x$

$x + 3$

$3x - 8$

△ ▷ **10.** The *perimeter* of the triangle is 85 feet. Find the lengths of its sides.

$2x$ $2x + 5$

$x^2 + 3$

△ **11.** The *area* of the parallelogram is 96 square miles. Find its base and height.

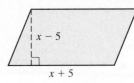

$x - 5$

$x + 5$

△ **12.** The *area* of the circle is 25π square kilometers. Find its radius.

x

Solve.

13. An object is thrown upward from the top of an 80-foot building with an initial velocity of 64 feet per second. The height h of the object after t seconds is given by the quadratic equation $h = -16t^2 + 64t + 80$. When will the object hit the ground?

14. A hang glider pilot accidentally drops her compass from the top of a 400-foot cliff. The height h of the compass after t seconds is given by the quadratic equation $h = -16t^2 + 400$. When will the compass hit the ground?

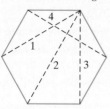

△ **15.** The width of a rectangle is 7 centimeters less than twice its length. Its area is 30 square centimeters. Find the dimensions of the rectangle.

△ **16.** The length of a rectangle is 9 inches more than its width. Its area is 112 square inches. Find the dimensions of the rectangle.

The equation $D = \dfrac{1}{2}n(n - 3)$ gives the number of diagonals D for a polygon with n sides. For example, a polygon with 6 sides has $D = \dfrac{1}{2} \cdot 6(6 - 3)$ or $D = 9$ diagonals. (See if you can count all 9 diagonals. Some are shown in the figure.) Use this equation, $D = \dfrac{1}{2}n(n - 3)$, for Exercises 17 through 20.

△ **17.** Find the number of diagonals for a polygon that has 12 sides.

△ **18.** Find the number of diagonals for a polygon that has 15 sides.

△ **19.** Find the number of sides n for a polygon that has 35 diagonals.

△ **20.** Find the number of sides n for a polygon that has 14 diagonals.

Solve.

21. The sum of a number and its square is 132. Find the number(s).

22. The sum of a number and its square is 182. Find the number(s).

23. The product of two consecutive room numbers is 210. Find the room numbers.

24. The product of two consecutive page numbers is 420. Find the page numbers.

25. A ladder is leaning against a building so that the distance from the ground to the top of the ladder is one foot less than the length of the ladder. Find the length of the ladder if the distance from the bottom of the ladder to the building is 5 feet.

26. Use the given figure to find the length of the guy wire.

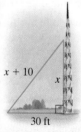

△ **27.** If the sides of a square are increased by 3 inches, the area becomes 64 square inches. Find the length of the sides of the original square.

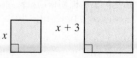

△ **28.** If the sides of a square are increased by 5 meters, the area becomes 100 square meters. Find the length of the sides of the original square.

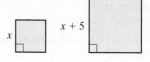

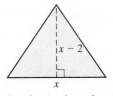

29. One leg of a right triangle is 4 millimeters longer than the smaller leg and the hypotenuse is 8 millimeters longer than the smaller leg. Find the lengths of the sides of the triangle.

30. One leg of a right triangle is 9 centimeters longer than the other leg and the hypotenuse is 45 centimeters. Find the lengths of the legs of the triangle.

31. The length of the base of a triangle is twice its height. If the area of the triangle is 100 square kilometers, find the height.

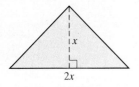

2x

32. The height of a triangle is 2 millimeters less than the base. If the area is 60 square millimeters, find the base.

x − 2

x

33. Find the length of the shorter leg of a right triangle if the longer leg is 12 feet more than the shorter leg and the hypotenuse is 12 feet less than twice the shorter leg.

34. Find the length of the shorter leg of a right triangle if the longer leg is 10 miles more than the shorter leg and the hypotenuse is 10 miles less than twice the shorter leg.

35. An object is dropped from 39 feet below the tip of the pinnacle atop one of the 1483-foot-tall Petronas Twin Towers in Kuala Lumpur, Malaysia. (*Source:* Council on Tall Buildings and Urban Habitat) The height h of the object after t seconds is given by the equation $h = -16t^2 + 1444$. Find how many seconds pass before the object reaches the ground.

36. An object is dropped from the top of 311 South Wacker Drive, a 961-foot-tall office building in Chicago. (*Source:* Council on Tall Buildings and Urban Habitat) The height h of the object after t seconds is given by the equation $h = -16t^2 + 961$. Find how many seconds pass before the object reaches the ground.

37. At the end of 2 years, P dollars invested at an interest rate r compounded annually increases to an amount, A dollars, given by

$$A = P(1 + r)^2$$

Find the interest rate if $100 increased to $144 in 2 years. Write your answer as a percent.

38. At the end of 2 years, P dollars invested at an interest rate r compounded annually increases to an amount, A dollars, given by

$$A = P(1 + r)^2$$

Find the interest rate if $2000 increased to $2420 in 2 years. Write your answer as a percent.

39. Find the dimensions of a rectangle whose width is 7 miles less than its length and whose area is 120 square miles.

40. Find the dimensions of a rectangle whose width is 2 inches less than half its length and whose area is 160 square inches.

41. If the cost, C, for manufacturing x units of a certain product is given by $C = x^2 - 15x + 50$, find the number of units manufactured at a cost of $9500.

42. If a switchboard handles n telephones, the number C of telephone connections it can make simultaneously is given by the equation $C = \dfrac{n(n - 1)}{2}$. Find how many telephones are handled by a switchboard making 120 telephone connections simultaneously.

REVIEW AND PREVIEW

The following double-line graph shows a comparison of the number of annual visitors (in millions) to Glacier National Park and Gettysburg National Military Park for the years shown. Use this graph to answer Exercises 43 through 50. See Section 3.1.

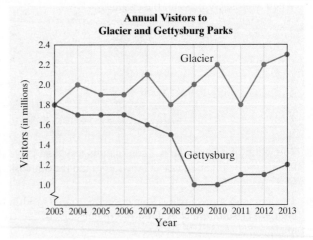

43. Approximate the number of visitors to Glacier National Park in 2011.

44. Approximate the number of visitors to Gettysburg National Military Park in 2011.

45. Approximate the number of visitors to Glacier National Park in 2013.

46. Approximate the number of visitors to Gettysburg National Military Park in 2013.

47. Determine the year that the colored lines in this graph intersect.

48. For what years on the graph is the number of visitors to Glacier Park greater than the number of visitors to Gettysburg Park?

49. In your own words, explain the meaning of the point of intersection in the graph.

50. Describe the trends shown in this graph and speculate as to why these trends have occurred.

Write each fraction in simplest form. See Section 1.3.

51. $\dfrac{20}{35}$ **52.** $\dfrac{24}{32}$ **53.** $\dfrac{27}{18}$

54. $\dfrac{15}{27}$ **55.** $\dfrac{14}{42}$ **56.** $\dfrac{45}{50}$

CONCEPT EXTENSIONS

△ **57.** Two boats travel at right angles to each other after leaving the same dock at the same time. One hour later, the boats are 17 miles apart. If one boat travels 7 miles per hour faster than the other boat, find the rate of each boat.

△ **58.** The side of a square equals the width of a rectangle. The length of the rectangle is 6 meters longer than its width. The sum of the areas of the square and the rectangle is 176 square meters. Find the side of the square.

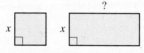

59. The sum of two numbers is 20, and the sum of their squares is 218. Find the numbers.

60. The sum of two numbers is 25, and the sum of their squares is 325. Find the numbers.

△ **61.** A rectangular pool is surrounded by a walk 4 meters wide. The pool is 6 meters longer than its width. If the total area of the pool and walk is 576 square meters more than the area of the pool, find the dimensions of the pool.

△ **62.** A rectangular garden is surrounded by a walk of uniform width. The area of the garden is 180 square yards. If the dimensions of the garden plus the walk are 16 yards by 24 yards, find the width of the walk.

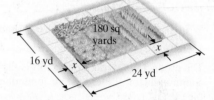

↘ **63.** Write down two numbers whose sum is 10. Square each number and find the sum of the squares. Use this work to write a word problem like Exercise 59. Then give the word problem to a classmate to solve.

↘ **64.** Write down two numbers whose sum is 12. Square each number and find the sum of the squares. Use this work to write a word problem like Exercise 60. Then give the word problem to a classmate to solve.

Chapter 6 **Vocabulary Check**

Fill in each blank with one of the words or phrases listed below. Not all choices will be used and some choices may be used more than once.

factoring	quadratic equation	perfect square trinomial	0
greatest common factor	hypotenuse	sum of two cubes	1
difference of two cubes	difference of two squares	triangle	leg

1. An equation that can be written in the form $ax^2 + bx + c = 0$ (with a not 0) is called a(n) _____.

2. _____ is the process of writing an expression as a product.

3. The _____ of a list of terms is the product of all common factors.

4. A trinomial that is the square of some binomial is called a(n) _____.

5. The expression $a^2 - b^2$ is called a(n) _____.

6. The expression $a^3 - b^3$ is called a(n) _____.

7. The expression $a^3 + b^3$ is called a(n) _____.

8. By the zero factor property, if the product of two numbers is 0, then at least one of the numbers must be _____.

9. In a right triangle, the side opposite the right angle is called the _____.

10. In a right triangle, each side adjacent to the right angle is called a _____.

11. The Pythagorean theorem states that $(\text{leg})^2 + (\text{leg})^2 = ($_____$)^2$.

Chapter 6 Highlights

DEFINITIONS AND CONCEPTS	EXAMPLES

Section 6.1   The Greatest Common Factor and Factoring by Grouping

Factoring is the process of writing an expression as a product.	Factor: $6 = 2 \cdot 3$ $x^2 + 5x + 6 = (x + 2)(x + 3)$
To Find the GCF of a List of Integers	Find the GCF of 12, 36, and 48.
Step 1. Write each number as a product of primes.	$12 = 2 \cdot 2 \cdot 3$
Step 2. Identify the common prime factors.	$36 = 2 \cdot 2 \cdot 3 \cdot 3$
Step 3. The product of all common factors is the greatest common factor. If there are no common prime factors, the GCF is 1.	$48 = 2 \cdot 2 \cdot 2 \cdot 2 \cdot 3$ $\text{GCF} = 2 \cdot 2 \cdot 3 = 12$
The GCF of a list of common variables raised to powers is the variable raised to the smallest exponent in the list.	The GCF of z^5, z^3, and z^{10} is z^3.
The GCF of a list of terms is the product of all common factors.	Find the GCF of $8x^2y$, $10x^3y^2$, and $26x^2y^3$. The GCF of 8, 10, and 26 is 2. The GCF of x^2, x^3, and x^2 is x^2. The GCF of y, y^2, and y^3 is y. The GCF of the terms is $2x^2y$.
To Factor by Grouping	Factor: $10ax + 15a - 6xy - 9y$
Step 1. Arrange the terms so that the first two terms have a common factor and the last two have a common factor.	**Step 1.** $10ax + 15a - 6xy - 9y$
Step 2. For each pair of terms, factor out the pair's GCF.	**Step 2.** $5a(2x + 3) - 3y(2x + 3)$
Step 3. If there is now a common binomial factor, factor it out.	**Step 3.** $(2x + 3)(5a - 3y)$
Step 4. If there is no common binomial factor, begin again, rearranging the terms differently. If no rearrangement leads to a common binomial factor, the polynomial cannot be factored by grouping.	

Section 6.2   Factoring Trinomials of the Form $x^2 + bx + c$

The product of these numbers is c. $x^2 + bx + c = (x + \square)(x + \square)$ The sum of these numbers is b.	Factor: $x^2 + 7x + 12$ $3 + 4 = 7 \qquad 3 \cdot 4 = 12$ $x^2 + 7x + 12 = (x + 3)(x + 4)$

DEFINITIONS AND CONCEPTS	EXAMPLES

Section 6.3   Factoring Trinomials of the Form $ax^2 + bx + c$ and Perfect Square Trinomials

To factor $ax^2 + bx + c$, try various combinations of factors of ax^2 and c until a middle term of bx is obtained when checking.	Factor: $3x^2 + 14x - 5$ Factors of $3x^2$: $3x, x$ Factors of -5: $-1, 5$ and $1, -5$. $$(3x - 1)(x + 5)$$ $$-1x$$ $$+ 15x$$ $$\overline{14x}\quad \textbf{Correct}\text{ middle term}$$
A **perfect square trinomial** is a trinomial that is the square of some binomial.	Perfect square trinomial = square of binomial $$x^2 + 4x + 4 = (x + 2)^2$$ $$25x^2 - 10x + 1 = (5x - 1)^2$$
Factoring Perfect Square Trinomials $$a^2 + 2ab + b^2 = (a + b)^2$$ $$a^2 - 2ab + b^2 = (a - b)^2$$	Factor. $$x^2 + 6x + 9 = x^2 + 2 \cdot x \cdot 3 + 3^2 = (x + 3)^2$$ $$4x^2 - 12x + 9 = (2x)^2 - 2 \cdot 2x \cdot 3 + 3^2 = (2x - 3)^2$$

Section 6.4   Factoring Trinomials of the Form $ax^2 + bx + c$ by Grouping

To Factor $ax^2 + bx + c$ by Grouping **Step 1.** Find two numbers whose product is $a \cdot c$ and whose sum is b. **Step 2.** Rewrite bx, using the factors found in Step 1. **Step 3.** Factor by grouping.	Factor: $3x^2 + 14x - 5$ **Step 1.** Find two numbers whose product is $3 \cdot (-5)$ or -15 and whose sum is 14. They are 15 and -1. **Step 2.** $3x^2 + 14x - 5$ $= 3x^2 + 15x - 1x - 5$ **Step 3.** $= 3x(x + 5) - 1(x + 5)$ $= (x + 5)(3x - 1)$

Section 6.5   Factoring Binomials

Difference of Squares $$a^2 - b^2 = (a + b)(a - b)$$	Factor. $$x^2 - 9 = x^2 - 3^2 = (x + 3)(x - 3)$$
Sum or Difference of Cubes $$a^3 + b^3 = (a + b)(a^2 - ab + b^2)$$ $$a^3 - b^3 = (a - b)(a^2 + ab + b^2)$$	$$y^3 + 8 = y^3 + 2^3 = (y + 2)(y^2 - 2y + 4)$$ $$125z^3 - 1 = (5z)^3 - 1^3 = (5z - 1)(25z^2 + 5z + 1)$$

Integrated Review—Choosing a Factoring Strategy

To Factor a Polynomial
 	
Step 1. Factor out the GCF.
 	
Step 2. **a.** If two terms
  i. $a^2 - b^2 = (a + b)(a - b)$
  ii. $a^3 - b^3 = (a - b)(a^2 + ab + b^2)$
  iii. $a^3 + b^3 = (a + b)(a^2 - ab + b^2)$
 	
  b. If three terms
  i. $a^2 + 2ab + b^2 = (a + b)^2$
  $a^2 - 2ab + b^2 = (a - b)^2$
 	
  ii. Methods in Sections 6.2 through 6.4
 	
  c. If four or more terms, try factoring by grouping.
	Factor: $2x^4 - 6x^2 - 8$
	
	Step 1. $2x^4 - 6x^2 - 8 = 2(x^4 - 3x^2 - 4)$
	
	Step 2. b. ii. $= 2(x^2 + 1)(x^2 - 4)$

(continued)

DEFINITIONS AND CONCEPTS	EXAMPLES

Integrated Review—Choosing a Factoring Strategy (continued)

Step 3. See if any factors can be factored further.

Step 4. Check by multiplying.

Step 3. $= 2(x^2 + 1)(x + 2)(x - 2)$

Step 4. Check by multiplying.

$$2(x^2 + 1)(x + 2)(x - 2) = 2(x^2 + 1)(x^2 - 4)$$
$$= 2(x^4 - 3x^2 - 4)$$
$$= 2x^4 - 6x^2 - 8$$

Section 6.6 Solving Quadratic Equations by Factoring

A **quadratic equation** is an equation that can be written in the form $ax^2 + bx + c = 0$ with a not 0.

The form $ax^2 + bx + c = 0$ is called the **standard form** of a quadratic equation.

Quadratic Equation	*Standard Form*
$x^2 = 16$	$x^2 - 16 = 0$
$y = -2y^2 + 5$	$2y^2 + y - 5 = 0$

Zero Factor Property

If a and b are real numbers and if $ab = 0$, then $a = 0$ or $b = 0$.

If $(x + 3)(x - 1) = 0$, then $x + 3 = 0$ or $x - 1 = 0$

To Solve Quadratic Equations by Factoring

Step 1. Write the equation in standard form: $ax^2 + bx + c = 0$.

Step 2. Factor the quadratic.

Step 3. Set each factor containing a variable equal to 0.

Step 4. Solve the equations.

Solve: $3x^2 = 13x - 4$

Step 1. $3x^2 - 13x + 4 = 0$

Step 2. $(3x - 1)(x - 4) = 0$

Step 3. $3x - 1 = 0$ or $x - 4 = 0$

Step 4. $3x = 1$ or $x = 4$

$$x = \frac{1}{3}$$

Step 5. Check in the original equation.

Step 5. Check both $\frac{1}{3}$ and 4 in the original equation.

Section 6.7 Quadratic Equations and Problem Solving

Problem-Solving Steps

A garden is in the shape of a rectangle whose length is two feet more than its width. If the area of the garden is 35 square feet, find its dimensions.

1. UNDERSTAND the problem.

1. Read and reread the problem. Guess a solution and check your guess.

Let x be the width of the rectangular garden. Then $x + 2$ is the length.

2. TRANSLATE.

2. In words:　　length　·　width　=　area

Translate:　　$(x + 2)$　·　x　=　35

DEFINITIONS AND CONCEPTS	EXAMPLES

Section 6.7   Quadratic Equations and Problem Solving (continued)

3. SOLVE.

4. INTERPRET.

3.
$$(x + 2)x = 35$$
$$x^2 + 2x - 35 = 0$$
$$(x - 5)(x + 7) = 0$$
$$x - 5 = 0 \quad \text{or} \quad x + 7 = 0$$
$$x = 5 \quad \text{or} \quad x = -7$$

4. Discard the solution of -7 since x represents width.

Check: If x is 5 feet then $x + 2 = 5 + 2 = 7$ feet. The area of a rectangle whose width is 5 feet and whose length is 7 feet is (5 feet)(7 feet) or 35 square feet.

State: The garden is 5 feet by 7 feet.

Chapter 6 **Review**

(6.1) *Complete the factoring.*

1. $6x^2 - 15x = 3x(\quad\quad)$

2. $2x^3y + 6x^2y^2 + 8xy^3 = 2xy(\quad\quad)$

Factor the GCF from each polynomial.

3. $20x^2 + 12x$

4. $6x^2y^2 - 3xy^3$

5. $3x(2x + 3) - 5(2x + 3)$

6. $5x(x + 1) - (x + 1)$

Factor each polynomial by grouping.

7. $3x^2 - 3x + 2x - 2$

8. $3a^2 + 9ab + 3b^2 + ab$

9. $10a^2 + 5ab + 7b^2 + 14ab$

10. $6x^2 + 10x - 3x - 5$

(6.2) *Factor each trinomial.*

11. $x^2 + 6x + 8$

12. $x^2 - 11x + 24$

13. $x^2 + x + 2$

14. $x^2 - x + 2$

15. $x^2 + 4xy - 12y^2$

16. $x^2 + 8xy + 15y^2$

17. $72 - 18x - 2x^2$

18. $32 + 12x - 4x^2$

19. $10a^3 - 110a^2 + 100a$

20. $5y^3 - 50y^2 + 120y$

21. To factor $x^2 + 2x - 48$, think of two numbers whose product is _____ and whose sum is _____.

22. What is the first step in factoring $3x^2 + 15x + 30$?

(6.3) *or* **(6.4)** *Factor each trinomial.*

23. $2x^2 + 13x + 6$

24. $4x^2 + 4x - 3$

25. $6x^2 + 5xy - 4y^2$

26. $18x^2 - 9xy - 20y^2$

27. $10y^3 + 25y^2 - 60y$

28. $60y^3 - 39y^2 + 6y$

29. $18x^2 - 60x + 50$

30. $4x^2 - 28xy + 49y^2$

(6.5) *Factor each binomial.*

31. $4x^2 - 9$

32. $9t^2 - 25s^2$

33. $16x^2 + y^2$

34. $x^3 - 8y^3$

35. $8x^3 + 27$

36. $2x^3 + 8x$

37. $54 - 2x^3y^3$

38. $9x^2 - 4y^2$

39. $16x^4 - 1$

40. $x^4 + 16$

(6.6) *Solve the following equations.*

41. $(x + 6)(x - 2) = 0$

42. $3x(x + 1)(7x - 2) = 0$

43. $4(5x + 1)(x + 3) = 0$

44. $x^2 + 8x + 7 = 0$

45. $x^2 - 2x - 24 = 0$

46. $x^2 + 10x = -25$

47. $x(x - 10) = -16$

48. $(3x - 1)(9x^2 - 6x + 1) = 0$

49. $56x^2 - 5x - 6 = 0$

50. $20x^2 - 7x - 6 = 0$

51. $5(3x + 2) = 4$

52. $6x^2 - 3x + 8 = 0$

53. $12 - 5t = -3$

54. $5x^3 + 20x^2 + 20x = 0$

55. $4t^3 - 5t^2 - 21t = 0$

56. Write a quadratic equation that has the two solutions 4 and 5.

(6.7) Use the given information to choose the correct dimensions.

△ **57.** The perimeter of a rectangle is 24 inches. The length is twice the width. Find the dimensions of the rectangle.

    a. 5 inches by 7 inches

    b. 5 inches by 10 inches

    c. 4 inches by 8 inches

    d. 2 inches by 10 inches

△ **58.** The area of a rectangle is 80 square meters. The length is one more than three times the width. Find the dimensions of the rectangle.

    a. 8 meters by 10 meters

    b. 4 meters by 13 meters

    c. 4 meters by 20 meters

    d. 5 meters by 16 meters

Use the given information to find the dimensions of each figure.

△ **59.** The *area* of the square is 81 square units. Find the length of a side.

x

△ **60.** The *perimeter* of the quadrilateral is 47 units. Find the lengths of the sides.

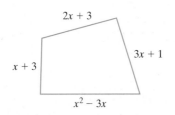

$2x + 3$

$3x + 1$

$x + 3$

$x^2 - 3x$

△ **61.** A flag for a local organization is in the shape of a rectangle whose length is 15 inches less than twice its width. If the area of the flag is 500 square inches, find its dimensions.

△ **62.** The base of a triangular sail is four times its height. If the area of the triangle is 162 square yards, find the base.

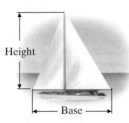

Height

Base

63. Find two consecutive positive integers whose product is 380.

64. Find two consecutive positive even integers whose product is 440.

65. A rocket is fired from the ground with an initial velocity of 440 feet per second. Its height h after t seconds is given by the equation

$$h = -16t^2 + 440t$$

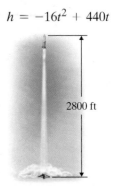

2800 ft

    a. Find how many seconds pass before the rocket reaches a height of 2800 feet. Explain why two answers are obtained.

    b. Find how many seconds pass before the rocket reaches the ground again.

△ **66.** An architect's squaring instrument is in the shape of a right triangle. Find the length of the longer leg of the right triangle if the hypotenuse is 8 centimeters longer than the longer leg and the shorter leg is 8 centimeters shorter than the longer leg.

MIXED REVIEW

Factor completely.

67. $7x - 63$

68. $11x(4x - 3) - 6(4x - 3)$

69. $m^2 - \dfrac{4}{25}$

70. $3x^3 - 4x^2 + 6x - 8$

71. $xy + 2x - y - 2$

72. $2x^2 + 2x - 24$

73. $3x^3 - 30x^2 + 27x$

74. $4x^2 - 81$

75. $2x^2 - 18$

76. $16x^2 - 24x + 9$

77. $5x^2 + 20x + 20$

78. $2x^2 + 5x - 12$

79. $4x^2y - 6xy^2$

80. $125x^3 + 27$

81. $24x^2 - 3x - 18$

82. $(x + 7)^2 - y^2$

83. $x^2(x + 3) - 4(x + 3)$

84. $54a^3b - 2b$

Write the perimeter of each figure as a simplified polynomial. Then factor each polynomial.

△ **85.**

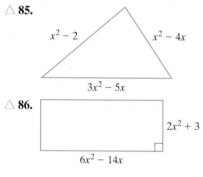

$x^2 - 2$ $x^2 - 4x$

$3x^2 - 5x$

△ **86.**

$2x^2 + 3$

$6x^2 - 14x$

Solve.

87. $2x^2 - x - 28 = 0$

88. $x^2 - 2x = 15$

89. $2x(x + 7)(x + 4) = 0$

90. $x(x - 5) = -6$

91. $x^2 = 16x$

Solve.

△ **92.** The perimeter of the following triangle is 48 inches. Find the lengths of its sides.

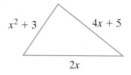

$x^2 + 3$ $4x + 5$

$2x$

93. The width of a rectangle is 4 inches less than its length. Its area is 12 square inches. Find the dimensions of the rectangle.

94. A 6-foot-tall person drops an object from the top of the Westin Peachtree Plaza in Atlanta, Georgia. The Westin building is 723 feet tall. (*Source: World Almanac* research) The height h of the object after t seconds is given by the equation $h = -16t^2 + 729$. Find how many seconds pass before the object reaches the ground.

723 ft

Write an expression for the area of the shaded region. Then write the expression as a factored polynomial.

△ **95.**

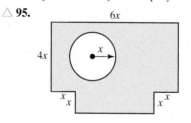

$6x$

$4x$

x

x x x x

1c

Chapter 6 Getting Ready for the Test

*All the exercises below are **Multiple Choice**. Choose the correct letter. Also, letters may be used more than once.*

▶ **1.** The greatest common factor of the terms of $10x^4 - 70x^3 + 2x^2 - 14x$ is

    A. $2x^2$ **B.** $2x$ **C.** $7x^2$ **D.** $7x$

▶ **2.** Choose the expression that is NOT a factored form of $9y^3 - 18y^2$.

    A. $9(y^3 - 2y^2)$ **B.** $9y(y^2 - 2y)$ **C.** $9y^2(y - 2)$ **D.** $9 \cdot y^3 - 18 \cdot y^2$

Identify each expression as:

    A. A factored expression or   **B.** Not a factored expression

▶ **3.** $(x - 1)(x + 5)$

▶ **4.** $z(z + 12)(z - 12)$

▶ **5.** $y(x - 6) + 1(x - 6)$

▶ **6.** $m \cdot m - 5 \cdot 5$

▶ 7. Choose the correct factored form for $4x^2 + 16$ or select "can't be factored."

   A. can't be factored   **B.** $4(x^2 + 4)$ **C.** $4(x + 2)^2$ **D.** $4(x + 2)(x - 2)$

▶ 8. Which of the binomials can't be factored using real numbers?

   A. $x^2 + 64$ **B.** $x^2 - 64$ **C.** $x^3 + 64$ **D.** $x^3 - 64$

▶ 9. To solve $x(x + 2) = 15$, which is an incorrect next step?

   A. $x^2 + 2x = 15$ **B.** $x(x + 2) - 15 = 0$ **C.** $x = 15$ and $x + 2 = 15$

Chapter 6 Test   MyMathLab®   YouTube™

Factor each polynomial completely. If a polynomial cannot be factored, write "prime."

▶ 1. $x^2 + 11x + 28$

▶ 2. $49 - m^2$

▶ 3. $y^2 + 22y + 121$

▶ 4. $4(a + 3) - y(a + 3)$

▶ 5. $x^2 + 4$

▶ 6. $y^2 - 8y - 48$

▶ 7. $x^2 + x - 10$

▶ 8. $9x^3 + 39x^2 + 12x$

▶ 9. $3a^2 + 3ab - 7a - 7b$

▶ 10. $3x^2 - 5x + 2$

▶ 11. $x^2 + 14xy + 24y^2$

▶ 12. $180 - 5x^2$

▶ 13. $6t^2 - t - 5$

▶ 14. $xy^2 - 7y^2 - 4x + 28$

▶ 15. $x - x^5$

▶ 16. $-xy^3 - x^3y$

▶ 17. $64x^3 - 1$

▶ 18. $8y^3 - 64$

Solve each equation.

▶ 19. $(x - 3)(x + 9) = 0$

▶ 20. $x^2 + 5x = 14$

▶ 21. $x(x + 6) = 7$

▶ 22. $3x(2x - 3)(3x + 4) = 0$

▶ 23. $5t^3 - 45t = 0$

▶ 24. $t^2 - 2t - 15 = 0$

▶ 25. $6x^2 = 15x$

Solve each problem.

▶ △ 26. A deck for a home is in the shape of a triangle. The length of the base of the triangle is 9 feet longer than its altitude. If the area of the triangle is 68 square feet, find the length of the base.

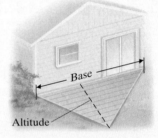

▶ 27. The sum of two numbers is 17 and the sum of their squares is 145. Find the numbers.

▶ 28. An object is dropped from the top of the Woolworth Building on Broadway in New York City. The height h of the object after t seconds is given by the equation

$$h = -16t^2 + 784$$

Find how many seconds pass before the object reaches the ground.

▶ △ 29. Find the lengths of the sides of a right triangle if the hypotenuse is 10 centimeters longer than the shorter leg and 5 centimeters longer than the longer leg.

Chapter 6 Cumulative Review

1. Translate each sentence into a mathematical statement.

   a. Nine is less than or equal to eleven.

   b. Eight is greater than one.

   c. Three is not equal to four.

2. Insert $<$ or $>$ in the space to make each statement true.

   a. $|-5|$ $|-3|$ **b.** $|0|$ $|-2|$

3. Simplify each fraction (write it in lowest terms).

   a. $\dfrac{42}{49}$ **b.** $\dfrac{11}{27}$ **c.** $\dfrac{88}{20}$

4. Evaluate $\dfrac{x}{y} + 5x$ if $x = 20$ and $y = 10$.

5. Simplify: $\dfrac{8 + 2 \cdot 3}{2^2 - 1}$

6. Evaluate $\dfrac{x}{y} + 5x$ if $x = -20$ and $y = 10$.

7. Add.

   a. $3 + (-7) + (-8)$

   b. $[7 + (-10)] + [-2 + |-4|]$

8. Evaluate $\dfrac{x}{y} + 5x$ if $x = -20$ and $y = -10$.

9. Multiply.
   a. $(-8)(4)$
   b. $14(-1)$
   c. $(-9)(-10)$

10. Simplify: $5 - 2(3x - 7)$

11. Simplify each expression by combining like terms.
    a. $7x - 3x$
    b. $10y^2 + y^2$
    c. $8x^2 + 2x - 3x$
    d. $9n^2 - 5n^2 + n^2$

12. Solve: $0.8y + 0.2(y - 1) = 1.8$

Solve.

13. $\dfrac{y}{7} = 20$

14. $\dfrac{x}{-7} = -4$

15. $-3x = 33$

16. $-\dfrac{2}{3}x = -22$

17. $8(2 - t) = -5t$

18. $-z = \dfrac{7z + 3}{5}$

19. Balsa wood sticks are commonly used to build models (for example, bridge models). A 48-inch balsa wood stick is to be cut into two pieces so that the longer piece is 3 times the shorter. Find the length of each piece.

20. Solve $3x + 9 \le 5(x - 1)$. Write the solution set using interval notation.

21. Graph the linear equation: $y = -\dfrac{1}{3}x + 2$

22. Is the ordered pair $(-1, 2)$ a solution of $-7x - 8y = -9$?

23. Find the slope and the y-intercept of the line whose equation is $3x - 4y = 4$.

24. Find the slope of the line through $(5, -6)$ and $(5, 2)$.

25. Evaluate each expression for the given value of x.
    a. $2x^3$; x is 5
    b. $\dfrac{9}{x^2}$; x is -3

26. Find the slope and y-intercept of the line whose equation is $7x - 3y = 2$.

27. Find the degree of each term.
    a. $3x^2$
    b. -2^3x^5
    c. y
    d. $12x^2yz^3$
    e. 5

28. Find an equation of the vertical line through $(0, 7)$.

29. Subtract: $(2x^3 + 8x^2 - 6x) - (2x^3 - x^2 + 1)$

30. Find an equation of the line with slope 4 and y-intercept $\left(0, \dfrac{1}{2}\right)$. Write the equation in standard form.

31. Multiply: $(3x + 2)(2x - 5)$

32. Write an equation of the line through $(-4, 0)$ and $(6, -1)$. Write the equation in standard form.

33. Multiply: $(3y + 1)^2$

34. Solve the system: $\begin{cases} -x + 3y = 18 \\ -3x + 2y = 19 \end{cases}$

35. Simplify by writing each expression with positive exponents only.
    a. 3^{-2}
    b. $2x^{-3}$
    c. $2^{-1} + 4^{-1}$
    d. $(-2)^{-4}$
    e. y^{-4}

36. Simplify: $\dfrac{(5a^7)^2}{a^5}$

37. Write each number in scientific notation.
    a. $367{,}000{,}000$
    b. 0.000003
    c. $20{,}520{,}000{,}000$
    d. 0.00085

38. Multiply: $(3x - 7y)^2$

39. Divide $x^2 + 7x + 12$ by $x + 3$ using long division.

40. Simplify: $\dfrac{(xy)^{-3}}{(x^5y^6)^3}$

41. Find the GCF of each list of terms.
    a. x^3, x^7, and x^5
    b. y, y^4, and y^7

Factor.

42. $z^3 + 7z + z^2 + 7$

43. $x^2 + 7x + 12$

44. $2x^3 + 2x^2 - 84x$

45. $8x^2 - 22x + 5$

46. $-4x^2 - 23x + 6$

47. $25a^2 - 9b^2$

48. $9xy^2 - 16x$

49. Solve: $(x - 3)(x + 1) = 0$

50. Solve: $x^2 - 13x = -36$

CHAPTER 7

Rational Expressions

7.1 Rational Functions and Simplifying Rational Expressions

7.2 Multiplying and Dividing Rational Expressions

7.3 Adding and Subtracting Rational Expressions with Common Denominators and Least Common Denominator

7.4 Adding and Subtracting Rational Expressions with Unlike Denominators

7.5 Solving Equations Containing Rational Expressions

Integrated Review—Summary on Rational Expressions

7.6 Proportion and Problem Solving with Rational Equations

7.7 Simplifying Complex Fractions

CHECK YOUR PROGRESS

Vocabulary Check
Chapter Highlights
Chapter Review
Getting Ready for the Test
Chapter Test
Cumulative Review

In this chapter, we expand our knowledge of algebraic expressions to include algebraic fractions, called *rational expressions*. We explore the operations of addition, subtraction, multiplication, and division using principles similar to the principles for numerical fractions.

Side Rear-View Mirror   Telescope   Magnifying Glass

Street Light Reflector   Sunglasses   Camera

What Do the Above Have in Common?

All the useful objects above contain convex mirrors or lenses or were made with convex mirrors or lenses. Basically, all of these objects were made using the rational equation below, called the Gaussian Mirror/Lens Formula. This equation or formula relates an object distance and image distance to the focal length. In general, the focal length is a measure of how strongly a lens converges or diverges light.

Of course, this is just one equation containing rational expressions. There are uses of rational expressions everywhere from health to sports statistics to driving safety. For some applications, see Section 7.1, Exercises 59 through 66, and Section 7.5, Exercises 43 through 52.

Gaussian Mirror/Lens Formula

$$\frac{1}{o} + \frac{1}{i} = \frac{1}{f}$$

$$\frac{1}{\text{object distance}} + \frac{1}{\text{image distance}} = \frac{1}{\text{focal length}}$$

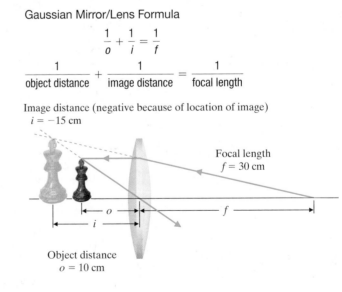

Image distance (negative because of location of image)
$i = -15$ cm

Focal length
$f = 30$ cm

Object distance
$o = 10$ cm

7.1 | Rational Functions and Simplifying Rational Expressions ▶

OBJECTIVES

1 Find the Domain of a Rational Function. ▶

2 Simplify or Write Rational Expressions in Lowest Terms. ▶

3 Write Equivalent Rational Expressions of the Form $-\dfrac{a}{b} = \dfrac{-a}{b} = \dfrac{a}{-b}$. ▶

4 Use Rational Functions in Applications. ▶

As we reviewed in Chapter 1, a rational number is a number that can be written as a quotient of integers. A **rational expression** is also a quotient; it is a quotient of polynomials.

> **Rational Expression**
>
> A rational expression is an expression that can be written in the form
> $$\frac{P}{Q},$$
> where P and Q are polynomials and $Q \neq 0$.

Rational Expressions

$$-\frac{2}{7} \qquad \frac{3y^3}{8} \qquad \frac{-4p}{p^3 + 2p + 1} \qquad \frac{5x^2 - 3x + 2}{3x + 7}$$

The first rational expression (or fraction) above is $-\dfrac{2}{7}$. For a negative fraction such as $-\dfrac{2}{7}$, recall from Section 1.7 that

$$-\frac{2}{7} = \frac{2}{-7} = \frac{-2}{7}$$

In general, for any fraction,

> $$\frac{-a}{b} = \frac{a}{-b} = -\frac{a}{b}, \qquad b \neq 0$$

This is also true for rational expressions. For example,

$$\underbrace{\frac{-(x + 2)}{x}}_{\uparrow} = \frac{x + 2}{-x} = -\frac{x + 2}{x}$$

Notice the parentheses.

Rational expressions are sometimes used to describe functions. For example, we call the function $f(x) = \dfrac{x^2 + 2}{x - 3}$ a **rational function** since $\dfrac{x^2 + 2}{x - 3}$ is a rational expression.

OBJECTIVE

1 **Finding the Domain of a Rational Function** ▶

As with fractions, a rational expression is **undefined** if the denominator is 0. If a variable in a rational expression is replaced with a number that makes the denominator 0, we say that the rational expression is **undefined** for this value of the variable. For example, the rational expression $\dfrac{x^2 + 2}{x - 3}$ is undefined when x is 3, because replacing x with 3 results in a denominator of 0. For this reason, we must exclude 3 from the domain of the function $f(x) = \dfrac{x^2 + 2}{x - 3}$.

The domain of f is then

$$\{x \mid x \text{ is a real number and } x \neq 3\}$$

"The set of all x such that x is a real number and x is not equal to 3."

In this section, we will use this set builder notation to write domains. Unless told otherwise, we assume that the domain of a function described by an equation is the set of all real numbers for which the equation is defined.

EXAMPLE 1 Find the domain of each rational function.

a. $f(x) = \dfrac{8x^3 + 7x^2 + 20}{2}$ **b.** $g(x) = \dfrac{5x^2 - 3}{x - 1}$ **c.** $f(x) = \dfrac{7x - 2}{x^2 - 2x - 15}$

Solution The domain of each function will contain all real numbers except those values that make the denominator 0.

a. No matter what the value of x, the denominator of $f(x) = \dfrac{8x^3 + 7x^2 + 20}{2}$ is never 0, so the domain of f is $\{x \mid x \text{ is a real number}\}$.

b. To find the values of x that make the denominator of $g(x)$ equal to 0, we solve the equation "denominator = 0":

$$x - 1 = 0, \quad \text{or} \quad x = 1$$

The domain must exclude 1 since the rational expression is undefined when x is 1. The domain of g is $\{x \mid x \text{ is a real number and } x \neq 1\}$.

c. We find the domain by setting the denominator equal to 0.

$$x^2 - 2x - 15 = 0 \quad \text{Set the denominator equal to 0 and solve.}$$
$$(x - 5)(x + 3) = 0$$
$$x - 5 = 0 \quad \text{or} \quad x + 3 = 0$$
$$x = 5 \quad \text{or} \quad x = -3$$

If x is replaced with 5 or with -3, the rational expression is undefined. The domain of f is $\{x \mid x \text{ is a real number and } x \neq 5, x \neq -3\}$. ☐

PRACTICE

1 Find the domain of each rational function.

a. $f(x) = \dfrac{4x^5 - 3x^2 + 2}{-6}$ **b.** $g(x) = \dfrac{6x^2 + 1}{x + 3}$ **c.** $h(x) = \dfrac{8x - 3}{x^2 - 5x + 6}$ ∎

✔ **CONCEPT CHECK**

For which of these values (if any) is the rational expression $\dfrac{x - 3}{x^2 + 2}$ undefined?

a. 2   **b.** 3   **c.** -2 **d.** 0   **e.** None of these

OBJECTIVE

2 Simplifying Rational Expressions ▶

Recall that a fraction is in lowest terms or simplest form if the numerator and denominator have no common factors other than 1 (or -1). For example, $\dfrac{3}{13}$ is in lowest terms since 3 and 13 have no common factors other than 1 (or -1).

To **simplify** a rational expression, or to write it in lowest terms, we use a method similar to simplifying a fraction.

Recall that to simplify a fraction, we essentially "remove factors of 1." Our ability to do this comes from these facts:

- If $c \neq 0$, then $\dfrac{c}{c} = 1$. For example, $\dfrac{7}{7} = 1$ and $\dfrac{-8.65}{-8.65} = 1$.

- $n \cdot 1 = n$. For example, $-5 \cdot 1 = -5$, $126.8 \cdot 1 = 126.8$, and $\dfrac{a}{b} \cdot 1 = \dfrac{a}{b}, b \neq 0$.

In other words, we have the following:

$$\frac{a \cdot c}{b \cdot c} = \frac{a}{b} \cdot \frac{c}{c} = \frac{a}{b}$$

$$\text{Since } \frac{a}{b} \cdot 1 = \frac{a}{b}$$

Let's practice simplifying a fraction by simplifying $\frac{15}{65}$.

$$\frac{15}{65} = \frac{3 \cdot 5}{13 \cdot 5} = \frac{3}{13} \cdot \frac{5}{5} = \frac{3}{13} \cdot 1 = \frac{3}{13}$$

Let's use the same technique and simplify the rational expression $\frac{x^2 - 9}{x^2 + x - 6}$.

$$\frac{x^2 - 9}{x^2 + x - 6} = \frac{(x - 3)(x + 3)}{(x - 2)(x + 3)} \qquad \text{Factor the numerator and the denominator.}$$

$$= \frac{(x - 3)\,(x + 3)}{(x - 2)\,(x + 3)} \qquad \text{Look for common factors.}$$

$$= \frac{x - 3}{x - 2} \cdot \frac{x + 3}{x + 3}$$

$$= \frac{x - 3}{x - 2} \cdot 1 \qquad \text{Write } \frac{x + 3}{x + 3} \text{ as 1.}$$

$$= \frac{x - 3}{x - 2} \qquad \text{Multiply to remove a factor of 1.}$$

This "removing a factor of 1" is stated in the principle below:

Fundamental Principle of Rational Expressions

For any rational expression $\frac{P}{Q}$ and any polynomial R, where $R \neq 0$,

$$\frac{PR}{QR} = \frac{P}{Q} \cdot \frac{R}{R} = \frac{P}{Q} \cdot 1 = \frac{P}{Q}$$

or, simply,

$$\frac{PR}{QR} = \frac{P}{Q}$$

In general, the following steps may be used to simplify rational expressions or to write a rational expression in lowest terms.

Simplifying or Writing a Rational Expression in Lowest Terms

Step 1. Completely factor the numerator and denominator of the rational expression.

Step 2. Divide out factors common to the numerator and denominator. (This is the same as "removing a factor of 1.")

For now, we assume that variables in a rational expression do not represent values that make the denominator 0.

EXAMPLE 2   Simplify each rational expression.

a. $\dfrac{2x^2}{10x^3 - 2x^2}$

b. $\dfrac{9x^2 + 13x + 4}{8x^2 + x - 7}$

(Continued on next page)

Solution

a. $\dfrac{2x^2}{10x^3 - 2x^2} = \dfrac{2x^2 \cdot 1}{2x^2(5x - 1)} = 1 \cdot \dfrac{1}{5x - 1} = \dfrac{1}{5x - 1}$

b. $\dfrac{9x^2 + 13x + 4}{8x^2 + x - 7} = \dfrac{(9x + 4)(x + 1)}{(8x - 7)(x + 1)}$ Factor the numerator and denominator.

$= \dfrac{9x + 4}{8x - 7} \cdot 1$ Since $\dfrac{x + 1}{x + 1} = 1$

$= \dfrac{9x + 4}{8x - 7}$ Simplest form □

PRACTICE

2 Simplify each rational expression.

a. $\dfrac{5z^4}{10z^5 - 5z^4}$

b. $\dfrac{5x^2 + 13x + 6}{6x^2 + 7x - 10}$ ∎

Just as for numerical fractions, we can use a shortcut notation. Remember that as long as exact factors in both the numerator and denominator are divided out, we are "removing a factor of 1." We will use the following notation to show this:

$\dfrac{x^2 - 9}{x^2 + x - 6} = \dfrac{(x - 3)(x + 3)}{(x - 2)(x + 3)}$ A factor of 1 is identified by the shading.

$= \dfrac{x - 3}{x - 2}$ Remove a factor of 1.

Thus, the rational expression $\dfrac{x^2 - 9}{x^2 + x - 6}$ has the same value as the rational expression $\dfrac{x - 3}{x - 2}$ for all values of x except 2 and -3. (Remember that when x is 2, the denominator of both rational expressions is 0 and when x is -3, the original rational expression has a denominator of 0.)

As we simplify rational expressions, we will assume that the simplified rational expression is equal to the original rational expression for all real numbers except those for which the original denominator is 0.

EXAMPLE 3 Simplify each rational expression.

a. $\dfrac{2 + x}{x + 2}$

b. $\dfrac{2 - x}{x - 2}$

Solution

a. $\dfrac{2 + x}{x + 2} = \dfrac{x + 2}{x + 2} = 1$ By the commutative property of addition, $2 + x = x + 2$.

b. $\dfrac{2 - x}{x - 2}$

The terms in the numerator of $\dfrac{2 - x}{x - 2}$ differ by sign from the terms of the denominator, so the polynomials are opposites of each other and the expression simplifies to -1. To see this, we factor out -1 from the numerator or the denominator. If -1 is factored from the numerator, then

$$\dfrac{2 - x}{x - 2} = \dfrac{-1(-2 + x)}{x - 2} = \dfrac{-1(x - 2)}{x - 2} = \dfrac{-1}{1} = -1$$

If -1 is factored from the denominator, the result is the same.

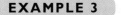

$$\dfrac{2 - x}{x - 2} = \dfrac{2 - x}{-1(-x + 2)} = \dfrac{2 - x}{-1(2 - x)} = \dfrac{1}{-1} = -1$$ □

Helpful Hint

When the numerator and the denominator of a rational expression are opposites of each other, the expression simplifies to -1.

PRACTICE
3   Simplify each rational expression.

a. $\dfrac{x + 3}{3 + x}$ b. $\dfrac{3 - x}{x - 3}$

EXAMPLE 4   Simplify: $\dfrac{18 - 2x^2}{x^2 - 2x - 3}$

Solution

$$\dfrac{18 - 2x^2}{x^2 - 2x - 3} = \dfrac{2(9 - x^2)}{(x + 1)(x - 3)}$$ Factor.

$$= \dfrac{2(3 + x)(3 - x)}{(x + 1)(x - 3)}$$ Factor completely.

$$= \dfrac{2(3 + x) \cdot -1\,(x - 3)}{(x + 1)\,(x - 3)}$$ Notice the opposites $3 - x$ and $x - 3$. Write $3 - x$ as $-1(x - 3)$ and simplify.

$$= -\dfrac{2(3 + x)}{x + 1}$$

PRACTICE
4   Simplify: $\dfrac{20 - 5x^2}{x^2 + x - 6}$

> **Helpful Hint**
>
> When simplifying a rational expression, we look for **common** *factors,* **not common** *terms.*
>
> $\dfrac{x \cdot (x + 2)}{x \cdot x} = \dfrac{x + 2}{x}$ $\dfrac{x + 2}{x}$
>
> Common factors. These   Common terms. There is
> can be divided out.   no factor of 1 that can be
>   generated.

✔ **CONCEPT CHECK**

Recall that we can only remove *factors* of 1. Which of the following are *not* true? Explain why.

a. $\dfrac{3 - 1}{3 + 5}$ simplifies to $-\dfrac{1}{5}$.   b. $\dfrac{2x + 10}{2}$ simplifies to $x + 5$.

c. $\dfrac{37}{72}$ simplifies to $\dfrac{3}{2}$.   d. $\dfrac{2x + 3}{2}$ simplifies to $x + 3$.

EXAMPLE 5   Simplify each rational expression.

a. $\dfrac{x^3 + 8}{2 + x}$ b. $\dfrac{2y^2 + 2}{y^3 - 5y^2 + y - 5}$

Solution

a. $\dfrac{x^3 + 8}{2 + x} = \dfrac{(x + 2)(x^2 - 2x + 4)}{x + 2}$ Factor the sum of the two cubes.

$$= x^2 - 2x + 4$$ Divide out common factors.

b. $\dfrac{2y^2 + 2}{y^3 - 5y^2 + y - 5} = \dfrac{2(y^2 + 1)}{(y^3 - 5y^2) + (y - 5)}$ Factor the numerator; group the denominator.

$$= \dfrac{2(y^2 + 1)}{y^2(y - 5) + 1(y - 5)}$$ Factor the denominator by grouping.

$$= \dfrac{2\,(y^2 + 1)}{(y - 5)\,(y^2 + 1)}$$

$$= \dfrac{2}{y - 5}$$ Divide out common factors.

(Continued on the next page)

PRACTICE
5 Simplify each rational expression.

a. $\dfrac{x^3 + 64}{4 + x}$

b. $\dfrac{5z^2 + 10}{z^3 - 3z^2 + 2z - 6}$

✔ **CONCEPT CHECK**

Does $\dfrac{n}{n+2}$ simplify to $\dfrac{1}{2}$? Why or why not?

OBJECTIVE

3 Writing Equivalent Forms of Rational Expressions ▶

From Example 3, we have

$$\frac{2+x}{x+2} = \frac{x+2}{x+2} = 1 \quad \text{and} \quad \frac{2-x}{x-2} = \frac{2-x}{-1(2-x)} = \frac{1}{-1} = -1.$$

When performing operations on rational expressions, equivalent forms of answers often result. For this reason, it is very important to be able to recognize equivalent answers.

EXAMPLE 6 List some equivalent forms of $-\dfrac{5x-1}{x+9}$.

<u>Solution</u> To do so, recall that $-\dfrac{a}{b} = \dfrac{-a}{b} = \dfrac{a}{-b}$. Thus

$$-\frac{5x-1}{x+9} = \frac{-(5x-1)}{x+9} = \frac{-5x+1}{x+9} \quad \text{or} \quad \frac{1-5x}{x+9}$$

Also,

$$-\frac{5x-1}{x+9} = \frac{5x-1}{-(x+9)} = \frac{5x-1}{-x-9} \quad \text{or} \quad \frac{5x-1}{-9-x}$$

Thus $-\dfrac{5x-1}{x+9} = \dfrac{-(5x-1)}{x+9} = \dfrac{-5x+1}{x+9} = \dfrac{5x-1}{-(x+9)} = \dfrac{5x-1}{-x-9}$ □

> **Helpful Hint**
>
> Remember, a negative sign in front of a fraction or rational expression may be moved to the numerator or the denominator, but *not* both.

PRACTICE
6 List some equivalent forms of $-\dfrac{x+3}{6x-11}$.

Keep in mind that many rational expressions may look different, but in fact be equivalent.

OBJECTIVE

4 Using Rational Functions in Applications ▶

Rational functions occur often in real-life situations.

EXAMPLE 7 Cost for Pressing Compact Discs

For the ICL Production Company, the rational function $C(x) = \dfrac{2.6x + 10{,}000}{x}$ describes the company's cost per disc of pressing x compact discs. Find the cost per disc for pressing:

a. 100 compact discs

b. 1000 compact discs

Solution

a. $C(100) = \dfrac{2.6(100) + 10,000}{100} = \dfrac{10,260}{100} = 102.6$

The cost per disc for pressing 100 compact discs is $102.60.

b. $C(1000) = \dfrac{2.6(1000) + 10,000}{1000} = \dfrac{12,600}{1000} = 12.6$

The cost per disc for pressing 1000 compact discs is $12.60. Notice that as more compact discs are produced, the cost per disc decreases. □

PRACTICE
7   A company's cost per tee shirt for silk screening x tee shirts is given by the rational function $C(x) = \dfrac{3.2x + 400}{x}$. Find the cost per tee shirt for printing:

a. 100 tee shirts   **b.** 1000 tee shirts ∎

Graphing Calculator Explorations

(Note: The information below about *connected* mode and *dot* mode may not apply to your graphing calculator.)

Recall that since the rational expression $\dfrac{7x - 2}{(x - 2)(x + 5)}$ is not defined when $x = 2$ or when $x = -5$, we say that the domain of the rational function $f(x) = \dfrac{7x - 2}{(x - 2)(x + 5)}$ is all real numbers except 2 and -5. This domain can be written as $\{x \mid x$ is a real number and $x \neq 2, x \neq -5\}$. This means that the graph of $f(x)$ should not cross the vertical lines $x = 2$ and $x = -5$. The graph of $f(x)$ in *connected* mode is to the left. In connected mode the graphing calculator tries to connect all dots of the graph so that the result is a smooth curve. This is what has happened in the graph. Notice that the graph appears to contain vertical lines at $x = 2$ and at $x = -5$. We know that this cannot happen because the function is not defined at $x = 2$ and at $x = -5$. We also know that this cannot happen because the graph of this function would not pass the vertical line test.

The graph of $f(x)$ in *dot* mode is to the left. In dot mode the graphing calculator will not connect dots with a smooth curve. Notice that the vertical lines have disappeared, and we have a better picture of the graph. The graph, however, actually appears more like the hand-drawn graph below. By using a Table feature, a Calculate Value feature, or by tracing, we can see that the function is not defined at $x = 2$ and at $x = -5$.

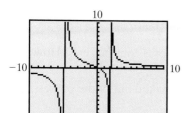

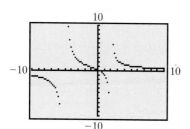

Find the domain of each rational function. Then graph each rational function and use the graph to confirm the domain.

1. $f(x) = \dfrac{x + 1}{x^2 - 4}$

2. $g(x) = \dfrac{5x}{x^2 - 9}$

3. $h(x) = \dfrac{x^2}{2x^2 + 7x - 4}$

4. $f(x) = \dfrac{3x + 2}{4x^2 - 19x - 5}$

✔ **Vocabulary, Readiness & Video Check**

Use the choices below to fill in each blank. Some choices may not be used.

1	true	rational	simplified	$\dfrac{-a}{-b}$	$\dfrac{-a}{b}$	$\dfrac{a}{-b}$
−1	false	domain	0			

1. A _____ expression is an expression that can be written as the quotient $\dfrac{P}{Q}$ of two polynomials P and Q as long as $Q \neq 0$.

2. A rational expression is undefined if the denominator is _____.

3. The _____ of the rational function $f(x) = \dfrac{2}{x}$ is $\{x \mid x \text{ is a real number and } x \neq 0\}$.

4. A rational expression is _____ if the numerator and denominator have no common factors other than 1 or −1.

5. The expression $\dfrac{x^2 + 2}{2 + x^2}$ simplifies to _____.

6. The expression $\dfrac{y - z}{z - y}$ simplifies to _____.

7. For a rational expression, $-\dfrac{a}{b} = $ _____ $= $ _____.

8. True or false: $\dfrac{a - 6}{a + 2} = \dfrac{-(a - 6)}{-(a + 2)} = \dfrac{-a + 6}{-a - 2}$. _____

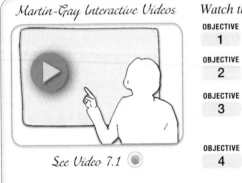

Martin-Gay Interactive Videos

See Video 7.1 ⦿

Watch the section lecture video and answer the following questions.

OBJECTIVE
1
9. Why can't the denominators of rational expressions be zero? How can we find the domain of a rational function?

OBJECTIVE
2
10. In ▦ Example 6, why isn't a factor of x divided out of the expression at the end?

OBJECTIVE
3
11. From ▦ Example 8, if we move a negative sign from in front of a rational expression to either the numerator or denominator, when do we insert parentheses and why?

OBJECTIVE
4
12. From ▦ Example 9, why do we subtract parts a. and b. to find the answer to part c.?

7.1 **Exercise Set** MyMathLab® ▶

Find the domain of each rational expression. See Example 1.

1. $f(x) = \dfrac{5x - 7}{4}$

2. $g(x) = \dfrac{4 - 3x}{2}$

3. $s(t) = \dfrac{t^2 + 1}{2t}$

4. $v(t) = -\dfrac{5t + t^2}{3t}$

▶ **5.** $f(x) = \dfrac{3x}{7 - x}$

6. $f(x) = \dfrac{-4x}{-2 + x}$

7. $f(x) = \dfrac{x}{3x - 1}$

8. $g(x) = \dfrac{-2}{2x + 5}$

9. $R(x) = \dfrac{3 + 2x}{x^3 + x^2 - 2x}$

10. $h(x) = \dfrac{5 - 3x}{2x^2 - 14x + 20}$

▶ **11.** $C(x) = \dfrac{x + 3}{x^2 - 4}$

12. $R(x) = \dfrac{5}{x^2 - 7x}$

Study Example 6. Then list four equivalent forms for each rational expression.

13. $-\dfrac{x - 10}{x + 8}$

▶ **14.** $-\dfrac{x + 11}{x - 4}$

15. $-\dfrac{5y - 3}{y - 12}$

16. $-\dfrac{8y - 1}{y - 15}$

MIXED PRACTICE

Simplify each expression. See Examples 2 through 5.

▶ **17.** $\dfrac{x + 7}{7 + x}$

18. $\dfrac{y + 9}{9 + y}$

▶ **19.** $\dfrac{x - 7}{7 - x}$

20. $\dfrac{y - 9}{9 - y}$

21. $\dfrac{2}{8x + 16}$

22. $\dfrac{3}{9x + 6}$

▶ **23.** $\dfrac{-5a - 5b}{a + b}$

24. $\dfrac{-4x - 4y}{x + y}$

25. $\dfrac{7x + 35}{x^2 + 5x}$

26. $\dfrac{9x + 99}{x^2 + 11x}$

27. $\dfrac{x + 5}{x^2 - 4x - 45}$

28. $\dfrac{x - 3}{x^2 - 6x + 9}$

29. $\dfrac{5x^2 + 11x + 2}{x + 2}$

30. $\dfrac{12x^2 + 4x - 1}{2x + 1}$

▶ **31.** $\dfrac{x^3 + 7x^2}{x^2 + 5x - 14}$

32. $\dfrac{x^4 - 10x^3}{x^2 - 17x + 70}$

33. $\dfrac{2x^2 - 8}{4x - 8}$

34. $\dfrac{5x^2 - 500}{35x + 350}$

▶ **35.** $\dfrac{4 - x^2}{x - 2}$

36. $\dfrac{49 - y^2}{y - 7}$

37. $\dfrac{11x^2 - 22x^3}{6x - 12x^2}$

38. $\dfrac{24y^2 - 8y^3}{15y - 5y^2}$

39. $\dfrac{x^2 + xy + 2x + 2y}{x + 2}$

40. $\dfrac{ab + ac + b^2 + bc}{b + c}$

41. $\dfrac{x^3 + 8}{x + 2}$

42. $\dfrac{x^3 + 64}{x + 4}$

43. $\dfrac{x^3 - 1}{1 - x}$

44. $\dfrac{3 - x}{x^3 - 27}$

45. $\dfrac{2xy + 5x - 2y - 5}{3xy + 4x - 3y - 4}$

46. $\dfrac{2xy + 2x - 3y - 3}{2xy + 4x - 3y - 6}$

47. $\dfrac{3x^2 - 5x - 2}{6x^3 + 2x^2 + 3x + 1}$

48. $\dfrac{2x^2 - x - 3}{2x^3 - 3x^2 + 2x - 3}$

49. $\dfrac{9x^2 - 15x + 25}{27x^3 + 125}$

50. $\dfrac{8x^3 - 27}{4x^2 + 6x + 9}$

MIXED PRACTICE

Simplify each expression. Then determine whether the given answer is correct. See Examples 3 through 6.

51. $\dfrac{9 - x^2}{x - 3}$; Answer: $-3 - x$

52. $\dfrac{100 - x^2}{x - 10}$; Answer: $-10 - x$

53. $\dfrac{7 - 34x - 5x^2}{25x^2 - 1}$; Answer: $\dfrac{x + 7}{-5x - 1}$

54. $\dfrac{2 - 15x - 8x^2}{64x^2 - 1}$; Answer: $\dfrac{x + 2}{-8x - 1}$

Find each function value. See Example 7.

55. If $f(x) = \dfrac{x + 8}{2x - 1}$, find $f(2), f(0),$ and $f(-1)$.

56. If $f(x) = \dfrac{x - 2}{-5 + x}$, find $f(-5), f(0),$ and $f(10)$.

57. If $g(x) = \dfrac{x^2 + 8}{x^3 - 25x}$, find $g(3), g(-2),$ and $g(1)$.

58. If $s(t) = \dfrac{t^3 + 1}{t^2 + 1}$, find $s(-1), s(1),$ and $s(2)$.

Solve. See Example 7.

▶ **59.** The total revenue from the sale of a popular book is approximated by the rational function $R(x) = \dfrac{1000x^2}{x^2 + 4}$, where x is the number of years since publication and $R(x)$ is the total revenue in millions of dollars.

   a. Find the total revenue at the end of the first year.

   b. Find the total revenue at the end of the second year.

   c. Find the revenue during the second year only.

   d. Find the domain of function R.

60. The function $f(x) = \dfrac{100,000x}{100 - x}$ models the cost in dollars for removing x percent of the pollutants from a bayou in which a nearby company dumped creosol.

   a. Find the cost of removing 20% of the pollutants from the bayou. [*Hint:* Find $f(20)$.]

   b. Find the cost of removing 60% of the pollutants and then 80% of the pollutants.

   c. Find $f(90)$, then $f(95)$, and then $f(99)$. What happens to the cost as x approaches 100%?

   d. Find the domain of function f.

61. The dose of medicine prescribed for a child depends on the child's age A in years and the adult dose D for the medication. Young's Rule is a formula used by pediatricians that gives a child's dose C as

$$C = \frac{DA}{A + 12}$$

Suppose that an 8-year-old child needs medication, and the normal adult dose is 1000 mg. What size dose should the child receive?

62. Calculating body-mass index is a way to gauge whether a person should lose weight. Doctors recommend that body-mass index values fall between 18.5 and 25. The formula for body-mass index B is

$$B = \frac{703w}{h^2}$$

where w is weight in pounds and h is height in inches. Should a 148-pound person who is 5 feet 6 inches tall lose weight?

63. Anthropologists and forensic scientists use a measure called the cephalic index to help classify skulls. The cephalic index of a skull with width W and length L from front to back is given by the formula

$$C = \frac{100W}{L}$$

A long skull has an index value less than 75, a medium skull has an index value between 75 and 85, and a broad skull has an index value over 85. Find the cephalic index of a skull that is 5 inches wide and 6.4 inches long. Classify the skull.

64. A company's gross profit margin P can be computed with the formula $P = \dfrac{R - C}{R}$, where R = the company's revenue and C = cost of goods sold. During a recent fiscal year, computer company Apple had revenues of $32.5 billion and cost of goods sold $21.3 billion. (*Source:* Apple, Inc.) What was Apple's gross profit margin in this year? Express the answer as a percent, rounded to the nearest tenth of a percent.

65. A baseball player's slugging average S can be calculated with the following formula:

$$S = \frac{h + d + 2t + 3r}{b}, \text{ where } h = \text{number of hits,}$$

d = number of doubles, t = number of triples, r = number of home runs, and b = number of at bats. In 2014, Jose Abreu of the Chicago White Sox led Major League Baseball in slugging average. During the 2014 season, Abreu had 556 at bats, 176 hits, 35 doubles, 2 triples, and 36 home runs. (*Source:* Major League Baseball) Calculate Abreu's slugging average. Round to three decimal places.

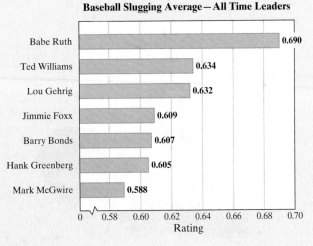

Baseball Slugging Average—All Time Leaders

Babe Ruth	0.690
Ted Williams	0.634
Lou Gehrig	0.632
Jimmie Foxx	0.609
Barry Bonds	0.607
Hank Greenberg	0.605
Mark McGwire	0.588

Rating: 0.58 0.60 0.62 0.64 0.66 0.68 0.70

Source: Baseball Almanac

66. To calculate a quarterback's rating in NCAA football, you may use the formula $\dfrac{100C + 330T - 200I + 8.4Y}{A}$, where C = the number of completed passes, A = the number of attempted passes, T = the number of touchdown passes, Y = the number of yards in the completed passes, and I = the number of interceptions. Marcus Mariota of the Oregon Ducks was selected as the 2014 winner of the Heisman Memorial Trophy as the Most Outstanding Football Player. Mariota, a junior quarterback, ended the season with 445 attempts, 304 completions, 4454 yards, 42 touchdowns, and only 4 interceptions. Calculate Mariota's quarterback rating for the 2014 season. (*Source:* NCAA) Round the answer to the nearest tenth.

REVIEW AND PREVIEW

Perform each indicated operation. See Section 1.3.

67. $\dfrac{1}{3} \cdot \dfrac{9}{11}$

68. $\dfrac{5}{27} \cdot \dfrac{2}{5}$

69. $\dfrac{1}{3} \div \dfrac{1}{4}$

70. $\dfrac{7}{8} \div \dfrac{1}{2}$

71. $\dfrac{13}{20} \div \dfrac{2}{9}$

72. $\dfrac{8}{15} \div \dfrac{5}{8}$

CONCEPT EXTENSIONS

Which of the following are incorrect and why? See the second Concept Check in this section.

73. $\dfrac{5a - 15}{5}$ simplifies to $a - 3$?

74. $\dfrac{7m - 9}{7}$ simplifies to $m - 9$?

75. $\dfrac{1 + 2}{1 + 3}$ simplifies to $\dfrac{2}{3}$?

76. $\dfrac{46}{54}$ simplifies to $\dfrac{6}{5}$?

Determine whether each rational expression can be simplified. If yes, does it simplify to 1, −1, or neither? (Do not actually simplify.)

77. $\dfrac{x}{x + 7}$

78. $\dfrac{x + 9}{x - 9}$

79. $\dfrac{3 + x}{x + 3}$

80. $\dfrac{8 + x}{x + 8}$

81. $\dfrac{5 - x}{x - 5}$

82. $\dfrac{x - 7}{-x + 7}$

83. Does $\dfrac{x}{x + 5}$ simplify to $\dfrac{1}{5}$? Why or why not?

84. Does $\dfrac{x + 7}{x}$ simplify to 7? Why or why not?

85. In your own words explain how to simplify a rational expression.

86. In your own words, explain how to find the domain of a rational function.

87. Graph a portion of the function $f(x) = \dfrac{20x}{100 - x}$. To do so, complete the given table, plot the points, and then connect the plotted points with a smooth curve. (*Note:* The domain of this function is all real numbers except 100. We are graphing just a portion of this function.)

x	0	10	30	50	70	90	95	99
y or $f(x)$								

88. The domain of the function $f(x) = \dfrac{1}{x}$ is all real numbers except 0. This means that the graph of this function will be in two pieces: one piece corresponding to x values less than 0 and one piece corresponding to x values greater than 0. Graph the function by completing the following tables, separately plotting the points, and connecting each set of plotted points with a smooth curve.

x	$\dfrac{1}{4}$	$\dfrac{1}{2}$	1	2	4
y or $f(x)$					

x	-4	-2	-1	$-\dfrac{1}{2}$	$-\dfrac{1}{4}$
y or $f(x)$					

How does the graph of $y = \dfrac{x^2 - 9}{x - 3}$ compare to the graph of $y = x + 3$? Recall that $\dfrac{x^2 - 9}{x - 3} = \dfrac{(x + 3)(x - 3)}{x - 3} = x + 3$ as

long as x is not 3. This means that the graph of $y = \dfrac{x^2 - 9}{x - 3}$ is the same as the graph of $y = x + 3$ with $x \neq 3$. To graph $y = \dfrac{x^2 - 9}{x - 3}$, then, graph the linear equation $y = x + 3$ and place an open dot on the graph at 3. This open dot or interruption of the line at 3 means $x \neq 3$.

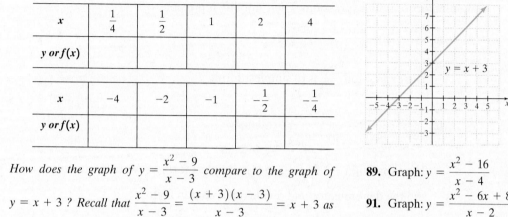

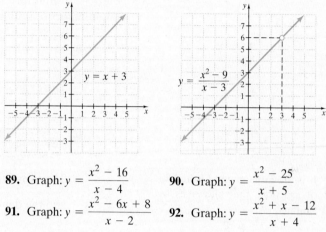

89. Graph: $y = \dfrac{x^2 - 16}{x - 4}$

90. Graph: $y = \dfrac{x^2 - 25}{x + 5}$

91. Graph: $y = \dfrac{x^2 - 6x + 8}{x - 2}$

92. Graph: $y = \dfrac{x^2 + x - 12}{x + 4}$

7.2 Multiplying and Dividing Rational Expressions ▶

OBJECTIVES

1 Multiply Rational Expressions. ▶

2 Divide Rational Expressions. ▶

3 Multiply or Divide Rational Expressions. ▶

4 Convert between Units of Measure. ▶

OBJECTIVE

1   Multiplying Rational Expressions ▶

Just as simplifying rational expressions is similar to simplifying number fractions, multiplying and dividing rational expressions is similar to multiplying and dividing number fractions.

Fractions	*Rational Expressions*
Multiply: $\dfrac{3}{5} \cdot \dfrac{10}{11}$	Multiply: $\dfrac{x - 3}{x + 5} \cdot \dfrac{2x + 10}{x^2 - 9}$

Multiply numerators and multiply denominators.

$$\dfrac{3}{5} \cdot \dfrac{10}{11} = \dfrac{3 \cdot 10}{5 \cdot 11} \qquad \dfrac{x - 3}{x + 5} \cdot \dfrac{2x + 10}{x^2 - 9} = \dfrac{(x - 3) \cdot (2x + 10)}{(x + 5) \cdot (x^2 - 9)}$$

Simplify by factoring numerators and denominators.

$$= \dfrac{3 \cdot 2 \cdot 5}{5 \cdot 11} \qquad\qquad = \dfrac{(x - 3) \cdot 2 (x + 5)}{(x + 5)(x + 3)(x - 3)}$$

Apply the fundamental principle.

$$= \dfrac{3 \cdot 2}{11} \text{ or } \dfrac{6}{11} \qquad\qquad = \dfrac{2}{x + 3}$$

Multiplying Rational Expressions

If $\dfrac{P}{Q}$ and $\dfrac{R}{S}$ are rational expressions, then

$$\dfrac{P}{Q} \cdot \dfrac{R}{S} = \dfrac{PR}{QS}, \qquad Q \neq 0, S \neq 0$$

To multiply rational expressions, multiply the numerators and multiply the denominators.

Note: Recall that for Sections 7.1 through 7.4, we assume variables in rational expressions have only those replacement values for which the expressions are defined.

> **EXAMPLE 1** Multiply.
>
> **a.** $\dfrac{25x}{2} \cdot \dfrac{1}{y^3}$
>
> **b.** $\dfrac{-7x^2}{5y} \cdot \dfrac{3y^5}{14x^2}$

Solution To multiply rational expressions, multiply the numerators and multiply the denominators of both expressions. Then simplify if possible.

a. $\dfrac{25x}{2} \cdot \dfrac{1}{y^3} = \dfrac{25x \cdot 1}{2 \cdot y^3} = \dfrac{25x}{2y^3}$

The expression $\dfrac{25x}{2y^3}$ is in simplest form.

b. $\dfrac{-7x^2}{5y} \cdot \dfrac{3y^5}{14x^2} = \dfrac{-7x^2 \cdot 3y^5}{5y \cdot 14x^2}$ Multiply.

The expression $\dfrac{-7x^2 \cdot 3y^5}{5y \cdot 14x^2}$ is not in simplest form, so we factor the numerator and the denominator and divide out common factors.

$$= \dfrac{-1 \cdot 7 \cdot 3 \cdot x^2 \cdot y \cdot y^4}{5 \cdot 2 \cdot 7 \cdot x^2 \cdot y}$$

$$= -\dfrac{3y^4}{10}$$

> **Helpful Hint**
>
> It is the Fundamental Principle of Fractions that allows us to simplify.

PRACTICE
1 Multiply.

a. $\dfrac{4a}{5} \cdot \dfrac{3}{b^2}$

b. $\dfrac{-3p^4}{q^2} \cdot \dfrac{2q^3}{9p^4}$

When multiplying rational expressions, it is usually best to factor each numerator and denominator before multiplying. This will help us when we divide out common factors to write the product in lowest terms.

> **EXAMPLE 2** Multiply: $\dfrac{x^2 + x}{3x} \cdot \dfrac{6}{5x + 5}$

Solution $\dfrac{x^2 + x}{3x} \cdot \dfrac{6}{5x + 5} = \dfrac{x(x + 1)}{3x} \cdot \dfrac{2 \cdot 3}{5(x + 1)}$ Factor numerators and denominators.

$$= \dfrac{x(x + 1) \cdot 2 \cdot 3}{3x \cdot 5 \,(x + 1)}$$ Multiply.

$$= \dfrac{2}{5}$$ Simplify by dividing out common factors.

PRACTICE
2 Multiply: $\dfrac{x^2 - x}{5x} \cdot \dfrac{15}{x^2 - 1}$

The following steps may be used to multiply rational expressions.

> **Multiplying Rational Expressions**
>
> **Step 1.** Completely factor numerators and denominators.
>
> **Step 2.** Multiply numerators and multiply denominators.
>
> **Step 3.** Simplify or write the product in lowest terms by dividing out common factors.

✔ **CONCEPT CHECK**

Which of the following is a true statement?

a. $\dfrac{1}{3} \cdot \dfrac{1}{2} = \dfrac{1}{5}$

b. $\dfrac{2}{x} \cdot \dfrac{5}{x} = \dfrac{10}{x}$

c. $\dfrac{3}{x} \cdot \dfrac{1}{2} = \dfrac{3}{2x}$

d. $\dfrac{x}{7} \cdot \dfrac{x+5}{4} = \dfrac{2x+5}{28}$

EXAMPLE 3   Multiply: $\dfrac{3x+3}{5x-5x^2} \cdot \dfrac{2x^2+x-3}{4x^2-9}$

Solution

$$\dfrac{3x+3}{5x-5x^2} \cdot \dfrac{2x^2+x-3}{4x^2-9} = \dfrac{3(x+1)}{5x(1-x)} \cdot \dfrac{(2x+3)(x-1)}{(2x-3)(2x+3)} \qquad \text{Factor.}$$

$$= \dfrac{3(x+1)(2x+3)(x-1)}{5x(1-x)(2x-3)(2x+3)} \qquad \text{Multiply.}$$

$$= \dfrac{3(x+1)(x-1)}{5x(1-x)(2x-3)} \qquad \begin{array}{l}\text{Divide out common}\\\text{factors.}\end{array}$$

Next, recall that $x - 1$ and $1 - x$ are opposites so that $x - 1 = -1(1 - x)$.

$$= \dfrac{3(x+1)(-1)(1-x)}{5x(1-x)(2x-3)} \qquad \begin{array}{l}\text{Write } x - 1 \text{ as}\\ -1(1-x).\end{array}$$

$$= \dfrac{-3(x+1)}{5x(2x-3)} \quad \text{or} \quad -\dfrac{3(x+1)}{5x(2x-3)} \qquad \begin{array}{l}\text{Divide out common}\\\text{factors.}\end{array} \qquad \square$$

PRACTICE
3   Multiply: $\dfrac{6-3x}{6x+6x^2} \cdot \dfrac{3x^2-2x-5}{x^2-4}$

OBJECTIVE
2   **Dividing Rational Expressions** ▶

We can divide by a rational expression in the same way we divide by a fraction. To divide by a fraction, multiply by its reciprocal.

> **Helpful Hint**
>
> Don't forget how to find reciprocals. The reciprocal of $\dfrac{a}{b}$ is $\dfrac{b}{a}, a \neq 0, b \neq 0$.

For example, to divide $\dfrac{3}{2}$ by $\dfrac{7}{8}$, multiply $\dfrac{3}{2}$ by $\dfrac{8}{7}$.

$$\dfrac{3}{2} \div \dfrac{7}{8} = \dfrac{3}{2} \cdot \dfrac{8}{7} = \dfrac{3 \cdot 4 \cdot 2}{2 \cdot 7} = \dfrac{12}{7}$$

Dividing Rational Expressions

If $\dfrac{P}{Q}$ and $\dfrac{R}{S}$ are rational expressions and $\dfrac{R}{S}$ is not 0, then

$$\dfrac{P}{Q} \div \dfrac{R}{S} = \dfrac{P}{Q} \cdot \dfrac{S}{R} = \dfrac{PS}{QR}$$

To divide two rational expressions, multiply the first rational expression by the reciprocal of the second rational expression.

Answer to Concept Check: c

EXAMPLE 4   Divide: $\dfrac{3x^3y^7}{40} \div \dfrac{4x^3}{y^2}$

Solution $\dfrac{3x^3y^7}{40} \div \dfrac{4x^3}{y^2} = \dfrac{3x^3y^7}{40} \cdot \dfrac{y^2}{4x^3}$ Multiply by the reciprocal of $\dfrac{4x^3}{y^2}$.

$= \dfrac{3x^3y^9}{160x^3}$

$= \dfrac{3y^9}{160}$ Simplify.   □

PRACTICE
4   Divide: $\dfrac{5a^3b^2}{24} \div \dfrac{10a^5}{6}$ ■

EXAMPLE 5   Divide: $\dfrac{(x+2)^2}{10} \div \dfrac{2x+4}{5}$

Solution

$\dfrac{(x+2)^2}{10} \div \dfrac{2x+4}{5} = \dfrac{(x+2)^2}{10} \cdot \dfrac{5}{2x+4}$ Multiply by the reciprocal of $\dfrac{2x+4}{5}$.

$= \dfrac{(x+2)(x+2) \cdot 5}{5 \cdot 2 \cdot 2 \cdot (x+2)}$ Factor and multiply.

> **Helpful Hint**
> Remember, **to Divide by a Rational Expression**, multiply by its reciprocal.

$= \dfrac{x+2}{4}$ Simplify.   □

PRACTICE
5   Divide: $\dfrac{(x-5)^2}{3} \div \dfrac{4x-20}{9}$ ■

The following may be used to divide by a rational expression.

> **Dividing by a Rational Expression**
> Multiply by its reciprocal.

EXAMPLE 6   Divide: $\dfrac{6x+2}{x^2-1} \div \dfrac{3x^2+x}{x-1}$

Solution

$\dfrac{6x+2}{x^2-1} \div \dfrac{3x^2+x}{x-1} = \dfrac{6x+2}{x^2-1} \cdot \dfrac{x-1}{3x^2+x}$ Multiply by the reciprocal.

$= \dfrac{2(3x+1)(x-1)}{(x+1)(x-1) \cdot x(3x+1)}$ Factor and multiply.

$= \dfrac{2}{x(x+1)}$ Simplify.   □

PRACTICE
6   Divide: $\dfrac{10x-2}{x^2-9} \div \dfrac{5x^2-x}{x+3}$ ■

EXAMPLE 7   Divide: $\dfrac{2x^2 - 11x + 5}{5x - 25} \div \dfrac{4x - 2}{10}$

Solution

$$\dfrac{2x^2 - 11x + 5}{5x - 25} \div \dfrac{4x - 2}{10} = \dfrac{2x^2 - 11x + 5}{5x - 25} \cdot \dfrac{10}{4x - 2} \quad \text{Multiply by the reciprocal.}$$

$$= \dfrac{(2x - 1)(x - 5) \cdot 2 \cdot 5}{5(x - 5) \cdot 2(2x - 1)} \quad \text{Factor and multiply.}$$

$$= \dfrac{1}{1} \quad \text{or} \quad 1 \qquad \text{Simplify.} \qquad \square$$

PRACTICE
7   Divide: $\dfrac{3x^2 - 11x - 4}{2x - 8} \div \dfrac{9x + 3}{6}$ ■

OBJECTIVE
3   Multiplying or Dividing Rational Expressions ▶

Let's make sure that we understand the difference between multiplying and dividing rational expressions.

Rational Expressions	
Multiplication	Multiply the numerators and multiply the denominators.
Division	Multiply by the reciprocal of the divisor.

EXAMPLE 8   Multiply or divide as indicated.

   a. $\dfrac{x - 4}{5} \cdot \dfrac{x}{x - 4}$ **b.** $\dfrac{x - 4}{5} \div \dfrac{x}{x - 4}$ **c.** $\dfrac{x^2 - 4}{2x + 6} \cdot \dfrac{x^2 + 4x + 3}{2 - x}$

Solution

   a. $\dfrac{x - 4}{5} \cdot \dfrac{x}{x - 4} = \dfrac{(x - 4) \cdot x}{5 \cdot (x - 4)} = \dfrac{x}{5}$

   b. $\dfrac{x - 4}{5} \div \dfrac{x}{x - 4} = \dfrac{x - 4}{5} \cdot \dfrac{x - 4}{x} = \dfrac{(x - 4)^2}{5x}$

   c. $\dfrac{x^2 - 4}{2x + 6} \cdot \dfrac{x^2 + 4x + 3}{2 - x} = \dfrac{(x - 2)(x + 2) \cdot (x + 1)(x + 3)}{2(x + 3) \cdot (2 - x)}$ Factor and multiply.

$$= \dfrac{(x - 2)(x + 2) \cdot (x + 1)(x + 3)}{2(x + 3) \cdot (2 - x)}$$

$$= \dfrac{-1(x + 2)(x + 1)}{2} \qquad \begin{array}{l} \text{Divide out com-} \\ \text{mon factors. Recall} \\ \text{that } \dfrac{x - 2}{2 - x} = -1 \end{array}$$

$$= -\dfrac{(x + 2)(x + 1)}{2} \qquad \qquad \square$$

PRACTICE
8   Multiply or divide as indicated.

   a. $\dfrac{y + 9}{8x} \cdot \dfrac{y + 9}{2x}$ **b.** $\dfrac{y + 9}{8x} \div \dfrac{y + 9}{2}$ **c.** $\dfrac{35x - 7x^2}{x^2 - 25} \cdot \dfrac{x^2 + 3x - 10}{x^2 + 4x}$ ■

OBJECTIVE

4 Converting Between Units of Measure

How many square inches are in 1 square foot?

How many cubic feet are in a cubic yard?

If you have trouble answering these questions, this section will be helpful to you.

Now that we know how to multiply fractions and rational expressions, we can use this knowledge to help us convert between units of measure. To do so, we will use **unit fractions**. A unit fraction is a fraction that equals 1. For example, since 12 in. = 1 ft, we have the unit fractions

$$\frac{12 \text{ in.}}{1 \text{ ft}} = 1 \quad \text{and} \quad \frac{1 \text{ ft}}{12 \text{ in.}} = 1$$

EXAMPLE 9   18 square feet = _____ square yards

Solution Let's multiply 18 square feet by a unit fraction that has square feet in the denominator and square yards in the numerator. From the diagram, you can see that

1 square yard = 9 square feet

Thus,

$$18 \text{ sq ft} = \frac{18 \text{ sq ft}}{1} \cdot 1 = \frac{\overset{2}{\cancel{18} \text{ sq ft}}}{1} \cdot \frac{1 \text{ sq yd}}{\underset{1}{\cancel{9} \text{ sq ft}}}$$

$$= \frac{2 \cdot 1}{1 \cdot 1} \text{ sq yd} = 2 \text{ sq yd}$$

Thus, 18 sq ft = 2 sq yd.

Draw a diagram of 18 sq ft to help you see that this is reasonable. ☐

(diagram: 1 yd = 3 ft, Area: 1 sq yd or 9 sq ft)

PRACTICE

9   288 square inches = _____ square feet ■

EXAMPLE 10   5.2 square yards = _____ square feet

Solution

$$5.2 \text{ sq yd} = \frac{5.2 \text{ sq yd}}{1} \cdot 1 = \frac{5.2 \text{ sq yd}}{1} \cdot \frac{9 \text{ sq ft}}{1 \text{ sq yd}} \quad \begin{matrix} \leftarrow \text{Units converting to} \\ \leftarrow \text{Units given} \end{matrix}$$

$$= \frac{5.2 \cdot 9}{1 \cdot 1} \text{ sq ft}$$

$$= 46.8 \text{ sq ft}$$

Thus, 5.2 sq yd = 46.8 sq ft.

Draw a diagram to see that this is reasonable. ☐

PRACTICE

10   3.5 square feet = _____ square inches ■

EXAMPLE 11   **Converting from Cubic Feet to Cubic Yards**

The largest building in the world by volume is The Boeing Company's Everett, Washington, factory complex, where Boeing's wide-body jetliners, the 747, 767, and 777, are built. The volume of this factory complex is 472,370,319 cubic feet. Find the volume of this Boeing facility in cubic yards. (*Source:* The Boeing Company)

<u>Solution</u> There are 27 cubic feet in 1 cubic yard. (See the diagram.)

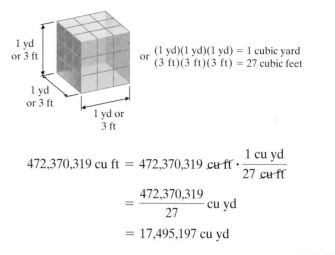

or $\dfrac{(1 \text{ yd})(1 \text{ yd})(1 \text{ yd}) = 1 \text{ cubic yard}}{(3 \text{ ft})(3 \text{ ft})(3 \text{ ft}) = 27 \text{ cubic feet}}$

1 yd
or 3 ft

1 yd
or 3 ft

1 yd or
3 ft

$$472{,}370{,}319 \text{ cu ft} = 472{,}370{,}319 \ \cancel{\text{cu ft}} \cdot \dfrac{1 \text{ cu yd}}{27 \ \cancel{\text{cu ft}}}$$

$$= \dfrac{472{,}370{,}319}{27} \text{ cu yd}$$

$$= 17{,}495{,}197 \text{ cu yd} \qquad \square$$

PRACTICE

11   The largest casino in the world is the Venetian, in Macau, on the southern tip of China. The gaming area for this casino is approximately 61,000 *square yards*. Find the size of the gaming area in *square feet*. (*Source: USA Today*) ■

Helpful Hint

When converting among units of measurement, if possible write the unit fraction so that **the numerator contains the units you are converting to** and **the denominator contains the original units**.

Unit fraction

$$48 \text{ in.} = \dfrac{48 \ \cancel{\text{in.}}}{1} \cdot \dfrac{1 \text{ ft}}{12 \ \cancel{\text{in.}}} \qquad \begin{array}{l} \leftarrow \text{Units converting to} \\ \leftarrow \text{Original units} \end{array}$$

$$= \dfrac{48}{12} \text{ ft} = 4 \text{ ft}$$

EXAMPLE 12   At the 2012 Summer Olympics, Jamaican athlete Usain Bolt won the gold medal in the men's 100-meter track event. He ran the distance at an average speed of 34.1 feet per second. Convert this speed to miles per hour. (*Source:* International Olympic Committee)

<u>Solution</u> Recall that 1 mile = 5280 feet and 1 hour = 3600 seconds $(60 \cdot 60)$.

Unit fractions

$$34.1 \text{ feet/second} = \dfrac{34.1 \text{ feet}}{1 \text{ second}} \cdot \dfrac{3600 \text{ seconds}}{1 \text{ hour}} \cdot \dfrac{1 \text{ mile}}{5280 \text{ feet}}$$

$$= \dfrac{34.1 \cdot 3600}{5280} \text{ miles/hour}$$

$$\approx 23.3 \text{ miles/hour (rounded to the nearest tenth)} \qquad \square$$

PRACTICE

12   The cheetah is the fastest land animal, being clocked at about 102.7 feet per second. Convert this to miles per hour. Round to the nearest tenth. (*Source: World Almanac and Book of Facts*) ■

✓ Vocabulary, Readiness & Video Check

Use one of the choices below to fill in the blank.

opposites   reciprocals

1. The expressions $\dfrac{x}{2y}$ and $\dfrac{2y}{x}$ are called _____ .

Multiply or divide as indicated.

2. $\dfrac{a}{b} \cdot \dfrac{c}{d} =$ _____

3. $\dfrac{a}{b} \div \dfrac{c}{d} =$ _____

4. $\dfrac{x}{7} \cdot \dfrac{x}{6} =$ _____

5. $\dfrac{x}{7} \div \dfrac{x}{6} =$ _____

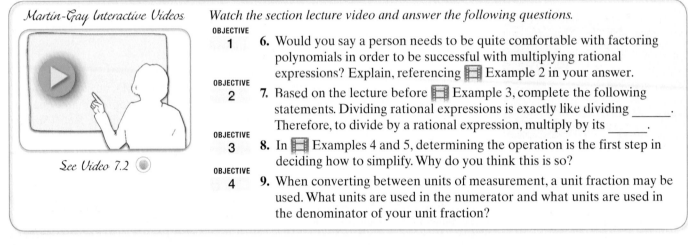

Martin-Gay Interactive Videos

See Video 7.2 ●

Watch the section lecture video and answer the following questions.

OBJECTIVE 1

6. Would you say a person needs to be quite comfortable with factoring polynomials in order to be successful with multiplying rational expressions? Explain, referencing ▦ Example 2 in your answer.

OBJECTIVE 2

7. Based on the lecture before ▦ Example 3, complete the following statements. Dividing rational expressions is exactly like dividing _____. Therefore, to divide by a rational expression, multiply by its _____.

OBJECTIVE 3

8. In ▦ Examples 4 and 5, determining the operation is the first step in deciding how to simplify. Why do you think this is so?

OBJECTIVE 4

9. When converting between units of measurement, a unit fraction may be used. What units are used in the numerator and what units are used in the denominator of your unit fraction?

7.2   Exercise Set   MyMathLab® ▶

Find each product and simplify if possible. See Examples 1 through 3.

1. $\dfrac{3x}{y^2} \cdot \dfrac{7y}{4x}$

2. $\dfrac{9x^2}{y} \cdot \dfrac{4y}{3x^3}$

▶ **3.** $\dfrac{8x}{2} \cdot \dfrac{x^5}{4x^2}$

4. $\dfrac{6x^2}{10x^3} \cdot \dfrac{5x}{12}$

5. $-\dfrac{5a^2b}{30a^2b^2} \cdot b^3$

6. $-\dfrac{9x^3y^2}{18xy^5} \cdot y^3$

7. $\dfrac{x}{2x-14} \cdot \dfrac{x^2-7x}{5}$

8. $\dfrac{4x-24}{20x} \cdot \dfrac{5}{x-6}$

9. $\dfrac{6x+6}{5} \cdot \dfrac{10}{36x+36}$

10. $\dfrac{x^2+x}{8} \cdot \dfrac{16}{x+1}$

11. $\dfrac{(m+n)^2}{m-n} \cdot \dfrac{m}{m^2+mn}$

12. $\dfrac{(m-n)^2}{m+n} \cdot \dfrac{m}{m^2-mn}$

13. $\dfrac{x^2-25}{x^2-3x-10} \cdot \dfrac{x+2}{x}$

14. $\dfrac{a^2-4a+4}{a^2-4} \cdot \dfrac{a+3}{a-2}$

15. $\dfrac{x^2+6x+8}{x^2+x-20} \cdot \dfrac{x^2+2x-15}{x^2+8x+16}$

16. $\dfrac{x^2+9x+20}{x^2-15x+44} \cdot \dfrac{x^2-11x+28}{x^2+12x+35}$

Find each quotient and simplify. See Examples 4 through 7.

17. $\dfrac{5x^7}{2x^5} \div \dfrac{15x}{4x^3}$

18. $\dfrac{9y^4}{6y} \div \dfrac{y^2}{3}$

19. $\dfrac{8x^2}{y^3} \div \dfrac{4x^2y^3}{6}$

20. $\dfrac{7a^2b}{3ab^2} \div \dfrac{21a^2b^2}{14ab}$

21. $\dfrac{(x-6)(x+4)}{4x} \div \dfrac{2x-12}{8x^2}$

22. $\dfrac{(x+3)^2}{5} \div \dfrac{5x+15}{25}$

23. $\dfrac{3x^2}{x^2-1} \div \dfrac{x^5}{(x+1)^2}$

24. $\dfrac{9x^5}{a^2-b^2} \div \dfrac{27x^2}{3b-3a}$

25. $\dfrac{m^2-n^2}{m+n} \div \dfrac{m}{m^2+nm}$

26. $\dfrac{(m-n)^2}{m+n} \div \dfrac{m^2-mn}{m}$

▶ **27.** $\dfrac{x+2}{7-x} \div \dfrac{x^2-5x+6}{x^2-9x+14}$

28. $\dfrac{x-3}{2-x} \div \dfrac{x^2+3x-18}{x^2+2x-8}$

29. $\dfrac{x^2+7x+10}{x-1} \div \dfrac{x^2+2x-15}{x-1}$

30. $\dfrac{x+1}{(x+1)(2x+3)} \div \dfrac{20x+100}{2x+3}$

MIXED PRACTICE

Multiply or divide as indicated. See Examples 1 through 8.

31. $\dfrac{5x-10}{12} \div \dfrac{4x-8}{8}$

32. $\dfrac{6x+6}{5} \div \dfrac{9x+9}{10}$

33. $\dfrac{x^2+5x}{8} \cdot \dfrac{9}{3x+15}$

34. $\dfrac{3x^2+12x}{6} \cdot \dfrac{9}{2x+8}$

35. $\dfrac{7}{6p^2+q} \div \dfrac{14}{18p^2+3q}$

36. $\dfrac{3x+6}{20} \div \dfrac{4x+8}{8}$

37. $\dfrac{3x+4y}{x^2+4xy+4y^2} \cdot \dfrac{x+2y}{2}$

38. $\dfrac{x^2-y^2}{3x^2+3xy} \cdot \dfrac{3x^2+6x}{3x^2-2xy-y^2}$

39. $\dfrac{(x+2)^2}{x-2} \div \dfrac{x^2-4}{2x-4}$

40. $\dfrac{x+3}{x^2-9} \div \dfrac{5x+15}{(x-3)^2}$

41. $\dfrac{x^2-4}{24x} \div \dfrac{2-x}{6xy}$

42. $\dfrac{3y}{3-x} \div \dfrac{12xy}{x^2-9}$

43. $\dfrac{a^2+7a+12}{a^2+5a+6} \cdot \dfrac{a^2+8a+15}{a^2+5a+4}$

44. $\dfrac{b^2+2b-3}{b^2+b-2} \cdot \dfrac{b^2-4}{b^2+6b+8}$

45. $\dfrac{5x-20}{3x^2+x} \cdot \dfrac{3x^2+13x+4}{x^2-16}$

46. $\dfrac{9x+18}{4x^2-3x} \cdot \dfrac{4x^2-11x+6}{x^2-4}$

47. $\dfrac{8n^2-18}{2n^2-5n+3} \div \dfrac{6n^2+7n-3}{n^2-9n+8}$

48. $\dfrac{36n^2-64}{3n^2+10n+8} \div \dfrac{3n^2-13n+12}{n^2-5n-14}$

49. Find the quotient of $\dfrac{x^2-9}{2x}$ and $\dfrac{x+3}{8x^4}$.

50. Find the quotient of $\dfrac{4x^2+4x+1}{4x+2}$ and $\dfrac{4x+2}{16}$.

Multiply or divide as indicated. Some of these expressions contain 4-term polynomials and sums and differences of cubes. See Examples 1 through 8.

51. $\dfrac{a^2+ac+ba+bc}{a-b} \div \dfrac{a+c}{a+b}$

52. $\dfrac{x^2+2x-xy-2y}{x^2-y^2} \div \dfrac{2x+4}{x+y}$

53. $\dfrac{3x^2+8x+5}{x^2+8x+7} \cdot \dfrac{x+7}{x^2+4}$

54. $\dfrac{16x^2+2x}{16x^2+10x+1} \cdot \dfrac{1}{4x^2+2x}$

55. $\dfrac{x^3+8}{x^2-2x+4} \cdot \dfrac{4}{x^2-4}$

56. $\dfrac{9y}{3y-3} \cdot \dfrac{y^3-1}{y^3+y^2+y}$

57. $\dfrac{a^2-ab}{6a^2+6ab} \div \dfrac{a^3-b^3}{a^2-b^2}$

58. $\dfrac{x^3+27y^3}{6x} \div \dfrac{x^2-9y^2}{x^2-3xy}$

Convert as indicated. See Examples 9 through 12.

59. 10 square feet = _____ square inches.

60. 1008 square inches = _____ square feet.

61. 45 square feet = _____ square yards.

62. 2 square yards = _____ square inches.

63. 3 cubic yards = _____ cubic feet.

64. 2 cubic yards = _____ cubic inches.

65. 50 miles per hour = _____ feet per second (round to the nearest whole).

66. 10 feet per second = _____ miles per hour (round to the nearest tenth).

67. 6.3 square yards = _____ square feet.

68. 3.6 square yards = _____ square feet.

69. In January 2010, the Burj Khalifa Tower officially became the tallest building in the world. This tower has a curtain wall (the exterior skin of the building) that is approximately 133,500 square yards. Convert this to square feet. (*Source:* Burj Khalifa)

70. The Pentagon, headquarters for the Department of Defense, contains 3,705,793 square feet of office and storage space. Convert this to square yards. Round to the nearest square yard. (*Source:* U.S. Department of Defense)

71. On February 14, 2014, Brian Smith set a new stock car world speed record of 396.7 feet per second on the Space Shuttle landing runway at The John F. Kennedy Space Center. Convert this speed to miles per hour. Round to the nearest tenth. (*Source:* Vox Media)

72. On October 4, 2004, the rocket plane *SpaceShipOne* shot to an altitude of more than 100 km for the second time inside a week to claim the $10 million Ansari X-Prize. At one point in its flight, *SpaceShipOne* was traveling past Mach 1, about 930 miles per hour. Find this speed in feet per second. (*Source:* Space.com)

REVIEW AND PREVIEW

Perform each indicated operation. See Section 1.3.

73. $\dfrac{1}{5}+\dfrac{4}{5}$

74. $\dfrac{3}{15}+\dfrac{6}{15}$

75. $\dfrac{9}{9}-\dfrac{19}{9}$

76. $\dfrac{4}{3}-\dfrac{8}{3}$

77. $\dfrac{6}{5}+\left(\dfrac{1}{5}-\dfrac{8}{5}\right)$

78. $-\dfrac{3}{2}+\left(\dfrac{1}{2}-\dfrac{3}{2}\right)$

Graph each linear equation. See Section 3.2.

79. $x-2y=6$

80. $5x-y=10$

CONCEPT EXTENSIONS

Identify each statement as true or false. If false, correct the multiplication. See the Concept Check in this section.

81. $\dfrac{4}{a} \cdot \dfrac{1}{b} = \dfrac{4}{ab}$

82. $\dfrac{2}{3} \cdot \dfrac{2}{4} = \dfrac{2}{7}$

83. $\dfrac{x}{5} \cdot \dfrac{x+3}{4} = \dfrac{2x+3}{20}$

84. $\dfrac{7}{a} \cdot \dfrac{3}{a} = \dfrac{21}{a}$

85. Find the area of the rectangle.

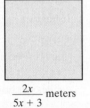

$\dfrac{2x}{x^2-25}$ feet

$\dfrac{x+5}{9x}$ feet

86. Find the area of the square.

$\dfrac{2x}{5x+3}$ meters

Multiply or divide as indicated.

87. $\left(\dfrac{x^2-y^2}{x^2+y^2} \div \dfrac{x^2-y^2}{3x}\right) \cdot \dfrac{x^2+y^2}{6}$

88. $\left(\dfrac{x^2-9}{x^2-1} \cdot \dfrac{x^2+2x+1}{2x^2+9x+9}\right) \div \dfrac{2x+3}{1-x}$

89. $\left(\dfrac{2a+b}{b^2} \cdot \dfrac{3a^2-2ab}{ab+2b^2}\right) \div \dfrac{a^2-3ab+2b^2}{5ab-10b^2}$

90. $\left(\dfrac{x^2y^2-xy}{4x-4y} \div \dfrac{3y-3x}{8x-8y}\right) \cdot \dfrac{y-x}{8}$

91. In your own words, explain how you multiply rational expressions.

92. Explain how dividing rational expressions is similar to dividing rational numbers.

7.3 Adding and Subtracting Rational Expressions with Common Denominators and Least Common Denominator ▶

OBJECTIVES

1 Add and Subtract Rational Expressions with the Same Denominator. ▶

2 Find the Least Common Denominator of a List of Rational Expressions. ▶

3 Write a Rational Expression as an Equivalent Expression Whose Denominator Is Given. ▶

OBJECTIVE

1 Adding and Subtracting Rational Expressions with the Same Denominator ▶

Like multiplication and division, addition and subtraction of rational expressions is similar to addition and subtraction of rational numbers. In this section, we add and subtract rational expressions with a common (or the same) denominator.

Add: $\dfrac{6}{5} + \dfrac{2}{5}$ | Add: $\dfrac{9}{x+2} + \dfrac{3}{x+2}$

Add the numerators and place the sum over the common denominator.

$\dfrac{6}{5} + \dfrac{2}{5} = \dfrac{6+2}{5}$ | $\dfrac{9}{x+2} + \dfrac{3}{x+2} = \dfrac{9+3}{x+2}$

$= \dfrac{8}{5}$ Simplify. | $= \dfrac{12}{x+2}$ Simplify.

Adding and Subtracting Rational Expressions with Common Denominators

If $\dfrac{P}{R}$ and $\dfrac{Q}{R}$ are rational expressions, then

$$\dfrac{P}{R} + \dfrac{Q}{R} = \dfrac{P+Q}{R} \qquad \text{and} \qquad \dfrac{P}{R} - \dfrac{Q}{R} = \dfrac{P-Q}{R}$$

To add or subtract rational expressions, add or subtract the numerators and place the sum or difference over the common denominator.

EXAMPLE 1   Add: $\dfrac{5m}{2n} + \dfrac{m}{2n}$

Solution $\dfrac{5m}{2n} + \dfrac{m}{2n} = \dfrac{5m + m}{2n}$ Add the numerators.

$\qquad\qquad\qquad = \dfrac{6m}{2n}$ Simplify the numerator by combining like terms.

$\qquad\qquad\qquad = \dfrac{3m}{n}$ Simplify by applying the fundamental principle.   □

PRACTICE
1   Add: $\dfrac{7a}{4b} + \dfrac{a}{4b}$ ■

EXAMPLE 2   Subtract: $\dfrac{2y}{2y - 7} - \dfrac{7}{2y - 7}$

Solution $\dfrac{2y}{2y - 7} - \dfrac{7}{2y - 7} = \dfrac{2y - 7}{2y - 7}$ Subtract the numerators.

$\qquad\qquad\qquad\qquad\qquad = \dfrac{1}{1}$ or   1   Simplify.   □

PRACTICE
2   Subtract: $\dfrac{3x}{3x - 2} - \dfrac{2}{3x - 2}$ ■

EXAMPLE 3   Subtract: $\dfrac{3x^2 + 2x}{x - 1} - \dfrac{10x - 5}{x - 1}$

Solution $\dfrac{3x^2 + 2x}{x - 1} - \dfrac{10x - 5}{x - 1} = \dfrac{(3x^2 + 2x) - (10x - 5)}{x - 1}$ Subtract the numerators. Notice the parentheses.

$\qquad\qquad\qquad\qquad\qquad\qquad = \dfrac{3x^2 + 2x - 10x + 5}{x - 1}$ Use the distributive property.

$\qquad\qquad\qquad\qquad\qquad\qquad = \dfrac{3x^2 - 8x + 5}{x - 1}$ Combine like terms.

$\qquad\qquad\qquad\qquad\qquad\qquad = \dfrac{(x - 1)(3x - 5)}{x - 1}$ Factor.

$\qquad\qquad\qquad\qquad\qquad\qquad = 3x - 5$ Simplify.   □

> **Helpful Hint**
> Parentheses are inserted so that the entire numerator, $10x - 5$, is subtracted.

PRACTICE
3   Subtract: $\dfrac{4x^2 + 15x}{x + 3} - \dfrac{8x + 15}{x + 3}$ ■

> **Helpful Hint**
> Notice how the numerator $10x - 5$ has been subtracted in Example 3.
> This − sign applies to the entire numerator, $10x - 5$. So parentheses are inserted here to indicate this.
>
> $$\dfrac{3x^2 + 2x}{x - 1} - \dfrac{10x - 5}{x - 1} = \dfrac{3x^2 + 2x - (10x - 5)}{x - 1}$$

OBJECTIVE

2   Finding the Least Common Denominator

To add and subtract fractions with **unlike** denominators, first find the least common denominator (LCD) and then write all fractions as equivalent fractions with the LCD.

For example, suppose we add $\dfrac{8}{3}$ and $\dfrac{2}{5}$. The LCD of denominators 3 and 5 is 15, since 15 is the least common multiple (LCM) of 3 and 5. That is, 15 is the smallest number that both 3 and 5 divide into evenly.

Next, rewrite each fraction so that its denominator is 15.

$$\frac{8}{3} + \frac{2}{5} = \frac{8(5)}{3(5)} + \frac{2(3)}{5(3)} = \frac{40}{15} + \frac{6}{15} = \frac{40 + 6}{15} = \frac{46}{15}$$

We are multiplying by 1.

To add or subtract rational expressions with unlike denominators, we also first find the LCD and then write all rational expressions as equivalent expressions with the LCD. The **least common denominator (LCD) of a list of rational expressions** is a polynomial of least degree whose factors include all the factors of the denominators in the list.

Finding the Least Common Denominator (LCD)

Step 1. Factor each denominator completely.

Step 2. The least common denominator (LCD) is the product of all unique factors found in Step 1, each raised to a power equal to the greatest number of times that the factor appears in any one factored denominator.

EXAMPLE 4   Find the LCD for each pair.

a. $\dfrac{1}{8}, \dfrac{3}{22}$

b. $\dfrac{7}{5x}, \dfrac{6}{15x^2}$

Solution

a. Start by finding the prime factorization of each denominator.

$$8 = 2 \cdot 2 \cdot 2 = 2^3 \quad \text{and}$$
$$22 = 2 \cdot 11$$

Next, write the product of all the unique factors, each raised to a power equal to the greatest number of times that the factor appears in any denominator.

The greatest number of times that the factor 2 appears is 3.

The greatest number of times that the factor 11 appears is 1.

$$\text{LCD} = 2^3 \cdot 11^1 = 8 \cdot 11 = 88$$

b. Factor each denominator.

$$5x = 5 \cdot x \quad \text{and}$$
$$15x^2 = 3 \cdot 5 \cdot x^2$$

The greatest number of times that the factor 5 appears is 1.

The greatest number of times that the factor 3 appears is 1.

The greatest number of times that the factor x appears is 2.

$$\text{LCD} = 3^1 \cdot 5^1 \cdot x^2 = 15x^2$$

PRACTICE

4   Find the LCD for each pair.

a. $\dfrac{3}{14}, \dfrac{5}{21}$

b. $\dfrac{4}{9y}, \dfrac{11}{15y^3}$

EXAMPLE 5   Find the LCD for each pair.

a. $\dfrac{7x}{x+2}$ and $\dfrac{5x^2}{x-2}$

b. $\dfrac{3}{x}$ and $\dfrac{6}{x+4}$

Solution

a. The denominators $x+2$ and $x-2$ are completely factored already. The factor $x+2$ appears once and the factor $x-2$ appears once.

$$\text{LCD} = (x+2)(x-2)$$

b. The denominators x and $x+4$ cannot be factored further. The factor x appears once and the factor $x+4$ appears once.

$$\text{LCD} = x(x+4)$$ □

PRACTICE
5   Find the LCD for each pair.

a. $\dfrac{16}{y-5}$ and $\dfrac{3y^3}{y-4}$

b. $\dfrac{8}{a}$ and $\dfrac{5}{a+2}$ ■

EXAMPLE 6   Find the LCD of $\dfrac{6m^2}{3m+15}$ and $\dfrac{2}{(m+5)^2}$.

Solution   We factor each denominator.

$$3m+15 = 3(m+5)$$
$$(m+5)^2 = (m+5)^2 \quad \text{This denominator is already factored.}$$

The greatest number of times that the factor 3 appears is 1.

The greatest number of times that the factor $m+5$ appears *in any one denominator* is 2.

$$\text{LCD} = 3(m+5)^2$$ □

PRACTICE
6   Find the LCD of $\dfrac{2x^3}{(2x-1)^2}$ and $\dfrac{5x}{6x-3}$.   ■

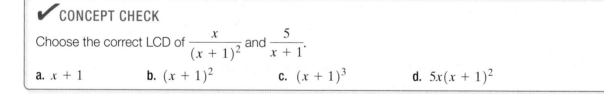

✔ **CONCEPT CHECK**

Choose the correct LCD of $\dfrac{x}{(x+1)^2}$ and $\dfrac{5}{x+1}$.

a. $x+1$ **b.** $(x+1)^2$ **c.** $(x+1)^3$ **d.** $5x(x+1)^2$

EXAMPLE 7   Find the LCD of $\dfrac{t-10}{t^2-t-6}$ and $\dfrac{t+5}{t^2+3t+2}$.

Solution   Start by factoring each denominator.

$$t^2-t-6 = (t-3)(t+2)$$
$$t^2+3t+2 = (t+1)(t+2)$$
$$\text{LCD} = (t-3)(t+2)(t+1)$$ □

PRACTICE
7   Find the LCD of $\dfrac{x-5}{x^2+5x+4}$ and $\dfrac{x+8}{x^2-16}$.   ■

Answer to Concept Check: b

EXAMPLE 8 Find the LCD of $\dfrac{2}{x-2}$ and $\dfrac{10}{2-x}$.

Solution The denominators $x - 2$ and $2 - x$ are opposites. That is, $2 - x = -1(x - 2)$. Use $x - 2$ or $2 - x$ as the LCD.

$$\text{LCD} = x - 2 \quad \text{or} \quad \text{LCD} = 2 - x$$ □

PRACTICE
8 Find the LCD of $\dfrac{5}{3-x}$ and $\dfrac{4}{x-3}$. ■

OBJECTIVE
3 Writing Equivalent Rational Expressions ▶

Next we practice writing a rational expression as an equivalent rational expression with a given denominator. To do this, we multiply by a form of 1. Recall that multiplying an expression by 1 produces an equivalent expression. In other words,

$$\frac{P}{Q} = \frac{P}{Q} \cdot 1 = \frac{P}{Q} \cdot \frac{R}{R} = \frac{PR}{QR}.$$

EXAMPLE 9 Write each rational expression as an equivalent rational expression with the given denominator.

a. $\dfrac{4b}{9a} = \dfrac{}{27a^2b}$ **b.** $\dfrac{7x}{2x+5} = \dfrac{}{6x+15}$

Solution

a. We can ask ourselves: "What do we multiply $9a$ by to get $27a^2b$?" The answer is $3ab$, since $9a(3ab) = 27a^2b$. So we multiply by 1 in the form of $\dfrac{3ab}{3ab}$.

$$\frac{4b}{9a} = \frac{4b}{9a} \cdot 1$$

$$= \frac{4b}{9a} \cdot \frac{3ab}{3ab}$$

$$= \frac{4b(3ab)}{9a(3ab)} = \frac{12ab^2}{27a^2b}$$

b. First, factor the denominator on the right.

$$\frac{7x}{2x+5} = \frac{}{3(2x+5)}$$

To obtain the denominator on the right from the denominator on the left, we multiply $\dfrac{7x}{2x+5}$ by 1 in the form of $\dfrac{3}{3}$.

$$\frac{7x}{2x+5} = \frac{7x}{2x+5} \cdot \frac{3}{3} = \frac{7x \cdot 3}{(2x+5) \cdot 3} = \frac{21x}{3(2x+5)} \text{ or } \frac{21x}{6x+15}$$ □

PRACTICE
9 Write each rational expression as an equivalent fraction with the given denominator.

a. $\dfrac{3x}{5y} = \dfrac{}{35xy^2}$ **b.** $\dfrac{9x}{4x+7} = \dfrac{}{8x+14}$ ■

EXAMPLE 10 Write the rational expression as an equivalent rational expression with the given denominator.

$$\frac{5}{x^2 - 4} = \frac{}{(x - 2)(x + 2)(x - 4)}$$

**Solution** First, factor the denominator $x^2 - 4$ as $(x - 2)(x + 2)$.

If we multiply the original denominator $(x - 2)(x + 2)$ by $x - 4$, the result is the new denominator $(x - 2)(x + 2)(x - 4)$. Thus, we multiply by 1 in the form of $\dfrac{x - 4}{x - 4}$.

$$\frac{5}{x^2 - 4} = \underbrace{\frac{5}{(x - 2)(x + 2)}}_{\substack{\text{Factored} \\ \text{denominator}}} = \frac{5}{(x - 2)(x + 2)} \cdot \frac{x - 4}{x - 4}$$

$$= \frac{5(x - 4)}{(x - 2)(x + 2)(x - 4)}$$

$$= \frac{5x - 20}{(x - 2)(x + 2)(x - 4)} \qquad \square$$

**PRACTICE
10** Write the rational expression as an equivalent rational expression with the given denominator.

$$\frac{3}{x^2 - 2x - 15} = \frac{}{(x - 2)(x + 3)(x - 5)}$$

✔ Vocabulary, Readiness & Video Check

Use the choices below to fill in each blank. Not all choices will be used.

$$\frac{9}{22} \qquad \frac{5}{22} \qquad \frac{9}{11} \qquad \frac{5}{11} \qquad \frac{ac}{b} \qquad \frac{a - c}{b} \qquad \frac{a + c}{b} \qquad \frac{5 - 6 + x}{x} \qquad \frac{5 - (6 + x)}{x}$$

1. $\dfrac{7}{11} + \dfrac{2}{11} =$ _____

2. $\dfrac{7}{11} - \dfrac{2}{11} =$ _____

3. $\dfrac{a}{b} + \dfrac{c}{b} =$ _____

4. $\dfrac{a}{b} - \dfrac{c}{b} =$ _____

5. $\dfrac{5}{x} - \dfrac{6 + x}{x} =$ _____

Martin-Gay Interactive Videos

See Video 7.3 ◉

Watch the section lecture video and answer the following questions.

OBJECTIVE 1
6. In ▦ Example 3, why is it important to place parentheses around the second numerator when writing as one expression?

OBJECTIVE 2
7. In ▦ Examples 4 and 5, we factor the denominators completely. How does this help determine the LCD?

OBJECTIVE 3
8. Based on ▦ Example 6, complete the following statements. To write an equivalent rational expression, you multiply the _____ of a rational expression by the same expression as the denominator. This means you're multiplying the original rational expression by a factor of _____ and therefore not changing the _____ of the original expression.

7.3 Exercise Set MyMathLab ▶

Add or subtract as indicated. Simplify the result if possible. See Examples 1 through 3.

1. $\dfrac{a+1}{13} + \dfrac{8}{13}$

2. $\dfrac{x+1}{7} + \dfrac{6}{7}$

3. $\dfrac{4m}{3n} + \dfrac{5m}{3n}$

4. $\dfrac{3p}{2q} + \dfrac{11p}{2q}$

5. $\dfrac{4m}{m-6} - \dfrac{24}{m-6}$

6. $\dfrac{8y}{y-2} - \dfrac{16}{y-2}$

▶ **7.** $\dfrac{9}{3+y} + \dfrac{y+1}{3+y}$

8. $\dfrac{9}{y+9} + \dfrac{y-5}{y+9}$

9. $\dfrac{5x^2+4x}{x-1} - \dfrac{6x+3}{x-1}$

10. $\dfrac{x^2+9x}{x+7} - \dfrac{4x+14}{x+7}$

11. $\dfrac{4a}{a^2+2a-15} - \dfrac{12}{a^2+2a-15}$

12. $\dfrac{3y}{y^2+3y-10} - \dfrac{6}{y^2+3y-10}$

▶ **13.** $\dfrac{2x+3}{x^2-x-30} - \dfrac{x-2}{x^2-x-30}$

14. $\dfrac{3x-1}{x^2+5x-6} - \dfrac{2x-7}{x^2+5x-6}$

15. $\dfrac{2x+1}{x-3} + \dfrac{3x+6}{x-3}$

16. $\dfrac{4p-3}{2p+7} + \dfrac{3p+8}{2p+7}$

17. $\dfrac{2x^2}{x-5} - \dfrac{25+x^2}{x-5}$

18. $\dfrac{6x^2}{2x-5} - \dfrac{25+2x^2}{2x-5}$

19. $\dfrac{5x+4}{x-1} - \dfrac{2x+7}{x-1}$

20. $\dfrac{7x+1}{x-4} - \dfrac{2x+21}{x-4}$

Find the LCD for each list of rational expressions. See Examples 4 through 8.

21. $\dfrac{19}{2x}, \dfrac{5}{4x^3}$

22. $\dfrac{17x}{4y^5}, \dfrac{2}{8y}$

▶ **23.** $\dfrac{9}{8x}, \dfrac{3}{2x+4}$

24. $\dfrac{1}{6y}, \dfrac{3x}{4y+12}$

25. $\dfrac{2}{x+3}, \dfrac{5}{x-2}$

26. $\dfrac{-6}{x-1}, \dfrac{4}{x+5}$

27. $\dfrac{x}{x+6}, \dfrac{10}{3x+18}$

28. $\dfrac{12}{x+5}, \dfrac{x}{4x+20}$

29. $\dfrac{8x^2}{(x-6)^2}, \dfrac{13x}{5x-30}$

30. $\dfrac{9x^2}{7x-14}, \dfrac{6x}{(x-2)^2}$

▶ **31.** $\dfrac{1}{3x+3}, \dfrac{7}{2x^2+4x+2}$

32. $\dfrac{19x+5}{4x-12}, \dfrac{3}{2x^2-12x+18}$

33. $\dfrac{5}{x-8}, \dfrac{3}{8-x}$

34. $\dfrac{2x+5}{3x-7}, \dfrac{5}{7-3x}$

35. $\dfrac{5x+1}{x^2+3x-4}, \dfrac{3x}{x^2+2x-3}$

36. $\dfrac{4}{x^2+4x+3}, \dfrac{4x-2}{x^2+10x+21}$

37. $\dfrac{2x}{3x^2+4x+1}, \dfrac{7}{2x^2-x-1}$

38. $\dfrac{3x}{4x^2+5x+1}, \dfrac{5}{3x^2-2x-1}$

39. $\dfrac{1}{x^2-16}, \dfrac{x+6}{2x^3-8x^2}$

40. $\dfrac{5}{x^2-25}, \dfrac{x+9}{3x^3-15x^2}$

Rewrite each rational expression as an equivalent rational expression with the given denominator. See Examples 9 and 10.

41. $\dfrac{3}{2x} = \dfrac{}{4x^2}$

42. $\dfrac{3}{9y^5} = \dfrac{}{72y^9}$

▶ **43.** $\dfrac{6}{3a} = \dfrac{}{12ab^2}$

44. $\dfrac{5}{4y^2x} = \dfrac{}{32y^3x^2}$

45. $\dfrac{9}{2x+6} = \dfrac{}{2y(x+3)}$

46. $\dfrac{4x+1}{3x+6} = \dfrac{}{3y(x+2)}$

▶ **47.** $\dfrac{9a+2}{5a+10} = \dfrac{}{5b(a+2)}$

48. $\dfrac{5+y}{2x^2+10} = \dfrac{}{4(x^2+5)}$

49. $\dfrac{x}{x^3+6x^2+8x} = \dfrac{}{x(x+4)(x+2)(x+1)}$

50. $\dfrac{5x}{x^3+2x^2-3x} = \dfrac{}{x(x-1)(x-5)(x+3)}$

51. $\dfrac{9y-1}{15x^2-30} = \dfrac{}{30x^2-60}$

52. $\dfrac{6m-5}{3x^2-9} = \dfrac{}{12x^2-36}$

MIXED PRACTICE SECTIONS 7.2 AND 7.3

Perform the indicated operations.

53. $\dfrac{5x}{7} + \dfrac{9x}{7}$

54. $\dfrac{5x}{7} \cdot \dfrac{9x}{7}$

55. $\dfrac{x+3}{4} \div \dfrac{2x-1}{4}$

56. $\dfrac{x+3}{4} - \dfrac{2x-1}{4}$

57. $\dfrac{x^2}{x-6} - \dfrac{5x+6}{x-6}$

58. $\dfrac{x^2+5x}{x^2-25} \cdot \dfrac{3x-15}{x^2}$

59. $\dfrac{-2x}{x^3 - 8x} + \dfrac{3x}{x^3 - 8x}$

60. $\dfrac{-2x}{x^3 - 8x} \div \dfrac{3x}{x^3 - 8x}$

61. $\dfrac{12x - 6}{x^2 + 3x} \cdot \dfrac{4x^2 + 13x + 3}{4x^2 - 1}$

62. $\dfrac{x^3 + 7x^2}{3x^3 - x^2} \div \dfrac{5x^2 + 36x + 7}{9x^2 - 1}$

REVIEW AND PREVIEW

Perform each indicated operation. See Section 1.3.

63. $\dfrac{2}{3} + \dfrac{5}{7}$

64. $\dfrac{9}{10} - \dfrac{3}{5}$

65. $\dfrac{1}{6} - \dfrac{3}{4}$

66. $\dfrac{11}{15} + \dfrac{5}{9}$

67. $\dfrac{1}{12} + \dfrac{3}{20}$

68. $\dfrac{7}{30} + \dfrac{3}{18}$

CONCEPT EXTENSIONS

For Exercises 69 and 70, see the Concept Check in this section.

69. Choose the correct LCD of $\dfrac{11a^3}{4a - 20}$ and $\dfrac{15a^3}{(a - 5)^2}$.

    a. $4a(a - 5)(a + 5)$ **b.** $a - 5$ **c.** $(a - 5)^2$

    d. $4(a - 5)^2$ **e.** $(4a - 20)(a - 5)^2$

70. Choose the correct LCD of $\dfrac{5}{14x^2}$ and $\dfrac{y}{6x^3}$.

    a. $84x^5$ **b.** $84x^3$

    c. $42x^3$ **d.** $42x^5$

For Exercises 71 and 72, an algebra student approaches you with each incorrect solution. Find the error and correct the work shown below.

71.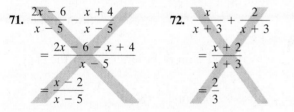
$$\dfrac{2x - 6}{x - 5} - \dfrac{x + 4}{x - 5}$$
$$= \dfrac{2x - 6 - x + 4}{x - 5}$$
$$= \dfrac{x - 2}{x - 5}$$

72.
$$\dfrac{x}{x + 3} + \dfrac{2}{x + 3}$$
$$= \dfrac{x + 2}{x + 3}$$
$$= \dfrac{2}{3}$$

Multiple choice. Select the correct result.

73. $\dfrac{3}{x} + \dfrac{y}{x} =$

    a. $\dfrac{3 + y}{x^2}$ **b.** $\dfrac{3 + y}{2x}$ **c.** $\dfrac{3 + y}{x}$

74. $\dfrac{3}{x} - \dfrac{y}{x} =$

    a. $\dfrac{3 - y}{x^2}$ **b.** $\dfrac{3 - y}{2x}$ **c.** $\dfrac{3 - y}{x}$

75. $\dfrac{3}{x} \cdot \dfrac{y}{x} =$

    a. $\dfrac{3y}{x}$ **b.** $\dfrac{3y}{x^2}$ **c.** $3y$

76. $\dfrac{3}{x} \div \dfrac{y}{x} =$

    a. $\dfrac{3}{y}$ **b.** $\dfrac{y}{3}$ **c.** $\dfrac{3}{x^2 y}$

Write each rational expression as an equivalent expression with a denominator of $x - 2$.

77. $\dfrac{5}{2 - x}$

78. $\dfrac{8y}{2 - x}$

79. $-\dfrac{7 + x}{2 - x}$

80. $\dfrac{x - 3}{-(x - 2)}$

△ **81.** A square has a side of length $\dfrac{5}{x - 2}$ meters. Express its perimeter as a rational expression.

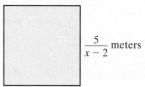
$\dfrac{5}{x - 2}$ meters

△ **82.** A trapezoid has sides of the indicated lengths. Find its perimeter.

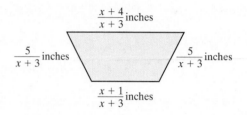
$\dfrac{x + 4}{x + 3}$ inches
$\dfrac{5}{x + 3}$ inches
$\dfrac{5}{x + 3}$ inches
$\dfrac{x + 1}{x + 3}$ inches

83. Write two rational expressions with the same denominator whose sum is $\dfrac{5}{3x - 1}$.

84. Write two rational expressions with the same denominator whose difference is $\dfrac{x - 7}{x^2 + 1}$.

85. The planet Mercury revolves around the Sun in 88 Earth days. It takes Jupiter 4332 Earth days to make one revolution around the Sun. (*Source:* National Space Science Data Center) If the two planets are aligned as shown in the figure, how long will it take for them to align again?

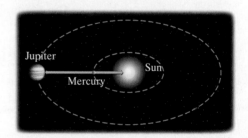

86. You are throwing a barbecue and you want to make sure that you purchase the same number of hot dogs as hot dog buns. Hot dogs come 8 to a package and hot dog buns come 12 to a package. What is the least number of each type of package you should buy?

87. Write some instructions to help a friend who is having difficulty finding the LCD of two rational expressions.

88. Explain why the LCD of the rational expressions $\dfrac{7}{x + 1}$ and $\dfrac{9x}{(x + 1)^2}$ is $(x + 1)^2$ and not $(x + 1)^3$.

89. In your own words, describe how to add or subtract two rational expressions with the same denominators.

90. Explain the similarities between subtracting $\dfrac{3}{8}$ from $\dfrac{7}{8}$ and subtracting $\dfrac{6}{x + 3}$ from $\dfrac{9}{x + 3}$.

7.4 Adding and Subtracting Rational Expressions with Unlike Denominators ▶

OBJECTIVE

1 Add and Subtract Rational Expressions with Unlike Denominators. ▶

OBJECTIVE

1 Adding and Subtracting Rational Expressions with Unlike Denominators ▶

Let's add $\frac{3}{8}$ and $\frac{1}{6}$. From the previous section, the LCD of 8 and 6 is 24. Now let's write equivalent fractions with denominator 24 by multiplying by different forms of 1.

$$\frac{3}{8} = \frac{3}{8} \cdot 1 = \frac{3}{8} \cdot \frac{3}{3} = \frac{3 \cdot 3}{8 \cdot 3} = \frac{9}{24}$$

$$\frac{1}{6} = \frac{1}{6} \cdot 1 = \frac{1}{6} \cdot \frac{4}{4} = \frac{1 \cdot 4}{6 \cdot 4} = \frac{4}{24}$$

Now that the denominators are the same, we may add.

$$\frac{3}{8} + \frac{1}{6} = \frac{9}{24} + \frac{4}{24} = \frac{9 + 4}{24} = \frac{13}{24}$$

We add or subtract rational expressions the same way. You may want to use the steps below.

Adding or Subtracting Rational Expressions with Unlike Denominators

Step 1. Find the LCD of the rational expressions.

Step 2. Rewrite each rational expression as an equivalent expression whose denominator is the LCD found in Step 1.

Step 3. Add or subtract numerators and write the sum or difference over the common denominator.

Step 4. Simplify or write the rational expression in simplest form.

EXAMPLE 1 Perform each indicated operation.

a. $\frac{a}{4} - \frac{2a}{8}$ **b.** $\frac{3}{10x^2} + \frac{7}{25x}$

Solution

a. First, we must find the LCD. Since $4 = 2^2$ and $8 = 2^3$, the LCD $= 2^3 = 8$. Next we write each fraction as an equivalent fraction with the denominator 8, then we subtract.

$$\frac{a}{4} - \frac{2a}{8} = \frac{a(2)}{4(2)} - \frac{2a}{8} = \frac{2a}{8} - \frac{2a}{8} = \frac{2a - 2a}{8} = \frac{0}{8} = 0$$

Multiplying the numerator and denominator by 2 is the same as multiplying by $\frac{2}{2}$ or 1.

b. Since $10x^2 = 2 \cdot 5 \cdot x \cdot x$ and $25x = 5 \cdot 5 \cdot x$, the LCD $= 2 \cdot 5^2 \cdot x^2 = 50x^2$. We write each fraction as an equivalent fraction with a denominator of $50x^2$.

$$\frac{3}{10x^2} + \frac{7}{25x} = \frac{3(5)}{10x^2(5)} + \frac{7(2x)}{25x(2x)}$$

$$= \frac{15}{50x^2} + \frac{14x}{50x^2}$$

$$= \frac{15 + 14x}{50x^2} \qquad \text{Add numerators. Write the sum over the common denominator.} \quad \square$$

PRACTICE

1   Perform each indicated operation.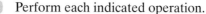

a. $\dfrac{2x}{5} - \dfrac{6x}{15}$

b. $\dfrac{7}{8a} + \dfrac{5}{12a^2}$

EXAMPLE 2   Subtract: $\dfrac{6x}{x^2 - 4} - \dfrac{3}{x + 2}$

**Solution**   Since $x^2 - 4 = (x + 2)(x - 2)$, the LCD $= (x - 2)(x + 2)$. We write equivalent expressions with the LCD as denominators.

$$\dfrac{6x}{x^2 - 4} - \dfrac{3}{x + 2} = \dfrac{6x}{(x - 2)(x + 2)} - \dfrac{3(x - 2)}{(x + 2)(x - 2)}$$

$$= \dfrac{6x - 3(x - 2)}{(x + 2)(x - 2)} \qquad \text{Subtract numerators. Write the difference over the common denominator.}$$

$$= \dfrac{6x - 3x + 6}{(x + 2)(x - 2)} \qquad \text{Apply the distributive property in the numerator.}$$

$$= \dfrac{3x + 6}{(x + 2)(x - 2)} \qquad \text{Combine like terms in the numerator.}$$

Next we factor the numerator to see if this rational expression can be simplified.

$$= \dfrac{3(x + 2)}{(x + 2)(x - 2)} \qquad \text{Factor.}$$

$$= \dfrac{3}{x - 2} \qquad \text{Divide out common factors to simplify.} \quad \square$$

PRACTICE

2   Subtract: $\dfrac{12x}{x^2 - 25} - \dfrac{6}{x + 5}$

EXAMPLE 3   Add: $\dfrac{2}{3t} + \dfrac{5}{t + 1}$

**Solution**   The LCD is $3t(t + 1)$. We write each rational expression as an equivalent rational expression with a denominator of $3t(t + 1)$.

$$\dfrac{2}{3t} + \dfrac{5}{t + 1} = \dfrac{2(t + 1)}{3t(t + 1)} + \dfrac{5(3t)}{(t + 1)(3t)}$$

$$= \dfrac{2(t + 1) + 5(3t)}{3t(t + 1)} \qquad \text{Add numerators. Write the sum over the common denominator.}$$

$$= \dfrac{2t + 2 + 15t}{3t(t + 1)} \qquad \text{Apply the distributive property in the numerator.}$$

$$= \dfrac{17t + 2}{3t(t + 1)} \qquad \text{Combine like terms in the numerator.} \quad \square$$

PRACTICE

3   Add: $\dfrac{3}{5y} + \dfrac{2}{y + 1}$

EXAMPLE 4   Subtract: $\dfrac{7}{x - 3} - \dfrac{9}{3 - x}$

**Solution**   To find a common denominator, we notice that $x - 3$ and $3 - x$ are opposites. That is, $3 - x = -(x - 3)$. We write the denominator $3 - x$ as $-(x - 3)$ and simplify.

(Continued on next page)

$$\frac{7}{x-3} - \frac{9}{3-x} = \frac{7}{x-3} - \frac{9}{-(x-3)}$$

$$= \frac{7}{x-3} - \frac{-9}{x-3} \qquad \text{Apply } \frac{a}{-b} = \frac{-a}{b}.$$

$$= \frac{7-(-9)}{x-3} \qquad \text{Subtract numerators. Write the difference over the common denominator.}$$

$$= \frac{16}{x-3}$$

PRACTICE
4 Subtract: $\dfrac{6}{x-5} - \dfrac{7}{5-x}$

EXAMPLE 5 Add: $1 + \dfrac{m}{m+1}$

<u>Solution</u> Recall that 1 is the same as $\dfrac{1}{1}$. The LCD of $\dfrac{1}{1}$ and $\dfrac{m}{m+1}$ is $m+1$.

$$1 + \frac{m}{m+1} = \frac{1}{1} + \frac{m}{m+1} \qquad \text{Write 1 as } \frac{1}{1}.$$

$$= \frac{1(m+1)}{1(m+1)} + \frac{m}{m+1} \qquad \begin{array}{l}\text{Multiply both the numerator and the} \\ \text{denominator of } \frac{1}{1} \text{ by } m+1.\end{array}$$

$$= \frac{m+1+m}{m+1} \qquad \begin{array}{l}\text{Add numerators. Write the sum over} \\ \text{the common denominator.}\end{array}$$

$$= \frac{2m+1}{m+1} \qquad \text{Combine like terms in the numerator.}$$

PRACTICE
5 Add: $2 + \dfrac{b}{b+3}$

EXAMPLE 6 Subtract: $\dfrac{3}{2x^2+x} - \dfrac{2x}{6x+3}$

<u>Solution</u> First, we factor the denominators.

$$\frac{3}{2x^2+x} - \frac{2x}{6x+3} = \frac{3}{x(2x+1)} - \frac{2x}{3(2x+1)}$$

The LCD is $3x(2x+1)$. We write equivalent expressions with denominators of $3x(2x+1)$.

$$= \frac{3(3)}{x(2x+1)(3)} - \frac{2x(x)}{3(2x+1)(x)}$$

$$= \frac{9-2x^2}{3x(2x+1)} \qquad \begin{array}{l}\text{Subtract numerators. Write the} \\ \text{difference over the common} \\ \text{denominator.}\end{array}$$

PRACTICE
6 Subtract: $\dfrac{5}{2x^2+3x} - \dfrac{3x}{4x+6}$

EXAMPLE 7 Add: $\dfrac{2x}{x^2 + 2x + 1} + \dfrac{x}{x^2 - 1}$

Solution First we factor the denominators.

$$\dfrac{2x}{x^2 + 2x + 1} + \dfrac{x}{x^2 - 1} = \dfrac{2x}{(x+1)(x+1)} + \dfrac{x}{(x+1)(x-1)}$$

Now we write the rational expressions as equivalent expressions with denominators of $(x+1)(x+1)(x-1)$, the LCD.

$$= \dfrac{2x(x-1)}{(x+1)(x+1)(x-1)} + \dfrac{x(x+1)}{(x+1)(x-1)(x+1)}$$

$$= \dfrac{2x(x-1) + x(x+1)}{(x+1)^2(x-1)}$$ Add numerators. Write the sum over the common denominator.

$$= \dfrac{2x^2 - 2x + x^2 + x}{(x+1)^2(x-1)}$$ Apply the distributive property in the numerator.

$$= \dfrac{3x^2 - x}{(x+1)^2(x-1)} \quad \text{or} \quad \dfrac{x(3x-1)}{(x+1)^2(x-1)}$$

The numerator was factored as a last step to see if the rational expression could be simplified further. Since there are no factors common to the numerator and the denominator, we can't simplify further.   □

PRACTICE
7   Add: $\dfrac{2x}{x^2 + 7x + 12} + \dfrac{3x}{x^2 - 9}$ ■

✔ Vocabulary, Readiness & Video Check

Match each exercise with the first step needed to perform the operation. Do not actually perform the operation.

1. $\dfrac{3}{4} - \dfrac{y}{4}$ **2.** $\dfrac{2}{a} \cdot \dfrac{3}{(a+6)}$ **3.** $\dfrac{x+1}{x} \div \dfrac{x-1}{x}$ **4.** $\dfrac{9}{x-2} - \dfrac{x}{x+2}$

A. Multiply the first rational expression by the reciprocal of the second rational expression.

B. Find the LCD. Write each expression as an equivalent expression with the LCD as denominator.

C. Multiply numerators and multiply denominators.

D. Subtract numerators. Place the difference over a common denominator.

Martin-Gay Interactive Videos

See Video 7.4 ●

Watch the section lecture video and answer the following question.

OBJECTIVE
1   **5.** What special case is shown in ▦ Example 2 and what's the purpose of presenting it?

7.4 Exercise Set MyMathLab▶

MIXED PRACTICE

Perform each indicated operation. Simplify if possible. See Examples 1 through 7.

1. $\dfrac{4}{2x} + \dfrac{9}{3x}$

2. $\dfrac{15}{7a} + \dfrac{8}{6a}$

3. $\dfrac{15a}{b} - \dfrac{6b}{5}$

4. $\dfrac{4c}{d} - \dfrac{8d}{5}$

▶ 5. $\dfrac{3}{x} + \dfrac{5}{2x^2}$

6. $\dfrac{14}{3x^2} + \dfrac{6}{x}$

7. $\dfrac{6}{x+1} + \dfrac{10}{2x+2}$

8. $\dfrac{8}{x+4} - \dfrac{3}{3x+12}$

9. $\dfrac{3}{x+2} - \dfrac{2x}{x^2-4}$

10. $\dfrac{5}{x-4} + \dfrac{4x}{x^2-16}$

11. $\dfrac{3}{4x} + \dfrac{8}{x-2}$

12. $\dfrac{5}{y^2} - \dfrac{y}{2y+1}$

▶ 13. $\dfrac{6}{x-3} + \dfrac{8}{3-x}$

14. $\dfrac{15}{y-4} + \dfrac{20}{4-y}$

15. $\dfrac{9}{x-3} + \dfrac{9}{3-x}$

16. $\dfrac{5}{a-7} + \dfrac{5}{7-a}$

17. $\dfrac{-8}{x^2-1} - \dfrac{7}{1-x^2}$

18. $\dfrac{-9}{25x^2-1} + \dfrac{7}{1-25x^2}$

19. $\dfrac{5}{x} + 2$

20. $\dfrac{7}{x^2} - 5x$

21. $\dfrac{5}{x-2} + 6$

22. $\dfrac{6y}{y+5} + 1$

▶ 23. $\dfrac{y+2}{y+3} - 2$

24. $\dfrac{7}{2x-3} - 3$

25. $\dfrac{-x+2}{x} - \dfrac{x-6}{4x}$

26. $\dfrac{-y+1}{y} - \dfrac{2y-5}{3y}$

27. $\dfrac{5x}{x+2} - \dfrac{3x-4}{x+2}$

28. $\dfrac{7x}{x-3} - \dfrac{4x+9}{x-3}$

29. $\dfrac{3x^4}{7} - \dfrac{4x^2}{21}$

30. $\dfrac{5x}{6} + \dfrac{11x^2}{2}$

31. $\dfrac{1}{x+3} - \dfrac{1}{(x+3)^2}$

32. $\dfrac{5x}{(x-2)^2} - \dfrac{3}{x-2}$

33. $\dfrac{4}{5b} + \dfrac{1}{b-1}$

34. $\dfrac{1}{y+5} + \dfrac{2}{3y}$

35. $\dfrac{2}{m} + 1$

36. $\dfrac{6}{x} - 1$

37. $\dfrac{2x}{x-7} - \dfrac{x}{x-2}$

38. $\dfrac{9x}{x-10} - \dfrac{x}{x-3}$

39. $\dfrac{6}{1-2x} - \dfrac{4}{2x-1}$

40. $\dfrac{10}{3n-4} - \dfrac{5}{4-3n}$

41. $\dfrac{7}{(x+1)(x-1)} + \dfrac{8}{(x+1)^2}$

42. $\dfrac{5}{(x+1)(x+5)} - \dfrac{2}{(x+5)^2}$

43. $\dfrac{x}{x^2-1} - \dfrac{2}{x^2-2x+1}$

44. $\dfrac{x}{x^2-4} - \dfrac{5}{x^2-4x+4}$

▶ 45. $\dfrac{3a}{2a+6} - \dfrac{a-1}{a+3}$

46. $\dfrac{1}{x+y} - \dfrac{y}{x^2-y^2}$

47. $\dfrac{y-1}{2y+3} + \dfrac{3}{(2y+3)^2}$

48. $\dfrac{x-6}{5x+1} + \dfrac{6}{(5x+1)^2}$

49. $\dfrac{5}{2-x} + \dfrac{x}{2x-4}$

50. $\dfrac{-1}{a-2} + \dfrac{4}{4-2a}$

51. $\dfrac{15}{x^2+6x+9} + \dfrac{2}{x+3}$

52. $\dfrac{2}{x^2+4x+4} + \dfrac{1}{x+2}$

53. $\dfrac{13}{x^2-5x+6} - \dfrac{5}{x-3}$

54. $\dfrac{-7}{y^2 - 3y + 2} - \dfrac{2}{y - 1}$

55. $\dfrac{70}{m^2 - 100} + \dfrac{7}{2(m + 10)}$

56. $\dfrac{27}{y^2 - 81} + \dfrac{3}{2(y + 9)}$

▶ **57.** $\dfrac{x + 8}{x^2 - 5x - 6} + \dfrac{x + 1}{x^2 - 4x - 5}$

58. $\dfrac{x + 4}{x^2 + 12x + 20} + \dfrac{x + 1}{x^2 + 8x - 20}$

59. $\dfrac{5}{4n^2 - 12n + 8} - \dfrac{3}{3n^2 - 6n}$

60. $\dfrac{6}{5y^2 - 25y + 30} - \dfrac{2}{4y^2 - 8y}$

MIXED PRACTICE

Perform the indicated operations. Addition, subtraction, multiplication, and division of rational expressions are included here.

61. $\dfrac{15x}{x + 8} \cdot \dfrac{2x + 16}{3x}$

62. $\dfrac{9z + 5}{15} \cdot \dfrac{5z}{81z^2 - 25}$

63. $\dfrac{8x + 7}{3x + 5} - \dfrac{2x - 3}{3x + 5}$

64. $\dfrac{2z^2}{4z - 1} - \dfrac{z - 2z^2}{4z - 1}$

65. $\dfrac{5a + 10}{18} \div \dfrac{a^2 - 4}{10a}$

66. $\dfrac{9}{x^2 - 1} \div \dfrac{12}{3x + 3}$

67. $\dfrac{5}{x^2 - 3x + 2} + \dfrac{1}{x - 2}$

68. $\dfrac{4}{2x^2 + 5x - 3} + \dfrac{2}{x + 3}$

REVIEW AND PREVIEW

Solve the following linear and quadratic equations. See Sections 2.3 and 6.6.

69. $3x + 5 = 7$

70. $5x - 1 = 8$

71. $2x^2 - x - 1 = 0$

72. $4x^2 - 9 = 0$

73. $4(x + 6) + 3 = -3$

74. $2(3x + 1) + 15 = -7$

CONCEPT EXTENSIONS

Perform each indicated operation.

75. $\dfrac{3}{x} - \dfrac{2x}{x^2 - 1} + \dfrac{5}{x + 1}$

76. $\dfrac{5}{x - 2} + \dfrac{7x}{x^2 - 4} - \dfrac{11}{x}$

77. $\dfrac{5}{x^2 - 4} + \dfrac{2}{x^2 - 4x + 4} - \dfrac{3}{x^2 - x - 6}$

78. $\dfrac{8}{x^2 + 6x + 5} - \dfrac{3x}{x^2 + 4x - 5} + \dfrac{2}{x^2 - 1}$

79. $\dfrac{9}{x^2 + 9x + 14} - \dfrac{3x}{x^2 + 10x + 21} + \dfrac{x + 4}{x^2 + 5x + 6}$

80. $\dfrac{x + 10}{x^2 - 3x - 4} - \dfrac{8}{x^2 + 6x + 5} - \dfrac{9}{x^2 + x - 20}$

81. A board of length $\dfrac{3}{x + 4}$ inches was cut into two pieces. If one piece is $\dfrac{1}{x - 4}$ inches, express the length of the other piece as a rational expression.

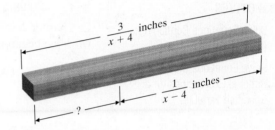

82. The length of a rectangle is $\dfrac{3}{y - 5}$ feet, while its width is $\dfrac{2}{y}$ feet. Find its perimeter and then find its area.

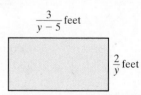

83. In ice hockey, penalty killing percentage is a statistic calculated as $1 - \dfrac{G}{P}$, where G = opponent's power play goals and P = opponent's power play opportunities. Simplify this expression.

84. The dose of medicine prescribed for a child depends on the child's age A in years and the adult dose D for the medication. Two expressions that give a child's dose are Young's Rule, $\dfrac{DA}{A + 12}$, and Cowling's Rule, $\dfrac{D(A + 1)}{24}$. Find an expression for the difference in the doses given by these expressions.

85. Explain when the LCD of the rational expressions in a sum is the product of the denominators.

86. Explain when the LCD is the same as one of the denominators of a rational expression to be added or subtracted.

△ **87.** Two angles are said to be complementary if the sum of their measures is 90°. If one angle measures $\dfrac{40}{x}$ degrees, find the measure of its complement.

△ **88.** Two angles are said to be supplementary if the sum of their measures is 180°. If one angle measures $\dfrac{x+2}{x}$ degrees, find the measure of its supplement.

\ **89.** In your own words, explain how to add two rational expressions with different denominators.

\ **90.** In your own words, explain how to subtract two rational expressions with different denominators.

7.5 Solving Equations Containing Rational Expressions ▶

OBJECTIVES

1 Solve Equations Containing Rational Expressions. ▶

2 Solve Equations Containing Rational Expressions for a Specified Variable. ▶

OBJECTIVE

1 Solving Equations Containing Rational Expressions ▶

In Chapter 2, we solved equations containing fractions. In this section, we continue the work we began in Chapter 2 by solving equations containing rational expressions.

Examples of Equations Containing Rational Expressions

$$\frac{x}{2} + \frac{8}{3} = \frac{1}{6} \quad \text{and} \quad \frac{4x}{x^2 + x - 30} + \frac{2}{x - 5} = \frac{1}{x + 6}$$

To solve equations such as these, use the multiplication property of equality to clear the equation of fractions by multiplying both sides of the equation by the LCD.

EXAMPLE 1 Solve: $\dfrac{x}{2} + \dfrac{8}{3} = \dfrac{1}{6}$

Solution The LCD of denominators 2, 3, and 6 is 6, so we multiply both sides of the equation by 6.

$$6\left(\frac{x}{2} + \frac{8}{3}\right) = 6\left(\frac{1}{6}\right)$$

Helpful Hint

Make sure that *each* term is multiplied by the LCD, 6.

$$6\left(\frac{x}{2}\right) + 6\left(\frac{8}{3}\right) = 6\left(\frac{1}{6}\right) \quad \text{Use the distributive property.}$$

$$3 \cdot x + 16 = 1 \qquad \text{Multiply and simplify.}$$

$$3x = -15 \qquad \text{Subtract 16 from both sides.}$$

$$x = -5 \qquad \text{Divide both sides by 3.}$$

Check: To check, we replace x with -5 in the original equation.

$$\frac{x}{2} + \frac{8}{3} = \frac{1}{6}$$

$$\frac{-5}{2} + \frac{8}{3} \overset{?}{=} \frac{1}{6} \qquad \text{Replace } x \text{ with } -5$$

$$\frac{1}{6} = \frac{1}{6} \qquad \text{True}$$

This number checks, so the solution is -5. ☐

PRACTICE

1 Solve: $\dfrac{x}{3} + \dfrac{4}{5} = \dfrac{2}{15}$

EXAMPLE 2   Solve: $\dfrac{t-4}{2} - \dfrac{t-3}{9} = \dfrac{5}{18}$

Solution   The LCD of denominators 2, 9, and 18 is 18, so we multiply both sides of the equation by 18.

$$18\left(\dfrac{t-4}{2} - \dfrac{t-3}{9}\right) = 18\left(\dfrac{5}{18}\right)$$

Helpful Hint
Multiply _each_ term by 18.

$$18\left(\dfrac{t-4}{2}\right) - 18\left(\dfrac{t-3}{9}\right) = 18\left(\dfrac{5}{18}\right) \quad \text{Use the distributive property.}$$

$$9(t-4) - 2(t-3) = 5 \qquad \text{Simplify.}$$

$$9t - 36 - 2t + 6 = 5 \qquad \text{Use the distributive property.}$$

$$7t - 30 = 5 \qquad \text{Combine like terms.}$$

$$7t = 35$$

$$t = 5 \qquad \text{Solve for } t.$$

Check:

$$\dfrac{t-4}{2} - \dfrac{t-3}{9} = \dfrac{5}{18}$$

$$\dfrac{5-4}{2} - \dfrac{5-3}{9} \overset{?}{=} \dfrac{5}{18} \qquad \text{Replace } t \text{ with 5.}$$

$$\dfrac{1}{2} - \dfrac{2}{9} \overset{?}{=} \dfrac{5}{18} \qquad \text{Simplify.}$$

$$\dfrac{5}{18} = \dfrac{5}{18} \qquad \text{True}$$

The solution is 5.   □

PRACTICE
2   Solve: $\dfrac{x+4}{4} - \dfrac{x-3}{3} = \dfrac{11}{12}$ ■

Recall from Section 7.1 that a rational expression is defined for all real numbers except those that make the denominator of the expression 0. This means that if an equation contains _rational expressions with variables in the denominator_, we must be certain that a proposed solution does not make any denominator 0. If replacing the variable with the proposed solution makes any denominator 0, the rational expression is undefined and this proposed solution must be rejected.

EXAMPLE 3   Solve: $3 - \dfrac{6}{x} = x + 8$

Solution   In this equation, 0 cannot be a solution because if x is 0, the rational expression $\dfrac{6}{x}$ is undefined. The LCD is x, so we multiply both sides of the equation by x.

$$x\left(3 - \dfrac{6}{x}\right) = x(x + 8)$$

Helpful Hint
Multiply _each_ term by x.

$$x(3) - x\left(\dfrac{6}{x}\right) = x \cdot x + x \cdot 8 \quad \text{Use the distributive property.}$$

$$3x - 6 = x^2 + 8x \qquad \text{Simplify.}$$

Now we write the quadratic equation in standard form and solve for x.

$$0 = x^2 + 5x + 6$$

$$0 = (x+3)(x+2) \qquad \text{Factor.}$$

$$x + 3 = 0 \quad \text{or} \quad x + 2 = 0 \quad \text{Set each factor equal to 0 and solve.}$$

$$x = -3 \qquad\qquad x = -2$$

(Continued on next page)

Notice that neither -3 nor -2 makes the denominator in the original equation equal to 0.

Check: To check these solutions, we replace x in the original equation by -3, and then by -2.

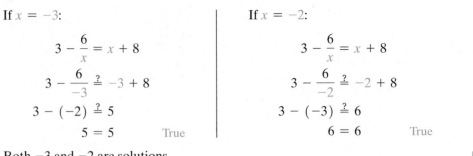

If $x = -3$:

$$3 - \frac{6}{x} = x + 8$$

$$3 - \frac{6}{-3} \overset{?}{=} -3 + 8$$

$$3 - (-2) \overset{?}{=} 5$$

$$5 = 5 \qquad \text{True}$$

If $x = -2$:

$$3 - \frac{6}{x} = x + 8$$

$$3 - \frac{6}{-2} \overset{?}{=} -2 + 8$$

$$3 - (-3) \overset{?}{=} 6$$

$$6 = 6 \qquad \text{True}$$

Both -3 and -2 are solutions. □

PRACTICE
3 Solve: $8 + \dfrac{7}{x} = x + 2$ ■

The following steps may be used to solve an equation containing rational expressions.

> **Solving an Equation Containing Rational Expressions**
>
> **Step 1.** Multiply both sides of the equation by the LCD of all rational expressions in the equation.
>
> **Step 2.** Remove any grouping symbols and solve the resulting equation.
>
> **Step 3.** Check the solution in the original equation.

EXAMPLE 4   Solve: $\dfrac{4x}{x^2 + x - 30} + \dfrac{2}{x - 5} = \dfrac{1}{x + 6}$

Solution The denominator $x^2 + x - 30$ factors as $(x + 6)(x - 5)$. The LCD is then $(x + 6)(x - 5)$, so we multiply both sides of the equation by this LCD.

$$(x + 6)(x - 5)\left(\frac{4x}{x^2 + x - 30} + \frac{2}{x - 5}\right) = (x + 6)(x - 5)\left(\frac{1}{x + 6}\right) \quad \text{Multiply by the LCD.}$$

$$(x + 6)(x - 5) \cdot \frac{4x}{x^2 + x - 30} + (x + 6)(x - 5) \cdot \frac{2}{x - 5} \quad \text{Apply the distributive property.}$$

$$= (x + 6)(x - 5) \cdot \frac{1}{x + 6}$$

$$4x + 2(x + 6) = x - 5 \quad \text{Simplify.}$$

$$4x + 2x + 12 = x - 5 \quad \text{Apply the distributive property.}$$

$$6x + 12 = x - 5 \quad \text{Combine like terms.}$$

$$5x = -17$$

$$x = -\frac{17}{5} \quad \text{Divide both sides by 5.}$$

Check: Check by replacing x with $-\dfrac{17}{5}$ in the original equation. The solution is $-\dfrac{17}{5}$.

□

PRACTICE
4 Solve: $\dfrac{6x}{x^2 - 5x - 14} - \dfrac{3}{x + 2} = \dfrac{1}{x - 7}$ ■

EXAMPLE 5 Solve: $\dfrac{2x}{x-4} = \dfrac{8}{x-4} + 1$

Solution Multiply both sides by the LCD, $x-4$.

$$(x-4)\left(\dfrac{2x}{x-4}\right) = (x-4)\left(\dfrac{8}{x-4}+1\right)$$
Multiply by the LCD. Notice that 4 cannot be a solution.

$$(x-4)\cdot\dfrac{2x}{x-4} = (x-4)\cdot\dfrac{8}{x-4} + (x-4)\cdot 1$$
Use the distributive property.

$$2x = 8 + (x-4)$$ Simplify.

$$2x = 4 + x$$

$$x = 4$$

Notice that 4 makes the denominators 0 in the original equation. Therefore, 4 is *not* a solution.

This equation has *no solution*.

PRACTICE 5 Solve: $\dfrac{7x}{x-2} = \dfrac{14}{x-2} + 4$

Helpful Hint

As we can see from Example 5, it is important to check the proposed solution(s) in the *original* equation.

✔ **CONCEPT CHECK**

When can we clear fractions by multiplying through by the LCD?

a. When adding or subtracting rational expressions
b. When solving an equation containing rational expressions
c. Both of these
d. Neither of these

EXAMPLE 6 Solve: $x + \dfrac{14}{x-2} = \dfrac{7x}{x-2} + 1$

Solution Notice the denominators in this equation. We can see that 2 can't be a solution. The LCD is $x-2$, so we multiply both sides of the equation by $x-2$.

$$(x-2)\left(x + \dfrac{14}{x-2}\right) = (x-2)\left(\dfrac{7x}{x-2} + 1\right)$$

$$(x-2)(x) + (x-2)\left(\dfrac{14}{x-2}\right) = (x-2)\left(\dfrac{7x}{x-2}\right) + (x-2)(1)$$

$$x^2 - 2x + 14 = 7x + x - 2$$ Simplify.

$$x^2 - 2x + 14 = 8x - 2$$ Combine like terms.

$$x^2 - 10x + 16 = 0$$ Write the quadratic equation in standard form.

$$(x-8)(x-2) = 0$$ Factor.

$$x - 8 = 0 \quad \text{or} \quad x - 2 = 0$$ Set each factor equal to 0.

$$x = 8 \qquad\qquad x = 2$$ Solve.

(Continued on next page)

As we have already noted, 2 can't be a solution of the original equation. So we need only replace x with 8 in the original equation. We find that 8 is a solution; the only solution is 8. □

PRACTICE
6 Solve: $x + \dfrac{x}{x-5} = \dfrac{5}{x-5} - 7$ ∎

OBJECTIVE
2 Solving Equations for a Specified Variable ▶

The last example in this section is an equation containing several variables, and we are directed to solve for one of the variables. The steps used in the preceding examples can be applied to solve equations for a specified variable as well.

EXAMPLE 7   Solve $\dfrac{1}{a} + \dfrac{1}{b} = \dfrac{1}{x}$ for x.

Solution This type of equation often models a work problem, as we shall see in Section 7.6. The LCD is abx, so we multiply both sides by abx.

$$abx\left(\frac{1}{a} + \frac{1}{b}\right) = abx\left(\frac{1}{x}\right)$$

$$abx\left(\frac{1}{a}\right) + abx\left(\frac{1}{b}\right) = abx \cdot \frac{1}{x}$$

$$bx + ax = ab \qquad \text{Simplify.}$$

$$x(b + a) = ab \qquad \text{Factor out } x \text{ from each term on the left side.}$$

$$\frac{x(b + a)}{b + a} = \frac{ab}{b + a} \qquad \text{Divide both sides by } b + a.$$

$$x = \frac{ab}{b + a} \qquad \text{Simplify.}$$

This equation is now solved for x. □

PRACTICE
7 Solve $\dfrac{1}{a} + \dfrac{1}{b} = \dfrac{1}{x}$ for b.   ∎

Graphing Calculator Explorations

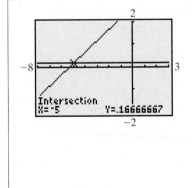

A graphing calculator may be used to check solutions of equations containing rational expressions. For example, to check the solution of Example 1, $\dfrac{x}{2} + \dfrac{8}{3} = \dfrac{1}{6}$, graph $Y_1 = \dfrac{x}{2} + \dfrac{8}{3}$ and $Y_2 = \dfrac{1}{6}$.

Use TRACE and ZOOM, or use INTERSECT, to find the point of intersection. The point of intersection has an x-value of -5, so the solution of the equation is -5.

Use a graphing calculator to check the examples of this section.

1. Example 2   **2.** Example 3

3. Example 5   **4.** Example 6

✓ Vocabulary, Readiness & Video Check

Multiple choice. Choose the correct response.

1. Multiply both sides of the equation $\dfrac{3x}{2} + 5 = \dfrac{1}{4}$ by 4. The result is:

   a. $3x + 5 = 1$ **b.** $6x + 5 = 1$ **c.** $6x + 20 = 1$ **d.** $6x + 9 = 1$

2. Multiply both sides of the equation $\dfrac{1}{x} - \dfrac{3}{5x} = 2$ by $5x$. The result is:

   a. $1 - 3 = 10x$ **b.** $5 - 3 = 10x$ **c.** $1 - 3 = 7x$ **d.** $5 - 3 = 7x$

Choose the correct LCD for the fractions in each equation.

3. Equation: $\dfrac{9}{x} + \dfrac{3}{4} = \dfrac{1}{12}$; LCD: _____

   a. $4x$ **b.** $12x$ **c.** $48x$ **d.** x

4. Equation: $\dfrac{8}{3x} - \dfrac{1}{x} = \dfrac{7}{9}$; LCD: _____

   a. x **b.** $3x$ **c.** $27x$ **d.** $9x$

5. Equation: $\dfrac{9}{x - 1} = \dfrac{7}{(x - 1)^2}$; LCD: _____

   a. $(x - 1)^2$ **b.** $x - 1$ **c.** $(x - 1)^3$ **d.** 63

6. Equation: $\dfrac{1}{x - 2} - \dfrac{3}{x^2 - 4} = 8$; LCD: _____

   a. $(x - 2)$ **b.** $x + 2$ **c.** $x^2 - 4$ **d.** $(x - 2)(x^2 - 4)$

Martin-Gay Interactive Videos

See Video 7.5 ◉

Watch the section lecture video and answer the following questions.

OBJECTIVE 1
7. After multiplying through by the LCD and then simplifying, why is it important to take a moment and determine whether you have a linear or a quadratic equation before you finish solving the problem?

OBJECTIVE 1
8. From ▦ Examples 2–5, what extra step is needed when checking solutions of an equation containing rational expressions?

OBJECTIVE 2
9. The steps for solving ▦ Example 6 for a specified variable are the same as what other steps? How do you treat this specified variable?

7.5 Exercise Set MyMathLab® ▷

Solve each equation and check each solution. See Examples 1 through 3.

1. $\dfrac{x}{5} + 3 = 9$ **2.** $\dfrac{x}{5} - 2 = 9$

3. $\dfrac{x}{2} + \dfrac{5x}{4} = \dfrac{x}{12}$ **4.** $\dfrac{x}{6} + \dfrac{4x}{3} = \dfrac{x}{18}$

5. $2 - \dfrac{8}{x} = 6$ **6.** $5 + \dfrac{4}{x} = 1$

7. $2 + \dfrac{10}{x} = x + 5$ **8.** $6 + \dfrac{5}{y} = y - \dfrac{2}{y}$

9. $\dfrac{a}{5} = \dfrac{a - 3}{2}$ **10.** $\dfrac{b}{5} = \dfrac{b + 2}{6}$

▷ 11. $\dfrac{x - 3}{5} + \dfrac{x - 2}{2} = \dfrac{1}{2}$ **12.** $\dfrac{a + 5}{4} + \dfrac{a + 5}{2} = \dfrac{a}{8}$

Solve each equation and check each proposed solution. See Examples 4 through 6.

13. $\dfrac{3}{2a - 5} = -1$ **14.** $\dfrac{6}{4 - 3x} = -3$

15. $\dfrac{4y}{y - 4} + 5 = \dfrac{5y}{y - 4}$ **16.** $\dfrac{2a}{a + 2} - 5 = \dfrac{7a}{a + 2}$

▶ 17. $2 + \dfrac{3}{a-3} = \dfrac{a}{a-3}$

18. $\dfrac{2y}{y-2} - \dfrac{4}{y-2} = 4$

19. $\dfrac{1}{x+3} + \dfrac{6}{x^2-9} = 1$

20. $\dfrac{1}{x+2} + \dfrac{4}{x^2-4} = 1$

21. $\dfrac{2y}{y+4} + \dfrac{4}{y+4} = 3$

22. $\dfrac{5y}{y+1} - \dfrac{3}{y+1} = 4$

23. $\dfrac{2x}{x+2} - 2 = \dfrac{x-8}{x-2}$

24. $\dfrac{4y}{y-3} - 3 = \dfrac{3y-1}{y+3}$

MIXED PRACTICE

Solve each equation. See Examples 1 through 6.

▶ 25. $\dfrac{2}{y} + \dfrac{1}{2} = \dfrac{5}{2y}$

26. $\dfrac{6}{3y} + \dfrac{3}{y} = 1$

27. $\dfrac{a}{a-6} = \dfrac{-2}{a-1}$

28. $\dfrac{5}{x-6} = \dfrac{x}{x-2}$

29. $\dfrac{11}{2x} + \dfrac{2}{3} = \dfrac{7}{2x}$

30. $\dfrac{5}{3} - \dfrac{3}{2x} = \dfrac{3}{2}$

31. $\dfrac{2}{x-2} + 1 = \dfrac{x}{x+2}$

32. $1 + \dfrac{3}{x+1} = \dfrac{x}{x-1}$

33. $\dfrac{x+1}{3} - \dfrac{x-1}{6} = \dfrac{1}{6}$

34. $\dfrac{3x}{5} - \dfrac{x-6}{3} = -\dfrac{2}{5}$

▶ 35. $\dfrac{t}{t-4} = \dfrac{t+4}{6}$

36. $\dfrac{15}{x+4} = \dfrac{x-4}{x}$

37. $\dfrac{y}{2y+2} + \dfrac{2y-16}{4y+4} = \dfrac{2y-3}{y+1}$

38. $\dfrac{1}{x+2} = \dfrac{4}{x^2-4} - \dfrac{1}{x-2}$

▶ 39. $\dfrac{4r-4}{r^2+5r-14} + \dfrac{2}{r+7} = \dfrac{1}{r-2}$

40. $\dfrac{3}{x+3} = \dfrac{12x+19}{x^2+7x+12} - \dfrac{5}{x+4}$

41. $\dfrac{x+1}{x+3} = \dfrac{x^2-11x}{x^2+x-6} - \dfrac{x-3}{x-2}$

42. $\dfrac{2t+3}{t-1} - \dfrac{2}{t+3} = \dfrac{5-6t}{t^2+2t-3}$

Solve each equation for the indicated variable. See Example 7.

43. $R = \dfrac{E}{I}$ for I (Electronics: resistance of a circuit)

44. $T = \dfrac{V}{Q}$ for Q (Water purification: settling time)

▶ 45. $T = \dfrac{2U}{B+E}$ for B (Merchandising: stock turnover rate)

46. $i = \dfrac{A}{t+B}$ for t (Hydrology: rainfall intensity)

47. $B = \dfrac{705w}{h^2}$ for w (Health: body-mass index)

△ 48. $\dfrac{A}{W} = L$ for W (Geometry: area of a rectangle)

49. $N = R + \dfrac{V}{G}$ for G (Urban forestry: tree plantings per year)

50. $C = \dfrac{D(A+1)}{24}$ for A (Medicine: Cowling's Rule for child's dose)

△ 51. $\dfrac{C}{\pi r} = 2$ for r (Geometry: circumference of a circle)

52. $W = \dfrac{CE^2}{2}$ for C (Electronics: energy stored in a capacitor)

53. $\dfrac{1}{y} + \dfrac{1}{3} = \dfrac{1}{x}$ for x

54. $\dfrac{1}{5} + \dfrac{2}{y} = \dfrac{1}{x}$ for x

REVIEW AND PREVIEW

TRANSLATING

Write each phrase as an expression.

55. The reciprocal of x

56. The reciprocal of $x + 1$

57. The reciprocal of x, added to the reciprocal of 2

58. The reciprocal of x, subtracted from the reciprocal of 5

Answer each question.

59. If a tank is filled in 3 hours, what fractional part of the tank is filled in 1 hour?

60. If a strip of beach is cleaned in 4 hours, what fractional part of the beach is cleaned in 1 hour?

Identify the x- and y-intercepts. See Section 3.3.

61. 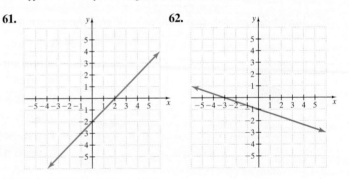   62.

63. 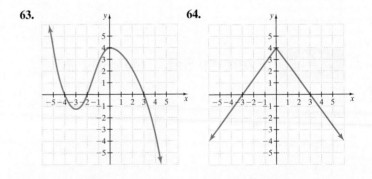   64.

CONCEPT EXTENSIONS

65. Explain the difference between solving an equation such as $\dfrac{x}{2} + \dfrac{3}{4} = \dfrac{x}{4}$ for x and performing an operation such as adding $\dfrac{x}{2} + \dfrac{3}{4}$.

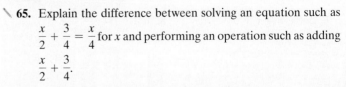

66. When solving an equation such as $\dfrac{y}{4} = \dfrac{y}{2} - \dfrac{1}{4}$, we may multiply all terms by 4. When subtracting two rational expressions such as $\dfrac{y}{2} - \dfrac{1}{4}$, we may not. Explain why.

Determine whether each of the following is an equation or an expression. If it is an equation, then solve it for its variable. If it is an expression, perform the indicated operation.

67. $\dfrac{1}{x} + \dfrac{5}{9}$

68. $\dfrac{1}{x} + \dfrac{5}{9} = \dfrac{2}{3}$

69. $\dfrac{5}{x-1} - \dfrac{2}{x} = \dfrac{5}{x(x-1)}$

70. $\dfrac{5}{x-1} - \dfrac{2}{x}$

Recall that two angles are supplementary if the sum of their measures is 180°. Find the measures of the following supplementary angles.

△ 71.

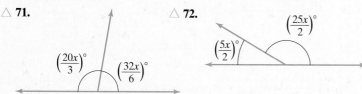

△ 72.

Recall that two angles are complementary if the sum of their measures is 90°. Find the measures of the following complementary angles.

△ 73.

△ 74.

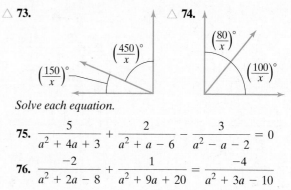

Solve each equation.

75. $\dfrac{5}{a^2 + 4a + 3} + \dfrac{2}{a^2 + a - 6} - \dfrac{3}{a^2 - a - 2} = 0$

76. $\dfrac{-2}{a^2 + 2a - 8} + \dfrac{1}{a^2 + 9a + 20} = \dfrac{-4}{a^2 + 3a - 10}$

Integrated Review   Summary on Rational Expressions

Sections 7.1–7.5

It is important to know the difference between performing operations with rational expressions and solving an equation containing rational expressions. Study the examples below.

Performing Operations with Rational Expressions

Adding: $\quad \dfrac{1}{x} + \dfrac{1}{x+5} = \dfrac{1 \cdot (x+5)}{x(x+5)} + \dfrac{1 \cdot x}{x(x+5)} = \dfrac{x+5+x}{x(x+5)} = \dfrac{2x+5}{x(x+5)}$

Subtracting: $\quad \dfrac{3}{x} - \dfrac{5}{x^2 y} = \dfrac{3 \cdot xy}{x \cdot xy} - \dfrac{5}{x^2 y} = \dfrac{3xy - 5}{x^2 y}$

Multiplying: $\quad \dfrac{2}{x} \cdot \dfrac{5}{x-1} = \dfrac{2 \cdot 5}{x(x-1)} = \dfrac{10}{x(x-1)}$

Dividing: $\quad \dfrac{4}{2x+1} \div \dfrac{x-3}{x} = \dfrac{4}{2x+1} \cdot \dfrac{x}{x-3} = \dfrac{4x}{(2x+1)(x-3)}$

Solving an Equation Containing Rational Expressions

To solve an equation containing rational expressions, we clear the equation of fractions by multiplying both sides by the LCD.

$$\dfrac{3}{x} - \dfrac{5}{x-1} = \dfrac{1}{x(x-1)} \qquad \text{Note that } x \text{ can't be 0 or 1.}$$

$$x(x-1)\left(\dfrac{3}{x}\right) - x(x-1)\left(\dfrac{5}{x-1}\right) = x(x-1) \cdot \dfrac{1}{x(x-1)} \qquad \text{Multiply both sides by the LCD.}$$

$$3(x-1) - 5x = 1 \qquad \text{Simplify.}$$

$$3x - 3 - 5x = 1 \qquad \text{Use the distributive property.}$$

$$-2x - 3 = 1 \qquad \text{Combine like terms.}$$

$$-2x = 4 \qquad \text{Add 3 to both sides.}$$

$$x = -2 \qquad \text{Divide both sides by } -2.$$

Determine whether each of the following is an equation or an expression. If it is an equation, solve it for its variable. If it is an expression, perform the indicated operation.

1. $\dfrac{1}{x} + \dfrac{2}{3}$

2. $\dfrac{3}{a} + \dfrac{5}{6}$

3. $\dfrac{1}{x} + \dfrac{2}{3} = \dfrac{3}{x}$

4. $\dfrac{3}{a} + \dfrac{5}{6} = 1$

5. $\dfrac{2}{x-1} - \dfrac{1}{x}$

6. $\dfrac{4}{x-3} - \dfrac{1}{x}$

7. $\dfrac{2}{x+1} - \dfrac{1}{x} = 1$

8. $\dfrac{4}{x-3} - \dfrac{1}{x} = \dfrac{6}{x(x-3)}$

9. $\dfrac{15x}{x+8} \cdot \dfrac{2x+16}{3x}$

10. $\dfrac{9z+5}{15} \cdot \dfrac{5z}{81z^2-25}$

11. $\dfrac{2x+1}{x-3} + \dfrac{3x+6}{x-3}$

12. $\dfrac{4p-3}{2p+7} + \dfrac{3p+8}{2p+7}$

13. $\dfrac{x+5}{7} = \dfrac{8}{2}$

14. $\dfrac{1}{2} = \dfrac{x-1}{8}$

15. $\dfrac{5a+10}{18} \div \dfrac{a^2-4}{10a}$

16. $\dfrac{9}{x^2-1} + \dfrac{12}{3x+3}$

17. $\dfrac{x+2}{3x-1} + \dfrac{5}{(3x-1)^2}$

18. $\dfrac{4}{(2x-5)^2} + \dfrac{x+1}{2x-5}$

19. $\dfrac{x-7}{x} - \dfrac{x+2}{5x}$

20. $\dfrac{10x-9}{x} - \dfrac{x-4}{3x}$

21. $\dfrac{3}{x+3} = \dfrac{5}{x^2-9} - \dfrac{2}{x-3}$

22. $\dfrac{9}{x^2-4} + \dfrac{2}{x+2} = \dfrac{-1}{x-2}$

23. Explain the difference between solving an equation, such as $\dfrac{x}{5} + \dfrac{3}{10} = \dfrac{x}{10}$, for x and performing an operation such as adding $\dfrac{x}{5} + \dfrac{3}{10}$.

24. When solving an equation such as $\dfrac{y}{10} = \dfrac{y}{5} - \dfrac{1}{10}$, we may multiply all terms by 10. When subtracting two rational expressions such as $\dfrac{y}{5} - \dfrac{1}{10}$, we may not. Explain why.

7.6 | Proportion and Problem Solving with Rational Equations ▷

OBJECTIVES

1 Solve Proportions. ▷
2 Use Proportions to Solve Problems. ▷
3 Solve Problems about Numbers. ▷
4 Solve Problems about Work. ▷
5 Solve Problems about Distance. ▷

OBJECTIVE

1 Solving Proportions ▷

A **ratio** is the quotient of two numbers or two quantities. For example, the ratio of 2 to 5 can be written as $\dfrac{2}{5}$, the quotient of 2 and 5.

If two ratios are equal, we say the ratios are **in proportion** to each other. A **proportion** is a mathematical statement that two ratios are equal.

For example, the equation $\dfrac{1}{2} = \dfrac{4}{8}$ is a proportion, as is $\dfrac{x}{5} = \dfrac{8}{10}$, because both sides of the equations are ratios. When we want to emphasize the equation as a proportion, we

read the proportion $\dfrac{1}{2} = \dfrac{4}{8}$ as "one is to two as four is to eight"

In a proportion, cross products are equal. To understand cross products, let's start with the proportion

$$\dfrac{a}{b} = \dfrac{c}{d}$$

and multiply both sides by the LCD, bd.

$$bd\left(\frac{a}{b}\right) = bd\left(\frac{c}{d}\right) \quad \text{Multiply both sides by the LCD, } bd.$$

$$\underset{\text{Cross product}}{\underbrace{ad}} = \underset{\text{Cross product}}{\underbrace{bc}} \quad \text{Simplify.}$$

Notice why ad and bc are called cross products.

$$ad \quad \frac{a}{b} = \frac{c}{d} \quad bc$$

Cross Products

If $\dfrac{a}{b} = \dfrac{c}{d}$, then $ad = bc$.

For example, if

$$\frac{1}{2} = \frac{4}{8}, \text{ then } 1 \cdot 8 = 2 \cdot 4 \text{ or}$$

$$8 = 8$$

Notice that a proportion contains four numbers (or expressions). If any three numbers are known, we can solve and find the fourth number.

EXAMPLE 1   Solve for x: $\dfrac{45}{x} = \dfrac{5}{7}$

Solution This is an equation with rational expressions as well as a proportion. Below are two ways to solve.

Since this is a rational equation, we can use the methods of the previous section.

$$\frac{45}{x} = \frac{5}{7}$$

$$7x \cdot \frac{45}{x} = 7x \cdot \frac{5}{7} \quad \text{Multiply both sides by the LCD, } 7x.$$

$$7 \cdot 45 = x \cdot 5 \quad \text{Divide out common factors.}$$

$$315 = 5x \quad \text{Multiply.}$$

$$\frac{315}{5} = \frac{5x}{5} \quad \text{Divide both sides by 5.}$$

$$63 = x \quad \text{Simplify.}$$

Since this is also a proportion, we may set cross products equal.

$$\frac{45}{x} = \frac{5}{7}$$

$$45 \cdot 7 = x \cdot 5 \quad \text{Set cross products equal.}$$

$$315 = 5x \quad \text{Multiply.}$$

$$\frac{315}{5} = \frac{5x}{5} \quad \text{Divide both sides by 5.}$$

$$63 = x \quad \text{Simplify.}$$

Check: Both methods give us a solution of 63. To check, substitute 63 for x in the original proportion. The solution is 63.   □

PRACTICE
1   Solve for x: $\dfrac{36}{x} = \dfrac{4}{11}$

In this section, if the rational equation is a proportion, we will use cross products to solve.

EXAMPLE 2 Solve for x: $\dfrac{x-5}{3} = \dfrac{x+2}{5}$

Solution

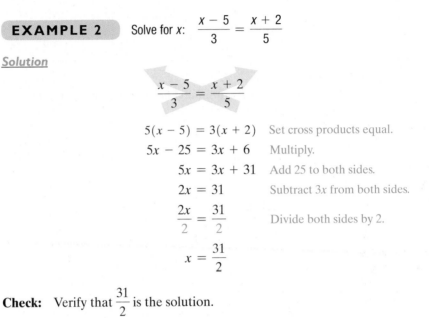

$$\dfrac{x-5}{3} = \dfrac{x+2}{5}$$

$5(x-5) = 3(x+2)$ Set cross products equal.

$5x - 25 = 3x + 6$ Multiply.

$5x = 3x + 31$ Add 25 to both sides.

$2x = 31$ Subtract $3x$ from both sides.

$\dfrac{2x}{2} = \dfrac{31}{2}$ Divide both sides by 2.

$x = \dfrac{31}{2}$

Check: Verify that $\dfrac{31}{2}$ is the solution. ☐

PRACTICE
2 Solve for x: $\dfrac{3x+2}{9} = \dfrac{x-1}{2}$ ■

OBJECTIVE

2 Using Proportions to Solve Problems

Proportions can be used to model and solve many real-life problems. When using proportions in this way, it is important to judge whether the solution is reasonable. Doing so helps us decide if the proportion has been formed correctly. We use the same problem-solving steps that were introduced in Section 2.4.

EXAMPLE 3 **Calculating the Cost of a Redbox Rental**

Not everyone is streaming movies. Many people still rent movies and video games from Redbox. If renting 3 movies costs $4.50, how much should 5 movies cost?

Solution

1. UNDERSTAND. Read and reread the problem. We know that the cost of renting 5 movies is more than the cost of renting three movies, or $4.50, and less than the cost of 6 rentals, which is double the cost of 3 rentals, or $2(\$4.50) = \$9.00$. Let's suppose that 5 rentals cost $7.00. To check, we see if 3 rentals is to 5 rentals as the *price* of three rentals is to the *price* of 5 rentals. In other words, we see if

$$\dfrac{3 \text{ rentals}}{5 \text{ rentals}} = \dfrac{price \text{ of 3 rentals}}{price \text{ of 5 rentals}}$$

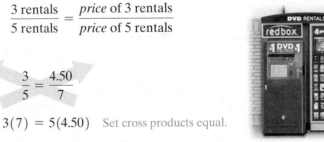

or

$$\dfrac{3}{5} = \dfrac{4.50}{7}$$

$3(7) = 5(4.50)$ Set cross products equal.

or

$21 = 22.5$ Not a true statement.

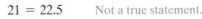

Thus, $7 is not correct, but we now have a better understanding of the problem. Let x = price of renting 5 videos.

2. TRANSLATE.

$$\frac{3 \text{ rentals}}{5 \text{ rentals}} = \frac{price \text{ of 3 rentals}}{price \text{ of 5 rentals}}$$

$$\frac{3}{5} = \frac{4.50}{x}$$

3. SOLVE.

$$\frac{3}{5} = \frac{4.50}{x}$$

$3x = 5(4.50)$ Set cross products equal.

$3x = 22.50$

$x = 7.50$ Divide both sides by **3**.

4. INTERPRET.

Check: Verify that 3 rentals is to 5 rentals as $4.50 is to $7.50. Also, notice that our solution is a reasonable one as discussed in Step 1.

State: Five rentals from Redbox cost $7.50.   ☐

PRACTICE

3   Four 2-liter bottles of Diet Pepsi cost $5.16. How much will seven 2-liter bottles cost?   ■

Helpful Hint

The proportion $\dfrac{5 \text{ rentals}}{3 \text{ rentals}} = \dfrac{price \text{ of 5 rentals}}{price \text{ of 3 rentals}}$ could also have been used to solve Example 3.

Notice that the cross products are the same.

Similar triangles have the same shape but not necessarily the same size. In similar triangles, the measures of corresponding angles are equal, and corresponding sides are in proportion.

If triangle ABC and triangle XYZ shown are similar, then we know that the measure of angle A = the measure of angle X, the measure of angle B = the measure of angle Y, and the measure of angle C = the measure of angle Z. We also know that corresponding sides are in proportion: $\dfrac{a}{x} = \dfrac{b}{y} = \dfrac{c}{z}$.

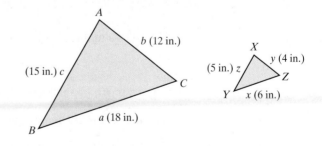

In this section, we will position similar triangles so that they have the same orientation.

To show that corresponding sides are in proportion for the triangles above, we write the ratios of the corresponding sides.

$$\frac{a}{x} = \frac{18}{6} = 3 \qquad \frac{b}{y} = \frac{12}{4} = 3 \qquad \frac{c}{z} = \frac{15}{5} = 3$$

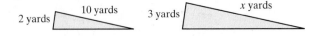

EXAMPLE 4   **Finding the Length of a Side of a Triangle**

If the following two triangles are similar, find the unknown length x.

Solution

1. UNDERSTAND. Read the problem and study the figure.

2. TRANSLATE. Since the triangles are similar, their corresponding sides are in proportion and we have

$$\frac{2}{3} = \frac{10}{x}$$

3. SOLVE. To solve, we multiply both sides by the LCD, $3x$, or cross multiply.

$$2x = 30$$
$$x = 15 \quad \text{Divide both sides by 2.}$$

4. INTERPRET.

Check: To check, replace x with 15 in the original proportion and see that a true statement results.

State: The unknown length is 15 yards.

PRACTICE
4   If the following two triangles are similar, find x.

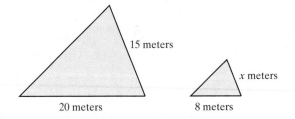

OBJECTIVE

3   Solving Problems about Numbers ▶

Let's continue to solve problems. The remaining problems are all modeled by rational equations.

EXAMPLE 5   **Finding an Unknown Number**

The quotient of a number and 6, minus $\frac{5}{3}$, is the quotient of the number and 2. Find the number.

Solution

1. UNDERSTAND. Read and reread the problem. Suppose that the unknown number is 2. Then we see if the quotient of 2 and 6, or $\frac{2}{6}$, minus $\frac{5}{3}$ is equal to the quotient of 2 and 2, or $\frac{2}{2}$.

$$\frac{2}{6} - \frac{5}{3} = \frac{1}{3} - \frac{5}{3} = -\frac{4}{3}, \text{ not } \frac{2}{2}$$

Don't forget that the purpose of a proposed solution is to better understand the problem.

Let x = the unknown number.

2. TRANSLATE.

In words:

the quotient of x and 6	minus	$\frac{5}{3}$	is	the quotient of x and 2
↓	↓	↓	↓	↓

Translate:

$$\frac{x}{6} \quad - \quad \frac{5}{3} \quad = \quad \frac{x}{2}$$

3. SOLVE. Here, we solve the equation $\frac{x}{6} - \frac{5}{3} = \frac{x}{2}$. We begin by multiplying both sides of the equation by the LCD, 6.

$$6\left(\frac{x}{6} - \frac{5}{3}\right) = 6\left(\frac{x}{2}\right)$$

$$6\left(\frac{x}{6}\right) - 6\left(\frac{5}{3}\right) = 6\left(\frac{x}{2}\right) \qquad \text{Apply the distributive property.}$$

$$x - 10 = 3x \qquad \text{Simplify.}$$

$$-10 = 2x \qquad \text{Subtract } x \text{ from both sides.}$$

$$\frac{-10}{2} = \frac{2x}{2} \qquad \text{Divide both sides by 2.}$$

$$-5 = x \qquad \text{Simplify.}$$

4. INTERPRET.

Check: To check, we verify that "the quotient of -5 and 6 minus $\frac{5}{3}$ is the quotient of -5 and 2," or $-\frac{5}{6} - \frac{5}{3} = -\frac{5}{2}$.

State: The unknown number is -5.   □

PRACTICE
5 The quotient of a number and 5, minus $\frac{3}{2}$, is the quotient of the number and 10. Find the number.   ∎

OBJECTIVE

4   Solving Problems about Work ▶

The next example is often called a work problem. Work problems usually involve people or machines doing a certain task.

EXAMPLE 6   **Finding Work Rates**

Sam Waterton and Frank Schaffer work in a plant that manufactures automobiles. Sam can complete a quality control tour of the plant in 3 hours, while his assistant, Frank, needs 7 hours to complete the same job. The regional manager is coming to inspect the plant facilities, so both Sam and Frank are directed to complete a quality control tour at the same time. How long will this take?

Solution

1. **UNDERSTAND.** Read and reread the problem. The key idea here is the relationship between the **time** (hours) it takes to complete the job and the **part of the job** completed in 1 unit of time (hour). For example, if the **time** it takes Sam to complete the job is 3 hours, the **part of the job** he can complete in 1 hour is $\frac{1}{3}$. Similarly, Frank can complete $\frac{1}{7}$ of the job in 1 hour.

Let $x =$ the **time** in hours it takes Sam and Frank to complete the job together. Then $\frac{1}{x} =$ the **part of the job** they complete in 1 hour.

(Continued on next page)

	Hours to Complete Total Job	*Part of Job Completed in 1 Hour*
Sam	3	$\dfrac{1}{3}$
Frank	7	$\dfrac{1}{7}$
Together	x	$\dfrac{1}{x}$

2. TRANSLATE.

In words:

part of job Sam completes in 1 hour	added to	part of job Frank completes in 1 hour	is equal to	part of job they complete together in 1 hour
↓	↓	↓	↓	↓

Translate:

$$\dfrac{1}{3} \quad + \quad \dfrac{1}{7} \quad = \quad \dfrac{1}{x}$$

3. SOLVE. Here, we solve the equation $\dfrac{1}{3} + \dfrac{1}{7} = \dfrac{1}{x}$. We begin by multiplying both sides of the equation by the LCD, $21x$.

$$21x\left(\dfrac{1}{3}\right) + 21x\left(\dfrac{1}{7}\right) = 21x\left(\dfrac{1}{x}\right)$$

$$7x + 3x = 21 \qquad\qquad \text{Simplify.}$$

$$10x = 21$$

$$x = \dfrac{21}{10} \quad \text{or} \quad 2\dfrac{1}{10} \text{ hours}$$

4. INTERPRET.

Check: Our proposed solution is $2\dfrac{1}{10}$ hours. This proposed solution is reasonable since $2\dfrac{1}{10}$ hours is more than half of Sam's time and less than half of Frank's time.

Check this solution in the originally *stated* problem.

State: Sam and Frank can complete the quality control tour in $2\dfrac{1}{10}$ hours. ☐

PRACTICE

6 Cindy Liu and Mary Beckwith own a landscaping company. Cindy can complete a certain garden planting in 3 hours, while Mary takes 4 hours to complete the same job. If both of them work together, how long will it take to plant the garden? ▪

✔ **CONCEPT CHECK**

Solve $E = mc^2$
a. for m.   **b.** for c^2.

Answers to Concept Check:

a. $m = \dfrac{E}{c^2}$ **b.** $c^2 = \dfrac{E}{m}$

OBJECTIVE

5 Solving Problems About Distance ▶

Next we look at a problem solved by the distance formula,

$$d = r \cdot t$$

EXAMPLE 7   **Finding Speeds of Vehicles**

A car travels 180 miles in the same time that a truck travels 120 miles. If the car's speed is 20 miles per hour faster than the truck's, find the car's speed and the truck's speed.

Solution

1. UNDERSTAND. Read and reread the problem. Suppose that the truck's speed is 45 miles per hour. Then the car's speed is 20 miles per hour more, or 65 miles per hour.

   We are given that the car travels 180 miles in the same time that the truck travels 120 miles. To find the time it takes the car to travel 180 miles, remember that since $d = rt$, we know that $\dfrac{d}{r} = t$.

Car's Time	*Truck's Time*
$t = \dfrac{d}{r} = \dfrac{180}{65} = 2\dfrac{50}{65} = 2\dfrac{10}{13}$ hours	$t = \dfrac{d}{r} = \dfrac{120}{45} = 2\dfrac{30}{45} = 2\dfrac{2}{3}$ hours

   Since the times are not the same, our proposed solution is not correct. But we have a better understanding of the problem.

   Let x = the speed of the truck.

   Since the car's speed is 20 miles per hour faster than the truck's, then

   $$x + 20 = \text{the speed of the car.}$$

   Use the formula $d = r \cdot t$ or **d**istance = **r**ate $\cdot$ **t**ime. Prepare a chart to organize the information in the problem.

   <table>
   <tr><th colspan="2">Helpful Hint</th><th></th><th>*Distance*</th><th>=</th><th>*Rate*</th><th>·</th><th>*Time*</th></tr>
   <tr><td colspan="2">If $d = r \cdot t$,
then $t = \dfrac{d}{r}$</td><td>*Truck*</td><td>120</td><td></td><td>x</td><td></td><td>$\begin{cases}\dfrac{120}{x} \leftarrow \text{distance} \\ \leftarrow \text{rate}\end{cases}$</td></tr>
   <tr><td colspan="2">or *time* $= \dfrac{distance}{rate}$.</td><td>*Car*</td><td>180</td><td></td><td>$x + 20$</td><td></td><td>$\begin{cases}\dfrac{180}{x + 20} \leftarrow \text{distance} \\ \leftarrow \text{rate}\end{cases}$</td></tr>
   </table>

2. TRANSLATE. Since the car and the truck travel the same amount of time, we have that

In words:	car's time	=	truck's time
	↓		↓
Translate:	$\dfrac{180}{x + 20}$	=	$\dfrac{120}{x}$

3. SOLVE. We begin by multiplying both sides of the equation by the LCD, $x(x + 20)$, or cross multiplying.

   $$\frac{180}{x + 20} = \frac{120}{x}$$

   $$180x = 120(x + 20)$$

   $180x = 120x + 2400$ Use the distributive property.

   $60x = 2400$ Subtract $120x$ from both sides.

   $x = 40$ Divide both sides by 60.

   (Continued on next page)

4. INTERPRET. The speed of the truck is 40 miles per hour. The speed of the car must then be $x + 20$ or 60 miles per hour.

Check: Find the time it takes the car to travel 180 miles and the time it takes the truck to travel 120 miles.

Car's Time	*Truck's Time*
$t = \dfrac{d}{r} = \dfrac{180}{60} = 3$ hours	$t = \dfrac{d}{r} = \dfrac{120}{40} = 3$ hours

Since both travel the same amount of time, the proposed solution is correct.

State: The car's speed is 60 miles per hour and the truck's speed is 40 miles per hour.   ☐

PRACTICE
7   A bus travels 180 miles in the same time that a car travels 240 miles. If the car's speed is 15 miles per hour faster than the speed of the bus, find the speed of the car and the speed of the bus.   ■

✔ Vocabulary, Readiness & Video Check

Without solving algebraically, select the best choice for each exercise.

1. One person can complete a job in 7 hours. A second person can complete the same job in 5 hours. How long will it take them to complete the job if they work together?

a. more than 7 hours

b. between 5 and 7 hours

c. less than 5 hours

2. One inlet pipe can fill a pond in 30 hours. A second inlet pipe can fill the same pond in 25 hours. How long before the pond is filled if both inlet pipes are on?

a. less than 25 hours

b. between 25 and 30 hours

c. more than 30 hours

TRANSLATING

Given the variable in the first column, use the phrase in the second column to translate into an expression and then continue to the phrase in the third column to translate into another expression.

3.	A number: x	The reciprocal of the number:	The reciprocal of the number, decreased by 3:
4.	A number: y	The reciprocal of the number:	The reciprocal of the number, increased by 2:
5.	A number: z	The sum of the number and 5:	The reciprocal of the sum of the number and 5:
6.	A number: x	The difference of the number and 1:	The reciprocal of the difference of the number and 1:
7.	A number: y	Twice the number:	Eleven divided by twice the number:
8.	A number: z	Triple the number:	Negative ten divided by triple the number:

Martin-Gay Interactive Videos

See Video 7.6 🔘

Watch the section lecture video and answer the following questions.

OBJECTIVE 1

9. Based on 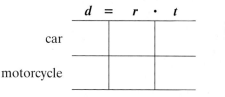 Examples 1 and 2, can proportions only be solved by using cross products? Explain.

OBJECTIVE 2

10. In 🎞 Example 3 we are told there are many ways to set up a correct proportion. Why does this fact make it even more important to check that your solution is reasonable?

OBJECTIVE 3

11. What words or phrases in 🎞 Example 5 told you to translate into an equation containing rational expressions?

OBJECTIVE 4

12. From 🎞 Example 6, how can you determine a somewhat reasonable answer to a work problem before you even begin to solve it?

OBJECTIVE 5

13. The following problem is worded like 🎞 Example 7 in the video, but using different quantities.

A car travels 325 miles in the same time that a motorcycle travels 290 miles. If the car's speed is 7 miles per hour more than the motorcycle's, find the speed of the car and the speed of the motorcycle. Fill in the table and set up an equation based on this problem (do not solve). Use 🎞 Example 7 in the video as a model for your work.

	d	$=$	r	$\cdot$	t
car					
motorcycle					

7.6   Exercise Set   MyMathLab® ▶

Solve each proportion. See Examples 1 and 2. For additional exercises on proportion and proportion applications, see Appendix B.

1. $\dfrac{2}{3} = \dfrac{x}{6}$

2. $\dfrac{x}{2} = \dfrac{16}{6}$

3. $\dfrac{x}{10} = \dfrac{5}{9}$

4. $\dfrac{9}{4x} = \dfrac{6}{2}$

5. $\dfrac{x+1}{2x+3} = \dfrac{2}{3}$

6. $\dfrac{x+1}{x+2} = \dfrac{5}{3}$

7. $\dfrac{9}{5} = \dfrac{12}{3x+2}$

8. $\dfrac{6}{11} = \dfrac{27}{3x-2}$

Solve. See Example 3.

9. The ratio of the weight of an object on Earth to the weight of the same object on Pluto is 100 to 3. If an elephant weighs 4100 pounds on Earth, find the elephant's weight on Pluto.

10. If a 170-pound person weighs approximately 65 pounds on Mars, about how much does a 9000-pound satellite weigh? Round your answer to the nearest pound.

11. There are 110 calories per 177.4 grams of Frosted Flakes cereal. Find how many calories are in 212.5 grams of this cereal. Round to the nearest whole calorie.

12. On an architect's blueprint, 1 inch corresponds to 4 feet. Find the length of a wall represented by a line that is $3\dfrac{7}{8}$ inches long on the blueprint.

Find the unknown length x or y in the following pairs of similar triangles. See Example 4.

△ **13.**

△ **14.**

△ **15.**

△ **16.**

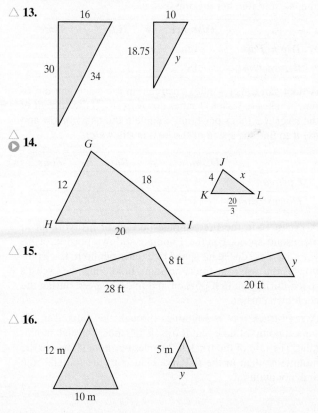

Solve the following. See Example 5.

17. Three times the reciprocal of a number equals 9 times the reciprocal of 6. Find the number.

18. Twelve divided by the sum of x and 2 equals the quotient of 4 and the difference of x and 2. Find x.

19. If twice a number added to 3 is divided by the number plus 1, the result is three halves. Find the number.

20. A number added to the product of 6 and the reciprocal of the number equals -5. Find the number.

See Example 6.

21. Smith Engineering found that an experienced surveyor surveys a roadbed in 4 hours. An apprentice surveyor needs 5 hours to survey the same stretch of road. If the two work together, find how long it takes them to complete the job.

22. An experienced bricklayer constructs a small wall in 3 hours. The apprentice completes the job in 6 hours. Find how long it takes if they work together.

23. In 2 minutes, a conveyor belt moves 300 pounds of recyclable aluminum from the delivery truck to a storage area. A smaller belt moves the same quantity of cans the same distance in 6 minutes. If both belts are used, find how long it takes to move the cans to the storage area.

24. Find how long it takes the conveyor belts described in Exercise 23 to move 1200 pounds of cans. (*Hint:* Think of 1200 pounds as four 300-pound jobs.)

See Example 7.

25. A jogger begins her workout by jogging to the park, a distance of 12 miles. She then jogs home at the same speed but along a different route. This return trip is 18 miles and her time is one hour longer. Complete the accompanying chart and use it to find her jogging speed.

	Distance	=	Rate	·	Time
Trip to Park	12				
Return Trip	18				

26. A boat can travel 9 miles upstream in the same amount of time it takes to travel 11 miles downstream. If the current of the river is 3 miles per hour, complete the chart below and use it to find the speed of the boat in still water.

	Distance	=	Rate	·	Time
Upstream	9		$r - 3$		
Downstream	11		$r + 3$		

27. A cyclist rode the first 20-mile portion of his workout at a constant speed. For the 16-mile cooldown portion of his workout, he reduced his speed by 2 miles per hour. Each portion of the workout took the same time. Find the cyclist's speed during the first portion and find his speed during the cooldown portion.

28. A semi-truck travels 300 miles through the flatland in the same amount of time that it travels 180 miles through mountains. The rate of the truck is 20 miles per hour slower in the mountains than in the flatland. Find both the flatland rate and mountain rate.

MIXED PRACTICE

Solve the following. See Examples 1 through 7. (Note: Some exercises can be modeled by equations without rational expressions.)

29. A human factors expert recommends that there be at least 9 square feet of floor space in a college classroom for every student in the class. Find the minimum floor space that 40 students need.

30. Due to space problems at a local university, a 20-foot by 12-foot conference room is converted into a classroom. Find the maximum number of students the room can accommodate. (See Exercise 29.)

31. One-fourth equals the quotient of a number and 8. Find the number.

32. Four times a number added to 5 is divided by 6. The result is $\frac{7}{2}$. Find the number.

33. Marcus and Tony work for Lombardo's Pipe and Concrete. Mr. Lombardo is preparing an estimate for a customer. He knows that Marcus lays a slab of concrete in 6 hours. Tony lays the same size slab in 4 hours. If both work on the job and the cost of labor is $45.00 per hour, decide what the labor estimate should be.

34. Mr. Dodson can paint his house by himself in 4 days. His son needs an additional day to complete the job if he works by himself. If they work together, find how long it takes to paint the house.

35. A pilot can travel 400 miles with the wind in the same amount of time as 336 miles against the wind. Find the speed of the wind if the pilot's speed in still air is 230 miles per hour.

36. A fisherman on Pearl River rows 9 miles downstream in the same amount of time he rows 3 miles upstream. If the current is 6 miles per hour, find how long it takes him to cover the 12 miles.

37. Find the unknown length y.

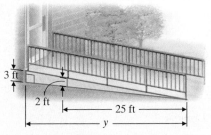

38. Find the unknown length y.

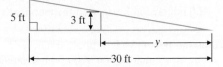

39. Suppose two trains leave Holbrook, Arizona, at the same time, traveling in opposite directions. One train travels 10 mph faster than the other. In 3.5 hours, the trains are 322 miles apart. Find the speed of each train.

40. Suppose two cars leave Brinkley, Arkansas, at the same time, traveling in opposite directions. One car travels 8 mph faster than the other car. In 2.5 hours, the cars are 280 miles apart. Find the speed of each car.

41. Two divided by the difference of a number and 3 minus 4 divided by the number plus 3, equals 8 times the reciprocal of the difference of the number squared and 9. What is the number?

42. If 15 times the reciprocal of a number is added to the ratio of 9 times the number minus 7 and the number plus 2, the result is 9. What is the number?

43. A pilot flies 630 miles with a tailwind of 35 miles per hour. Against the wind, he flies only 455 miles in the same amount of time. Find the rate of the plane in still air.

44. A marketing manager travels 1080 miles in a corporate jet and then an additional 240 miles by car. If the car ride takes one hour longer than the jet ride takes, and if the rate of the jet is 6 times the rate of the car, find the time the manager travels by jet and find the time the manager travels by car.

45. To mix weed killer with water correctly, it is necessary to mix 8 teaspoons of weed killer with 2 gallons of water. Find how many gallons of water are needed to mix with the entire box if it contains 36 teaspoons of weed killer.

46. The directions for a certain bug spray concentrate is to mix 3 ounces of concentrate with 2 gallons of water. How many ounces of concentrate are needed to mix with 5 gallons of water?

47. A boater travels 16 miles per hour on the water on a still day. During one particular windy day, he finds that he travels 48 miles with the wind behind him in the same amount of time that he travels 16 miles into the wind. Find the rate of the wind.

Let x be the rate of the wind.

	r	$\times$	t	$=$	d
with wind	$16 + x$				48
into wind	$16 - x$				16

48. The current on a portion of the Mississippi River is 3 miles per hour. A barge can go 6 miles upstream in the same amount of time it takes to go 10 miles downstream. Find the speed of the boat in still water.

Let x be the speed of the boat in still water.

	r	$\times$	t	$=$	d
upstream	$x - 3$				6
downstream	$x + 3$				10

49. Two hikers are 11 miles apart and walking toward each other. They meet in 2 hours. Find the rate of each hiker if one hiker walks 1.1 mph faster than the other.

50. On a 255-mile trip, Gary Alessandrini traveled at an average speed of 70 mph, got a speeding ticket, and then traveled at 60 mph for the remainder of the trip. If the entire trip took 4.5 hours and the speeding ticket stop took 30 minutes, how long did Gary speed before getting stopped?

51. One custodian cleans a suite of offices in 3 hours. When a second worker is asked to join the regular custodian, the job takes only $1\frac{1}{2}$ hours. How long does it take the second worker to do the same job alone?

52. One person proofreads copy for a small newspaper in 4 hours. If a second proofreader is also employed, the job can be done in $2\frac{1}{2}$ hours. How long does it take the second proofreader to do the same job alone?

△ **53.** An architect is completing the plans for a triangular deck. Use the diagram below to find the unknown dimension.

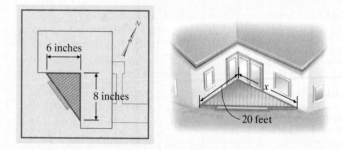

△ **54.** A student wishes to make a small model of a triangular mainsail to study the effects of wind on the sail. The smaller model will be the same shape as a regular-size sailboat's mainsail. Use the following diagram to find the unknown dimensions.

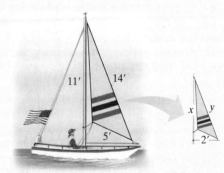

55. The manufacturers of cans of salted mixed nuts state that the ratio of peanuts to other nuts is 3 to 2. If 324 peanuts are in a can, find how many other nuts should also be in the can.

56. There are 1280 calories in a 14-ounce portion of Eagle Brand Milk. Find how many calories are in 2 ounces of Eagle Brand Milk.

57. A jet plane traveling at 500 mph overtakes a propeller plane traveling at 200 mph that had a 2-hour head start. How far from the starting point are the planes?

58. How long will it take a bus traveling at 60 miles per hour to overtake a car traveling at 40 miles per hour if the car had a 1.5-hour head start?

59. One pipe fills a storage pool in 20 hours. A second pipe fills the same pool in 15 hours. When a third pipe is added and all three are used to fill the pool, it takes only 6 hours. Find how long it takes the third pipe to do the job.

60. One pump fills a tank in 9 hours. A second pump fills the same tank in 6 hours. When a third pump is added and all three are used to fill the tank, it takes only 3 hours. Find how long it takes the third pump to fill the tank.

61. A car travels 280 miles in the same time that a motorcycle travels 240 miles. If the car's speed is 10 miles per hour more than the motorcycle's, find the speed of the car and the speed of the motorcycle.

62. A bus traveled on a straight road for 3 hours at an average speed 20 miles per hour faster than it traveled on a winding road. The time spent on the winding road was 4 hours. Find the average speed on the straight road if the entire trip was 305 miles.

63. In 6 hours, an experienced cook prepares enough pies to supply a local restaurant's daily order. Another cook prepares the same number of pies in 7 hours. Together with a third cook, they prepare the pies in 2 hours. Find how long it takes the third cook to prepare the pies alone.

64. Mrs. Smith balances the company books in 8 hours. It takes her assistant 12 hours to do the same job. If they work together, find how long it takes them to balance the books.

65. The quotient of a number and 3, minus 1, equals $\frac{5}{3}$. Find the number.

66. The quotient of a number and 5, minus 1, equals $\frac{7}{5}$. Find the number.

67. Currently, the Toyota Camry is the best-selling car in the world. Suppose that during a test drive of two Camrys, one car travels 224 miles in the same time that the second car travels 175 miles. If the speed of the first car is 14 miles per hour faster than the speed of the second car, find the speed of both cars. (*Source: Kelley Blue Book*)

68. The second best-selling car is the Honda Accord. A driver of this car took a day trip along the California coastline driving at two speeds. He drove 70 miles at a slower speed and 300 miles at a speed 40 miles per hour faster. If the time spent driving the faster speed was twice that spent at the slower speed, find the two speeds during the trip. (*Source: Kelley Blue Book*)

69. A pilot can fly an MD-11 2160 miles with the wind in the same time she can fly 1920 miles against the wind. If the speed of the wind is 30 mph, find the speed of the plane in still air. (*Source:* Air Transport Association of America)

70. A pilot can fly a DC-10 1365 miles against the wind in the same time he can fly 1575 miles with the wind. If the speed of the plane in still air is 490 miles per hour, find the speed of the wind. (*Source:* Air Transport Association of America)

Given that the following pairs of triangles are similar, find each unknown length.

△ **71.**

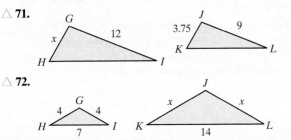

△ **72.**

△ **73.**

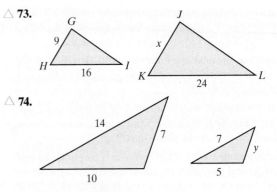

△ **74.**

REVIEW AND PREVIEW

Find the slope of the line through each pair of points. Use the slope to determine whether the line is vertical, horizontal, or moves upward or downward from left to right. See Section 3.4.

75. $(-2, 5), (4, -3)$

76. $(0, 4), (2, 10)$

77. $(-3, -6), (1, 5)$

78. $(-2, 7), (3, -2)$

79. $(3, 7), (3, -2)$

80. $(0, -4), (2, -4)$

CONCEPT EXTENSIONS

The following bar graph shows the capacity of the United States to generate electricity from the wind in the years shown. Use this graph for Exercises 81 and 82.

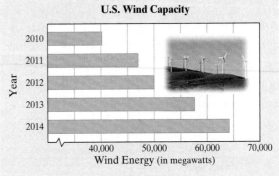

U.S. Wind Capacity

Source: American Wind Energy Association

81. Find the approximate megawatt capacity in 2014.

82. Find the approximate megawatt capacity in 2013.

In general, 1000 megawatts will serve the average electricity needs of 560,000 people. Use this fact and the preceding graph to answer Exercises 83 and 84.

83. In 2014, the number of megawatts that were generated from wind would serve the electricity needs of how many people?

84. How many megawatts of electricity are needed to serve the city or town in which you live?

For Exercises 85 and 86 decide whether we can immediately use cross products to solve for x. Do not actually solve.

85. $\frac{2-x}{5} = \frac{1+x}{3}$

86. $\frac{2}{5} - x = \frac{1+x}{3}$

Solve.

87. One pump fills a tank 3 times as fast as another pump. If the pumps work together, they fill the tank in 21 minutes. How long does it take each pump to fill the tank?

88. It takes 9 hours for pump A to fill a tank alone. Pump B takes 15 hours to fill the same tank alone. If pumps A, B, and C are used, the tank fills in 5 hours. How long does it take pump C to fill the tank alone?

89. For what value of x is $\dfrac{x}{x-1}$ in proportion to $\dfrac{x+1}{x}$? Explain your result.

90. If x is 10, is $\dfrac{2}{x}$ in proportion to $\dfrac{x}{50}$? Explain why or why not.

91. Person A can complete a job in 5 hours, and person B can complete the same job in 3 hours. Without solving algebraically, discuss reasonable and unreasonable answers for how long it would take them to complete the job together.

92. A hyena spots a giraffe 0.5 mile away and begins running toward it. The giraffe starts running away from the hyena just as the hyena begins running toward it. A hyena can run at a speed of 40 mph and a giraffe can run at 32 mph. How long will it take for the hyena to overtake the giraffe? (*Source: World Almanac and Book of Facts*)

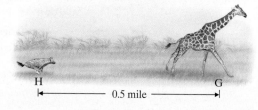

H   G

|←———— 0.5 mile ————→|

Solve. See the Concept Check in this section.

Solve $D = RT$

93. for R **94.** for T

7.7 Simplifying Complex Fractions ▶

OBJECTIVES

1 Simplify Complex Fractions by Simplifying the Numerator and Denominator and Then Dividing. ▶

2 Simplify Complex Fractions by Multiplying by a Common Denominator. ▶

3 Simplify Expressions with Negative Exponents. ▶

A rational expression whose numerator, denominator, or both contain one or more rational expressions is called a **complex rational expression** or a **complex fraction.**

Complex Fractions

$$\dfrac{\frac{1}{a}}{\frac{b}{2}} \qquad \dfrac{\frac{x}{2y^2}}{\frac{6x-2}{9y}} \qquad \dfrac{x+\frac{1}{y}}{y+1}$$

The parts of a complex fraction are

$$\dfrac{\left.\dfrac{x}{y+2}\right\}}{\left.7+\dfrac{1}{y}\right\}}$$

← Numerator of complex fraction
← Main fraction bar
← Denominator of complex fraction

Our goal in this section is to simplify complex fractions. A complex fraction is simplified when it is in the form $\dfrac{P}{Q}$, where P and Q are polynomials that have no common factors. Two methods of simplifying complex fractions are introduced. The first method evolves from the definition of a fraction as a quotient.

OBJECTIVE

1 Simplifying Complex Fractions: Method 1 ▶

Simplifying a Complex Fraction: Method I

Step 1. Simplify the numerator and the denominator of the complex fraction so that each is a single fraction.

Step 2. Perform the indicated division by multiplying the numerator of the complex fraction by the reciprocal of the denominator of the complex fraction.

Step 3. Simplify if possible.

EXAMPLE 1 Simplify each complex fraction.

a. $\dfrac{\dfrac{2x}{27y^2}}{\dfrac{6x^2}{9}}$
b. $\dfrac{\dfrac{5x}{x+2}}{\dfrac{10}{x-2}}$
c. $\dfrac{\dfrac{x}{y^2}+\dfrac{1}{y}}{\dfrac{y}{x^2}+\dfrac{1}{x}}$

Solution

a. The numerator of the complex fraction is already a single fraction, and so is the denominator. Perform the indicated division by multiplying the numerator, $\dfrac{2x}{27y^2}$, by the reciprocal of the denominator, $\dfrac{6x^2}{9}$. Then simplify.

$$\dfrac{\dfrac{2x}{27y^2}}{\dfrac{6x^2}{9}} = \dfrac{2x}{27y^2} \div \dfrac{6x^2}{9}$$

$$= \dfrac{2x}{27y^2} \cdot \dfrac{9}{6x^2} \qquad \text{Multiply by the reciprocal of } \dfrac{6x^2}{9}.$$

$$= \dfrac{2x \cdot 9}{27y^2 \cdot 6x^2}$$

$$= \dfrac{1}{9xy^2}$$

<table>
<tr><td>

Helpful Hint

Both the numerator and denominator are single fractions, so we perform the indicated division.

</td></tr>
</table>

b. $\dfrac{\left\{\dfrac{5x}{x+2}\right.}{\left\{\dfrac{10}{x-2}\right.} = \dfrac{5x}{x+2} \div \dfrac{10}{x-2} = \dfrac{5x}{x+2} \cdot \dfrac{x-2}{10}$ Multiply by the reciprocal of $\dfrac{10}{x-2}$.

$$= \dfrac{5x(x-2)}{2 \cdot 5(x+2)}$$

$$= \dfrac{x(x-2)}{2(x+2)} \qquad \text{Simplify.}$$

c. First simplify the numerator and the denominator of the complex fraction separately so that each is a single fraction. Then perform the indicated division.

$$\dfrac{\dfrac{x}{y^2}+\dfrac{1}{y}}{\dfrac{y}{x^2}+\dfrac{1}{x}} = \dfrac{\dfrac{x}{y^2}+\dfrac{1 \cdot y}{y \cdot y}}{\dfrac{y}{x^2}+\dfrac{1 \cdot x}{x \cdot x}} \qquad \begin{array}{l}\text{Simplify the numerator. The LCD is } y^2.\\[6pt]\text{Simplify the denominator. The LCD is } x^2.\end{array}$$

$$= \dfrac{\dfrac{x+y}{y^2}}{\dfrac{y+x}{x^2}} \qquad \text{Add.}$$

$$= \dfrac{x+y}{y^2} \cdot \dfrac{x^2}{y+x} \qquad \text{Multiply by the reciprocal of } \dfrac{y+x}{x^2}.$$

$$= \dfrac{x^2(x+y)}{y^2(y+x)}$$

$$= \dfrac{x^2}{y^2} \qquad \text{Simplify.} \qquad \square$$

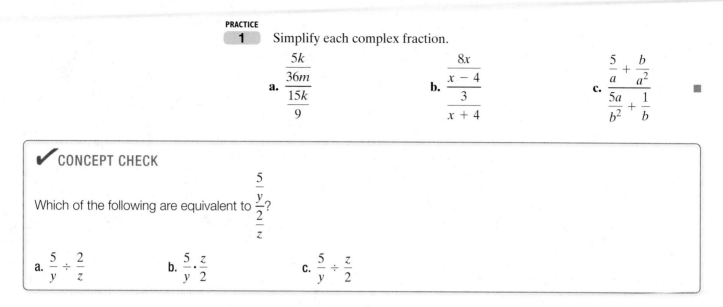

Simplify each complex fraction.

a. $\dfrac{\dfrac{5k}{36m}}{\dfrac{15k}{9}}$

b. $\dfrac{\dfrac{8x}{x-4}}{\dfrac{3}{x+4}}$

c. $\dfrac{\dfrac{5}{a}+\dfrac{b}{a^2}}{\dfrac{5a}{b^2}+\dfrac{1}{b}}$

✔ CONCEPT CHECK

Which of the following are equivalent to $\dfrac{\dfrac{5}{y}}{\dfrac{2}{z}}$?

a. $\dfrac{5}{y} \div \dfrac{2}{z}$

b. $\dfrac{5}{y} \cdot \dfrac{z}{2}$

c. $\dfrac{5}{y} \div \dfrac{z}{2}$

OBJECTIVE

2 Simplifying Complex Fractions: Method 2 ▶

Next we look at another method of simplifying complex fractions. With this method, we multiply the numerator and the denominator of the complex fraction by the LCD of all fractions in the complex fraction.

Simplifying a Complex Fraction: Method 2

Step 1. Multiply the numerator and the denominator of the complex fraction by the LCD of the fractions in both the numerator and the denominator.

Step 2. Simplify.

EXAMPLE 2 Simplify each complex fraction.

a. $\dfrac{\dfrac{5x}{x+2}}{\dfrac{10}{x-2}}$

b. $\dfrac{\dfrac{x}{y^2}+\dfrac{1}{y}}{\dfrac{y}{x^2}+\dfrac{1}{x}}$

Solution

a. Notice we are reworking Example 1(b) using method 2. The least common denominator of $\dfrac{5x}{x+2}$ and $\dfrac{10}{x-2}$ is $(x+2)(x-2)$. Multiply both the numerator, $\dfrac{5x}{x+2}$, and the denominator, $\dfrac{10}{x-2}$, by the LCD.

$$\dfrac{\dfrac{5x}{x+2}}{\dfrac{10}{x-2}} = \dfrac{\left(\dfrac{5x}{x+2}\right)\cdot(x+2)(x-2)}{\left(\dfrac{10}{x-2}\right)\cdot(x+2)(x-2)} \quad \text{Multiply numerator and denominator by the LCD.}$$

$$= \dfrac{5x\cdot(x-2)}{2\cdot 5\cdot(x+2)} \quad \text{Simplify.}$$

$$= \dfrac{x(x-2)}{2(x+2)} \quad \text{Simplify.}$$

b. Here, we are reworking Example 1(c) using method 2. The least common denominator of $\dfrac{x}{y^2},\dfrac{1}{y},\dfrac{y}{x^2}$, and $\dfrac{1}{x}$ is x^2y^2.

(Continued on next page)

$$\frac{\dfrac{x}{y^2} + \dfrac{1}{y}}{\dfrac{y}{x^2} + \dfrac{1}{x}} = \frac{\left(\dfrac{x}{y^2} + \dfrac{1}{y}\right) \cdot x^2 y^2}{\left(\dfrac{y}{x^2} + \dfrac{1}{x}\right) \cdot x^2 y^2}$$ Multiply the numerator and denominator by the LCD.

$$= \frac{\dfrac{x}{y^2} \cdot x^2 y^2 + \dfrac{1}{y} \cdot x^2 y^2}{\dfrac{y}{x^2} \cdot x^2 y^2 + \dfrac{1}{x} \cdot x^2 y^2}$$ Use the distributive property.

$$= \frac{x^3 + x^2 y}{y^3 + xy^2}$$ Simplify.

$$= \frac{x^2(x + y)}{y^2(y + x)}$$ Factor.

$$= \frac{x^2}{y^2}$$ Simplify.   □

PRACTICE

2   Use method 2 to simplify.

a. $\dfrac{\dfrac{8x}{x-4}}{\dfrac{3}{x+4}}$ **b.** $\dfrac{\dfrac{b}{a^2} + \dfrac{1}{a}}{\dfrac{a}{b^2} + \dfrac{1}{b}}$ ■

OBJECTIVE

3   Simplifying Expressions with Negative Exponents ▶

If an expression contains negative exponents, write the expression as an equivalent expression with positive exponents.

EXAMPLE 3   Simplify:

$$\frac{x^{-1} + 2xy^{-1}}{x^{-2} - x^{-2}y^{-1}}$$

<u>Solution</u> This fraction does not appear to be a complex fraction. If we write it by using only positive exponents, however, we see that it is a complex fraction.

$$\frac{x^{-1} + 2xy^{-1}}{x^{-2} - x^{-2}y^{-1}} = \frac{\dfrac{1}{x} + \dfrac{2x}{y}}{\dfrac{1}{x^2} - \dfrac{1}{x^2 y}}$$

The LCD of $\dfrac{1}{x}, \dfrac{2x}{y}, \dfrac{1}{x^2}$, and $\dfrac{1}{x^2 y}$ is $x^2 y$. Multiply both the numerator and denominator by $x^2 y$.

$$= \frac{\left(\dfrac{1}{x} + \dfrac{2x}{y}\right) \cdot x^2 y}{\left(\dfrac{1}{x^2} - \dfrac{1}{x^2 y}\right) \cdot x^2 y}$$

$$= \frac{\dfrac{1}{x} \cdot x^2 y + \dfrac{2x}{y} \cdot x^2 y}{\dfrac{1}{x^2} \cdot x^2 y - \dfrac{1}{x^2 y} \cdot x^2 y}$$ Apply the distributive property.

$$= \frac{xy + 2x^3}{y - 1} \quad \text{or} \quad \frac{x(y + 2x^2)}{y - 1}$$ Simplify. □

PRACTICE
3 Simplify: $\dfrac{3x^{-1} + x^{-2}y^{-1}}{y^{-2} + xy^{-1}}$

EXAMPLE 4 Simplify: $\dfrac{(2x)^{-1} + 1}{2x^{-1} - 1}$

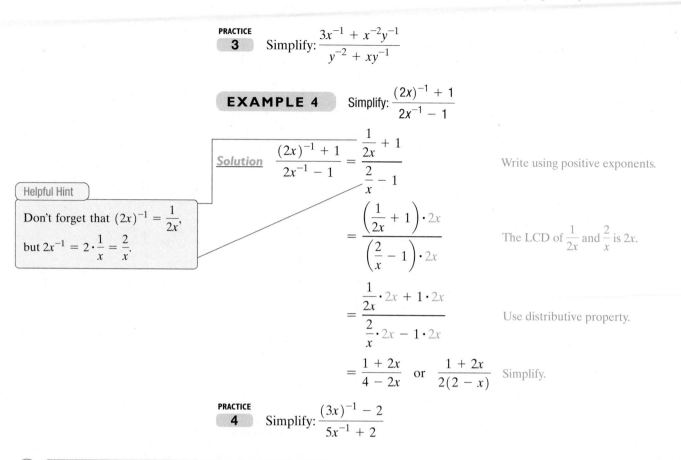

Solution $\dfrac{(2x)^{-1} + 1}{2x^{-1} - 1} = \dfrac{\dfrac{1}{2x} + 1}{\dfrac{2}{x} - 1}$ Write using positive exponents.

Helpful Hint

Don't forget that $(2x)^{-1} = \dfrac{1}{2x}$,

but $2x^{-1} = 2 \cdot \dfrac{1}{x} = \dfrac{2}{x}$.

$= \dfrac{\left(\dfrac{1}{2x} + 1\right) \cdot 2x}{\left(\dfrac{2}{x} - 1\right) \cdot 2x}$ The LCD of $\dfrac{1}{2x}$ and $\dfrac{2}{x}$ is $2x$.

$= \dfrac{\dfrac{1}{2x} \cdot 2x + 1 \cdot 2x}{\dfrac{2}{x} \cdot 2x - 1 \cdot 2x}$ Use distributive property.

$= \dfrac{1 + 2x}{4 - 2x}$ or $\dfrac{1 + 2x}{2(2 - x)}$ Simplify.

PRACTICE
4 Simplify: $\dfrac{(3x)^{-1} - 2}{5x^{-1} + 2}$

Vocabulary, Readiness & Video Check

Complete the steps by writing the simplified complex fraction.

1. $\dfrac{\dfrac{7}{x}}{\dfrac{1}{x} + \dfrac{z}{x}} = \dfrac{x\left(\dfrac{7}{x}\right)}{x\left(\dfrac{1}{x}\right) + x\left(\dfrac{z}{x}\right)} = $ _____

2. $\dfrac{\dfrac{x}{4}}{\dfrac{x^2}{2} + \dfrac{1}{4}} = \dfrac{4\left(\dfrac{x}{4}\right)}{4\left(\dfrac{x^2}{2}\right) + 4\left(\dfrac{1}{4}\right)} = $ _____

Write with positive exponents.

3. $x^{-2} = $ _____

4. $y^{-3} = $ _____

5. $2x^{-1} = $ _____

6. $(2x)^{-1} = $ _____

7. $(9y)^{-1} = $ _____

8. $9y^{-2} = $ _____

Martin-Gay Interactive Videos

See Video 7.7

Watch the section lecture video and answer the following questions.

OBJECTIVE 1

9. From 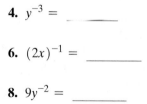 Example 2, before you can rewrite the complex fraction as division, describe how it must appear.

OBJECTIVE 2

10. How does finding an LCD in method 2, as in Example 3, differ from finding an LCD in method 1? In your answer, mention the purpose of the LCD in each method.

OBJECTIVE 3

11. Based on Example 4, what connection is there between negative exponents and complex fractions?

7.7 Exercise Set MyMathLab ▶

Simplify each complex fraction. See Examples 1 and 2.

▶ **1.** $\dfrac{\dfrac{10}{3x}}{\dfrac{5}{6x}}$

2. $\dfrac{\dfrac{15}{2x}}{\dfrac{5}{6x}}$

3. $\dfrac{1 + \dfrac{2}{5}}{2 + \dfrac{3}{5}}$

4. $\dfrac{2 + \dfrac{1}{7}}{3 - \dfrac{4}{7}}$

5. $\dfrac{\dfrac{4}{x - 1}}{\dfrac{x}{x - 1}}$

6. $\dfrac{\dfrac{x}{x + 2}}{\dfrac{2}{x + 2}}$

7. $\dfrac{1 - \dfrac{2}{x}}{x + \dfrac{4}{9x}}$

8. $\dfrac{5 - \dfrac{3}{x}}{x + \dfrac{2}{3x}}$

▶ **9.** $\dfrac{\dfrac{4x^2 - y^2}{xy}}{\dfrac{2}{y} - \dfrac{1}{x}}$

10. $\dfrac{\dfrac{x^2 - 9y^2}{xy}}{\dfrac{1}{y} - \dfrac{3}{x}}$

11. $\dfrac{\dfrac{x + 1}{3}}{\dfrac{2x - 1}{6}}$

12. $\dfrac{\dfrac{x + 3}{12}}{\dfrac{4x - 5}{15}}$

13. $\dfrac{\dfrac{2}{x} + \dfrac{3}{x^2}}{\dfrac{4}{x^2} - \dfrac{9}{x}}$

14. $\dfrac{\dfrac{2}{x^2} + \dfrac{1}{x}}{\dfrac{4}{x^2} - \dfrac{1}{x}}$

15. $\dfrac{\dfrac{1}{x} + \dfrac{2}{x^2}}{x + \dfrac{8}{x^2}}$

16. $\dfrac{\dfrac{1}{y} + \dfrac{3}{y^2}}{y + \dfrac{27}{y^2}}$

17. $\dfrac{\dfrac{4}{5 - x} + \dfrac{5}{x - 5}}{\dfrac{2}{x} + \dfrac{3}{x - 5}}$

18. $\dfrac{\dfrac{3}{x - 4} - \dfrac{2}{4 - x}}{\dfrac{2}{x - 4} - \dfrac{2}{x}}$

▶ **19.** $\dfrac{\dfrac{x + 2}{x} - \dfrac{2}{x - 1}}{\dfrac{x + 1}{x} + \dfrac{x + 1}{x - 1}}$

20. $\dfrac{\dfrac{5}{a + 2} - \dfrac{1}{a - 2}}{\dfrac{3}{2 + a} + \dfrac{6}{2 - a}}$

21. $\dfrac{\dfrac{2}{x} + 3}{\dfrac{4}{x^2} - 9}$

22. $\dfrac{2 + \dfrac{1}{x}}{4x - \dfrac{1}{x}}$

23. $\dfrac{1 - \dfrac{x}{y}}{\dfrac{x^2}{y^2} - 1}$

24. $\dfrac{1 - \dfrac{2}{x}}{x - \dfrac{4}{x}}$

25. $\dfrac{\dfrac{-2x}{x - y}}{\dfrac{y}{x^2}}$

26. $\dfrac{\dfrac{7y}{x^2 + xy}}{\dfrac{y^2}{x^2}}$

27. $\dfrac{\dfrac{2}{x} + \dfrac{1}{x^2}}{\dfrac{y}{x^2}}$

28. $\dfrac{\dfrac{5}{x^2} - \dfrac{2}{x}}{\dfrac{1}{x} + 2}$

29. $\dfrac{\dfrac{x}{9} - \dfrac{1}{x}}{1 + \dfrac{3}{x}}$

30. $\dfrac{\dfrac{x}{4} - \dfrac{4}{x}}{1 - \dfrac{4}{x}}$

31. $\dfrac{\dfrac{x - 1}{x^2 - 4}}{1 + \dfrac{1}{x - 2}}$

32. $\dfrac{\dfrac{x + 3}{x^2 - 9}}{1 + \dfrac{1}{x - 3}}$

33. $\dfrac{\dfrac{2}{x + 5} + \dfrac{4}{x + 3}}{\dfrac{3x + 13}{x^2 + 8x + 15}}$

34. $\dfrac{\dfrac{2}{x + 2} + \dfrac{6}{x + 7}}{\dfrac{4x + 13}{x^2 + 9x + 14}}$

Simplify. See Examples 3 and 4.

35. $\dfrac{x^{-1}}{x^{-2} + y^{-2}}$

36. $\dfrac{a^{-3} + b^{-1}}{a^{-2}}$

▶ **37.** $\dfrac{2a^{-1} + 3b^{-2}}{a^{-1} - b^{-1}}$

38. $\dfrac{x^{-1} + y^{-1}}{3x^{-2} + 5y^{-2}}$

39. $\dfrac{1}{x - x^{-1}}$

40. $\dfrac{x^{-2}}{x + 3x^{-1}}$

41. $\dfrac{a^{-1} + 1}{a^{-1} - 1}$

42. $\dfrac{a^{-1} - 4}{4 + a^{-1}}$

43. $\dfrac{3x^{-1} + (2y)^{-1}}{x^{-2}}$

44. $\dfrac{5x^{-2} - 3y^{-1}}{x^{-1} + y^{-1}}$

45. $\dfrac{2a^{-1} + (2a)^{-1}}{a^{-1} + 2a^{-2}}$

46. $\dfrac{a^{-1} + 2a^{-2}}{2a^{-1} + (2a)^{-1}}$

47. $\dfrac{5x^{-1} + 2y^{-1}}{x^{-2}y^{-2}}$

48. $\dfrac{x^{-2}y^{-2}}{5x^{-1} + 2y^{-1}}$

49. $\dfrac{5x^{-1} - 2y^{-1}}{25x^{-2} - 4y^{-2}}$

50. $\dfrac{3x^{-1} + 3y^{-1}}{4x^{-2} - 9y^{-2}}$

REVIEW AND PREVIEW

Simplify. See Section 5.1.

51. $\dfrac{3x^3y^2}{12x}$

52. $\dfrac{-36xb^3}{9xb^2}$

53. $\dfrac{144x^5y^5}{-16x^2y}$

54. $\dfrac{48x^3y^2}{-4xy}$

Solve the following. See Section 3.6.

55. If $P(x) = -x^2$, find $P(-3)$.

56. If $f(x) = x^2 - 6$, find $f(-1)$.

CONCEPT EXTENSIONS

Solve. See the Concept Check in this section.

57. Which of the following are equivalent to $\dfrac{\dfrac{x+1}{9}}{\dfrac{y-2}{5}}$?

a. $\dfrac{x+1}{9} \div \dfrac{y-2}{5}$ **b.** $\dfrac{x+1}{9} \cdot \dfrac{y-2}{5}$ **c.** $\dfrac{x+1}{9} \cdot \dfrac{5}{y-2}$

58. Which of the following are equivalent to $\dfrac{\dfrac{a}{7}}{\dfrac{b}{13}}$?

a. $\dfrac{a}{7} \cdot \dfrac{b}{13}$ **b.** $\dfrac{a}{7} \div \dfrac{b}{13}$ **c.** $\dfrac{a}{7} \div \dfrac{13}{b}$ **d.** $\dfrac{a}{7} \cdot \dfrac{13}{b}$

59. When the source of a sound is traveling toward a listener, the pitch that the listener hears due to the Doppler effect is given by the complex rational expression $\dfrac{a}{1 - \dfrac{s}{770}}$, where a is the actual pitch of the sound and s is the speed of the sound source. Simplify this expression.

60. In baseball, the earned run average (ERA) statistic gives the average number of earned runs scored on a pitcher per game. It is computed with the following expression: $\dfrac{E}{\dfrac{I}{9}}$, where E is the number of earned runs scored on a pitcher and I is the total number of innings pitched by the pitcher. Simplify this expression.

61. Which of the following are equivalent to $\dfrac{\dfrac{1}{x}}{\dfrac{3}{y}}$?

a. $\dfrac{1}{x} \div \dfrac{3}{y}$ **b.** $\dfrac{1}{x} \cdot \dfrac{y}{3}$ **c.** $\dfrac{1}{x} \div \dfrac{y}{3}$

62. Which of the following are equivalent to $\dfrac{\dfrac{5}{2}}{a}$?

a. $\dfrac{5}{1} \div \dfrac{2}{a}$ **b.** $\dfrac{1}{5} \div \dfrac{2}{a}$ **c.** $\dfrac{5}{1} \cdot \dfrac{2}{a}$

63. In your own words, explain one method for simplifying a complex fraction.

64. Explain your favorite method for simplifying a complex fraction and why.

Simplify.

65. $\dfrac{1}{1 + (1 + x)^{-1}}$

66. $\dfrac{(x + 2)^{-1} + (x - 2)^{-1}}{(x^2 - 4)^{-1}}$

67. $\dfrac{x}{1 - \dfrac{1}{1 + \dfrac{1}{x}}}$

68. $\dfrac{x}{1 - \dfrac{1}{1 - \dfrac{1}{x}}}$

69. $\dfrac{\dfrac{2}{y^2} - \dfrac{5}{xy} - \dfrac{3}{x^2}}{\dfrac{2}{y^2} + \dfrac{7}{xy} + \dfrac{3}{x^2}}$

70. $\dfrac{\dfrac{2}{x^2} - \dfrac{1}{xy} - \dfrac{1}{y^2}}{\dfrac{1}{x^2} - \dfrac{3}{xy} + \dfrac{2}{y^2}}$

71. $\dfrac{3(a + 1)^{-1} + 4a^{-2}}{(a^3 + a^2)^{-1}}$

72. $\dfrac{9x^{-1} - 5(x - y)^{-1}}{4(x - y)^{-1}}$

*In the study of calculus, the difference quotient $\dfrac{f(a + h) - f(a)}{h}$ is often found and simplified. Find and simplify this quotient for each function f(x) by following steps **a** through **d**.*

a. *Find $(a + h)$.* **b.** *Find $f(a)$.*

c. *Use steps **a** and **b** to find $\dfrac{f(a + h) - f(a)}{h}$*

d. *Simplify the result of step **c**.*

73. $f(x) = \dfrac{1}{x}$

74. $f(x) = \dfrac{5}{x}$

75. $\dfrac{3}{x + 1}$

76. $\dfrac{2}{x^2}$

Chapter 7 Vocabulary Check

Fill in each blank with one of the words or phrases listed below. Not all choices will be used.

least common denominator   simplifying   reciprocals   numerator $\dfrac{-a}{b}$ $\dfrac{a}{-b}$

cross products   ratio   proportion

rational expression   domain   complex fraction   denominator $\dfrac{-a}{-b}$

1. A(n) _____ is an expression that can be written in the form $\dfrac{P}{Q}$, where P and Q are polynomials and Q is not 0.

2. In a(n) _____, the numerator or denominator or both may contain fractions.

3. For a rational expression, $-\dfrac{a}{b} =$ _____ = _____.

4. A rational expression is undefined when the _____ is 0.

5. The process of writing a rational expression in lowest terms is called _____.

6. The expressions $\dfrac{2x}{7}$ and $\dfrac{7}{2x}$ are called _____.

7. The _____ of a list of rational expressions is a polynomial of least degree whose factors include all factors of the denominators in the list.

8. A(n) _____ is the quotient of two numbers.

9. $\dfrac{x}{2} = \dfrac{7}{16}$ is an example of a(n) _____.

10. If $\dfrac{a}{b} = \dfrac{c}{d}$, then ad and bc are called _____.

11. The _____ of the rational function $f(x) = \dfrac{1}{x - 3}$ is $\{x \mid x \text{ is a real number}, x \neq 3\}$.

Chapter 7 Highlights

DEFINITIONS AND CONCEPTS   **EXAMPLES**

Section 7.1   Rational Functions and Simplifying Rational Expressions

A **rational expression** is an expression that can be written in the form $\dfrac{P}{Q}$, where P and Q are polynomials and Q does not equal 0.

$$\frac{7y^3}{4}, \quad \frac{x^2 + 6x + 1}{x - 3}, \quad \frac{-5}{s^3 + 8}$$

To find values for which a rational expression is undefined, find values for which the denominator is 0.

Find any values for which the expression $\dfrac{5y}{y^2 - 4y + 3}$ is undefined.

$$y^2 - 4y + 3 = 0 \quad \text{Set the denominator equal to 0.}$$
$$(y - 3)(y - 1) = 0 \quad \text{Factor.}$$
$$y - 3 = 0 \quad \text{or} \quad y - 1 = 0 \quad \text{Set each factor equal to 0.}$$
$$y = 3 \qquad\qquad y = 1 \quad \text{Solve.}$$

The expression is undefined when y is 3 and when y is 1.

To Simplify a Rational Expression

Step 1. Factor the numerator and denominator.

Step 2. Divide out factors common to the numerator and denominator. (This is the same as removing a factor of 1.)

A **rational function** is a function described by a rational expression.

Simplify: $\dfrac{4x + 20}{x^2 - 25}$

$$\frac{4x + 20}{x^2 - 25} = \frac{4(x + 5)}{(x + 5)(x - 5)} = \frac{4}{x - 5}$$

$$f(x) = \frac{2x - 6}{7}, \quad h(t) = \frac{t^2 - 3t + 5}{t - 1}$$

DEFINITIONS AND CONCEPTS	EXAMPLES

Section 7.2 Multiplying and Dividing Rational Expressions

To Multiply Rational Expressions

Step 1. Factor numerators and denominators.

Step 2. Multiply numerators and multiply denominators.

Step 3. Write the product in simplest form.

$$\frac{P}{Q} \cdot \frac{R}{S} = \frac{PR}{QS}$$

Multiply: $\dfrac{4x + 4}{2x - 3} \cdot \dfrac{2x^2 + x - 6}{x^2 - 1}$

$$\frac{4x + 4}{2x - 3} \cdot \frac{2x^2 + x - 6}{x^2 - 1} = \frac{4(x + 1)}{2x - 3} \cdot \frac{(2x - 3)(x + 2)}{(x + 1)(x - 1)}$$

$$= \frac{4(x + 1)(2x - 3)(x + 2)}{(2x - 3)(x + 1)(x - 1)}$$

$$= \frac{4(x + 2)}{x - 1}$$

To Divide by a Rational Expression

To divide by a rational expression, multiply by the reciprocal.

$$\frac{P}{Q} \div \frac{R}{S} = \frac{P}{Q} \cdot \frac{S}{R} = \frac{PS}{QR}$$

Divide: $\dfrac{15x + 5}{3x^2 - 14x - 5} \div \dfrac{15}{3x - 12}$

$$\frac{15x + 5}{3x^2 - 14x - 5} \div \frac{15}{3x - 12} = \frac{5(3x + 1)}{(3x + 1)(x - 5)} \cdot \frac{3(x - 4)}{3 \cdot 5}$$

$$= \frac{x - 4}{x - 5}$$

Section 7.3 Adding and Subtracting Rational Expressions with Common Denominators and Least Common Denominator

To Add or Subtract Rational Expressions with the Same Denominator

To add or subtract rational expressions with the same denominator, add or subtract numerators and place the sum or difference over the common denominator.

$$\frac{P}{R} + \frac{Q}{R} = \frac{P + Q}{R}$$

$$\frac{P}{R} - \frac{Q}{R} = \frac{P - Q}{R}$$

Perform indicated operations.

$$\frac{5}{x + 1} + \frac{x}{x + 1} = \frac{5 + x}{x + 1}$$

$$\frac{2y + 7}{y^2 - 9} - \frac{y + 4}{y^2 - 9} = \frac{(2y + 7) - (y + 4)}{y^2 - 9}$$

$$= \frac{2y + 7 - y - 4}{y^2 - 9}$$

$$= \frac{y + 3}{(y + 3)(y - 3)}$$

$$= \frac{1}{y - 3}$$

To Find the Least Common Denominator (LCD)

Step 1. Factor the denominators.

Step 2. The LCD is the product of all unique factors, each raised to a power equal to the greatest number of times that it appears in any one factored denominator.

Find the LCD for

$$\frac{7x}{x^2 + 10x + 25} \text{ and } \frac{11}{3x^2 + 15x}$$

$$x^2 + 10x + 25 = (x + 5)(x + 5)$$

$$3x^2 + 15x = 3x(x + 5)$$

LCD is $3x(x + 5)(x + 5)$ or $3x(x + 5)^2$

Section 7.4 Adding and Subtracting Rational Expressions with Unlike Denominators

To Add or Subtract Rational Expressions with Unlike Denominators

Step 1. Find the LCD.

Step 2. Rewrite each rational expression as an equivalent expression whose denominator is the LCD.

Perform the indicated operation.

$$\frac{9x + 3}{x^2 - 9} - \frac{5}{x - 3}$$

$$= \frac{9x + 3}{(x + 3)(x - 3)} - \frac{5}{x - 3}$$

(continued)

DEFINITIONS AND CONCEPTS	EXAMPLES

Section 7.4   Adding and Subtracting Rational Expressions with Unlike Denominators (continued)

Step 3. Add or subtract numerators and place the sum or difference over the common denominator.

Step 4. Write the result in simplest form.

LCD is $(x + 3)(x - 3)$.

$$= \frac{9x + 3}{(x + 3)(x - 3)} - \frac{5(x + 3)}{(x - 3)(x + 3)}$$

$$= \frac{9x + 3 - 5(x + 3)}{(x + 3)(x - 3)}$$

$$= \frac{9x + 3 - 5x - 15}{(x + 3)(x - 3)}$$

$$= \frac{4x - 12}{(x + 3)(x - 3)}$$

$$= \frac{4(x - 3)}{(x + 3)(x - 3)} = \frac{4}{x + 3}$$

Section 7.5   Solving Equations Containing Rational Expressions

To Solve an Equation Containing Rational Expressions

Step 1. Multiply both sides of the equation by the LCD of all rational expressions in the equation.

Step 2. Remove any grouping symbols and solve the resulting equation.

Step 3. Check the solution in the original equation.

Solve: $\dfrac{5x}{x + 2} + 3 = \dfrac{4x - 6}{x + 2}$

$$(x + 2)\left(\frac{5x}{x + 2} + 3\right) = (x + 2)\left(\frac{4x - 6}{x + 2}\right)$$

$$(x + 2)\left(\frac{5x}{x + 2}\right) + (x + 2)(3) = (x + 2)\left(\frac{4x - 6}{x + 2}\right)$$

$$5x + 3x + 6 = 4x - 6$$

$$4x = -12$$

$$x = -3$$

The solution checks and the solution is -3.

Section 7.6   Proportion and Problem Solving with Rational Equations

A **ratio** is the quotient of two numbers or two quantities.
A **proportion** is a mathematical statement that two ratios are equal.

Cross products

$$\text{If } \frac{a}{b} = \frac{c}{d}, \text{ then } ad = bc.$$

Proportions

$$\frac{2}{3} = \frac{8}{12} \qquad \frac{x}{7} = \frac{15}{35}$$

Cross Products

$2 \cdot 12$ or 24 $\qquad\qquad$ $3 \cdot 8$ or 24

$$\frac{2}{3} = \frac{8}{12}$$

Solve: $\dfrac{3}{4} = \dfrac{x}{x - 1}$

$$\frac{3}{4} = \frac{x}{x - 1}$$

$$3(x - 1) = 4x \qquad \text{Set cross products equal.}$$

$$3x - 3 = 4x$$

$$-3 = x$$

DEFINITIONS AND CONCEPTS	EXAMPLES

Section 7.6   Proportion and Problem Solving with Rational Equations (continued)

Problem-Solving Steps

1. UNDERSTAND. Read and reread the problem.

A small plane and a car leave Kansas City, Missouri, and head for Minneapolis, Minnesota, a distance of 450 miles. The speed of the plane is 3 times the speed of the car, and the plane arrives 6 hours ahead of the car. Find the speed of the car.

Let x = the speed of the car.

Then $3x$ = the speed of the plane.

	Distance	**= Rate ·**	**Time**
Car	450	x	$\dfrac{450}{x}\left(\dfrac{\text{distance}}{\text{rate}}\right)$
Plane	450	$3x$	$\dfrac{450}{3x}\left(\dfrac{\text{distance}}{\text{rate}}\right)$

2. TRANSLATE.

In words: plane's time   +   6 hours   =   car's time

$$\downarrow \qquad\qquad \downarrow \qquad\qquad \downarrow$$

Translate: $\dfrac{450}{3x}$ +   6   + $\dfrac{450}{x}$

3. SOLVE.

$$\frac{450}{3x} + 6 = \frac{450}{x}$$

$$3x\left(\frac{450}{3x}\right) + 3x(6) = 3x\left(\frac{450}{x}\right)$$

$$450 + 18x = 1350$$

$$18x = 900$$

$$x = 50$$

4. INTERPRET.

Check this solution in the originally stated problem. **State** the conclusion: The speed of the car is 50 miles per hour.

Section 7.7   Simplifying Complex Fractions

Method 1: Simplify the numerator and the denominator so that each is a single fraction. Then perform the indicated division and simplify if possible.

Simplify: $\dfrac{\dfrac{x+2}{x}}{x - \dfrac{4}{x}}$

Method 1: $\dfrac{\dfrac{x+2}{x}}{\dfrac{x \cdot x}{1 \cdot x} - \dfrac{4}{x}} = \dfrac{\dfrac{x+2}{x}}{\dfrac{x^2 - 4}{x}}$

$$= \frac{x+2}{x} \cdot \frac{x}{(x+2)(x-2)} = \frac{1}{x-2}$$

Method 2: Multiply the numerator and the denominator of the complex fraction by the LCD of the fractions in both the numerator and the denominator. Then simplify if possible.

Method 2: $\dfrac{\left(\dfrac{x+2}{x}\right) \cdot x}{\left(x - \dfrac{4}{x}\right) \cdot x} = \dfrac{x+2}{x \cdot x - \dfrac{4}{x} \cdot x}$

$$= \frac{x+2}{x^2-4} = \frac{x+2}{(x+2)(x-2)} = \frac{1}{x-2}$$

Chapter 7 Review

(7.1) Find the domain for each rational function.

1. $f(x) = \dfrac{3 - 5x}{7}$

2. $g(x) = \dfrac{2x + 4}{11}$

3. $f(x) = \dfrac{-3x^2}{x - 5}$

4. $h(x) = \dfrac{4x}{3x - 12}$

5. $f(x) = \dfrac{x^3 + 2}{x^2 + 8x}$

6. $G(x) = \dfrac{20}{3x^2 - 48}$

Simplify each rational expression.

7. $\dfrac{x + 12}{12 - x}$

8. $\dfrac{2x}{2x^2 - 2x}$

9. $\dfrac{x + 7}{x^2 - 49}$

10. $\dfrac{2x^2 + 4x - 30}{x^2 + x - 20}$

Simplify each expression. This section contains four-term polynomials and sums and differences of two cubes.

11. $\dfrac{x^2 + xa + xb + ab}{x^2 - xc + bx - bc}$

12. $\dfrac{x^2 + 5x - 2x - 10}{x^2 - 3x - 2x + 6}$

13. $\dfrac{4 - x}{x^3 - 64}$

14. $\dfrac{x^2 - 4}{x^3 + 8}$

The average cost (per bookcase) of manufacturing x bookcases is given by the rational function

$$C(x) = \dfrac{35x + 4200}{x}$$

15. Find the average cost per bookcase of manufacturing 50 bookcases.

16. Find the average cost per bookcase of manufacturing 100 bookcases.

(7.2) Perform each indicated operation and simplify.

17. $\dfrac{15x^3y^2}{z} \cdot \dfrac{z}{5xy^3}$

18. $\dfrac{-y^3}{8} \cdot \dfrac{9x^2}{y^3}$

19. $\dfrac{x^2 - 9}{x^2 - 4} \cdot \dfrac{x - 2}{x + 3}$

20. $\dfrac{2x + 5}{x - 6} \cdot \dfrac{2x}{-x + 6}$

21. $\dfrac{x^2 - 5x - 24}{x^2 - x - 12} \div \dfrac{x^2 - 10x + 16}{x^2 + x - 6}$

22. $\dfrac{4x + 4y}{xy^2} \div \dfrac{3x + 3y}{x^2y}$

23. $\dfrac{x^2 + x - 42}{x - 3} \cdot \dfrac{(x - 3)^2}{x + 7}$

24. $\dfrac{2a + 2b}{3} \cdot \dfrac{a - b}{a^2 - b^2}$

25. $\dfrac{2x^2 - 9x + 9}{8x - 12} \div \dfrac{x^2 - 3x}{2x}$

26. $\dfrac{x^2 - y^2}{x^2 + xy} \div \dfrac{3x^2 - 2xy - y^2}{3x^2 + 6x}$

27. $\dfrac{x - y}{4} \div \dfrac{y^2 - 2y - xy + 2x}{16x + 24}$

28. $\dfrac{5 + x}{7} \div \dfrac{xy + 5y - 3x - 15}{7y - 35}$

(7.3) Perform each indicated operation and simplify.

29. $\dfrac{x}{x^2 + 9x + 14} + \dfrac{7}{x^2 + 9x + 14}$

30. $\dfrac{x}{x^2 + 2x - 15} + \dfrac{5}{x^2 + 2x - 15}$

31. $\dfrac{4x - 5}{3x^2} - \dfrac{2x + 5}{3x^2}$

32. $\dfrac{9x + 7}{6x^2} - \dfrac{3x + 4}{6x^2}$

Find the LCD of each pair of rational expressions.

33. $\dfrac{x + 4}{2x}, \dfrac{3}{7x}$

34. $\dfrac{x - 2}{x^2 - 5x - 24}, \dfrac{3}{x^2 + 11x + 24}$

Rewrite each rational expression as an equivalent expression whose denominator is the given polynomial.

35. $\dfrac{5}{7x} = \dfrac{}{14x^3y}$

36. $\dfrac{9}{4y} = \dfrac{}{16y^3x}$

37. $\dfrac{x + 2}{x^2 + 11x + 18} = \dfrac{}{(x + 2)(x - 5)(x + 9)}$

38. $\dfrac{3x - 5}{x^2 + 4x + 4} = \dfrac{}{(x + 2)^2(x + 3)}$

(7.4) Perform each indicated operation and simplify.

39. $\dfrac{4}{5x^2} - \dfrac{6}{y}$

40. $\dfrac{2}{x - 3} - \dfrac{4}{x - 1}$

41. $\dfrac{4}{x + 3} - 2$

42. $\dfrac{3}{x^2 + 2x - 8} + \dfrac{2}{x^2 - 3x + 2}$

43. $\dfrac{2x - 5}{6x + 9} - \dfrac{4}{2x^2 + 3x}$

44. $\dfrac{x - 1}{x^2 - 2x + 1} - \dfrac{x + 1}{x - 1}$

Find the perimeter and the area of each figure.

△ **45.**

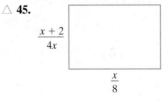

46.

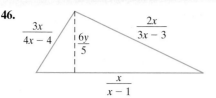

(7.5) *Solve each equation.*

47. $\dfrac{n}{10} = 9 - \dfrac{n}{5}$

48. $\dfrac{2}{x+1} - \dfrac{1}{x-2} = -\dfrac{1}{2}$

49. $\dfrac{y}{2y+2} + \dfrac{2y-16}{4y+4} = \dfrac{y-3}{y+1}$

50. $\dfrac{2}{x-3} - \dfrac{4}{x+3} = \dfrac{8}{x^2-9}$

51. $\dfrac{x-3}{x+1} - \dfrac{x-6}{x+5} = 0$

52. $x + 5 = \dfrac{6}{x}$

Solve the equation for the indicated variable.

53. $\dfrac{4A}{5b} = x^2$, for b

54. $\dfrac{x}{7} + \dfrac{y}{8} = 10$, for y

(7.6) *Solve each proportion.*

55. $\dfrac{x}{2} = \dfrac{12}{4}$

56. $\dfrac{20}{1} = \dfrac{x}{25}$

57. $\dfrac{2}{x-1} = \dfrac{3}{x+3}$

58. $\dfrac{4}{y-3} = \dfrac{2}{y-3}$

Solve.

59. A machine can process 300 parts in 20 minutes. Find how many parts can be processed in 45 minutes.

60. As his consulting fee, Mr. Visconti charges $90.00 per day. Find how much he charges for 3 hours of consulting. Assume an 8-hour work day.

61. Five times the reciprocal of a number equals the sum of $\dfrac{3}{2}$ the reciprocal of the number and $\dfrac{7}{6}$. What is the number?

62. The reciprocal of a number equals the reciprocal of the difference of 4 and the number. Find the number.

63. A car travels 90 miles in the same time that a car traveling 10 miles per hour slower travels 60 miles. Find the speed of each car.

64. The current in a bayou near Lafayette, Louisiana, is 4 miles per hour. A paddle boat travels 48 miles upstream in the same amount of time it takes to travel 72 miles downstream. Find the speed of the boat in still water.

65. When Mark and Maria manicure Mr. Stergeon's lawn, it takes them 5 hours. If Mark works alone, it takes 7 hours. Find how long it takes Maria alone.

66. It takes pipe A 20 days to fill a fish pond. Pipe B takes 15 days. Find how long it takes both pipes together to fill the pond.

Given that the pairs of triangles are similar, find each unknown length x.

△ **67.**

△ **68.**

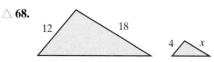

(7.7) *Simplify each complex fraction.*

69. $\dfrac{\dfrac{5x}{27}}{-\dfrac{10xy}{21}}$

70. $\dfrac{\dfrac{3}{5} + \dfrac{2}{7}}{\dfrac{1}{5} + \dfrac{5}{6}}$

71. $\dfrac{3 - \dfrac{1}{y}}{2 - \dfrac{1}{y}}$

72. $\dfrac{\dfrac{6}{x+2} + 4}{\dfrac{8}{x+2} - 4}$

73. $\dfrac{\dfrac{x-3}{x+3} + \dfrac{x+3}{x-3}}{\dfrac{x-3}{x+3} - \dfrac{x+3}{x-3}}$

74. $\dfrac{\dfrac{3}{x-1} - \dfrac{2}{1-x}}{\dfrac{2}{x-1} - \dfrac{2}{x}}$

75. $\dfrac{x + y^{-1}}{\dfrac{x}{y}}$

76. $\dfrac{x - xy^{-1}}{\dfrac{1+x}{y}}$

MIXED REVIEW

Simplify each rational expression.

77. $\dfrac{4x+12}{8x^2+24x}$

78. $\dfrac{x^3 - 6x^2 + 9x}{x^2 + 4x - 21}$

Perform the indicated operations and simplify.

79. $\dfrac{x^2+9x+20}{x^2-25} \cdot \dfrac{x^2-9x+20}{x^2+8x+16}$

80. $\dfrac{x^2-x-72}{x^2-x-30} \div \dfrac{x^2+6x-27}{x^2-9x+18}$

81. $\dfrac{x}{x^2-36} + \dfrac{6}{x^2-36}$

82. $\dfrac{5x-1}{4x} - \dfrac{3x-2}{4x}$

83. $\dfrac{4}{3x^2+8x-3} + \dfrac{2}{3x^2-7x+2}$

84. $\dfrac{3x}{x^2+9x+14} - \dfrac{6x}{x^2+4x-21}$

Solve.

85. $\dfrac{4}{a-1} + 2 = \dfrac{3}{a-1}$

86. $\dfrac{x}{x+3} + 4 = \dfrac{x}{x+3}$

Solve.

87. The quotient of twice a number and three, minus one-sixth, is the quotient of the number and two. Find the number.

88. Mr. Crocker can paint his house by himself in three days. His son will need an additional day to complete the job if he works alone. If they work together, find how long it takes to paint the house.

Given that the following pairs of triangles are similar, find each unknown length.

89.

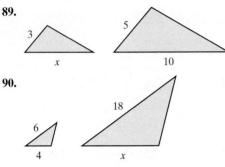

90.

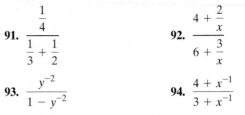

Simplify each complex fraction.

91. $\dfrac{\dfrac{1}{4}}{\dfrac{1}{3} + \dfrac{1}{2}}$

92. $\dfrac{4 + \dfrac{2}{x}}{6 + \dfrac{3}{x}}$

93. $\dfrac{y^{-2}}{1 - y^{-2}}$

94. $\dfrac{4 + x^{-1}}{3 + x^{-1}}$

Chapter 7 Getting Ready for the Test

MULTIPLE CHOICE *Select the correct choice.*

1. Choose the expression that is equivalent to $\dfrac{-x}{4 - x}$.

 A. $\dfrac{1}{4}$ **B.** $-\dfrac{1}{4}$ **C.** $\dfrac{x}{4 - x}$ **D.** $\dfrac{x}{x - 4}$

2. For which of these values (if any) is the expression $\dfrac{x + 3}{x^2 + 9}$ undefined?

 A. -3 **B.** 3 **C.** -3 and 3 **D.** 0 **E.** none of these

MATCHING *Match each rational expression to its simplified form. Letters may be used more than once.*

3. $\dfrac{y - 6}{6 - y}$

4. $\dfrac{y + 3}{3 + y}$

 A. 1

 B. -1

5. $\dfrac{x - 2}{-2 + x}$

6. $\dfrac{m - 4}{m + 4}$

 C. neither 1 nor -1

MULTIPLE CHOICE *Select the correct choice.*

7. $\dfrac{8}{x^2} \cdot \dfrac{4}{x^2} =$

 A. $\dfrac{32}{x^2}$ **B.** $\dfrac{2}{x^2}$ **C.** $\dfrac{32}{x^4}$ **D.** 2 **E.** $\dfrac{1}{2}$

8. $\dfrac{8}{x^2} \div \dfrac{4}{x^2} =$

 A. $\dfrac{32}{x^2}$ **B.** $\dfrac{2}{x^2}$ **C.** $\dfrac{32}{x^4}$ **D.** 2 **E.** $\dfrac{1}{2}$

9. $\dfrac{8}{x^2} + \dfrac{4}{x^2} =$

 A. $\dfrac{32}{x^2}$ **B.** $\dfrac{2}{x^2}$ **C.** $\dfrac{12}{x^4}$ **D.** $\dfrac{12}{x^2}$

10. $\dfrac{7x}{x - 1} - \dfrac{5 + 2x}{x - 1} =$

 A. 5 **B.** $\dfrac{9x - 5}{x - 1}$ **C.** $\dfrac{5}{x - 1}$ **D.** $\dfrac{14}{x - 1}$

11. The LCD of $\dfrac{9}{25x}$ and $\dfrac{z}{10x^3}$ is

 A. $250x^4$ **B.** $250x$ **C.** $50x^4$ **D.** $50x^3$

▶ **12.** The LCD of $\dfrac{5}{4x + 8}$ and $\dfrac{9}{8x - 8}$ is

    A. $(4x + 8)(8x - 8)$ **B.** $32(x + 2)(x - 1)$ **C.** $4(x + 2)(x - 1)$ **D.** $8(x + 2)(x - 1)$

MULTIPLE CHOICE *Identify each as an*   **A.** *expression or* **B.** *equation.*
Letters may be used more than once or not at all.

▶ **13.** $\dfrac{5}{x} + \dfrac{1}{3}$ ▶ **14.** $\dfrac{5}{x} + \dfrac{1}{3} = \dfrac{2}{x}$ ▶ **15.** $\dfrac{a + 5}{11} = 9$ ▶ **16.** $\dfrac{a + 5}{11} \cdot 9$

MULTIPLE CHOICE *Select the correct choice.*

▶ **17.** Multiply the given equation through by the LCD of its terms. Choose the correct equivalent equation once this is done.

    Given Equation: $\dfrac{x + 3}{4} + \dfrac{5}{6} = 3$

    A. $(x + 3) + 5 = 3$ **B.** $3(x + 3) + 2 \cdot 5 = 3$ **C.** $3(x + 3) + 2 \cdot 5 = 12 \cdot 3$ **D.** $6(x + 3) + 4 \cdot 5 = 3$

▶ **18.** Multiply the given equation through by the LCD of its terms. Choose the correct equivalent equation once this is done.

    Given equation: $3 - \dfrac{10x}{4(x + 1)} = \dfrac{5}{6(x + 1)}$

    A. $3 - 10x = 5$ **B.** $3 - 3 \cdot 10x = 2 \cdot 5$ **C.** $3 \cdot 12(x + 1) - 3 \cdot 10x = 2 \cdot 5$ **D.** $4(x + 1) - 3 \cdot 10x = 2 \cdot 5$

▶ **19.** Translate into an equation. Let x be the unknown number. "The quotient of a number and 5 equals the sum of that number and 12."

    A. $\dfrac{x}{5} = x + 12$ **B.** $\dfrac{5}{x} = x + 12$ **C.** $\dfrac{x}{5} = x \cdot 12$ **D.** $\dfrac{x}{5} \cdot (x + 12)$

▶ **20.** Write $\dfrac{2x^{-1}}{y^{-2} + (5x)^{-1}}$ without negative exponents.

    A. $\dfrac{\frac{2}{x}}{\frac{1}{y^2} + \frac{1}{5x}}$ **B.** $\dfrac{\frac{1}{2x}}{\frac{1}{y^2} + \frac{1}{5x}}$ **C.** $\dfrac{y^2 + 5x}{2x}$ **D.** $\dfrac{\frac{2}{x}}{\frac{1}{y^2} + \frac{5}{x}}$

Chapter 7 Test   MyMathLab®   YouTube

▶ **1.** Find the domain of the rational function

$$g(x) = \frac{9x^2 - 9}{x^2 + 4x + 3}$$

▶ **2.** For a certain computer desk, the average cost C (in dollars) per desk manufactured is

$$C = \frac{100x + 3000}{x}$$

where x is the number of desks manufactured.

  a. Find the average cost per desk when manufacturing 200 computer desks.

  b. Find the average cost per desk when manufacturing 1000 computer desks.

Simplify each rational expression.

▶ **3.** $\dfrac{3x - 6}{5x - 10}$ ▶ **4.** $\dfrac{x + 6}{x^2 + 12x + 36}$

▶ **5.** $\dfrac{x + 3}{x^3 + 27}$ ▶ **6.** $\dfrac{2m^3 - 2m^2 - 12m}{m^2 - 5m + 6}$

▶ **7.** $\dfrac{ay + 3a + 2y + 6}{ay + 3a + 5y + 15}$ ▶ **8.** $\dfrac{y - x}{x^2 - y^2}$

Perform the indicated operation and simplify if possible.

▶ **9.** $\dfrac{3}{x - 1} \cdot (5x - 5)$

▶ **10.** $\dfrac{y^2 - 5y + 6}{2y + 4} \cdot \dfrac{y + 2}{2y - 6}$

▶ **11.** $\dfrac{15x}{2x + 5} - \dfrac{6 - 4x}{2x + 5}$

▶ **12.** $\dfrac{5a}{a^2 - a - 6} - \dfrac{2}{a - 3}$

▶ **13.** $\dfrac{6}{x^2 - 1} + \dfrac{3}{x + 1}$

▶ **14.** $\dfrac{x^2 - 9}{x^2 - 3x} \div \dfrac{xy + 5x + 3y + 15}{2x + 10}$

15. $\dfrac{x+2}{x^2+11x+18} + \dfrac{5}{x^2-3x-10}$

Solve each equation.

16. $\dfrac{4}{y} - \dfrac{5}{3} = \dfrac{-1}{5}$

17. $\dfrac{5}{y+1} = \dfrac{4}{y+2}$

18. $\dfrac{a}{a-3} = \dfrac{3}{a-3} - \dfrac{3}{2}$

19. $x - \dfrac{14}{x-1} = 4 - \dfrac{2x}{x-1}$

20. $\dfrac{10}{x^2-25} = \dfrac{3}{x+5} + \dfrac{1}{x-5}$

Simplify each complex fraction.

21. $\dfrac{\frac{5x^2}{yz^2}}{\frac{10x}{z^3}}$

22. $\dfrac{5 - \frac{1}{y^2}}{\frac{1}{y} + \frac{2}{y^2}}$

23. $\dfrac{\frac{b}{a} - \frac{a}{b}}{\frac{1}{b} + \frac{1}{a}}$

24. In a sample of 85 fluorescent bulbs, 3 were found to be defective. At this rate, how many defective bulbs should be found in 510 bulbs?

25. One number plus five times its reciprocal is equal to six. Find the number.

26. A pleasure boat traveling down the Red River takes the same time to go 14 miles upstream as it takes to go 16 miles downstream. If the current of the river is 2 miles per hour, find the speed of the boat in still water.

27. An inlet pipe can fill a tank in 12 hours. A second pipe can fill the tank in 15 hours. If both pipes are used, find how long it takes to fill the tank.

28. Given that the two triangles are similar, find x.

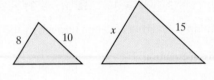

Chapter 7 Cumulative Review

TRANSLATING

1. Write each sentence as an equation or inequality. Let x represent the unknown number.

   a. The quotient of 15 and a number is 4.

   b. Three subtracted from 12 is a number.

   c. Four times a number, added to 17, is not equal to 21.

   d. Triple a number is less than 48.

2. Write each sentence as an equation. Let x represent the unknown number.

   a. The difference of 12 and a number is -45.

   b. The product of 12 and a number is -45.

   c. A number less 10 is twice the number.

3. Rajiv Puri invested part of his \$20,000 inheritance in a mutual fund account that pays 7% simple interest yearly and the rest in a certificate of deposit that pays 9% simple interest yearly. At the end of one year, Rajiv's investments earned \$1550. Find the amount he invested at each rate.

4. The number of non-business bankruptcies has increased over the years. In 2002, the number of non-business bankruptcies was 80,000 less than twice the number in 1994. If the total of non-business bankruptcies for these two years is 2,290,000 find the number of non-business bankruptcies for each year. (*Source:* American Bankruptcy Institute)

5. Graph $x - 3y = 6$ by finding and plotting intercepts.

6. Find the slope of the line whose equation is $7x + 2y = 9$.

7. Use the product rule to simplify each expression.

   a. $4^2 \cdot 4^5$

   b. $x^4 \cdot x^6$

   c. $y^3 \cdot y$

   d. $y^3 \cdot y^2 \cdot y^7$

   e. $(-5)^7 \cdot (-5)^8$

   f. $a^2 \cdot b^2$

8. Simplify.

   a. $\dfrac{x^9}{x^7}$

   b. $\dfrac{x^{19}y^5}{xy}$

   c. $(x^5y^2)^3$

   d. $(-3a^2b)(5a^3b)$

9. Subtract $(5z - 7)$ from the sum of $(8z + 11)$ and $(9z - 2)$.

10. Subtract $(9x^2 - 6x + 2)$ from $(x + 1)$.

11. Multiply: $(3a + b)^3$

12. Multiply: $(2x+1)(5x^2 - x + 2)$

13. Use a special product to square each binomial.

   a. $(t+2)^2$

   b. $(p-q)^2$

   c. $(2x+5)^2$

   d. $(x^2 - 7y)^2$

14. Multiply.

   a. $(x+9)^2$

   b. $(2x+1)(2x-1)$

   c. $8x(x^2+1)(x^2-1)$

15. Simplify each expression. Write results using positive exponents only.

   a. $\dfrac{1}{x^{-3}}$

   b. $\dfrac{1}{3^{-4}}$

   c. $\dfrac{p^{-4}}{q^{-9}}$

   d. $\dfrac{5^{-3}}{2^{-5}}$

16. Simplify. Write results with positive exponents only.

   a. 5^{-3}

   b. $\dfrac{9}{x^{-7}}$

   c. $\dfrac{11^{-1}}{7^{-2}}$

17. Divide: $\dfrac{4x^2 + 7 + 8x^3}{2x+3}$

18. Divide $(4x^3 - 9x + 2)$ by $(x-4)$.

19. Find the GCF of each list of numbers.

    a. 28 and 40

    b. 55 and 21

    c. 15, 18, and 66

20. Find the GCF of $9x^2$, $6x^3$, and $21x^5$.

Factor.

21. $-9a^5 + 18a^2 - 3a$

22. $7x^6 - 7x^5 + 7x^4$

23. $3m^2 - 24m - 60$

24. $-2a^2 + 10a + 12$

25. $3x^2 + 11x + 6$

26. $10m^2 - 7m + 1$

27. $x^2 + 12x + 36$

28. $4x^2 + 12x + 9$

29. $x^2 + 4$

30. $x^2 - 4$

31. $x^3 + 8$

32. $27y^3 - 1$

33. $2x^3 + 3x^2 - 2x - 3$

34. $3x^3 + 5x^2 - 12x - 20$

35. $12m^2 - 3n^2$

36. $x^5 - x$

37. Solve: $x(2x - 7) = 4$

38. Solve: $3x^2 + 5x = 2$

39. Find the x-intercepts of the graph of $y = x^2 - 5x + 4$.

40. Find the x-intercepts of the graph of $y = x^2 - x - 6$.

41. The height of a triangular sail is 2 meters less than twice the length of the base. If the sail has an area of 30 square meters, find the length of its base and the height.

42. The height of a parallelogram is 5 feet more than three times its base. If the area of the parallelogram is 182 square feet, find the length of its base and height.

43. Simplify: $\dfrac{18 - 2x^2}{x^2 - 2x - 3}$

44. Simplify: $\dfrac{2x^2 - 50}{4x^4 - 20x^3}$

45. Divide: $\dfrac{6x + 2}{x^2 - 1} \div \dfrac{3x^2 + x}{x - 1}$

46. Multiply: $\dfrac{6x^2 - 18x}{3x^2 - 2x} \cdot \dfrac{15x - 10}{x^2 - 9}$

47. Simplify: $\dfrac{(2x)^{-1} + 1}{2x^{-1} - 1}$

48. Simplify: $\dfrac{\dfrac{m}{3} + \dfrac{n}{6}}{\dfrac{m + n}{12}}$

Inequalities and Absolute Value

9.1   Compound Inequalities

9.2   Absolute Value Equations

9.3   Absolute Value Inequalities

Integrated Review—
Solving Compound
Inequalities and Absolute
Value Equations and
Inequalities

9.4   Graphing Linear
Inequalities in Two
Variables and
Systems of Linear
Inequalities

✓ CHECK YOUR PROGRESS

Vocabulary Check

Chapter Highlights

Chapter Review

Getting Ready for the Test

Chapter Test

Cumulative Review

Mathematics is a tool for solving problems in such diverse fields as transportation, engineering, economics, medicine, business, and biology. We solve problems using mathematics by modeling real-world phenomena with mathematical equations or inequalities. Our ability to solve problems using mathematics, then, depends in part on our ability to solve different types of equations and inequalities. This chapter includes solving absolute value equations and inequalities and other types of inequalities.

Growth of Social Network Users

Whatever your interests, there are many social media choices that fit your preferences. For example, we may check on family in Facebook, tweet latest activities, look for new ideas in Pinterest, or go to Instagram or WhatsApp or Tumblr. In a recent year, U.S. users spent more than 121.8 billion minutes monthly on social media. This is consistent over much of the world. The following graph demonstrates the current and projected growth in social network users worldwide.

In Section 9.3, Exercises 83 and 84, we will find the projected growth in the number of social network users worldwide as well as the percent of increase.

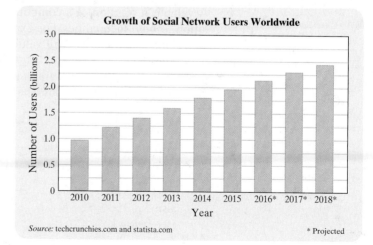

9.1 Compound Inequalities

OBJECTIVES

1 Find the Intersection of Two Sets.

2 Solve Compound Inequalities Containing **and**.

3 Find the Union of Two Sets.

4 Solve Compound Inequalities Containing **or**.

Two inequalities joined by the word **and** or **or** are called **compound inequalities.**

Compound Inequalities

$$x + 3 < 8 \quad and \quad x > 2$$

$$\frac{2x}{3} \geq 5 \quad or \quad -x + 10 < 7$$

OBJECTIVE

1 Finding the Intersection of Two Sets

The solution set of a compound inequality formed by the word **and** is the **intersection** of the solution sets of the two inequalities. We use the symbol ∩ to represent "intersection."

Intersection of Two Sets

The intersection of two sets, A and B, is the set of all elements common to both sets. A intersect B is denoted by $A \cap B$.

$A \cap B$

A B

EXAMPLE 1 If $A = \{x \,|\, x$ is an even number greater than 0 and less than 10$\}$ and $B = \{3, 4, 5, 6\}$, find $A \cap B$.

Solution Let's list the elements in set A.

$$A = \{2, 4, 6, 8\}$$

The numbers 4 and 6 are in sets A and B. The intersection is $\{4, 6\}$. □

PRACTICE

1 If $A = \{x \,|\, x$ is an odd number greater than 0 and less than 10$\}$ and $B = \{1, 2, 3, 4\}$, find $A \cap B$. ■

OBJECTIVE

2 Solving Compound Inequalities Containing "and"

A value is a solution of a compound inequality formed by the word **and** if it is a solution of *both* inequalities. For example, the solution set of the compound inequality $x \leq 5$ and $x \geq 3$ contains all values of x that make the inequality $x \leq 5$ a true statement **and** the inequality $x \geq 3$ a true statement. The first graph shown below is the graph of $x \leq 5$, the second graph is the graph of $x \geq 3$, and the third graph shows the intersection of the two graphs. The third graph is the graph of $x \leq 5$ **and** $x \geq 3$.

$\{x \,\|\, x \leq 5\}$	⟵─┼─┼─┼─┼─┼─┼─┤─┼─⟶ −1 0 1 2 3 4 5 6	$(-\infty, 5]$
$\{x \,\|\, x \geq 3\}$	⟵─┼─┼─┼─┼─┼─┼─┼─⟶ −1 0 1 2 3 4 5 6	$[3, \infty)$
$\{x \,\|\, x \leq 5 \text{ and } x \geq 3\}$ also $\{x \,\|\, 3 \leq x \leq 5\}$ (see below)	⟵─┼─┼─┼─┼─┼━━━┤─┼─⟶ −1 0 1 2 3 4 5 6	$[3,5]$

Since $x \geq 3$ is the same as $3 \leq x$, the compound inequality $3 \leq x$ and $x \leq 5$ can be written in a more compact form as $3 \leq x \leq 5$. The solution set $\{x \,|\, 3 \leq x \leq 5\}$ includes all numbers that are greater than or equal to 3 and at the same time less than or equal to 5.

In interval notation, the set $\{x \,|\, x \leq 5 \text{ and } x \geq 3\}$ or the set $\{x \,|\, 3 \leq x \leq 5\}$ is written as $[3, 5]$.

> **Helpful Hint**
>
> Don't forget that some compound inequalities containing "and" can be written in a more compact form.
>
> | Compound Inequality | Compact Form | Interval Notation |
> |---|---|---|
> | $2 \le x$ and $x \le 6$ | $2 \le x \le 6$ | $[2, 6]$ |
>
> Graph:
>
> $0 \quad 1 \quad 2 \quad 3 \quad 4 \quad 5 \quad 6 \quad 7$

EXAMPLE 2   Solve: $x - 7 < 2$ *and* $2x + 1 < 9$

Solution First we solve each inequality separately.

$$
\begin{array}{ccc}
x - 7 < 2 & and & 2x + 1 < 9 \\
x < 9 & and & 2x < 8 \\
x < 9 & and & x < 4
\end{array}
$$

Now we can graph the two intervals on two number lines and find their intersection. Their intersection is shown on the third number line.

$\{x \mid x < 9\}$

$(-\infty, 9)$

$3 \quad 4 \quad 5 \quad 6 \quad 7 \quad 8 \quad 9 \quad 10$

$\{x \mid x < 4\}$

$(-\infty, 4)$

$3 \quad 4 \quad 5 \quad 6 \quad 7 \quad 8 \quad 9 \quad 10$

$\{x \mid x < 9 \text{ and } x < 4\} = \{x \mid x < 4\}$ $(-\infty, 4)$

$3 \quad 4 \quad 5 \quad 6 \quad 7 \quad 8 \quad 9 \quad 10$

The solution set is $(-\infty, 4)$.

PRACTICE

2 Solve $x + 3 < 8$ *and* $2x - 1 < 3$. Write the solution set in interval notation.

EXAMPLE 3   Solve: $2x \ge 0$ *and* $4x - 1 \le -9$

Solution First we solve each inequality separately.

$$
\begin{array}{ccc}
2x \ge 0 & and & 4x - 1 \le -9 \\
x \ge 0 & and & 4x \le -8 \\
x \ge 0 & and & x \le -2
\end{array}
$$

Now we can graph the two intervals and find their intersection.

$\{x \mid x \ge 0\}$

$[0, \infty)$

$-3 \; -2 \; -1 \quad 0 \quad 1 \quad 2 \quad 3 \quad 4$

$\{x \mid x \le -2\}$

$(-\infty, -2]$

$-3 \; -2 \; -1 \quad 0 \quad 1 \quad 2 \quad 3 \quad 4$

$\{x \mid x \ge 0 \text{ and } x \le -2\} = \varnothing$ $\varnothing$

There is no number that is greater than or equal to 0 *and* less than or equal to -2. The solution set can be written as $\{\ \}$ or $\varnothing$.

PRACTICE

3 Solve $4x \le 0$ *and* $3x + 2 > 8$. Write the solution set in interval notation.

> **Helpful Hint**
>
> Example 3 shows that some compound inequalities have no solution. Also, some have all real numbers as solutions.

To solve a compound inequality written in a compact form, such as $2 < 4 - x < 7$, we get x alone in the "middle part." Since a compound inequality is really two inequalities in one statement, we must perform the same operations on all three parts of the inequality. For example:

$$2 < 4 - x < 7 \text{ means } 2 < 4 - x \quad and \quad 4 - x < 7,$$

EXAMPLE 4   Solve: $2 < 4 - x < 7$

Solution To get x alone, we first subtract 4 from all three parts.

$$2 < 4 - x < 7$$

$$2 - 4 < 4 - x - 4 < 7 - 4 \quad \text{Subtract 4 from all three parts.}$$

$$-2 < -x < 3 \quad \text{Simplify.}$$

$$\frac{-2}{-1} > \frac{-x}{-1} > \frac{3}{-1} \quad \text{Divide all three parts by } -1 \text{ and reverse the inequality symbols.}$$

$$2 > x > -3$$

Helpful Hint
Don't forget to reverse both inequality symbols.

This is equivalent to $-3 < x < 2$.

The solution set in interval notation is $(-3, 2)$, and its graph is shown.

PRACTICE
4   Solve $3 < 5 - x < 9$. Write the solution set in interval notation.

EXAMPLE 5   Solve: $-1 \leq \frac{2x}{3} + 5 \leq 2$

Solution First, clear the inequality of fractions by multiplying all three parts by the LCD, 3.

$$-1 \leq \frac{2x}{3} + 5 \leq 2$$

$$3(-1) \leq 3\left(\frac{2x}{3} + 5\right) \leq 3(2) \quad \text{Multiply all three parts by the LCD, 3.}$$

$$-3 \leq 2x + 15 \leq 6 \quad \text{Use the distributive property and multiply.}$$

$$-3 - 15 \leq 2x + 15 - 15 \leq 6 - 15 \quad \text{Subtract 15 from all three parts.}$$

$$-18 \leq 2x \leq -9 \quad \text{Simplify.}$$

$$\frac{-18}{2} \leq \frac{2x}{2} \leq \frac{-9}{2} \quad \text{Divide all three parts by 2.}$$

$$-9 \leq x \leq -\frac{9}{2} \quad \text{Simplify.}$$

The graph of the solution is shown.

The solution set in interval notation is $\left[-9, -\frac{9}{2}\right]$.

PRACTICE
5   Solve $-4 \leq \frac{x}{2} - 1 \leq 3$. Write the solution set in interval notation.

OBJECTIVE

3 Finding the Union of Two Sets ▶

The solution set of a compound inequality formed by the word **or** is the **union** of the solution sets of the two inequalities. We use the symbol $\cup$ to denote "union."

> **Helpful Hint**
>
> The word *either* in this definition means "one or the other or both."

Union of Two Sets

The **union** of two sets, A and B, is the set of elements that belong to *either* of the sets. A union B is denoted by $A \cup B$.

$$A \quad B$$
$$\underbrace{\qquad\qquad}_{A \cup B}$$

EXAMPLE 6 If $A = \{x \mid x \text{ is an even number greater than 0 and less than 10}\}$ and $B = \{3, 4, 5, 6\}$, find $A \cup B$.

Solution Recall from Example 1 that $A = \{2, 4, 6, 8\}$. The numbers that are in either set or both sets are $\{2, 3, 4, 5, 6, 8\}$. This set is the union. □

PRACTICE

6 If $A = \{x \mid x \text{ is an odd number greater than 0 and less than 10}\}$ and $B = \{2, 3, 4, 5, 6\}$, find $A \cup B$. ▪

OBJECTIVE

4 Solving Compound Inequalities Containing "or" ▶

A value is a solution of a compound inequality formed by the word **or** if it is a solution of **either** inequality. For example, the solution set of the compound inequality $x \leq 1$ **or** $x \geq 3$ contains all numbers that make the inequality $x \leq 1$ a true statement **or** the inequality $x \geq 3$ a true statement.

$\{x \mid x \leq 1\}$ ⟵———————⟶ $(-\infty, 1]$
　　　　　　　　　　　　−1　0　1　2　3　4　5　6

$\{x \mid x \geq 3\}$ ⟵———————⟶ $[3, \infty)$
　　　　　　　　　　　　−1　0　1　2　3　4　5　6

$\{x \mid x \leq 1 \text{ or } x \geq 3\}$ ⟵———————⟶ $(-\infty, 1] \cup [3, \infty)$
　　　　　　　　　　　　　　　　−1　0　1　2　3　4　5　6

In interval notation, the set $\{x \mid x \leq 1 \text{ or } x \geq 3\}$ is written as $(-\infty, 1] \cup [3, \infty)$.

EXAMPLE 7 Solve: $5x - 3 \leq 10 \text{ or } x + 1 \geq 5$

Solution First we solve each inequality separately.

$$5x - 3 \leq 10 \quad or \quad x + 1 \geq 5$$
$$5x \leq 13 \quad or \quad x \geq 4$$
$$x \leq \frac{13}{5} \quad or \quad x \geq 4$$

Now we can graph each interval and find their union.

$\left\{ x \mid x \leq \dfrac{13}{5} \right\}$ ⟵———————⟶ $\left(-\infty, \dfrac{13}{5} \right]$
　　　　　　　　　　　　　　−1　0　1　2　3　4　5　6

$\{x \mid x \geq 4\}$ ⟵———————⟶ $[4, \infty)$
　　　　　　　　　　　　−1　0　1　2　3　4　5　6

$\left\{ x \mid x \leq \dfrac{13}{5} \text{ or } x \geq 4 \right\}$ ⟵———————⟶ $\left(-\infty, \dfrac{13}{5} \right] \cup [4, \infty)$
　　　　　　　　　　　　　　　　　−1　0　1　2　3　4　5　6

Continued on next page

The solution set is $\left(-\infty, \dfrac{13}{5}\right] \cup [4, \infty)$.

PRACTICE
7   Solve $8x + 5 \leq 8$ or $x - 1 \geq 2$. Write the solution set in interval notation.

EXAMPLE 8   Solve: $-2x - 5 < -3$ *or* $6x < 0$

Solution   First we solve each inequality separately.

$$-2x - 5 < -3 \quad or \quad 6x < 0$$
$$-2x < 2 \quad\ \ or \quad\ \ x < 0$$
$$x > -1 \quad or \quad\ \ x < 0$$

Now we can graph each interval and find their union.

$\{x \mid x > -1\}$ $(-1, \infty)$

$\{x \mid x < 0\}$ $(-\infty, 0)$

$\{x \mid x > -1 \ or \ x < 0\}$ $(-\infty, \infty)$

$= $ all real numbers

The solution set is $(-\infty, \infty)$.

PRACTICE
8   Solve $-3x - 2 > -8$ *or* $5x > 0$. Write the solution set in interval notation.

✔ **CONCEPT CHECK**
Which of the following is *not* a correct way to represent the set of all numbers between -3 and 5?
a. $\{x \mid -3 < x < 5\}$ **b.** $-3 < x$ *or* $x < 5$
c. $(-3, 5)$ **d.** $x > -3$ *and* $x < 5$

Answer to Concept Check:
b is not correct

✔ | **Vocabulary, Readiness & Video Check**

Use the choices below to fill in each blank.

    or $\cup$ $\varnothing$

    and $\cap$ compound

1. Two inequalities joined by the word "and" or "or" are called _____ inequalities.

2. The word _____ means intersection.

3. The word _____ means union.

4. The symbol _____ represents intersection.

5. The symbol _____ represents union.

6. The symbol _____ is the empty set.

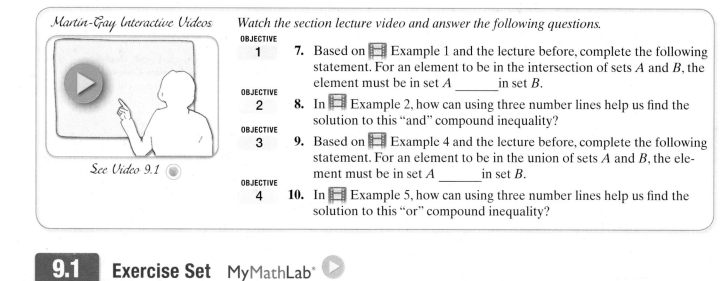

Watch the section lecture video and answer the following questions.

OBJECTIVE 1

7. Based on ▥ Example 1 and the lecture before, complete the following statement. For an element to be in the intersection of sets A and B, the element must be in set A _____ in set B.

OBJECTIVE 2

8. In ▥ Example 2, how can using three number lines help us find the solution to this "and" compound inequality?

OBJECTIVE 3

9. Based on ▥ Example 4 and the lecture before, complete the following statement. For an element to be in the union of sets A and B, the element must be in set A _____ in set B.

OBJECTIVE 4

10. In ▥ Example 5, how can using three number lines help us find the solution to this "or" compound inequality?

See Video 9.1

9.1   Exercise Set   MyMathLab®

MIXED PRACTICE

If $A = \{x \mid x \text{ is an even integer}\}$, $B = \{x \mid x \text{ is an odd integer}\}$, $C = \{2, 3, 4, 5\}$, and $D = \{4, 5, 6, 7\}$, list the elements of each set. See Examples 1 and 6.

1. $C \cup D$
2. $C \cap D$
3. $A \cap D$
4. $A \cup D$
5. $A \cup B$
6. $A \cap B$
7. $B \cap D$
8. $B \cup D$
9. $B \cup C$
10. $B \cap C$
11. $A \cap C$
12. $A \cup C$

Solve each compound inequality. Graph the solution set and write it in interval notation. See Examples 2 and 3.

13. $x < 1$ and $x > -3$
14. $x \le 0$ and $x \ge -2$
15. $x \le -3$ and $x \ge -2$
16. $x < 2$ and $x > 4$
17. $x < -1$ and $x < 1$
18. $x \ge -4$ and $x > 1$

Solve each compound inequality. Write solutions in interval notation. See Examples 2 and 3.

19. $x + 1 \ge 7$ and $3x - 1 \ge 5$
20. $x + 2 \ge 3$ and $5x - 1 \ge 9$
21. $4x + 2 \le -10$ and $2x \le 0$
22. $2x + 4 > 0$ and $4x > 0$
23. $-2x < -8$ and $x - 5 < 5$
24. $-7x \le -21$ and $x - 20 \le -15$

Solve each compound inequality. See Examples 4 and 5.

25. $5 < x - 6 < 11$
26. $-2 \le x + 3 \le 0$
27. $-2 \le 3x - 5 \le 7$
28. $1 < 4 + 2x < 7$
29. $1 \le \frac{2}{3}x + 3 \le 4$
30. $-2 < \frac{1}{2}x - 5 < 1$
31. $-5 \le \frac{-3x + 1}{4} \le 2$
32. $-4 \le \frac{-2x + 5}{3} \le 1$

Solve each compound inequality. Graph the solution set and write it in interval notation. See Examples 7 and 8.

33. $x < 4$ or $x < 5$
34. $x \ge -2$ or $x \le 2$
35. $x \le -4$ or $x \ge 1$
36. $x < 0$ or $x < 1$
37. $x > 0$ or $x < 3$
38. $x \ge -3$ or $x \le -4$

Solve each compound inequality. Write solutions in interval notation. See Examples 7 and 8.

39. $-2x \le -4$ or $5x - 20 \ge 5$
40. $-5x \le 10$ or $3x - 5 \ge 1$
41. $x + 4 < 0$ or $6x > -12$
42. $x + 9 < 0$ or $4x > -12$
43. $3(x - 1) < 12$ or $x + 7 > 10$
44. $5(x - 1) \ge -5$ or $5 + x \le 11$

MIXED PRACTICE

Solve each compound inequality. Write solutions in interval notation. See Examples 1 through 8.

45. $x < \frac{2}{3}$ and $x > -\frac{1}{2}$
46. $x < \frac{5}{7}$ and $x < 1$
47. $x < \frac{2}{3}$ or $x > -\frac{1}{2}$
48. $x < \frac{5}{7}$ or $x < 1$
49. $0 \le 2x - 3 \le 9$
50. $3 < 5x + 1 < 11$
51. $\frac{1}{2} < x - \frac{3}{4} < 2$

52. $\dfrac{2}{3} < x + \dfrac{1}{2} < 4$

53. $x + 3 \geq 3 \ and \ x + 3 \leq 2$

54. $2x - 1 \geq 3 \ and \ -x > 2$

55. $3x \geq 5 \ or \ -\dfrac{5}{8}x - 6 > 1$

56. $\dfrac{3}{8}x + 1 \leq 0 \ or \ -2x < -4$

57. $0 < \dfrac{5 - 2x}{3} < 5$

58. $-2 < \dfrac{-2x - 1}{3} < 2$

59. $-6 < 3(x - 2) \leq 8$

60. $-5 < 2(x + 4) < 8$

61. $-x + 5 > 6 \ and \ 1 + 2x \leq -5$

62. $5x \leq 0 \ and \ -x + 5 < 8$

▶ **63.** $3x + 2 \leq 5 \ or \ 7x > 29$

64. $-x < 7 \ or \ 3x + 1 < -20$

65. $5 - x > 7 \ and \ 2x + 3 \geq 13$

66. $-2x < -6 \ or \ 1 - x > -2$

67. $-\dfrac{1}{2} \leq \dfrac{4x - 1}{6} < \dfrac{5}{6}$

68. $-\dfrac{1}{2} \leq \dfrac{3x - 1}{10} < \dfrac{1}{2}$

69. $\dfrac{1}{15} < \dfrac{8 - 3x}{15} < \dfrac{4}{5}$

70. $-\dfrac{1}{4} < \dfrac{6 - x}{12} < -\dfrac{1}{6}$

71. $0.3 < 0.2x - 0.9 < 1.5$

72. $-0.7 \leq 0.4x + 0.8 < 0.5$

REVIEW AND PREVIEW

Evaluate the following. See Sections 1.5 and 1.6.

73. $|-7| - |19|$

74. $|-7 - 19|$

75. $-(-6) - |-10|$

76. $|-4| - (-4) + |-20|$

Find by inspection all values for x that make each equation true.

77. $|x| = 7$ **78.** $|x| = 5$

79. $|x| = 0$

80. $|x| = -2$

CONCEPT EXTENSIONS

Use the graph to answer Exercises 81 and 82.

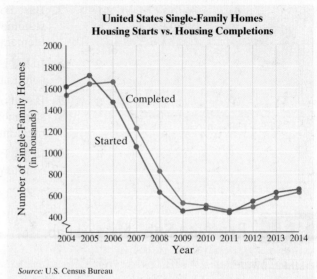

**United States Single-Family Homes
Housing Starts vs. Housing Completions**

Source: U.S. Census Bureau

81. For which years were the number of single-family housing starts greater than 1500 and the number of single-family home completions greater than 1500?

82. For which years were the number of single-family housing starts less than 500 or the number of single-family housing completions greater than 1500?

83. In your own words, describe how to find the union of two sets.

84. In your own words, describe how to find the intersection of two sets.

*Solve each compound inequality for x. See the example below. To solve $x - 6 < 3x < 2x + 5$, notice that this inequality contains a variable not only in the middle but also on the left and the right. When this occurs, we solve by rewriting the inequality using the word **and**.*

$$x - 6 < 3x \quad and \quad 3x < 2x + 5$$
$$-6 < 2x \quad and \quad x < 5$$
$$-3 < x$$
$$x > -3 \quad and \quad x < 5$$

$$x > -3$$

$$x < 5$$

$$-3 < x < 5 \ or \ (-3, 5)$$

85. $2x - 3 < 3x + 1 < 4x - 5$

86. $x + 3 < 2x + 1 < 4x + 6$

87. $-3(x - 2) \leq 3 - 2x \leq 10 - 3x$

88. $7x - 1 \leq 7 + 5x \leq 3(1 + 2x)$

89. $5x - 8 < 2(2 + x) < -2(1 + 2x)$

90. $1 + 2x < 3(2 + x) < 1 + 4x$

The formula for converting Fahrenheit temperatures to Celsius temperatures is $C = \dfrac{5}{9}(F - 32)$. Use this formula for Exercises 91 and 92.

91. During a recent year, the temperatures in Chicago ranged from $-29°C$ to $35°C$. Use a compound inequality to convert these temperatures to Fahrenheit temperatures.

92. In Oslo, the average temperature ranges from $-10°C$ to $18°C$. Use a compound inequality to convert these temperatures to the Fahrenheit scale.

Solve.

93. Christian D'Angelo has scores of 68, 65, 75, and 78 on his algebra tests. Use a compound inequality to find the scores he can make on his final exam to receive a C in the course. The final exam counts as two tests, and a C is received if the final course average is from 70 to 79.

94. Wendy Wood has scores of 80, 90, 82, and 75 on her chemistry tests. Use a compound inequality to find the range of scores she can make on her final exam to receive a B in the course. The final exam counts as two tests, and a B is received if the final course average is from 80 to 89.

9.2 | Absolute Value Equations

OBJECTIVE

1 Solve Absolute Value Equations.

OBJECTIVE

1   Solving Absolute Value Equations

In Chapter 1, we defined the absolute value of a number as its distance from 0 on a number line.

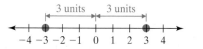

$$|-2| = 2 \text{ and } |3| = 3$$

In this section, we concentrate on solving equations containing the absolute value of a variable or a variable expression. Examples of absolute value equations are

$$|x| = 3 \qquad -5 = |2y + 7| \qquad |z - 6.7| = |3z + 1.2|$$

Since distance and absolute value are so closely related, absolute value equations and inequalities (see Section 9.3) are extremely useful in solving distance-type problems such as calculating the possible error in a measurement.

For the absolute value equation $|x| = 3$, its solution set will contain all numbers whose distance from 0 is 3 units. Two numbers are 3 units away from 0 on the number line: 3 and -3.

Thus, the solution set of the equation $|x| = 3$ is $\{3, -3\}$. This suggests the following:

Solving Equations of the Form $|X| = a$

If a is a positive number, then $|X| = a$ is equivalent to $X = a$ or $X = -a$.

EXAMPLE 1   Solve: $|p| = 2$

<u>Solution</u>   Since 2 is positive, $|p| = 2$ is equivalent to $p = 2$ or $p = -2$.

To check, let $p = 2$ and then $p = -2$ in the original equation.

$|p| = 2$ Original equation	$|p| = 2$ Original equation
$|2| \overset{?}{=} 2$ Let $p = 2$.	$|-2| \overset{?}{=} 2$ Let $p = -2$.
$2 = 2$ True	$2 = 2$ True

The solutions are 2 and -2 or the solution set is $\{2, -2\}$.

PRACTICE

1   Solve: $|q| = 13$

If the expression inside the absolute value bars is more complicated than a single variable, we can still apply the absolute value property.

> **Helpful Hint**
>
> For the equation $|X| = a$ in the box on the previous page, X can be a single variable or a variable expression.

EXAMPLE 2 Solve: $|5w + 3| = 7$

Solution Here the expression inside the absolute value bars is $5w + 3$. If we think of the expression $5w + 3$ as X in the absolute value property, we see that $|X| = 7$ is equivalent to

$$X = 7 \quad \text{or} \quad X = -7$$

Then substitute $5w + 3$ for X, and we have

$$5w + 3 = 7 \quad \text{or} \quad 5w + 3 = -7$$

Solve these two equations for w.

$$
\begin{aligned}
5w + 3 &= 7 &\text{or} \quad 5w + 3 &= -7 \\
5w &= 4 &\text{or} \quad 5w &= -10 \\
w &= \frac{4}{5} &\text{or} \quad w &= -2
\end{aligned}
$$

Check: To check, let $w = -2$ and then $w = \frac{4}{5}$ in the original equation.

Let $w = -2$

$$|5(-2) + 3| \stackrel{?}{=} 7$$
$$|-10 + 3| \stackrel{?}{=} 7$$
$$|-7| \stackrel{?}{=} 7$$
$$7 = 7 \quad \text{True}$$

Let $w = \frac{4}{5}$

$$\left|5\left(\frac{4}{5}\right) + 3\right| \stackrel{?}{=} 7$$
$$|4 + 3| \stackrel{?}{=} 7$$
$$|7| \stackrel{?}{=} 7$$
$$7 = 7 \quad \text{True}$$

Both solutions check, and the solutions are -2 and $\frac{4}{5}$ or the solution set is $\left\{-2, \frac{4}{5}\right\}$. ☐

PRACTICE
2 Solve: $|2x - 3| = 5$

EXAMPLE 3 Solve: $\left|\dfrac{x}{2} - 1\right| = 11$

Solution $\left|\dfrac{x}{2} - 1\right| = 11$ is equivalent to

$$\frac{x}{2} - 1 = 11 \quad \text{or} \quad \frac{x}{2} - 1 = -11$$

$$2\left(\frac{x}{2} - 1\right) = 2(11) \quad \text{or} \quad 2\left(\frac{x}{2} - 1\right) = 2(-11) \quad \text{Clear fractions.}$$

$$x - 2 = 22 \quad \text{or} \quad x - 2 = -22 \quad \text{Apply the distributive property.}$$

$$x = 24 \quad \text{or} \quad x = -20$$

The solutions are 24 and -20. ☐

PRACTICE
3 Solve: $\left|\dfrac{x}{5} + 1\right| = 15$

To apply the absolute value property, first make sure that the absolute value expression is isolated.

> **Helpful Hint**
>
> If the equation has a single absolute value expression containing variables, isolate the absolute value expression first.

EXAMPLE 4   Solve: $|2x| + 5 = 7$

Solution We want the absolute value expression alone on one side of the equation, so begin by subtracting 5 from both sides. Then apply the absolute value property.

$$|2x| + 5 = 7$$
$$|2x| = 2 \qquad \text{Subtract 5 from both sides.}$$
$$2x = 2 \quad \text{or} \quad 2x = -2$$
$$x = 1 \quad \text{or} \quad x = -1$$

The solutions are -1 and 1.   □

PRACTICE
4   Solve: $|3x| + 8 = 14$ ■

EXAMPLE 5   Solve: $|y| = 0$

Solution We are looking for all numbers whose distance from 0 is zero units. The only number is 0. The solution is 0.   □

PRACTICE
5   Solve: $|z| = 0$ ■

The next two examples illustrate a special case for absolute value equations. This special case occurs when an isolated absolute value is equal to a negative number.

EXAMPLE 6   Solve: $2|x| + 25 = 23$

Solution First, isolate the absolute value.

$$2|x| + 25 = 23$$
$$2|x| = -2 \quad \text{Subtract 25 from both sides.}$$
$$|x| = -1 \quad \text{Divide both sides by 2.}$$

The absolute value of a number is never negative, so this equation has no solution. The solution set is { } or $\varnothing$.   □

PRACTICE
6   Solve: $3|z| + 9 = 7$ ■

EXAMPLE 7   Solve: $\left| \dfrac{3x + 1}{2} \right| = -2$

Solution Again, the absolute value of any expression is never negative, so no solution exists. The solution set is { } or $\varnothing$.   □

PRACTICE
7   Solve: $\left| \dfrac{5x + 3}{4} \right| = -8$ ■

Given two absolute value expressions, we might ask, when are the absolute values of two expressions equal? To see the answer, notice that

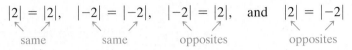

$$|2| = |2|, \quad |-2| = |-2|, \quad |-2| = |2|, \quad \text{and} \quad |2| = |-2|$$

same   same   opposites   opposites

Two absolute value expressions are equal when the expressions inside the absolute value bars are equal to or are opposites of each other.

EXAMPLE 8 Solve: $|3x + 2| = |5x - 8|$

Solution This equation is true if the expressions inside the absolute value bars are equal to or are opposites of each other.

$$3x + 2 = 5x - 8 \quad \text{or} \quad 3x + 2 = -(5x - 8)$$

Next, solve each equation.

$$
\begin{aligned}
3x + 2 &= 5x - 8 & \text{or} \quad 3x + 2 &= -5x + 8 \\
-2x + 2 &= -8 & \text{or} \quad 8x + 2 &= 8 \\
-2x &= -10 & \text{or} \quad 8x &= 6 \\
x &= 5 & \text{or} \quad x &= \frac{3}{4}
\end{aligned}
$$

The solutions are $\frac{3}{4}$ and 5. □

PRACTICE

8 Solve: $|2x + 4| = |3x - 1|$

EXAMPLE 9 Solve: $|x - 3| = |5 - x|$

Solution

$$
\begin{aligned}
x - 3 &= 5 - x & \text{or} \quad x - 3 &= -(5 - x) \\
2x - 3 &= 5 & \text{or} \quad x - 3 &= -5 + x \\
2x &= 8 & \text{or} \quad x - 3 - x &= -5 + x - x \\
x &= 4 & \text{or} \quad -3 &= -5 \qquad \text{False}
\end{aligned}
$$

Recall from Section 2.3 that when an equation simplifies to a false statement, the equation has no solution. Thus, the only solution for the original absolute value equation is 4. □

PRACTICE

9 Solve: $|x - 2| = |8 - x|$

✔ **CONCEPT CHECK**

True or false? Absolute value equations always have two solutions. Explain your answer.

The following box summarizes the methods shown for solving absolute value equations.

Absolute Value Equations

$|X| = a$
$\begin{cases} \text{If } a \text{ is positive, then solve } X = a \text{ or } X = -a. \\ \text{If } a \text{ is 0, solve } X = 0. \\ \text{If } a \text{ is negative, the equation } |X| = a \text{ has no solution.} \end{cases}$

$|X| = |Y|$ Solve $X = Y$ or $X = -Y$.

Vocabulary, Readiness & Video Check

Match each absolute value equation with the equivalent statement.

1. $|x - 2| = 5$

2. $|x - 2| = 0$

3. $|x - 2| = |x + 3|$

4. $|x + 3| = 5$

5. $|x + 3| = -5$

A. $x - 2 = 0$

B. $x - 2 = x + 3$ or $x - 2 = -(x + 3)$

C. $x - 2 = 5$ or $x - 2 = -5$

D. $\varnothing$

E. $x + 3 = 5$ or $x + 3 = -5$

Martin-Gay Interactive Videos

Watch the section lecture videos and answer the following question.

OBJECTIVE 1

6. As explained in Example 3, why is a positive in the rule "$|X| = a$ is equivalent to $X = a$ or $X = -a$"?

See Video 9.2

9.2 Exercise Set MyMathLab®

Solve each absolute value equation. See Examples 1 through 7.

1. $|x| = 7$

2. $|y| = 15$

3. $|3x| = 12.6$

4. $|6n| = 12.6$

5. $|2x - 5| = 9$

6. $|6 + 2n| = 4$

7. $\left|\dfrac{x}{2} - 3\right| = 1$

8. $\left|\dfrac{n}{3} + 2\right| = 4$

9. $|z| + 4 = 9$

10. $|x| + 1 = 3$

11. $|3x| + 5 = 14$

12. $|2x| - 6 = 4$

13. $|2x| = 0$

14. $|7z| = 0$

15. $|4n + 1| + 10 = 4$

16. $|3z - 2| + 8 = 1$

17. $|5x - 1| = 0$

18. $|3y + 2| = 0$

Solve. See Examples 8 and 9.

19. $|5x - 7| = |3x + 11|$

20. $|9y + 1| = |6y + 4|$

21. $|z + 8| = |z - 3|$

22. $|2x - 5| = |2x + 5|$

MIXED PRACTICE

Solve each absolute value equation. See Examples 1 through 9.

23. $|x| = 4$

24. $|x| = 1$

25. $|y| = 0$

26. $|y| = 8$

27. $|z| = -2$

28. $|y| = -9$

29. $|7 - 3x| = 7$

30. $|4m + 5| = 5$

31. $|6x| - 1 = 11$

32. $|7z| + 1 = 22$

33. $|4p| = -8$

34. $|5m| = -10$

35. $|x - 3| + 3 = 7$

36. $|x + 4| - 4 = 1$

37. $\left|\dfrac{z}{4} + 5\right| = -7$

38. $\left|\dfrac{c}{5} - 1\right| = -2$

39. $|9v - 3| = -8$

40. $|1 - 3b| = -7$

41. $|8n + 1| = 0$

42. $|5x - 2| = 0$

43. $|1 + 6c| - 7 = -3$

44. $|2 + 3m| - 9 = -7$

45. $|5x + 1| = 11$

46. $|8 - 6c| = 1$

47. $|4x - 2| = |-10|$

48. $|3x + 5| = |-4|$

49. $|5x + 1| = |4x - 7|$

50. $|3 + 6n| = |4n + 11|$

51. $|6 + 2x| = -|-7|$

52. $|4 - 5y| = -|-3|$

53. $|2x - 6| = |10 - 2x|$

54. $|4n + 5| = |4n + 3|$

55. $\left|\dfrac{2x - 5}{3}\right| = 7$

56. $\left|\dfrac{1 + 3n}{4}\right| = 4$

57. $2 + |5n| = 17$

58. $8 + |4m| = 24$

59. $\left|\dfrac{2x - 1}{3}\right| = |-5|$

60. $\left|\dfrac{5x + 2}{2}\right| = |-6|$

61. $|2y - 3| = |9 - 4y|$

62. $|5z - 1| = |7 - z|$

63. $\left|\dfrac{3n + 2}{8}\right| = |-1|$

64. $\left|\dfrac{2r - 6}{5}\right| = |-2|$

65. $|x + 4| = |7 - x|$

66. $|8 - y| = |y + 2|$

67. $\left|\dfrac{8c - 7}{3}\right| = -|-5|$

68. $\left|\dfrac{5d + 1}{6}\right| = -|-9|$

REVIEW AND PREVIEW

The circle graph shows the types of cheese produced in the United States in 2014. Use this graph to answer Exercises 69 through 72. See Section 2.6.

U.S. Cheese¹ Production by Variety, 2014

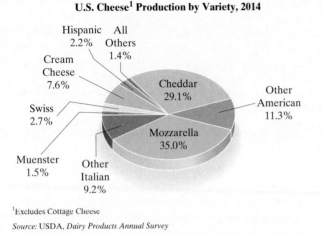

¹Excludes Cottage Cheese

Source: USDA, Dairy Products Annual Survey

69. In 2014, cheddar cheese made up what percent of U.S. cheese production?

70. Which cheese had the highest U.S. production in 2014?

71. A circle contains 360°. Find the number of degrees found in the 9.2% sector for Other Italian Cheese.

72. In 2014, the total production of cheeses above in the United States was 11,201,000,000 pounds. Find the amount of cream cheese produced during that year.

List five integer solutions of each inequality. See Section 1.2.

73. $|x| \leq 3$

74. $|x| \geq -2$

75. $|y| > -10$

76. $|y| < 0$

CONCEPT EXTENSIONS

Without going through a solution procedure, determine the solution of each absolute value equation or inequality.

77. $|x - 7| = -4$

78. $|x - 7| < -4$

79. Write an absolute value equation representing all numbers x whose distance from 0 is 5 units.

80. Write an absolute value equation representing all numbers x whose distance from 0 is 2 units.

81. Explain why some absolute value equations have two solutions.

82. Explain why some absolute value equations have one solution.

83. Write an absolute value equation representing all numbers x whose distance from 1 is 5 units.

84. Write an absolute value equation representing all numbers x whose distance from 7 is 2 units.

85. Describe how solving an absolute value equation such as $|2x - 1| = 3$ is similar to solving an absolute value equation such as $|2x - 1| = |x - 5|$.

86. Describe how solving an absolute value equation such as $|2x - 1| = 3$ is different from solving an absolute value equation such as $|2x - 1| = |x - 5|$.

Write each as an equivalent absolute value equation.

87. $x = 6$ or $x = -6$

88. $2x - 1 = 4$ or $2x - 1 = -4$

89. $x - 2 = 3x - 4$ or $x - 2 = -(3x - 4)$

90. For what value(s) of c will an absolute value equation of the form $|ax + b| = c$ have

  a. one solution?

  b. no solution?

  c. two solutions?

9.3 Absolute Value Inequalities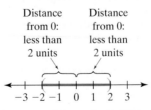

OBJECTIVES

1 Solve Absolute Value Inequalities of the Form $|X| < a$.

2 Solve Absolute Value Inequalities of the Form $|X| > a$.

OBJECTIVE

1 Solving Absolute Value Inequalities of the Form $|X| < a$

The solution set of an absolute value inequality such as $|x| < 2$ contains all numbers whose distance from 0 is less than 2 units, as shown below.

Distance from 0: less than 2 units   Distance from 0: less than 2 units

$$-3 \;\; -2 \;\; -1 \;\; 0 \;\; 1 \;\; 2 \;\; 3$$

The solution set is $\{x | -2 < x < 2\}$, or $(-2, 2)$ in interval notation.

EXAMPLE 1 Solve $|x| \leq 3$ and graph the solution set.

Solution The solution set of this inequality contains all numbers whose distance from 0 is less than or equal to 3. Thus 3, −3, and all numbers between 3 and −3 are in the solution set.

The solution set is $[-3, 3]$.

PRACTICE
1   Solve $|x| < 5$ and graph the solution set.

In general, we have the following.

> **Solving Absolute Value Inequalities of the Form $|X| < a$**
>
> If a is a positive number, then $|X| < a$ is equivalent to $-a < X < a$.

This property also holds true for the inequality symbol $\leq$.

EXAMPLE 2   Solve $|m - 6| < 2$ for m and graph the solution set.

Solution   Replace X with $m - 6$ and a with 2 in the preceding property, and we see that

$$|m - 6| < 2 \quad \text{is equivalent to} \quad -2 < m - 6 < 2$$

Solve this compound inequality for m by adding 6 to all three parts.

$$-2 < m - 6 < 2$$
$$-2 + 6 < m - 6 + 6 < 2 + 6 \qquad \text{Add 6 to all three parts.}$$
$$4 < m < 8 \qquad\qquad\qquad \text{Simplify.}$$

The solution set is $(4, 8)$, and its graph is shown.

PRACTICE
2   Solve $|b + 1| < 3$ for b and graph the solution set.

> **Helpful Hint**
>
> Before using an absolute value inequality property, isolate the absolute value expression on one side of the inequality.

EXAMPLE 3   Solve $|5x + 1| + 1 \leq 10$ for x and graph the solution set.

Solution   First, isolate the absolute value expression by subtracting 1 from both sides.

$$|5x + 1| + 1 \leq 10$$
$$|5x + 1| \leq 10 - 1 \quad \text{Subtract 1 from both sides.}$$
$$|5x + 1| \leq 9 \qquad\quad \text{Simplify.}$$

Since 9 is positive, we apply the absolute value property for $|X| \leq a$.

$$-9 \leq 5x + 1 \leq 9$$
$$-9 - 1 \leq 5x + 1 - 1 \leq 9 - 1 \quad \text{Subtract 1 from all three parts.}$$
$$-10 \leq 5x \leq 8 \qquad\qquad\quad \text{Simplify.}$$
$$-2 \leq x \leq \frac{8}{5} \qquad\qquad\qquad \text{Divide all three parts by 5.}$$

The solution set is $\left[-2, \dfrac{8}{5}\right]$, and the graph is shown above.

PRACTICE
3   Solve $|3x - 2| + 5 \leq 9$ for x and graph the solution set.

EXAMPLE 4 Solve for x: $\left| 2x - \dfrac{1}{10} \right| < -13$

__Solution__ The absolute value of a number is always nonnegative and can never be less than −13. Thus this absolute value inequality has no solution. The solution set is { } or ∅. ☐

PRACTICE
4 Solve for x: $\left| 3x + \dfrac{5}{8} \right| < -4$ ■

EXAMPLE 5 Solve for x: $\left| \dfrac{2(x + 1)}{3} \right| \leq 0$

__Solution__ Recall that "≤" means "is less than or equal to." The absolute value of any expression will never be less than 0, but it may be equal to 0. Thus, to solve $\left| \dfrac{2(x + 1)}{3} \right| \leq 0$, we solve $\left| \dfrac{2(x + 1)}{3} \right| = 0$

$$\dfrac{2(x + 1)}{3} = 0$$

$$3\left[\dfrac{2(x + 1)}{3} \right] = 3(0) \quad \text{Clear the equation of fractions.}$$

$$2x + 2 = 0 \quad \text{Apply the distributive property.}$$

$$2x = -2 \quad \text{Subtract 2 from both sides.}$$

$$x = -1 \quad \text{Divide both sides by 2.}$$

The solution set is $\{-1\}$. ☐

PRACTICE
5 Solve for x: $\left| \dfrac{3(x - 2)}{5} \right| \leq 0$ ■

OBJECTIVE
2 Solving Absolute Value Inequalities of the Form $|X| > a$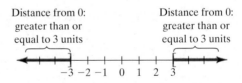

Let us now solve an absolute value inequality of the form $|X| > a$, such as $|x| \geq 3$. The solution set contains all numbers whose distance from 0 is 3 or more units. Thus the graph of the solution set contains 3 and all points to the right of 3 on the number line or −3 and all points to the left of −3 on the number line.

Distance from 0:   Distance from 0:
greater than or   greater than or
equal to 3 units   equal to 3 units

−3 −2 −1 0 1 2 3

This solution set is written as $\{x | x \leq -3 \text{ or } x \geq 3\}$. In interval notation, the solution is $(-\infty, -3] \cup [3, \infty)$, since "or" means "union." In general, we have the following.

Solving Absolute Value Inequalities of the Form $|X| > a$

If a is a positive number, then $|X| > a$ is equivalent to $X < -a$ or $X > a$.

This property also holds true for the inequality symbol ≥.

EXAMPLE 6 Solve for y: $|y - 3| > 7$

__Solution__ Since 7 is positive, we apply the property for $|X| > a$.

$$|y - 3| > 7 \text{ is equivalent to } y - 3 < -7 \text{ or } y - 3 > 7$$

Next, solve the compound inequality.

$$y - 3 < -7 \qquad \text{or} \qquad y - 3 > 7$$
$$y - 3 + 3 < -7 + 3 \qquad \text{or} \qquad y - 3 + 3 > 7 + 3 \qquad \text{Add 3 to both sides.}$$
$$y < -4 \qquad \text{or} \qquad y > 10 \qquad \text{Simplify.}$$

The solution set is $(-\infty, -4) \cup (10, \infty)$, and its graph is shown.

PRACTICE
6   Solve for y: $|y + 4| \geq 6$

Example 7 illustrates another special case of absolute value inequalities when an isolated absolute value expression is less than, less than or equal to, greater than, or greater than or equal to a negative number or 0.

EXAMPLE 7   Solve: $|2x + 9| + 5 > 3$

Solution   First isolate the absolute value expression by subtracting 5 from both sides.

$$|2x + 9| + 5 > 3$$
$$|2x + 9| + 5 - 5 > 3 - 5 \qquad \text{Subtract 5 from both sides.}$$
$$|2x + 9| > -2 \qquad \text{Simplify.}$$

The absolute value of any number is always nonnegative and thus is always greater than -2. This inequality and the original inequality are true for all values of x. The solution set is $\{x | x \text{ is a real number}\}$ or $(-\infty, \infty)$, and its graph is shown.

PRACTICE
7   Solve $|4x + 3| + 5 > 3$. Graph the solution set.

✔ **CONCEPT CHECK**
Without taking any solution steps, how do you know that the absolute value inequality $|3x - 2| > -9$ has a solution? What is its solution?

EXAMPLE 8   Solve: $\left|\dfrac{x}{3} - 1\right| - 7 \geq -5$

Solution   First, isolate the absolute value expression by adding 7 to both sides.

$$\left|\frac{x}{3} - 1\right| - 7 \geq -5$$

$$\left|\frac{x}{3} - 1\right| - 7 + 7 \geq -5 + 7 \qquad \text{Add 7 to both sides.}$$

$$\left|\frac{x}{3} - 1\right| \geq 2 \qquad \text{Simplify.}$$

Next, write the absolute value inequality as an equivalent compound inequality and solve.

$$\frac{x}{3} - 1 \leq -2 \qquad \text{or} \qquad \frac{x}{3} - 1 \geq 2$$

$$3\left(\frac{x}{3} - 1\right) \leq 3(-2) \qquad \text{or} \qquad 3\left(\frac{x}{3} - 1\right) \geq 3(2) \qquad \text{Clear the inequalities of fractions.}$$

$$x - 3 \leq -6 \qquad \text{or} \qquad x - 3 \geq 6 \qquad \text{Apply the distributive property.}$$

$$x \leq -3 \qquad \text{or} \qquad x \geq 9 \qquad \text{Add 3 to both sides.}$$

Answer to Concept Check:
$(-\infty, \infty)$ since the absolute value is always nonnegative

Continued on next page

The solution set is $(-\infty, -3] \cup [9, \infty)$, and its graph is shown.

$$\xleftarrow{}\underset{-6\,-4\,-2\ \ 0\ \ 2\ \ 4\ \ 6\ \ 8\ \ 10\ 12}{\overset{-3 \qquad\qquad\qquad 9}{|\!-\!|\!-\!|\!-\!|\!-\!|\!-\!|\!-\!|\!-\!|}}\xrightarrow{}$$

PRACTICE
8 Solve $\left|\dfrac{x}{2} - 3\right| - 5 > -2$. Graph the solution set.

The following box summarizes the types of absolute value equations and inequalities.

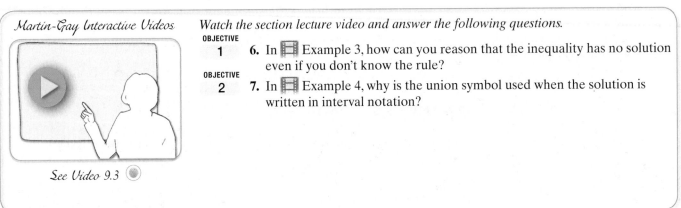

Solving Absolute Value Equations and Inequalities with $a > 0$	
Algebraic Solution	**Solution Graph**
$\lvert X \rvert = a$ is equivalent to $X = a$ or $X = -a$.	
$\lvert X \rvert < a$ is equivalent to $-a < X < a$.	
$\lvert X \rvert > a$ is equivalent to $X < -a$ or $X > a$.	

✔ Vocabulary, Readiness & Video Check

Match each absolute value statement with the equivalent statement.

1. $\lvert 2x + 1 \rvert = 3$

2. $\lvert 2x + 1 \rvert \le 3$

3. $\lvert 2x + 1 \rvert < 3$

4. $\lvert 2x + 1 \rvert \ge 3$

5. $\lvert 2x + 1 \rvert > 3$

A. $2x + 1 > 3$ or $2x + 1 < -3$

B. $2x + 1 \ge 3$ or $2x + 1 \le -3$

C. $-3 < 2x + 1 < 3$

D. $2x + 1 = 3$ or $2x + 1 = -3$

E. $-3 \le 2x + 1 \le 3$

Martin-Gay Interactive Videos

Watch the section lecture video and answer the following questions.

OBJECTIVE 1
6. In ▦ Example 3, how can you reason that the inequality has no solution even if you don't know the rule?

OBJECTIVE 2
7. In ▦ Example 4, why is the union symbol used when the solution is written in interval notation?

See Video 9.3 ◉

9.3 Exercise Set MyMathLab ▸

Solve each inequality. Then graph the solution set and write it in interval notation. See Examples 1 through 4.

1. $\lvert x \rvert \le 4$

2. $\lvert x \rvert < 6$

3. $\lvert x - 3 \rvert < 2$

4. $\lvert y - 7 \rvert \le 5$

5. $\lvert x + 3 \rvert < 2$

6. $\lvert x + 4 \rvert < 6$

7. $\lvert 2x + 7 \rvert \le 13$

8. $\lvert 5x - 3 \rvert \le 18$

9. $\lvert x \rvert + 7 \le 12$

10. $\lvert x \rvert + 6 \le 7$

▸ **11.** $\lvert 3x - 1 \rvert < -5$

12. $\lvert 8x - 3 \rvert < -2$

13. $\lvert x - 6 \rvert - 7 \le -1$

14. $\lvert z + 2 \rvert - 7 < -3$

Solve each inequality. Graph the solution set and write it in interval notation. See Examples 6 through 8.

▸ **15.** $\lvert x \rvert > 3$

16. $\lvert y \rvert \ge 4$

17. $\lvert x + 10 \rvert \ge 14$

18. $\lvert x - 9 \rvert \ge 2$

19. $\lvert x \rvert + 2 > 6$

20. $\lvert x \rvert - 1 > 3$

21. $\lvert 5x \rvert > -4$

22. $\lvert 4x - 11 \rvert > -1$

23. $\lvert 6x - 8 \rvert + 3 > 7$

24. $\lvert 10 + 3x \rvert + 1 > 2$

Solve each inequality. Graph the solution set and write it in interval notation. See Example 5.

25. $|x| \leq 0$

26. $|x| \geq 0$

27. $|8x + 3| > 0$

28. $|5x - 6| < 0$

MIXED PRACTICE

Solve each inequality. Graph the solution set and write it in interval notation. See Examples 1 through 8.

29. $|x| \leq 2$

30. $|z| < 8$

31. $|y| > 1$

32. $|x| \geq 10$

33. $|x - 3| < 8$

34. $|-3 + x| \leq 10$

35. $|0.6x - 3| > 0.6$

36. $|1 + 0.3x| \geq 0.1$

37. $5 + |x| \leq 2$

38. $8 + |x| < 1$

39. $|x| > -4$

40. $|x| \leq -7$

41. $|2x - 7| \leq 11$

42. $|5x + 2| < 8$

43. $|x + 5| + 2 \geq 8$

44. $|-1 + x| - 6 > 2$

45. $|x| > 0$

46. $|x| < 0$

47. $9 + |x| > 7$

48. $5 + |x| \geq 4$

49. $6 + |4x - 1| \leq 9$

50. $-3 + |5x - 2| \leq 4$

51. $\left|\dfrac{2}{3}x + 1\right| > 1$

52. $\left|\dfrac{3}{4}x - 1\right| \geq 2$

53. $|5x + 3| < -6$

54. $|4 + 9x| \geq -6$

55. $\left|\dfrac{8x - 3}{4}\right| \leq 0$

56. $\left|\dfrac{5x + 6}{2}\right| \leq 0$

57. $|1 + 3x| + 4 < 5$

58. $|7x - 3| - 1 \leq 10$

59. $\left|\dfrac{x + 6}{3}\right| > 2$

60. $\left|\dfrac{7 + x}{2}\right| \geq 4$

61. $-15 + |2x - 7| \leq -6$

62. $-9 + |3 + 4x| < -4$

63. $\left|2x + \dfrac{3}{4}\right| - 7 \leq -2$

64. $\left|\dfrac{3}{5} + 4x\right| - 6 < -1$

MIXED PRACTICE

Solve each equation or inequality for x. (Sections 9.2, 9.3)

65. $|2x - 3| < 7$

66. $|2x - 3| > 7$

67. $|2x - 3| = 7$

68. $|5 - 6x| = 29$

69. $|x - 5| \geq 12$

70. $|x + 4| \geq 20$

71. $|9 + 4x| = 0$

72. $|9 + 4x| \geq 0$

73. $|2x + 1| + 4 < 7$

74. $8 + |5x - 3| \geq 11$

75. $|3x - 5| + 4 = 5$

76. $|5x - 3| + 2 = 4$

77. $|x + 11| = -1$

78. $|4x - 4| = -3$

79. $\left|\dfrac{2x - 1}{3}\right| = 6$

80. $\left|\dfrac{6 - x}{4}\right| = 5$

81. $\left|\dfrac{3x - 5}{6}\right| > 5$

82. $\left|\dfrac{4x - 7}{5}\right| < 2$

REVIEW AND PREVIEW

Solve. See Section 2.4.

Many companies predict the growth or decline of various social network use. The following data is from Techcrunchies, a technical information site. Notice that the first table is the predicted increase in the number of people using social network sites worldwide (in millions) and the second is the predicted percent increase in the number of social network site users worldwide.

83. Use the middle column in the table to find the predicted number of social network site users for each year.

Year	Increase in Social Network Users	Predicted Number
2015	$2x$	
2016	$2x + 170$	
2017	$3x - 650$	
Total	6380 million	

84. Use the middle column in the table to find the predicted percent of increase in the number of social network site users for each year.

Year	Percent of Increase in Social Network Users	Predicted Percent of Increase
2015	x	
2016	$3x - 11$	
2017	$2x + 11$	
Total	66%	

Consider the equation $3x - 4y = 12$. For each value of x or y given, find the corresponding value of the other variable that makes the statement true. See Section 2.5.

85. If $x = 2$, find y.

86. If $y = -1$, find x.

87. If $y = -3$, find x.

88. If $x = 4$, find y.

CONCEPT EXTENSIONS

89. Write an absolute value inequality representing all numbers x whose distance from 0 is less than 7 units.

90. Write an absolute value inequality representing all numbers x whose distance from 0 is greater than 4 units.

91. Write $-5 \leq x \leq 5$ as an equivalent inequality containing an absolute value.

92. Write $x > 1$ or $x < -1$ as an equivalent inequality containing an absolute value.

93. Describe how solving $|x - 3| = 5$ is different from solving $|x - 3| < 5$.

94. Describe how solving $|x + 4| = 0$ is similar to solving $|x + 4| \leq 0$.

The expression $|x_T - x|$ *is defined to be the absolute error in x, where* x_T *is the true value of a quantity and x is the measured value or value as stored in a computer.*

95. If the true value of a quantity is 3.5 and the absolute error must be less than 0.05, find the acceptable measured values.

96. If the true value of a quantity is 0.2 and the approximate value stored in a computer is $\dfrac{51}{256}$, find the absolute error.

Integrated Review Solving Compound Inequalities and Absolute Value
Equations and Inequalities

Sections 9.1–9.3

Solve each equation or inequality. Write inequality solution sets in interval notation. For inequalities containing "and" or "or", also graph the solution set notation.

1. $x < 7$ *and* $x > -5$

2. $x < 7$ *or* $x > -5$

3. $|4x - 3| = 1$

4. $|2x + 1| < 5$

5. $|6x| - 9 \geq -3$

6. $|x - 7| = |2x + 11|$

7. $-5 \leq \dfrac{3x - 8}{2} \leq 2$

8. $|9x - 1| = -3$

9. $3x + 2 \leq 5$ *or* $-3x \geq 0$

10. $3x + 2 \leq 5$ *and* $-3x \geq 0$

11. $|3 - x| - 5 \leq -2$

12. $\left|\dfrac{4x + 1}{5}\right| = |-1|$

Match each equation or inequality on the left with the equivalent statement on the right.

13. $|2x + 1| = 5$

14. $|2x + 1| < 5$

15. $|2x + 1| > 5$

16. $x < 3$ *or* $x < 5$

17. $x < 3$ *and* $x < 5$

A. $2x + 1 > 5$ or $2x + 1 < -5$

B. $2x + 1 = 5$ or $2x + 1 = -5$

C. $x < 5$

D. $x < 3$

E. $-5 < 2x + 1 < 5$

9.4 Graphing Linear Inequalities in Two Variables and Systems of Linear Inequalities

OBJECTIVE

1 Graph a Linear Inequality in Two Variables.

2 Solve a System of Linear Inequalities.

In this section, we first learn to graph a single linear inequality in two variables. Then we solve systems of linear inequalities.

Recall that a linear equation in two variables is an equation that can be written in the form $Ax + By = C$ where $A, B,$ and C are real numbers and A and B are not both 0. The definition of a linear inequality is the same except that the equal sign is replaced with an inequality sign.

A **linear inequality in two variables** is an inequality that can be written in one of the forms:

$$Ax + By < C \qquad Ax + By \leq C$$
$$Ax + By > C \qquad Ax + By \geq C$$

where $A, B,$ and C are real numbers and A and B are not both 0. Just as for linear equations in x and y, an ordered pair is a **solution** of an inequality in x and y if replacing the variables by coordinates of the ordered pair results in a true statement.

OBJECTIVE

1 Graphing Linear Inequalities in Two Variables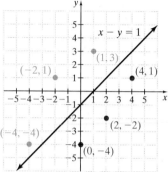

The linear equation $x - y = 1$ is graphed next. Recall that all points on the line correspond to ordered pairs that satisfy the equation $x - y = 1$.

Notice the line defined by $x - y = 1$ divides the rectangular coordinate system plane into 2 sides. All points on one side of the line satisfy the inequality $x - y < 1$ and all points on the other side satisfy the inequality $x - y > 1$. The graph below shows a few examples of this.

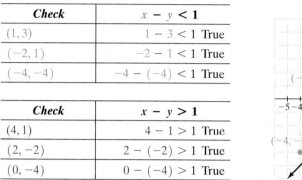

Check	$x - y < 1$
$(1, 3)$	$1 - 3 < 1$ True
$(-2, 1)$	$-2 - 1 < 1$ True
$(-4, -4)$	$-4 - (-4) < 1$ True

Check	$x - y > 1$
$(4, 1)$	$4 - 1 > 1$ True
$(2, -2)$	$2 - (-2) > 1$ True
$(0, -4)$	$0 - (-4) > 1$ True

The graph of $x - y < 1$ is the region shaded blue, and the graph of $x - y > 1$ is the region shaded red below.

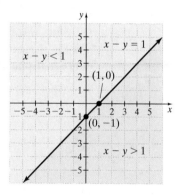

The region to the left of the line and the region to the right of the line are called **half-planes.** Every line divides the plane (similar to a sheet of paper extending indefinitely in all directions) into two half-planes; the line is called the **boundary.**

Recall that the inequality $x - y \leq 1$ means

$$x - y = 1 \quad \text{or} \quad x - y < 1$$

Thus, the graph of $x - y \leq 1$ is the half-plane $x - y < 1$ along with the boundary line $x - y = 1$.

Graphing a Linear Inequality in Two Variables

Step 1. Graph the boundary line found by replacing the inequality sign with an equal sign. If the inequality sign is $>$ or $<$, graph a dashed boundary line (indicating that the points on the line are not solutions of the inequality). If the inequality sign is $\geq$ or $\leq$, graph a solid boundary line (indicating that the points on the line are solutions of the inequality).

Step 2. Choose a point, *not* on the boundary line, as a test point. Substitute the coordinates of this test point into the *original* inequality.

Step 3. If a true statement is obtained in Step 2, shade the half-plane that contains the test point. If a false statement is obtained, shade the half-plane that does not contain the test point.

EXAMPLE 1 Graph: $x + y < 7$

Solution

Step 1. First we graph the boundary line by graphing the equation $x + y = 7$. We graph this boundary as a dashed line because the inequality sign is $<$, and thus the points on the line are not solutions of the inequality $x + y < 7$.

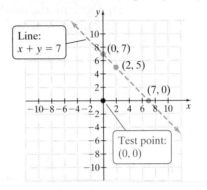

Step 2. Next, we choose a test point, being careful not to choose a point on the boundary line. We choose $(0, 0)$. Substitute the coordinates of $(0, 0)$ into $x + y < 7$.

$$x + y < 7 \quad \text{Original inequality}$$

$$0 + 0 \overset{?}{<} 7 \quad \text{Replace } x \text{ with 0 and } y \text{ with 0.}$$

$$0 < 7 \quad \text{True}$$

Step 3. Since the result is a true statement, $(0, 0)$ is a solution of $x + y < 7$, and every point in the same half-plane as $(0, 0)$ is also a solution. To indicate this, shade the entire half-plane containing $(0, 0)$, as shown.

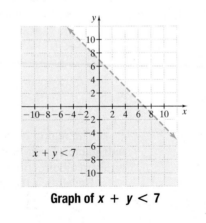

Graph of $x + y < 7$

PRACTICE

1 Graph: $x + y > 5$

✔ **CONCEPT CHECK**

Determine whether $(0, 0)$ is included in the graph of

a. $y \geq 2x + 3$ **b.** $x < 7$ **c.** $2x - 3y < 6$

EXAMPLE 2 Graph: $2x - y \geq 3$

Solution

Step 1. We graph the boundary line by graphing $2x - y = 3$. We draw this line as a solid line because the inequality sign is $\geq$, and thus the points on the line are solutions of $2x - y \geq 3$.

Answers to Concept Check:
a. no   **b.** yes   **c.** yes

Step 2. Once again, $(0, 0)$ is a convenient test point since it is not on the boundary line. We substitute 0 for x and 0 for y into the original inequality.

$$2x - y \geq 3$$

$$2(0) - 0 \geq 3 \quad \text{Let } x = 0 \text{ and } y = 0.$$

$$0 \geq 3 \quad \text{False}$$

Step 3. Since the statement is false, no point in the half-plane containing $(0, 0)$ is a solution. Therefore, we shade the half-plane that does not contain $(0, 0)$. Every point in the shaded half-plane and every point on the boundary line is a solution of $2x - y \geq 3$.

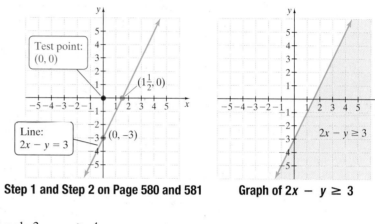

Step 1 and Step 2 on Page 580 and 581   **Graph of $2x - y \geq 3$**

PRACTICE

2   Graph: $3x - y \geq 4$

Helpful Hint

When graphing an inequality, make sure the test point is substituted into the **original inequality.** For Example 2, we substituted the test point $(0, 0)$ into the **original inequality** $2x - y \geq 3$, *not* $2x - y = 3$.

EXAMPLE 3   Graph: $x > 2y$

Solution

Step 1. We find the boundary line by graphing $x = 2y$. The boundary line is a dashed line since the inequality symbol is $>$.

Step 2. We cannot use $(0, 0)$ as a test point because it is a point on the boundary line. We choose instead $(0, 2)$.

$$x > 2y$$

$$0 > 2(2) \quad \text{Let } x = 0 \text{ and } y = 2.$$

$$0 > 4 \quad \text{False}$$

Step 3. Since the statement is false, we shade the half-plane that does not contain the test point $(0, 2)$, as shown.

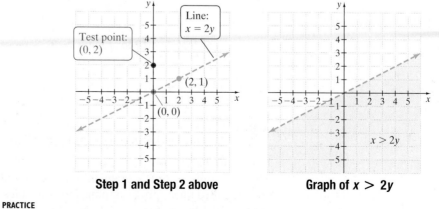

Step 1 and Step 2 above   **Graph of $x > 2y$**

PRACTICE

3   Graph: $x > 3y$

EXAMPLE 4 Graph: $5x + 4y \leq 20$

Solution We graph the solid boundary line $5x + 4y = 20$ and choose $(0,0)$ as the test point.

$$5x + 4y \leq 20$$
$$5(0) + 4(0) \overset{?}{\leq} 20 \quad \text{Let } x = 0 \text{ and } y = 0.$$
$$0 \leq 20 \quad \text{True}$$

We shade the half-plane that contains $(0,0)$, as shown.

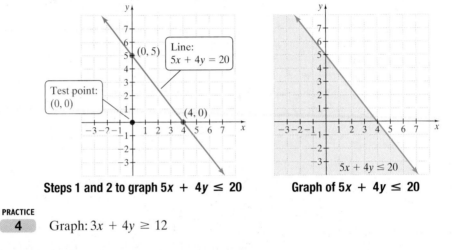

Steps 1 and 2 to graph $5x + 4y \leq 20$ Graph of $5x + 4y \leq 20$

PRACTICE
4   Graph: $3x + 4y \geq 12$

EXAMPLE 5 Graph: $y > 3$

Solution We graph the dashed boundary line $y = 3$ and choose $(0,0)$ as the test point. (Recall that the graph of $y = 3$ is a horizontal line with y-intercept 3.)

$$y > 3$$
$$0 \overset{?}{>} 3 \quad \text{Let } y = 0.$$
$$0 > 3 \quad \text{False}$$

We shade the half-plane that does not contain $(0,0)$, as shown.

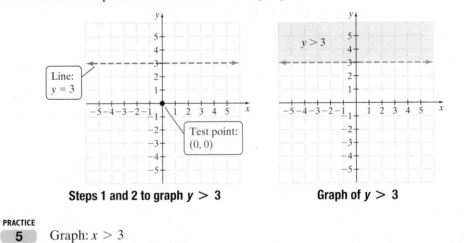

Steps 1 and 2 to graph $y > 3$ Graph of $y > 3$

PRACTICE
5   Graph: $x > 3$

OBJECTIVE
2   Solving Systems of Linear Inequalities ▶

Just as two linear equations make a system of linear equations, two linear inequalities make a **system of linear inequalities.** Systems of inequalities are very important in a process called linear programming. Many businesses use linear programming to find the most profitable way to use limited resources such as employees, machines, or buildings.

A **solution of a system of linear inequalities** is an ordered pair that satisfies each inequality in the system. The set of all such ordered pairs is the solution set of the system. Graphing this set gives us a picture of the solution set. We can graph a system of inequalities by graphing each inequality in the system and identifying the region of overlap.

EXAMPLE 6   Graph the solution of the system: $\begin{cases} 3x \geq y \\ x + 2y \leq 8 \end{cases}$

Solution We begin by graphing each inequality on the same set of axes. The graph of the solution region of the system is the region contained in the graphs of both inequalities. It is their intersection.

First, graph $3x \geq y$. The boundary line is the graph of $3x = y$. Sketch a solid boundary line since the inequality $3x \geq y$ means $3x > y$ or $3x = y$. The test point $(1, 0)$ satisfies the inequality, so shade the half-plane that includes $(1, 0)$.

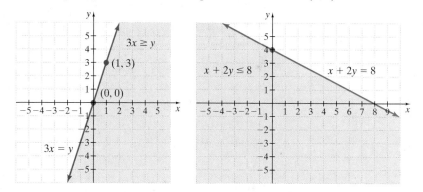

Next, graph $x + 2y \leq 8$ on the same set of axes. (For clarity, the graph of $x + 2y \leq 8$ is shown on a separate set of axes.) Sketch a solid boundary line $x + 2y = 8$. The test point $(0, 0)$ satisfies the inequality $x + 2y \leq 8$, so shade the half-plane that includes $(0, 0)$.

An ordered pair solution of the system must satisfy both inequalities. These solutions are points that lie in both shaded regions. The solution region of the system is the purple shaded region as seen below. This solution region includes parts of both boundary lines.

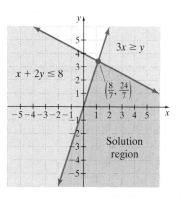

PRACTICE

6   Graph the solution of the system: $\begin{cases} 4x \leq y \\ x + 3y \geq 9 \end{cases}$

In linear programming, it is sometimes necessary to find the coordinates of the **corner point:** the point at which two boundary lines intersect. To find the point of intersection, solve the related linear system

$$\begin{cases} 3x = y \\ x + 2y = 8 \end{cases}$$

by the substitution method or the addition method. The lines intersect at $\left(\dfrac{8}{7}, \dfrac{24}{7} \right)$, the corner point of the graph.

Graphing the Solution Region of a System of Linear Inequalities

Step 1. Graph each inequality in the system on the same set of axes.

Step 2. The solutions (or solution region) of the system are the points common to the graphs of all the inequalities in the system.

EXAMPLE 7 Graph the solution of the system: $\begin{cases} x - y < 2 \\ x + 2y > -1 \end{cases}$

Solution Graph both inequalities on the same set of axes. Both boundary lines are dashed lines since the inequality symbols are $<$ and $>$. The solution region of the system is the region shown by the purple shading. In this example, the boundary lines are not a part of the solution.

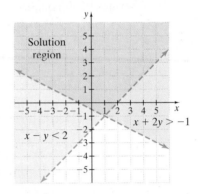

PRACTICE

7 Graph the solution of the system: $\begin{cases} x - y > 4 \\ x + 3y < -4 \end{cases}$

EXAMPLE 8 Graph the solution of the system: $\begin{cases} -3x + 4y < 12 \\ x \geq 2 \end{cases}$

Solution Graph both inequalities on the same set of axes.

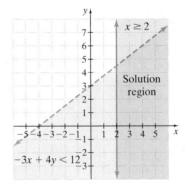

The solution region of the system is the purple shaded region, including a portion of the line $x = 2$.

PRACTICE

8 Graph the solution of the system: $\begin{cases} y \leq 6 \\ -2x + 5y > 10 \end{cases}$

✓ **Vocabulary, Readiness & Video Check**

Use the choices below to fill in each blank. Some choices may be used more than once and some not at all.

true	$x < 3$	$y < 3$	half-planes	yes
false	$x \leq 3$	$y \leq 3$	linear inequality in two variables	no

1. The statement $5x - 6y < 7$ is an example of a(n) _____.

2. A boundary line divides a plane into two regions called _____.

3. True or false: The graph of $5x - 6y < 7$ includes its corresponding boundary line. _____

4. True or false: When graphing a linear inequality, to determine which side of the boundary line to shade, choose a point *not* on the boundary line. _____

5. True or false: The boundary line for the inequality $5x - 6y < 7$ is the graph of $5x - 6y = 7$.

_____

6. The graph of _____ is

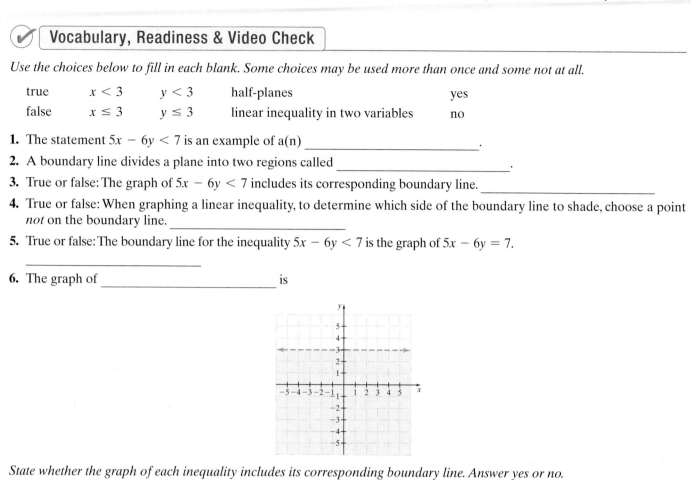

State whether the graph of each inequality includes its corresponding boundary line. Answer yes or no.

7. $y \geq x + 4$ **8.** $x - y > -7$ **9.** $y \geq x$ **10.** $x > 0$

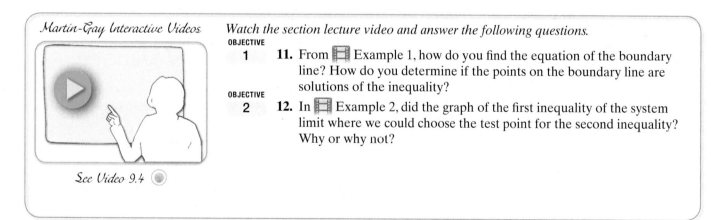

Martin-Gay Interactive Videos

Watch the section lecture video and answer the following questions.

OBJECTIVE
1

11. From ▦ Example 1, how do you find the equation of the boundary line? How do you determine if the points on the boundary line are solutions of the inequality?

OBJECTIVE
2

12. In ▦ Example 2, did the graph of the first inequality of the system limit where we could choose the test point for the second inequality? Why or why not?

See Video 9.4 ⦿

9.4   Exercise Set MyMathLab® ▶

Determine whether the ordered pairs given are solutions of the linear inequality in two variables.

1. $x - y > 3$; $(2, -1)$, $(5, 1)$

2. $y - x < -2$; $(2, 1)$, $(5, -1)$

3. $3x - 5y \leq -4$; $(-1, -1)$, $(4, 0)$

4. $2x + y \geq 10$; $(-1, -4)$, $(5, 0)$

5. $x < -y$; $(0, 2)$, $(-5, 1)$

6. $y > 3x$; $(0, 0)$, $(-1, -4)$

MIXED PRACTICE

Graph each inequality. See Examples 1 through 5.

7. $x + y \leq 1$ **8.** $x + y \geq -2$

9. $2x + y > -4$ **10.** $x + 3y \leq 3$

11. $x + 6y \leq -6$ **12.** $7x + y > -14$

13. $2x + 5y > -10$ **14.** $5x + 2y \leq 10$

15. $x + 2y \leq 3$ **16.** $2x + 3y > -5$

▶ **17.** $2x + 7y > 5$ **18.** $3x + 5y \le -2$

19. $x - 2y \ge 3$ **20.** $4x + y \le 2$

21. $5x + y < 3$ **22.** $x + 2y > -7$

23. $4x + y < 8$ **24.** $9x + 2y \ge -9$

25. $y \ge 2x$ **26.** $x < 5y$ **27.** $x \ge 0$

28. $y \le 0$ **29.** $y \le -3$ **30.** $x > -\dfrac{2}{3}$

31. $2x - 7y > 0$ **32.** $5x + 2y \le 0$ **33.** $3x - 7y \ge 0$

34. $-2x - 9y > 0$ **35.** $x > y$ **36.** $x \le -y$

37. $x - y \le 6$ **38.** $x - y > 10$ **39.** $-\dfrac{1}{4}y + \dfrac{1}{3}x > 1$

40. $\dfrac{1}{2}x - \dfrac{1}{3}y \le -1$ **41.** $-x < 0.4y$ **42.** $0.3x \ge 0.1y$

In Exercises 43–48, match each graph with its inequality.

  a. $x > 2$ **b.** $y < 2$ **c.** $y < 2x$

  d. $y \le -3x$ **e.** $2x + 3y < 6$ **f.** $3x + 2y > 6$

43.

44.

45.

46.

47.

48.

Graph the solution of each system of linear inequalities. See Examples 6 through 8.

49. $\begin{cases} y \ge x + 1 \\ y \ge 3 - x \end{cases}$ **50.** $\begin{cases} y \ge x - 3 \\ y \ge -1 - x \end{cases}$

51. $\begin{cases} y < 3x - 4 \\ y \le x + 2 \end{cases}$ **52.** $\begin{cases} y \le 2x + 1 \\ y > x + 2 \end{cases}$

53. $\begin{cases} y \le -2x - 2 \\ y \ge x + 4 \end{cases}$ **54.** $\begin{cases} y \le 2x + 4 \\ y \ge -x - 5 \end{cases}$

55. $\begin{cases} y \ge -x + 2 \\ y \le 2x + 5 \end{cases}$ **56.** $\begin{cases} y \ge x - 5 \\ y \le -3x + 3 \end{cases}$

▶ **57.** $\begin{cases} x \ge 3y \\ x + 3y \le 6 \end{cases}$ **58.** $\begin{cases} -2x < y \\ x + 2y < 3 \end{cases}$

59. $\begin{cases} y + 2x \ge 0 \\ 5x - 3y \le 12 \end{cases}$ **60.** $\begin{cases} y + 2x \le 0 \\ 5x + 3y \ge -2 \end{cases}$

61. $\begin{cases} 3x - 4y \ge -6 \\ 2x + y \le 7 \end{cases}$ **62.** $\begin{cases} 4x - y \ge -2 \\ 2x + 3y \le -8 \end{cases}$

63. $\begin{cases} x \le 2 \\ y \ge -3 \end{cases}$ **64.** $\begin{cases} x \ge -3 \\ y \ge -2 \end{cases}$

▶ **65.** $\begin{cases} y \ge 1 \\ x < -3 \end{cases}$ **66.** $\begin{cases} y > 2 \\ x \ge -1 \end{cases}$

67. $\begin{cases} 2x + 3y < -8 \\ x \ge -4 \end{cases}$ **68.** $\begin{cases} 3x + 2y \le 6 \\ x < 2 \end{cases}$

69. $\begin{cases} 2x - 5y \le 9 \\ y \le -3 \end{cases}$ **70.** $\begin{cases} 2x + 5y \le -10 \\ y \ge 1 \end{cases}$

71. $\begin{cases} y \ge \dfrac{1}{2}x + 2 \\ y \le \dfrac{1}{2}x - 3 \end{cases}$ **72.** $\begin{cases} y \ge -\dfrac{3}{2}x + 3 \\ y < -\dfrac{3}{2}x + 6 \end{cases}$

REVIEW AND PREVIEW

Evaluate each expression for the given replacement value. See Section 5.1.

73. x^2 if x is -5 **74.** x^3 if x is -5

75. $2x^3$ if x is -1 **76.** $3x^2$ if x is -1

CONCEPT EXTENSIONS

Determine whether $(1, 1)$ is included in each graph. See the Concept Check in this section.

77. $3x + 4y < 8$ **78.** $y > 5x$

79. $y \ge -\dfrac{1}{2}x$ **80.** $x > 3$

81. Write an inequality whose solutions are all pairs of numbers x and y whose sum is at least 13. Graph the inequality.

82. Write an inequality whose solutions are all the pairs of numbers x and y whose sum is at most -4. Graph the inequality.

83. Explain why a point on the boundary line should not be chosen as the test point.

84. Describe the graph of a linear inequality.

85. The price for a taxi cab in a small city is $2.50 per mile, x, while traveling, and $0.25 every minute, y, while waiting. If you have $20 to spend on a cab ride, the inequality

$$2.5x + 0.25y \le 20$$

represents your situation. Graph this inequality in the first quadrant only.

86. A word processor charges $22 per hour, x, for typing a first draft, and $15 per hour, y, for making changes and typing a second draft. If you need a document typed and have $100, the inequality

$$22x + 15y \leq 100$$

represents your situation. Graph the inequality in the first quadrant only.

87. In Exercises 85 and 86, why were you instructed to graph each inequality in the first quadrant only?

88. Scott Sambracci and Sara Thygeson are planning their wedding. They have calculated that they want the cost of their wedding ceremony, x, plus the cost of their reception, y, to be no more than $5000.

 a. Write an inequality describing this relationship.

 b. Graph this inequality.

 c. Why should we be interested in only quadrant I of this graph?

89. It's the end of the budgeting period for Dennis Fernandes, and he has $500 left in his budget for car rental expenses. He plans to spend this budget on a sales trip throughout southern Texas. He will rent a car that costs $30 per day and $0.15 per mile, and he can spend no more than $500.

 a. Write an inequality describing this situation. Let x = number of days and let y = number of miles.

 b. Graph this inequality.

 c. Why should we be interested in only quadrant I of this graph?

90. Explain how to decide which region to shade to show the solution region of the following system.

$$\begin{cases} x \geq 3 \\ y \geq -2 \end{cases}$$

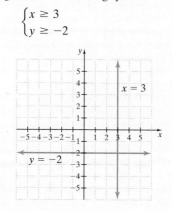

For each system of inequalities, choose the corresponding graph.

91. $\begin{cases} y < 5 \\ x > 3 \end{cases}$ **92.** $\begin{cases} y > 5 \\ x < 3 \end{cases}$ **93.** $\begin{cases} y \leq 5 \\ x < 3 \end{cases}$

94. $\begin{cases} y > 5 \\ x \geq 3 \end{cases}$

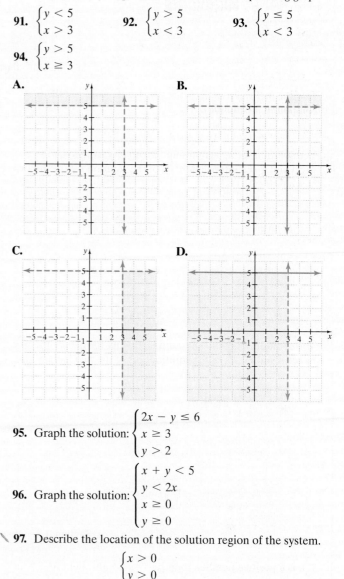

95. Graph the solution: $\begin{cases} 2x - y \leq 6 \\ x \geq 3 \\ y > 2 \end{cases}$

96. Graph the solution: $\begin{cases} x + y < 5 \\ y < 2x \\ x \geq 0 \\ y \geq 0 \end{cases}$

97. Describe the location of the solution region of the system.

$$\begin{cases} x > 0 \\ y > 0 \end{cases}$$

Chapter 9 Vocabulary Check

Fill in each blank with one of the words or phrases listed below.

compound inequality   solution   system of linear inequalities

absolute value   union   intersection

1. The statement "$x < 5$ or $x > 7$" is called a(n) _____.

2. The _____ of two sets is the set of all elements common to both sets.

3. The _____ of two sets is the set of all elements that belong to either of the sets.

4. A number's distance from 0 is called its _____.

5. When a variable in an equation is replaced by a number and the resulting equation is true, then that number is called a(n) _____ of the equation.

6. Two or more linear inequalities are called a(n) _____.

Chapter 9 Highlights

DEFINITIONS AND CONCEPTS	EXAMPLES

Section 9.1 Compound Inequalities

Two inequalities joined by the word **and** or **or** are called **compound inequalities.**

Compound Inequalities

$$x - 7 \leq 4 \quad \text{and} \quad x \geq -21$$
$$2x + 7 > x - 3 \quad \text{or} \quad 5x + 2 > -3$$

The solution set of a compound inequality formed by the word **and** is the **intersection, ∩,** of the solution sets of the two inequalities.

Solve for x:

$$x < 5 \text{ and } x < 3$$

$\{x \mid x < 5\}$ $(-\infty, 5)$

$\{x \mid x < 3\}$ $(-\infty, 3)$

$\{x \mid x < 3$ and $x < 5\}$ $(-\infty, 3)$

The solution set of a compound inequality formed by the word **or** is the **union, ∪,** of the solution sets of the two inequalities.

Solve for x:

$$x - 2 \geq -3 \quad \text{or} \quad 2x \leq -4$$
$$x \geq -1 \quad \text{or} \quad x \leq -2$$

$\{x \mid x \geq -1\}$ $[-1, \infty)$

$\{x \mid x \leq -2\}$ $(-\infty, -2]$

$\{x \mid x \leq -2$ or $x \geq -1\}$ $(-\infty, -2]$ $\cup [-1, \infty)$

Section 9.2 Absolute Value Equations

If a is a positive number, then $|x| = a$ is equivalent to $x = a$ or $x = -a$.

Solve for y:

$$|5y - 1| - 7 = 4$$

$|5y - 1| = 11$ Add 7.

$5y - 1 = 11$ or $5y - 1 = -11$

$5y = 12$ or $5y = -10$ Add 1.

$y = \dfrac{12}{5}$ or $y = -2$ Divide by 5.

The solutions are -2 and $\dfrac{12}{5}$.

If a is negative, then $|x| = a$ has no solution.

Solve for x:

$$\left|\frac{x}{2} - 7\right| = -1$$

The solution set is $\{ \ \}$ or $\varnothing$.

DEFINITIONS AND CONCEPTS	EXAMPLES

Section 9.2   Absolute Value Equations (continued)

If an absolute value equation is of the form $|x| = |y|$, solve $x = y$ or $x = -y$.

Solve for x:

$$|x - 7| = |2x + 1|$$

$$x - 7 = 2x + 1 \quad \text{or} \quad x - 7 = -(2x + 1)$$
$$x = 2x + 8 \quad \text{or} \quad x - 7 = -2x - 1$$
$$-x = 8 \quad \text{or} \quad x = -2x + 6$$
$$x = -8 \quad \text{or} \quad 3x = 6$$
$$x = 2$$

The solutions are -8 and 2.

Section 9.3   Absolute Value Inequalities

If a is a positive number, then $|x| < a$ is equivalent to $-a < x < a$.

Solve for y:

$$|y - 5| \le 3$$
$$-3 \le y - 5 \le 3$$
$$-3 + 5 \le y - 5 + 5 \le 3 + 5 \quad \text{Add 5.}$$
$$2 \le y \le 8$$

The solution set is $[2, 8]$.

If a is a positive number, then $|x| > a$ is equivalent to $x < -a$ or $x > a$.

Solve for x:

$$\left| \frac{x}{2} - 3 \right| > 7$$

$$\frac{x}{2} - 3 < -7 \quad \text{or} \quad \frac{x}{2} - 3 > 7$$
$$x - 6 < -14 \quad \text{or} \quad x - 6 > 14 \quad \text{Multiply by 2.}$$
$$x < -8 \quad \text{or} \quad x > 20 \quad \text{Add 6.}$$

The solution set is $(-\infty, -8) \cup (20, \infty)$.

Section 9.4   Graphing Linear Inequalities in Two Variables and Systems of Linear Inequalities

A **linear inequality in two variables** is an inequality that can be written in one of the forms:

$$Ax + By < C \qquad Ax + By \le C$$
$$Ax + By > C \qquad Ax + By \ge C$$

To graph a linear inequality

1. Graph the boundary line by graphing the related equation. Draw the line solid if the inequality symbol is $\le$ or $\ge$. Draw the line dashed if the inequality symbol is $<$ or $>$.

2. Choose a test point not on the line. Substitute its coordinates into the original inequality.

3. If the resulting inequality is true, shade the half-plane that contains the test point. If the inequality is not true, shade the half-plane that does not contain the test point.

Linear Inequalities

$$2x - 5y < 6 \qquad x \ge -5$$
$$y > -8x \qquad y \le 2$$

Graph $2x - y \le 4$.

1. Graph $2x - y = 4$. Draw a solid line because the inequality symbol is $\le$.

2. Check the test point $(0, 0)$ in the inequality $2x - y \le 4$.
$$2 \cdot 0 - 0 \le 4 \quad \text{Let } x = 0 \text{ and } y = 0.$$
$$0 \le 4 \quad \text{True}$$

3. The inequality is true, so we shade the half-plane containing $(0, 0)$.

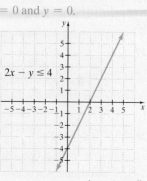

(continued)

DEFINITIONS AND CONCEPTS   EXAMPLES

Section 9.4   Graphing Linear Inequalities in Two Variables and Systems of Linear Inequalities   (continued)

A system of linear inequalities consists of two or more linear inequalities.

To graph a system of inequalities, graph each inequality in the system. The overlapping region is the solution of the system.

System of Linear Inequalities

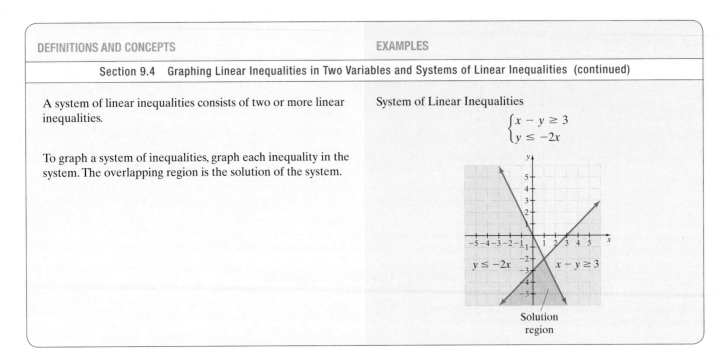

$$\begin{cases} x - y \geq 3 \\ y \leq -2x \end{cases}$$

Solution region

Chapter 9   Review

(9.1) *Solve each inequality. Write your answers in interval notation.*

1. $-3 < 4(2x - 1) < 12$

2. $-2 \leq 8 + 5x < -1$

3. $\dfrac{1}{6} < \dfrac{4x - 3}{3} \leq \dfrac{4}{5}$

4. $-6 < x - (3 - 4x) < -3$

5. $3x - 5 > 6$ *or* $-x < -5$

6. $x \leq 2$ *and* $x > -5$

(9.2) *Solve each absolute value equation.*

7. $|8 - x| = 3$ **8.** $|x - 7| = 9$

9. $|-3x + 4| = 7$ **10.** $|2x + 9| = 9$

11. $5 + |6x + 1| = 5$ **12.** $|3x - 2| + 6 = 10$

13. $|5 - 6x| + 8 = 3$ **14.** $-5 = |4x - 3|$

15. $\left|\dfrac{3x - 7}{4}\right| = 2$ **16.** $-4 = \left|\dfrac{x - 3}{2}\right| - 5$

17. $|6x + 1| = |15 + 4x|$ **18.** $|x - 3| = |x + 5|$

(9.3) *Solve each absolute value inequality. Graph the solution set and write it in interval notation.*

19. $|5x - 1| < 9$

20. $|6 + 4x| \geq 10$

21. $|3x| - 8 > 1$

22. $9 + |5x| < 24$

23. $|6x - 5| \leq -1$

24. $|6x - 5| \leq 5$

25. $\left|3x + \dfrac{2}{5}\right| \geq 4$

26. $|5x - 3| > 2$

27. $\left|\dfrac{x}{3} + 6\right| - 8 > -5$

28. $\left|\dfrac{4(x - 1)}{7}\right| + 10 < 2$

(9.4) *Graph the following inequalities.*

29. $3x - 4y \leq 0$ **30.** $3x - 4y \geq 0$

31. $x + 6y < 6$ **32.** $y \leq -4$

33. $y \geq -7$ **34.** $x \geq -y$

Graph the solution region of the following systems of linear inequalities.

35. $\begin{cases} y \geq 2x - 3 \\ y \leq -2x + 1 \end{cases}$ **36.** $\begin{cases} y \leq -3x - 3 \\ y \leq 2x + 7 \end{cases}$

37. $\begin{cases} x + 2y > 0 \\ x - y \leq 6 \end{cases}$ **38.** $\begin{cases} 4x - y \leq 0 \\ 3x - 2y \geq -5 \end{cases}$

39. $\begin{cases} 3x - 2y \leq 4 \\ 2x + y \geq 5 \end{cases}$ **40.** $\begin{cases} -2x + 3y > -7 \\ x \geq -2 \end{cases}$

MIXED REVIEW

Solve. If an inequality, write your solutions in interval notation.

41. $0 \le \dfrac{2(3x + 4)}{5} \le 3$

42. $x \le 2 \text{ or } x > -5$

43. $-2x \le 6 \text{ and } -2x + 3 < -7$

44. $|7x| - 26 = -5$

45. $\left|\dfrac{9 - 2x}{5}\right| = -3$

46. $|x - 3| = |7 + 2x|$

47. $|6x - 5| \ge -1$

48. $\left|\dfrac{4x - 3}{5}\right| < 1$

Graph the solutions.

49. $-x \le y$

50. $x + y > -2$

51. $\begin{cases} -3x + 2y > -1 \\ \qquad\quad y < -2 \end{cases}$

52. $\begin{cases} x - 2y \ge \ \ 7 \\ x + \ y \le -5 \end{cases}$

Chapter 9 Getting Ready for the Test

MULTIPLE CHOICE *For Exercises 1 and 2, choose the correct interval notation for each set.*

1. $\{x \mid x \le -11\}$
   A. $(-\infty, -11]$ **B.** $[-11, \infty)$ **C.** $[-11, 11]$ **D.** $(-\infty, -11)$

2. $\{x \mid -5 < x\}$
   A. $(-\infty, -5)$ **B.** $(-5, \infty)$ **C.** $(-5, 5)$ **D.** $(-\infty, -5]$

3. Choose the solution of $|x - 3| = 7$ by checking the given numbers in the original equation.
   A. $\{-7, 7\}$ **B.** $\{-10, 10\}$ **C.** $\{4, 10\}$ **D.** $\{-4, 10\}$

MATCHING *Match each equation or inequality with an equivalent statement. Letters may be used more than once or not at all.*

   A. $5x - 2 = 4 \text{ or } 5x - 2 = -4$ **B.** $5x = 6 \text{ or } 5x = -6$ **C.** $-4 \le 5x - 2 \le 4$
   D. $-6 \le 5x \le 6$ **E.** $5x - 2 \ge 4 \text{ or } 5x - 2 \le -4$ **F.** $5x \ge 6 \text{ or } 5x \le -6$

4. $|5x - 2| \le 4$ **5.** $|5x - 2| = 4$

6. $|5x - 2| \ge 4$ **7.** $|5x| - 2 = 4$

MATCHING *Match each equation or inequality with its solution. Letters may be used more than once or not at all.*

   A. no solution, or $\varnothing$ **B.** $(-\infty, \infty)$

8. $|x + 3| = -9$ **9.** $|x + 3| < -9$ **10.** $|x + 3| > -9$

MATCHING *Match each system with the graph of its solution region.*

11. $\begin{cases} x \le -3 \\ y \le 3 \end{cases}$ **12.** $\begin{cases} x \le -3 \\ y \ge 3 \end{cases}$ **13.** $\begin{cases} x \ge -3 \\ y \ge 3 \end{cases}$ **14.** $\begin{cases} x \ge -3 \\ y \le 3 \end{cases}$

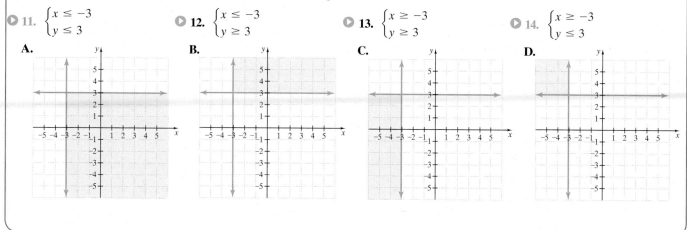

Chapter 9 Test   MyMathLab® You Tube

Solve each equation or inequality.

1. $|6x - 5| - 3 = -2$

2. $|8 - 2t| = -6$

3. $|x - 5| = |x + 2|$

4. $-3 < 2(x - 3) \le 4$

5. $|3x + 1| > 5$

6. $|x - 5| - 4 < -2$

7. $x \le -2$ and $x \le -5$

8. $x \le -2$ or $x \le -5$

9. $-x > 1$ and $3x + 3 \ge x - 3$

10. $6x + 1 > 5x + 4$ or $1 - x > -4$

11. $\left|\dfrac{5x - 7}{2}\right| = 4$

12. $\left|17x - \dfrac{1}{5}\right| > -2$

13. $-1 \le \dfrac{2x - 5}{3} < 2$

Graph each linear inequality.

14. $y > -4x$

15. $2x - 3y > -6$

Graph the solutions of the following systems of linear inequalities.

16. $\begin{cases} y + 2x \le 4 \\ \qquad y \ge 2 \end{cases}$

17. $\begin{cases} 2y - x \ge 1 \\ x + y \ge -4 \end{cases}$

Chapter 9 Cumulative Review

1. Find the value of each expression when $x = 2$ and $y = -5$.

    a. $\dfrac{x - y}{12 + x}$ **b.** $x^2 - 3y$

2. Find the value of each expression when $x = -4$ and $y = 7$.

    a. $\dfrac{x - y}{7 - x}$ **b.** $x^2 + 2y$

3. Simplify each expression.

    a. $\dfrac{(-12)(-3) + 3}{-7 - (-2)}$ **b.** $\dfrac{2(-3)^2 - 20}{-5 + 4}$

4. Simplify each expression.

    a. $\dfrac{4(-3) - (-6)}{-8 + 4}$ **b.** $\dfrac{3 + (-3)(-2)^3}{-1 - (-4)}$

5. Simplify each expression by combining like terms.

    a. $2x + 3x + 5 + 2$

    b. $-5a - 3 + a + 2$

    c. $4y - 3y^2$

    d. $2.3x + 5x - 6$

    e. $-\dfrac{1}{2}b + b$

6. Simplify each expression by combining like terms.

    a. $4x - 3 + 7 - 5x$

    b. $-6y + 3y - 8 + 8y$

    c. $2 + 8.1a + a - 6$

    d. $2x^2 - 2x$

7. Solve: $2x + 3x - 5 + 7 = 10x + 3 - 6x - 4$

8. Solve: $6y - 11 + 4 + 2y = 8 + 15y - 8y$

9. Complete the table for the equation $y = 3x$.

x	y
-1	
	0
	-9

10. Complete the table for the equation $2x + y = 6$.

x	y
0	
	-2
3	

11. Identify the x- and y-intercepts.

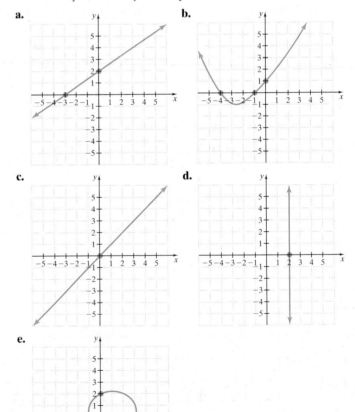

12. Identify the *x*- and *y*-intercepts.

a.

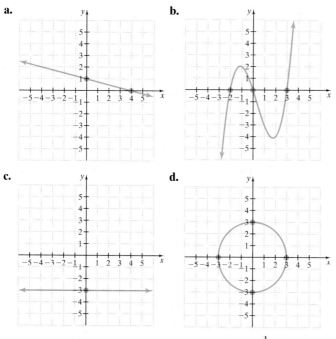

b.

c.

d.

13. Determine whether the graphs of $y = -\frac{1}{5}x + 1$ and $2x + 10y = 3$ are parallel lines, perpendicular lines, or neither.

14. Determine whether the graphs of $y = 3x + 7$ and $x + 3y = -15$ are parallel lines, perpendicular lines, or neither.

15. Find an equation of the line with *y*-intercept $(0, -3)$ and slope of $\frac{1}{4}$.

16. Find an equation of the line with *y*-intercept $(0, 4)$ and slope of -2.

17. Find an equation of the line parallel to the line $y = 5$ and passing through $(-2, -3)$.

18. Find an equation of the line perpendicular to $y = 2x + 4$ and passing through $(1, 5)$.

19. Which of the following linear equations are functions?
a. $y = x$
b. $y = 2x + 1$
c. $y = 5$
d. $x = -1$

20. Which of the following linear equations are functions?
a. $2x + 3 = y$ **b.** $x + 4 = 0$
c. $\frac{1}{2}y = 2x$ **d.** $y = 0$

21. Determine whether $(12, 6)$ is a solution of the system.
$$\begin{cases} 2x - 3y = 6 \\ x = 2y \end{cases}$$

22. State whether each of the following ordered pairs is a solution of the system.
$$\begin{cases} 2x + y = 4 \\ x + y = 2 \end{cases}$$
a. $(1, 1)$
b. $(2, 0)$

23. Add $(11x^3 - 12x^2 + x - 3)$ and $(x^3 - 10x + 5)$.

24. Combine like terms to simplify.
$4a^2 + 3a - 2a^2 + 7a - 5$.

25. Factor: $x^2 + 7yx + 6y^2$

26. Factor: $3x^2 + 15x + 18$

27. Divide: $\frac{3x^3y^7}{40} \div \frac{4x^3}{y^2}$

28. Divide: $\frac{12x^2y^3}{5} \div \frac{3y^2}{x}$

29. Subtract: $\frac{2y}{2y - 7} - \frac{7}{2y - 7}$

30. Subtract: $\frac{-4x^2}{x + 1} - \frac{4x}{x + 1}$

31. Add: $\frac{2x}{x^2 + 2x + 1} + \frac{x}{x^2 - 1}$

32. Add: $\frac{3x}{x^2 + 5x + 6} + \frac{1}{x^2 + 2x - 3}$

33. Solve: $\frac{x}{2} + \frac{8}{3} = \frac{1}{6}$

34. Solve: $\frac{1}{21} + \frac{x}{7} = \frac{5}{3}$

35. Solve the following system of equations by graphing.
$$\begin{cases} 2x + y = 7 \\ 2y = -4x \end{cases}$$

36. Solve the following system by graphing.
$$\begin{cases} y = x + 2 \\ 2x + y = 5 \end{cases}$$

37. Solve the system.
$$\begin{cases} 7x - 3y = -14 \\ -3x + y = 6 \end{cases}$$

38. Solve the system.
$$\begin{cases} 5x + y = 3 \\ y = -5x \end{cases}$$

39. Solve the system.
$$\begin{cases} 3x - 2y = 2 \\ -9x + 6y = -6 \end{cases}$$

40. Solve the system.
$$\begin{cases} -2x + y = 7 \\ 6x - 3y = -21 \end{cases}$$

41. Graph the solution of the system.

$$\begin{cases} -3x + 4y < 12 \\ x \geq 2 \end{cases}$$

42. Graph the solution of the system.

$$\begin{cases} 2x - y \leq 6 \\ y \geq 2 \end{cases}$$

43. Simplify the following.

a. $x^7 \cdot x^4$

b. $\left(\dfrac{t}{2}\right)^4$

c. $(9y^5)^2$

44. Simplify.

a. $\left(\dfrac{-6x}{y^3}\right)^3$

b. $\dfrac{(2b^2)^5}{a^2b^7}$

c. $\dfrac{(3y)^2}{y^2}$

d. $\dfrac{(x^2y^4)^2}{xy^3}$

45. Solve: $(5x - 1)(2x^2 + 15x + 18) = 0$

46. Solve: $(x + 1)(2x^2 - 3x - 5) = 0$

47. Solve: $\dfrac{45}{x} = \dfrac{5}{7}$

48. Solve: $\dfrac{2x + 7}{3} = \dfrac{x - 6}{2}$

Rational Exponents, Radicals, and Complex Numbers

10.1 Radicals and Radical Functions

10.2 Rational Exponents

10.3 Simplifying Radical Expressions

10.4 Adding, Subtracting, and Multiplying Radical Expressions

10.5 Rationalizing Denominators and Numerators of Radical Expressions

Integrated Review—Radicals and Rational Exponents

10.6 Radical Equations and Problem Solving

10.7 Complex Numbers

✓ CHECK YOUR PROGRESS

Vocabulary Check

Chapter Highlights

Chapter Review

Getting Ready for the Test

Chapter Test

Cumulative Review

In this chapter, radical notation is reviewed, and then rational exponents are introduced. As the name implies, rational exponents are exponents that are rational numbers. We present an interpretation of rational exponents that is consistent with the meaning and rules already established for integer exponents, and we present two forms of notation for roots: radical and exponent. We conclude this chapter with complex numbers, a natural extension of the real number system.

What Is Zorbing?

New Zealand is the home of some great extreme adventures. For example, bungee jumping, base jumping, and zorbing originated in New Zealand. Invented in 1995, zorbing is climbing inside a large, double-chambered ball and rolling down a hillside track. The creators have also provided zorbs for a show at Sea World, San Diego, created snow zorbing, and produced the zurf, which is zorbing at the beach. Since its inception, zorbing has spread throughout the world, including a site in Amesbury, Massachusetts.

NASA has even investigated using a zorb-like rover to investigate Mars, called the tumbleweed rover.

In Section 10.3, Exercises 125 and 126, we will explore aspects of zorbs and zorbing.

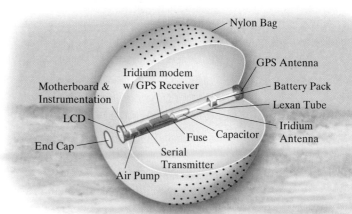

Tumbleweed Rover Architecture

If volume V or surface area A are known, then radius r can be calculated using

$$r = \sqrt[3]{\frac{3V}{4\pi}} \text{ or } r = \sqrt{\frac{A}{4\pi}}$$

10.1 | Radicals and Radical Functions

OBJECTIVES

1 Find Square Roots.
2 Approximate Roots.
3 Find Cube Roots.
4 Find nth Roots.
5 Find $\sqrt[n]{a^n}$ Where a Is a Real Number.
6 Graph Square and Cube Root Functions.

OBJECTIVE

1   Finding Square Roots

Recall from Section 8.2 that to find a **square root** of a number a, we find a number that was squared to get a.

Thus, because

$$5^2 = 25 \quad \text{and} \quad (-5)^2 = 25,$$

both 5 and -5 are square roots of 25.

Recall that we denote the **nonnegative**, or **principal**, **square root** with the **radical sign**.

$$\sqrt{25} = 5$$

We denote the **negative square root** with the **negative radical sign**.

$$-\sqrt{25} = -5$$

An expression containing a radical sign is called a **radical expression**. An expression within, or "under," a radical sign is called a **radicand**.

radical expression: $\sqrt{a}$ ⟵ radical sign
                              ⟵ radicand

> **Principal and Negative Square Roots**
>
> If a is a nonnegative number, then
>
> $\sqrt{a}$ is the **principal**, or **nonnegative**, **square root** of a
> $-\sqrt{a}$ is the **negative square root** of a

▶ **EXAMPLE 1**   Simplify. Assume that all variables represent nonnegative real numbers.

a. $\sqrt{36}$ **b.** $\sqrt{0}$ **c.** $\sqrt{\dfrac{4}{49}}$ **d.** $\sqrt{0.25}$

e. $\sqrt{x^6}$ **f.** $\sqrt{9x^{12}}$ **g.** $-\sqrt{81}$ **h.** $\sqrt{-81}$

Solution

a. $\sqrt{36} = 6$ because $6^2 = 36$ and 6 is not negative.

b. $\sqrt{0} = 0$ because $0^2 = 0$ and 0 is not negative.

c. $\sqrt{\dfrac{4}{49}} = \dfrac{2}{7}$ because $\left(\dfrac{2}{7}\right)^2 = \dfrac{4}{49}$ and $\dfrac{2}{7}$ is not negative.

d. $\sqrt{0.25} = 0.5$ because $(0.5)^2 = 0.25$.

e. $\sqrt{x^6} = x^3$ because $(x^3)^2 = x^6$.

f. $\sqrt{9x^{12}} = 3x^6$ because $(3x^6)^2 = 9x^{12}$.

g. $-\sqrt{81} = -9$. The negative in front of the radical indicates the negative square root of 81.

h. $\sqrt{-81}$ is not a real number.   □

PRACTICE

1   Simplify. Assume that all variables represent nonnegative real numbers.

a. $\sqrt{49}$ **b.** $\sqrt{\dfrac{0}{1}}$ **c.** $\sqrt{\dfrac{16}{81}}$ **d.** $\sqrt{0.64}$

e. $\sqrt{z^8}$ **f.** $\sqrt{16b^4}$ **g.** $-\sqrt{36}$ **h.** $\sqrt{-36}$ ■

Recall from Section 8.2 our discussion of the square root of a negative number. For example, can we simplify $\sqrt{-4}$? That is, can we find a real number whose square is -4? No, there is no real number whose square is -4, and we say that $\sqrt{-4}$ is not a real number. In general:

The square root of a negative number is not a real number.

Helpful Hint

- Remember: $\sqrt{0} = 0$.
- Don't forget that the square root of a negative number is not a real number. For example,

$$\sqrt{-9} \text{ is not a real number}$$

because there is no real number that when multiplied by itself would give a product of -9. In Section 10.7, we will see what kind of a number $\sqrt{-9}$ is.

OBJECTIVE

2   Approximating Roots ▶

Recall that numbers such as 1, 4, 9, and 25 are called **perfect squares,** since $1 = 1^2, 4 = 2^2, 9 = 3^2$, and $25 = 5^2$. Square roots of perfect square radicands simplify to rational numbers. What happens when we try to simplify a root such as $\sqrt{3}$? Since there is no rational number whose square is 3, $\sqrt{3}$ is not a rational number. It is called an **irrational number,** and we can find a decimal **approximation** of it. To find decimal approximations, use a calculator. For example, an approximation for $\sqrt{3}$ is

$$\sqrt{3} \approx 1.732$$
$$\uparrow$$
approximation symbol

To see if the approximation is reasonable, notice that since

$$1 < 3 < 4,$$
$$\sqrt{1} < \sqrt{3} < \sqrt{4}, \text{ or}$$
$$1 < \sqrt{3} < 2.$$

1 and 4 are perfect squares closest to but less than and greater than 3, respectively.

We found $\sqrt{3} \approx 1.732$, a number between 1 and 2, so our result is reasonable.

EXAMPLE 2   Use a calculator to approximate $\sqrt{20}$. Round the approximation to 3 decimal places and check to see that your approximation is reasonable.

Solution
$$\sqrt{20} \approx 4.472$$

Is this reasonable? Since $16 < 20 < 25$, $\sqrt{16} < \sqrt{20} < \sqrt{25}$, or $4 < \sqrt{20} < 5$. The approximation is between 4 and 5 and thus is reasonable.   □

PRACTICE

2   Use a calculator to approximate $\sqrt{45}$. Round the approximation to three decimal places and check to see that your approximation is reasonable.   ■

OBJECTIVE

3   Finding Cube Roots ▶

Finding roots can be extended to other roots such as cube roots. For example, since $2^3 = 8$, we call 2 the **cube root** of 8. In symbols, we write

$$\sqrt[3]{8} = 2$$

Cube Root

The **cube root** of a real number a is written as $\sqrt[3]{a}$, and

$$\sqrt[3]{a} = b \text{ only if } b^3 = a$$

From this definition, we have

$$\sqrt[3]{64} = 4 \text{ since } 4^3 = 64$$
$$\sqrt[3]{-27} = -3 \text{ since } (-3)^3 = -27$$
$$\sqrt[3]{x^3} = x \text{ since } x^3 = x^3$$

Notice that, unlike with square roots, *it is possible to have a negative radicand when finding a cube root.* This is so because the *cube* of a negative number is a negative number. Therefore, the *cube root* of a negative number is a negative number.

EXAMPLE 3 Find the cube roots.

a. $\sqrt[3]{1}$ **b.** $\sqrt[3]{-64}$ **c.** $\sqrt[3]{\dfrac{8}{125}}$ **d.** $\sqrt[3]{x^6}$ **e.** $\sqrt[3]{-27x^{15}}$

Solution

a. $\sqrt[3]{1} = 1$ because $1^3 = 1$.

b. $\sqrt[3]{-64} = -4$ because $(-4)^3 = -64$.

c. $\sqrt[3]{\dfrac{8}{125}} = \dfrac{2}{5}$ because $\left(\dfrac{2}{5}\right)^3 = \dfrac{8}{125}$.

d. $\sqrt[3]{x^6} = x^2$ because $(x^2)^3 = x^6$.

e. $\sqrt[3]{-27x^{15}} = -3x^5$ because $(-3x^5)^3 = -27x^{15}$. □

PRACTICE
3 Find the cube roots.

a. $\sqrt[3]{-1}$ **b.** $\sqrt[3]{27}$ **c.** $\sqrt[3]{\dfrac{27}{64}}$ **d.** $\sqrt[3]{x^{12}}$ **e.** $\sqrt[3]{-8x^3}$ ■

OBJECTIVE
4 Finding *n*th Roots ▶

Just as we can raise a real number to powers other than 2 or 3, we can find roots other than square roots and cube roots. In fact, we can find the **nth root** of a number, where *n* is any natural number. In symbols, the *n*th root of *a* is written as $\sqrt[n]{a}$, where *n* is called the **index.** The index 2 is usually omitted for square roots.

> **Helpful Hint**
>
> If the index is even, such as $\sqrt{}, \sqrt[4]{}, \sqrt[6]{}$, and so on, the radicand must be nonnegative for the root to be a real number. For example,
>
> $$\sqrt[4]{16} = 2, \text{ but } \sqrt[4]{-16} \text{ is not a real number.}$$
> $$\sqrt[6]{64} = 2, \text{ but } \sqrt[6]{-64} \text{ is not a real number.}$$
>
> If the index is odd, such as $\sqrt[3]{}, \sqrt[5]{}$, and so on, the radicand may be any real number. For example,
>
> $$\sqrt[3]{64} = 4 \quad \text{and} \quad \sqrt[3]{-64} = -4$$
> $$\sqrt[5]{32} = 2 \quad \text{and} \quad \sqrt[5]{-32} = -2$$

✔ **CONCEPT CHECK**
Which one is not a real number?

a. $\sqrt[3]{-15}$ **b.** $\sqrt[4]{-15}$ **c.** $\sqrt[5]{-15}$ **d.** $\sqrt{(-15)^2}$

Answer to Concept Check: b

EXAMPLE 4   Simplify the following expressions.

a. $\sqrt[4]{81}$ b. $\sqrt[5]{-243}$ c. $-\sqrt{25}$ d. $\sqrt[4]{-81}$ e. $\sqrt[3]{64x^3}$

Solution

a. $\sqrt[4]{81} = 3$ because $3^4 = 81$ and 3 is positive.

b. $\sqrt[5]{-243} = -3$ because $(-3)^5 = -243$.

c. $-\sqrt{25} = -5$ because -5 is the opposite of $\sqrt{25}$.

d. $\sqrt[4]{-81}$ is not a real number. There is no real number that, when raised to the fourth power, is -81.

e. $\sqrt[3]{64x^3} = 4x$ because $(4x)^3 = 64x^3$.   □

PRACTICE
4   Simplify the following expressions.

a. $\sqrt[4]{10,000}$ b. $\sqrt[5]{-1}$ c. $-\sqrt{81}$ d. $\sqrt[4]{-625}$ e. $\sqrt[3]{27x^9}$ ■

OBJECTIVE

5   Finding $\sqrt[n]{a^n}$ Where a Is a Real Number ▶

Recall that the notation $\sqrt{a^2}$ indicates the positive square root of a^2 only. For example,

$$\sqrt{(-7)^2} = \sqrt{49} = 7$$

When variables are present in the radicand and it is _unclear whether the variable represents a positive number or a negative number_, absolute value bars are sometimes needed to ensure that the result is a positive number. For example,

$$\sqrt{x^2} = |x|$$

This ensures that the result is positive. This same situation may occur when the index is any _even_ positive integer. When the index is any _odd_ positive integer, absolute value bars are not necessary.

Finding $\sqrt[n]{a^n}$

If n is an _even_ positive integer, then $\sqrt[n]{a^n} = |a|$.

If n is an _odd_ positive integer, then $\sqrt[n]{a^n} = a$.

EXAMPLE 5   Simplify.

a. $\sqrt{(-3)^2}$ b. $\sqrt{x^2}$ c. $\sqrt[4]{(x-2)^4}$ d. $\sqrt[3]{(-5)^3}$

e. $\sqrt[5]{(2x-7)^5}$ f. $\sqrt{25x^2}$ g. $\sqrt{x^2 + 2x + 1}$

Solution

a. $\sqrt{(-3)^2} = |-3| = 3$ When the index is even, the absolute value bars ensure that our result is not negative.

b. $\sqrt{x^2} = |x|$

c. $\sqrt[4]{(x-2)^4} = |x-2|$

d. $\sqrt[3]{(-5)^3} = -5$

e. $\sqrt[5]{(2x-7)^5} = 2x - 7$ Absolute value bars are not needed when the index is odd.

f. $\sqrt{25x^2} = 5|x|$

g. $\sqrt{x^2 + 2x + 1} = \sqrt{(x+1)^2} = |x+1|$ □

(Continued on next page)

PRACTICE

5 Simplify.

a. $\sqrt{(-4)^2}$ b. $\sqrt{x^{14}}$ c. $\sqrt[4]{(x + 7)^4}$ d. $\sqrt[3]{(-7)^3}$

e. $\sqrt[5]{(3x - 5)^5}$ f. $\sqrt{49x^2}$ g. $\sqrt{x^2 + 16x + 64}$

OBJECTIVE

6 Graphing Square and Cube Root Functions ▶

Recall that an equation in x and y describes a function if each x-value is paired with exactly one y-value. With this in mind, does the equation

$$y = \sqrt{x}$$

describe a function? First, notice that replacement values for x must be nonnegative real numbers, since $\sqrt{x}$ is not a real number if $x < 0$. The notation $\sqrt{x}$ denotes the principal square root of x, so for every nonnegative number x, there is exactly one number, $\sqrt{x}$. Therefore, $y = \sqrt{x}$ describes a function, and we may write it as

$$f(x) = \sqrt{x}$$

In general, radical functions are functions of the form

$$f(x) = \sqrt[n]{x}.$$

Recall that the domain of a function in x is the set of all possible replacement values for x. This means that if n is even, the domain is the set of all nonnegative numbers, or $\{x \mid x \geq 0\}$ or $[0, \infty)$. If n is odd, the domain is the set of all real numbers, or $(-\infty, \infty)$. Keep this in mind as we find function values.

EXAMPLE 6 If $f(x) = \sqrt{x - 4}$ and $g(x) = \sqrt[3]{x + 2}$, find each function value.

a. $f(8)$ b. $f(6)$ c. $g(-1)$ d. $g(1)$

Solution

a. $f(8) = \sqrt{8 - 4} = \sqrt{4} = 2$ b. $f(6) = \sqrt{6 - 4} = \sqrt{2}$

c. $g(-1) = \sqrt[3]{-1 + 2} = \sqrt[3]{1} = 1$ d. $g(1) = \sqrt[3]{1 + 2} = \sqrt[3]{3}$ □

PRACTICE

6 If $f(x) = \sqrt{x + 5}$ and $g(x) = \sqrt[3]{x - 3}$, find each function value.

a. $f(11)$ b. $f(-1)$ c. $g(11)$ d. $g(-6)$

Helpful Hint

Notice that for the function $f(x) = \sqrt{x - 4}$, the domain includes all real numbers that make the radicand ≥ 0. To see what numbers these are, solve $x - 4 \geq 0$ and find that $x \geq 4$. The domain is $\{x \mid x \geq 4\}$, or $[4, \infty)$.

The domain of the cube root function $g(x) = \sqrt[3]{x + 2}$ is the set of real numbers, or $(-\infty, \infty)$.

EXAMPLE 7 Graph the square root function: $f(x) = \sqrt{x}$

Solution To graph, we identify the domain, evaluate the function for several values of x, plot the resulting points, and connect the points with a smooth curve. Since $\sqrt{x}$ is not a real number for negative values of x, the domain of this function is the set of all non-negative numbers, $\{x \mid x \geq 0\}$, or $[0, \infty)$. We have approximated $\sqrt{3}$ in the table on the next page to help us locate the point corresponding to $(3, \sqrt{3})$.

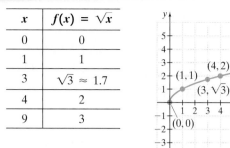

x	$f(x) = \sqrt{x}$
0	0
1	1
3	$\sqrt{3} \approx 1.7$
4	2
9	3

Notice that the graph of this function passes the vertical line test, as expected.   ☐

PRACTICE
7   Graph the square root function: $h(x) = \sqrt{x + 2}$ ■

The equation $f(x) = \sqrt[3]{x}$ also describes a function. Here, x may be any real number, so the domain of this function is the set of all real numbers, or $(-\infty, \infty)$. A few function values are given next.

$$f(0) = \sqrt[3]{0} = 0$$
$$f(1) = \sqrt[3]{1} = 1$$
$$f(-1) = \sqrt[3]{-1} = -1$$
$$f(6) = \sqrt[3]{6}$$
$$f(-6) = \sqrt[3]{-6}$$
$$f(8) = \sqrt[3]{8} = 2$$
$$f(-8) = \sqrt[3]{-8} = -2$$

Here, there is no rational number whose cube is 6. Thus, the radicals do not simplify to rational numbers.

EXAMPLE 8   Graph the function: $f(x) = \sqrt[3]{x}$

Solution To graph, we identify the domain, plot points, and connect the points with a smooth curve. The domain of this function is the set of all real numbers. The table comes from the function values obtained earlier. We have approximated $\sqrt[3]{6}$ and $\sqrt[3]{-6}$ for graphing purposes.

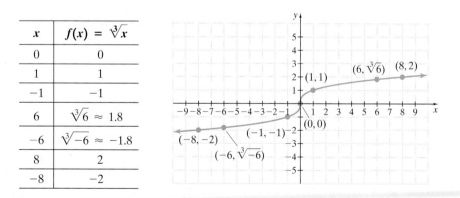

x	$f(x) = \sqrt[3]{x}$
0	0
1	1
-1	-1
6	$\sqrt[3]{6} \approx 1.8$
-6	$\sqrt[3]{-6} \approx -1.8$
8	2
-8	-2

The graph of this function passes the vertical line test, as expected.   ☐

PRACTICE
8   Graph the function: $f(x) = \sqrt[3]{x} - 4$ ■

✔ **Vocabulary, Readiness & Video Check**

Use the choices below to fill in each blank. Not all choices will be used.

is	cubes	$-\sqrt{a}$	radical sign	index
is not	squares	$\sqrt{-a}$	radicand	

1. In the expression $\sqrt[n]{a}$, the n is called the _____, the $\sqrt{}$ is called the _____, and a is called the _____.

2. If $\sqrt{a}$ is the positive square root of a, $a \neq 0$, then _____ is the negative square root of a.

3. The square root of a negative number _____ a real number.

4. Numbers such as 1, 4, 9, and 25 are called perfect _____, whereas numbers such as 1, 8, 27, and 125 are called perfect _____.

Fill in the blank.

5. The domain of the function $f(x) = \sqrt{x}$ is _____.

6. The domain of the function $f(x) = \sqrt[3]{x}$ is _____.

7. If $f(16) = 4$, the corresponding ordered pair is _____.

8. If $g(-8) = -2$, the corresponding ordered pair is _____.

Martin-Gay Interactive Videos

See Video 10.1 ⬤

Watch the section lecture video and answer the following questions.

OBJECTIVE 1
9. From ▦ Examples 5 and 6, when simplifying radicals containing variables with exponents, describe a shortcut you can use.

OBJECTIVE 2
10. From ▦ Example 9, how can you determine a reasonable approximation for a non-perfect square root without using a calculator?

OBJECTIVE 3
11. From ▦ Example 11, what is an important difference between the square root and the cube root of a negative number?

OBJECTIVE 4
12. From ▦ Example 12, what conclusion is made about the even root of a negative number?

OBJECTIVE 5
13. From the lecture before ▦ Example 17, why do you think no absolute value bars are used when n is odd?

OBJECTIVE 6
14. In ▦ Example 19, the domain is found by looking at the graph. How can the domain be found by looking at the function?

10.1 Exercise Set MyMathLab® ▸

Simplify. Assume that variables represent nonnegative real numbers. See Example 1.

1. $\sqrt{100}$

2. $\sqrt{400}$

3. $\sqrt{\dfrac{1}{4}}$

4. $\sqrt{\dfrac{9}{25}}$

5. $\sqrt{0.0001}$

6. $\sqrt{0.04}$

7. $-\sqrt{36}$

8. $-\sqrt{9}$

9. $\sqrt{x^{10}}$

10. $\sqrt{x^{16}}$

11. $\sqrt{16y^6}$

12. $\sqrt{64y^{20}}$

Use a calculator to approximate each square root to 3 decimal places. Check to see that each approximation is reasonable. See Example 2.

13. $\sqrt{7}$

14. $\sqrt{11}$

▶ **15.** $\sqrt{38}$

16. $\sqrt{56}$

17. $\sqrt{200}$

18. $\sqrt{300}$

Find each cube root. See Example 3.

19. $\sqrt[3]{64}$

20. $\sqrt[3]{27}$

▶ **21.** $\sqrt[3]{\dfrac{1}{8}}$

22. $\sqrt[3]{\dfrac{27}{64}}$

23. $\sqrt[3]{-1}$

24. $\sqrt[3]{-125}$

25. $\sqrt[3]{x^{12}}$

26. $\sqrt[3]{x^{15}}$

▶ **27.** $\sqrt[3]{-27x^9}$

28. $\sqrt[3]{-64x^6}$

Find each root. Assume that all variables represent nonnegative real numbers. See Example 4.

29. $-\sqrt[4]{16}$

30. $\sqrt[5]{-243}$

▶ **31.** $\sqrt[4]{-16}$

32. $\sqrt{-16}$

▶ **33.** $\sqrt[5]{-32}$

34. $\sqrt[5]{-1}$

35. $\sqrt[5]{x^{20}}$

36. $\sqrt[4]{x^{20}}$

▶ **37.** $\sqrt[6]{64x^{12}}$

38. $\sqrt[5]{-32x^{15}}$

39. $\sqrt{81x^4}$

40. $\sqrt[4]{81x^4}$

41. $\sqrt[4]{256x^8}$

42. $\sqrt{256x^8}$

Simplify. Assume that the variables represent any real number. See Example 5.

▶ **43.** $\sqrt{(-8)^2}$

44. $\sqrt{(-7)^2}$

▶ **45.** $\sqrt[3]{(-8)^3}$

46. $\sqrt[5]{(-7)^5}$

47. $\sqrt{4x^2}$

48. $\sqrt[4]{16x^4}$

49. $\sqrt[3]{x^3}$

50. $\sqrt[5]{x^5}$

▶ **51.** $\sqrt{(x-5)^2}$

52. $\sqrt{(y-6)^2}$

53. $\sqrt{x^2+4x+4}$
(*Hint:* Factor the polynomial first.)

54. $\sqrt{x^2-8x+16}$
(*Hint:* Factor the polynomial first.)

MIXED PRACTICE

Simplify each radical. Assume that all variables represent positive real numbers.

55. $-\sqrt{121}$

56. $-\sqrt[3]{125}$

57. $\sqrt[3]{8x^3}$

58. $\sqrt{16x^8}$

59. $\sqrt{y^{12}}$

60. $\sqrt[3]{y^{12}}$

61. $\sqrt{25a^2b^{20}}$

62. $\sqrt{9x^4y^6}$

63. $\sqrt[3]{-27x^{12}y^9}$

64. $\sqrt[3]{-8a^{21}b^6}$

65. $\sqrt[4]{a^{16}b^4}$

66. $\sqrt[4]{x^8y^{12}}$

▶ **67.** $\sqrt[5]{-32x^{10}y^5}$

68. $\sqrt[5]{-243x^5z^{15}}$

69. $\sqrt{\dfrac{25}{49}}$

70. $\sqrt{\dfrac{4}{81}}$

71. $\sqrt{\dfrac{x^{20}}{4y^2}}$

72. $\sqrt{\dfrac{y^{10}}{9x^6}}$

73. $-\sqrt[3]{\dfrac{z^{21}}{27x^3}}$

74. $-\sqrt[3]{\dfrac{64a^3}{b^9}}$

75. $\sqrt[4]{\dfrac{x^4}{16}}$

76. $\sqrt[4]{\dfrac{y^4}{81x^4}}$

If $f(x)=\sqrt{2x+3}$ and $g(x)=\sqrt[3]{x-8}$, find the following function values. See Example 6.

77. $f(0)$

78. $g(0)$

79. $g(7)$

80. $f(-1)$

81. $g(-19)$

82. $f(3)$

83. $f(2)$

84. $g(1)$

Identify the domain and then graph each function. See Example 7.

▶ **85.** $f(x)=\sqrt{x}+2$

86. $f(x)=\sqrt{x}-2$

87. $f(x)=\sqrt{x-3}$; use the following table.

x	$f(x)$
3	
4	
7	
12	

88. $f(x)=\sqrt{x+1}$; use the following table.

x	$f(x)$
-1	
0	
3	
8	

Identify the domain and then graph each function. See Example 8.

89. $f(x)=\sqrt[3]{x}+1$

90. $f(x)=\sqrt[3]{x}-2$

91. $g(x)=\sqrt[3]{x-1}$; use the following table.

x	$g(x)$
1	
2	
0	
9	
-7	

92. $g(x)=\sqrt[3]{x+1}$; use the following table.

x	$g(x)$
-1	
0	
-2	
7	
-9	

REVIEW AND PREVIEW

Simplify each exponential expression. See Sections 5.1 and 5.5.

93. $(-2x^3y^2)^5$

94. $(4y^6z^7)^3$

95. $(-3x^2y^3z^5)(20x^5y^7)$

96. $(-14a^5bc^2)(2abc^4)$

97. $\dfrac{7x^{-1}y}{14(x^5y^2)^{-2}}$

98. $\dfrac{(2a^{-1}b^2)^3}{(8a^2b)^{-2}}$

CONCEPT EXTENSIONS

Determine whether the following are real numbers. See the Concept Check in this section.

99. $\sqrt{-17}$

100. $\sqrt[3]{-17}$

101. $\sqrt[10]{-17}$

102. $\sqrt[15]{-17}$

Choose the correct letter or letters. No pencil is needed, just think your way through these.

103. Which radical is not a real number?

   a. $\sqrt{3}$ **b.** $-\sqrt{11}$ **c.** $\sqrt[3]{-10}$ **d.** $\sqrt{-10}$

104. Which radical(s) simplify to 3?

   a. $\sqrt{9}$ **b.** $\sqrt{-9}$ **c.** $\sqrt[3]{27}$ **d.** $\sqrt[3]{-27}$

105. Which radical(s) simplify to −3?

   a. $\sqrt{9}$ **b.** $\sqrt{-9}$ **c.** $\sqrt[3]{27}$ **d.** $\sqrt[3]{-27}$

106. Which radical does not simplify to a whole number?

   a. $\sqrt{64}$ **b.** $\sqrt[3]{64}$ **c.** $\sqrt{8}$ **d.** $\sqrt[3]{8}$

For Exercises 107 through 110, do not use a calculator.

107. $\sqrt{160}$ is closest to

   a. 10   **b.** 13   **c.** 20   **d.** 40

108. $\sqrt{1000}$ is closest to

   a. 10   **b.** 30   **c.** 100   **d.** 500

△ **109.** The perimeter of the triangle is closest to

   a. 12   **b.** 18

   c. 66   **d.** 132

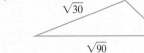

110. The length of the bent wire is closest to

   a. 5   **b.** $\sqrt{28}$

   c. 7   **d.** 14

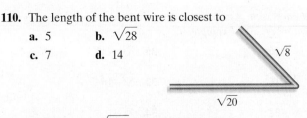

111. Explain why $\sqrt{-64}$ is not a real number.

112. Explain why $\sqrt[3]{-64}$ is a real number.

The Mosteller formula for calculating adult body surface area is $B = \sqrt{\dfrac{hw}{3131}}$, where B is an individual's body surface area in square meters, h is the individual's height in inches, and w is the individual's weight in pounds. Use this information to answer Exercises 113 and 114. Round answers to 2 decimal places.

△ **113.** Find the body surface area of an individual who is 66 inches tall and who weighs 135 pounds.

△ **114.** Find the body surface area of an individual who is 74 inches tall and who weighs 225 pounds.

115. Escape velocity is the minimum speed that an object must reach to escape the pull of a planet's gravity. Escape velocity v is given by the equation $v = \sqrt{\dfrac{2Gm}{r}}$, where m is the mass of the planet, r is its radius, and G is the universal gravitational constant, which has a value of $G = 6.67 \times 10^{-11}$ m^3/kg·s^2. The mass of Earth is 5.97×10^{24} kg, and its radius is 6.37×10^6 m. Use this information to find the escape velocity for Earth in meters per second. Round to the nearest whole number. (*Source*: National Space Science Data Center)

116. Use the formula from Exercise 115 to determine the escape velocity for the moon. The mass of the moon is 7.35×10^{22} kg, and its radius is 1.74×10^6 m. Round to the nearest whole number. (*Source*: National Space Science Data Center)

117. Suppose a classmate tells you that $\sqrt{13} \approx 5.7$. Without a calculator, how can you convince your classmate that he or she must have made an error?

118. Suppose a classmate tells you that $\sqrt[3]{10} \approx 3.2$. Without a calculator, how can you convince your friend that he or she must have made an error?

Use a graphing calculator to verify the domain of each function and its graph.

119. Exercise 85   **120.** Exercise 86

121. Exercise 89   **122.** Exercise 90

10.2 | Rational Exponents ▷

OBJECTIVES

1 Understand the Meaning of $a^{1/n}$. ▷

2 Understand the Meaning of $a^{m/n}$. ▷

3 Understand the Meaning of $a^{-m/n}$. ▷

4 Use Rules for Exponents to Simplify Expressions That Contain Rational Exponents. ▷

5 Use Rational Exponents to Simplify Radical Expressions. ▷

OBJECTIVE

1   Understanding the Meaning of $a^{1/n}$ ▷

So far in this text, we have not defined expressions with rational exponents such as $3^{1/2}$, $x^{2/3}$, and $-9^{-1/4}$. We will define these expressions so that the rules for exponents will apply to these rational exponents as well.

Suppose that $x = 5^{1/3}$. Then

$$x^3 = (5^{1/3})^3 = 5^{1/3 \cdot 3} = 5^1 \text{ or } 5$$

using rules
for exponents

Since $x^3 = 5$, x is the number whose cube is 5, or $x = \sqrt[3]{5}$. Notice that we also know that $x = 5^{1/3}$. This means

$$5^{1/3} = \sqrt[3]{5}$$

Definition of $a^{1/n}$

If n is a positive integer greater than 1 and $\sqrt[n]{a}$ is a real number, then

$$a^{1/n} = \sqrt[n]{a}$$

Notice that the denominator of the rational exponent corresponds to the index of the radical.

EXAMPLE I   Use radical notation to write the following. Simplify if possible.

a. $4^{1/2}$ **b.** $64^{1/3}$ **c.** $x^{1/4}$ **d.** $0^{1/6}$ **e.** $-9^{1/2}$ **f.** $(81x^8)^{1/4}$ **g.** $5y^{1/3}$

Solution

a. $4^{1/2} = \sqrt{4} = 2$ **b.** $64^{1/3} = \sqrt[3]{64} = 4$

c. $x^{1/4} = \sqrt[4]{x}$ **d.** $0^{1/6} = \sqrt[6]{0} = 0$

e. $-9^{1/2} = -\sqrt{9} = -3$ **f.** $(81x^8)^{1/4} = \sqrt[4]{81x^8} = 3x^2$

g. $5y^{1/3} = 5\sqrt[3]{y}$ ☐

PRACTICE

1   Use radical notation to write the following. Simplify if possible.

a. $36^{1/2}$ **b.** $1000^{1/3}$ **c.** $x^{1/3}$ **d.** $1^{1/4}$

e. $-64^{1/2}$ **f.** $(125x^9)^{1/3}$ **g.** $3x^{1/4}$ ■

OBJECTIVE

2   Understanding the Meaning of $a^{m/n}$ ▷

As we expand our use of exponents to include $\dfrac{m}{n}$, we define their meaning so that rules for exponents still hold true. For example, by properties of exponents,

$$8^{2/3} = (8^{1/3})^2 = (\sqrt[3]{8})^2 \quad \text{or}$$
$$8^{2/3} = (8^2)^{1/3} = \sqrt[3]{8^2}$$

Definition of $a^{m/n}$

If m and n are positive integers greater than 1 with $\dfrac{m}{n}$ in simplest form, then

$$a^{m/n} = \sqrt[n]{a^m} = (\sqrt[n]{a})^m$$

as long as $\sqrt[n]{a}$ is a real number.

Notice that the denominator n of the rational exponent corresponds to the index of the radical. The numerator m of the rational exponent indicates that the base is to be raised to the mth power. This means

$$8^{2/3} = \sqrt[3]{8^2} = \sqrt[3]{64} = 4 \quad \text{or}$$

$$8^{2/3} = (\sqrt[3]{8})^2 = 2^2 = 4$$

From simplifying $8^{2/3}$, can you see that it doesn't matter whether you raise to a power first and then take the nth root or you take the nth root first and then raise to a power?

> **Helpful Hint**
>
> Most of the time, $(\sqrt[n]{a})^m$ will be easier to calculate than $\sqrt[n]{a^m}$.

EXAMPLE 2 Use radical notation to write the following. Then simplify if possible.

    a. $4^{3/2}$ **b.** $-16^{3/4}$ **c.** $(-27)^{2/3}$

    d. $\left(\dfrac{1}{9}\right)^{3/2}$ **e.** $(4x - 1)^{3/5}$

Solution

    a. $4^{3/2} = (\sqrt{4})^3 = 2^3 = 8$ **b.** $-16^{3/4} = -(\sqrt[4]{16})^3 = -(2)^3 = -8$

    c. $(-27)^{2/3} = (\sqrt[3]{-27})^2 = (-3)^2 = 9$ **d.** $\left(\dfrac{1}{9}\right)^{3/2} = \left(\sqrt{\dfrac{1}{9}}\right)^3 = \left(\dfrac{1}{3}\right)^3 = \dfrac{1}{27}$

    e. $(4x - 1)^{3/5} = \sqrt[5]{(4x - 1)^3}$ □

PRACTICE
2   Use radical notation to write the following. Simplify if possible.

    a. $16^{3/2}$ **b.** $-1^{3/5}$ **c.** $-(81)^{3/4}$

    d. $\left(\dfrac{1}{25}\right)^{3/2}$ **e.** $(3x + 2)^{5/9}$ ■

> **Helpful Hint**
>
> The *denominator* of a rational exponent is the index of the corresponding radical. For example, $x^{1/5} = \sqrt[5]{x}$ and $z^{2/3} = \sqrt[3]{z^2}$, or $z^{2/3} = (\sqrt[3]{z})^2$.

OBJECTIVE
3 **Understanding the Meaning of** $a^{-m/n}$ ▶

The rational exponents we have given meaning to exclude negative rational numbers. To complete the set of definitions, we define $a^{-m/n}$.

> **Definition of** $a^{-m/n}$
>
> $$a^{-m/n} = \dfrac{1}{a^{m/n}}$$
>
> as long as $a^{m/n}$ is a nonzero real number.

EXAMPLE 3 Write each expression with a positive exponent, and then simplify.

    a. $16^{-3/4}$ **b.** $(-27)^{-2/3}$

Solution

    a. $16^{-3/4} = \dfrac{1}{16^{3/4}} = \dfrac{1}{(\sqrt[4]{16})^3} = \dfrac{1}{2^3} = \dfrac{1}{8}$

    b. $(-27)^{-2/3} = \dfrac{1}{(-27)^{2/3}} = \dfrac{1}{(\sqrt[3]{-27})^2} = \dfrac{1}{(-3)^2} = \dfrac{1}{9}$ □

PRACTICE

3 Write each expression with a positive exponent; then simplify.

    a. $9^{-3/2}$ **b.** $(-64)^{-2/3}$

Helpful Hint

If an expression contains a negative rational exponent, such as $9^{-3/2}$, you may want to first write the expression with a positive exponent and then interpret the rational exponent. Notice that the sign of the base is not affected by the sign of its exponent. For example,

$$9^{-3/2} = \frac{1}{9^{3/2}} = \frac{1}{(\sqrt{9})^3} = \frac{1}{27}$$

Also,

$$(-27)^{-1/3} = \frac{1}{(-27)^{1/3}} = -\frac{1}{3}$$

OBJECTIVE

4 **Using Rules for Exponents to Simplify Expressions** ▶

It can be shown that the properties of integer exponents hold for rational exponents. By using these properties and definitions, we can now simplify expressions that contain rational exponents.

    These rules are repeated here for review.

    Note: For the remainder of this chapter, we will assume that variables represent positive real numbers. Since this is so, we need not insert absolute value bars when we simplify even roots.

Summary of Exponent Rules

If m and n are rational numbers, and a, b, and c are numbers for which the expressions below exist, then

Product rule for exponents: $a^m \cdot a^n = a^{m+n}$

Power rule for exponents: $(a^m)^n = a^{m \cdot n}$

Power rules for products and quotients: $(ab)^n = a^n b^n$ and

$$\left(\frac{a}{c}\right)^n = \frac{a^n}{c^n}, c \neq 0$$

Quotient rule for exponents: $\dfrac{a^m}{a^n} = a^{m-n}, a \neq 0$

Zero exponent: $a^0 = 1, a \neq 0$

Negative exponent: $a^{-n} = \dfrac{1}{a^n}, a \neq 0$

EXAMPLE 4   Use properties of exponents to simplify. Write results with only positive exponents.

    a. $b^{1/3} \cdot b^{5/3}$ **b.** $x^{1/2}x^{1/3}$ **c.** $\dfrac{7^{1/3}}{7^{4/3}}$

    d. $y^{-4/7} \cdot y^{6/7}$ **e.** $\dfrac{(2x^{2/5}y^{-1/3})^5}{x^2 y}$

(Continued on next page)

Solution

a. $b^{1/3} \cdot b^{5/3} = b^{(1/3+5/3)} = b^{6/3} = b^2$ Use the product rule.

b. $x^{1/2}x^{1/3} = x^{(1/2+1/3)} = x^{3/6+2/6} = x^{5/6}$ Use the product rule.

c. $\dfrac{7^{1/3}}{7^{4/3}} = 7^{1/3-4/3} = 7^{-3/3} = 7^{-1} = \dfrac{1}{7}$ Use the quotient rule.

d. $y^{-4/7} \cdot y^{6/7} = y^{-4/7+6/7} = y^{2/7}$ Use the product rule.

e. We begin by using the power rule $(ab)^m = a^m b^m$ to simplify the numerator.

$$\frac{(2x^{2/5}y^{-1/3})^5}{x^2y} = \frac{2^5(x^{2/5})^5(y^{-1/3})^5}{x^2y} = \frac{32x^2y^{-5/3}}{x^2y} \quad \text{Use the power rule and simplify}$$

$$= 32x^{2-2}y^{-5/3-3/3} \quad \text{Apply the quotient rule.}$$

$$= 32x^0y^{-8/3}$$

$$= \frac{32}{y^{8/3}} \qquad\qquad\qquad \square$$

PRACTICE

4   Use properties of exponents to simplify.

a. $y^{2/3} \cdot y^{8/3}$ **b.** $x^{3/5} \cdot x^{1/4}$ **c.** $\dfrac{9^{2/7}}{9^{9/7}}$

d. $b^{4/9} \cdot b^{-2/9}$ **e.** $\dfrac{(3x^{1/4}y^{-2/3})^4}{x^4y}$

EXAMPLE 5   Multiply.

a. $z^{2/3}(z^{1/3} - z^5)$ **b.** $(x^{1/3} - 5)(x^{1/3} + 2)$

Solution

a. $z^{2/3}(z^{1/3} - z^5) = z^{2/3}z^{1/3} - z^{2/3}z^5$ Apply the distributive property.

$$= z^{(2/3+1/3)} - z^{(2/3+5)} \quad \text{Use the product rule.}$$

$$= z^{3/3} - z^{(2/3+15/3)}$$

$$= z - z^{17/3}$$

b. $(x^{1/3} - 5)(x^{1/3} + 2) = x^{2/3} + 2x^{1/3} - 5x^{1/3} - 10$ Think of $(x^{1/3} - 5)$ and

$$= x^{2/3} - 3x^{1/3} - 10 \qquad \begin{array}{l}(x^{1/3} + 2) \text{ as 2 binomials,}\\ \text{then multiply using FOIL.}\end{array}$$

$\square$

PRACTICE

5   Multiply.

a. $x^{3/5}(x^{1/3} - x^2)$ **b.** $(x^{1/2} + 6)(x^{1/2} - 2)$

EXAMPLE 6   Factor $x^{-1/2}$ from the expression $3x^{-1/2} - 7x^{5/2}$. Assume that all variables represent positive numbers.

Solution

$$3x^{-1/2} - 7x^{5/2} = (x^{-1/2})(3) - (x^{-1/2})(7x^{6/2})$$

$$= x^{-1/2}(3 - 7x^3)$$

To check, multiply $x^{-1/2}(3 - 7x^3)$ to see that the product is $3x^{-1/2} - 7x^{5/2}$. $\square$

PRACTICE

6   Factor $x^{-1/5}$ from the expression $2x^{-1/5} - 7x^{4/5}$.

OBJECTIVE

5   Using Rational Exponents to Simplify Radical Expressions ▷

Some radical expressions are easier to simplify when we first write them with rational exponents. Next, use properties of exponents to simplify the expression, and then convert it back to radical notation.

EXAMPLE 7   Use rational exponents to simplify. Assume that variables represent positive numbers.

a. $\sqrt[8]{x^4}$ b. $\sqrt[6]{25}$ c. $\sqrt[4]{r^2 s^6}$

Solution

a. $\sqrt[8]{x^4} = x^{4/8} = x^{1/2} = \sqrt{x}$

b. $\sqrt[6]{25} = 25^{1/6} = (5^2)^{1/6} = 5^{2/6} = 5^{1/3} = \sqrt[3]{5}$

c. $\sqrt[4]{r^2 s^6} = (r^2 s^6)^{1/4} = r^{2/4} s^{6/4} = r^{1/2} s^{3/2} = (rs^3)^{1/2} = \sqrt{rs^3}$ □

PRACTICE

7   Use rational exponents to simplify. Assume that the variables represent positive numbers.

a. $\sqrt[9]{x^3}$ b. $\sqrt[4]{36}$ c. $\sqrt[8]{a^4 b^2}$ ■

EXAMPLE 8   Use rational exponents to write as a single radical.

a. $\sqrt{x} \cdot \sqrt[4]{x}$ b. $\dfrac{\sqrt{x}}{\sqrt[3]{x}}$ c. $\sqrt[3]{3} \cdot \sqrt{2}$

Solution

a. $\sqrt{x} \cdot \sqrt[4]{x} = x^{1/2} \cdot x^{1/4} = x^{1/2 + 1/4}$
$$= x^{3/4} = \sqrt[4]{x^3}$$

b. $\dfrac{\sqrt{x}}{\sqrt[3]{x}} = \dfrac{x^{1/2}}{x^{1/3}} = x^{1/2 - 1/3} = x^{3/6 - 2/6}$
$$= x^{1/6} = \sqrt[6]{x}$$

c. $\sqrt[3]{3} \cdot \sqrt{2} = 3^{1/3} \cdot 2^{1/2}$ Write with rational exponents.
$$= 3^{2/6} \cdot 2^{3/6}$$ Write the exponents so that they have the same denominator.
$$= (3^2 \cdot 2^3)^{1/6}$$ Use $a^n b^n = (ab)^n$
$$= \sqrt[6]{3^2 \cdot 2^3}$$ Write with radical notation.
$$= \sqrt[6]{72}$$ Multiply $3^2 \cdot 2^3$.   □

PRACTICE

8   Use rational exponents to write each of the following as a single radical.

a. $\sqrt[3]{x} \cdot \sqrt[4]{x}$ b. $\dfrac{\sqrt[3]{y}}{\sqrt[5]{y}}$ c. $\sqrt[3]{5} \cdot \sqrt[3]{3}$ ■

✔ | **Vocabulary, Readiness & Video Check**

Answer each true or false.

1. $9^{-1/2}$ is a positive number. _____

2. $9^{-1/2}$ is a whole number. _____

3. $\dfrac{1}{a^{-m/n}} = a^{m/n}$ (where $a^{m/n}$ is a nonzero real number). _____

Fill in the blank with the correct choice.

4. To simplify $x^{2/3} \cdot x^{1/5}$, _____ the exponents.

    a. add   **b.** subtract   **c.** multiply   **d.** divide

5. To simplify $(x^{2/3})^{1/5}$, _____ the exponents.

    a. add   **b.** subtract   **c.** multiply   **d.** divide

6. To simplify $\dfrac{x^{2/3}}{x^{1/5}}$, _____ the exponents.

    a. add   **b.** subtract   **c.** multiply   **d.** divide

---

Martin-Gay Interactive Videos

Watch the section lecture video and answer the following questions.

OBJECTIVE 1

7. After studying ▦ Example 2, write $-(3x)^{1/5}$ in radical notation.

OBJECTIVE 2

8. From ▦ Examples 3 and 4, in a fractional exponent, what do the numerator and denominator each represent in radical form?

OBJECTIVE 3

9. Based on ▦ Example 5, complete the following statements. A negative fractional exponent will move a base from the numerator to the _____ with the fractional exponent becoming _____.

OBJECTIVE 4

10. Based on ▦ Examples 7–9, complete the following statements. Assume you have an expression with fractional exponents. If applying the product rule of exponents, you _____ the exponents. If applying the quotient rule of exponents, you _____ the exponents. If applying the power rule of exponents, you _____ the exponents.

OBJECTIVE 5

11. From ▦ Example 10, describe a way to simplify a radical of a variable raised to a power if the index and the exponent have a common factor.

See Video 10.2

10.2 Exercise Set   MyMathLab®

Use radical notation to write each expression. Simplify if possible.
See Example 1.

1. $49^{1/2}$ **2.** $64^{1/3}$

3. $27^{1/3}$ **4.** $8^{1/3}$

5. $\left(\dfrac{1}{16}\right)^{1/4}$ **6.** $\left(\dfrac{1}{64}\right)^{1/2}$

7. $169^{1/2}$ **8.** $81^{1/4}$

9. $2m^{1/3}$ **10.** $(2m)^{1/3}$

11. $(9x^4)^{1/2}$ **12.** $(16x^8)^{1/2}$

13. $(-27)^{1/3}$ **14.** $-64^{1/2}$

15. $-16^{1/4}$ **16.** $(-32)^{1/5}$

Use radical notation to write each expression. Simplify if possible.
See Example 2.

17. $16^{3/4}$ **18.** $4^{5/2}$

19. $(-64)^{2/3}$ **20.** $(-8)^{4/3}$

21. $(-16)^{3/4}$ **22.** $(-9)^{3/2}$

23. $(2x)^{3/5}$ **24.** $2x^{3/5}$

25. $(7x+2)^{2/3}$ **26.** $(x-4)^{3/4}$

27. $\left(\dfrac{16}{9}\right)^{3/2}$ **28.** $\left(\dfrac{49}{25}\right)^{3/2}$

Write with positive exponents. Simplify if possible. See Example 3.

29. $8^{-4/3}$ **30.** $64^{-2/3}$

31. $(-64)^{-2/3}$ **32.** $(-8)^{-4/3}$

33. $(-4)^{-3/2}$ **34.** $(-16)^{-5/4}$

35. $x^{-1/4}$ **36.** $y^{-1/6}$

37. $\dfrac{1}{a^{-2/3}}$ **38.** $\dfrac{1}{n^{-8/9}}$

39. $\dfrac{5}{7x^{-3/4}}$ **40.** $\dfrac{2}{3y^{-5/7}}$

Use the properties of exponents to simplify each expression. Write with positive exponents. See Example 4.

41. $a^{2/3}a^{5/3}$ **42.** $b^{9/5}b^{8/5}$

43. $x^{-2/5} \cdot x^{7/5}$ **44.** $y^{4/3} \cdot y^{-1/3}$

45. $3^{1/4} \cdot 3^{3/8}$ **46.** $5^{1/2} \cdot 5^{1/6}$

47. $\dfrac{y^{1/3}}{y^{1/6}}$ **48.** $\dfrac{x^{3/4}}{x^{1/8}}$

49. $(4u^2)^{3/2}$ **50.** $(32^{1/5}x^{2/3})^3$

51. $\dfrac{b^{1/2}b^{3/4}}{-b^{1/4}}$ **52.** $\dfrac{a^{1/4}a^{-1/2}}{a^{2/3}}$

53. $\dfrac{(x^3)^{1/2}}{x^{7/2}}$

54. $\dfrac{y^{11/3}}{(y^5)^{1/3}}$

55. $\dfrac{(3x^{1/4})^3}{x^{1/12}}$

56. $\dfrac{(2x^{1/5})^4}{x^{3/10}}$

57. $\dfrac{(y^3z)^{1/6}}{y^{-1/2}z^{1/3}}$

58. $\dfrac{(m^2n)^{1/4}}{m^{-1/2}n^{5/8}}$

59. $\dfrac{(x^3y^2)^{1/4}}{(x^{-5}y^{-1})^{-1/2}}$

60. $\dfrac{(a^{-2}b^3)^{1/8}}{(a^{-3}b)^{-1/4}}$

Multiply. See Example 5.

61. $y^{1/2}(y^{1/2} - y^{2/3})$

62. $x^{1/2}(x^{1/2} + x^{3/2})$

63. $x^{2/3}(x - 2)$

64. $3x^{1/2}(x + y)$

65. $(2x^{1/3} + 3)(2x^{1/3} - 3)$

66. $(y^{1/2} + 5)(y^{1/2} + 5)$

Factor the given factor from the expression. See Example 6.

67. $x^{8/3}; x^{8/3} + x^{10/3}$

68. $x^{3/2}; x^{5/2} - x^{3/2}$

69. $x^{1/5}; x^{2/5} - 3x^{1/5}$

70. $x^{2/7}; x^{3/7} - 2x^{2/7}$

71. $x^{-1/3}; 5x^{-1/3} + x^{2/3}$

72. $x^{-3/4}; x^{-3/4} + 3x^{1/4}$

Use rational exponents to simplify each radical. Assume that all variables represent positive numbers. See Example 7.

73. $\sqrt[6]{x^3}$

74. $\sqrt[9]{a^3}$

75. $\sqrt[6]{4}$

76. $\sqrt[4]{36}$

77. $\sqrt[4]{16x^2}$

78. $\sqrt[8]{4y^2}$

79. $\sqrt[8]{x^4y^4}$

80. $\sqrt[9]{y^6z^3}$

81. $\sqrt[12]{a^8b^4}$

82. $\sqrt[10]{a^5b^5}$

83. $\sqrt[4]{(x + 3)^2}$

84. $\sqrt[8]{(y + 1)^4}$

Use rational exponents to write as a single radical expression. See Example 8.

85. $\sqrt[3]{y} \cdot \sqrt[5]{y^2}$

86. $\sqrt[3]{y^2} \cdot \sqrt[6]{y}$

87. $\dfrac{\sqrt[3]{b^2}}{\sqrt[4]{b}}$

88. $\dfrac{\sqrt[4]{a}}{\sqrt[5]{a}}$

89. $\sqrt[3]{x} \cdot \sqrt[4]{x} \cdot \sqrt[8]{x^3}$

90. $\sqrt[6]{y} \cdot \sqrt[3]{y} \cdot \sqrt[5]{y^2}$

91. $\dfrac{\sqrt[3]{a^2}}{\sqrt[6]{a}}$

92. $\dfrac{\sqrt[5]{b^2}}{\sqrt[10]{b^3}}$

93. $\sqrt{3} \cdot \sqrt[3]{4}$

94. $\sqrt[3]{5} \cdot \sqrt{2}$

95. $\sqrt[5]{7} \cdot \sqrt[3]{y}$

96. $\sqrt[4]{5} \cdot \sqrt[3]{x}$

97. $\sqrt{5r} \cdot \sqrt[3]{s}$

98. $\sqrt[3]{b} \cdot \sqrt[5]{4a}$

REVIEW AND PREVIEW

Write each integer as a product of two integers such that one of the factors is a perfect square. For example, write 18 as 9 · 2 because 9 is a perfect square.

99. 75

100. 20

101. 48

102. 45

Write each integer as a product of two integers such that one of the factors is a perfect cube. For example, write 24 as 8 · 3 because 8 is a perfect cube.

103. 16

104. 56

105. 54

106. 80

CONCEPT EXTENSIONS

Choose the correct letter for each exercise. Letters will be used more than once. No pencil is needed. Just think about the meaning of each expression.

A = 2, B = −2, C = not a real number

107. $4^{1/2}$ _____

108. $-4^{1/2}$ _____

109. $(-4)^{1/2}$ _____

110. $8^{1/3}$ _____

111. $-8^{1/3}$ _____

112. $(-8)^{1/3}$ _____

Basal metabolic rate (BMR) is the number of calories per day a person needs to maintain life. A person's basal metabolic rate $B(w)$ in calories per day can be estimated with the function $B(w) = 70w^{3/4}$, where w is the person's weight in kilograms. Use this information to answer Exercises 113 and 114.

113. Estimate the BMR for a person who weighs 60 kilograms. Round to the nearest calorie. (*Note:* 60 kilograms is approximately 132 pounds.)

114. Estimate the BMR for a person who weighs 90 kilograms. Round to the nearest calorie. (*Note:* 90 kilograms is approximately 198 pounds.)

The number of cellular telephone subscribers in the United States from 2010–2015 can be modeled by $f(x) = 236x^{1/20}$, where $f(x)$ is the number of cellular telephone subscriptions in millions, x years after 2010. (Source: International Telecommunications Union) Use this information to answer Exercises 115 and 116.

115. Use this model to estimate the number of cellular telephone subscriptions in 2015. Round to the nearest tenth of a million.

116. Predict the number of cellular telephone subscriptions in 2020. Round to the nearest tenth of a million.

117. Explain how writing x^{-7} with positive exponents is similar to writing $x^{-1/4}$ with positive exponents.

118. Explain how writing $2x^{-5}$ with positive exponents is similar to writing $2x^{-3/4}$ with positive exponents.

Fill in each box with the correct expression.

119. $\square \cdot a^{2/3} = a^{3/3}$, or a

120. $\square \cdot x^{1/8} = x^{4/8}$, or $x^{1/2}$

121. $\dfrac{\square}{x^{-2/5}} = x^{3/5}$

122. $\dfrac{\square}{y^{-3/4}} = y^{4/4}$, or y

Use a calculator to write a four-decimal-place approximation of each number.

123. $8^{1/4}$

124. $20^{1/5}$

125. $18^{3/5}$

126. $76^{5/7}$

127. In physics, the speed of a wave traveling over a stretched string with tension t and density u is given by the expression $\dfrac{\sqrt{t}}{\sqrt{u}}$. Write this expression with rational exponents.

128. In electronics, the angular frequency of oscillations in a certain type of circuit is given by the expression $(LC)^{-1/2}$. Use radical notation to write this expression.

10.3 Simplifying Radical Expressions ▷

OBJECTIVES

1 Use the Product Rule for Radicals. ▷

2 Use the Quotient Rule for Radicals. ▷

3 Simplify Radicals. ▷

4 Use the Distance and Midpoint Formulas. ▷

OBJECTIVE

1 Using the Product Rule ▷

It is possible to simplify some radicals that do not evaluate to rational numbers. To do so, we use a product rule and a quotient rule for radicals. To discover the product rule, notice the following pattern.

$$\sqrt{9} \cdot \sqrt{4} = 3 \cdot 2 = 6$$
$$\sqrt{9 \cdot 4} = \sqrt{36} = 6$$

Since both expressions simplify to 6, it is true that

$$\sqrt{9} \cdot \sqrt{4} = \sqrt{9 \cdot 4}$$

This pattern suggests the following product rule for radicals.

> **Product Rule for Radicals**
>
> If $\sqrt[n]{a}$ and $\sqrt[n]{b}$ are real numbers, then
>
> $$\sqrt[n]{a} \cdot \sqrt[n]{b} = \sqrt[n]{ab}$$

Notice that the product rule is the relationship $a^{1/n} \cdot b^{1/n} = (ab)^{1/n}$ stated in radical notation.

EXAMPLE 1 Multiply.

a. $\sqrt{3} \cdot \sqrt{5}$

b. $\sqrt{21} \cdot \sqrt{x}$

c. $\sqrt[3]{4} \cdot \sqrt[3]{2}$

d. $\sqrt[4]{5y^2} \cdot \sqrt[4]{2x^3}$

e. $\sqrt{\dfrac{2}{a}} \cdot \sqrt{\dfrac{b}{3}}$

Solution

a. $\sqrt{3} \cdot \sqrt{5} = \sqrt{3 \cdot 5} = \sqrt{15}$

b. $\sqrt{21} \cdot \sqrt{x} = \sqrt{21x}$

c. $\sqrt[3]{4} \cdot \sqrt[3]{2} = \sqrt[3]{4 \cdot 2} = \sqrt[3]{8} = 2$

d. $\sqrt[4]{5y^2} \cdot \sqrt[4]{2x^3} = \sqrt[4]{5y^2 \cdot 2x^3} = \sqrt[4]{10y^2x^3}$

e. $\sqrt{\dfrac{2}{a}} \cdot \sqrt{\dfrac{b}{3}} = \sqrt{\dfrac{2}{a} \cdot \dfrac{b}{3}} = \sqrt{\dfrac{2b}{3a}}$ ☐

PRACTICE

1 Multiply.

a. $\sqrt{5} \cdot \sqrt{7}$

b. $\sqrt{13} \cdot \sqrt{z}$

c. $\sqrt[4]{125} \cdot \sqrt[4]{5}$

d. $\sqrt[3]{5y} \cdot \sqrt[3]{3x^2}$

e. $\sqrt{\dfrac{5}{m}} \cdot \sqrt{\dfrac{t}{2}}$

■

OBJECTIVE

2 Using the Quotient Rule ▶

To discover a quotient rule for radicals, notice the following pattern.

$$\sqrt{\frac{4}{9}} = \frac{2}{3}$$

$$\frac{\sqrt{4}}{\sqrt{9}} = \frac{2}{3}$$

Since both expressions simplify to $\frac{2}{3}$, it is true that

$$\sqrt{\frac{4}{9}} = \frac{\sqrt{4}}{\sqrt{9}}$$

This pattern suggests the following quotient rule for radicals.

Quotient Rule for Radicals

If $\sqrt[n]{a}$ and $\sqrt[n]{b}$ are real numbers and $\sqrt[n]{b}$ is not zero, then

$$\sqrt[n]{\frac{a}{b}} = \frac{\sqrt[n]{a}}{\sqrt[n]{b}}$$

Notice that the quotient rule is the relationship $\left(\dfrac{a}{b}\right)^{1/n} = \dfrac{a^{1/n}}{b^{1/n}}$ stated in radical notation. We can use the quotient rule to simplify radical expressions by reading the rule from left to right or to divide radicals by reading the rule from right to left.

For example,

$$\sqrt{\frac{x}{16}} = \frac{\sqrt{x}}{\sqrt{16}} = \frac{\sqrt{x}}{4} \qquad \text{Using } \sqrt[n]{\frac{a}{b}} = \frac{\sqrt[n]{a}}{\sqrt[n]{b}}$$

$$\frac{\sqrt{75}}{\sqrt{3}} = \sqrt{\frac{75}{3}} = \sqrt{25} = 5 \qquad \text{Using } \frac{\sqrt[n]{a}}{\sqrt[n]{b}} = \sqrt[n]{\frac{a}{b}}$$

Note: *Recall that from Section 10.2 on, we assume that variables represent positive real numbers. Since this is so, we need not insert absolute value bars when we simplify even roots.*

EXAMPLE 2 Use the quotient rule to simplify.

a. $\sqrt{\dfrac{25}{49}}$ **b.** $\sqrt{\dfrac{x}{9}}$ **c.** $\sqrt[3]{\dfrac{8}{27}}$ **d.** $\sqrt[4]{\dfrac{3}{16y^4}}$

Solution

a. $\sqrt{\dfrac{25}{49}} = \dfrac{\sqrt{25}}{\sqrt{49}} = \dfrac{5}{7}$ **b.** $\sqrt{\dfrac{x}{9}} = \dfrac{\sqrt{x}}{\sqrt{9}} = \dfrac{\sqrt{x}}{3}$

c. $\sqrt[3]{\dfrac{8}{27}} = \dfrac{\sqrt[3]{8}}{\sqrt[3]{27}} = \dfrac{2}{3}$ **d.** $\sqrt[4]{\dfrac{3}{16y^4}} = \dfrac{\sqrt[4]{3}}{\sqrt[4]{16y^4}} = \dfrac{\sqrt[4]{3}}{2y}$ ☐

PRACTICE

2 Use the quotient rule to simplify.

a. $\sqrt{\dfrac{36}{49}}$ **b.** $\sqrt{\dfrac{z}{16}}$ **c.** $\sqrt[3]{\dfrac{125}{8}}$ **d.** $\sqrt[4]{\dfrac{5}{81x^8}}$ ◼

OBJECTIVE

3 Simplifying Radicals ▶

Both the product and quotient rules can be used to simplify a radical. If the product rule is read from right to left, we have that

$$\sqrt[n]{ab} = \sqrt[n]{a} \cdot \sqrt[n]{b}.$$

This is used to simplify the following radicals.

EXAMPLE 3 Simplify the following.

    a. $\sqrt{50}$ **b.** $\sqrt[3]{24}$ **c.** $\sqrt{26}$ **d.** $\sqrt[4]{32}$

Solution

a. Factor 50 such that one factor is the largest perfect square that divides 50. The largest perfect square factor of 50 is 25, so we write 50 as $25 \cdot 2$ and use the product rule for radicals to simplify.

$$\sqrt{50} = \sqrt{25 \cdot 2} = \sqrt{25} \cdot \sqrt{2} = 5\sqrt{2}$$

    ↑ The largest perfect square factor of 50

> **Helpful Hint**
>
> Don't forget that, for example, $5\sqrt{2}$ means $5 \cdot \sqrt{2}$.

b. $\sqrt[3]{24} = \sqrt[3]{8 \cdot 3} = \sqrt[3]{8} \cdot \sqrt[3]{3} = 2\sqrt[3]{3}$

    ↑ The largest perfect cube factor of 24

c. $\sqrt{26}$ The largest perfect square factor of 26 is 1, so $\sqrt{26}$ cannot be simplified further.

d. $\sqrt[4]{32} = \sqrt[4]{16 \cdot 2} = \sqrt[4]{16} \cdot \sqrt[4]{2} = 2\sqrt[4]{2}$

    ↑ The largest fourth power factor of 32 □

PRACTICE

3 Simplify the following.

    a. $\sqrt{98}$ **b.** $\sqrt[3]{54}$ **c.** $\sqrt{35}$ **d.** $\sqrt[4]{243}$ ∎

After simplifying a radical such as a square root, always check the radicand to see that it contains no other perfect square factors. It may, if the largest perfect square factor of the radicand was not originally recognized. For example,

$$\sqrt{200} = \sqrt{4 \cdot 50} = \sqrt{4} \cdot \sqrt{50} = 2\sqrt{50}$$

Notice that the radicand 50 still contains the perfect square factor 25. This is because 4 is not the largest perfect square factor of 200. We continue as follows.

$$2\sqrt{50} = 2\sqrt{25 \cdot 2} = 2 \cdot \sqrt{25} \cdot \sqrt{2} = 2 \cdot 5 \cdot \sqrt{2} = 10\sqrt{2}$$

The radical is now simplified since 2 contains no perfect square factors (other than 1).

> **Helpful Hint**
>
> To help you recognize largest perfect power factors of a radicand, it will help if you are familiar with some perfect powers. A few are listed below.
>
> Perfect Squares   1,   4,   9,   16,   25,   36,   49,   64,   81,   100,   121,   144
> 1^2 2^2 3^2 4^2 5^2 6^2 7^2 8^2 9^2 10^2 11^2 12^2
>
> Perfect Cubes   1,   8,   27,   64,   125
> 1^3 2^3 3^3 4^3 5^3
>
> Perfect Fourth   1,   16,   81,   256
> Powers 1^4 2^4 3^4 4^4

> In general, we say that a radicand of the form $\sqrt[n]{a}$ is simplified when the radicand a contains no factors that are perfect nth powers (other than 1 or -1).

EXAMPLE 4   Use the product rule to simplify.

a. $\sqrt{25x^3}$ b. $\sqrt[3]{54x^6y^8}$ c. $\sqrt[4]{81z^{11}}$

Solution

a. $\sqrt{25x^3} = \sqrt{25x^2 \cdot x}$ Find the largest perfect square factor.

$= \sqrt{25x^2} \cdot \sqrt{x}$ Apply the product rule.

$= 5x\sqrt{x}$ Simplify.

b. $\sqrt[3]{54x^6y^8} = \sqrt[3]{27 \cdot 2 \cdot x^6 \cdot y^6 \cdot y^2}$ Factor the radicand and identify perfect cube factors.

$= \sqrt[3]{27x^6y^6 \cdot 2y^2}$

$= \sqrt[3]{27x^6y^6} \cdot \sqrt[3]{2y^2}$ Apply the product rule.

$= 3x^2y^2\sqrt[3]{2y^2}$ Simplify.

c. $\sqrt[4]{81z^{11}} = \sqrt[4]{81 \cdot z^8 \cdot z^3}$ Factor the radicand and identify perfect fourth power factors.

$= \sqrt[4]{81z^8} \cdot \sqrt[4]{z^3}$ Apply the product rule.

$= 3z^2\sqrt[4]{z^3}$ Simplify.   □

PRACTICE

4   Use the product rule to simplify.

a. $\sqrt{36z^7}$ b. $\sqrt[3]{32p^4q^7}$ c. $\sqrt[4]{16x^{15}}$ ■

EXAMPLE 5   Use the quotient rule to divide, and simplify if possible.

a. $\dfrac{\sqrt{20}}{\sqrt{5}}$ b. $\dfrac{\sqrt{50x}}{2\sqrt{2}}$ c. $\dfrac{7\sqrt[3]{48x^4y^8}}{\sqrt[3]{6y^2}}$ d. $\dfrac{2\sqrt[4]{32a^8b^6}}{\sqrt[4]{a^{-1}b^2}}$

Solution

a. $\dfrac{\sqrt{20}}{\sqrt{5}} = \sqrt{\dfrac{20}{5}}$ Apply the quotient rule.

$= \sqrt{4}$ Simplify.

$= 2$ Simplify.

b. $\dfrac{\sqrt{50x}}{2\sqrt{2}} = \dfrac{1}{2} \cdot \sqrt{\dfrac{50x}{2}}$ Apply the quotient rule.

$= \dfrac{1}{2} \cdot \sqrt{25x}$ Simplify.

$= \dfrac{1}{2} \cdot \sqrt{25} \cdot \sqrt{x}$ Factor $25x$.

$= \dfrac{1}{2} \cdot 5 \cdot \sqrt{x}$ Simplify.

$= \dfrac{5}{2}\sqrt{x}$

c. $\dfrac{7\sqrt[3]{48x^4y^8}}{\sqrt[3]{6y^2}} = 7 \cdot \sqrt[3]{\dfrac{48x^4y^8}{6y^2}}$ Apply the quotient rule.

$= 7 \cdot \sqrt[3]{8x^4y^6}$ Simplify.

$= 7\sqrt[3]{8x^3y^6 \cdot x}$ Factor.

$= 7 \cdot \sqrt[3]{8x^3y^6} \cdot \sqrt[3]{x}$ Apply the product rule.

$= 7 \cdot 2xy^2 \cdot \sqrt[3]{x}$ Simplify.

$= 14xy^2\sqrt[3]{x}$

(Continued on next page)

d. $\dfrac{2\sqrt[4]{32a^8b^6}}{\sqrt[4]{a^{-1}b^2}} = 2\sqrt[4]{\dfrac{32a^8b^6}{a^{-1}b^2}} = 2\sqrt[4]{32a^9b^4} = 2\sqrt[4]{16 \cdot a^8 \cdot b^4 \cdot 2 \cdot a}$

$= 2\sqrt[4]{16a^8b^4} \cdot \sqrt[4]{2a} = 2 \cdot 2a^2b \cdot \sqrt[4]{2a} = 4a^2b\sqrt[4]{2a}$ ☐

PRACTICE

5 Use the quotient rule to divide and simplify.

a. $\dfrac{\sqrt{80}}{\sqrt{5}}$ **b.** $\dfrac{\sqrt{98z}}{3\sqrt{2}}$ **c.** $\dfrac{5\sqrt[3]{40x^5y^7}}{\sqrt[3]{5y}}$ **d.** $\dfrac{3\sqrt[5]{64x^9y^8}}{\sqrt[5]{x^{-1}y^2}}$ ∎

✔ **CONCEPT CHECK**

Find and correct the error:

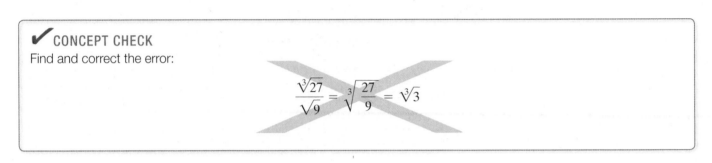

OBJECTIVE

4 Using the Distance and Midpoint Formulas ▶

Now that we know how to simplify radicals, we can derive and use the distance formula. The midpoint formula is often confused with the distance formula, so to clarify both, we will also review the midpoint formula.

The Cartesian coordinate system helps us visualize a distance between points. To find the distance between two points, we use the distance formula, which is derived from the Pythagorean theorem.

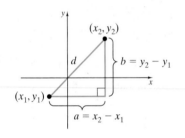

To find the distance d between two points (x_1, y_1) and (x_2, y_2) as shown to the left, notice that the length of leg a is $x_2 - x_1$ and that the length of leg b is $y_2 - y_1$.

Thus, the Pythagorean theorem tells us that

$$d^2 = a^2 + b^2$$

or

$$d^2 = (x_2 - x_1)^2 + (y_2 - y_1)^2$$

or

$$d = \sqrt{(x_2 - x_1)^2 + (y_2 - y_1)^2}$$

This formula gives us the distance between any two points on the real plane.

Distance Formula

The distance d between two points (x_1, y_1) and (x_2, y_2) is given by

$$d = \sqrt{(x_2 - x_1)^2 + (y_2 - y_1)^2}$$

EXAMPLE 6 Find the distance between $(2, -5)$ and $(1, -4)$. Give the exact distance and a three-decimal-place approximation.

Solution To use the distance formula, it makes no difference which point we call (x_1, y_1) and which point we call (x_2, y_2). We will let $(x_1, y_1) = (2, -5)$ and $(x_2, y_2) = (1, -4)$.

$$d = \sqrt{(x_2 - x_1)^2 + (y_2 - y_1)^2}$$
$$= \sqrt{(1 - 2)^2 + [-4 - (-5)]^2}$$
$$= \sqrt{(-1)^2 + (1)^2}$$
$$= \sqrt{1 + 1}$$
$$= \sqrt{2} \approx 1.414$$

The distance between the two points is exactly $\sqrt{2}$ units, or approximately 1.414 units.

PRACTICE

6 Find the distance between $(-3, 7)$ and $(-2, 3)$. Give the exact distance and a three-decimal-place approximation.

The **midpoint** of a line segment is the **point** located exactly halfway between the two endpoints of the line segment. On the graph to the left, the point M is the midpoint of line segment PQ. Thus, the distance between M and P equals the distance between M and Q.

Note: We usually need no knowledge of roots to calculate the midpoint of a line segment. We review midpoint here only because it is often confused with the distance between two points.

The x-coordinate of M is at half the distance between the x-coordinates of P and Q, and the y-coordinate of M is at half the distance between the y-coordinates of P and Q. That is, the x-coordinate of M is the average of the x-coordinates of P and Q; the y-coordinate of M is the average of the y-coordinates of P and Q.

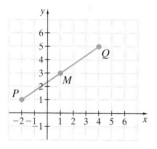

Midpoint Formula

The midpoint of the line segment whose endpoints are (x_1, y_1) and (x_2, y_2) is the point with coordinates

$$\left(\frac{x_1 + x_2}{2}, \frac{y_1 + y_2}{2} \right)$$

EXAMPLE 7 Find the midpoint of the line segment that joins points $P(-3, 3)$ and $Q(1, 0)$.

Solution Use the midpoint formula. It makes no difference which point we call (x_1, y_1) or which point we call (x_2, y_2). Let $(x_1, y_1) = (-3, 3)$ and $(x_2, y_2) = (1, 0)$.

$$\text{midpoint} = \left(\frac{x_1 + x_2}{2}, \frac{y_1 + y_2}{2} \right)$$
$$= \left(\frac{-3 + 1}{2}, \frac{3 + 0}{2} \right)$$
$$= \left(\frac{-2}{2}, \frac{3}{2} \right)$$
$$= \left(-1, \frac{3}{2} \right)$$

The midpoint of the segment is $\left(-1, \dfrac{3}{2} \right)$.

PRACTICE

7 Find the midpoint of the line segment that joins points $P(5, -2)$ and $Q(8, -6)$.

Helpful Hint

The distance between two points is a distance. The midpoint of a line segment is the point halfway between the endpoints of the segment.

distance—measured in units

midpoint—it is a point

✔ Vocabulary, Readiness & Video Check

Use the choices below to fill in each blank. Some choices may be used more than once.

distance   midpoint   point

1. The _____ of a line segment is the _____ exactly halfway between the two endpoints of the line segment.

2. The _____ between two points is a distance, measured in units.

3. The _____ formula is $d = \sqrt{(x_2 - x_1)^2 + (y_2 - y_1)^2}$.

4. The _____ formula is $\left(\dfrac{x_1 + x_2}{2}, \dfrac{y_1 + y_2}{2}\right)$.

Martin-Gay Interactive Videos

See Video 10.3 ⦿

Watch the section lecture video and answer the following questions.

OBJECTIVE 1
5. From ▦ Example 1 and the lecture before, in order to apply the product rule for radicals, what must be true about the indexes of the radicals being multiplied?

OBJECTIVE 2
6. From ▦ Examples 2–6, when might you apply the quotient rule (in either direction) in order to simplify a fractional radical expression?

OBJECTIVE 3
7. From ▦ Example 8, we know that an even power of a variable is a perfect square factor of the variable, leaving no factor in the radicand once simplified. Therefore, what must be true about the power of any variable left in the radicand of a simplified square root? Explain.

OBJECTIVE 4
8. From ▦ Example 10, the formula uses the coordinates of two points similar to the slope formula. What caution should you take when replacing values in the formula?

OBJECTIVE 4
9. Based on ▦ Example 11, complete the following statement. The x-value of the midpoint is the _____ of the x-values of the endpoints, and the y-value of the midpoint is the _____ of the y-values of the endpoints.

10.3 Exercise Set MyMathLab ▶

Use the product rule to multiply. See Example 1.

1. $\sqrt{7} \cdot \sqrt{2}$

2. $\sqrt{11} \cdot \sqrt{10}$

3. $\sqrt[4]{8} \cdot \sqrt[4]{2}$

4. $\sqrt[4]{27} \cdot \sqrt[4]{3}$

5. $\sqrt[3]{4} \cdot \sqrt[3]{9}$

6. $\sqrt[3]{10} \cdot \sqrt[3]{5}$

▶ 7. $\sqrt{2} \cdot \sqrt{3x}$

8. $\sqrt{3y} \cdot \sqrt{5x}$

9. $\sqrt{\dfrac{7}{x}} \cdot \sqrt{\dfrac{2}{y}}$

10. $\sqrt{\dfrac{6}{m}} \cdot \sqrt{\dfrac{n}{5}}$

11. $\sqrt[4]{4x^3} \cdot \sqrt[4]{5}$

12. $\sqrt[4]{ab^2} \cdot \sqrt[4]{27ab}$

Use the quotient rule to simplify. See Examples 2 and 3.

▶ 13. $\sqrt{\dfrac{6}{49}}$

14. $\sqrt{\dfrac{8}{81}}$

15. $\sqrt{\dfrac{2}{49}}$

16. $\sqrt{\dfrac{5}{121}}$

▶ 17. $\sqrt[4]{\dfrac{x^3}{16}}$

18. $\sqrt[4]{\dfrac{y}{81x^4}}$

19. $\sqrt[3]{\dfrac{4}{27}}$

20. $\sqrt[3]{\dfrac{3}{64}}$

21. $\sqrt[4]{\dfrac{8}{x^8}}$

22. $\sqrt[4]{\dfrac{a^3}{81}}$

23. $\sqrt[3]{\dfrac{2x}{81y^{12}}}$

24. $\sqrt[3]{\dfrac{3}{8x^6}}$

25. $\sqrt{\dfrac{x^2y}{100}}$

26. $\sqrt{\dfrac{y^2z}{36}}$

▶ **27.** $\sqrt{\dfrac{5x^2}{4y^2}}$

28. $\sqrt{\dfrac{y^{10}}{9x^6}}$

29. $-\sqrt[3]{\dfrac{z^7}{27x^3}}$

30. $-\sqrt[3]{\dfrac{64a}{b^9}}$

Simplify. See Examples 3 and 4.

▶ **31.** $\sqrt{32}$

32. $\sqrt{27}$

33. $\sqrt[3]{192}$

34. $\sqrt[3]{108}$

35. $5\sqrt{75}$

36. $3\sqrt{8}$

37. $\sqrt{24}$

38. $\sqrt{20}$

39. $\sqrt{100x^5}$

40. $\sqrt{64y^9}$

41. $\sqrt[3]{16y^7}$

42. $\sqrt[3]{64y^9}$

43. $\sqrt[4]{a^8b^7}$

44. $\sqrt[5]{32z^{12}}$

45. $\sqrt{y^5}$

46. $\sqrt[3]{y^5}$

▶ **47.** $\sqrt{25a^2b^3}$

48. $\sqrt{9x^5y^7}$

▶ **49.** $\sqrt[5]{-32x^{10}y}$

50. $\sqrt[5]{-243z^9}$

51. $\sqrt[3]{50x^{14}}$

52. $\sqrt[3]{40y^{10}}$

53. $-\sqrt{32a^8b^7}$

54. $-\sqrt{20ab^6}$

55. $\sqrt{9x^7y^9}$

56. $\sqrt{12r^9s^{12}}$

57. $\sqrt[3]{125r^9s^{12}}$

58. $\sqrt[3]{8a^6b^9}$

59. $\sqrt[4]{32x^{12}y^5}$

60. $\sqrt[4]{162x^7y^{20}}$

Use the quotient rule to divide. Then simplify if possible. See Example 5.

▶ **61.** $\dfrac{\sqrt{14}}{\sqrt{7}}$

62. $\dfrac{\sqrt{45}}{\sqrt{9}}$

63. $\dfrac{\sqrt[3]{24}}{\sqrt[3]{3}}$

64. $\dfrac{\sqrt[3]{10}}{\sqrt[3]{2}}$

65. $\dfrac{5\sqrt[4]{48}}{\sqrt[4]{3}}$

66. $\dfrac{7\sqrt[4]{162}}{\sqrt[4]{2}}$

▶ **67.** $\dfrac{\sqrt{x^5y^3}}{\sqrt{xy}}$

68. $\dfrac{\sqrt{a^7b^6}}{\sqrt{a^3b^2}}$

69. $\dfrac{8\sqrt[3]{54m^7}}{\sqrt[3]{2m}}$

70. $\dfrac{\sqrt[3]{128x^3}}{-3\sqrt[3]{2x}}$

71. $\dfrac{3\sqrt{100x^2}}{2\sqrt{2x^{-1}}}$

72. $\dfrac{\sqrt{270y^2}}{5\sqrt{3y^{-4}}}$

73. $\dfrac{\sqrt[4]{96a^{10}b^3}}{\sqrt[4]{3a^2b^3}}$

74. $\dfrac{\sqrt[4]{160x^{10}y^5}}{\sqrt[4]{2x^2y^2}}$

75. $\dfrac{\sqrt[5]{64x^{10}y^3}}{\sqrt[5]{2x^3y^{-7}}}$

76. $\dfrac{\sqrt[5]{192x^6y^{12}}}{\sqrt[5]{2x^{-1}y^{-3}}}$

Find the distance between each pair of points. Give the exact distance and a three-decimal-place approximation. See Example 6.

77. $(5, 1)$ and $(8, 5)$

78. $(2, 3)$ and $(14, 8)$

▶ **79.** $(-3, 2)$ and $(1, -3)$

80. $(3, -2)$ and $(-4, 1)$

81. $(-9, 4)$ and $(-8, 1)$

82. $(-5, -2)$ and $(-6, -6)$

83. $(0, -\sqrt{2})$ and $(\sqrt{3}, 0)$

84. $(-\sqrt{5}, 0)$ and $(0, \sqrt{7})$

85. $(1.7, -3.6)$ and $(-8.6, 5.7)$

86. $(9.6, 2.5)$ and $(-1.9, -3.7)$

Find the midpoint of the line segment whose endpoints are given. See Example 7.

87. $(6, -8), (2, 4)$

88. $(3, 9), (7, 11)$

▶ **89.** $(-2, -1), (-8, 6)$

90. $(-3, -4), (6, -8)$

91. $(7, 3), (-1, -3)$

92. $(-2, 5), (-1, 6)$

93. $\left(\dfrac{1}{2}, \dfrac{3}{8}\right), \left(-\dfrac{3}{2}, \dfrac{5}{8}\right)$

94. $\left(-\dfrac{2}{5}, \dfrac{7}{15}\right), \left(-\dfrac{2}{5}, -\dfrac{4}{15}\right)$

95. $(\sqrt{2}, 3\sqrt{5}), (\sqrt{2}, -2\sqrt{5})$

96. $(\sqrt{8}, -\sqrt{12}), (3\sqrt{2}, 7\sqrt{3})$

97. $(4.6, -3.5), (7.8, -9.8)$

98. $(-4.6, 2.1), (-6.7, 1.9)$

REVIEW AND PREVIEW

Perform each indicated operation. See Sections 2.1, 5.3, and 5.4.

99. $6x + 8x$

100. $(6x)(8x)$

101. $(2x + 3)(x - 5)$

102. $(2x + 3) + (x - 5)$

103. $9y^2 - 8y^2$

104. $(9y^2)(-8y^2)$

105. $-3(x + 5)$

106. $-3 + x + 5$

107. $(x - 4)^2$

108. $(2x + 1)^2$

CONCEPT EXTENSIONS

Answer true or false. Assume all radicals represent nonzero real numbers.

109. $\sqrt[n]{a} \cdot \sqrt[n]{b} = \sqrt[n]{ab}$, _____

110. $\sqrt[3]{7} \cdot \sqrt[3]{11} = \sqrt[3]{18}$, _____

111. $\sqrt[3]{7} \cdot \sqrt{11} = \sqrt{77}$, _____

112. $\sqrt{x^7y^8} = \sqrt{x^7} \cdot \sqrt{y^8}$, _____

113. $\dfrac{\sqrt[n]{a}}{\sqrt[n]{b}} = \sqrt[n]{\dfrac{a}{b}}$, _____

114. $\dfrac{\sqrt[3]{12}}{\sqrt[3]{4}} = \sqrt[3]{8}$, _____

Find and correct the error. See the Concept Check in this section.

115. $\dfrac{\sqrt[3]{64}}{\sqrt{64}} = \sqrt[3]{\dfrac{64}{64}} = \sqrt[3]{1} = 1$ ✗

116. $\dfrac{\sqrt[4]{16}}{\sqrt{4}} = \sqrt[4]{\dfrac{16}{4}} = \sqrt[4]{4}$ ✗

Simplify. Assume variables represent positive numbers.

117. $\sqrt[5]{x^{35}}$

118. $\sqrt[6]{y^{48}}$

119. $\sqrt[4]{a^{12}b^4c^{20}}$

120. $\sqrt[3]{a^9b^{21}c^3}$

121. $\sqrt[3]{z^{32}}$

122. $\sqrt[5]{x^{49}}$

123. $\sqrt{q^{17}r^{40}s^7}$

124. $\sqrt[4]{p^{11}q^4r^{45}}$

125. The formula for the radius r of a sphere with surface area A is given by $r = \sqrt{\dfrac{A}{4\pi}}$. Calculate the radius of a standard zorb whose outside surface area is 32.17 square meters. Round to the nearest tenth. (A zorb is a large inflated ball within a ball in which a person, strapped inside, may choose to roll down a hill. *Source:* Zorb, Ltd.)

126. NASA has investigated using a zorb-like Mars explorer, called the tumbleweed rover, to explore the Martian plains using wind power alone. Researchers have determined that the optimal rover would need to be efficient at catching any breeze, light enough to move easily, and large enough to roll over any rocks in its path. (*Source:* NASA)

a. If scientists determine that the volume of the sphere-shaped tumbleweed rover should be approximately 4200 cubic feet, find the radius for the rover rounded to the nearest tenth. The formula for the radius r of a sphere with volume V is given by $r = \sqrt[3]{\dfrac{3V}{4\pi}}$.

b. One of the designs being considered for further investigation is the so-called box kite drawn below. Here, in addition to a sphere, there are three disks that look like three great circles at right angles to each other with an exoskeleton to protect the "kites." Find the total area of three great circles each with a diameter of 6 meters. Round to the nearest tenth of a square meter.

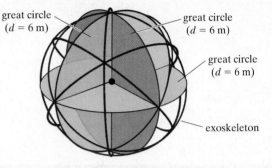

great circle ($d = 6$ m)

great circle ($d = 6$ m)

great circle ($d = 6$ m)

exoskeleton

Box Kite design

c. Do you think the box kite design is better than the sphere-alone design? Why or why not?

127. The formula for the lateral surface area A of a cone with height h and radius r is given by

$$A = \pi r \sqrt{r^2 + h^2}$$

a. Find the lateral surface area of a cone whose height is 3 centimeters and whose radius is 4 centimeters.

b. Approximate to two decimal places the lateral surface area of a cone whose height is 7.2 feet and whose radius is 6.8 feet.

128. Before Mount Vesuvius, a volcano in Italy, erupted violently in 79 C.E., its height was 4190 feet. Vesuvius was roughly cone-shaped, and its base had a radius of approximately 25,200 feet. Use the formula for the lateral surface area of a cone, given in Exercise 127, to approximate the surface area this volcano had before it erupted. (*Source:* Global Volcanism Network)

4190 ft

25,200 ft

10.4 Adding, Subtracting, and Multiplying Radical Expressions ▶

OBJECTIVES

1 Add or Subtract Radical Expressions. ▶

2 Multiply Radical Expressions. ▶

OBJECTIVE

1 Adding or Subtracting Radical Expressions ▶

We have learned that sums or differences of like terms can be simplified. To simplify these sums or differences, we use the distributive property. For example,

$$2x + 3x = (2 + 3)x = 5x \quad \text{and} \quad 7x^2y - 4x^2y = (7 - 4)x^2y = 3x^2y$$

The distributive property can also be used to add **like radicals.**

Like Radicals

Radicals with the same index and the same radicand are like radicals.

For example, $2\sqrt{7} + 3\sqrt{7} = (2 + 3)\sqrt{7} = 5\sqrt{7}$. Also,

Like radicals

$$5\sqrt{3x} - 7\sqrt{3x} = (5 - 7)\sqrt{3x} = -2\sqrt{3x}$$

The expression $2\sqrt{7} + 2\sqrt[3]{7}$ cannot be simplified further since $2\sqrt{7}$ and $2\sqrt[3]{7}$ are not like radicals.

Unlike radicals

EXAMPLE 1   Add or subtract as indicated. Assume all variables represent positive real numbers.

    a. $4\sqrt{11} + 8\sqrt{11}$ **b.** $5\sqrt[3]{3x} - 7\sqrt[3]{3x}$ **c.** $4\sqrt{5} + 4\sqrt[3]{5}$

Solution

    a. $4\sqrt{11} + 8\sqrt{11} = (4 + 8)\sqrt{11} = 12\sqrt{11}$

    b. $5\sqrt[3]{3x} - 7\sqrt[3]{3x} = (5 - 7)\sqrt[3]{3x} = -2\sqrt[3]{3x}$

    c. $4\sqrt{5} + 4\sqrt[3]{5}$

        This expression cannot be simplified since $4\sqrt{5}$ and $4\sqrt[3]{5}$ do not contain like radicals. $\square$

PRACTICE

1   Add or subtract as indicated.

    a. $3\sqrt{17} + 5\sqrt{17}$ **b.** $7\sqrt[3]{5z} - 12\sqrt[3]{5z}$ **c.** $3\sqrt{2} + 5\sqrt[3]{2}$ ∎

When adding or subtracting radicals, always check first to see whether any radicals can be simplified.

✔ **CONCEPT CHECK**

True or false?

$$\sqrt{a} + \sqrt{b} = \sqrt{a + b}$$

Explain.

EXAMPLE 2   Add or subtract. Assume that variables represent positive real numbers.

    a. $\sqrt{20} + 2\sqrt{45}$ **b.** $\sqrt[3]{54} - 5\sqrt[3]{16} + \sqrt[3]{2}$ **c.** $\sqrt{27x} - 2\sqrt{9x} + \sqrt{72x}$

    d. $\sqrt[3]{98} + \sqrt{98}$ **e.** $\sqrt[3]{48y^4} + \sqrt[3]{6y^4}$

Solution   First, simplify each radical. Then add or subtract any like radicals.

    a. $\sqrt{20} + 2\sqrt{45} = \sqrt{4 \cdot 5} + 2\sqrt{9 \cdot 5}$ Factor 20 and 45.

                    $= \sqrt{4} \cdot \sqrt{5} + 2 \cdot \sqrt{9} \cdot \sqrt{5}$ Use the product rule.

                    $= 2 \cdot \sqrt{5} + 2 \cdot 3 \cdot \sqrt{5}$ Simplify $\sqrt{4}$ and $\sqrt{9}$.

                    $= 2\sqrt{5} + 6\sqrt{5}$

                    $= 8\sqrt{5}$ Add like radicals.

    b. $\sqrt[3]{54} - 5\sqrt[3]{16} + \sqrt[3]{2}$

                $= \sqrt[3]{27} \cdot \sqrt[3]{2} - 5 \cdot \sqrt[3]{8} \cdot \sqrt[3]{2} + \sqrt[3]{2}$ Factor and use the product rule.

                $= 3 \cdot \sqrt[3]{2} - 5 \cdot 2 \cdot \sqrt[3]{2} + \sqrt[3]{2}$ Simplify $\sqrt[3]{27}$ and $\sqrt[3]{8}$.

                $= 3\sqrt[3]{2} - 10\sqrt[3]{2} + \sqrt[3]{2}$ Write $5 \cdot 2$ as 10.

                $= -6\sqrt[3]{2}$ Combine like radicals.

(Continued on next page)

Answer to Concept Check:
false; answers may vary

c. $\sqrt{27x} - 2\sqrt{9x} + \sqrt{72x}$

$= \sqrt{9} \cdot \sqrt{3x} - 2 \cdot \sqrt{9} \cdot \sqrt{x} + \sqrt{36} \cdot \sqrt{2x}$ Factor and use the product rule.

$= 3 \cdot \sqrt{3x} - 2 \cdot 3 \cdot \sqrt{x} + 6 \cdot \sqrt{2x}$ Simplify $\sqrt{9}$ and $\sqrt{36}$.

$= 3\sqrt{3x} - 6\sqrt{x} + 6\sqrt{2x}$ Write $2 \cdot 3$ as 6.

> **Helpful Hint**
>
> None of these terms contain like radicals. We can simplify no further.

d. $\sqrt[3]{98} + \sqrt{98} = \sqrt[3]{98} + \sqrt{49} \cdot \sqrt{2}$ Factor and use the product rule.

$= \sqrt[3]{98} + 7\sqrt{2}$ No further simplification is possible.

e. $\sqrt[3]{48y^4} + \sqrt[3]{6y^4} = \sqrt[3]{8y^3} \cdot \sqrt[3]{6y} + \sqrt[3]{y^3} \cdot \sqrt[3]{6y}$ Factor and use the product rule.

$= 2y\sqrt[3]{6y} + y\sqrt[3]{6y}$ Simplify $\sqrt[3]{8y^3}$ and $\sqrt[3]{y^3}$.

$= 3y\sqrt[3]{6y}$ Combine like radicals. ☐

PRACTICE
2 Add or subtract.

a. $\sqrt{24} + 3\sqrt{54}$ **b.** $\sqrt[3]{24} - 4\sqrt[3]{81} + \sqrt[3]{3}$ **c.** $\sqrt{75x} - 3\sqrt{27x} + \sqrt{12x}$
d. $\sqrt{40} + \sqrt[3]{40}$ **e.** $\sqrt[3]{81x^4} + \sqrt[3]{3x^4}$ ■

Let's continue to assume that variables represent positive real numbers.

EXAMPLE 3 Add or subtract as indicated.

a. $\dfrac{\sqrt{45}}{4} - \dfrac{\sqrt{5}}{3}$

b. $\sqrt[3]{\dfrac{7x}{8}} + 2\sqrt[3]{7x}$

Solution

a. $\dfrac{\sqrt{45}}{4} - \dfrac{\sqrt{5}}{3} = \dfrac{3\sqrt{5}}{4} - \dfrac{\sqrt{5}}{3}$ To subtract, notice that the LCD is 12.

$= \dfrac{3\sqrt{5} \cdot 3}{4 \cdot 3} - \dfrac{\sqrt{5} \cdot 4}{3 \cdot 4}$ Write each expression as an equivalent expression with a denominator of 12.

$= \dfrac{9\sqrt{5}}{12} - \dfrac{4\sqrt{5}}{12}$ Multiply factors in the numerator and the denominator.

$= \dfrac{5\sqrt{5}}{12}$ Subtract.

b. $\sqrt[3]{\dfrac{7x}{8}} + 2\sqrt[3]{7x} = \dfrac{\sqrt[3]{7x}}{\sqrt[3]{8}} + 2\sqrt[3]{7x}$ Apply the quotient rule for radicals.

$= \dfrac{\sqrt[3]{7x}}{2} + 2\sqrt[3]{7x}$ Simplify.

$= \dfrac{\sqrt[3]{7x}}{2} + \dfrac{2\sqrt[3]{7x} \cdot 2}{2}$ Write each expression as an equivalent expression with a denominator of 2.

$= \dfrac{\sqrt[3]{7x}}{2} + \dfrac{4\sqrt[3]{7x}}{2}$

$= \dfrac{5\sqrt[3]{7x}}{2}$ Add. ☐

PRACTICE
3 Add or subtract as indicated.

a. $\dfrac{\sqrt{28}}{3} - \dfrac{\sqrt{7}}{4}$

b. $\sqrt[3]{\dfrac{6y}{64}} + 3\sqrt[3]{6y}$ ■

OBJECTIVE

2   Multiplying Radical Expressions ▶

We can multiply radical expressions by using many of the same properties used to multiply polynomial expressions. For instance, to multiply $\sqrt{2}(\sqrt{6} - 3\sqrt{2})$, we use the distributive property and multiply $\sqrt{2}$ by each term inside the parentheses.

$$\sqrt{2}(\sqrt{6} - 3\sqrt{2}) = \sqrt{2}(\sqrt{6}) - \sqrt{2}(3\sqrt{2}) \quad \text{Use the distributive property.}$$

$$= \sqrt{2 \cdot 6} - 3\sqrt{2 \cdot 2}$$

$$= \sqrt{2 \cdot 2 \cdot 3} - 3 \cdot 2 \quad \text{Use the product rule for radicals.}$$

$$= 2\sqrt{3} - 6$$

EXAMPLE 4   Multiply.

a. $\sqrt{3}(5 + \sqrt{30})$ **b.** $(\sqrt{5} - \sqrt{6})(\sqrt{7} + 1)$ **c.** $(7\sqrt{x} + 5)(3\sqrt{x} - \sqrt{5})$

d. $(4\sqrt{3} - 1)^2$ **e.** $(\sqrt{2x} - 5)(\sqrt{2x} + 5)$ **f.** $(\sqrt{x - 3} + 5)^2$

Solution

a. $\sqrt{3}(5 + \sqrt{30}) = \sqrt{3}(5) + \sqrt{3}(\sqrt{30})$

$$= 5\sqrt{3} + \sqrt{3 \cdot 30}$$

$$= 5\sqrt{3} + \sqrt{3 \cdot 3 \cdot 10}$$

$$= 5\sqrt{3} + 3\sqrt{10}$$

b. To multiply, we can use the FOIL method.

$$\begin{array}{cccc} & \text{First} & \text{Outer} & \text{Inner} & \text{Last} \end{array}$$

$$(\sqrt{5} - \sqrt{6})(\sqrt{7} + 1) = \sqrt{5} \cdot \sqrt{7} + \sqrt{5} \cdot 1 - \sqrt{6} \cdot \sqrt{7} - \sqrt{6} \cdot 1$$

$$= \sqrt{35} + \sqrt{5} - \sqrt{42} - \sqrt{6}$$

c. $(7\sqrt{x} + 5)(3\sqrt{x} - \sqrt{5}) = 7\sqrt{x}(3\sqrt{x}) - 7\sqrt{x}(\sqrt{5}) + 5(3\sqrt{x}) - 5(\sqrt{5})$

$$= 21x - 7\sqrt{5x} + 15\sqrt{x} - 5\sqrt{5}$$

d. $(4\sqrt{3} - 1)^2 = (4\sqrt{3} - 1)(4\sqrt{3} - 1)$

$$= 4\sqrt{3}(4\sqrt{3}) - 4\sqrt{3}(1) - 1(4\sqrt{3}) - 1(-1)$$

$$= 16 \cdot 3 - 4\sqrt{3} - 4\sqrt{3} + 1$$

$$= 48 - 8\sqrt{3} + 1$$

$$= 49 - 8\sqrt{3}$$

e. $(\sqrt{2x} - 5)(\sqrt{2x} + 5) = \sqrt{2x} \cdot \sqrt{2x} + 5\sqrt{2x} - 5\sqrt{2x} - 5 \cdot 5$

$$= 2x - 25$$

f. $(\sqrt{x - 3} + 5)^2 = (\sqrt{x - 3})^2 + 2 \cdot \sqrt{x - 3} \cdot 5 + 5^2$

$$\begin{array}{ccccccc} \uparrow & \uparrow & \uparrow & \uparrow\uparrow & \uparrow & \uparrow & \uparrow \\ a & b & a^2 & +2\cdot & a & \cdot b & + b^2 \end{array}$$

$$= x - 3 + 10\sqrt{x - 3} + 25 \quad \text{Simplify.}$$

$$= x + 22 + 10\sqrt{x - 3} \quad \text{Combine like terms.} \qquad \square$$

PRACTICE

4   Multiply.

a. $\sqrt{5}(2 + \sqrt{15})$ **b.** $(\sqrt{2} - \sqrt{5})(\sqrt{6} + 2)$

c. $(3\sqrt{z} - 4)(2\sqrt{z} + 3)$ **d.** $(\sqrt{6} - 3)^2$

e. $(\sqrt{5x} + 3)(\sqrt{5x} - 3)$ **f.** $(\sqrt{x + 2} + 3)^2$

■

✔ Vocabulary, Readiness & Video Check

Complete the table with "Like" or "Unlike."

Terms	Like or Unlike Radical Terms?
1. $\sqrt{7}, \sqrt[3]{7}$	
2. $\sqrt[3]{x^2 y}, \sqrt[3]{yx^2}$	
3. $\sqrt[3]{abc}, \sqrt[3]{cba}$	
4. $2x\sqrt{5}, 2x\sqrt{10}$	

Simplify. Assume that all variables represent positive real numbers.

5. $2\sqrt{3} + 4\sqrt{3} =$ _____

6. $5\sqrt{7} + 3\sqrt{7} =$ _____

7. $8\sqrt{x} - \sqrt{x} =$ _____

8. $3\sqrt{y} - \sqrt{y} =$ _____

9. $7\sqrt[3]{x} + \sqrt[3]{x} =$ _____

10. $8\sqrt[3]{z} + \sqrt[3]{z} =$ _____

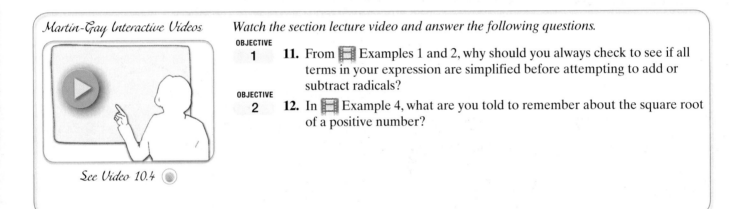

Martin-Gay Interactive Videos

Watch the section lecture video and answer the following questions.

OBJECTIVE 1

11. From ▦ Examples 1 and 2, why should you always check to see if all terms in your expression are simplified before attempting to add or subtract radicals?

OBJECTIVE 2

12. In ▦ Example 4, what are you told to remember about the square root of a positive number?

See Video 10.4 ◉

10.4 Exercise Set MyMathLab® ▶

Add or subtract. See Examples 1 through 3.

1. $\sqrt{8} - \sqrt{32}$

2. $\sqrt{27} - \sqrt{75}$

3. $2\sqrt{2x^3} + 4x\sqrt{8x}$

4. $3\sqrt{45x^3} + x\sqrt{5x}$

▶ **5.** $2\sqrt{50} - 3\sqrt{125} + \sqrt{98}$

6. $4\sqrt{32} - \sqrt{18} + 2\sqrt{128}$

7. $\sqrt[3]{16x} - \sqrt[3]{54x}$

8. $2\sqrt[3]{3a^4} - 3a\sqrt[3]{81a}$

9. $\sqrt{9b^3} - \sqrt{25b^3} + \sqrt{49b^3}$

10. $\sqrt{4x^7} + 9x^2\sqrt{x^3} - 5x\sqrt{x^5}$

11. $\dfrac{5\sqrt{2}}{3} + \dfrac{2\sqrt{2}}{5}$

12. $\dfrac{\sqrt{3}}{2} + \dfrac{4\sqrt{3}}{3}$

▶ **13.** $\sqrt[3]{\dfrac{11}{8}} - \dfrac{\sqrt[3]{11}}{6}$

14. $\dfrac{2\sqrt[3]{4}}{7} - \dfrac{\sqrt[3]{4}}{14}$

15. $\dfrac{\sqrt{20x}}{9} + \sqrt{\dfrac{5x}{9}}$

16. $\dfrac{3x\sqrt{7}}{5} + \sqrt{\dfrac{7x^2}{100}}$

17. $7\sqrt{9} - 7 + \sqrt{3}$

18. $\sqrt{16} - 5\sqrt{10} + 7$

19. $2 + 3\sqrt{y^2} - 6\sqrt{y^2} + 5$

20. $3\sqrt{7} - \sqrt[3]{x} + 4\sqrt{7} - 3\sqrt[3]{x}$

21. $3\sqrt{108} - 2\sqrt{18} - 3\sqrt{48}$

22. $-\sqrt{75} + \sqrt{12} - 3\sqrt{3}$

23. $-5\sqrt[3]{625} + \sqrt[3]{40}$

24. $-2\sqrt[3]{108} - \sqrt[3]{32}$

25. $a^3\sqrt{9ab^3} - \sqrt{25a^7b^3} + \sqrt{16a^7b^3}$

26. $\sqrt{4x^7y^5} + 9x^2\sqrt{x^3y^5} - 5xy\sqrt{x^5y^3}$

27. $5y\sqrt{8y} + 2\sqrt{50y^3}$

28. $3\sqrt{8x^2y^3} - 2x\sqrt{32y^3}$

29. $\sqrt[3]{54xy^3} - 5\sqrt[3]{2xy^3} + y\sqrt[3]{128x}$

30. $2\sqrt[3]{24x^3y^4} + 4x\sqrt[3]{81y^4}$

31. $6\sqrt[3]{11} + 8\sqrt{11} - 12\sqrt{11}$

32. $3\sqrt[3]{5} + 4\sqrt{5} - 8\sqrt{5}$

33. $-2\sqrt[4]{x^7} + 3\sqrt[4]{16x^7} - x\sqrt[4]{x^3}$

34. $6\sqrt[3]{24x^3} - 2\sqrt[3]{81x^3} - x\sqrt[3]{3}$

35. $\dfrac{4\sqrt{3}}{3} - \dfrac{\sqrt{12}}{3}$

36. $\dfrac{\sqrt{45}}{10} + \dfrac{7\sqrt{5}}{10}$

37. $\dfrac{\sqrt[3]{8x^4}}{7} + \dfrac{3x\sqrt[3]{x}}{7}$

38. $\dfrac{\sqrt[4]{48}}{5x} - \dfrac{2\sqrt[4]{3}}{10x}$

39. $\sqrt{\dfrac{28}{x^2}} + \sqrt{\dfrac{7}{4x^2}}$

40. $\dfrac{\sqrt{99}}{5x} - \sqrt{\dfrac{44}{x^2}}$

41. $\sqrt[3]{\dfrac{16}{27}} - \dfrac{\sqrt[3]{54}}{6}$

42. $\dfrac{\sqrt[3]{3}}{10} + \sqrt[3]{\dfrac{24}{125}}$

43. $-\dfrac{\sqrt[3]{2x^4}}{9} + \sqrt[3]{\dfrac{250x^4}{27}}$

44. $\dfrac{\sqrt[3]{y^5}}{8} + \dfrac{5y\sqrt[3]{y^2}}{4}$

△ 45. Find the perimeter of the trapezoid.

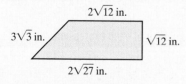

△ 46. Find the perimeter of the triangle.

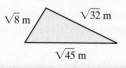

Multiply and then simplify if possible. See Example 4.

▶ 47. $\sqrt{7}(\sqrt{5} + \sqrt{3})$

48. $\sqrt{5}(\sqrt{15} - \sqrt{35})$

49. $(\sqrt{5} - \sqrt{2})^2$

50. $(3x - \sqrt{2})(3x - \sqrt{2})$

51. $\sqrt{3x}(\sqrt{3} - \sqrt{x})$

52. $\sqrt{5y}(\sqrt{y} + \sqrt{5})$

53. $(2\sqrt{x} - 5)(3\sqrt{x} + 1)$

54. $(8\sqrt{y} + z)(4\sqrt{y} - 1)$

55. $(\sqrt[3]{a} - 4)(\sqrt[3]{a} + 5)$

56. $(\sqrt[3]{a} + 2)(\sqrt[3]{a} + 7)$

57. $6(\sqrt{2} - 2)$

58. $\sqrt{5}(6 - \sqrt{5})$

59. $\sqrt{2}(\sqrt{2} + x\sqrt{6})$

60. $\sqrt{3}(\sqrt{3} - 2\sqrt{5x})$

▶ 61. $(2\sqrt{7} + 3\sqrt{5})(\sqrt{7} - 2\sqrt{5})$

62. $(\sqrt{6} - 4\sqrt{2})(3\sqrt{6} + \sqrt{2})$

63. $(\sqrt{x} - y)(\sqrt{x} + y)$

64. $(\sqrt{3x} + 2)(\sqrt{3x} - 2)$

65. $(\sqrt{3} + x)^2$

66. $(\sqrt{y} - 3x)^2$

67. $(\sqrt{5x} - 2\sqrt{3x})(\sqrt{5x} - 3\sqrt{3x})$

68. $(5\sqrt{7x} - \sqrt{2x})(4\sqrt{7x} + 6\sqrt{2x})$

69. $(\sqrt[3]{4} + 2)(\sqrt[3]{2} - 1)$

70. $(\sqrt[3]{3} + \sqrt[3]{2})(\sqrt[3]{9} - \sqrt[3]{4})$

71. $(\sqrt[3]{x} + 1)(\sqrt[3]{x^2} - \sqrt[3]{x} + 1)$

72. $(\sqrt[3]{3x} + 2)(\sqrt[3]{9x^2} - 2\sqrt[3]{3x} + 4)$

73. $(\sqrt{x - 1} + 5)^2$

74. $(\sqrt{3x + 1} + 2)^2$

75. $(\sqrt{2x + 5} - 1)^2$

76. $(\sqrt{x - 6} - 7)^2$

REVIEW AND PREVIEW

Factor each numerator and denominator. Then simplify if possible. See Section 7.1.

77. $\dfrac{2x - 14}{2}$

78. $\dfrac{8x - 24y}{4}$

79. $\dfrac{7x - 7y}{x^2 - y^2}$

80. $\dfrac{x^3 - 8}{4x - 8}$

81. $\dfrac{6a^2b - 9ab}{3ab}$

82. $\dfrac{14r - 28r^2s^2}{7rs}$

83. $\dfrac{-4 + 2\sqrt{3}}{6}$

84. $\dfrac{-5 + 10\sqrt{7}}{5}$

CONCEPT EXTENSIONS

△ 85. Find the perimeter and area of the rectangle.

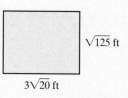

△ **86.** Find the area and perimeter of the trapezoid. (*Hint:* The area of a trapezoid is the product of half the height $6\sqrt{3}$ meters and the sum of the bases $2\sqrt{63}$ and $7\sqrt{7}$ meters.)

$2\sqrt{63}$ m

$2\sqrt{27}$ m

$6\sqrt{3}$ m

$7\sqrt{7}$ m

87. a. Add: $\sqrt{3} + \sqrt{3}$

    b. Multiply: $\sqrt{3} \cdot \sqrt{3}$

    c. Describe the differences in parts **a** and **b**.

88. a. Add: $2\sqrt{5} + \sqrt{5}$

    b. Multiply: $2\sqrt{5} \cdot \sqrt{5}$

    c. Describe the differences in parts **a** and **b**.

89. Multiply: $(\sqrt{2} + \sqrt{3} - 1)^2$

90. Multiply: $(\sqrt{5} - \sqrt{2} + 1)^2$

91. Explain how simplifying $2x + 3x$ is similar to simplifying $2\sqrt{x} + 3\sqrt{x}$.

92. Explain how multiplying $(x - 2)(x + 3)$ is similar to multiplying $(\sqrt{x} - \sqrt{2})(\sqrt{x} + 3)$.

10.5 Rationalizing Denominators and Numerators of Radical Expressions

OBJECTIVES

1 Rationalize Denominators.

2 Rationalize Denominators Having Two Terms.

3 Rationalize Numerators.

OBJECTIVE

1 Rationalizing Denominators of Radical Expressions

Often in mathematics, it is helpful to write a radical expression such as $\dfrac{\sqrt{3}}{\sqrt{2}}$ either without a radical in the denominator or without a radical in the numerator. The process of writing this expression as an equivalent expression but without a radical in the denominator is called **rationalizing the denominator.** To rationalize the denominator of $\dfrac{\sqrt{3}}{\sqrt{2}}$, we use the fundamental principle of fractions and multiply the numerator and the denominator by $\sqrt{2}$. Recall that this is the same as multiplying by $\dfrac{\sqrt{2}}{\sqrt{2}}$, which simplifies to 1.

$$\frac{\sqrt{3}}{\sqrt{2}} = \frac{\sqrt{3} \cdot \sqrt{2}}{\sqrt{2} \cdot \sqrt{2}} = \frac{\sqrt{6}}{\sqrt{4}} = \frac{\sqrt{6}}{2}$$

In this section, we continue to assume that variables represent positive real numbers.

EXAMPLE I Rationalize the denominator of each expression.

    a. $\dfrac{2}{\sqrt{5}}$ **b.** $\dfrac{2\sqrt{16}}{\sqrt{9x}}$ **c.** $\sqrt[3]{\dfrac{1}{2}}$

Solution

    a. To rationalize the denominator, we multiply the numerator and denominator by a factor that makes the radicand in the denominator a perfect square.

$$\frac{2}{\sqrt{5}} = \frac{2 \cdot \sqrt{5}}{\sqrt{5} \cdot \sqrt{5}} = \frac{2\sqrt{5}}{5} \quad \text{The denominator is now rationalized.}$$

    b. First, we simplify the radicals and then rationalize the denominator.

$$\frac{2\sqrt{16}}{\sqrt{9x}} = \frac{2(4)}{3\sqrt{x}} = \frac{8}{3\sqrt{x}}$$

To rationalize the denominator, multiply the numerator and denominator by $\sqrt{x}$. Then

$$\frac{8}{3\sqrt{x}} = \frac{8 \cdot \sqrt{x}}{3\sqrt{x} \cdot \sqrt{x}} = \frac{8\sqrt{x}}{3x}$$

c. $\sqrt[3]{\dfrac{1}{2}} = \dfrac{\sqrt[3]{1}}{\sqrt[3]{2}} = \dfrac{1}{\sqrt[3]{2}}$. Now we rationalize the denominator. Since $\sqrt[3]{2}$ is a cube root, we want to multiply by a value that will make the radicand 2 a perfect cube. If we multiply $\sqrt[3]{2}$ by $\sqrt[3]{2^2}$, we get $\sqrt[3]{2^3} = \sqrt[3]{8} = 2$.

$$\frac{1 \cdot \sqrt[3]{2^2}}{\sqrt[3]{2} \cdot \sqrt[3]{2^2}} = \frac{\sqrt[3]{4}}{\sqrt[3]{2^3}} = \frac{\sqrt[3]{4}}{2}$$ Multiply the numerator and denominator by $\sqrt[3]{2^2}$ and then simplify.   □

PRACTICE
1   Rationalize the denominator of each expression.

a. $\dfrac{5}{\sqrt{3}}$ **b.** $\dfrac{3\sqrt{25}}{\sqrt{4x}}$ **c.** $\sqrt[3]{\dfrac{2}{9}}$ ■

✔ **CONCEPT CHECK**
Determine the smallest number both the numerator and denominator can be multiplied by to rationalize the denominator of the radical expression.

a. $\dfrac{1}{\sqrt[3]{7}}$ **b.** $\dfrac{1}{\sqrt[4]{8}}$

EXAMPLE 2   Rationalize the denominator of $\sqrt{\dfrac{7x}{3y}}$.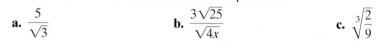

Solution $\sqrt{\dfrac{7x}{3y}} = \dfrac{\sqrt{7x}}{\sqrt{3y}}$ Use the quotient rule. No radical may be simplified further.

$= \dfrac{\sqrt{7x} \cdot \sqrt{3y}}{\sqrt{3y} \cdot \sqrt{3y}}$ Multiply numerator and denominator by $\sqrt{3y}$ so that the radicand in the denominator is a perfect square.

$= \dfrac{\sqrt{21xy}}{3y}$ Use the product rule in the numerator and denominator. Remember that $\sqrt{3y} \cdot \sqrt{3y} = 3y$.   □

PRACTICE
2   Rationalize the denominator of $\sqrt{\dfrac{3z}{5y}}$.   ■

EXAMPLE 3   Rationalize the denominator of $\dfrac{\sqrt[4]{x}}{\sqrt[4]{81y^5}}$.

Solution   First, simplify each radical if possible.

$\dfrac{\sqrt[4]{x}}{\sqrt[4]{81y^5}} = \dfrac{\sqrt[4]{x}}{\sqrt[4]{81y^4} \cdot \sqrt[4]{y}}$ Use the product rule in the denominator.

$= \dfrac{\sqrt[4]{x}}{3y\sqrt[4]{y}}$ Write $\sqrt[4]{81y^4}$ as $3y$.

$= \dfrac{\sqrt[4]{x} \cdot \sqrt[4]{y^3}}{3y\sqrt[4]{y} \cdot \sqrt[4]{y^3}}$ Multiply numerator and denominator by $\sqrt[4]{y^3}$ so that the radicand in the denominator is a perfect fourth power.

$= \dfrac{\sqrt[4]{xy^3}}{3y\sqrt[4]{y^4}}$ Use the product rule in the numerator and denominator.

$= \dfrac{\sqrt[4]{xy^3}}{3y^2}$ In the denominator, $\sqrt[4]{y^4} = y$ and $3y \cdot y = 3y^2$.   □

Answer to Concept Check:
a. $\sqrt[3]{7^2}$ or $\sqrt[3]{49}$ **b.** $\sqrt[4]{2}$

PRACTICE
3   Rationalize the denominator of $\dfrac{\sqrt[3]{z^2}}{\sqrt[3]{27x^4}}$.   ■

2 Rationalizing Denominators Having Two Terms ▶

Remember the product of the sum and difference of two terms?

$$(a + b)(a - b) = a^2 - b^2$$

These two expressions are called **conjugates** of each other.

To rationalize a numerator or denominator that is a sum or difference of two terms, we use conjugates. To see how and why this works, let's rationalize the denominator of the expression $\dfrac{5}{\sqrt{3} - 2}$. To do so, we multiply both the numerator and the denominator by $\sqrt{3} + 2$, the **conjugate** of the denominator $\sqrt{3} - 2$, and see what happens.

$$\frac{5}{\sqrt{3} - 2} = \frac{5(\sqrt{3} + 2)}{(\sqrt{3} - 2)(\sqrt{3} + 2)}$$

$$= \frac{5(\sqrt{3} + 2)}{(\sqrt{3})^2 - 2^2} \quad \text{Multiply the sum and difference of two terms: } (a + b)(a - b) = a^2 - b^2.$$

$$= \frac{5(\sqrt{3} + 2)}{3 - 4}$$

$$= \frac{5(\sqrt{3} + 2)}{-1}$$

$$= -5(\sqrt{3} + 2) \quad \text{or} \quad -5\sqrt{3} - 10$$

Notice in the denominator that the product of $(\sqrt{3} - 2)$ and its conjugate, $(\sqrt{3} + 2)$, is -1. In general, the product of an expression and its conjugate will contain no radical terms. This is why, when rationalizing a denominator or a numerator containing two terms, we multiply by its conjugate. Examples of conjugates are

$$\sqrt{a} - \sqrt{b} \quad \text{and} \quad \sqrt{a} + \sqrt{b}$$
$$x + \sqrt{y} \quad \text{and} \quad x - \sqrt{y}$$

EXAMPLE 4 Rationalize each denominator.

a. $\dfrac{2}{3\sqrt{2} + 4}$ **b.** $\dfrac{\sqrt{6} + 2}{\sqrt{5} - \sqrt{3}}$ **c.** $\dfrac{2\sqrt{m}}{3\sqrt{x} + \sqrt{m}}$

Solution

a. Multiply the numerator and denominator by the conjugate of the denominator, $3\sqrt{2} + 4$.

$$\frac{2}{3\sqrt{2} + 4} = \frac{2(3\sqrt{2} - 4)}{(3\sqrt{2} + 4)(3\sqrt{2} - 4)}$$

$$= \frac{2(3\sqrt{2} - 4)}{(3\sqrt{2})^2 - 4^2}$$

$$= \frac{2(3\sqrt{2} - 4)}{18 - 16}$$

$$= \frac{2(3\sqrt{2} - 4)}{2}, \quad \text{or} \quad 3\sqrt{2} - 4$$

It is often useful to leave a numerator in factored form to help determine whether the expression can be simplified.

b. Multiply the numerator and denominator by the conjugate of $\sqrt{5} - \sqrt{3}$.

$$\frac{\sqrt{6} + 2}{\sqrt{5} - \sqrt{3}} = \frac{(\sqrt{6} + 2)(\sqrt{5} + \sqrt{3})}{(\sqrt{5} - \sqrt{3})(\sqrt{5} + \sqrt{3})}$$

$$= \frac{\sqrt{6}\sqrt{5} + \sqrt{6}\sqrt{3} + 2\sqrt{5} + 2\sqrt{3}}{(\sqrt{5})^2 - (\sqrt{3})^2}$$

$$= \frac{\sqrt{30} + \sqrt{18} + 2\sqrt{5} + 2\sqrt{3}}{5 - 3}$$

$$= \frac{\sqrt{30} + 3\sqrt{2} + 2\sqrt{5} + 2\sqrt{3}}{2}$$

c. Multiply by the conjugate of $3\sqrt{x} + \sqrt{m}$ to eliminate the radicals from the denominator.

$$\frac{2\sqrt{m}}{3\sqrt{x} + \sqrt{m}} = \frac{2\sqrt{m}(3\sqrt{x} - \sqrt{m})}{(3\sqrt{x} + \sqrt{m})(3\sqrt{x} - \sqrt{m})} = \frac{6\sqrt{mx} - 2m}{(3\sqrt{x})^2 - (\sqrt{m})^2}$$

$$= \frac{6\sqrt{mx} - 2m}{9x - m} \qquad \square$$

PRACTICE
4   Rationalize each denominator.

a. $\dfrac{5}{3\sqrt{5} + 2}$ **b.** $\dfrac{\sqrt{2} + 5}{\sqrt{3} - \sqrt{5}}$ **c.** $\dfrac{3\sqrt{x}}{2\sqrt{x} + \sqrt{y}}$ ■

OBJECTIVE
3   Rationalizing Numerators ▶

As mentioned earlier, it is also often helpful to write an expression such as $\dfrac{\sqrt{3}}{\sqrt{2}}$ as an equivalent expression without a radical in the numerator. This process is called **rationalizing the numerator**. To rationalize the numerator of $\dfrac{\sqrt{3}}{\sqrt{2}}$, we multiply the numerator and the denominator by $\sqrt{3}$.

$$\frac{\sqrt{3}}{\sqrt{2}} = \frac{\sqrt{3} \cdot \sqrt{3}}{\sqrt{2} \cdot \sqrt{3}} = \frac{\sqrt{9}}{\sqrt{6}} = \frac{3}{\sqrt{6}}$$

EXAMPLE 5   Rationalize the numerator of $\dfrac{\sqrt{7}}{\sqrt{45}}$.

Solution First we simplify $\sqrt{45}$.

$$\frac{\sqrt{7}}{\sqrt{45}} = \frac{\sqrt{7}}{\sqrt{9 \cdot 5}} = \frac{\sqrt{7}}{3\sqrt{5}}$$

Next we rationalize the numerator by multiplying the numerator and the denominator by $\sqrt{7}$.

$$\frac{\sqrt{7}}{3\sqrt{5}} = \frac{\sqrt{7} \cdot \sqrt{7}}{3\sqrt{5} \cdot \sqrt{7}} = \frac{7}{3\sqrt{5 \cdot 7}} = \frac{7}{3\sqrt{35}} \qquad \square$$

PRACTICE
5   Rationalize the numerator of $\dfrac{\sqrt{32}}{\sqrt{80}}$. ■

EXAMPLE 6 Rationalize the numerator of $\dfrac{\sqrt[3]{2x^2}}{\sqrt[3]{5y}}$.

Solution The numerator and the denominator of this expression are already simplified. To rationalize the numerator, $\sqrt[3]{2x^2}$, we multiply the numerator and denominator by a factor that will make the radicand a perfect cube. If we multiply $\sqrt[3]{2x^2}$ by $\sqrt[3]{4x}$, we get $\sqrt[3]{8x^3} = 2x$.

$$\frac{\sqrt[3]{2x^2}}{\sqrt[3]{5y}} = \frac{\sqrt[3]{2x^2} \cdot \sqrt[3]{4x}}{\sqrt[3]{5y} \cdot \sqrt[3]{4x}} = \frac{\sqrt[3]{8x^3}}{\sqrt[3]{20xy}} = \frac{2x}{\sqrt[3]{20xy}}$$

□

PRACTICE
6 Rationalize the numerator of $\dfrac{\sqrt[3]{5b}}{\sqrt[3]{2a}}$.

■

EXAMPLE 7 Rationalize the numerator of $\dfrac{\sqrt{x} + 2}{5}$.

Solution We multiply the numerator and the denominator by the conjugate of the numerator, $\sqrt{x} + 2$.

$$\frac{\sqrt{x} + 2}{5} = \frac{(\sqrt{x} + 2)(\sqrt{x} - 2)}{5(\sqrt{x} - 2)} \qquad \text{Multiply by } \sqrt{x} - 2, \text{ the conjugate of } \sqrt{x} + 2.$$

$$= \frac{(\sqrt{x})^2 - 2^2}{5(\sqrt{x} - 2)} \qquad (a + b)(a - b) = a^2 - b^2$$

$$= \frac{x - 4}{5(\sqrt{x} - 2)}$$

□

PRACTICE
7 Rationalize the numerator of $\dfrac{\sqrt{x} - 3}{4}$.

■

✔ Vocabulary, Readiness & Video Check

Use the choices below to fill in each blank. Not all choices will be used.

rationalizing the numerator   conjugate $\dfrac{\sqrt{3}}{\sqrt{3}}$

rationalizing the denominator $\dfrac{5}{5}$

1. The _____ of $a + b$ is $a - b$.

2. The process of writing an equivalent expression, but without a radical in the denominator, is called
_____.

3. The process of writing an equivalent expression, but without a radical in the numerator, is called _____.

4. To rationalize the denominator of $\dfrac{5}{\sqrt{3}}$, we multiply by _____.

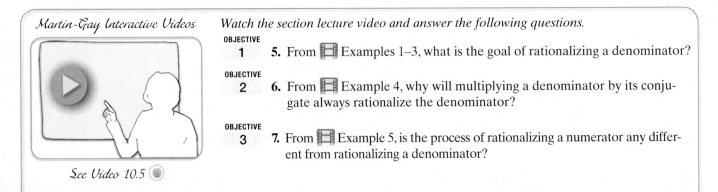

Martin-Gay Interactive Videos

Watch the section lecture video and answer the following questions.

OBJECTIVE
1 5. From Examples 1–3, what is the goal of rationalizing a denominator?

OBJECTIVE
2 6. From Example 4, why will multiplying a denominator by its conjugate always rationalize the denominator?

OBJECTIVE
3 7. From Example 5, is the process of rationalizing a numerator any different from rationalizing a denominator?

See Video 10.5 ◉

10.5   Exercise Set   MyMathLab® ▶

Rationalize each denominator. See Examples 1 through 3.

▶ **1.** $\dfrac{\sqrt{2}}{\sqrt{7}}$

2. $\dfrac{\sqrt{3}}{\sqrt{2}}$

3. $\sqrt{\dfrac{1}{5}}$

4. $\sqrt{\dfrac{1}{2}}$

5. $\sqrt{\dfrac{4}{x}}$

6. $\sqrt{\dfrac{25}{y}}$

▶ **7.** $\dfrac{4}{\sqrt[3]{3}}$

8. $\dfrac{6}{\sqrt[3]{9}}$

▶ **9.** $\dfrac{3}{\sqrt{8x}}$

10. $\dfrac{5}{\sqrt{27a}}$

11. $\dfrac{3}{\sqrt[3]{4x^2}}$

12. $\dfrac{5}{\sqrt[3]{3y}}$

13. $\dfrac{9}{\sqrt{3a}}$

14. $\dfrac{x}{\sqrt{5}}$

15. $\dfrac{3}{\sqrt[3]{2}}$

16. $\dfrac{5}{\sqrt[3]{9}}$

17. $\dfrac{2\sqrt{3}}{\sqrt{7}}$

18. $\dfrac{-5\sqrt{2}}{\sqrt{11}}$

19. $\sqrt{\dfrac{2x}{5y}}$

20. $\sqrt{\dfrac{13a}{2b}}$

21. $\sqrt[3]{\dfrac{3}{5}}$

22. $\sqrt[3]{\dfrac{7}{10}}$

23. $\sqrt{\dfrac{3x}{50}}$

24. $\sqrt{\dfrac{11y}{45}}$

25. $\dfrac{1}{\sqrt{12z}}$

26. $\dfrac{1}{\sqrt{32x}}$

27. $\dfrac{\sqrt[3]{2y^2}}{\sqrt[3]{9x^2}}$

28. $\dfrac{\sqrt[3]{3x}}{\sqrt[3]{4y^4}}$

29. $\sqrt[4]{\dfrac{81}{8}}$

30. $\sqrt[4]{\dfrac{1}{9}}$

31. $\sqrt[4]{\dfrac{16}{9x^7}}$

32. $\sqrt[5]{\dfrac{32}{m^6 n^{13}}}$

33. $\dfrac{5a}{\sqrt[5]{8a^9 b^{11}}}$

34. $\dfrac{9y}{\sqrt[4]{4y^9}}$

Write the conjugate of each expression.

35. $\sqrt{2} + x$

36. $\sqrt{3} + y$

37. $5 - \sqrt{a}$

38. $6 - \sqrt{b}$

39. $-7\sqrt{5} + 8\sqrt{x}$

40. $-9\sqrt{2} - 6\sqrt{y}$

Rationalize each denominator. See Example 4.

41. $\dfrac{6}{2 - \sqrt{7}}$

42. $\dfrac{3}{\sqrt{7} - 4}$

▶ **43.** $\dfrac{-7}{\sqrt{x} - 3}$

44. $\dfrac{-8}{\sqrt{y} + 4}$

45. $\dfrac{\sqrt{2} - \sqrt{3}}{\sqrt{2} + \sqrt{3}}$

46. $\dfrac{\sqrt{3} + \sqrt{4}}{\sqrt{2} - \sqrt{3}}$

47. $\dfrac{\sqrt{a} + 1}{2\sqrt{a} - \sqrt{b}}$

48. $\dfrac{2\sqrt{a} - 3}{2\sqrt{a} + \sqrt{b}}$

49. $\dfrac{8}{1 + \sqrt{10}}$

50. $\dfrac{-3}{\sqrt{6} - 2}$

51. $\dfrac{\sqrt{x}}{\sqrt{x} + \sqrt{y}}$

52. $\dfrac{2\sqrt{a}}{2\sqrt{x} - \sqrt{y}}$

53. $\dfrac{2\sqrt{3} + \sqrt{6}}{4\sqrt{3} - \sqrt{6}}$

54. $\dfrac{4\sqrt{5} + \sqrt{2}}{2\sqrt{5} - \sqrt{2}}$

Rationalize each numerator. See Examples 5 and 6.

55. $\sqrt{\dfrac{5}{3}}$

56. $\sqrt{\dfrac{3}{2}}$

▶ **57.** $\sqrt{\dfrac{18}{5}}$

58. $\sqrt{\dfrac{12}{7}}$

59. $\dfrac{\sqrt{4x}}{7}$

60. $\dfrac{\sqrt{3x^5}}{6}$

61. $\dfrac{\sqrt[3]{5y^2}}{\sqrt[3]{4x}}$

62. $\dfrac{\sqrt[3]{4x}}{\sqrt[3]{z^4}}$

63. $\sqrt{\dfrac{2}{5}}$

64. $\sqrt{\dfrac{3}{7}}$

65. $\dfrac{\sqrt{2x}}{11}$

66. $\dfrac{\sqrt{y}}{7}$

67. $\sqrt[3]{\dfrac{7}{8}}$

68. $\sqrt[3]{\dfrac{25}{2}}$

69. $\dfrac{\sqrt[3]{3x^5}}{10}$

70. $\sqrt[3]{\dfrac{9y}{7}}$

71. $\sqrt{\dfrac{18x^4 y^6}{3z}}$

72. $\sqrt{\dfrac{8x^5 y}{2z}}$

Rationalize each numerator. See Example 7.

73. $\dfrac{2 - \sqrt{11}}{6}$

74. $\dfrac{\sqrt{15} + 1}{2}$

75. $\dfrac{2 - \sqrt{7}}{-5}$

76. $\dfrac{\sqrt{5} + 2}{\sqrt{2}}$

77. $\dfrac{\sqrt{x} + 3}{\sqrt{x}}$

78. $\dfrac{5 + \sqrt{2}}{\sqrt{2x}}$

79. $\dfrac{\sqrt{2} - 1}{\sqrt{2} + 1}$

80. $\dfrac{\sqrt{8} - \sqrt{3}}{\sqrt{2} + \sqrt{3}}$

81. $\dfrac{\sqrt{x} + 1}{\sqrt{x} - 1}$

82. $\dfrac{\sqrt{x} + \sqrt{y}}{\sqrt{x} - \sqrt{y}}$

REVIEW AND PREVIEW

Solve each equation. See Sections 2.3 and 6.6.

83. $2x - 7 = 3(x - 4)$ **84.** $9x - 4 = 7(x - 2)$

85. $(x - 6)(2x + 1) = 0$ **86.** $(y + 2)(5y + 4) = 0$

87. $x^2 - 8x = -12$ **88.** $x^3 = x$

CONCEPT EXTENSIONS

 89. The formula of the radius r of a sphere with surface area A is

$$r = \sqrt{\frac{A}{4\pi}}$$

Rationalize the denominator of the radical expression in this formula.

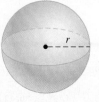

 **90.** The formula for the radius r of a cone with height 7 centimeters and volume V is

$$r = \sqrt{\frac{3V}{7\pi}}$$

Rationalize the numerator of the radical expression in this formula.

91. Given $\dfrac{\sqrt{5y^3}}{\sqrt{12x^3}}$, rationalize the denominator by following parts **a** and **b**.

  a. Multiply the numerator and denominator by $\sqrt{12x^3}$.

  b. Multiply the numerator and denominator by $\sqrt{3x}$.

  c. What can you conclude from parts **a** and **b**?

92. Given $\dfrac{\sqrt[3]{5y}}{\sqrt[3]{4}}$, rationalize the denominator by following parts **a** and **b**.

  a. Multiply the numerator and denominator by $\sqrt[3]{16}$.

  b. Multiply the numerator and denominator by $\sqrt[3]{2}$.

  c. What can you conclude from parts **a** and **b**?

Determine the smallest number both the numerator and denominator should be multiplied by to rationalize the denominator of the radical expression. See the Concept Check in this section.

93. $\dfrac{9}{\sqrt[3]{5}}$ **94.** $\dfrac{5}{\sqrt{27}}$

95. When rationalizing the denominator of $\dfrac{\sqrt{5}}{\sqrt{7}}$, explain why both the numerator and the denominator must be multiplied by $\sqrt{7}$.

96. When rationalizing the numerator of $\dfrac{\sqrt{5}}{\sqrt{7}}$, explain why both the numerator and the denominator must be multiplied by $\sqrt{5}$.

97. Explain why rationalizing the denominator does not change the value of the original expression.

98. Explain why rationalizing the numerator does not change the value of the original expression.

Integrated Review — Radicals and Rational Exponents

Sections 10.1–10.5

Throughout this review, assume that all variables represent positive real numbers.

Find each root.

1. $\sqrt{81}$ **2.** $\sqrt[3]{-8}$ **3.** $\sqrt[4]{\dfrac{1}{16}}$ **4.** $\sqrt{x^6}$

5. $\sqrt[3]{y^9}$ **6.** $\sqrt{4y^{10}}$ **7.** $\sqrt[5]{-32y^5}$ **8.** $\sqrt[4]{81b^{12}}$

Use radical notation to write each expression. Simplify if possible.

9. $36^{1/2}$ **10.** $(3y)^{1/4}$ **11.** $64^{-2/3}$ **12.** $(x + 1)^{3/5}$

Use the properties of exponents to simplify each expression. Write with positive exponents.

13. $y^{-1/6} \cdot y^{7/6}$ **14.** $\dfrac{(2x^{1/3})^4}{x^{5/6}}$ **15.** $\dfrac{x^{1/4}x^{3/4}}{x^{-1/4}}$ **16.** $4^{1/3} \cdot 4^{2/5}$

Use rational exponents to simplify each radical.

17. $\sqrt[3]{8x^6}$ **18.** $\sqrt[12]{a^9b^6}$

Use rational exponents to write each as a single radical expression.

19. $\sqrt[4]{x} \cdot \sqrt{x}$ **20.** $\sqrt{5} \cdot \sqrt[3]{2}$

Simplify.

21. $\sqrt{40}$

22. $\sqrt[4]{16x^7y^{10}}$

23. $\sqrt[3]{54x^4}$

24. $\sqrt[5]{-64b^{10}}$

Multiply or divide. Then simplify if possible.

25. $\sqrt{5} \cdot \sqrt{x}$

26. $\sqrt[3]{8x} \cdot \sqrt[3]{8x^2}$

27. $\dfrac{\sqrt{98y^6}}{\sqrt{2y}}$

28. $\dfrac{\sqrt[4]{48a^9b^3}}{\sqrt[4]{ab^3}}$

Perform each indicated operation.

29. $\sqrt{20} - \sqrt{75} + 5\sqrt{7}$

30. $\sqrt[3]{54y^4} - y\sqrt[3]{16y}$

31. $\sqrt{3}(\sqrt{5} - \sqrt{2})$

32. $(\sqrt{7} + \sqrt{3})^2$

33. $(2x - \sqrt{5})(2x + \sqrt{5})$

34. $(\sqrt{x+1} - 1)^2$

Rationalize each denominator.

35. $\sqrt{\dfrac{7}{3}}$

36. $\dfrac{5}{\sqrt[3]{2x^2}}$

37. $\dfrac{\sqrt{3} - \sqrt{7}}{2\sqrt{3} + \sqrt{7}}$

Rationalize each numerator.

38. $\sqrt{\dfrac{7}{3}}$

39. $\sqrt[3]{\dfrac{9y}{11}}$

40. $\dfrac{\sqrt{x} - 2}{\sqrt{x}}$

10.6 Radical Equations and Problem Solving ▷

OBJECTIVES

1 Solve Equations That Contain Radical Expressions. ▷

2 Use the Pythagorean Theorem to Model Problems. ▷

OBJECTIVE

1   Solving Equations That Contain Radical Expressions ▷

In this section, we present techniques to solve equations containing radical expressions such as

$$\sqrt{2x - 3} = 9$$

We use the power rule to help us solve these radical equations.

> **Power Rule**
>
> If both sides of an equation are raised to the same power, **all** solutions of the original equation are **among** the solutions of the new equation.

This property *does not* say that raising both sides of an equation to a power yields an equivalent equation. A solution of the new equation *may or may not* be a solution of the original equation. For example, $(-2)^2 = 2^2$, but $-2 \neq 2$. Thus, *each solution of the new equation must be checked* to make sure it is a solution of the original equation. Recall that a proposed solution that is not a solution of the original equation is called an **extraneous solution**.

EXAMPLE 1   Solve: $\sqrt{2x - 3} = 9$

Solution We use the power rule to square both sides of the equation to eliminate the radical.

$$\sqrt{2x - 3} = 9$$
$$(\sqrt{2x - 3})^2 = 9^2$$
$$2x - 3 = 81$$
$$2x = 84$$
$$x = 42$$

Now we check the solution in the original equation.

(Continued on next page)

Check:

$$\sqrt{2x - 3} = 9$$

$$\sqrt{2(42) - 3} \stackrel{?}{=} 9 \quad \text{Let } x = 42.$$

$$\sqrt{84 - 3} \stackrel{?}{=} 9$$

$$\sqrt{81} \stackrel{?}{=} 9$$

$$9 = 9 \quad \text{True}$$

The solution checks, so we conclude that the solution is 42, or the solution set is $\{42\}$. □

PRACTICE
1 Solve: $\sqrt{3x - 5} = 7$ ■

To solve a radical equation, first isolate a radical on one side of the equation.

EXAMPLE 2 Solve: $\sqrt{-10x - 1} + 3x = 0$

Solution First, isolate the radical on one side of the equation. To do this, we subtract $3x$ from both sides.

$$\sqrt{-10x - 1} + 3x = 0$$

$$\sqrt{-10x - 1} + 3x - 3x = 0 - 3x$$

$$\sqrt{-10x - 1} = -3x$$

Next we use the power rule to eliminate the radical.

$$(\sqrt{-10x - 1})^2 = (-3x)^2$$

$$-10x - 1 = 9x^2$$

Since this is a quadratic equation, we can set the equation equal to 0 and try to solve by factoring.

$$9x^2 + 10x + 1 = 0$$

$$(9x + 1)(x + 1) = 0 \quad \text{Factor.}$$

$$9x + 1 = 0 \quad \text{or} \quad x + 1 = 0 \quad \text{Set each factor equal to 0.}$$

$$x = -\frac{1}{9} \quad \text{or} \quad x = -1$$

Check: Let $x = -\frac{1}{9}$.

$$\sqrt{-10x - 1} + 3x = 0$$

$$\sqrt{-10\left(-\frac{1}{9}\right) - 1} + 3\left(-\frac{1}{9}\right) \stackrel{?}{=} 0$$

$$\sqrt{\frac{10}{9} - \frac{9}{9}} - \frac{3}{9} \stackrel{?}{=} 0$$

$$\sqrt{\frac{1}{9}} - \frac{1}{3} \stackrel{?}{=} 0$$

$$\frac{1}{3} - \frac{1}{3} = 0 \quad \text{True}$$

Let $x = -1$.

$$\sqrt{-10x - 1} + 3x = 0$$

$$\sqrt{-10(-1) - 1} + 3(-1) \stackrel{?}{=} 0$$

$$\sqrt{10 - 1} - 3 \stackrel{?}{=} 0$$

$$\sqrt{9} - 3 \stackrel{?}{=} 0$$

$$3 - 3 = 0 \quad \text{True}$$

Both solutions check. The solutions are $-\frac{1}{9}$ and -1, or the solution set is $\left\{-\frac{1}{9}, -1\right\}$. □

PRACTICE
2 Solve: $\sqrt{16x - 3} - 4x = 0$ ■

The following steps may be used to solve a radical equation.

Solving a Radical Equation

Step 1. Isolate one radical on one side of the equation.

Step 2. Raise each side of the equation to a power equal to the index of the radical and simplify.

Step 3. If the equation still contains a radical term, repeat Steps 1 and 2. If not, solve the equation.

Step 4. Check all proposed solutions in the original equation.

EXAMPLE 3   Solve: $\sqrt[3]{x+1} + 5 = 3$

Solution   First we isolate the radical by subtracting 5 from both sides of the equation.

$$\sqrt[3]{x+1} + 5 = 3$$
$$\sqrt[3]{x+1} = -2$$

Next we raise both sides of the equation to the third power to eliminate the radical.

$$(\sqrt[3]{x+1})^3 = (-2)^3$$
$$x + 1 = -8$$
$$x = -9$$

The solution checks in the original equation, so the solution is -9.

PRACTICE
3   Solve: $\sqrt[3]{x-2} + 1 = 3$

EXAMPLE 4   Solve: $\sqrt{4-x} = x - 2$

Solution

$$\sqrt{4-x} = x - 2$$
$$(\sqrt{4-x})^2 = (x-2)^2$$
$$4 - x = x^2 - 4x + 4$$
$$x^2 - 3x = 0 \qquad \text{Write the quadratic equation in standard form.}$$
$$x(x-3) = 0 \qquad \text{Factor.}$$
$$x = 0 \quad \text{or} \quad x - 3 = 0 \qquad \text{Set each factor equal to 0.}$$
$$x = 3$$

Check:

$$\sqrt{4-x} = x - 2 \qquad\qquad\qquad \sqrt{4-x} = x - 2$$
$$\sqrt{4-0} \stackrel{?}{=} 0 - 2 \quad \text{Let } x = 0. \qquad \sqrt{4-3} \stackrel{?}{=} 3 - 2 \quad \text{Let } x = 3.$$
$$2 = -2 \quad \text{False} \qquad\qquad\qquad 1 = 1 \quad \text{True}$$

The proposed solution 3 checks, but 0 does not. Since 0 is an extraneous solution, the only solution is 3.

PRACTICE
4   Solve: $\sqrt{16+x} = x - 4$

Helpful Hint

In Example 4, notice that $(x-2)^2 = x^2 - 4x + 4$. Make sure binomials are squared correctly.

✔ **CONCEPT CHECK**

How can you immediately tell that the equation $\sqrt{2y + 3} = -4$ has no real solution?

EXAMPLE 5   Solve: $\sqrt{2x + 5} + \sqrt{2x} = 3$

Solution We get one radical alone by subtracting $\sqrt{2x}$ from both sides.

$$\sqrt{2x + 5} + \sqrt{2x} = 3$$
$$\sqrt{2x + 5} = 3 - \sqrt{2x}$$

Now we use the power rule to begin eliminating the radicals. First we square both sides.

$$(\sqrt{2x + 5})^2 = (3 - \sqrt{2x})^2$$
$$2x + 5 = 9 - 6\sqrt{2x} + 2x \quad \text{Multiply } (3 - \sqrt{2x})(3 - \sqrt{2x}).$$

There is still a radical in the equation, so we get a radical alone again. Then we square both sides.

$2x + 5 = 9 - 6\sqrt{2x} + 2x$	
$6\sqrt{2x} = 4$	Get the radical alone.
$36(2x) = 16$	Square both sides of the equation to eliminate the radical.
$72x = 16$	Multiply.
$x = \dfrac{16}{72}$	Solve.
$x = \dfrac{2}{9}$	Simplify.

The proposed solution, $\dfrac{2}{9}$, checks in the original equation. The solution is $\dfrac{2}{9}$.   □

PRACTICE
5   Solve: $\sqrt{8x + 1} + \sqrt{3x} = 2$

Helpful Hint

Make sure expressions are squared correctly. In Example 5, we squared $(3 - \sqrt{2x})$ as

$$(3 - \sqrt{2x})^2 = (3 - \sqrt{2x})(3 - \sqrt{2x})$$
$$= 3 \cdot 3 - 3\sqrt{2x} - 3\sqrt{2x} + \sqrt{2x} \cdot \sqrt{2x}$$
$$= 9 - 6\sqrt{2x} + 2x$$

✔ **CONCEPT CHECK**

What is wrong with the following solution?

$$\sqrt{2x + 5} + \sqrt{4 - x} = 8$$
$$(\sqrt{2x + 5} + \sqrt{4 - x})^2 = 8^2$$
$$(2x + 5) + (4 - x) = 64$$
$$x + 9 = 64$$
$$x = 55$$

Answers to Concept Checks:
answers may vary;
$(\sqrt{2x + 5} + \sqrt{4 - x})^2$ is not
$(2x + 5) + (4 - x)$.

OBJECTIVE

2   Using the Pythagorean Theorem ▶

Recall that the Pythagorean theorem states that in a right triangle, the length of the hypotenuse squared equals the sum of the lengths of each of the legs squared.

Pythagorean Theorem

If a and b are the lengths of the legs of a right triangle and c is the length of the hypotenuse, then $a^2 + b^2 = c^2$.

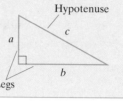

◁ **EXAMPLE 6**   Find the length of the unknown leg of the right triangle.

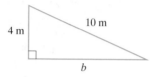

Solution   In the formula $a^2 + b^2 = c^2$, c is the hypotenuse. Here, $c = 10$, the length of the hypotenuse, and $a = 4$. We solve for b. Then $a^2 + b^2 = c^2$ becomes

$$4^2 + b^2 = 10^2$$
$$16 + b^2 = 100$$
$$b^2 = 84 \quad \text{Subtract 16 from both sides.}$$
$$b = \pm\sqrt{84} = \pm\sqrt{4\cdot 21} = \pm 2\sqrt{21}$$

Since b is a length and thus is positive, we will use the positive value only. The unknown leg of the triangle is $2\sqrt{21}$ meters long.   ☐

PRACTICE

6   Find the length of the unknown leg of the right triangle.

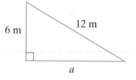

                                                                                    ■

◁ **EXAMPLE 7**   **Calculating Placement of a Wire**

A 50-foot supporting wire is to be attached to a 75-foot antenna. Because of surrounding buildings, sidewalks, and roadways, the wire must be anchored exactly 20 feet from the base of the antenna.

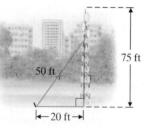

a. How high from the base of the antenna is the wire attached?

b. Local regulations require that a supporting wire be attached at a height no less than $\dfrac{3}{5}$ of the total height of the antenna. From part (a), have local regulations been met?

Solution

1. UNDERSTAND. Read and reread the problem. From the diagram, we notice that a right triangle is formed with hypotenuse 50 feet and one leg 20 feet. Let x be the height from the base of the antenna to the attached wire.

(Continued on next page)

2. TRANSLATE. Use the Pythagorean theorem.

$$a^2 + b^2 = c^2$$
$$20^2 + x^2 = 50^2 \quad a = 20, c = 50$$

3. SOLVE.

$$20^2 + x^2 = 50^2$$
$$400 + x^2 = 2500$$
$$x^2 = 2100 \qquad \text{Subtract 400 from both sides.}$$
$$x = \pm\sqrt{2100}$$
$$= \pm 10\sqrt{21}$$

4. INTERPRET. *Check* the work and *state* the solution.

Check: We will use only the positive value, $x = 10\sqrt{21}$, because x represents length. The wire is attached exactly $10\sqrt{21}$ feet from the base of the pole, or approximately 45.8 feet.

State: The supporting wire must be attached at a height no less than $\frac{3}{5}$ of the total height of the antenna. This height is $\frac{3}{5}$ (75 feet), or 45 feet. Since we know from part (a) that the wire is to be attached at a height of approximately 45.8 feet, local regulations have been met. □

PRACTICE
7 Keith Robinson bought two Siamese fighting fish, but when he got home, he found he only had one rectangular tank that was 12 in. long, 7 in. wide, and 5 in. deep. Since the fish must be kept separated, he needed to insert a plastic divider in the diagonal of the tank. He already has a piece that is 5 in. in one dimension, but how long must it be to fit corner to corner in the tank? ■

Graphing Calculator Explorations

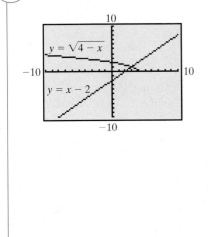

We can use a graphing calculator to solve radical equations. For example, to use a graphing calculator to approximate the solutions of the equation solved in Example 4, we graph the following.

$$Y_1 = \sqrt{4 - x} \quad \text{and} \quad Y_2 = x - 2$$

The x-value of the point of intersection is the solution. Use the Intersect feature or the Zoom and Trace features of your graphing calculator to see that the solution is 3.

Use a graphing calculator to solve each radical equation. Round all solutions to the nearest hundredth.

1. $\sqrt{x + 7} = x$　　　　　　　　　**2.** $\sqrt{3x + 5} = 2x$

3. $\sqrt{2x + 1} = \sqrt{2x} + 2$　　　　　**4.** $\sqrt{10x - 1} = \sqrt{-10x + 10} - 1$

5. $1.2x = \sqrt{3.1x + 5}$　　　　　　　**6.** $\sqrt{1.9x^2 - 2.2} = -0.8x + 3$

Vocabulary, Readiness & Video Check

Use the choices below to fill in each blank. Not all choices will be used.

hypotenuse	right	$x^2 + 25$	$16 - 8\sqrt{7x} + 7x$
extraneous solution	legs	$x^2 - 10x + 25$	$16 + 7x$

1. A proposed solution that is not a solution of the original equation is called a(n) _____.

2. The Pythagorean theorem states that $a^2 + b^2 = c^2$ where a and b are the lengths of the _____ of a(n) _____ triangle and c is the length of the _____.

3. The square of $x - 5$, or $(x - 5)^2 = $ _____ .

4. The square of $4 - \sqrt{7x}$, or $(4 - \sqrt{7x})^2 = $ _____ .

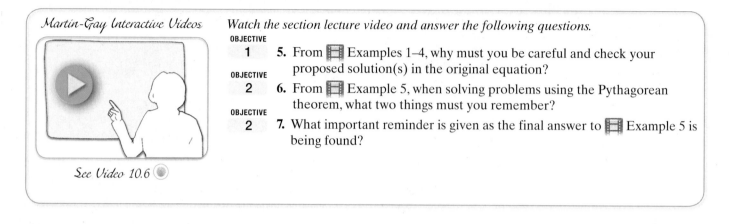

Martin-Gay Interactive Videos

Watch the section lecture video and answer the following questions.

OBJECTIVE 1

5. From Examples 1–4, why must you be careful and check your proposed solution(s) in the original equation?

OBJECTIVE 2

6. From Example 5, when solving problems using the Pythagorean theorem, what two things must you remember?

OBJECTIVE 2

7. What important reminder is given as the final answer to Example 5 is being found?

See Video 10.6

10.6 Exercise Set   MyMathLab®

Solve. See Examples 1 and 2.

1. $\sqrt{2x} = 4$

2. $\sqrt{3x} = 3$

3. $\sqrt{x - 3} = 2$

4. $\sqrt{x + 1} = 5$

5. $\sqrt{2x} = -4$

6. $\sqrt{5x} = -5$

7. $\sqrt{4x - 3} - 5 = 0$

8. $\sqrt{x - 3} - 1 = 0$

9. $\sqrt{2x - 3} - 2 = 1$

10. $\sqrt{3x + 3} - 4 = 8$

Solve. See Example 3.

11. $\sqrt[3]{6x} = -3$

12. $\sqrt[3]{4x} = -2$

13. $\sqrt[3]{x - 2} - 3 = 0$

14. $\sqrt[3]{2x - 6} - 4 = 0$

Solve. See Examples 4 and 5.

15. $\sqrt{13 - x} = x - 1$

16. $\sqrt{2x - 3} = 3 - x$

17. $x - \sqrt{4 - 3x} = -8$

18. $2x + \sqrt{x + 1} = 8$

19. $\sqrt{y + 5} = 2 - \sqrt{y - 4}$

20. $\sqrt{x + 3} + \sqrt{x - 5} = 3$

21. $\sqrt{x - 3} + \sqrt{x + 2} = 5$

22. $\sqrt{2x - 4} - \sqrt{3x + 4} = -2$

MIXED PRACTICE

Solve. See Examples 1 through 5.

23. $\sqrt{3x - 2} = 5$

24. $\sqrt{5x - 4} = 9$

25. $-\sqrt{2x} + 4 = -6$

26. $-\sqrt{3x + 9} = -12$

27. $\sqrt{3x + 1} + 2 = 0$

28. $\sqrt{3x + 1} - 2 = 0$

29. $\sqrt[4]{4x + 1} - 2 = 0$

30. $\sqrt[4]{2x - 9} - 3 = 0$

31. $\sqrt{4x - 3} = 7$

32. $\sqrt{3x + 9} = 6$

33. $\sqrt[3]{6x - 3} - 3 = 0$

34. $\sqrt[3]{3x + 4} = 7$

35. $\sqrt[3]{2x - 3} - 2 = -5$

36. $\sqrt[3]{x - 4} - 5 = -7$

37. $\sqrt{x + 4} = \sqrt{2x - 5}$

38. $\sqrt{3y + 6} = \sqrt{7y - 6}$

39. $x - \sqrt{1 - x} = -5$

40. $x - \sqrt{x - 2} = 4$

41. $\sqrt[3]{-6x - 1} = \sqrt[3]{-2x - 5}$

42. $\sqrt[3]{-4x - 3} = \sqrt[3]{-x - 15}$

43. $\sqrt{5x - 1} - \sqrt{x + 2} = 3$

44. $\sqrt{2x - 1} - 4 = -\sqrt{x - 4}$

45. $\sqrt{2x - 1} = \sqrt{1 - 2x}$

46. $\sqrt{7x - 4} = \sqrt{4 - 7x}$

47. $\sqrt{3x + 4} - 1 = \sqrt{2x + 1}$

48. $\sqrt{x - 2} + 3 = \sqrt{4x + 1}$

49. $\sqrt{y + 3} - \sqrt{y - 3} = 1$

50. $\sqrt{x + 1} - \sqrt{x - 1} = 2$

Find the length of the unknown side of each triangle. See Example 6.

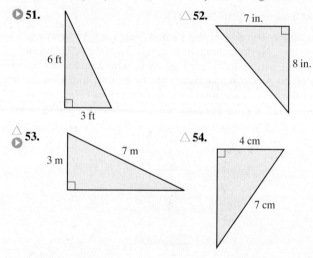

51. 6 ft, 3 ft

52. 7 in., 8 in.

53. 3 m, 7 m

54. 4 cm, 7 cm

Find the length of the unknown side of each triangle. Give the exact length and a one-decimal-place approximation. See Example 6.

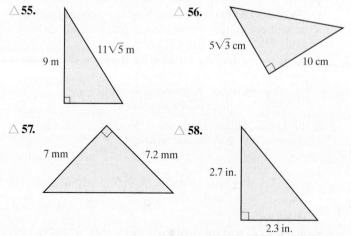

55. 9 m, $11\sqrt{5}$ m

56. $5\sqrt{3}$ cm, 10 cm

57. 7 mm, 7.2 mm

58. 2.7 in., 2.3 in.

Solve. Give exact answers and two-decimal-place approximations where appropriate. For Exercises 59 and 60, the solutions have been started for you. See Example 7.

59. A wire is needed to support a vertical pole 15 feet tall. The cable will be anchored to a stake 8 feet from the base of the pole. How much cable is needed?

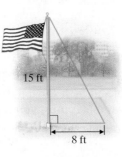

15 ft

8 ft

Start the solution:

1. UNDERSTAND the problem. Reread it as many times as needed. Notice that a right triangle is formed with legs of length 8 ft and 15 ft.
   Since we are looking for how much cable is needed, let

   x = amount of cable needed.

2. TRANSLATE into an equation. We use the Pythagorean theorem. (Fill in the blanks below.)

   $$a^2 \quad + \quad b^2 \quad = \quad c^2$$
   $$\downarrow \qquad\qquad \downarrow$$
   $$\underline{\quad}^2 \quad + \quad \underline{\quad}^2 \quad = \quad x^2$$

   Finish with:

3. SOLVE and 4. INTERPRET

60. The tallest structure in the United States is a TV tower in Blanchard, North Dakota. Its height is 2063 feet. A 2382-foot length of wire is to be used as a guy wire attached to the top of the tower. Approximate to the nearest foot how far from the base of the tower the guy wire must be anchored. (*Source:* U.S. Geological Survey)

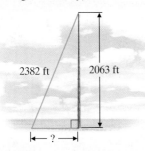

2382 ft 2063 ft

← ? →

Start the solution:

1. UNDERSTAND the problem. Reread it as many times as needed. Notice that a right triangle is formed with hypotenuse 2382 feet and one leg 2063 feet.
   Since we are looking for how far from the base of the tower the guy wire is anchored, let

   x = distance from base of tower to where guy wire is anchored.

2. TRANSLATE into an equation. We use the Pythagorean theorem. (Fill in the blanks below.)

   $$a^2 \quad + \quad b^2 \quad = \quad c^2$$
   $$\downarrow \qquad\qquad \downarrow$$
   $$\underline{\quad}^2 \quad + \quad x^2 \quad = \quad \underline{\quad}^2$$

   Finish with:

3. SOLVE and 4. INTERPRET

△ **61.** A spotlight is mounted on the eaves of a house 12 feet above the ground. A flower bed runs between the house and the sidewalk, so the closest a ladder can be placed to the house is 5 feet. How long of a ladder is needed so that an electrician can reach the place where the light is mounted?

12 ft

5 ft

△ **62.** A wire is to be attached to support a telephone pole. Because of surrounding buildings, sidewalks, and roadways, the wire must be anchored exactly 15 feet from the base of the pole. Telephone company workers have only 30 feet of cable, and 2 feet of that must be used to attach the cable to the pole and to the stake on the ground. How high from the base of the pole can the wire be attached?

← 15 ft →

△ **63.** The radius of the moon is 1080 miles. Use the formula for the radius r of a sphere given its surface area A,

$$r = \sqrt{\frac{A}{4\pi}}$$

to find the surface area of the moon. Round to the nearest square mile. (*Source:* National Space Science Data Center)

64. Police departments find it very useful to be able to approximate the speed of a car when they are given the distance that the car skidded before it came to a stop. If the road surface is wet concrete, the function $S(x) = \sqrt{10.5x}$ is used, where $S(x)$ is the speed of the car in miles per hour and x is the distance skidded in feet. Find how fast a car was moving if it skidded 280 feet on wet concrete.

65. The formula $v = \sqrt{2gh}$ gives the velocity v, in feet per second, of an object when it falls h feet accelerated by gravity g, in feet per second squared. If g is approximately 32 feet per second squared, find how far an object has fallen if its velocity is 80 feet per second.

66. Two tractors are pulling a tree stump from a field. If two forces A and B pull at right angles (90°) to each other, the size of the resulting force R is given by the formula $R = \sqrt{A^2 + B^2}$. If tractor A is exerting 600 pounds of force and the resulting force is 850 pounds, find how much force tractor B is exerting.

In psychology, it has been suggested that the number S of nonsense syllables that a person can repeat consecutively depends on his or her IQ score I according to the equation $S = 2\sqrt{I} - 9$.

67. Use this relationship to estimate the IQ of a person who can repeat 11 nonsense syllables consecutively.

68. Use this relationship to estimate the IQ of a person who can repeat 15 nonsense syllables consecutively.

*The **period** of a pendulum is the time it takes for the pendulum to make one full back-and-forth swing. The period of a pendulum depends on the length of the pendulum. The formula for the period P, in seconds, is $P = 2\pi\sqrt{\dfrac{l}{32}}$, where l is the length of the pendulum in feet. Use this formula for Exercises 69 through 74.*

69. Find the period of a pendulum whose length is 2 feet. Give the exact answer and a two-decimal-place approximation.

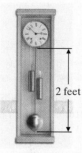

2 feet

70. Klockit sells a 43-inch lyre pendulum. Find the period of this pendulum. Round your answer to two decimal places. (*Hint:* First convert inches to feet.)

71. Find the length of a pendulum whose period is 4 seconds. Round your answer to two decimal places.

72. Find the length of a pendulum whose period is 3 seconds. Round your answer to two decimal places.

73. Study the relationship between period and pendulum length in Exercises 69 through 72 and make a conjecture about this relationship.

74. Galileo experimented with pendulums. He supposedly made conjectures about pendulums of equal length with different bob weights. Try this experiment. Make two pendulums 3 feet long. Attach a heavy weight (lead) to one and a light weight (a cork) to the other. Pull both pendulums back the same angle measure and release. Make a conjecture from your observations.

If the three lengths of the sides of a triangle are known, Heron's formula can be used to find its area. If a, b, and c are the lengths of the three sides, Heron's formula for area is

$$A = \sqrt{s(s-a)(s-b)(s-c)}$$

where s is half the perimeter of the triangle, or $s = \dfrac{1}{2}(a+b+c)$.

Use this formula to find the area of each triangle. Give the exact answer and then a two-decimal-place approximation.

△ **75.**   △ **76.**

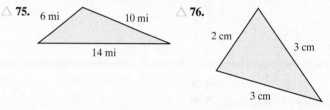

77. Describe when Heron's formula might be useful.

78. In your own words, explain why you think s in Heron's formula is called the *semiperimeter*.

The maximum distance $D(h)$ in kilometers that a person can see from a height h kilometers above the ground is given by the function $D(h) = 111.7\sqrt{h}$. Use this function for Exercises 79 and 80. Round your answers to two decimal places.

79. Find the height that would allow a person to see 80 kilometers.

80. Find the height that would allow a person to see 40 kilometers.

REVIEW AND PREVIEW

Use the vertical line test to determine whether each graph represents the graph of a function. See Section 3.6.

81.   **82.**

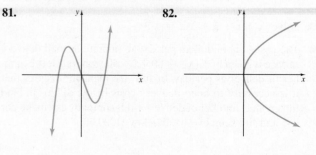

83.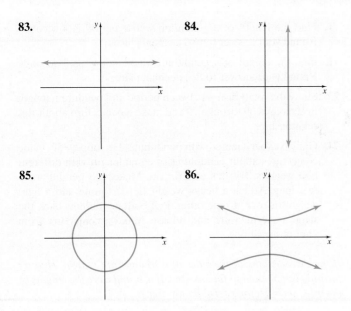

84.

85.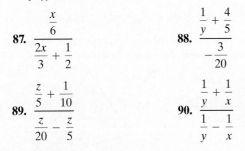

86.

Simplify. See Section 7.7.

87. $\dfrac{\dfrac{x}{6}}{\dfrac{2x}{3} + \dfrac{1}{2}}$

88. $\dfrac{\dfrac{1}{y} + \dfrac{4}{5}}{-\dfrac{3}{20}}$

89. $\dfrac{\dfrac{z}{5} + \dfrac{1}{10}}{\dfrac{z}{20} - \dfrac{z}{5}}$

90. $\dfrac{\dfrac{1}{y} + \dfrac{1}{x}}{\dfrac{1}{y} - \dfrac{1}{x}}$

CONCEPT EXTENSIONS

Find the error in each solution and correct. See the second Concept Check in this section.

91.
$$\sqrt{5x - 1} + 4 = 7$$
$$(\sqrt{5x - 1} + 4)^2 = 7^2$$
$$5x - 1 + 16 = 49$$
$$5x = 34$$
$$x = \frac{34}{5}$$

92.
$$\sqrt{2x + 3} + 4 = 1$$
$$\sqrt{2x + 3} = 5$$
$$(\sqrt{2x + 3})^2 = 5^2$$
$$2x + 3 = 25$$
$$2x = 22$$
$$x = 11$$

93. Solve: $\sqrt{\sqrt{x + 3}} + \sqrt{x} = \sqrt{3}$

94. The cost $C(x)$ in dollars per day to operate a small delivery service is given by $C(x) = 80\sqrt[3]{x} + 500$, where x is the number of deliveries per day. In July, the manager decides that it is necessary to keep delivery costs below $1220.00. Find the greatest number of deliveries this company can make per day and still keep overhead below $1220.00.

95. Consider the equations $\sqrt{2x} = 4$ and $\sqrt[3]{2x} = 4$.
   a. Explain the difference in solving these equations.
   b. Explain the similarity in solving these equations.

96. Explain why proposed solutions of radical equations must be checked in the original equation.

For Exercises 97 through 100, see the example below.

Example
Solve $(t^2 - 3t) - 2\sqrt{t^2 - 3t} = 0$.

Solution

Substitution can be used to make this problem somewhat simpler. Since $t^2 - 3t$ occurs more than once, let $x = t^2 - 3t$.

$$(t^2 - 3t) - 2\sqrt{t^2 - 3t} = 0$$
$$x - 2\sqrt{x} = 0 \quad \text{Let } x = t^2 - 3t.$$
$$x = 2\sqrt{x}$$
$$x^2 = (2\sqrt{x})^2$$
$$x^2 = 4x$$
$$x^2 - 4x = 0$$
$$x(x - 4) = 0$$
$$x = 0 \quad \text{or} \quad x - 4 = 0$$
$$x = 4$$

Now we "undo" the substitution by replacing x with $t^2 - 3t$.

$$x = 0$$
$$t^2 - 3t = 0 \quad \text{Replace } x \text{ with } t^2 - 3t.$$
$$t(t - 3) = 0 \quad \text{Factor.}$$
$$t = 0 \quad \text{or} \quad t - 3 = 0$$
$$t = 3$$

Replace x with $t^2 - 3t$ in $x = 4$.

$$x = 4$$
$$t^2 - 3t = 4 \quad \text{Replace } x \text{ with } t^2 - 3t.$$
$$t^2 - 3t - 4 = 0 \quad \text{Subtract 4.}$$
$$(t - 4)(t + 1) = 0 \quad \text{Factor.}$$
$$t - 4 = 0 \quad \text{or} \quad t + 1 = 0$$
$$t = 4 \qquad\qquad t = -1$$

In this problem, we have four possible solutions for t: $0, 3, 4$, and -1. All four solutions check in the original equation, so the solutions are $-1, 0, 3, 4$.

Solve. See the preceding example.

97. $3\sqrt{x^2 - 8x} = x^2 - 8x$

98. $\sqrt{(x^2 - x)} + 7 = 2(x^2 - x) - 1$

99. $7 - (x^2 - 3x) = \sqrt{(x^2 - 3x)} + 5$

100. $x^2 + 6x = 4\sqrt{x^2 + 6x}$

10.7 Complex Numbers

OBJECTIVES

1 Write Square Roots of Negative Numbers in the Form bi.

2 Add or Subtract Complex Numbers.

3 Multiply Complex Numbers.

4 Divide Complex Numbers.

5 Raise i to Powers.

OBJECTIVE

1 Writing Numbers in the Form bi

Our work with radical expressions has excluded expressions such as $\sqrt{-16}$ because $\sqrt{-16}$ is not a real number; there is no real number whose square is -16. In this section, we discuss a number system that includes roots of negative numbers. This number system is the **complex number system,** and it includes the set of real numbers as a subset. The complex number system allows us to solve equations such as $x^2 + 1 = 0$ that have no real number solutions. The set of complex numbers includes the **imaginary unit.**

Imaginary Unit

The imaginary unit, written i, is the number whose square is -1. That is,
$$i^2 = -1 \quad \text{and} \quad i = \sqrt{-1}$$

To write the square root of a negative number in terms of i, use the property that if a is a positive number, then
$$\sqrt{-a} = \sqrt{-1} \cdot \sqrt{a}$$
$$= i \cdot \sqrt{a}$$

Using i, we can write $\sqrt{-16}$ as
$$\sqrt{-16} = \sqrt{-1 \cdot 16} = \sqrt{-1} \cdot \sqrt{16} = i \cdot 4, \text{ or } 4i$$

EXAMPLE 1 Write with i notation.

a. $\sqrt{-36}$ **b.** $\sqrt{-5}$ **c.** $-\sqrt{-20}$

Solution

a. $\sqrt{-36} = \sqrt{-1 \cdot 36} = \sqrt{-1} \cdot \sqrt{36} = i \cdot 6, \text{ or } 6i$

b. $\sqrt{-5} = \sqrt{-1(5)} = \sqrt{-1} \cdot \sqrt{5} = i\sqrt{5}.$

c. $-\sqrt{-20} = -\sqrt{-1 \cdot 20} = -\sqrt{-1} \cdot \sqrt{4 \cdot 5} = -i \cdot 2\sqrt{5} = -2i\sqrt{5}$

> **Helpful Hint**
>
> Since $\sqrt{5}i$ can easily be confused with $\sqrt{5i}$, we write $\sqrt{5}i$ as $i\sqrt{5}$.

PRACTICE

1 Write with i notation.

a. $\sqrt{-4}$ **b.** $\sqrt{-7}$ **c.** $-\sqrt{-18}$

The product rule for radicals does not necessarily hold true for imaginary numbers. *To multiply square roots of negative numbers, first we write each number in terms of the imaginary unit i.* For example, to multiply $\sqrt{-4}$ and $\sqrt{-9}$, we first write each number in the form bi.
$$\sqrt{-4}\sqrt{-9} = 2i(3i) = 6i^2 = 6(-1) = -6 \quad \text{Correct}$$

We will also use this method to simplify quotients of square roots of negative numbers. Why? The product rule does not work for this example. In other words,
$$\sqrt{-4} \cdot \sqrt{-9} = \sqrt{(-4)(-9)} = \sqrt{36} = 6 \quad \text{Incorrect}$$

EXAMPLE 2 Multiply or divide as indicated.

a. $\sqrt{-3} \cdot \sqrt{-5}$ b. $\sqrt{-36} \cdot \sqrt{-1}$ c. $\sqrt{8} \cdot \sqrt{-2}$ d. $\dfrac{\sqrt{-125}}{\sqrt{5}}$

Solution

a. $\sqrt{-3} \cdot \sqrt{-5} = i\sqrt{3}(i\sqrt{5}) = i^2\sqrt{15} = -1\sqrt{15} = -\sqrt{15}$

b. $\sqrt{-36} \cdot \sqrt{-1} = 6i(i) = 6i^2 = 6(-1) = -6$

c. $\sqrt{8} \cdot \sqrt{-2} = 2\sqrt{2}(i\sqrt{2}) = 2i(\sqrt{2}\sqrt{2}) = 2i(2) = 4i$

d. $\dfrac{\sqrt{-125}}{\sqrt{5}} = \dfrac{i\sqrt{125}}{\sqrt{5}} = i\sqrt{25} = 5i$

PRACTICE

2 Multiply or divide as indicated.

a. $\sqrt{-5} \cdot \sqrt{-6}$ b. $\sqrt{-9} \cdot \sqrt{-1}$ c. $\sqrt{125} \cdot \sqrt{-5}$ d. $\dfrac{\sqrt{-27}}{\sqrt{3}}$

Now that we have practiced working with the imaginary unit, we define complex numbers.

Complex Numbers

A **complex number** is a number that can be written in the form $a + bi$, where a and b are real numbers.

Notice that the set of real numbers is a subset of the complex numbers since any real number can be written in the form of a complex number. For example,

$$16 = 16 + 0i$$

In general, a complex number $a + bi$ is a real number if $b = 0$. Also, a complex number is called a **pure imaginary number** or an imaginary number if $a = 0$ and $b \neq 0$. For example,

$$3i = 0 + 3i \quad \text{and} \quad i\sqrt{7} = 0 + i\sqrt{7}$$

are pure imaginary numbers.

The following diagram shows the relationship between complex numbers and their subsets.

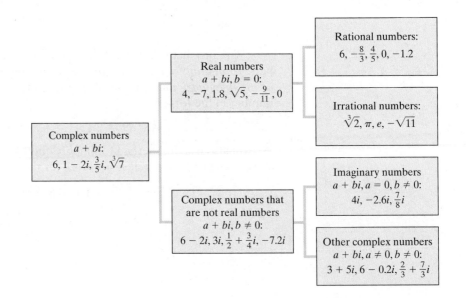

✔ **CONCEPT CHECK**

True or false? Every complex number is also a real number.

OBJECTIVE

2   Adding or Subtracting Complex Numbers ▶

Two complex numbers $a + bi$ and $c + di$ are equal if and only if $a = c$ and $b = d$. Complex numbers can be added or subtracted by adding or subtracting their real parts and then adding or subtracting their imaginary parts.

Sum or Difference of Complex Numbers

If $a + bi$ and $c + di$ are complex numbers, then their sum is

$$(a + bi) + (c + di) = (a + c) + (b + d)i$$

Their difference is

$$(a + bi) - (c + di) = a + bi - c - di = (a - c) + (b - d)i$$

EXAMPLE 3   Add or subtract the complex numbers. Write the sum or difference in the form $a + bi$.

a. $(2 + 3i) + (-3 + 2i)$ **b.** $5i - (1 - i)$ **c.** $(-3 - 7i) - (-6)$

Solution

a. $(2 + 3i) + (-3 + 2i) = (2 - 3) + (3 + 2)i = -1 + 5i$

b. $5i - (1 - i) = 5i - 1 + i$
$$= -1 + (5 + 1)i$$
$$= -1 + 6i$$

c. $(-3 - 7i) - (-6) = -3 - 7i + 6$
$$= (-3 + 6) - 7i$$
$$= 3 - 7i$$ □

PRACTICE

3   Add or subtract the complex numbers. Write the sum or difference in the form $a + bi$.

a. $(3 - 5i) + (-4 + i)$ **b.** $4i - (3 - i)$ **c.** $(-5 - 2i) - (-8)$ ■

OBJECTIVE

3   Multiplying Complex Numbers ▶

To multiply two complex numbers of the form $a + bi$, we multiply as though they are binomials. Then we use the relationship $i^2 = -1$ to simplify.

EXAMPLE 4   Multiply the complex numbers. Write the product in the form $a + bi$.

a. $-7i \cdot 3i$ **b.** $3i(2 - i)$ **c.** $(2 - 5i)(4 + i)$

d. $(2 - i)^2$ **e.** $(7 + 3i)(7 - 3i)$

Solution

a. $-7i \cdot 3i = -21i^2$
$$= -21(-1)   \text{Replace } i^2 \text{ with } -1.$$
$$= 21 + 0i$$

(Continued on next page)

b. $3i(2 - i) = 3i \cdot 2 - 3i \cdot i$ Use the distributive property.

$\qquad\qquad = 6i - 3i^2$ Multiply.

$\qquad\qquad = 6i - 3(-1)$ Replace i^2 with -1.

$\qquad\qquad = 6i + 3$

$\qquad\qquad = 3 + 6i$ Use the FOIL order below. (First, Outer, Inner, Last)

c. $(2 - 5i)(4 + i) = 2(4) + 2(i) - 5i(4) - 5i(i)$

$\qquad\qquad\qquad\qquad\quad$ F $\qquad$ O $\qquad$ I $\qquad$ L

$\qquad\qquad\qquad = 8 + 2i - 20i - 5i^2$

$\qquad\qquad\qquad = 8 - 18i - 5(-1)$ $\qquad\qquad\qquad\qquad i^2 = -1$

$\qquad\qquad\qquad = 8 - 18i + 5$

$\qquad\qquad\qquad = 13 - 18i$

d. $(2 - i)^2 = (2 - i)(2 - i)$

$\qquad\qquad = 2(2) - 2(i) - 2(i) + i^2$

$\qquad\qquad = 4 - 4i + (-1)$ $\qquad\qquad\qquad i^2 = -1$

$\qquad\qquad = 3 - 4i$

e. $(7 + 3i)(7 - 3i) = 7(7) - 7(3i) + 3i(7) - 3i(3i)$

$\qquad\qquad\qquad = 49 - 21i + 21i - 9i^2$

$\qquad\qquad\qquad = 49 - 9(-1)$ $\qquad\qquad\qquad\qquad i^2 = -1$

$\qquad\qquad\qquad = 49 + 9$

$\qquad\qquad\qquad = 58 + 0i$ $\qquad\qquad\qquad\qquad\qquad\qquad\qquad\qquad$ □

PRACTICE

4   Multiply the complex numbers. Write the product in the form $a + bi$.

a. $-4i \cdot 5i$ $\qquad\qquad$ **b.** $5i(2 + i)$ $\qquad\qquad$ **c.** $(2 + 3i)(6 - i)$

d. $(3 - i)^2$ $\qquad\qquad$ **e.** $(9 + 2i)(9 - 2i)$ $\qquad\qquad\qquad$ ■

Notice that if you add, subtract, or multiply two complex numbers, just like real numbers, the result is a complex number.

OBJECTIVE

4   Dividing Complex Numbers ▶

From Example 4(e), notice that the product of $7 + 3i$ and $7 - 3i$ is a real number. These two complex numbers are called **complex conjugates** of one another. In general, we have the following definition.

Complex Conjugates

The complex numbers $(a + bi)$ and $(a - bi)$ are called **complex conjugates** of each other, and

$$(a + bi)(a - bi) = a^2 + b^2.$$

To see that the product of a complex number $a + bi$ and its conjugate $a - bi$ is the real number $a^2 + b^2$, we multiply.

$$(a + bi)(a - bi) = a^2 - abi + abi - b^2i^2$$
$$= a^2 - b^2(-1)$$
$$= a^2 + b^2$$

We use complex conjugates to divide by a complex number.

EXAMPLE 5   Divide. Write in the form $a + bi$.

a. $\dfrac{2 + i}{1 - i}$ **b.** $\dfrac{7}{3i}$

Solution

a. Multiply the numerator and denominator by the complex conjugate of $1 - i$ to eliminate the imaginary number in the denominator.

$$\frac{2 + i}{1 - i} = \frac{(2 + i)(1 + i)}{(1 - i)(1 + i)}$$

$$= \frac{2(1) + 2(i) + 1(i) + i^2}{1^2 - i^2}$$

$$= \frac{2 + 3i - 1}{1 + 1} \qquad i^2 = -1.$$

$$= \frac{1 + 3i}{2} \quad \text{or} \quad \frac{1}{2} + \frac{3}{2}i$$

b. Multiply the numerator and denominator by the conjugate of $3i$. Note that $3i = 0 + 3i$, so its conjugate is $0 - 3i$ or $-3i$.

$$\frac{7}{3i} = \frac{7(-3i)}{(3i)(-3i)} = \frac{-21i}{-9i^2} = \frac{-21i}{-9(-1)} = \frac{-21i}{9} = \frac{-7i}{3} \quad \text{or} \quad 0 - \frac{7}{3}i \quad \square$$

PRACTICE

5   Divide. Write in the form $a + bi$.

a. $\dfrac{4 - i}{3 + i}$ **b.** $\dfrac{5}{2i}$ ∎

Helpful Hint

Recall that division can be checked by multiplication.

To check that $\dfrac{2 + i}{1 - i} = \dfrac{1}{2} + \dfrac{3}{2}i$, in Example 5(a), multiply $\left(\dfrac{1}{2} + \dfrac{3}{2}i\right)(1 - i)$ to verify that the product is $2 + i$.

OBJECTIVE

5   Finding Powers of i ▶

We can use the fact that $i^2 = -1$ to find higher powers of i. To find i^3, we rewrite it as the product of i^2 and i.

$$i^3 = i^2 \cdot i = (-1)i = -i$$
$$i^4 = i^2 \cdot i^2 = (-1) \cdot (-1) = 1$$

We continue this process and use the fact that $i^4 = 1$ and $i^2 = -1$ to simplify i^5 and i^6.

$$i^5 = i^4 \cdot i = 1 \cdot i = i$$
$$i^6 = i^4 \cdot i^2 = 1 \cdot (-1) = -1$$

If we continue finding powers of i, we generate the following pattern. Notice that the values i, -1, $-i$, and 1 repeat as i is raised to higher and higher powers.

$i^1 = i$	$i^5 = i$	$i^9 = i$
$i^2 = -1$	$i^6 = -1$	$i^{10} = -1$
$i^3 = -i$	$i^7 = -i$	$i^{11} = -i$
$i^4 = 1$	$i^8 = 1$	$i^{12} = 1$

This pattern allows us to find other powers of i. To do so, we will use the fact that $i^4 = 1$ and rewrite a power of i in terms of i^4. For example,

$$i^{22} = i^{20} \cdot i^2 = (i^4)^5 \cdot i^2 = 1^5 \cdot (-1) = 1 \cdot (-1) = -1.$$

EXAMPLE 6 Find the following powers of i.

a. i^7 b. i^{20} c. i^{46} d. i^{-12}

Solution

a. $i^7 = i^4 \cdot i^3 = 1(-i) = -i$

b. $i^{20} = (i^4)^5 = 1^5 = 1$

c. $i^{46} = i^{44} \cdot i^2 = (i^4)^{11} \cdot i^2 = 1^{11}(-1) = -1$

d. $i^{-12} = \dfrac{1}{i^{12}} = \dfrac{1}{(i^4)^3} = \dfrac{1}{(1)^3} = \dfrac{1}{1} = 1$

PRACTICE
6 Find the following powers of i.

a. i^9 b. i^{16} c. i^{34} d. i^{-24}

✔ Vocabulary, Readiness & Video Check

Use the choices below to fill in each blank. Not all choices will be used.

-1	$\sqrt{-1}$	real	imaginary unit
1	$\sqrt{1}$	complex	pure imaginary

1. A(n) _____ number is one that can be written in the form $a + bi$, where a and b are real numbers.

2. In the complex number system, i denotes the _____.

3. $i^2 = $ _____

4. $i = $ _____

5. A complex number, $a + bi$, is a(n) _____ number if $b = 0$.

6. A complex number, $a + bi$, is a(n) _____ number if $a = 0$ and $b \neq 0$.

Martin-Gay Interactive Videos

See Video 10.7 ⊙

Watch the section lecture video and answer the following questions.

OBJECTIVE 1
7. From ▦ Example 4, with what rule must you be especially careful when working with imaginary numbers and why?

OBJECTIVE 2
8. In ▦ Examples 5 and 6, what is the process of adding and subtracting complex numbers compared to? What important reminder is given about i?

OBJECTIVE 3
9. In ▦ Examples 7 and 8, what part of the definition of the imaginary unit i may be used during the multiplication of complex numbers to help simplify products?

OBJECTIVE 4
10. In ▦ Example 9, using complex conjugates to divide complex numbers is compared to what process?

OBJECTIVE 5
11. From the lecture before ▦ Example 10, what are the first four powers of i whose values keep repeating?

10.7 Exercise Set MyMathLab®

Simplify. See Example 1.

1. $\sqrt{-81}$ **2.** $\sqrt{-49}$ **3.** $\sqrt{-7}$

4. $\sqrt{-3}$ **5.** $-\sqrt{16}$ **6.** $-\sqrt{4}$

7. $\sqrt{-64}$ **8.** $\sqrt{-100}$

Write in terms of i. See Example 1.

9. $\sqrt{-24}$ **10.** $\sqrt{-32}$

11. $-\sqrt{-36}$ **12.** $-\sqrt{-121}$

13. $8\sqrt{-63}$ **14.** $4\sqrt{-20}$

15. $-\sqrt{54}$ **16.** $\sqrt{-63}$

Multiply or divide. See Example 2.

17. $\sqrt{-2} \cdot \sqrt{-7}$ **18.** $\sqrt{-11} \cdot \sqrt{-3}$

19. $\sqrt{-5} \cdot \sqrt{-10}$ **20.** $\sqrt{-2} \cdot \sqrt{-6}$

21. $\sqrt{16} \cdot \sqrt{-1}$ **22.** $\sqrt{3} \cdot \sqrt{-27}$

23. $\dfrac{\sqrt{-9}}{\sqrt{3}}$ **24.** $\dfrac{\sqrt{49}}{\sqrt{-10}}$

25. $\dfrac{\sqrt{-80}}{\sqrt{-10}}$ **26.** $\dfrac{\sqrt{-40}}{\sqrt{-8}}$

Add or subtract. Write the sum or difference in the form a + bi. See Example 3.

27. $(4 - 7i) + (2 + 3i)$ **28.** $(2 - 4i) - (2 - i)$

29. $(6 + 5i) - (8 - i)$ **30.** $(8 - 3i) + (-8 + 3i)$

31. $6 - (8 + 4i)$ **32.** $(9 - 4i) - 9$

Multiply. Write the product in the form a + bi. See Example 4.

33. $-10i \cdot -4i$ **34.** $-2i \cdot -11i$

35. $6i(2 - 3i)$ **36.** $5i(4 - 7i)$

37. $(\sqrt{3} + 2i)(\sqrt{3} - 2i)$ **38.** $(\sqrt{5} - 5i)(\sqrt{5} + 5i)$

39. $(4 - 2i)^2$ **40.** $(6 - 3i)^2$

Write each quotient in the form a + bi. See Example 5.

41. $\dfrac{4}{i}$ **42.** $\dfrac{5}{6i}$

43. $\dfrac{7}{4 + 3i}$ **44.** $\dfrac{9}{1 - 2i}$

45. $\dfrac{3 + 5i}{1 + i}$ **46.** $\dfrac{6 + 2i}{4 - 3i}$

47. $\dfrac{5 - i}{3 - 2i}$ **48.** $\dfrac{6 - i}{2 + i}$

MIXED PRACTICE

Perform each indicated operation. Write the result in the form a + bi.

49. $(7i)(-9i)$ **50.** $(-6i)(-4i)$

51. $(6 - 3i) - (4 - 2i)$ **52.** $(-2 - 4i) - (6 - 8i)$

53. $-3i(-1 + 9i)$ **54.** $-5i(-2 + i)$

55. $\dfrac{4 - 5i}{2i}$ **56.** $\dfrac{6 + 8i}{3i}$

57. $(4 + i)(5 + 2i)$ **58.** $(3 + i)(2 + 4i)$

59. $(6 - 2i)(3 + i)$ **60.** $(2 - 4i)(2 - i)$

61. $(8 - 3i) + (2 + 3i)$ **62.** $(7 + 4i) + (4 - 4i)$

63. $(1 - i)(1 + i)$ **64.** $(6 + 2i)(6 - 2i)$

65. $\dfrac{16 + 15i}{-3i}$ **66.** $\dfrac{2 - 3i}{-7i}$

67. $(9 + 8i)^2$ **68.** $(4 - 7i)^2$

69. $\dfrac{2}{3 + i}$ **70.** $\dfrac{5}{3 - 2i}$

71. $(5 - 6i) - 4i$ **72.** $(6 - 2i) + 7i$

73. $\dfrac{2 - 3i}{2 + i}$ **74.** $\dfrac{6 + 5i}{6 - 5i}$

75. $(2 + 4i) + (6 - 5i)$ **76.** $(5 - 3i) + (7 - 8i)$

77. $(\sqrt{6} + i)(\sqrt{6} - i)$ **78.** $(\sqrt{14} - 4i)(\sqrt{14} + 4i)$

79. $4(2 - i)^2$ **80.** $9(2 - i)^2$

Find each power of i. See Example 6.

81. i^8 **82.** i^{10} **83.** i^{21} **84.** i^{15}

85. i^{11} **86.** i^{40} **87.** i^{-6} **88.** i^{-9}

89. $(2i)^6$ **90.** $(5i)^4$ **91.** $(-3i)^5$ **92.** $(-2i)^7$

REVIEW AND PREVIEW

Recall that the sum of the measures of the angles of a triangle is 180°. Find the unknown angle in each triangle.

93.   **94.**

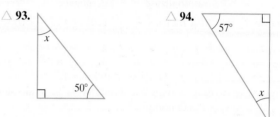

Use synthetic division to divide the following. See Section 5.7.

95. $(x^3 - 6x^2 + 3x - 4) \div (x - 1)$

96. $(5x^4 - 3x^2 + 2) \div (x + 2)$

Thirty people were recently polled about the average monthly balance in their checking accounts. The results of this poll are shown in the following histogram. Use this graph to answer Exercises 97 through 102. See Section 3.1.

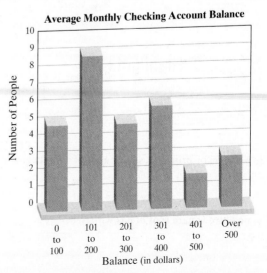

Average Monthly Checking Account Balance

97. How many people polled reported an average checking balance of $201 to $300?

98. How many people polled reported an average checking balance of $0 to $100?

99. How many people polled reported an average checking balance of $200 or less?

100. How many people polled reported an average checking balance of $301 or more?

101. What percent of people polled reported an average checking balance of $201 to $300? Round to the nearest tenth of a percent.

102. What percent of people polled reported an average checking balance of $0 to $100? Round to the nearest tenth of a percent.

CONCEPT EXTENSIONS

Write in the form a + bi.

103. $i^3 - i^4$

104. $i^8 - i^7$

105. $i^6 + i^8$

106. $i^4 + i^{12}$

107. $2 + \sqrt{-9}$

108. $5 - \sqrt{-16}$

109. $\dfrac{6 + \sqrt{-18}}{3}$

110. $\dfrac{4 - \sqrt{-8}}{2}$

111. $\dfrac{5 - \sqrt{-75}}{10}$

112. $\dfrac{7 + \sqrt{-98}}{14}$

113. Describe how to find the conjugate of a complex number.

114. Explain why the product of a complex number and its complex conjugate is a real number.

Simplify.

115. $(8 - \sqrt{-3}) - (2 + \sqrt{-12})$

116. $(8 - \sqrt{-4}) - (2 + \sqrt{-16})$

117. Determine whether $2i$ is a solution of $x^2 + 4 = 0$.

118. Determine whether $-1 + i$ is a solution of $x^2 + 2x = -2$.

Chapter 10 Vocabulary Check

Fill in each blank with one of the words or phrases listed below.

index	rationalizing	conjugate	principal square root	cube root	midpoint
complex number	like radicals	radicand	imaginary unit	distance	

1. The _____ of $\sqrt{3} + 2$ is $\sqrt{3} - 2$.

2. The _____ of a positive number a is written as $\sqrt{a}$.

3. The process of writing a radical expression as an equivalent expression but without a radical in the denominator is called _____ the denominator.

4. The _____, written i, is the number whose square is -1.

5. The _____ of a number is written as $\sqrt[3]{a}$.

6. In the notation $\sqrt[n]{a}$, n is called the _____ and a is called the _____.

7. Radicals with the same index and the same radicand are called _____.

8. A(n) _____ is a number that can be written in the form $a + bi$, where a and b are real numbers.

9. The _____ formula is $d = \sqrt{(x_2 - x_1)^2 + (y_2 - y_1)^2}$.

10. The _____ formula is $\left(\dfrac{x_1 + x_2}{2}, \dfrac{y_1 + y_2}{2} \right)$.

Chapter 10 Highlights

DEFINITIONS AND CONCEPTS	EXAMPLES
Section 10.1 Radicals and Radical Functions	

DEFINITIONS AND CONCEPTS	EXAMPLES
The **positive**, or **principal**, **square root** of a nonnegative number a is written as $\sqrt{a}$. $\qquad \sqrt{a} = b$ only if $b^2 = a$ and $b \geq 0$ The **negative square root** of a is written as $-\sqrt{a}$.	$\sqrt{36} = 6 \qquad \sqrt{\dfrac{9}{100}} = \dfrac{3}{10}$ $-\sqrt{36} = -6 \qquad -\sqrt{0.04} = -0.2$

DEFINITIONS AND CONCEPTS	EXAMPLES

Section 10.1 Radicals and Radical Functions (continued)

The **cube root** of a real number a is written as $\sqrt[3]{a}$.

$$\sqrt[3]{a} = b \text{ only if } b^3 = a$$

If n is an even positive integer, then $\sqrt[n]{a^n} = |a|$.

If n is an odd positive integer, then $\sqrt[n]{a^n} = a$.

A **radical function** in x is a function defined by an expression containing a root of x.

$$\sqrt[3]{27} = 3 \qquad \sqrt[3]{-\frac{1}{8}} = -\frac{1}{2}$$

$$\sqrt[3]{y^6} = y^2 \qquad \sqrt[3]{64x^9} = 4x^3$$

$$\sqrt{(-3)^2} = |-3| = 3$$

$$\sqrt[3]{(-7)^3} = -7$$

If $f(x) = \sqrt{x} + 2$,

$$f(1) = \sqrt{(1)} + 2 = 1 + 2 = 3$$

$$f(3) = \sqrt{(3)} + 2 \approx 3.73$$

Section 10.2 Rational Exponents

$a^{1/n} = \sqrt[n]{a}$ if $\sqrt[n]{a}$ is a real number.

If m and n are positive integers greater than 1 with $\dfrac{m}{n}$ in lowest terms and $\sqrt[n]{a}$ is a real number, then

$$a^{m/n} = \sqrt[n]{a^m} = \left(\sqrt[n]{a}\right)^m$$

$a^{-m/n} = \dfrac{1}{a^{m/n}}$ as long as $a^{m/n}$ is a nonzero number.

Exponent rules are true for rational exponents.

$$81^{1/2} = \sqrt{81} = 9$$

$$(-8x^3)^{1/3} = \sqrt[3]{-8x^3} = -2x$$

$$4^{5/2} = \left(\sqrt{4}\right)^5 = 2^5 = 32$$

$$27^{2/3} = \left(\sqrt[3]{27}\right)^2 = 3^2 = 9$$

$$16^{-3/4} = \frac{1}{16^{3/4}} = \frac{1}{\left(\sqrt[4]{16}\right)^3} = \frac{1}{2^3} = \frac{1}{8}$$

$$x^{2/3} \cdot x^{-5/6} = x^{2/3-5/6} = x^{-1/6} = \frac{1}{x^{1/6}}$$

$$(8^4)^{1/2} = 8^2 = 64$$

$$\frac{a^{4/5}}{a^{-2/5}} = a^{4/5-(-2/5)} = a^{6/5}$$

Section 10.3 Simplifying Radical Expressions

Product and Quotient Rules

If $\sqrt[n]{a}$ and $\sqrt[n]{b}$ are real numbers,

$$\sqrt[n]{a} \cdot \sqrt[n]{b} = \sqrt[n]{a \cdot b}$$

$$\frac{\sqrt[n]{a}}{\sqrt[n]{b}} = \sqrt[n]{\frac{a}{b}}, \text{ provided } \sqrt[n]{b} \neq 0$$

A radical of the form $\sqrt[n]{a}$ is **simplified** when a contains no factors that are perfect nth powers.

Multiply or divide as indicated:

$$\sqrt{11} \cdot \sqrt{3} = \sqrt{33}$$

$$\frac{\sqrt[3]{40x}}{\sqrt[3]{5x}} = \sqrt[3]{8} = 2$$

$$\sqrt{40} = \sqrt{4 \cdot 10} = 2\sqrt{10}$$

$$\sqrt{36x^5} = \sqrt{36x^4 \cdot x} = 6x^2\sqrt{x}$$

$$\sqrt[3]{24x^7y^3} = \sqrt[3]{8x^6y^3 \cdot 3x} = 2x^2y\sqrt[3]{3x}$$

Distance Formula

The distance d between two points (x_1, y_1) and (x_2, y_2) is given by

$$d = \sqrt{(x_2 - x_1)^2 + (y_2 - y_1)^2}$$

Find the distance between points $(-1, 6)$ and $(-2, -4)$.
Let $(x_1, y_1) = (-1, 6)$ and $(x_2, y_2) = (-2, -4)$.

$$d = \sqrt{(x_2 - x_1)^2 + (y_2 - y_1)^2}$$

$$= \sqrt{(-2 - (-1))^2 + (-4 - 6)^2}$$

$$= \sqrt{1 + 100} = \sqrt{101}$$

(continued)

DEFINITIONS AND CONCEPTS	EXAMPLES

Section 10.3   Simplifying Radical Expressions (continued)

Midpoint Formula

The midpoint of the line segment whose endpoints are (x_1, y_1) and (x_2, y_2) is the point with coordinates

$$\left(\frac{x_1 + x_2}{2}, \frac{y_1 + y_2}{2}\right)$$

Find the midpoint of the line segment whose endpoints are $(-1, 6)$ and $(-2, -4)$.

$$\left(\frac{-1 + (-2)}{2}, \frac{6 + (-4)}{2}\right)$$

The midpoint is $\left(-\dfrac{3}{2}, 1\right)$.

Section 10.4   Adding, Subtracting, and Multiplying Radical Expressions

Radicals with the same index and the same radicand are **like radicals.**

The distributive property can be used to add like radicals.

$$5\sqrt{6} + 2\sqrt{6} = (5 + 2)\sqrt{6} = 7\sqrt{6}$$

$$-\sqrt[3]{3x} - 10\sqrt[3]{3x} + 3\sqrt[3]{10x}$$

$$= (-1 - 10)\sqrt[3]{3x} + 3\sqrt[3]{10x}$$

$$= -11\sqrt[3]{3x} + 3\sqrt[3]{10x}$$

Radical expressions are multiplied by using many of the same properties used to multiply polynomials.

Multiply.

$$(\sqrt{5} - \sqrt{2x})(\sqrt{2} + \sqrt{2x})$$

$$= \sqrt{10} + \sqrt{10x} - \sqrt{4x} - 2x$$

$$= \sqrt{10} + \sqrt{10x} - 2\sqrt{x} - 2x$$

$$(2\sqrt{3} - \sqrt{8x})(2\sqrt{3} + \sqrt{8x})$$

$$= 4(3) - 8x = 12 - 8x$$

Section 10.5   Rationalizing Denominators and Numerators of Radical Expressions

The **conjugate** of $a + b$ is $a - b$.

The conjugate of $\sqrt{7} + \sqrt{3}$ is $\sqrt{7} - \sqrt{3}$.

The process of writing the denominator of a radical expression without a radical is called **rationalizing the denominator.**

Rationalize each denominator.

$$\frac{\sqrt{5}}{\sqrt{3}} = \frac{\sqrt{5} \cdot \sqrt{3}}{\sqrt{3} \cdot \sqrt{3}} = \frac{\sqrt{15}}{3}$$

$$\frac{6}{\sqrt{7} + \sqrt{3}} = \frac{6(\sqrt{7} - \sqrt{3})}{(\sqrt{7} + \sqrt{3})(\sqrt{7} - \sqrt{3})}$$

$$= \frac{6(\sqrt{7} - \sqrt{3})}{7 - 3}$$

$$= \frac{6(\sqrt{7} - \sqrt{3})}{4} = \frac{3(\sqrt{7} - \sqrt{3})}{2}$$

DEFINITIONS AND CONCEPTS	EXAMPLES

Section 10.5   Rationalizing Denominators and Numerators of Radical Expressions (continued)

The process of writing the numerator of a radical expression without a radical is called **rationalizing the numerator**.

Rationalize each numerator.

$$\frac{\sqrt[3]{9}}{\sqrt[3]{5}} = \frac{\sqrt[3]{9} \cdot \sqrt[3]{3}}{\sqrt[3]{5} \cdot \sqrt[3]{3}} = \frac{\sqrt[3]{27}}{\sqrt[3]{15}} = \frac{3}{\sqrt[3]{15}}$$

$$\frac{\sqrt{9} + \sqrt{3x}}{12} = \frac{(\sqrt{9} + \sqrt{3x})(\sqrt{9} - \sqrt{3x})}{12(\sqrt{9} - \sqrt{3x})}$$

$$= \frac{9 - 3x}{12(\sqrt{9} - \sqrt{3x})}$$

$$= \frac{3(3 - x)}{3 \cdot 4(3 - \sqrt{3x})} = \frac{3 - x}{4(3 - \sqrt{3x})}$$

Section 10.6   Radical Equations and Problem Solving

To Solve a Radical Equation

Step 1. Write the equation so that one radical is by itself on one side of the equation.

Step 2. Raise each side of the equation to a power equal to the index of the radical and simplify.

Step 3. If the equation still contains a radical, repeat Steps 1 and 2. If not, solve the equation.

Step 4. Check all proposed solutions in the original equation.

Solve: $x = \sqrt{4x + 9} + 3$

1. $x - 3 = \sqrt{4x + 9}$

2. $(x - 3)^2 = (\sqrt{4x + 9})^2$
   $x^2 - 6x + 9 = 4x + 9$

3. $x^2 - 10x = 0$
   $x(x - 10) = 0$
   $x = 0$ or $x = 10$

4. The proposed solution 10 checks, but 0 does not. The solution is 10.

Section 10.7   Complex Numbers

$i^2 = -1$ and $i = \sqrt{-1}$

A **complex number** is a number that can be written in the form $a + bi$, where a and b are real numbers.

Simplify: $\sqrt{-9}$

$$\sqrt{-9} = \sqrt{-1 \cdot 9} = \sqrt{-1} \cdot \sqrt{9} = i \cdot 3 \text{ or } 3i$$

Complex Numbers	*Written in Form a + bi*
12	$12 + 0i$
$-5i$	$0 + (-5)i$
$-2 - 3i$	$-2 + (-3)i$

Multiply,

$$\sqrt{-3} \cdot \sqrt{-7} = i\sqrt{3} \cdot i\sqrt{7}$$
$$= i^2 \sqrt{21}$$
$$= -\sqrt{21}$$

To add or subtract complex numbers, add or subtract their real parts and then add or subtract their imaginary parts.

Perform each indicated operation.

$$(-3 + 2i) - (7 - 4i) = -3 + 2i - 7 + 4i$$
$$= -10 + 6i$$

To multiply complex numbers, multiply as though they are binomials.

$$(-7 - 2i)(6 + i) = -42 - 7i - 12i - 2i^2$$
$$= -42 - 19i - 2(-1)$$
$$= -42 - 19i + 2$$
$$= -40 - 19i$$

(continued)

DEFINITIONS AND CONCEPTS	EXAMPLES

Section 10.7   Complex Numbers (continued)

The complex numbers $(a + bi)$ and $(a - bi)$ are called **complex conjugates**.

The complex conjugate of $(3 + 6i)$ is $(3 - 6i)$.

Their product is a real number:

$$(3 - 6i)(3 + 6i) = 9 - 36i^2$$
$$= 9 - 36(-1) = 9 + 36 = 45$$

To divide complex numbers, multiply the numerator and the denominator by the conjugate of the denominator.

Divide.

$$\frac{4}{2 - i} = \frac{4(2 + i)}{(2 - i)(2 + i)}$$
$$= \frac{4(2 + i)}{4 - i^2}$$
$$= \frac{4(2 + i)}{5}$$
$$= \frac{8 + 4i}{5} = \frac{8}{5} + \frac{4}{5}i$$

Chapter 10   Review

(10.1) *Find the root. Assume that all variables represent positive numbers.*

1. $\sqrt{81}$ **2.** $\sqrt[4]{81}$

3. $\sqrt[3]{-8}$ **4.** $\sqrt[4]{-16}$

5. $-\sqrt{\dfrac{1}{49}}$ **6.** $\sqrt{x^{64}}$

7. $-\sqrt{36}$ **8.** $\sqrt[3]{64}$

9. $\sqrt[3]{-a^6 b^9}$ **10.** $\sqrt{16a^4 b^{12}}$

11. $\sqrt[5]{32a^5 b^{10}}$ **12.** $\sqrt[5]{-32x^{15} y^{20}}$

13. $\sqrt{\dfrac{x^{12}}{36y^2}}$ **14.** $\sqrt[3]{\dfrac{27y^3}{z^{12}}}$

Simplify. Use absolute value bars when necessary.

15. $\sqrt{(-x)^2}$ **16.** $\sqrt[4]{(x^2 - 4)^4}$

17. $\sqrt[3]{(-27)^3}$ **18.** $\sqrt[5]{(-5)^5}$

19. $-\sqrt[5]{x^5}$ **20.** $-\sqrt[3]{x^3}$

21. $\sqrt[4]{16(2y + z)^4}$ **22.** $\sqrt{25(x - y)^2}$

23. $\sqrt[5]{y^5}$ **24.** $\sqrt[6]{x^6}$

25. Let $f(x) = \sqrt{x} + 3$.
   a. Find $f(0)$ and $f(9)$.
   b. Find the domain of $f(x)$.
   c. Graph $f(x)$.

26. Let $g(x) = \sqrt[3]{x} - 3$.
   a. Find $g(11)$ and $g(20)$.
   b. Find the domain $g(x)$.
   c. Graph $g(x)$.

(10.2) *Evaluate.*

27. $\left(\dfrac{1}{81}\right)^{1/4}$ **28.** $\left(-\dfrac{1}{27}\right)^{1/3}$

29. $(-27)^{-1/3}$ **30.** $(-64)^{-1/3}$

31. $-9^{3/2}$ **32.** $64^{-1/3}$

33. $(-25)^{5/2}$ **34.** $\left(\dfrac{25}{49}\right)^{-3/2}$

35. $\left(\dfrac{8}{27}\right)^{-2/3}$ **36.** $\left(-\dfrac{1}{36}\right)^{-1/4}$

Write with rational exponents.

37. $\sqrt[3]{x^2}$ **38.** $\sqrt[5]{5x^2 y^3}$

Write using radical notation.

39. $y^{4/5}$ **40.** $5(xy^2 z^5)^{1/3}$

41. $(x + 2)^{-1/3}$ **42.** $(x + 2y)^{-1/2}$

Simplify each expression. Assume that all variables represent positive real numbers. Write with only positive exponents.

43. $a^{1/3} a^{4/3} a^{1/2}$ **44.** $\dfrac{b^{1/3}}{b^{4/3}}$

45. $(a^{1/2} a^{-2})^3$ **46.** $(x^{-3} y^6)^{1/3}$

47. $\left(\dfrac{b^{3/4}}{a^{-1/2}}\right)^8$ **48.** $\dfrac{x^{1/4} x^{-1/2}}{x^{2/3}}$

49. $\left(\dfrac{49c^{5/3}}{a^{-1/4} b^{5/6}}\right)^{-1}$ **50.** $a^{-1/4}(a^{5/4} - a^{9/4})$

Use a calculator and write a three-decimal-place approximation of each number.

51. $\sqrt{20}$

52. $\sqrt[3]{-39}$

53. $\sqrt[4]{726}$

54. $56^{1/3}$

55. $-78^{3/4}$

56. $105^{-2/3}$

Use rational exponents to write each as a single radical.

57. $\sqrt[3]{2} \cdot \sqrt{7}$

58. $\sqrt[3]{3} \cdot \sqrt[4]{x}$

(10.3) Perform each indicated operation and then simplify if possible. Assume that all variables represent positive real numbers.

59. $\sqrt{3} \cdot \sqrt{8}$

60. $\sqrt[3]{7y} \cdot \sqrt[3]{x^2 z}$

61. $\dfrac{\sqrt{44x^3}}{\sqrt{11x}}$

62. $\dfrac{\sqrt[4]{a^6 b^{13}}}{\sqrt[4]{a^2 b}}$

Simplify.

63. $\sqrt{60}$

64. $-\sqrt{75}$

65. $\sqrt[3]{162}$

66. $\sqrt[3]{-32}$

67. $\sqrt{36x^7}$

68. $\sqrt[3]{24a^5 b^7}$

69. $\sqrt{\dfrac{p^{17}}{121}}$

70. $\sqrt[3]{\dfrac{y^5}{27x^6}}$

71. $\sqrt[4]{\dfrac{xy^6}{81}}$

72. $\sqrt{\dfrac{2x^3}{49y^4}}$

△ The formula for the radius r of a circle of area A is $r = \sqrt{\dfrac{A}{\pi}}$. Use this for Exercises 73 and 74.

73. Find the exact radius of a circle whose area is 25 square meters.

74. Approximate to two decimal places the radius of a circle whose area is 104 square inches.

Find the distance between each pair of points. Give the exact value and a three-decimal-place approximation.

75. $(-6, 3)$ and $(8, 4)$

76. $(-4, -6)$ and $(-1, 5)$

77. $(-1, 5)$ and $(2, -3)$

78. $(-\sqrt{2}, 0)$ and $(0, -4\sqrt{6})$

79. $(-\sqrt{5}, -\sqrt{11})$ and $(-\sqrt{5}, -3\sqrt{11})$

80. $(7.4, -8.6)$ and $(-1.2, 5.6)$

Find the midpoint of each line segment whose endpoints are given.

81. $(2, 6); (-12, 4)$

82. $(-6, -5); (-9, 7)$

83. $(4, -6); (-15, 2)$

84. $\left(0, -\dfrac{3}{8}\right); \left(\dfrac{1}{10}, 0\right)$

85. $\left(\dfrac{3}{4}, -\dfrac{1}{7}\right); \left(-\dfrac{1}{4}, -\dfrac{3}{7}\right)$

86. $(\sqrt{3}, -2\sqrt{6}); (\sqrt{3}, -4\sqrt{6})$

(10.4) Perform each indicated operation. Assume that all variables represent positive real numbers.

87. $\sqrt{20} + \sqrt{45} - 7\sqrt{5}$

88. $x\sqrt{75x} - \sqrt{27x^3}$

89. $\sqrt[3]{128} + \sqrt[3]{250}$

90. $3\sqrt[4]{32a^5} - a\sqrt[4]{162a}$

91. $\dfrac{5}{\sqrt{4}} + \dfrac{\sqrt{3}}{3}$

92. $\sqrt{\dfrac{8}{x^2}} - \sqrt{\dfrac{50}{16x^2}}$

93. $2\sqrt{50} - 3\sqrt{125} + \sqrt{98}$

94. $2a\sqrt[4]{32b^5} - 3b\sqrt[4]{162a^4 b} + \sqrt[4]{2a^4 b^5}$

Multiply and then simplify if possible. Assume that all variables represent positive real numbers.

95. $\sqrt{3}(\sqrt{27} - \sqrt{3})$

96. $(\sqrt{x} - 3)^2$

97. $(\sqrt{5} - 5)(2\sqrt{5} + 2)$

98. $(2\sqrt{x} - 3\sqrt{y})(2\sqrt{x} + 3\sqrt{y})$

99. $(\sqrt{a} + 3)(\sqrt{a} - 3)$

100. $(\sqrt[3]{a} + 2)^2$

101. $(\sqrt[3]{5x} + 9)(\sqrt[3]{5x} - 9)$

102. $(\sqrt[3]{a} + 4)(\sqrt[3]{a^2} - 4\sqrt[3]{a} + 16)$

(10.5) Rationalize each denominator. Assume that all variables represent positive real numbers.

103. $\dfrac{3}{\sqrt{7}}$

104. $\sqrt{\dfrac{x}{12}}$

105. $\dfrac{5}{\sqrt[3]{4}}$

106. $\sqrt{\dfrac{24x^5}{3y}}$

107. $\sqrt[3]{\dfrac{15x^6 y^7}{z^2}}$

108. $\sqrt[4]{\dfrac{81}{8x^{10}}}$

109. $\dfrac{3}{\sqrt{y} - 2}$

110. $\dfrac{\sqrt{2} - \sqrt{3}}{\sqrt{2} + \sqrt{3}}$

Rationalize each numerator. Assume that all variables represent positive real numbers.

111. $\dfrac{\sqrt{11}}{3}$

112. $\sqrt{\dfrac{18}{y}}$

113. $\dfrac{\sqrt[3]{9}}{7}$

114. $\sqrt{\dfrac{24x^5}{3y^2}}$

115. $\sqrt[3]{\dfrac{xy^2}{10z}}$

116. $\dfrac{\sqrt{x} + 5}{-3}$

(10.6) Solve each equation.

117. $\sqrt{y - 7} = 5$

118. $\sqrt{2x} + 10 = 4$

119. $\sqrt[3]{2x - 6} = 4$

120. $\sqrt{x + 6} = \sqrt{x + 2}$

121. $2x - 5\sqrt{x} = 3$

122. $\sqrt{x + 9} = 2 + \sqrt{x - 7}$

Find each unknown length.

△ **123.**

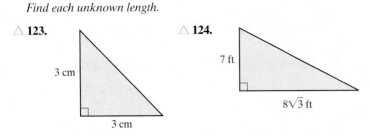

3 cm

3 cm

△ **124.**

7 ft

$8\sqrt{3}$ ft

△ **125.** Craig and Daniel Cantwell want to determine the distance *x* across a pond on their property. They are able to measure the distances shown on the following diagram. Find how wide the pond is at the crossing point indicated by the triangle to the nearest tenth of a foot.

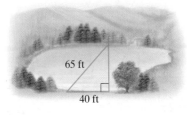

65 ft

40 ft

△ **126.** Andrea Roberts, a pipefitter, needs to connect two underground pipelines that are offset by 3 feet, as pictured in the diagram. Neglecting the joints needed to join the pipes, find the length of the shortest possible connecting pipe rounded to the nearest hundredth of a foot.

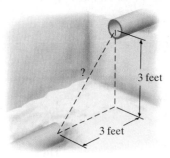

?

3 feet

3 feet

(10.7) *Perform each indicated operation and simplify. Write the results in the form a + bi.*

127. $\sqrt{-8}$

128. $-\sqrt{-6}$

129. $\sqrt{-4} + \sqrt{-16}$

130. $\sqrt{-2} \cdot \sqrt{-5}$

131. $(12 - 6i) + (3 + 2i)$

132. $(-8 - 7i) - (5 - 4i)$

133. $(2i)^6$

134. $(3i)^4$

135. $-3i(6 - 4i)$

136. $(3 + 2i)(1 + i)$

137. $(2 - 3i)^2$

138. $(\sqrt{6} - 9i)(\sqrt{6} + 9i)$

139. $\dfrac{2 + 3i}{2i}$

140. $\dfrac{1 + i}{-3i}$

MIXED REVIEW

Simplify. Use absolute value bars when necessary.

141. $\sqrt[3]{x^3}$

142. $\sqrt{(x + 2)^2}$

Simplify. Assume that all variables represent positive real numbers. If necessary, write answers with positive exponents only.

143. $-\sqrt{100}$

144. $\sqrt[3]{-x^{12}y^3}$

145. $\sqrt[4]{\dfrac{y^{20}}{16x^{12}}}$

146. $9^{1/2}$

147. $64^{-1/2}$

148. $\left(\dfrac{27}{64}\right)^{-2/3}$

149. $\dfrac{(x^{2/3}x^{-3})^3}{x^{-1/2}}$

150. $\sqrt{200x^9}$

151. $\sqrt{\dfrac{3n^3}{121m^{10}}}$

152. $3\sqrt{20} - 7x\sqrt[3]{40} + 3\sqrt[3]{5x^3}$

153. $(2\sqrt{x} - 5)^2$

154. Find the distance between $(-3, 5)$ and $(-8, 9)$.

155. Find the midpoint of the line segment joining $(-3, 8)$ and $(11, 24)$.

Rationalize each denominator.

156. $\dfrac{7}{\sqrt{13}}$

157. $\dfrac{2}{\sqrt{x} + 3}$

Solve.

158. $\sqrt{x + 2} = x$

159. $\sqrt{2x - 1} + 2 = x$

1c

Chapter 10 Getting Ready for the Test

MULTIPLE CHOICE *Select the correct choice.*

▶ **1.** Which radical simplifies to -4?

    A. $\sqrt{16}$ **B.** $\sqrt{-16}$ **C.** $\sqrt[3]{64}$ **D.** $\sqrt[3]{-64}$

▶ **2.** Which radical does not simplify to a whole number?

    A. $\sqrt{16}$ **B.** $\sqrt[3]{16}$ **C.** $\sqrt{64}$ **D.** $\sqrt[3]{64}$

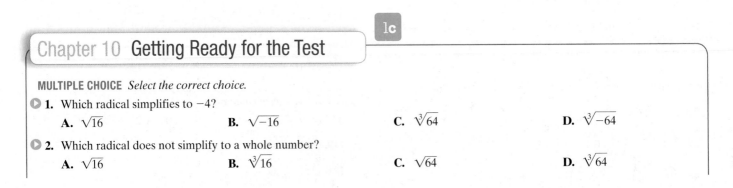

For Exercises 3–6, identify each as **A.** *a real number or* **B.** *not a real number.*

▶ **3.** $\sqrt{5}$ ▶ **4.** $\sqrt{-11}$ ▶ **5.** $\sqrt[3]{-9}$ ▶ **6.** $-\sqrt{17}$

MATCHING *Match each expression with its simplified form. Letters may be used more than once or not at all.*

▶ **7.** $25^{1/2}$ **A.** 5

▶ **8.** $(-25)^{1/2}$ **B.** -5

▶ **9.** $(-125)^{1/3}$ **C.** not a real number

▶ **10.** $-25^{1/2}$

MULTIPLE CHOICE *For Exercises 11–14, identify each statement as* **A.** *true or* **B.** *false.*

▶ **11.** $\sqrt{5} \cdot \sqrt{10} = \sqrt{15}$ ▶ **12.** $\sqrt[3]{4} \cdot \sqrt[3]{9} = \sqrt[3]{36}$ ▶ **13.** $\dfrac{\sqrt{12}}{\sqrt{6}} = \sqrt{2}$

▶ **14.** $\dfrac{\sqrt[3]{10}}{\sqrt[3]{4}} = \sqrt[3]{6}$ ▶ **15.** $\sqrt{2} + \sqrt{3} = \sqrt{5}$ ▶ **16.** $\sqrt[3]{7} + \sqrt{7} = \sqrt[4]{7}$

MULTIPLE CHOICE *Select the correct choice.*

▶ **17.** Which expression simplifies to x?

  A. $x^{1/2} + x^{1/2}$ **B.** $x^{1/2} \cdot x^{1/2}$ **C.** $\left(x^{1/2}\right)^2$ **D.** both B and C   **E.** A, B, and C

▶ **18.** To rationalize the numerator of $\dfrac{\sqrt{x} - 3}{\sqrt{x}}$, we multiply by:

  A. $\dfrac{\sqrt{x}}{\sqrt{x} + 3}$ **B.** $\dfrac{\sqrt{x}}{\sqrt{x}}$ **C.** $\dfrac{\sqrt{x} + 3}{\sqrt{x} + 3}$ **D.** $\dfrac{\sqrt{x} + 3}{\sqrt{x}}$

▶ **19.** Square both sides of the equation $\sqrt{x + 1} = 3 + \sqrt{x - 1}$. The result is:

  A. $x + 1 = 9 + (x - 1)$ **B.** $x + 1 = 9 + 6\sqrt{x - 1} + (x - 1)$ **C.** $x + 1 = 6 + (x - 1)$

▶ **20.** $(5 - 2i)^2 =$

  A. $25 + 4i$ **B.** 21   **C.** 29   **D.** $21 - 20i$

▶ **21.** The expression $\dfrac{3 + \sqrt{-9}}{3}$ simplifies to:

  A. $1 + i$ **B.** $3i$ **C.** $1 + 3i$ **D.** $2i$

Chapter 10 Test   MyMathLab®   You Tube™

Raise to the power or find the root. Assume that all variables represent positive numbers. Write with only positive exponents.

▶ **1.** $\sqrt{216}$ ▶ **2.** $-\sqrt[4]{x^{64}}$

▶ **3.** $\left(\dfrac{1}{125}\right)^{1/3}$ ▶ **4.** $\left(\dfrac{1}{125}\right)^{-1/3}$

▶ **5.** $\left(\dfrac{8x^3}{27}\right)^{2/3}$ ▶ **6.** $\sqrt[3]{-a^{18}b^9}$

▶ **7.** $\left(\dfrac{64c^{4/3}}{a^{-2/3}b^{5/6}}\right)^{1/2}$ ▶ **8.** $a^{-2/3}(a^{5/4} - a^3)$

Find the root. Use absolute value bars when necessary.

▶ **9.** $\sqrt[4]{(4xy)^4}$ ▶ **10.** $\sqrt[3]{(-27)^3}$

Rationalize the denominator. Assume that all variables represent positive numbers.

▶ **11.** $\sqrt{\dfrac{9}{y}}$ ▶ **12.** $\dfrac{4 - \sqrt{x}}{4 + 2\sqrt{x}}$ ▶ **13.** $\dfrac{\sqrt[3]{ab}}{\sqrt[3]{ab^2}}$

▶ **14.** Rationalize the numerator of $\dfrac{\sqrt{6} + x}{8}$ and simplify.

Perform the indicated operations. Assume that all variables represent positive numbers.

▶ **15.** $\sqrt{125x^3} - 3\sqrt{20x^3}$

▶ **16.** $\sqrt{3}(\sqrt{16} - \sqrt{2})$

▶ **17.** $(\sqrt{x} + 1)^2$

▶ **18.** $(\sqrt{2} - 4)(\sqrt{3} + 1)$

▶ **19.** $(\sqrt{5} + 5)(\sqrt{5} - 5)$

Use a calculator to approximate each to three decimal places.

▶ **20.** $\sqrt{561}$ ▶ **21.** $386^{-2/3}$

Solve.

▶ **22.** $x = \sqrt{x - 2} + 2$

▶ **23.** $\sqrt{x^2 - 7} + 3 = 0$

▶ **24.** $\sqrt[3]{x + 5} = \sqrt[3]{2x - 1}$

Perform the indicated operation and simplify. Write the result in the form $a + bi$.

▶ **25.** $\sqrt{-2}$ ▶ **26.** $-\sqrt{-8}$

▶ **27.** $(12 - 6i) - (12 - 3i)$ ▶ **28.** $(6 - 2i)(6 + 2i)$

▶ 29. $(4 + 3i)^2$

▶ 30. $\dfrac{1 + 4i}{1 - i}$

▶ 31. Find x.

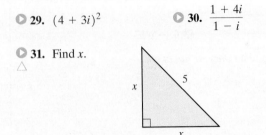

▶ 32. Identify the domain of $g(x)$. Then complete the accompanying table and graph $g(x)$.

$$g(x) = \sqrt{x + 2}$$

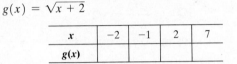

x	-2	-1	2	7
$g(x)$				

▶ 33. Find the distance between the points $(-6, 3)$ and $(-8, -7)$.

▶ 34. Find the distance between the points $(-2\sqrt{5}, \sqrt{10})$ and $(-\sqrt{5}, 4\sqrt{10})$.

▶ 35. Find the midpoint of the line segment whose endpoints are $(-2, -5)$ and $(-6, 12)$.

▶ 36. Find the midpoint of the line segment whose endpoints are $\left(-\dfrac{2}{3}, -\dfrac{1}{5}\right)$ and $\left(-\dfrac{1}{3}, \dfrac{4}{5}\right)$.

Solve.

▶ 37. The function $V(r) = \sqrt{2.5r}$ can be used to estimate the maximum safe velocity V in miles per hour at which a car can travel if it is driven along a curved road with a *radius of curvature r* in feet. To the nearest whole number, find the maximum safe speed if a cloverleaf exit on an expressway has a radius of curvature of 300 feet.

▶ 38. Use the formula from Exercise 37 to find the radius of curvature if the safe velocity is 30 mph.

Chapter 10 **Cumulative Review**

1. Simplify each expression.
   a. $-3 + [(-2 - 5) - 2]$
   b. $2^3 - |10| + [-6 - (-5)]$

2. Simplify each expression.
   a. $2(x - 3) + (5x + 3)$
   b. $4(3x + 2) - 3(5x - 1)$
   c. $7x + 2(x - 7) - 3x$

3. Solve: $\dfrac{x}{2} - 1 = \dfrac{2}{3}x - 3$

4. Solve: $\dfrac{a - 1}{2} + a = 2 - \dfrac{2a + 7}{8}$

5. A 48-inch balsa wood stick is to be cut into two pieces so that the longer piece is 3 times the shorter. Find the length of each piece.

6. The Smith family owns a lake house 121.5 miles from home. If it takes them $4\dfrac{1}{2}$ hours to drive round-trip from their house to their lake house, find their average speed.

7. Without graphing, determine the number of solutions of the system.
   $$\begin{cases} 3x - y = 4 \\ x + 2y = 8 \end{cases}$$

8. Solve: $|3x - 2| + 5 = 5$

9. Solve the system: $\begin{cases} x + 2y = 7 \\ 2x + 2y = 13 \end{cases}$

10. Solve: $\left|\dfrac{x}{2} - 1\right| \le 0$

11. Solve the system: $\begin{cases} 2x - y = 7 \\ 8x - 4y = 1 \end{cases}$

12. Graph: $y = |x - 2|$

13. Lynn Pike, a pharmacist, needs 70 liters of a 50% alcohol solution. She has available a 30% alcohol solution and an 80% alcohol solution. How many liters of each solution should she mix to obtain 70 liters of a 50% alcohol solution?

14. Find the domain and the range of each relation. Use the vertical line test to determine whether each graph is the graph of a function.

   a.

   b.

   c.

   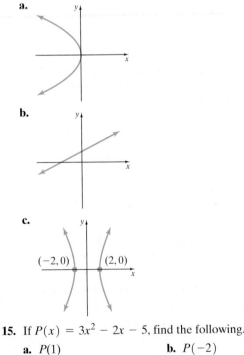

15. If $P(x) = 3x^2 - 2x - 5$, find the following.
   a. $P(1)$ **b.** $P(-2)$

16. Graph: $f(x) = -2$

17. Divide $6m^2 + 2m$ by $2m$.

18. Find the slope of $y = -3$.

19. Use synthetic division to divide $2x^3 - x^2 - 13x + 1$ by $x - 3$.

20. Solve the system.

$$\begin{cases} \dfrac{x}{6} - \dfrac{y}{2} = 1 \\[2mm] \dfrac{x}{3} - \dfrac{y}{4} = 2 \end{cases}$$

21. Factor: $40 - 13t + t^2$

22. At a seasonal clearance sale, Nana Long spent $33.75. She paid $3.50 for tee-shirts and $4.25 for shorts. If she bought 9 items, how many of each item did she buy?

23. Simplify each rational expression.

a. $\dfrac{x^3 + 8}{2 + x}$

b. $\dfrac{2y^2 + 2}{y^3 - 5y^2 + y - 5}$

24. Use scientific notation to simplify and write the answer in scientific notation. $\dfrac{0.0000035 \times 4000}{0.28}$

25. Solve: $|x - 3| = |5 - x|$

26. Subtract $(2x - 5)$ from the sum of $(5x^2 - 3x + 6)$ and $(4x^2 + 5x - 3)$.

27. Subtract: $\dfrac{3x^2 + 2x}{x - 1} - \dfrac{10x - 5}{x - 1}$

28. Multiply and simplify the product if possible.

a. $(y - 2)(3y + 4)$

b. $(3y - 1)(2y^2 + 3y - 1)$

29. Add: $1 + \dfrac{m}{m + 1}$

30. Factor: $x^3 - x^2 + 4x - 4$

31. Simply each complex fraction.

a. $\dfrac{\dfrac{5x}{x + 2}}{\dfrac{10}{x - 2}}$

b. $\dfrac{\dfrac{x}{y^2} + \dfrac{1}{y}}{\dfrac{y}{x^2} + \dfrac{1}{x}}$

32. Simplify each rational expression.

a. $\dfrac{a^3 - 8}{2 - a}$

b. $\dfrac{3a^2 - 3}{a^3 + 5a^2 - a - 5}$

33. Solve: $|5x + 1| + 1 \le 10$

34. Perform the indicated operations.

a. $\dfrac{3}{xy^2} - \dfrac{2}{3x^2 y}$

b. $\dfrac{5x}{x + 3} - \dfrac{2x}{x - 3}$

c. $\dfrac{x}{x - 2} - \dfrac{5}{2 - x}$

35. If the following two triangles are similar, find the unknown length x.

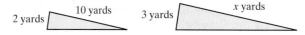

36. Simplify each complex fraction.

a. $\dfrac{\dfrac{y - 2}{16}}{\dfrac{2y + 3}{12}}$

b. $\dfrac{\dfrac{x}{16} - \dfrac{1}{x}}{1 - \dfrac{4}{x}}$

37. Find the cube roots.

a. $\sqrt[3]{1}$

b. $\sqrt[3]{-64}$

c. $\sqrt[3]{\dfrac{8}{125}}$

d. $\sqrt[3]{x^6}$

e. $\sqrt[3]{-27x^{15}}$

38. Divide $x^3 - 2x^2 + 3x - 6$ by $x - 2$.

39. Write each expression with a positive exponent, and then simplify.

a. $16^{-3/4}$

b. $(-27)^{-2/3}$

40. Use synthetic division to divide $4y^3 - 12y^2 - y + 12$ by $y - 3$.

41. Rationalize the numerator of $\dfrac{\sqrt{x} + 2}{5}$.

42. Solve: $\dfrac{28}{9 - a^2} = \dfrac{2a}{a - 3} + \dfrac{6}{a + 3}$

43. Suppose that u varies inversely as w. If u is 3 when w is 5, find the constant of variation and the inverse variation equation.

44. Suppose that y varies directly as x. If $y = 0.51$ when $x = 3$, find the constant of variation and the direct variation equation.

Quadratic Equations and Functions

11.1 Solving Quadratic Equations by Completing the Square

11.2 Solving Quadratic Equations by the Quadratic Formula

11.3 Solving Equations by Using Quadratic Methods

Integrated Review—Summary on Solving Quadratic Equations

11.4 Nonlinear Inequalities in One Variable

11.5 Quadratic Functions and Their Graphs

11.6 Further Graphing of Quadratic Functions

CHECK YOUR PROGRESS

Vocabulary Check

Chapter Highlights

Chapter Review

Getting Ready for the Test

Chapter Test

Cumulative Review

An important part of the study of algebra is learning to model and solve problems. Often, the model of a problem is a quadratic equation or a function containing a second-degree polynomial. In this chapter, we continue the work begun in Chapter 6, when we solved polynomial equations in one variable by factoring. Two additional methods of solving quadratic equations are analyzed as well as methods of solving nonlinear inequalities in one variable.

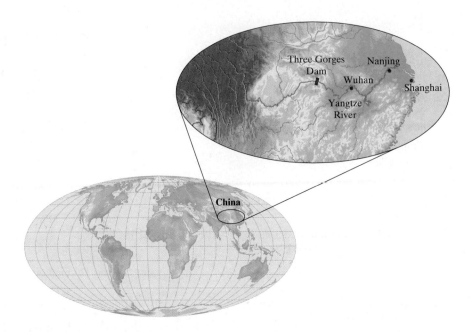

Why Are Dams Built?

One type of a dam is a man-made structure built across a river. Dams are built primarily to control river flow, improve navigation, provide reservoirs for fresh water, or to produce hydroelectric power. The Three Gorges Dam in China is the largest operating hydroelectric facility. While this dam produces the most electricity of any dam in the world, it is only 610 feet in height.

In Section 11.1, Exercises 81 and 82, we will examine the height of some of the great dams.

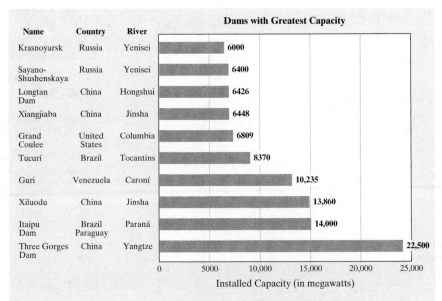

Name	Country	River	Dams with Greatest Capacity
Krasnoyarsk	Russia	Yenisei	6000
Sayano-Shushenskaya	Russia	Yenisei	6400
Longtan Dam	China	Hongshui	6426
Xiangjiaba	China	Jinsha	6448
Grand Coulee	United States	Columbia	6809
Tucurí	Brazil	Tocantins	8370
Guri	Venezuela	Caroní	10,235
Xiluodu	China	Jinsha	13,860
Itaipu Dam	Brazil Paraguay	Paraná	14,000
Three Gorges Dam	China	Yangtze	22,500

Installed Capacity (in megawatts)

Source: U.S. Committee on Large Dams of the International Commission on Large Dams   Note: 1 megawatt = 1,000,000,000

11.1 Solving Quadratic Equations by Completing the Square ▶

OBJECTIVES

1 Use the Square Root Property to Solve Quadratic Equations. ▶

2 Solve Quadratic Equations by Completing the Square. ▶

3 Use Quadratic Equations to Solve Problems. ▶

OBJECTIVE

1   Using the Square Root Property ▶

In Chapter 6, we solved quadratic equations by factoring. Recall that a **quadratic,** or **second-degree, equation** is an equation that can be written in the form $ax^2 + bx + c = 0$, where a, b, and c are real numbers and a is not 0. To solve a quadratic equation such as $x^2 = 9$ by factoring, we use the zero factor property. To use the zero factor property, the equation must first be written in standard form, $ax^2 + bx + c = 0$.

$$x^2 = 9$$
$$x^2 - 9 = 0 \qquad \text{Subtract 9 from both sides.}$$
$$(x + 3)(x - 3) = 0 \qquad \text{Factor.}$$
$$x + 3 = 0 \quad \text{or} \quad x - 3 = 0 \quad \text{Set each factor equal to 0.}$$
$$x = -3 \qquad\qquad x = 3 \quad \text{Solve.}$$

The solution set is $\{-3, 3\}$, the positive and negative square roots of 9. Not all quadratic equations can be solved by factoring, so we need to explore other methods. Notice that the solutions of the equation $x^2 = 9$ are two numbers whose square is 9.

$$3^2 = 9 \qquad \text{and} \qquad (-3)^2 = 9$$

Thus, we can solve the equation $x^2 = 9$ by taking the square root of both sides. Be sure to include both $\sqrt{9}$ and $-\sqrt{9}$ as solutions since both $\sqrt{9}$ and $-\sqrt{9}$ are numbers whose square is 9.

$$x^2 = 9$$
$$\sqrt{x^2} = \pm\sqrt{9} \qquad \text{The notation } \pm\sqrt{9} \text{ (read as ``plus or minus } \sqrt{9}\text{'')}$$
$$x = \pm 3 \qquad \text{indicates the pair of numbers } +\sqrt{9} \text{ and } -\sqrt{9}.$$

This illustrates the square root property.

Square Root Property

If b is a real number and if $a^2 = b$, then $a = \pm\sqrt{b}$.

Helpful Hint

The notation ± 3, for example, is read as "plus or minus 3." It is a shorthand notation for the pair of numbers $+3$ and -3.

EXAMPLE 1   Use the square root property to solve $x^2 = 50$.

Solution

$$x^2 = 50$$
$$x = \pm\sqrt{50} \qquad \text{Use the square root property.}$$
$$x = \pm 5\sqrt{2} \qquad \text{Simplify the radical.}$$

Check: Let $x = 5\sqrt{2}$.   Let $x = -5\sqrt{2}$.

$$x^2 = 50 \qquad\qquad\qquad x^2 = 50$$
$$(5\sqrt{2})^2 \stackrel{?}{=} 50 \qquad\qquad (-5\sqrt{2})^2 \stackrel{?}{=} 50$$
$$25 \cdot 2 \stackrel{?}{=} 50 \qquad\qquad\quad 25 \cdot 2 \stackrel{?}{=} 50$$
$$50 = 50 \quad \text{True} \qquad\qquad 50 = 50 \quad \text{True}$$

The solutions are $5\sqrt{2}$ and $-5\sqrt{2}$, or the solution set is $\{-5\sqrt{2}, 5\sqrt{2}\}$. ☐

PRACTICE

1   Use the square root property to solve $x^2 = 32$.

EXAMPLE 2 Use the square root property to solve $2x^2 - 14 = 0$.

Solution First we get the squared variable alone on one side of the equation.

$$2x^2 - 14 = 0$$
$$2x^2 = 14 \qquad \text{Add 14 to both sides.}$$
$$x^2 = 7 \qquad \text{Divide both sides by 2.}$$
$$x = \pm\sqrt{7} \qquad \text{Use the square root property.}$$

Check to see that the solutions are $\sqrt{7}$ and $-\sqrt{7}$, or the solution set is $\{-\sqrt{7}, \sqrt{7}\}$. ☐

PRACTICE
2 Use the square root property to solve $5x^2 - 50 = 0$. ■

EXAMPLE 3 Use the square root property to solve $(x + 1)^2 = 12$.

Solution

$$(x + 1)^2 = 12$$
$$x + 1 = \pm\sqrt{12} \qquad \text{Use the square root property.}$$
$$x + 1 = \pm 2\sqrt{3} \qquad \text{Simplify the radical.}$$
$$x = -1 \pm 2\sqrt{3} \qquad \text{Subtract 1 from both sides.}$$

> **Helpful Hint**
>
> Don't forget that $-1 \pm 2\sqrt{3}$, for example, means $-1 + 2\sqrt{3}$ and $-1 - 2\sqrt{3}$. In other words, the equation in Example 3 has two solutions.

Check: Below is a check for $-1 + 2\sqrt{3}$. The check for $-1 - 2\sqrt{3}$ is almost the same and is left for you to do on your own.

$$(x + 1)^2 = 12$$
$$(-1 + 2\sqrt{3} + 1)^2 \stackrel{?}{=} 12$$
$$(2\sqrt{3})^2 \stackrel{?}{=} 12$$
$$4 \cdot 3 \stackrel{?}{=} 12$$
$$12 = 12 \qquad \text{True}$$

The solutions are $-1 + 2\sqrt{3}$ and $-1 - 2\sqrt{3}$. ☐

PRACTICE
3 Use the square root property to solve $(x + 3)^2 = 20$. ■

EXAMPLE 4 Use the square root property to solve $(2x - 5)^2 = -16$.

Solution

$$(2x - 5)^2 = -16$$
$$2x - 5 = \pm\sqrt{-16} \qquad \text{Use the square root property.}$$
$$2x - 5 = \pm 4i \qquad \text{Simplify the radical.}$$
$$2x = 5 \pm 4i \qquad \text{Add 5 to both sides.}$$
$$x = \frac{5 \pm 4i}{2} \qquad \text{Divide both sides by 2.}$$

The solutions are $\dfrac{5 + 4i}{2}$ and $\dfrac{5 - 4i}{2}$. ☐

PRACTICE
4 Use the square root property to solve $(5x - 2)^2 = -9$. ■

✔ CONCEPT CHECK

How do you know just by looking that $(x - 2)^2 = -4$ has complex but not real solutions?

OBJECTIVE

2   Solving by Completing the Square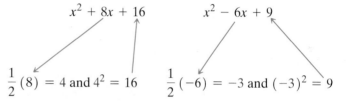

Notice from Examples 3 and 4 that, if we write a quadratic equation so that one side is the square of a binomial, we can solve by using the square root property. To write the square of a binomial, we write perfect square trinomials. Recall that a perfect square trinomial is a trinomial that can be factored into two identical binomial factors.

Perfect Square Trinomials	*Factored Form*
$x^2 + 8x + 16$	$(x + 4)^2$
$x^2 - 6x + 9$	$(x - 3)^2$
$x^2 + 3x + \dfrac{9}{4}$	$\left(x + \dfrac{3}{2}\right)^2$

Notice that for each perfect square trinomial in x, **the constant term of the trinomial is the square of half the coefficient of the x-term.** For example,

$$x^2 + 8x + 16 \qquad\qquad x^2 - 6x + 9$$

$$\frac{1}{2}(8) = 4 \text{ and } 4^2 = 16 \qquad \frac{1}{2}(-6) = -3 \text{ and } (-3)^2 = 9$$

The process of writing a quadratic equation so that one side is a perfect square trinomial is called **completing the square.**

EXAMPLE 5   Solve $p^2 + 2p = 4$ by completing the square.

Solution   First, add the square of half the coefficient of p to both sides so that the resulting trinomial will be a perfect square trinomial. The coefficient of p is 2.

$$\frac{1}{2}(2) = 1 \quad \text{and} \quad 1^2 = 1$$

Add 1 to both sides of the original equation.

$$p^2 + 2p = 4$$
$$p^2 + 2p + 1 = 4 + 1 \quad \text{Add 1 to both sides.}$$
$$(p + 1)^2 = 5 \qquad \text{Factor the trinomial; simplify the right side.}$$

We may now use the square root property and solve for p.

$$p + 1 = \pm\sqrt{5} \qquad \text{Use the square root property.}$$
$$p = -1 \pm \sqrt{5} \quad \text{Subtract 1 from both sides.}$$

Notice that there are two solutions: $-1 + \sqrt{5}$ and $-1 - \sqrt{5}$.   □

PRACTICE

5   Solve $b^2 + 4b = 3$ by completing the square.   ■

EXAMPLE 6   Solve $m^2 - 7m - 1 = 0$ for m by completing the square.

Solution   First, add 1 to both sides of the equation so that the left side has no constant term.

$$m^2 - 7m - 1 = 0$$
$$m^2 - 7m = 1$$

(Continued on next page)

Now find the constant term that makes the left side a perfect square trinomial by squaring half the coefficient of m. Add this constant to both sides of the equation.

$$\frac{1}{2}(-7) = -\frac{7}{2} \quad \text{and} \quad \left(-\frac{7}{2}\right)^2 = \frac{49}{4}$$

$$m^2 - 7m + \frac{49}{4} = 1 + \frac{49}{4} \qquad \text{Add } \frac{49}{4} \text{ to both sides of the equation.}$$

$$\left(m - \frac{7}{2}\right)^2 = \frac{53}{4} \qquad \begin{array}{l}\text{Factor the perfect square trinomial} \\ \text{and simplify the right side.}\end{array}$$

$$m - \frac{7}{2} = \pm\sqrt{\frac{53}{4}} \qquad \text{Apply the square root property.}$$

$$m = \frac{7}{2} \pm \frac{\sqrt{53}}{2} \qquad \text{Add } \frac{7}{2} \text{ to both sides and simplify } \sqrt{\frac{53}{4}}.$$

$$m = \frac{7 \pm \sqrt{53}}{2} \qquad \text{Simplify.}$$

The solutions are $\dfrac{7 + \sqrt{53}}{2}$ and $\dfrac{7 - \sqrt{53}}{2}$. □

PRACTICE

6 Solve $p^2 - 3p + 1 = 0$ by completing the square. ■

The following steps may be used to solve a quadratic equation such as $ax^2 + bx + c = 0$ by completing the square. This method may be used whether or not the polynomial $ax^2 + bx + c$ is factorable.

> **Solving a Quadratic Equation in x by Completing the Square**
>
> **Step 1.** If the coefficient of x^2 is 1, go to Step 2. Otherwise, divide both sides of the equation by the coefficient of x^2.
>
> **Step 2.** Isolate all variable terms on one side of the equation.
>
> **Step 3.** Complete the square for the resulting binomial by adding the square of half of the coefficient of x to both sides of the equation.
>
> **Step 4.** Factor the resulting perfect square trinomial and write it as the square of a binomial.
>
> **Step 5.** Use the square root property to solve for x.

EXAMPLE 7 Solve: $2x^2 - 8x + 3 = 0$

Solution Our procedure for finding the constant term to complete the square works only if the coefficient of the squared variable term is 1. Therefore, to solve this equation, the first step is to divide both sides by 2, the coefficient of x^2.

$$2x^2 - 8x + 3 = 0$$

Step 1. $x^2 - 4x + \dfrac{3}{2} = 0 \qquad$ Divide both sides by 2.

Step 2. $x^2 - 4x = -\dfrac{3}{2} \qquad$ Subtract $\dfrac{3}{2}$ from both sides.

Next find the square of half of -4.

$$\frac{1}{2}(-4) = -2 \quad \text{and} \quad (-2)^2 = 4$$

Add 4 to both sides of the equation to complete the square.

Step 3. $x^2 - 4x + 4 = -\dfrac{3}{2} + 4$

Step 4. $(x - 2)^2 = \dfrac{5}{2}$ Factor the perfect square and simplify the right side.

Step 5. $x - 2 = \pm\sqrt{\dfrac{5}{2}}$ Apply the square root property.

$x - 2 = \pm\dfrac{\sqrt{10}}{2}$ Rationalize the denominator.

$x = 2 \pm \dfrac{\sqrt{10}}{2}$ Add 2 to both sides.

$= \dfrac{4}{2} \pm \dfrac{\sqrt{10}}{2}$ Find a common denominator.

$= \dfrac{4 \pm \sqrt{10}}{2}$ Simplify.

The solutions are $\dfrac{4 + \sqrt{10}}{2}$ and $\dfrac{4 - \sqrt{10}}{2}$.   □

PRACTICE
7   Solve: $3x^2 - 12x + 1 = 0$ ■

EXAMPLE 8   Solve $3x^2 - 9x + 8 = 0$ by completing the square.

Solution $3x^2 - 9x + 8 = 0$

Step 1. $x^2 - 3x + \dfrac{8}{3} = 0$ Divide both sides of the equation by 3.

Step 2. $x^2 - 3x = -\dfrac{8}{3}$ Subtract $\dfrac{8}{3}$ from both sides.

Since $\dfrac{1}{2}(-3) = -\dfrac{3}{2}$ and $\left(-\dfrac{3}{2}\right)^2 = \dfrac{9}{4}$, we add $\dfrac{9}{4}$ to both sides of the equation.

Step 3. $x^2 - 3x + \dfrac{9}{4} = -\dfrac{8}{3} + \dfrac{9}{4}$

Step 4. $\left(x - \dfrac{3}{2}\right)^2 = -\dfrac{5}{12}$ Factor the perfect square trinomial.

Step 5. $x - \dfrac{3}{2} = \pm\sqrt{-\dfrac{5}{12}}$ Apply the square root property.

$x - \dfrac{3}{2} = \pm\dfrac{i\sqrt{5}}{2\sqrt{3}}$ Simplify the radical.

$x - \dfrac{3}{2} = \pm\dfrac{i\sqrt{15}}{6}$ Rationalize the denominator.

$x = \dfrac{3}{2} \pm \dfrac{i\sqrt{15}}{6}$ Add $\dfrac{3}{2}$ to both sides.

$= \dfrac{9}{6} \pm \dfrac{i\sqrt{15}}{6}$ Find a common denominator.

$= \dfrac{9 \pm i\sqrt{15}}{6}$ Simplify.

The solutions are $\dfrac{9 + i\sqrt{15}}{6}$ and $\dfrac{9 - i\sqrt{15}}{6}$.   □

PRACTICE
8   Solve $2x^2 - 5x + 7 = 0$ by completing the square.   ■

OBJECTIVE

3 Solving Problems Modeled by Quadratic Equations ▶

Recall the **simple interest** formula $I = Prt$, where I is the interest earned, P is the principal, r is the rate of interest, and t is time in years. If $100 is invested at a simple interest rate of 5% annually, at the end of 3 years the total interest I earned is

$$I = P \cdot r \cdot t$$

or

$$I = 100 \cdot 0.05 \cdot 3 = \$15$$

and the new principal is

$$\$100 + \$15 = \$115$$

Most of the time, the interest computed on money borrowed or money deposited is **compound interest.** Compound interest, unlike simple interest, is computed on original principal *and* on interest already earned. To see the difference between simple interest and compound interest, suppose that $100 is invested at a rate of 5% compounded annually. To find the total amount of money at the end of 3 years, we calculate as follows.

$$I = P \cdot r \cdot t$$

First year: Interest = $\$100 \cdot 0.05 \cdot 1 = \$5.00$
New principal = $\$100.00 + \$5.00 = \$105.00$

Second year: Interest = $\$105.00 \cdot 0.05 \cdot 1 = \$5.25$
New principal = $\$105.00 + \$5.25 = \$110.25$

Third year: Interest = $\$110.25 \cdot 0.05 \cdot 1 \approx \$5.51$
New principal = $\$110.25 + \$5.51 = \$115.76$

At the end of the third year, the total compound interest earned is $15.76, whereas the total simple interest earned is $15.

It is tedious to calculate compound interest as we did above, so we use a compound interest formula. The formula for calculating the total amount of money when interest is compounded annually is

$$A = P(1 + r)^t$$

where P is the original investment, r is the interest rate per compounding period, and t is the number of periods. For example, the amount of money A at the end of 3 years if $100 is invested at 5% compounded annually is

$$A = \$100(1 + 0.05)^3 \approx \$100(1.1576) = \$115.76$$

as we previously calculated.

EXAMPLE 9 Finding Interest Rates

Use the formula $A = P(1 + r)^t$ to find the interest rate r if $2000 compounded annually grows to $2420 in 2 years.

Solution

1. UNDERSTAND the problem. Since the $2000 is compounded annually, we use the compound interest formula. For this example, make sure that you understand the formula for compounding interest annually.

2. TRANSLATE. We substitute the given values into the formula.

$$A = P(1 + r)^t$$
$$2420 = 2000(1 + r)^2 \quad \text{Let } A = 2420, P = 2000, \text{ and } t = 2.$$

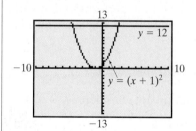

3. SOLVE. Solve the equation for r.

$$2420 = 2000(1 + r)^2$$

$$\frac{2420}{2000} = (1 + r)^2 \qquad \text{Divide both sides by 2000.}$$

$$\frac{121}{100} = (1 + r)^2 \qquad \text{Simplify the fraction.}$$

$$\pm\sqrt{\frac{121}{100}} = 1 + r \qquad \text{Use the square root property.}$$

$$\pm\frac{11}{10} = 1 + r \qquad \text{Simplify.}$$

$$-1 \pm \frac{11}{10} = r$$

$$-\frac{10}{10} \pm \frac{11}{10} = r$$

$$\frac{1}{10} = r \quad \text{or} \quad -\frac{21}{10} = r$$

4. INTERPRET. The rate cannot be negative, so we reject $-\dfrac{21}{10}$.

Check: $\dfrac{1}{10} = 0.10 = 10\%$ per year. If we invest $2000 at 10% compounded annually, in 2 years the amount in the account would be $2000(1 + 0.10)^2 = 2420$ dollars, the desired amount.

State: The interest rate is 10% compounded annually. □

PRACTICE

9   Use the formula from Example 9 to find the interest rate r if $5000 compounded annually grows to $5618 in 2 years. ■

Graphing Calculator Explorations

In Section 6.6, we showed how we can use a grapher to approximate real number solutions of a quadratic equation written in standard form. We can also use a grapher to solve a quadratic equation when it is not written in standard form. For example, to solve $(x + 1)^2 = 12$, the quadratic equation in Example 3, we graph the following on the same set of axes. Use Xmin $= -10$, Xmax $= 10$, Ymin $= -13$, and Ymax $= 13$.

$$Y_1 = (x + 1)^2 \quad \text{and} \quad Y_2 = 12$$

Use the Intersect feature or the Zoom and Trace features to locate the points of intersection of the graphs. (See your manuals for specific instructions.) The x-values of these points are the solutions of $(x + 1)^2 = 12$. The solutions, rounded to two decimal places, are 2.46 and -4.46.

Check to see that these numbers are approximations of the exact solutions $-1 \pm 2\sqrt{3}$.

Use a graphing calculator to solve each quadratic equation. Round all solutions to the nearest hundredth.

1. $x(x - 5) = 8$ **2.** $x(x + 2) = 5$

3. $x^2 + 0.5x = 0.3x + 1$ **4.** $x^2 - 2.6x = -2.2x + 3$

5. Use a graphing calculator and solve $(2x - 5)^2 = -16$, Example 4 in this section, using the window

$$Xmin = -20$$
$$Xmax = 20$$
$$Xscl = 1$$
$$Ymin = -20$$
$$Ymax = 20$$
$$Yscl = 1$$

Explain the results. Compare your results with the solution found in Example 4.

6. What are the advantages and disadvantages of using a graphing calculator to solve quadratic equations?

✓ Vocabulary, Readiness & Video Check

Use the choices below to fill in each blank. Not all choices will be used.

binomial	$\sqrt{b}$	$\pm\sqrt{b}$	b^2	9	25	completing the square
quadratic	$-\sqrt{b}$	$\dfrac{b}{2}$	$\left(\dfrac{b}{2}\right)^2$	3	5	

1. By the square root property, if b is a real number, and $a^2 = b$, then $a = $ _____.

2. A _____ equation can be written in the form $ax^2 + bx + c = 0, a \neq 0$.

3. The process of writing a quadratic equation so that one side is a perfect square trinomial is called _____.

4. A perfect square trinomial is one that can be factored as a _____ squared.

5. To solve $x^2 + 6x = 10$ by completing the square, add _____ to both sides.

6. To solve $x^2 + bx = c$ by completing the square, add _____ to both sides.

Martin-Gay Interactive Videos

Watch the section lecture video and answer the following questions.

OBJECTIVE 1

7. From ▦ Examples 2 and 3, explain a step you can perform so that you may easily apply the square root property to $2x^2 = 16$. Explain why you perform this step.

OBJECTIVE 2

8. In ▦ Example 5, why is the equation first divided through by 3?

OBJECTIVE 3

9. In ▦ Example 6, why is the negative solution not considered?

See Video 11.1 ◉

11.1 Exercise Set   MyMathLab ▸

Use the square root property to solve each equation. These equations have real number solutions. See Examples 1 through 3.

▸ 1. $x^2 = 16$

2. $x^2 = 49$

3. $x^2 - 7 = 0$

4. $x^2 - 11 = 0$

5. $x^2 = 18$

6. $y^2 = 20$

7. $3z^2 - 30 = 0$

8. $2x^2 - 4 = 0$

9. $(x + 5)^2 = 9$

10. $(y - 3)^2 = 4$

▸ 11. $(z - 6)^2 = 18$

12. $(y + 4)^2 = 27$

13. $(2x - 3)^2 = 8$

14. $(4x + 9)^2 = 6$

Use the square root property to solve each equation. See Examples 1 through 4.

15. $x^2 + 9 = 0$

16. $x^2 + 4 = 0$

▸ 17. $x^2 - 6 = 0$

18. $y^2 - 10 = 0$

19. $2z^2 + 16 = 0$

20. $3p^2 + 36 = 0$

21. $(3x - 1)^2 = -16$

22. $(4y + 2)^2 = -25$

23. $(z + 7)^2 = 5$

24. $(x + 10)^2 = 11$

25. $(x + 3)^2 + 8 = 0$

26. $(y - 4)^2 + 18 = 0$

Add the proper constant to each binomial so that the resulting trinomial is a perfect square trinomial. Then factor the trinomial.

27. $x^2 + 16x + $ _____

28. $y^2 + 2y + $ _____

29. $z^2 - 12z + $ _____

30. $x^2 - 8x + $ _____

31. $p^2 + 9p + $ _____

32. $n^2 + 5n + $ _____

33. $x^2 + x + $ _____

34. $y^2 - y + $ _____

MIXED PRACTICE

Solve each equation by completing the square. These equations have real number solutions. See Examples 5 through 7.

35. $x^2 + 8x = -15$

36. $y^2 + 6y = -8$

▶ **37.** $x^2 + 6x + 2 = 0$

38. $x^2 - 2x - 2 = 0$

39. $x^2 + x - 1 = 0$

40. $x^2 + 3x - 2 = 0$

41. $x^2 + 2x - 5 = 0$

42. $x^2 - 6x + 3 = 0$

43. $y^2 + y - 7 = 0$

44. $x^2 - 7x - 1 = 0$

45. $3p^2 - 12p + 2 = 0$

46. $2x^2 + 14x - 1 = 0$

47. $4y^2 - 2 = 12y$

48. $6x^2 - 3 = 6x$

49. $2x^2 + 7x = 4$

50. $3x^2 - 4x = 4$

51. $x^2 + 8x + 1 = 0$

52. $x^2 - 10x + 2 = 0$

▶ **53.** $3y^2 + 6y - 4 = 0$

54. $2y^2 + 12y + 3 = 0$

55. $2x^2 - 3x - 5 = 0$

56. $5x^2 + 3x - 2 = 0$

Solve each equation by completing the square. See Examples 5 through 8.

57. $y^2 + 2y + 2 = 0$

58. $x^2 + 4x + 6 = 0$

59. $y^2 + 6y - 8 = 0$

60. $y^2 + 10y - 26 = 0$

61. $2a^2 + 8a = -12$

62. $3x^2 + 12x = -14$

63. $5x^2 + 15x - 1 = 0$

64. $16y^2 + 16y - 1 = 0$

65. $2x^2 - x + 6 = 0$

66. $4x^2 - 2x + 5 = 0$

67. $x^2 + 10x + 28 = 0$

68. $y^2 + 8y + 18 = 0$

69. $z^2 + 3z - 4 = 0$

70. $y^2 + y - 2 = 0$

71. $2x^2 - 4x = -3$

72. $9x^2 - 36x = -40$

73. $3x^2 + 3x = 5$

74. $10y^2 - 30y = 2$

Use the formula $A = P(1 + r)^t$ to solve Exercises 75 through 78. See Example 9.

▶ **75.** Find the rate r at which \$3000 compounded annually grows to \$4320 in 2 years.

76. Find the rate r at which \$800 compounded annually grows to \$882 in 2 years.

77. Find the rate at which \$15,000 compounded annually grows to \$16,224 in 2 years.

78. Find the rate at which \$2000 compounded annually grows to \$2880 in 2 years.

Neglecting air resistance, the distance $s(t)$ in feet traveled by a freely falling object is given by the function $s(t) = 16t^2$, where t is time in seconds. Use this formula to solve Exercises 79 through 82. Round answers to two decimal places.

79. The Petronas Towers in Kuala Lumpur, completed in 1998, are the tallest buildings in Malaysia. Each tower is 1483 feet tall. How long would it take an object to fall to the ground from the top of one of the towers? (*Source:* Council on Tall Buildings and Urban Habitat, Lehigh University)

80. The Burj Khalifa, the tallest building in the world, was completed in 2010 in Dubai. It is estimated to be 2717 feet tall. How long would it take an object to fall to the ground from the top of the building? (*Source:* Council on Tall Buildings and Urban Habitat)

81. The Three Gorges Dam, while producing the most electricity of any dam in the world, is only 610 feet tall. How long would it take an object to fall from the top to the base of the dam? (*Source:* U.S. Committee on Large Dams of the International Commission on Large Dams)

82. The Hoover Dam, located on the Colorado River on the border of Nevada and Arizona near Las Vegas, is 725 feet tall. How long would it take an object to fall from the top to the base of the dam? (*Source:* U.S. Committee on Large Dams of the International Commission on Large Dams)

Solve.

△ **83.** The area of a square room is 225 square feet. Find the dimensions of the room.

△ **84.** The area of a circle is 36π square inches. Find the radius of the circle.

△ **85.** An isosceles right triangle has legs of equal length. If the hypotenuse is 20 centimeters long, find the length of each leg.

△ **86.** The top of a square coffee table has a diagonal that measures 30 inches. Find the length of each side of the top of the coffee table.

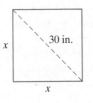

REVIEW AND PREVIEW

Simplify each expression. See Section 10.1.

87. $\dfrac{1}{2} - \sqrt{\dfrac{9}{4}}$ **88.** $\dfrac{9}{10} - \sqrt{\dfrac{49}{100}}$

Simplify each expression. See Section 10.5.

89. $\dfrac{6 + 4\sqrt{5}}{2}$ **90.** $\dfrac{10 - 20\sqrt{3}}{2}$

91. $\dfrac{3 - 9\sqrt{2}}{6}$ **92.** $\dfrac{12 - 8\sqrt{7}}{16}$

Evaluate $\sqrt{b^2 - 4ac}$ for each set of values. See Section 10.3.

93. $a = 2, b = 4, c = -1$ **94.** $a = 1, b = 6, c = 2$

95. $a = 3, b = -1, c = -2$ **96.** $a = 1, b = -3, c = -1$

CONCEPT EXTENSIONS

Without solving, determine whether the solutions of each equation are real numbers or complex but not real numbers. See the Concept Check in this section.

97. $(x + 1)^2 = -1$

98. $(y - 5)^2 = -9$

99. $3z^2 = 10$

100. $4x^2 = 17$

101. $(2y - 5)^2 + 7 = 3$

102. $(3m + 2)^2 + 4 = 1$

Find two possible missing terms so that each is a perfect square trinomial.

103. $x^2 + \quad + 16$ **104.** $y^2 + \quad + 9$

105. $z^2 + \quad + \dfrac{25}{4}$ **106.** $x^2 + \quad + \dfrac{1}{4}$

107. In your own words, explain how to calculate the number that will complete the square on an expression such as $x^2 - 5x$.

108. In your own words, what is the difference between simple interest and compound interest?

109. If you are depositing money in an account that pays 4%, would you prefer the interest to be simple or compound? Explain your answer.

110. If you are borrowing money at a rate of 10%, would you prefer the interest to be simple or compound? Explain your answer.

A common equation used in business is a demand equation. It expresses the relationship between the unit price of some commodity and the quantity demanded. For Exercises 111 and 112, p represents the unit price and x represents the quantity demanded in thousands.

111. A manufacturing company has found that the demand equation for a certain type of scissors is given by the equation $p = -x^2 + 47$. Find the demand for the scissors if the price is $11 per pair.

112. Acme, Inc., sells desk lamps and has found that the demand equation for a certain style of desk lamp is given by the equation $p = -x^2 + 15$. Find the demand for the desk lamp if the price is $7 per lamp.

11.2 Solving Quadratic Equations by the Quadratic Formula ▷

OBJECTIVES

1 Solve Quadratic Equations by Using the Quadratic Formula. ▷

2 Determine the Number and Type of Solutions of a Quadratic Equation by Using the Discriminant. ▷

3 Solve Problems Modeled by Quadratic Equations. ▷

OBJECTIVE

1   Solving Quadratic Equations by Using the Quadratic Formula ▷

Any quadratic equation can be solved by completing the square. Since the same sequence of steps is repeated each time we complete the square, let's complete the square for a general quadratic equation, $ax^2 + bx + c = 0, a \neq 0$. By doing so, we find a pattern for the solutions of a quadratic equation known as the **quadratic formula.**

Recall that to complete the square for an equation such as $ax^2 + bx + c = 0$, we first divide both sides by the coefficient of x^2.

$$ax^2 + bx + c = 0$$

$$x^2 + \frac{b}{a}x + \frac{c}{a} = 0 \qquad \text{Divide both sides by } a, \text{ the coefficient of } x^2.$$

$$x^2 + \frac{b}{a}x = -\frac{c}{a} \qquad \text{Subtract the constant } \frac{c}{a} \text{ from both sides.}$$

Next, find the square of half $\frac{b}{a}$, the coefficient of x.

$$\frac{1}{2}\left(\frac{b}{a}\right) = \frac{b}{2a} \quad \text{and} \quad \left(\frac{b}{2a}\right)^2 = \frac{b^2}{4a^2}$$

Add this result to both sides of the equation.

$$x^2 + \frac{b}{a}x + \frac{b^2}{4a^2} = -\frac{c}{a} + \frac{b^2}{4a^2} \qquad \text{Add } \frac{b^2}{4a^2} \text{ to both sides.}$$

$$x^2 + \frac{b}{a}x + \frac{b^2}{4a^2} = \frac{-c \cdot 4a}{a \cdot 4a} + \frac{b^2}{4a^2} \qquad \begin{array}{l}\text{Find a common denominator}\\\text{on the right side.}\end{array}$$

$$x^2 + \frac{b}{a}x + \frac{b^2}{4a^2} = \frac{b^2 - 4ac}{4a^2} \qquad \text{Simplify the right side.}$$

$$\left(x + \frac{b}{2a}\right)^2 = \frac{b^2 - 4ac}{4a^2} \qquad \begin{array}{l}\text{Factor the perfect square}\\\text{trinomial on the left side.}\end{array}$$

$$x + \frac{b}{2a} = \pm\sqrt{\frac{b^2 - 4ac}{4a^2}} \qquad \text{Apply the square root property.}$$

$$x + \frac{b}{2a} = \pm\frac{\sqrt{b^2 - 4ac}}{2a} \qquad \text{Simplify the radical.}$$

$$x = -\frac{b}{2a} \pm \frac{\sqrt{b^2 - 4ac}}{2a} \qquad \text{Subtract } \frac{b}{2a} \text{ from both sides.}$$

$$x = \frac{-b \pm \sqrt{b^2 - 4ac}}{2a} \qquad \text{Simplify.}$$

This equation identifies the solutions of the general quadratic equation in standard form and is called the quadratic formula. It can be used to solve any equation written in standard form $ax^2 + bx + c = 0$ as long as a is not 0.

Quadratic Formula

A quadratic equation written in the form $ax^2 + bx + c = 0$ has the solutions

$$x = \frac{-b \pm \sqrt{b^2 - 4ac}}{2a}$$

EXAMPLE 1 Solve $3x^2 + 16x + 5 = 0$ for x.

Solution This equation is in standard form, so $a = 3$, $b = 16$, and $c = 5$. Substitute these values into the quadratic formula.

$$x = \frac{-b \pm \sqrt{b^2 - 4ac}}{2a} \qquad \text{Quadratic formula}$$

$$= \frac{-16 \pm \sqrt{16^2 - 4(3)(5)}}{2 \cdot 3} \qquad \text{Use } a = 3, b = 16, \text{ and } c = 5.$$

$$= \frac{-16 \pm \sqrt{256 - 60}}{6}$$

$$= \frac{-16 \pm \sqrt{196}}{6} = \frac{-16 \pm 14}{6}$$

$$x = \frac{-16 + 14}{6} = -\frac{1}{3} \quad \text{or} \quad x = \frac{-16 - 14}{6} = -\frac{30}{6} = -5$$

The solutions are $-\dfrac{1}{3}$ and -5, or the solution set is $\left\{ -\dfrac{1}{3}, -5 \right\}$.

PRACTICE

1 Solve $3x^2 - 5x - 2 = 0$ for x.

Helpful Hint
To replace a, b, and c correctly in the quadratic formula, write the quadratic equation in standard form $ax^2 + bx + c = 0$.

EXAMPLE 2 Solve: $2x^2 - 4x = 3$

Solution First write the equation in standard form by subtracting 3 from both sides.

$$2x^2 - 4x - 3 = 0$$

Now $a = 2$, $b = -4$, and $c = -3$. Substitute these values into the quadratic formula.

$$x = \frac{-b \pm \sqrt{b^2 - 4ac}}{2a}$$

$$= \frac{-(-4) \pm \sqrt{(-4)^2 - 4(2)(-3)}}{2 \cdot 2}$$

$$= \frac{4 \pm \sqrt{16 + 24}}{4}$$

$$= \frac{4 \pm \sqrt{40}}{4} = \frac{4 \pm 2\sqrt{10}}{4}$$

$$= \frac{2(2 \pm \sqrt{10})}{2 \cdot 2} = \frac{2 \pm \sqrt{10}}{2}$$

The solutions are $\dfrac{2 + \sqrt{10}}{2}$ and $\dfrac{2 - \sqrt{10}}{2}$, or the solution set is $\left\{ \dfrac{2 - \sqrt{10}}{2}, \dfrac{2 + \sqrt{10}}{2} \right\}$.

PRACTICE

2 Solve: $3x^2 - 8x = 2$

Helpful Hint
To simplify the expression $\dfrac{4 \pm 2\sqrt{10}}{4}$ in the preceding example, note that 2 is factored out of both terms of the numerator _before_ simplifying. $$\frac{4 \pm 2\sqrt{10}}{4} = \frac{2(2 \pm \sqrt{10})}{2 \cdot 2} = \frac{2 \pm \sqrt{10}}{2}$$

For the quadratic equation $x^2 = 7$, choose the correct substitution for a, b, and c in the standard form $ax^2 + bx + c = 0$.
a. $a = 1, b = 0,$ and $c = -7$
b. $a = 1, b = 0,$ and $c = 7$
c. $a = 0, b = 0,$ and $c = 7$
d. $a = 1, b = 1,$ and $c = -7$

EXAMPLE 3   Solve: $\dfrac{1}{4}m^2 - m + \dfrac{1}{2} = 0$

Solution We could use the quadratic formula with $a = \dfrac{1}{4}, b = -1,$ and $c = \dfrac{1}{2}.$ Instead, we find a simpler, equivalent standard form equation whose coefficients are not fractions.

Multiply both sides of the equation by the LCD 4 to clear fractions.

$$4\left(\frac{1}{4}m^2 - m + \frac{1}{2}\right) = 4 \cdot 0$$

$$m^2 - 4m + 2 = 0 \qquad \text{Simplify.}$$

Substitute $a = 1, b = -4,$ and $c = 2$ into the quadratic formula and simplify.

$$m = \frac{-(-4) \pm \sqrt{(-4)^2 - 4(1)(2)}}{2 \cdot 1} = \frac{4 \pm \sqrt{16 - 8}}{2}$$

$$= \frac{4 \pm \sqrt{8}}{2} = \frac{4 \pm 2\sqrt{2}}{2} = \frac{2(2 \pm \sqrt{2})}{2}$$

$$= 2 \pm \sqrt{2}$$

The solutions are $2 + \sqrt{2}$ and $2 - \sqrt{2}$. □

PRACTICE
3   Solve: $\dfrac{1}{8}x^2 - \dfrac{1}{4}x - 2 = 0$ ■

EXAMPLE 4   Solve: $x = -3x^2 - 3$

Solution The equation in standard form is $3x^2 + x + 3 = 0$. Thus, let $a = 3, b = 1,$ and $c = 3$ in the quadratic formula.

$$x = \frac{-1 \pm \sqrt{1^2 - 4(3)(3)}}{2 \cdot 3} = \frac{-1 \pm \sqrt{1 - 36}}{6} = \frac{-1 \pm \sqrt{-35}}{6} = \frac{-1 \pm i\sqrt{35}}{6}$$

The solutions are $\dfrac{-1 + i\sqrt{35}}{6}$ and $\dfrac{-1 - i\sqrt{35}}{6}$. □

PRACTICE
4   Solve: $x = -2x^2 - 2$ ■

What is the first step in solving $-3x^2 = 5x - 4$ using the quadratic formula?

In Example 1, the equation $3x^2 + 16x + 5 = 0$ had two real roots, $-\dfrac{1}{3}$ and -5.

In Example 4, the equation $3x^2 + x + 3 = 0$ (written in standard form) had no real roots. How do their related graphs compare? Recall that the x-intercepts of $f(x) = 3x^2 + 16x + 5$ occur where $f(x) = 0$ or where $3x^2 + 16x + 5 = 0$.

Answer to Concept Checks:
a;
Write the equation in standard form.

Since this equation has two real roots, the graph has two x-intercepts. Similarly, since the equation $3x^2 + x + 3 = 0$ has no real roots, the graph of $f(x) = 3x^2 + x + 3$ has no x-intercepts.

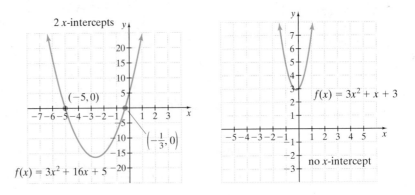

OBJECTIVE

2 Using the Discriminant

In the quadratic formula, $x = \dfrac{-b \pm \sqrt{b^2 - 4ac}}{2a}$, the radicand $b^2 - 4ac$ is called the **discriminant** because, by knowing its value, we can **discriminate** among the possible number and type of solutions of a quadratic equation. Possible values of the discriminant and their meanings are summarized next.

Discriminant

The following table corresponds the discriminant $b^2 - 4ac$ of a quadratic equation of the form $ax^2 + bx + c = 0$ with the number and type of solutions of the equation.

$b^2 - 4ac$	*Number and Type of Solutions*
Positive	Two real solutions
Zero	One real solution
Negative	Two complex but not real solutions

EXAMPLE 5 Use the discriminant to determine the number and type of solutions of each quadratic equation.

a. $x^2 + 2x + 1 = 0$ **b.** $3x^2 + 2 = 0$ **c.** $2x^2 - 7x - 4 = 0$

Solution

a. In $x^2 + 2x + 1 = 0$, $a = 1$, $b = 2$, and $c = 1$. Thus,

$$b^2 - 4ac = 2^2 - 4(1)(1) = 0$$

Since $b^2 - 4ac = 0$, this quadratic equation has one real solution.

b. In this equation, $a = 3$, $b = 0$, $c = 2$. Then $b^2 - 4ac = 0 - 4(3)(2) = -24$. Since $b^2 - 4ac$ is negative, the quadratic equation has two complex but not real solutions.

c. In this equation, $a = 2$, $b = -7$, and $c = -4$. Then

$$b^2 - 4ac = (-7)^2 - 4(2)(-4) = 81$$

Since $b^2 - 4ac$ is positive, the quadratic equation has two real solutions. ☐

PRACTICE

5 Use the discriminant to determine the number and type of solutions of each quadratic equation.

a. $x^2 - 6x + 9 = 0$ **b.** $x^2 - 3x - 1 = 0$ **c.** $7x^2 + 11 = 0$

The discriminant helps us determine the number and type of solutions of a quadratic equation, $ax^2 + bx + c = 0$. Recall that the solutions of this equation are the same as the x-intercepts of its related graph $f(x) = ax^2 + bx + c$. This means that the discriminant of $ax^2 + bx + c = 0$ also tells us the number of x-intercepts for the graph of $f(x) = ax^2 + bx + c$ or, equivalently, $y = ax^2 + bx + c$.

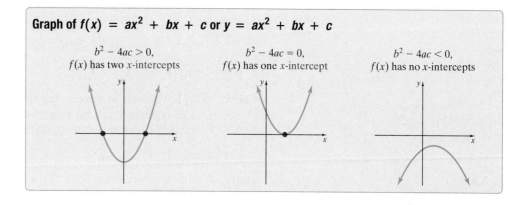

Graph of $f(x) = ax^2 + bx + c$ or $y = ax^2 + bx + c$

$b^2 - 4ac > 0$,	$b^2 - 4ac = 0$,	$b^2 - 4ac < 0$,
$f(x)$ has two x-intercepts	$f(x)$ has one x-intercept	$f(x)$ has no x-intercepts

OBJECTIVE

3   Solving Problems Modeled by Quadratic Equations ▶

The quadratic formula is useful in solving problems that are modeled by quadratic equations.

△ **EXAMPLE 6**   **Calculating Distance Saved**

At a local university, students often leave the sidewalk and cut across the lawn to save walking distance. Given the diagram below of a favorite place to cut across the lawn, approximate how many feet of walking distance a student saves by cutting across the lawn instead of walking on the sidewalk.

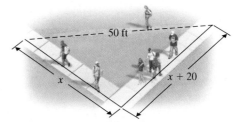

50 ft
x $x + 20$

Solution

1. UNDERSTAND. Read and reread the problem. In the diagram, notice that a triangle is formed. Since the corner of the block forms a right angle, we use the Pythagorean theorem for right triangles. You may want to review this theorem.

2. TRANSLATE. By the Pythagorean theorem, we have

$$\text{In words: } (\text{leg})^2 + (\text{leg})^2 = (\text{hypotenuse})^2$$
$$\text{Translate: } x^2 + (x + 20)^2 = 50^2$$

3. SOLVE. Use the quadratic formula to solve.

$$x^2 + x^2 + 40x + 400 = 2500 \quad \text{Square } (x + 20) \text{ and 50.}$$
$$2x^2 + 40x - 2100 = 0 \quad \text{Set the equation equal to 0.}$$
$$x^2 + 20x - 1050 = 0 \quad \text{Divide by 2.}$$

(Continued on next page)

Here, $a = 1, b = 20, c = -1050$. By the quadratic formula,

$$x = \frac{-20 \pm \sqrt{20^2 - 4(1)(-1050)}}{2 \cdot 1}$$

$$= \frac{-20 \pm \sqrt{400 + 4200}}{2} = \frac{-20 \pm \sqrt{4600}}{2}$$

$$= \frac{-20 \pm \sqrt{100 \cdot 46}}{2} = \frac{-20 \pm 10\sqrt{46}}{2}$$

$$= -10 \pm 5\sqrt{46} \quad \text{Simplify.}$$

4. INTERPRET.

Check: We have two results using the quadratic formula. The length of a side of a triangle can't be negative, so we reject $-10 - 5\sqrt{46}$. Since $-10 + 5\sqrt{46} \approx 24$ feet, the walking distance along the sidewalk is

$$x + (x + 20) \approx 24 + (24 + 20) = 68 \text{ feet.}$$

State: A student saves about $68 - 50$ or 18 feet of walking distance by cutting across the lawn. □

PRACTICE

6 Given the diagram, approximate to the nearest foot how many feet of walking distance a person can save by cutting across the lawn instead of walking on the sidewalk. ■

EXAMPLE 7 Calculating Landing Time

An object is thrown upward from the top of a 200-foot cliff with a velocity of 12 feet per second. The height h in feet of the object after t seconds is

$$h = -16t^2 + 12t + 200$$

How long after the object is thrown will it strike the ground? Round to the nearest tenth of a second.

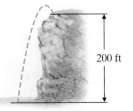

200 ft

Solution

1. UNDERSTAND. Read and reread the problem.

2. TRANSLATE. Since we want to know when the object strikes the ground, we want to know when the height $h = 0$, or

$$0 = -16t^2 + 12t + 200$$

3. SOLVE. First we divide both sides of the equation by -4.

$$0 = 4t^2 - 3t - 50 \quad \text{Divide both sides by } -4.$$

Here, $a = 4, b = -3$, and $c = -50$. By the quadratic formula,

$$t = \frac{-(-3) \pm \sqrt{(-3)^2 - 4(4)(-50)}}{2 \cdot 4}$$

$$= \frac{3 \pm \sqrt{9 + 800}}{8}$$

$$= \frac{3 \pm \sqrt{809}}{8}$$

4. INTERPRET.

Check: We check our calculations from the quadratic formula. Since the time won't be negative, we reject the proposed solution

$$\frac{3 - \sqrt{809}}{8}.$$

State: The time it takes for the object to strike the ground is exactly

$$\frac{3 + \sqrt{809}}{8} \text{ seconds} \approx 3.9 \text{ seconds}.$$ □

PRACTICE

7 A toy rocket is shot upward from the top of a 45-foot-tall building, with an initial velocity of 20 feet per second. The height h in feet of the rocket after t seconds is

$$h = -16t^2 + 20t + 45$$

How long after the rocket is launched will it strike the ground? Round to the nearest tenth of a second. ■

✔ Vocabulary, Readiness & Video Check

Fill in each blank.

1. The quadratic formula is _____ .

2. For $2x^2 + x + 1 = 0$, if $a = 2$, then $b =$ _____ and $c =$ _____ .

3. For $5x^2 - 5x - 7 = 0$, if $a = 5$, then $b =$ _____ and $c =$ _____ .

4. For $7x^2 - 4 = 0$, if $a = 7$, then $b =$ _____ and $c =$ _____ .

5. For $x^2 + 9 = 0$, if $c = 9$, then $a =$ _____ and $b =$ _____ .

6. The correct simplified form of $\dfrac{5 \pm 10\sqrt{2}}{5}$ is _____ .

   a. $1 \pm 10\sqrt{2}$ **b.** $2\sqrt{2}$ **c.** $1 \pm 2\sqrt{2}$ **d.** $\pm 5\sqrt{2}$

Martin-Gay Interactive Videos

See Video 11.2 ⦿

Watch the section lecture video and answer the following questions.

OBJECTIVE 1

7. Based on ▦ Examples 1–3, answer the following.
  a. Must a quadratic equation be written in standard form in order to use the quadratic formula? Why or why not?
  b. Must fractions be cleared from an equation before using the quadratic formula? Why or why not?

OBJECTIVE 2

8. Based on ▦ Example 4 and the lecture before, complete the following statements. The discriminant is the _____ in the quadratic formula and can be used to find the number and type of solutions of a quadratic equation without _____ the equation. To use the discriminant, the quadratic equation needs to be written in _____ form.

OBJECTIVE 3

9. In ▦ Example 5, the value of x is found, which is then used to find the dimensions of the triangle. Yet all this work still does not solve the problem. Explain.

11.2 Exercise Set MyMathLab ▶

Use the quadratic formula to solve each equation. These equations have real number solutions only. See Examples 1 through 3.

1. $m^2 + 5m - 6 = 0$

2. $p^2 + 11p - 12 = 0$

3. $2y = 5y^2 - 3$

4. $5x^2 - 3 = 14x$

5. $x^2 - 6x + 9 = 0$

6. $y^2 + 10y + 25 = 0$

▶ **7.** $x^2 + 7x + 4 = 0$

8. $y^2 + 5y + 3 = 0$

9. $8m^2 - 2m = 7$

10. $11n^2 - 9n = 1$

11. $3m^2 - 7m = 3$

12. $x^2 - 13 = 5x$

13. $\frac{1}{2}x^2 - x - 1 = 0$

14. $\frac{1}{6}x^2 + x + \frac{1}{3} = 0$

15. $\frac{2}{5}y^2 + \frac{1}{5}y = \frac{3}{5}$

16. $\frac{1}{8}x^2 + x = \frac{5}{2}$

17. $\frac{1}{3}y^2 = y + \frac{1}{6}$

18. $\frac{1}{2}y^2 = y + \frac{1}{2}$

19. $x^2 + 5x = -2$

20. $y^2 - 8 = 4y$

21. $(m + 2)(2m - 6) = 5(m - 1) - 12$

22. $7p(p - 2) + 2(p + 4) = 3$

MIXED PRACTICE

Use the quadratic formula to solve each equation. These equations have real solutions and complex but not real solutions. See Examples 1 through 4.

23. $x^2 + 6x + 13 = 0$

24. $x^2 + 2x + 2 = 0$

▶ **25.** $(x + 5)(x - 1) = 2$

26. $x(x + 6) = 2$

27. $6 = -4x^2 + 3x$

28. $2 = -9x^2 - x$

29. $\frac{x^2}{3} - x = \frac{5}{3}$

30. $\frac{x^2}{2} - 3 = -\frac{9}{2}x$

31. $10y^2 + 10y + 3 = 0$

32. $3y^2 + 6y + 5 = 0$

33. $x(6x + 2) = 3$

34. $x(7x + 1) = 2$

▶ **35.** $\frac{2}{5}y^2 + \frac{1}{5}y + \frac{3}{5} = 0$

36. $\frac{1}{8}x^2 + x + \frac{5}{2} = 0$

37. $\frac{1}{2}y^2 = y - \frac{1}{2}$

38. $\frac{2}{3}x^2 - \frac{20}{3}x = -\frac{100}{6}$

39. $(n - 2)^2 = 2n$

40. $\left(p - \frac{1}{2}\right)^2 = \frac{p}{2}$

Use the discriminant to determine the number and type of solutions of each equation. See Example 5.

41. $x^2 - 5 = 0$

42. $x^2 - 7 = 0$

43. $4x^2 + 12x = -9$

44. $9x^2 + 1 = 6x$

45. $3x = -2x^2 + 7$

46. $3x^2 = 5 - 7x$

▶ **47.** $6 = 4x - 5x^2$

48. $8x = 3 - 9x^2$

49. $9x - 2x^2 + 5 = 0$

50. $5 - 4x + 12x^2 = 0$

Solve. See Examples 6 and 7.

▶ **51.** Nancy, Thelma, and John Varner live on a corner lot. Often, neighborhood children cut across their lot to save walking distance. Given the diagram below, approximate to the nearest foot how many feet of walking distance is saved by cutting across their property instead of walking around the lot.

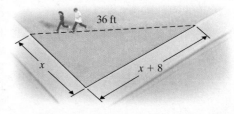

△ **52.** Given the diagram below, approximate to the nearest foot how many feet of walking distance a person saves by cutting across the lawn instead of walking on the sidewalk.

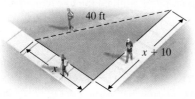

40 ft

$x + 10$

x

△ **53.** The hypotenuse of an isosceles right triangle is 2 centimeters longer than either of its legs. Find the exact length of each side. (*Hint:* An isosceles right triangle is a right triangle whose legs are the same length.)

△ **54.** The hypotenuse of an isosceles right triangle is one meter longer than either of its legs. Find the length of each side.

△ **55.** Bailey's rectangular dog pen for his Irish setter must have an area of 400 square feet. Also, the length must be 10 feet longer than the width. Find the dimensions of the pen.

? ? ?

△ **56.** An entry in the Peach Festival Poster Contest must be rectangular and have an area of 1200 square inches. Furthermore, its length must be 20 inches longer than its width. Find the dimensions each entry must have.

△ **57.** A holding pen for cattle must be square and have a diagonal length of 100 meters.

 a. Find the length of a side of the pen.

 b. Find the area of the pen.

△ **58.** A rectangle is three times longer than it is wide. It has a diagonal of length 50 centimeters.

 a. Find the dimensions of the rectangle.

 b. Find the perimeter of the rectangle.

50 cm

△ **59.** The heaviest reported door in the world is the 708.6-ton radiation shield door in the National Institute for Fusion Science at Toki, Japan. If the height of the door is 1.1 feet longer than its width, and its front area (neglecting depth) is 1439.9 square feet, find its width and height [Interesting note: the door is 6.6 feet thick.] (*Source: Guinness World Records*)

△ **60.** Christi and Robbie Wegmann are constructing a rectangular stained glass window whose length is 7.3 inches longer than its width. If the area of the window is 569.9 square inches, find its width and length.

△ **61.** The base of a triangle is four more than twice its height. If the area of the triangle is 42 square centimeters, find its base and height.

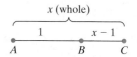

x

62. If a point B divides a line segment such that the smaller portion is to the larger portion as the larger is to the whole, the whole is the length of the *golden ratio*.

x (whole)

1 $x - 1$

A B C

The golden ratio was thought by the Greeks to be the most pleasing to the eye, and many of their buildings contained numerous examples of the golden ratio. The value of the golden ratio is the positive solution of

$$\begin{array}{c}(\text{smaller}) \\ (\text{larger})\end{array} \quad \frac{x - 1}{1} = \frac{1}{x} \quad \begin{array}{c}(\text{larger}) \\ (\text{whole})\end{array}$$

Find this value.

The Wollomombi Falls in Australia have a height of 1100 feet. A pebble is thrown upward from the top of the falls with an initial velocity of 20 feet per second. The height of the pebble h after t seconds is given by the equation $h = -16t^2 + 20t + 1100$. Use this equation for Exercises 63 and 64.

63. How long after the pebble is thrown will it hit the ground? Round to the nearest tenth of a second.

64. How long after the pebble is thrown will it be 550 feet from the ground? Round to the nearest tenth of a second.

A ball is thrown downward from the top of a 180-foot building with an initial velocity of 20 feet per second. The height of the ball h after t seconds is given by the equation $h = -16t^2 - 20t + 180$. Use this equation to answer Exercises 65 and 66.

65. How long after the ball is thrown will it strike the ground? Round the result to the nearest tenth of a second.

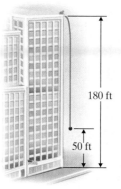

180 ft

50 ft

66. How long after the ball is thrown will it be 50 feet from the ground? Round the result to the nearest tenth of a second.

REVIEW AND PREVIEW

Solve each equation. See Sections 7.5 and 10.6.

67. $\sqrt{5x - 2} = 3$

68. $\sqrt{y + 2} + 7 = 12$

69. $\dfrac{1}{x} + \dfrac{2}{5} = \dfrac{7}{x}$

70. $\dfrac{10}{z} = \dfrac{5}{z} - \dfrac{1}{3}$

Factor. See Sections 6.2 through 6.5.

71. $x^4 + x^2 - 20$

72. $4y^4 + 23y^2 - 6$

73. $z^4 - 13z^2 + 36$

74. $x^4 - 1$

CONCEPT EXTENSIONS

For each quadratic equation, choose the correct substitution for a, b, and c in the standard form $ax^2 + bx + c = 0$.

75. $x^2 = -10$
  a. $a = 1, b = 0, c = -10$
  b. $a = 1, b = 0, c = 10$
  c. $a = 0, b = 1, c = -10$
  d. $a = 1, b = 1, c = 10$

76. $x^2 + 5 = -x$
  a. $a = 1, b = 5, c = -1$
  b. $a = 1, b = -1, c = 5$
  c. $a = 1, b = 5, c = 1$
  d. $a = 1, b = 1, c = 5$

77. Solve Exercise 1 by factoring. Explain the result.

78. Solve Exercise 2 by factoring. Explain the result.

Use the quadratic formula and a calculator to approximate each solution to the nearest tenth.

79. $2x^2 - 6x + 3 = 0$

80. $3.6x^2 + 1.8x - 4.3 = 0$

The accompanying graph shows the daily low temperatures for one week in New Orleans, Louisiana.

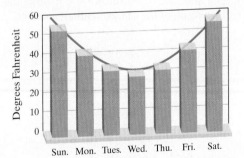

81. Between which days of the week was there the greatest decrease in the low temperature?

82. Between which days of the week was there the greatest increase in the low temperature?

83. Which day of the week had the lowest low temperature?

84. Use the graph to estimate the low temperature on Thursday.

Notice that the shape of the temperature graph is similar to the curve drawn. In fact, this graph can be modeled by the quadratic function $f(x) = 3x^2 - 18x + 56$, where $f(x)$ is the temperature in degrees Fahrenheit and x is the number of days from Sunday. (This graph is shown in blue.) Use this function to answer Exercises 85 and 86.

85. Use the quadratic function given to approximate the temperature on Thursday. Does your answer agree with the graph?

86. Use the function given and the quadratic formula to find when the temperature was 35° F. [*Hint:* Let $f(x) = 35$ and solve for x.] Round your answer to one decimal place and interpret your result. Does your answer agree with the graph?

Solve.

87. The number of Internet users worldwide (in millions) can be modeled by the quadratic equation $f(x) = 5x^2 + 55x + 29$, where $f(x)$ is the number of Internet users worldwide in millions of users, and x is the number of years after 1995. (*Source:* Data from International Telecommunications Union)
  a. Find the number of Internet users worldwide in 2015.
  b. If the trend described in this model continues, find in what year after 1995 the worldwide users of the Internet will reach 4500 million.

88. While the number of farms in the United States was decreasing through the late twentieth century and the early twenty-first century, the average size of farms was increasing. This may be due to consolidation of existing farmlands. The equation $f(x) = -0.5x^2 + 4x + 429$ models the size of the average farm, where $f(x)$ is farm size in acres, and x represents the number of years after 2011. (*Source:* Based on data from the National Agricultural Statistics Service)
  a. Find the size of the average farm in 2012. Round to the nearest acre.
  b. Find the size of the average farm in 2014. Round to the nearest acre.

89. The amount of money spent in restaurants in the United States x years after 1970 can be modeled by $f(x) = 0.2x^2 + 5.1x + 45.3$, where $f(x)$ is the amount of money spent in restaurants (in billions of dollars), and x is the number of years since 1970.
  a. Find the amount the American public spent in restaurants in 2015. Round to the nearest tenth of a billion.
  b. According to this model, in what year after 1970 was the amount of money spent in restaurants $400 billion?
  c. According to this model, in what year after 1970 will the amount of money spent on restaurants equal $1000 billion?

90. The relationship between body weight and the Recommended Dietary Allowance (RDA) for vitamin A in children up to age 10 is modeled by the quadratic equation $y = 0.149x^2 - 4.475x + 406.478$, where y is the RDA for vitamin A in micrograms for a child whose weight is x pounds. (*Source:* Based on data from the Food and Nutrition Board, National Academy of Sciences–Institute of Medicine, 1989)

    a. Determine the vitamin A requirements of a child who weighs 35 pounds.

    b. What is the weight of a child whose RDA of vitamin A is 600 micrograms? Round your answer to the nearest pound.

The solutions of the quadratic equation $ax^2 + bx + c = 0$ *are* $\dfrac{-b + \sqrt{b^2 - 4ac}}{2a}$ *and* $\dfrac{-b - \sqrt{b^2 - 4ac}}{2a}$.

91. Show that the sum of these solutions is $\dfrac{-b}{a}$.

92. Show that the product of these solutions is $\dfrac{c}{a}$.

Use the quadratic formula to solve each quadratic equation.

93. $3x^2 - \sqrt{12}x + 1 = 0$
    (*Hint:* $a = 3, b = -\sqrt{12}, c = 1$)

94. $5x^2 + \sqrt{20}x + 1 = 0$

95. $x^2 + \sqrt{2}x + 1 = 0$

96. $x^2 - \sqrt{2}x + 1 = 0$

97. $2x^2 - \sqrt{3}x - 1 = 0$

98. $7x^2 + \sqrt{7}x - 2 = 0$

99. Use a graphing calculator to solve Exercises 63 and 65.

100. Use a graphing calculator to solve Exercises 64 and 66.

Recall that the discriminant also tells us the number of x-intercepts of the related function.

101. Check the results of Exercise 49 by graphing $y = 9x - 2x^2 + 5$.

102. Check the results of Exercise 50 by graphing $y = 5 - 4x + 12x^2$.

11.3   Solving Equations by Using Quadratic Methods ▶

OBJECTIVES

1 Solve Various Equations That Are Quadratic in Form. ▶

2 Solve Problems That Lead to Quadratic Equations. ▶

OBJECTIVE

1   Solving Equations That Are Quadratic in Form ▶

In this section, we discuss various types of equations that can be solved in part by using the methods for solving quadratic equations. We call these equations ones that are quadratic in form.

Once each equation is simplified, you may want to use these steps when deciding which method to use to solve the quadratic equation.

> **Solving a Quadratic Equation**
>
> **Step 1.** If the equation is in the form $(ax + b)^2 = c$, use the square root property and solve. If not, go to Step 2.
>
> **Step 2.** Write the equation in standard form: $ax^2 + bx + c = 0$.
>
> **Step 3.** Try to solve the equation by the factoring method. If not possible, go to Step 4.
>
> **Step 4.** Solve the equation by the quadratic formula.

The first example is a radical equation that becomes a quadratic equation once we square both sides.

EXAMPLE 1   Solve: $x - \sqrt{x} - 6 = 0$

Solution Recall that to solve a radical equation, first get the radical alone on one side of the equation. Then square both sides.

$$x - 6 = \sqrt{x} \qquad \text{Add } \sqrt{x} \text{ to both sides.}$$
$$(x - 6)^2 = \left(\sqrt{x}\right)^2 \qquad \text{Square both sides.}$$
$$x^2 - 12x + 36 = x$$
$$x^2 - 13x + 36 = 0 \qquad \text{Set the equation equal to 0.}$$
$$(x - 9)(x - 4) = 0$$
$$x - 9 = 0 \quad \text{or} \quad x - 4 = 0$$
$$x = 9 \qquad\qquad x = 4$$

(Continued on next page)

Check:

Let $x = 9$ Let $x = 4$

$x - \sqrt{x} - 6 = 0$ $x - \sqrt{x} - 6 = 0$

$9 - \sqrt{9} - 6 \stackrel{?}{=} 0$ $4 - \sqrt{4} - 6 \stackrel{?}{=} 0$

$9 - 3 - 6 \stackrel{?}{=} 0$ $4 - 2 - 6 \stackrel{?}{=} 0$

$0 = 0$ True $-4 = 0$ False

The solution is 9 or the solution set is {9}.   □

PRACTICE
1   Solve: $x - \sqrt{x + 1} - 5 = 0$ ■

EXAMPLE 2   Solve: $\dfrac{3x}{x - 2} - \dfrac{x + 1}{x} = \dfrac{6}{x(x - 2)}$

Solution In this equation, x cannot be either 2 or 0 because these values cause denominators to equal zero. To solve for x, we first multiply both sides of the equation by $x(x - 2)$ to clear the fractions. By the distributive property, this means that we multiply each term by $x(x - 2)$.

$$x(x - 2)\left(\frac{3x}{x - 2}\right) - x(x - 2)\left(\frac{x + 1}{x}\right) = x(x - 2)\left[\frac{6}{x(x - 2)}\right]$$

$$3x^2 - (x - 2)(x + 1) = 6 \quad \text{Simplify.}$$
$$3x^2 - (x^2 - x - 2) = 6 \quad \text{Multiply.}$$
$$3x^2 - x^2 + x + 2 = 6$$
$$2x^2 + x - 4 = 0 \quad \text{Simplify.}$$

This equation cannot be factored using integers, so we solve by the quadratic formula.

$$x = \frac{-1 \pm \sqrt{1^2 - 4(2)(-4)}}{2 \cdot 2} \quad \begin{array}{l} \text{Use } a = 2, b = 1, \text{ and } c = -4 \\ \text{in the quadratic formula.} \end{array}$$

$$= \frac{-1 \pm \sqrt{1 + 32}}{4} \quad \text{Simplify.}$$

$$= \frac{-1 \pm \sqrt{33}}{4}$$

Neither proposed solution will make the denominators 0.

The solutions are $\dfrac{-1 + \sqrt{33}}{4}$ and $\dfrac{-1 - \sqrt{33}}{4}$ or the solution set is $\left\{\dfrac{-1 + \sqrt{33}}{4}, \dfrac{-1 - \sqrt{33}}{4}\right\}$.   □

PRACTICE
2   Solve: $\dfrac{5x}{x + 1} - \dfrac{x + 4}{x} = \dfrac{3}{x(x + 1)}$ ■

EXAMPLE 3   Solve: $p^4 - 3p^2 - 4 = 0$

Solution First we factor the trinomial.

$$p^4 - 3p^2 - 4 = 0$$
$$(p^2 - 4)(p^2 + 1) = 0 \quad\quad\quad \text{Factor.}$$
$$(p - 2)(p + 2)(p^2 + 1) = 0 \quad\quad\quad \text{Factor further.}$$
$$p - 2 = 0 \quad \text{or} \quad p + 2 = 0 \quad \text{or} \quad p^2 + 1 = 0 \quad \begin{array}{l} \text{Set each factor equal} \\ \text{to 0 and solve.} \end{array}$$
$$p = 2 \quad\quad\quad\quad p = -2 \quad\quad\quad\quad p^2 = -1$$
$$p = \pm\sqrt{-1} = \pm i$$

The solutions are 2, −2, i and −i.

PRACTICE

3   Solve: $p^4 - 7p^2 - 144 = 0$

> **Helpful Hint**
>
> Example 3 can be solved using substitution also. Think of $p^4 - 3p^2 - 4 = 0$ as
>
> $$(p^2)^2 - 3p^2 - 4 = 0 \quad \text{Then let } x = p^2 \text{ and solve and substitute back.}$$
> $$\text{The solutions will be the same.}$$
>
> $$x^2 - 3x - 4 = 0$$

✔ **CONCEPT CHECK**

a. True or false? The maximum number of solutions that a quadratic equation can have is 2.
b. True or false? The maximum number of solutions that an equation in quadratic form can have is 2.

EXAMPLE 4   Solve: $(x - 3)^2 - 3(x - 3) - 4 = 0$

Solution   Notice that the quantity $(x - 3)$ is repeated in this equation. Sometimes it is helpful to substitute a variable (in this case other than x) for the repeated quantity. We will let $y = x - 3$. Then

$$(x - 3)^2 - 3(x - 3) - 4 = 0$$

becomes

$$y^2 - 3y - 4 = 0 \quad \text{Let } x - 3 = y.$$
$$(y - 4)(y + 1) = 0 \quad \text{Factor.}$$

To solve, we use the zero factor property.

$$y - 4 = 0 \quad \text{or} \quad y + 1 = 0 \quad \text{Set each factor equal to 0.}$$
$$y = 4 \qquad\qquad y = -1 \quad \text{Solve.}$$

> **Helpful Hint**
>
> When using substitution, don't forget to substitute back to the original variable.

To find values of x, we substitute back. That is, we substitute $x - 3$ for y.

$$x - 3 = 4 \quad \text{or} \quad x - 3 = -1$$
$$x = 7 \qquad\qquad x = 2$$

Both 2 and 7 check. The solutions are 2 and 7.

PRACTICE

4   Solve: $(x + 2)^2 - 2(x + 2) - 3 = 0$

EXAMPLE 5   Solve: $x^{2/3} - 5x^{1/3} + 6 = 0$

Solution   The key to solving this equation is recognizing that $x^{2/3} = (x^{1/3})^2$. We replace $x^{1/3}$ with m so that

$$(x^{1/3})^2 - 5x^{1/3} + 6 = 0$$

becomes

$$m^2 - 5m + 6 = 0$$

Now we solve by factoring.

$$m^2 - 5m + 6 = 0$$
$$(m - 3)(m - 2) = 0 \qquad\qquad\qquad \text{Factor.}$$
$$m - 3 = 0 \quad \text{or} \quad m - 2 = 0 \quad \text{Set each factor equal to 0.}$$
$$m = 3 \qquad\qquad m = 2$$

Answer to Concept Check:
a. true   **b.** false

(Continued on next page)

Since $m = x^{1/3}$, we have

$$x^{1/3} = 3 \qquad \text{or} \quad x^{1/3} = 2$$
$$x = 3^3 = 27 \quad \text{or} \qquad x = 2^3 = 8$$

Both 8 and 27 check. The solutions are 8 and 27.

PRACTICE

5   Solve: $x^{2/3} - 5x^{1/3} + 4 = 0$

OBJECTIVE

2   Solving Problems That Lead to Quadratic Equations   ▶

The next example is a work problem. This problem is modeled by a rational equation that simplifies to a quadratic equation.

EXAMPLE 6   **Finding Work Time**

Together, an experienced word processor and an apprentice word processor can create a word document in 6 hours. Alone, the experienced word processor can create the document 2 hours faster than the apprentice word processor can. Find the time in which each person can create the word document alone.

Solution

1. **UNDERSTAND.** Read and reread the problem. The key idea here is the relationship between the *time* (hours) it takes to complete the job and the *part of the job* completed in one unit of time (hour). For example, because they can complete the job together in 6 hours, the *part of the job* they can complete in 1 hour is $\frac{1}{6}$.

   Let

   $x = $ the *time* in hours it takes the apprentice word processor to complete the job alone, and

   $x - 2 = $ the *time* in hours it takes the experienced word processor to complete the job alone.

   We can summarize in a chart the information discussed.

	Total Hours to Complete Job	*Part of Job Completed in 1 Hour*
Apprentice Word Processor	x	$\dfrac{1}{x}$
Experienced Word Processor	$x - 2$	$\dfrac{1}{x - 2}$
Together	6	$\dfrac{1}{6}$

2. **TRANSLATE.**

In words:	part of job completed by apprentice word processor in 1 hour	added to	part of job completed by experienced word processor in 1 hour	is equal to	part of job completed together in 1 hour
	↓	↓	↓	↓	↓
Translate:	$\dfrac{1}{x}$	$+$	$\dfrac{1}{x - 2}$	$=$	$\dfrac{1}{6}$

3. SOLVE.

$$\frac{1}{x} + \frac{1}{x-2} = \frac{1}{6}$$

$$6x(x-2)\left(\frac{1}{x} + \frac{1}{x-2}\right) = 6x(x-2)\cdot\frac{1}{6}$$ Multiply both sides by the LCD $6x(x-2)$.

$$6x(x-2)\cdot\frac{1}{x} + 6x(x-2)\cdot\frac{1}{x-2} = 6x(x-2)\cdot\frac{1}{6}$$ Use the distributive property.

$$6(x-2) + 6x = x(x-2)$$

$$6x - 12 + 6x = x^2 - 2x$$

$$0 = x^2 - 14x + 12$$

Now we can substitute $a = 1, b = -14$, and $c = 12$ into the quadratic formula and simplify.

$$x = \frac{-(-14) \pm \sqrt{(-14)^2 - 4(1)(12)}}{2\cdot1} = \frac{14 \pm \sqrt{148}}{2}^*$$

Using a calculator or a square root table, we see that $\sqrt{148} \approx 12.2$ rounded to one decimal place. Thus,

$$x \approx \frac{14 \pm 12.2}{2}$$

$$x \approx \frac{14 + 12.2}{2} = 13.1 \quad \text{or} \quad x \approx \frac{14 - 12.2}{2} = 0.9$$

4. INTERPRET.

Check: If the apprentice word processor completes the job alone in 0.9 hours, the experienced word processor completes the job alone in $x - 2 = 0.9 - 2 = -1.1$ hours. Since this is not possible, we reject the solution of 0.9. The approximate solution thus is 13.1 hours.

State: The apprentice word processor can complete the job alone in approximately 13.1 hours, and the experienced word processor can complete the job alone in approximately

$$x - 2 = 13.1 - 2 = 11.1 \text{ hours} \qquad \square$$

PRACTICE

6 Together, Katy and Steve can groom all the dogs at the Barkin' Doggie Day Care in 4 hours. Alone, Katy can groom the dogs 1 hour faster than Steve can groom the dogs alone. Find the time in which each of them can groom the dogs alone. ▪

EXAMPLE 7 **Finding Driving Speeds**

Beach and Fargo are about 400 miles apart. A salesperson travels from Fargo to Beach one day at a certain speed. She returns to Fargo the next day and drives 10 mph faster. Her total travel time was $14\frac{2}{3}$ hours. Find her speed to Beach and the return speed to Fargo.

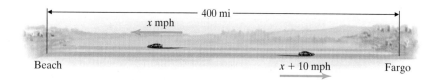

*This expression can be simplified further, but this will suffice because we are approximating.

(Continued on next page)

Solution

1. **UNDERSTAND.** Read and reread the problem. Let

$$x = \text{the speed to Beach, so}$$
$$x + 10 = \text{the return speed to Fargo.}$$

Then organize the given information in a table.

Helpful Hint

Since $d = rt, t = \dfrac{d}{r}$. The time column was completed using $\dfrac{d}{r}$.

	distance	= rate	· time	
To Beach	400	x	$\dfrac{400}{x}$	← distance ← rate
Return to Fargo	400	$x + 10$	$\dfrac{400}{x + 10}$	← distance ← rate

2. **TRANSLATE.**

In words: time to Beach   +   return time to Fargo   = $14\dfrac{2}{3}$ hours

$$\text{Translate:} \quad \frac{400}{x} \quad + \quad \frac{400}{x + 10} \quad = \quad \frac{44}{3}$$

3. **SOLVE.**

$$\frac{400}{x} + \frac{400}{x + 10} = \frac{44}{3}$$

$$\frac{100}{x} + \frac{100}{x + 10} = \frac{11}{3} \qquad \text{Divide both sides by 4.}$$

$$3x(x + 10)\left(\frac{100}{x} + \frac{100}{x + 10}\right) = 3x(x + 10) \cdot \frac{11}{3} \qquad \text{Multiply both sides by the LCD } 3x(x + 10).$$

$$3x(x + 10) \cdot \frac{100}{x} + 3x(x + 10) \cdot \frac{100}{x + 10} = 3x(x + 10) \cdot \frac{11}{3} \qquad \text{Use the distributive property.}$$

$$3(x + 10) \cdot 100 + 3x \cdot 100 = x(x + 10) \cdot 11$$

$$300x + 3000 + 300x = 11x^2 + 110x$$

$$0 = 11x^2 - 490x - 3000 \qquad \text{Set equation equal to 0.}$$

$$0 = (11x + 60)(x - 50) \qquad \text{Factor.}$$

$$11x + 60 = 0 \quad \text{or} \quad x - 50 = 0 \qquad \text{Set each factor equal to 0.}$$

$$x = -\frac{60}{11} \text{ or } -5\frac{5}{11}; \quad x = 50$$

4. **INTERPRET.**

Check: The speed is not negative, so it's not $-5\dfrac{5}{11}$. The number 50 does check.

State: The speed to Beach was 50 mph, and her return speed to Fargo was 60 mph. □

PRACTICE

7   The 36-km S-shaped Hangzhou Bay Bridge is the longest cross-sea bridge in the world, linking Ningbo and Shanghai, China. A merchant drives over the bridge one morning from Ningbo to Shanghai in very heavy traffic and returns home that night driving 50 km per hour faster. The total travel time was 1.3 hours. Find the speed to Shanghai and the return speed to Ningbo. ■

Vocabulary, Readiness & Video Check

Martin-Gay Interactive Videos

See Video 11.3

Watch the section lecture video and answer the following questions.

OBJECTIVE 1

1. From Examples 1 and 2, what's the main thing to remember when using a substitution in order to solve an equation by quadratic methods?

OBJECTIVE 2

2. In Example 4, the translated equation is actually a rational equation. Explain how we end up solving it using quadratic methods.

11.3 Exercise Set MyMathLab®

Solve. See Example 1.

1. $2x = \sqrt{10 + 3x}$

2. $3x = \sqrt{8x + 1}$

3. $x - 2\sqrt{x} = 8$

4. $x - \sqrt{2x} = 4$

5. $\sqrt{9x} = x + 2$

6. $\sqrt{16x} = x + 3$

Solve. See Example 2.

7. $\dfrac{2}{x} + \dfrac{3}{x - 1} = 1$

8. $\dfrac{6}{x^2} = \dfrac{3}{x + 1}$

9. $\dfrac{3}{x} + \dfrac{4}{x + 2} = 2$

10. $\dfrac{5}{x - 2} + \dfrac{4}{x + 2} = 1$

11. $\dfrac{7}{x^2 - 5x + 6} = \dfrac{2x}{x - 3} - \dfrac{x}{x - 2}$

12. $\dfrac{11}{2x^2 + x - 15} = \dfrac{5}{2x - 5} - \dfrac{x}{x + 3}$

Solve. See Example 3.

13. $p^4 - 16 = 0$

14. $x^4 + 2x^2 - 3 = 0$

15. $4x^4 + 11x^2 = 3$

16. $z^4 = 81$

17. $z^4 - 13z^2 + 36 = 0$

18. $9x^4 + 5x^2 - 4 = 0$

Solve. See Examples 4 and 5.

19. $x^{2/3} - 3x^{1/3} - 10 = 0$

20. $x^{2/3} + 2x^{1/3} + 1 = 0$

21. $(5n + 1)^2 + 2(5n + 1) - 3 = 0$

22. $(m - 6)^2 + 5(m - 6) + 4 = 0$

23. $2x^{2/3} - 5x^{1/3} = 3$

24. $3x^{2/3} + 11x^{1/3} = 4$

25. $1 + \dfrac{2}{3t - 2} = \dfrac{8}{(3t - 2)^2}$

26. $2 - \dfrac{7}{x + 6} = \dfrac{15}{(x + 6)^2}$

27. $20x^{2/3} - 6x^{1/3} - 2 = 0$

28. $4x^{2/3} + 16x^{1/3} = -15$

MIXED PRACTICE

Solve. See Examples 1 through 5.

29. $a^4 - 5a^2 + 6 = 0$

30. $x^4 - 12x^2 + 11 = 0$

31. $\dfrac{2x}{x - 2} + \dfrac{x}{x + 3} = -\dfrac{5}{x + 3}$

32. $\dfrac{5}{x - 3} + \dfrac{x}{x + 3} = \dfrac{19}{x^2 - 9}$

33. $(p + 2)^2 = 9(p + 2) - 20$

34. $2(4m - 3)^2 - 9(4m - 3) = 5$

35. $2x = \sqrt{11x + 3}$

36. $4x = \sqrt{2x + 3}$

37. $x^{2/3} - 8x^{1/3} + 15 = 0$

38. $x^{2/3} - 2x^{1/3} - 8 = 0$

39. $y^3 + 9y - y^2 - 9 = 0$

40. $x^3 + x - 3x^2 - 3 = 0$

41. $2x^{2/3} + 3x^{1/3} - 2 = 0$

42. $6x^{2/3} - 25x^{1/3} - 25 = 0$

43. $x^{-2} - x^{-1} - 6 = 0$

44. $y^{-2} - 8y^{-1} + 7 = 0$

45. $x - \sqrt{x} = 2$

46. $x - \sqrt{3x} = 6$

47. $\dfrac{x}{x-1} + \dfrac{1}{x+1} = \dfrac{2}{x^2-1}$

48. $\dfrac{x}{x-5} + \dfrac{5}{x+5} = -\dfrac{1}{x^2-25}$

49. $p^4 - p^2 - 20 = 0$

50. $x^4 - 10x^2 + 9 = 0$

51. $(x+3)(x^2 - 3x + 9) = 0$

52. $(x-6)(x^2 + 6x + 36) = 0$

53. $1 = \dfrac{4}{x-7} + \dfrac{5}{(x-7)^2}$

54. $3 + \dfrac{1}{2p+4} = \dfrac{10}{(2p+4)^2}$

55. $27y^4 + 15y^2 = 2$

56. $8z^4 + 14z^2 = -5$

57. $x - \sqrt{19 - 2x} - 2 = 0$

58. $x - \sqrt{17 - 4x} - 3 = 0$

Solve. For Exercises 59 and 60, the solutions have been started for you. See Examples 6 and 7.

59. Roma Sherry drove 330 miles from her hometown to Tucson. During her return trip, she was able to increase her speed by 11 miles per hour. If her return trip took 1 hour less time, find her original speed and her speed returning home.

Start the solution:

1. UNDERSTAND the problem. Reread it as many times as needed. Let

$$x = \text{original speed, and}$$
$$x + 11 = \text{return-trip speed.}$$

Organize the information in a table.

	distance =	rate ·	time	
To Tucson	330	x	$\dfrac{330}{x}$	← distance ← rate
Return trip	330	___	$\dfrac{330}{\_\_\_}$	← distance ← rate

2. TRANSLATE into an equation. (Fill in the blanks below.)

time to Tucson	equals	return trip time	plus	1 hour
↓	↓	↓	↓	↓
___	=	___	+	1

Finish with:

3. SOLVE and **4.** INTERPRET

60. A salesperson drove to Portland, a distance of 300 miles. During the last 80 miles of his trip, heavy rainfall forced him to decrease his speed by 15 miles per hour. If his total driving time was 6 hours, find his original speed and his speed during the rainfall.

Start the solution:

1. UNDERSTAND the problem. Reread it as many times as needed. Let

$$x = \text{original speed, and}$$
$$x - 15 = \text{rainfall speed.}$$

Organize the information in a table.

	distance =	rate ·	time	
First part of trip	300 − 80, or 220	x	$\dfrac{220}{x}$	← distance ← rate
Heavy rainfall part of trip	80	$x - 15$	$\dfrac{80}{\_\_\_}$	← distance ← rate

2. TRANSLATE into an equation. (Fill in the blanks below.)

time during first part of trip	plus	time during heavy rainfall	equals	6 hr
↓	↓	↓	↓	↓
___	+	___	=	6

Finish with:

3. SOLVE and **4.** INTERPRET

61. A jogger ran 3 miles, decreased her speed by 1 mile per hour, and then ran another 4 miles. If her total time jogging was $1\dfrac{3}{5}$ hours, find her speed for each part of her run.

62. Mark Keaton's workout consists of jogging for 3 miles and then riding his bike for 5 miles at a speed 4 miles per hour faster than he jogs. If his total workout time is 1 hour, find his jogging speed and his biking speed.

63. A Chinese restaurant in Mandeville, Louisiana, has a large goldfish pond around the restaurant. Suppose that an inlet pipe and a hose together can fill the pond in 8 hours. The inlet pipe alone can complete the job in one hour less time than the hose alone. Find the time that the hose can complete the job alone and the time that the inlet pipe can complete the job alone. Round each to the nearest tenth of an hour.

64. A water tank on a farm in Flatonia, Texas, can be filled with a large inlet pipe and a small inlet pipe in 3 hours. The large inlet pipe alone can fill the tank in 2 hours less time than the small inlet pipe alone. Find the time to the nearest tenth of an hour each pipe can fill the tank alone.

65. Bill Shaughnessy and his son Billy can clean the house together in 4 hours. When the son works alone, it takes him an hour longer to clean than it takes his dad alone. Find how long to the nearest tenth of an hour it takes the son to clean alone.

66. Together, Noodles and Freckles eat a 50-pound bag of dog food in 30 days. Noodles by himself eats a 50-pound bag in 2 weeks less time than Freckles does by himself. How many days to the nearest whole day would a 50-pound bag of dog food last Freckles?

67. The product of a number and 4 less than the number is 96. Find the number.

68. A whole number increased by its square is two more than twice itself. Find the number.

△ **69.** Suppose that an open box is to be made from a square sheet of cardboard by cutting out squares from each corner as shown and then folding along the dotted lines. If the box is to have a volume of 300 cubic inches, find the original dimensions of the sheet of cardboard.

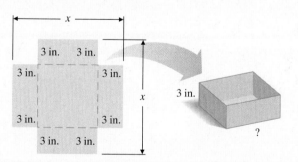

a. The ? in the drawing above will be the length (and the width) of the box as shown. Represent this length in terms of x.

b. Use the formula for volume of a box, $V = l \cdot w \cdot h$, to write an equation in x.

c. Solve the equation for x and give the dimensions of the sheet of cardboard. Check your solution.

△ **70.** Suppose that an open box is to be made from a square sheet of cardboard by cutting out squares from each corner as shown and then folding along the dotted lines. If the box is to have

a volume of 128 cubic inches, find the original dimensions of the sheet of cardboard.

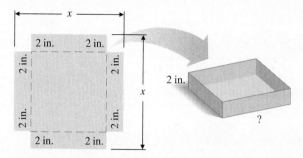

a. The ? in the drawing above will be the length (and the width) of the box as shown. Represent this length in terms of x.

b. Use the formula for volume of a box, $V = l \cdot w \cdot h$, to write an equation in x.

c. Solve the equation for x and give the dimensions of the sheet of cardboard. Check your solution.

△ **71.** A sprinkler that sprays water in a circular pattern is to be used to water a square garden. If the area of the garden is 920 square feet, find the smallest whole number *radius* that the sprinkler can be adjusted to so that the entire garden is watered.

△ **72.** Suppose that a square field has an area of 6270 square feet. See Exercise 71 and find the sprinkler radius.

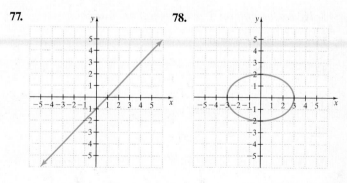

REVIEW AND PREVIEW

Solve each inequality. See Section 2.8.

73. $\dfrac{5x}{3} + 2 \le 7$

74. $\dfrac{2x}{3} + \dfrac{1}{6} \ge 2$

75. $\dfrac{y-1}{15} > -\dfrac{2}{5}$

76. $\dfrac{z-2}{12} < \dfrac{1}{4}$

Find the domain and range of each graphed relation. Decide which relations are also functions. See Section 3.6.

77.

78.

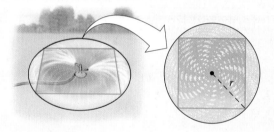

79. **80.**

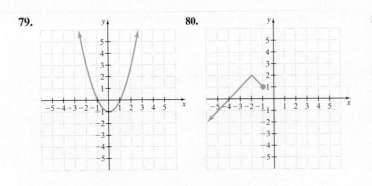

CONCEPT EXTENSIONS

Solve.

81. $5y^3 + 45y - 5y^2 - 45 = 0$

82. $10x^3 + 10x - 30x^2 - 30 = 0$

83. $3x^{-2} - 3x^{-1} - 18 = 0$

84. $2y^{-2} - 16y^{-1} + 14 = 0$

85. $2x^3 = -54$

86. $y^3 - 216 = 0$

87. Write a polynomial equation that has three solutions: 2, 5, and -7.

88. Write a polynomial equation that has three solutions: 0, $2i$, and $-2i$.

89. In 2015, the Daytona 500 race was extended to 203 laps, which increased the race distance to 507.5 miles. Dale Earnhardt Jr. won the 2014 Daytona 500 race but came in third in the 2015 race. Joey Logano, who won the 2015 race, completed the 203-lap race in 3 hours, 5 minutes, and 15 seconds. Logano's average speed for the race was 1.193 seconds per lap faster than that of Earnhardt. (Source: Nascar)

    a. Find Joey Logano's average race speed (miles per hour) for the 2015 Daytona 500. Round to the nearest hundredth.

    b. Find Joey Logano's average lap time (seconds per lap) for the 2015 Daytona 500. Round to the nearest thousandth.

    c. Find Dale Earnhart Jr.'s average lap time.

    d. Find Dale Earnhardt Jr.'s average race speed (miles per hour).

90. Use a graphing calculator to solve Exercise 29. Compare the solution with the solution from Exercise 29. Explain any differences.

Integrated Review   Summary on Solving Quadratic Equations

Sections 11.1–11.3

Use the square root property to solve each equation.

1. $x^2 - 10 = 0$

2. $x^2 - 14 = 0$

3. $(x - 1)^2 = 8$

4. $(x + 5)^2 = 12$

Solve each equation by completing the square.

5. $x^2 + 2x - 12 = 0$

6. $x^2 - 12x + 11 = 0$

7. $3x^2 + 3x = 5$

8. $16y^2 + 16y = 1$

Use the quadratic formula to solve each equation.

9. $2x^2 - 4x + 1 = 0$

10. $\dfrac{1}{2}x^2 + 3x + 2 = 0$

11. $x^2 + 4x = -7$

12. $x^2 + x = -3$

Solve each equation. Use a method of your choice.

13. $x^2 + 3x + 6 = 0$

14. $2x^2 + 18 = 0$

15. $x^2 + 17x = 0$

16. $4x^2 - 2x - 3 = 0$

17. $(x - 2)^2 = 27$

18. $\dfrac{1}{2}x^2 - 2x + \dfrac{1}{2} = 0$

19. $3x^2 + 2x = 8$

20. $2x^2 = -5x - 1$

21. $x(x - 2) = 5$

22. $x^2 - 31 = 0$

23. $5x^2 - 55 = 0$

24. $5x^2 + 55 = 0$

25. $x(x + 5) = 66$

26. $5x^2 + 6x - 2 = 0$

27. $2x^2 + 3x = 1$

28. $x - \sqrt{13 - 3x} - 3 = 0$

29. $\dfrac{5x}{x - 2} - \dfrac{x + 1}{x} = \dfrac{3}{x(x - 2)}$

Solve.

△ **30.** The diagonal of a square room measures 20 feet. Find the exact length of a side of the room. Then approximate the length to the nearest tenth of a foot.

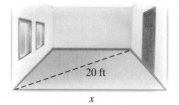

20 ft

x

31. Together, Jack and Lucy Hoag can prepare a crawfish boil for a large party in 4 hours. Lucy alone can complete the job in 2 hours less time than Jack alone. Find the time that each person can prepare the crawfish boil alone. Round each time to the nearest tenth of an hour.

32. Diane Gray exercises at Total Body Gym. On the treadmill, she runs 5 miles, then increases her speed by 1 mile per hour and runs an additional 2 miles. If her total time on the treadmill is $1\dfrac{1}{3}$ hours, find her speed during each part of her run.

11.4 Nonlinear Inequalities in One Variable ▶

OBJECTIVES

1 Solve Polynomial Inequalities of Degree 2 or Greater. ▶

2 Solve Inequalities That Contain Rational Expressions with Variables in the Denominator. ▶

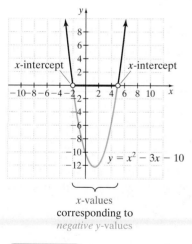

x-intercept

x-intercept

$y = x^2 - 3x - 10$

x-values corresponding to *negative y*-values

Helpful Hint

The related equation is found by replacing the inequality symbol with "=".

OBJECTIVE

1 Solving Polynomial Inequalities ▶

Just as we can solve linear inequalities in one variable, so can we also solve quadratic inequalities in one variable. A **quadratic inequality** is an inequality that can be written so that one side is a quadratic expression and the other side is 0. Here are examples of quadratic inequalities in one variable. Each is written in **standard form.**

$$x^2 - 10x + 7 \le 0 \qquad 3x^2 + 2x - 6 > 0$$
$$2x^2 + 9x - 2 < 0 \qquad x^2 - 3x + 11 \ge 0$$

A solution of a quadratic inequality in one variable is a value of the variable that makes the inequality a true statement.

The value of an expression such as $x^2 - 3x - 10$ will sometimes be positive, sometimes negative, and sometimes 0, depending on the value substituted for x. To solve the inequality $x^2 - 3x - 10 < 0$, we are looking for all values of x that make the expression $x^2 - 3x - 10$ **less than 0**, or **negative.** To understand how we find these values, we'll study the graph of the quadratic function $y = x^2 - 3x - 10$.

Notice that the x-values for which y is positive are separated from the x values for which y is negative by the x-intercepts. (Recall that the x-intercepts correspond to values of x for which $y = 0$.) Thus, the solution set of $x^2 - 3x - 10 < 0$ consists of all real numbers from -2 to 5 or, in interval notation, $(-2, 5)$.

It is not necessary to graph $y = x^2 - 3x - 10$ to solve the related inequality $x^2 - 3x - 10 < 0$. Instead, we can draw a number line representing the x-axis and keep the following in mind: *A region on the number line for which the value of* $x^2 - 3x - 10$ *is positive is separated from a region on the number line for which the value of* $x^2 - 3x - 10$ *is negative by a value for which the expression is 0.*

Let's find these values for which the expression is 0 by solving the related equation:

$$x^2 - 3x - 10 \stackrel{!}{=} 0$$
$$(x - 5)(x + 2) = 0 \qquad \text{Factor.}$$
$$x - 5 = 0 \quad \text{or} \quad x + 2 = 0 \qquad \text{Set each factor equal to 0.}$$
$$x = 5 \qquad\qquad x = -2 \qquad \text{Solve.}$$

These two numbers, -2 and 5, divide the number line into three regions. We will call the regions A, B, and C. These regions are important because, if the value of $x^2 - 3x - 10$ is negative when a number from a region is substituted for x, then $x^2 - 3x - 10$ is negative when any number in that region is substituted for x. The same is true if the value of $x^2 - 3x - 10$ is positive for a particular value of x in a region.

To see whether the inequality $x^2 - 3x - 10 < 0$ is true or false in each region, we choose a test point from each region and substitute its value for x in the inequality $x^2 - 3x - 10 < 0$. If the resulting inequality is true, the region containing the test point is a solution region.

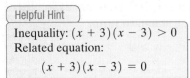

Region	Test Point Value	$(x - 5)(x + 2) < 0$	Result
A	-3	$(-8)(-1) < 0$	False
B	0	$(-5)(2) < 0$	True
C	6	$(1)(8) < 0$	False

The values in region B satisfy the inequality. The numbers -2 and 5 are not included in the solution set since the inequality symbol is $<$. The solution set is $(-2, 5)$, and its graph is shown.

$$
\begin{array}{ccc}
A & B & C \\
\text{F}\ {-2} & \text{T}\quad 5 & \text{F}
\end{array}
$$

EXAMPLE 1   Solve: $(x + 3)(x - 3) > 0$

Solution First we solve the related equation, $(x + 3)(x - 3) = 0$.

$$(x + 3)(x - 3) = 0$$
$$x + 3 = 0 \quad \text{or} \quad x - 3 = 0$$
$$x = -3 \qquad\qquad x = 3$$

Helpful Hint

Inequality: $(x + 3)(x - 3) > 0$
Related equation:
$$(x + 3)(x - 3) = 0$$

The two numbers -3 and 3 separate the number line into three regions, A, B, and C.

$$
\begin{array}{ccc}
A & B & C \\
-3 & 3 &
\end{array}
$$

Now we substitute the value of a test point from each region. If the test value satisfies the inequality, every value in the region containing the test value is a solution.

Region	Test Point Value	$(x + 3)(x - 3) > 0$	Result
A	-4	$(-1)(-7) > 0$	True
B	0	$(3)(-3) > 0$	False
C	4	$(7)(1) > 0$	True

The points in regions A and C satisfy the inequality. The numbers -3 and 3 are not included in the solution since the inequality symbol is $>$. The solution set is $(-\infty, -3) \cup (3, \infty)$, and its graph is shown.

$$
\begin{array}{ccc}
A & B & C \\
\text{T}\ {-3} & \text{F}\quad 3 & \text{T}
\end{array}
$$

PRACTICE

1   Solve: $(x - 4)(x + 3) > 0$

The following steps may be used to solve a polynomial inequality.

Solving a Polynomial Inequality

Step 1. Solve the related equation.

Step 2. Separate the number line into regions with the solutions from Step 1.

Step 3. For each region, choose a test point and determine whether its value satisfies the *original inequality*.

Step 4. The solution set includes the regions whose test point value is a solution. If the inequality symbol is $\leq$ or $\geq$, the values from Step 1 are solutions; if $<$ or $>$, they are not.

✔ CONCEPT CHECK

When choosing a test point in Step 3, why would the solutions from Step 2 not make good choices for test points?

EXAMPLE 2   Solve: $x^2 - 4x \leq 0$

<u>Solution</u> First we solve the related equation, $x^2 - 4x = 0$.

$$x^2 - 4x = 0$$
$$x(x - 4) = 0$$
$$x = 0 \quad \text{or} \quad x = 4$$

The numbers 0 and 4 separate the number line into three regions, A, B, and C.

We check a test value in each region in the original inequality. Values in region B satisfy the inequality. The numbers 0 and 4 are included in the solution since the inequality symbol is $\leq$. The solution set is $[0, 4]$, and its graph is shown.

PRACTICE
2   Solve: $x^2 - 8x \leq 0$

EXAMPLE 3   Solve: $(x + 2)(x - 1)(x - 5) \leq 0$

<u>Solution</u> First we solve $(x + 2)(x - 1)(x - 5) = 0$. By inspection, we see that the solutions are -2, 1, and 5. They separate the number line into four regions, A, B, C, and D. Next we check test points from each region.

Region	Test Point Value	$(x + 2)(x - 1)(x - 5) \leq 0$	Result
A	-3	$(-1)(-4)(-8) \leq 0$	True
B	0	$(2)(-1)(-5) \leq 0$	False
C	2	$(4)(1)(-3) \leq 0$	True
D	6	$(8)(5)(1) \leq 0$	False

Answer to Concept Check:
The solutions found in Step 2 have a value of 0 in the original inequality.

(Continued on next page)

The solution set is $(-\infty, -2] \cup [1, 5]$, and its graph is shown. We include the numbers $-2, 1,$ and 5 because the inequality symbol is $\leq$.

$$
\begin{array}{c}
 \quad A \quad\quad B \quad C \quad\quad D \\
\longleftarrow\!\!\!\!-\!\!\!\!-\!\!\!\!-\!\!\!\!\underset{\text{T}\ -2\ \ \text{F}\ \ 1\ \ \text{T}\ 5\ \ \text{F}}{\rule{0pt}{1em}}\!\!\!\!-\!\!\!\!-\!\!\!\!\longrightarrow
\end{array}
$$

□

PRACTICE
3 Solve: $(x + 3)(x - 2)(x + 1) \leq 0$
■

OBJECTIVE
2 Solving Rational Inequalities ▶

Inequalities containing rational expressions with variables in the denominator are solved by using a similar procedure.

EXAMPLE 4 Solve: $\dfrac{x + 2}{x - 3} \leq 0$

Solution First we find all values that make the denominator equal to 0. To do this, we solve $x - 3 = 0$ and find that $x = 3$.

Next, we solve the related equation $\dfrac{x + 2}{x - 3} = 0$.

$$\frac{x + 2}{x - 3} = 0$$

$$x + 2 = 0 \quad \text{Multiply both sides by the LCD, } x - 3.$$

$$x = -2$$

Now we place these numbers on a number line and proceed as before, checking test point values in the original inequality.

$$
\begin{array}{c}
 \quad A \quad\quad B \quad\quad C \\
\longleftarrow\!\!\!\!-\!\!\!\!-\!\!\!\!\underset{-2 \quad\quad 3}{\rule{0pt}{1em}|\quad\quad|}\!\!\!\!-\!\!\!\!-\!\!\!\!\longrightarrow
\end{array}
$$

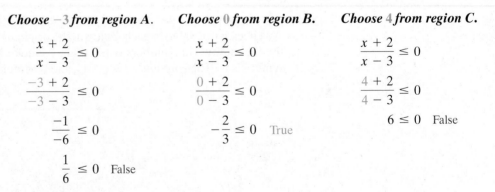

Choose −3 from region A.

$$\frac{x + 2}{x - 3} \leq 0$$

$$\frac{-3 + 2}{-3 - 3} \leq 0$$

$$\frac{-1}{-6} \leq 0$$

$$\frac{1}{6} \leq 0 \quad \text{False}$$

Choose 0 from region B.

$$\frac{x + 2}{x - 3} \leq 0$$

$$\frac{0 + 2}{0 - 3} \leq 0$$

$$-\frac{2}{3} \leq 0 \quad \text{True}$$

Choose 4 from region C.

$$\frac{x + 2}{x - 3} \leq 0$$

$$\frac{4 + 2}{4 - 3} \leq 0$$

$$6 \leq 0 \quad \text{False}$$

The solution set is $[-2, 3)$. This interval includes -2 because -2 satisfies the original inequality. This interval does not include 3 because 3 would make the denominator 0.

$$
\begin{array}{c}
 \quad A \quad\quad B \quad\quad C \\
\longleftarrow\!\!\!\!-\!\!\!\!-\!\!\!\!\underset{\text{F}\ -2\quad \text{T}\quad 3\ \ \text{F}}{\rule{0pt}{1em}[\quad\quad)}\!\!\!\!-\!\!\!\!-\!\!\!\!\longrightarrow
\end{array}
$$

□

PRACTICE
4 Solve: $\dfrac{x - 5}{x + 4} \leq 0$
■

The following steps may be used to solve a rational inequality with variables in the denominator.

Solving a Rational Inequality

Step 1. Solve for values that make all denominators 0.

Step 2. Solve the related equation.

Step 3. Separate the number line into regions with the solutions from Steps 1 and 2.

Step 4. For each region, choose a test point and determine whether its value satisfies the *original inequality*.

Step 5. The solution set includes the regions whose test point value is a solution. Check whether to include values from Step 2. Be sure *not* to include values that make any denominator 0.

EXAMPLE 5   Solve: $\dfrac{5}{x+1} < -2$

Solution   First we find values for x that make the denominator equal to 0.

$$x + 1 = 0$$
$$x = -1$$

Next we solve $\dfrac{5}{x+1} = -2$.

$$(x + 1) \cdot \frac{5}{x + 1} = (x + 1) \cdot -2 \quad \text{Multiply both sides by the LCD, } x + 1.$$

$$5 = -2x - 2 \qquad \text{Simplify.}$$

$$7 = -2x$$

$$-\frac{7}{2} = x$$

We use these two solutions to divide a number line into three regions and choose test points. Only a test point value from region B satisfies the *original inequality*. The solution set is $\left(-\dfrac{7}{2}, -1 \right)$, and its graph is shown.

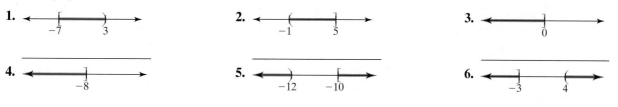

PRACTICE
5   Solve: $\dfrac{7}{x+3} < 5$

Vocabulary, Readiness & Video Check

Write the graphed solution set in interval notation.

1. $\xleftarrow{\hspace{1cm}} \overset{[\hspace{1.2cm})}{\underset{-7 \qquad 3}{\rule{2cm}{0pt}}} \xrightarrow{\hspace{1cm}}$

2. $\xleftarrow{\hspace{1cm}} \overset{(\hspace{1.2cm}]}{\underset{-1 \qquad 5}{\rule{2cm}{0pt}}} \xrightarrow{\hspace{1cm}}$

3. $\xleftarrow{\hspace{1cm}} \overset{]}{\underset{0}{\rule{1cm}{0pt}}} \xrightarrow{\hspace{1cm}}$

4. $\xleftarrow{\hspace{1cm}} \overset{]}{\underset{-8}{\rule{1cm}{0pt}}} \xrightarrow{\hspace{1cm}}$

5. $\xleftarrow{\hspace{1cm}} \overset{)\hspace{1.2cm}[}{\underset{-12 \qquad -10}{\rule{2cm}{0pt}}} \xrightarrow{\hspace{1cm}}$

6. $\xleftarrow{\hspace{1cm}} \overset{]\hspace{1.2cm}(}{\underset{-3 \qquad 4}{\rule{2cm}{0pt}}} \xrightarrow{\hspace{1cm}}$

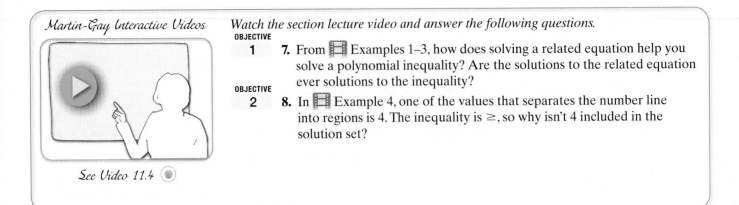

Watch the section lecture video and answer the following questions.

OBJECTIVE
1

7. From ▦ Examples 1–3, how does solving a related equation help you solve a polynomial inequality? Are the solutions to the related equation ever solutions to the inequality?

OBJECTIVE
2

8. In ▦ Example 4, one of the values that separates the number line into regions is 4. The inequality is ≥, so why isn't 4 included in the solution set?

See Video 11.4

11.4 Exercise Set   MyMathLab®

Solve each polynomial inequality. Write the solution set in interval notation. See Examples 1 through 3.

1. $(x + 1)(x + 5) > 0$

2. $(x + 1)(x + 5) \le 0$

▶ **3.** $(x - 3)(x + 4) \le 0$

4. $(x + 4)(x - 1) > 0$

5. $x^2 - 7x + 10 \le 0$

6. $x^2 + 8x + 15 \ge 0$

7. $3x^2 + 16x < -5$

8. $2x^2 - 5x < 7$

9. $(x - 6)(x - 4)(x - 2) > 0$

10. $(x - 6)(x - 4)(x - 2) \le 0$

11. $x(x - 1)(x + 4) \le 0$

12. $x(x - 6)(x + 2) > 0$

13. $(x^2 - 9)(x^2 - 4) > 0$

14. $(x^2 - 16)(x^2 - 1) \le 0$

Solve each inequality. Write the solution set in interval notation. See Example 4.

15. $\dfrac{x + 7}{x - 2} < 0$

16. $\dfrac{x - 5}{x - 6} > 0$

17. $\dfrac{5}{x + 1} > 0$

18. $\dfrac{3}{y - 5} < 0$

▶ **19.** $\dfrac{x + 1}{x - 4} \ge 0$

20. $\dfrac{x + 1}{x - 4} \le 0$

Solve each inequality. Write the solution set in interval notation. See Example 5.

21. $\dfrac{3}{x - 2} < 4$

22. $\dfrac{-2}{y + 3} > 2$

23. $\dfrac{x^2 + 6}{5x} \ge 1$

24. $\dfrac{y^2 + 15}{8y} \le 1$

25. $\dfrac{x + 2}{x - 3} < 1$

26. $\dfrac{x - 1}{x + 4} > 2$

MIXED PRACTICE

Solve each inequality. Write the solution set in interval notation.

27. $(2x - 3)(4x + 5) \le 0$

28. $(6x + 7)(7x - 12) > 0$

▶ **29.** $x^2 > x$

30. $x^2 < 25$

31. $(2x - 8)(x + 4)(x - 6) \le 0$

32. $(3x - 12)(x + 5)(2x - 3) \ge 0$

33. $6x^2 - 5x \ge 6$

34. $12x^2 + 11x \le 15$

35. $4x^3 + 16x^2 - 9x - 36 > 0$

36. $x^3 + 2x^2 - 4x - 8 < 0$

▶ **37.** $x^4 - 26x^2 + 25 \ge 0$

38. $16x^4 - 40x^2 + 9 \le 0$

39. $(2x - 7)(3x + 5) > 0$

40. $(4x - 9)(2x + 5) < 0$

41. $\dfrac{x}{x - 10} < 0$

42. $\dfrac{x + 10}{x - 10} > 0$

43. $\dfrac{x - 5}{x + 4} \geq 0$

44. $\dfrac{x - 3}{x + 2} \leq 0$

45. $\dfrac{x(x + 6)}{(x - 7)(x + 1)} \geq 0$

46. $\dfrac{(x - 2)(x + 2)}{(x + 1)(x - 4)} \leq 0$

47. $\dfrac{-1}{x - 1} > -1$

48. $\dfrac{4}{y + 2} < -2$

49. $\dfrac{x}{x + 4} \leq 2$

50. $\dfrac{4x}{x - 3} \geq 5$

51. $\dfrac{z}{z - 5} \geq 2z$

52. $\dfrac{p}{p + 4} \leq 3p$

53. $\dfrac{(x + 1)^2}{5x} > 0$

54. $\dfrac{(2x - 3)^2}{x} < 0$

REVIEW AND PREVIEW

Recall that the graph of $f(x) + K$ is the same as the graph of $f(x)$ shifted K units upward if $K > 0$ and $|K|$ units downward if $K < 0$. Use the graph of $f(x) = |x|$ below to sketch the graph of each function. See Section 8.3.

55. $g(x) = |x| + 2$

56. $H(x) = |x| - 2$

57. $G(x) = |x| - 1$

58. $h(x) = |x| + 5$

Use the graph of $f(x) = x^2$ below to sketch the graph of each function.

59. $F(x) = x^2 - 3$

60. $h(x) = x^2 - 4$

61. $H(x) = x^2 + 1$

62. $g(x) = x^2 + 3$

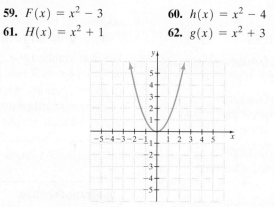

CONCEPT EXTENSIONS

63. Explain why $\dfrac{x + 2}{x - 3} > 0$ and $(x + 2)(x - 3) > 0$ have the same solutions.

64. Explain why $\dfrac{x + 2}{x - 3} \geq 0$ and $(x + 2)(x - 3) \geq 0$ do not have the same solutions.

Find all numbers that satisfy each of the following.

65. A number minus its reciprocal is less than zero. Find the numbers.

66. Twice a number added to its reciprocal is nonnegative. Find the numbers.

67. The total profit function $P(x)$ for a company producing x thousand units is given by

$$P(x) = -2x^2 + 26x - 44$$

Find the values of x for which the company makes a profit. (*Hint:* The company makes a profit when $P(x) > 0$.)

68. A projectile is fired straight up from the ground with an initial velocity of 80 feet per second. Its height $s(t)$ in feet at any time t is given by the function

$$s(t) = -16t^2 + 80t$$

Find the interval of time for which the height of the projectile is greater than 96 feet.

Use a graphing calculator to check each exercise.

69. Exercise 37

70. Exercise 38

71. Exercise 39

72. Exercise 40

11.5 Quadratic Functions and Their Graphs ▶

OBJECTIVES

1 Graph Quadratic Functions of the Form $f(x) = x^2 + k$. ▶

2 Graph Quadratic Functions of the Form $f(x) = (x - h)^2$. ▶

3 Graph Quadratic Functions of the Form $f(x) = (x - h)^2 + k$. ▶

4 Graph Quadratic Functions of the Form $f(x) = ax^2$. ▶

5 Graph Quadratic Functions of the Form $f(x) = a(x - h)^2 + k$. ▶

OBJECTIVE

1 Graphing $f(x) = x^2 + k$ ▶

We first graphed the quadratic equation $y = x^2$ in Section 8.2. In Sections 8.2 and 8.3, we learned that this graph defines a function, and we wrote $y = x^2$ as $f(x) = x^2$. In those sections, we discovered that the graph of a quadratic function is a parabola opening upward or downward. In this section, we continue our study of quadratic functions and their graphs. (Much of the contents of this section is a review of shifting and reflecting techniques from Section 8.3, but specific to quadratic functions.)

First, let's recall the definition of a quadratic function.

> **Quadratic Function**
>
> A quadratic function is a function that can be written in the form $f(x) = ax^2 + bx + c$, where $a, b,$ and c are real numbers and $a \neq 0$.

Notice that equations of the form $y = ax^2 + bx + c$, where $a \neq 0$, define quadratic functions, since y is a function of x or $y = f(x)$.

Recall that if $a > 0$, the parabola opens upward and if $a < 0$, the parabola opens downward. Also, the vertex of a parabola is the lowest point if the parabola opens upward and the highest point if the parabola opens downward. The axis of symmetry is the vertical line that passes through the vertex.

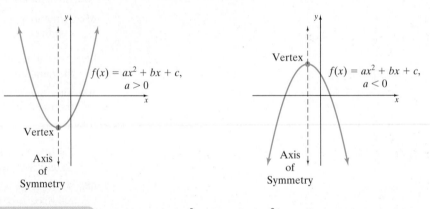

EXAMPLE 1 Graph $f(x) = x^2$ and $g(x) = x^2 + 6$ on the same set of axes.

<u>Solution</u> First we construct a table of values for $f(x)$ and plot the points. Notice that for each x-value, the corresponding value of $g(x)$ must be 6 more than the corresponding value of $f(x)$ since $f(x) = x^2$ and $g(x) = x^2 + 6$. In other words, the graph of $g(x) = x^2 + 6$ is the same as the graph of $f(x) = x^2$ shifted upward 6 units. The axis of symmetry for both graphs is the y-axis.

x	$f(x) = x^2$	$g(x) = x^2 + 6$
-2	4	10
-1	1	7
0	0	6
1	1	7
2	4	10

Each y-value is increased by 6.

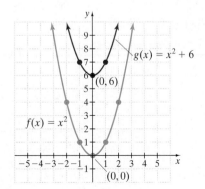

PRACTICE

1 Graph $f(x) = x^2$ and $g(x) = x^2 - 4$ on the same set of axes.

In general, we have the following properties.

> **Graphing the Parabola Defined by $f(x) = x^2 + k$**
>
> If k is positive, the graph of $f(x) = x^2 + k$ is the graph of $y = x^2$ shifted upward k units.
> If k is negative, the graph of $f(x) = x^2 + k$ is the graph of $y = x^2$ shifted downward $|k|$ units.
> The vertex is $(0, k)$, and the axis of symmetry is the y-axis.

EXAMPLE 2   Graph each function.

   a. $F(x) = x^2 + 2$ 　　　　　　　　　　　 **b.** $g(x) = x^2 - 3$

Solution

   a. $F(x) = x^2 + 2$

   The graph of $F(x) = x^2 + 2$ is obtained by shifting the graph of $y = x^2$ upward 2 units.

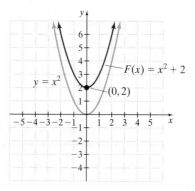

   b. $g(x) = x^2 - 3$

   The graph of $g(x) = x^2 - 3$ is obtained by shifting the graph of $y = x^2$ downward 3 units.

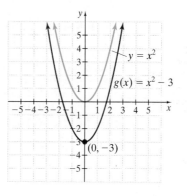

PRACTICE

2　Graph each function.

   a. $f(x) = x^2 - 5$ 　　　　　　 **b.** $g(x) = x^2 + 3$

OBJECTIVE

2　Graphing $f(x) = (x - h)^2$ ▶

Now we will graph functions of the form $f(x) = (x - h)^2$.

EXAMPLE 3 Graph $f(x) = x^2$ and $g(x) = (x - 2)^2$ on the same set of axes.

Solution By plotting points, we see that for each x-value, the corresponding value of $g(x)$ is the same as the value of $f(x)$ when the x-value is increased by 2. Thus, the graph of $g(x) = (x - 2)^2$ is the graph of $f(x) = x^2$ shifted to the right 2 units. The axis of symmetry for the graph of $g(x) = (x - 2)^2$ is also shifted 2 units to the right and is the line $x = 2$.

x	$f(x) = x^2$	x	$g(x) = (x - 2)^2$
-2	4	0	4
-1	1	1	1
0	0	2	0
1	1	3	1
2	4	4	4

Each x-value increased by 2 corresponds to same y-value.

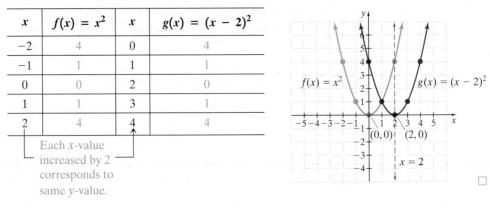

PRACTICE
3 Graph $f(x) = x^2$ and $g(x) = (x + 6)^2$ on the same set of axes.

In general, we have the following properties.

Graphing the Parabola Defined by $f(x) = (x - h)^2$

If h is positive, the graph of $f(x) = (x - h)^2$ is the graph of $y = x^2$ shifted to the right h units.
If h is negative, the graph of $f(x) = (x - h)^2$ is the graph of $y = x^2$ shifted to the left $|h|$ units.
The vertex is $(h, 0)$, and the axis of symmetry is the vertical line $x = h$.

EXAMPLE 4 Graph each function.

a. $G(x) = (x - 3)^2$ **b.** $F(x) = (x + 1)^2$

Solution

a. The graph of $G(x) = (x - 3)^2$ is obtained by shifting the graph of $y = x^2$ to the right 3 units. The graph of $G(x)$ is below on the left.

b. The equation $F(x) = (x + 1)^2$ can be written as $F(x) = [x - (-1)]^2$. The graph of $F(x) = [x - (-1)]^2$ is obtained by shifting the graph of $y = x^2$ to the left 1 unit. The graph of $F(x)$ is below on the right.

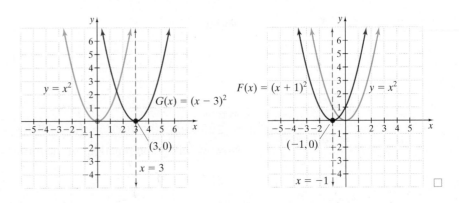

PRACTICE
4 Graph each function.

  a. $G(x) = (x + 4)^2$ **b.** $H(x) = (x - 7)^2$

OBJECTIVE
3 Graphing $f(x) = (x - h)^2 + k$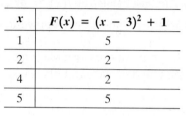

As we will see in graphing functions of the form $f(x) = (x - h)^2 + k$, it is possible to combine vertical and horizontal shifts.

Graphing the Parabola Defined by $f(x) = (x - h)^2 + k$

The parabola has the same shape as $y = x^2$.
The vertex is (h, k), and the axis of symmetry is the vertical line $x = h$.

EXAMPLE 5 Graph: $F(x) = (x - 3)^2 + 1$

Solution The graph of $F(x) = (x - 3)^2 + 1$ is the graph of $y = x^2$ shifted 3 units to the right and 1 unit up. The vertex is then $(3, 1)$, and the axis of symmetry is $x = 3$. A few ordered pair solutions are plotted to aid in graphing.

x	$F(x) = (x - 3)^2 + 1$
1	5
2	2
4	2
5	5

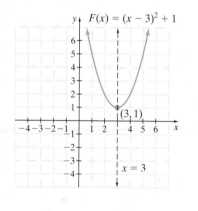

PRACTICE
5 Graph: $f(x) = (x + 2)^2 + 2$

OBJECTIVE
4 Graphing $f(x) = ax^2$

Next, we discover the change in the shape of the graph when the coefficient of x^2 is not 1.

EXAMPLE 6 Graph $f(x) = x^2$, $g(x) = 3x^2$, and $h(x) = \frac{1}{2}x^2$ on the same set of axes.

Solution Comparing the tables of values, we see that for each x-value, the corresponding value of $g(x)$ is triple the corresponding value of $f(x)$. Similarly, the value of $h(x)$ is half the value of $f(x)$.

x	$f(x) = x^2$
-2	4
-1	1
0	0
1	1
2	4

x	$g(x) = 3x^2$
-2	12
-1	3
0	0
1	3
2	12

x	$h(x) = \frac{1}{2}x^2$
-2	2
-1	$\frac{1}{2}$
0	0
1	$\frac{1}{2}$
2	2

(Continued on next page)

The result is that the graph of $g(x) = 3x^2$ is narrower than the graph of $f(x) = x^2$, and the graph of $h(x) = \dfrac{1}{2}x^2$ is wider. The vertex for each graph is $(0, 0)$, and the axis of symmetry is the y-axis.

Additional ordered-pair solutions are shown on the graph.

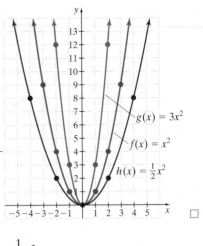

PRACTICE

6 Graph $f(x) = x^2$, $g(x) = 4x^2$, and $h(x) = \dfrac{1}{4}x^2$ on the same set of axes. ∎

Graphing the Parabola Defined by $f(x) = ax^2$

If a is positive, the parabola opens upward, and if a is negative, the parabola opens downward.
If $|a| > 1$, the graph of the parabola is narrower than the graph of $y = x^2$.
If $|a| < 1$, the graph of the parabola is wider than the graph of $y = x^2$.

EXAMPLE 7 Graph: $f(x) = -2x^2$

Solution Because $a = -2$, a negative value, this parabola opens downward. Since $|-2| = 2$ and $2 > 1$, the parabola is narrower than the graph of $y = x^2$. The vertex is $(0, 0)$, and the axis of symmetry is the y-axis. We verify this by plotting a few points.

x	$f(x) = -2x^2$
-2	-8
-1	-2
0	0
1	-2
2	-8

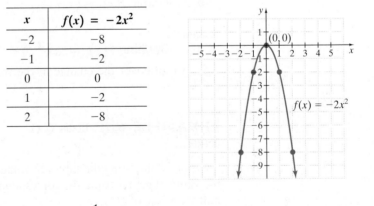

PRACTICE

7 Graph: $f(x) = -\dfrac{1}{2}x^2$ ∎

OBJECTIVE

5 Graphing $f(x) = a(x - h)^2 + k$ ▶

Now we will see the shape of the graph of a quadratic function of the form $f(x) = a(x - h)^2 + k$.

EXAMPLE 8 Graph $g(x) = \frac{1}{2}(x + 2)^2 + 5$. Find the vertex and the axis of symmetry.

<u>Solution</u> The function $g(x) = \frac{1}{2}(x + 2)^2 + 5$ may be written as $g(x) = \frac{1}{2}[x - (-2)]^2 + 5$. Thus, this graph is the same as the graph of $y = x^2$ shifted 2 units to the left and 5 units up, and it is wider because a is $\frac{1}{2}$. The vertex is $(-2, 5)$, and the axis of symmetry is $x = -2$. We plot a few points to verify.

x	$g(x) = \frac{1}{2}(x + 2)^2 + 5$
-4	7
-3	$5\frac{1}{2}$
-2	5
-1	$5\frac{1}{2}$
0	7

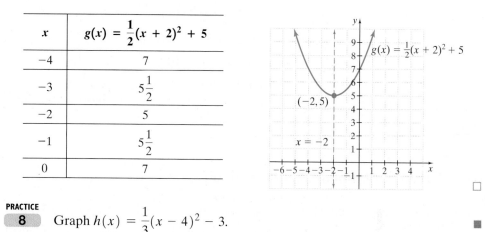

PRACTICE

8 Graph $h(x) = \frac{1}{3}(x - 4)^2 - 3$.

In general, the following holds.

Graph of a Quadratic Function

The graph of a quadratic function written in the form $f(x) = a(x - h)^2 + k$ is a parabola with vertex (h, k).

If $a > 0$, the parabola opens upward.
If $a < 0$, the parabola opens downward.

The axis of symmetry is the line whose equation is $x = h$.

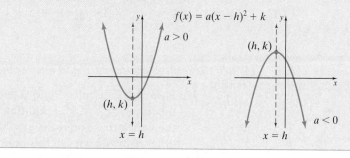

✔ **CONCEPT CHECK**

Which description of the graph of $f(x) = -0.35(x + 3)^2 - 4$ is correct?
a. The graph opens downward and has its vertex at $(-3, 4)$.
b. The graph opens upward and has its vertex at $(-3, 4)$.
c. The graph opens downward and has its vertex at $(-3, -4)$.
d. The graph is narrower than the graph of $y = x^2$.

Answer to Concept Check: **c**

Graphing Calculator Explorations

Use a graphing calculator to graph the first function of each pair that follows. Then use its graph to predict the graph of the second function. Check your prediction by graphing both on the same set of axes.

1. $F(x) = \sqrt{x};\ G(x) = \sqrt{x} + 1$

2. $g(x) = x^3;\ H(x) = x^3 - 2$

3. $H(x) = |x|;\ f(x) = |x - 5|$

4. $h(x) = x^3 + 2;\ g(x) = (x - 3)^3 + 2$

5. $f(x) = |x + 4|;\ F(x) = |x + 4| + 3$

6. $G(x) = \sqrt{x} - 2;\ g(x) = \sqrt{x - 4} - 2$

✓ Vocabulary, Readiness & Video Check

Use the choices below to fill in each blank. Some choices will be used more than once.

upward   highest   parabola   downward   lowest   quadratic

1. A(n) _____ function is one that can be written in the form $f(x) = ax^2 + bx + c, a \neq 0$.

2. The graph of a quadratic function is a(n) _____ opening _____ or _____ .

3. If $a > 0$, the graph of the quadratic function opens _____ .

4. If $a < 0$, the graph of the quadratic function opens _____ .

5. The vertex of a parabola is the _____ point if $a > 0$.

6. The vertex of a parabola is the _____ point if $a < 0$.

State the vertex of the graph of each quadratic function.

7. $f(x) = x^2$ **8.** $f(x) = -5x^2$ **9.** $g(x) = (x - 2)^2$ **10.** $g(x) = (x + 5)^2$

11. $f(x) = 2x^2 + 3$ **12.** $h(x) = x^2 - 1$ **13.** $g(x) = (x + 1)^2 + 5$ **14.** $h(x) = (x - 10)^2 - 7$

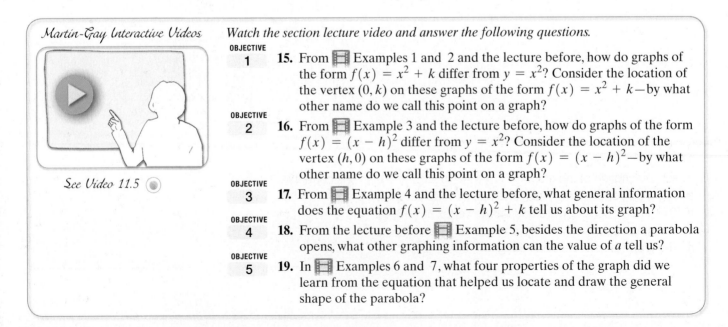

Martin-Gay Interactive Videos

See Video 11.5

Watch the section lecture video and answer the following questions.

OBJECTIVE 1

15. From ▦ Examples 1 and 2 and the lecture before, how do graphs of the form $f(x) = x^2 + k$ differ from $y = x^2$? Consider the location of the vertex $(0, k)$ on these graphs of the form $f(x) = x^2 + k$—by what other name do we call this point on a graph?

OBJECTIVE 2

16. From ▦ Example 3 and the lecture before, how do graphs of the form $f(x) = (x - h)^2$ differ from $y = x^2$? Consider the location of the vertex $(h, 0)$ on these graphs of the form $f(x) = (x - h)^2$—by what other name do we call this point on a graph?

OBJECTIVE 3

17. From ▦ Example 4 and the lecture before, what general information does the equation $f(x) = (x - h)^2 + k$ tell us about its graph?

OBJECTIVE 4

18. From the lecture before ▦ Example 5, besides the direction a parabola opens, what other graphing information can the value of a tell us?

OBJECTIVE 5

19. In ▦ Examples 6 and 7, what four properties of the graph did we learn from the equation that helped us locate and draw the general shape of the parabola?

11.5 Exercise Set MyMathLab®

MIXED PRACTICE

Sketch the graph of each quadratic function. Label the vertex and sketch and label the axis of symmetry. See Examples 1 through 5.

1. $f(x) = x^2 - 1$

2. $g(x) = x^2 + 3$

3. $h(x) = x^2 + 5$

4. $h(x) = x^2 - 4$

5. $g(x) = x^2 + 7$

6. $f(x) = x^2 - 2$

7. $f(x) = (x - 5)^2$

8. $g(x) = (x + 5)^2$

9. $h(x) = (x + 2)^2$

10. $H(x) = (x - 1)^2$

11. $G(x) = (x + 3)^2$

12. $f(x) = (x - 6)^2$

13. $f(x) = (x - 2)^2 + 5$

14. $g(x) = (x - 6)^2 + 1$

15. $h(x) = (x + 1)^2 + 4$

16. $G(x) = (x + 3)^2 + 3$

17. $g(x) = (x + 2)^2 - 5$

18. $h(x) = (x + 4)^2 - 6$

Sketch the graph of each quadratic function. Label the vertex and sketch and label the axis of symmetry. See Examples 6 and 7.

19. $H(x) = 2x^2$

20. $f(x) = 5x^2$

21. $h(x) = \dfrac{1}{3}x^2$

22. $f(x) = -\dfrac{1}{4}x^2$

23. $g(x) = -x^2$

24. $g(x) = -3x^2$

Sketch the graph of each quadratic function. Label the vertex and sketch and label the axis of symmetry. See Example 8.

25. $f(x) = 2(x - 1)^2 + 3$

26. $g(x) = 4(x - 4)^2 + 2$

27. $h(x) = -3(x + 3)^2 + 1$

28. $f(x) = -(x - 2)^2 - 6$

29. $H(x) = \dfrac{1}{2}(x - 6)^2 - 3$

30. $G(x) = \dfrac{1}{5}(x + 4)^2 + 3$

MIXED PRACTICE

Sketch the graph of each quadratic function. Label the vertex and sketch and label the axis of symmetry.

31. $f(x) = -(x - 2)^2$

32. $g(x) = -(x + 6)^2$

33. $F(x) = -x^2 + 4$

34. $H(x) = -x^2 + 10$

35. $F(x) = 2x^2 - 5$

36. $g(x) = \dfrac{1}{2}x^2 - 2$

37. $h(x) = (x - 6)^2 + 4$

38. $f(x) = (x - 5)^2 + 2$

39. $F(x) = \left(x + \dfrac{1}{2}\right)^2 - 2$

40. $H(x) = \left(x + \dfrac{1}{2}\right)^2 - 3$

41. $F(x) = \dfrac{3}{2}(x + 7)^2 + 1$

42. $g(x) = -\dfrac{3}{2}(x - 1)^2 - 5$

43. $f(x) = \dfrac{1}{4}x^2 - 9$

44. $H(x) = \dfrac{3}{4}x^2 - 2$

45. $G(x) = 5\left(x + \dfrac{1}{2}\right)^2$

46. $F(x) = 3\left(x - \dfrac{3}{2}\right)^2$

47. $h(x) = -(x - 1)^2 - 1$

48. $f(x) = -3(x + 2)^2 + 2$

49. $g(x) = \sqrt{3}(x + 5)^2 + \dfrac{3}{4}$

50. $G(x) = \sqrt{5}(x - 7)^2 - \dfrac{1}{2}$

51. $h(x) = 10(x + 4)^2 - 6$

52. $h(x) = 8(x + 1)^2 + 9$

53. $f(x) = -2(x - 4)^2 + 5$

54. $G(x) = -4(x + 9)^2 - 1$

REVIEW AND PREVIEW

Add the proper constant to each binomial so that the resulting trinomial is a perfect square trinomial. See Section 11.1.

55. $x^2 + 8x$

56. $y^2 + 4y$

57. $z^2 - 16z$

58. $x^2 - 10x$

59. $y^2 + y$

60. $z^2 - 3z$

Solve by completing the square. See Section 11.1.

61. $x^2 + 4x = 12$

62. $y^2 + 6y = -5$

63. $z^2 + 10z - 1 = 0$

64. $x^2 + 14x + 20 = 0$

65. $z^2 - 8z = 2$

66. $y^2 - 10y = 3$

CONCEPT EXTENSIONS

Solve. See the Concept Check in this section.

67. Which description of $f(x) = -213(x - 0.1)^2 + 3.6$ is correct?

Graph Opens	Vertex
a. upward	$(0.1, 3.6)$
b. upward	$(-213, 3.6)$
c. downward	$(0.1, 3.6)$
d. downward	$(-0.1, 3.6)$

68. Which description of $f(x) = 5\left(x + \dfrac{1}{2}\right)^2 + \dfrac{1}{2}$ is correct?

Graph Opens	Vertex
a. upward	$\left(\dfrac{1}{2}, \dfrac{1}{2}\right)$
b. upward	$\left(-\dfrac{1}{2}, \dfrac{1}{2}\right)$
c. downward	$\left(\dfrac{1}{2}, -\dfrac{1}{2}\right)$
d. downward	$\left(-\dfrac{1}{2}, -\dfrac{1}{2}\right)$

Write the equation of the parabola that has the same shape as $f(x) = 5x^2$ but with the following vertex.

69. $(2, 3)$

70. $(1, 6)$

71. $(-3, 6)$

72. $(4, -1)$

The shifting properties covered in this section apply to the graphs of all functions. Given the graph of $y = f(x)$ below, sketch the graph of each of the following.

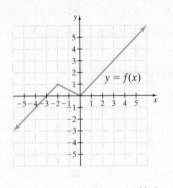

73. $y = f(x) + 1$

74. $y = f(x) - 2$

75. $y = f(x - 3)$

76. $y = f(x + 3)$

77. $y = f(x + 2) + 2$

78. $y = f(x - 1) + 1$

79. The quadratic function $f(x) = 12.5x^2 - 64x + 135$ approximates the annual retail sales from online shopping in the United States from 2005 through 2014, where x is the number of years past 2005 and $f(x)$ is the annual retail sales in billions of dollars. (*Source:* Based on data from the U.S. Bureau of the Census and the Retail Association of America)

  a. Use this function to find the online retail sales in the United States for 2013.

  b. Use this function to predict the online retail sales in the United States for 2020.

80. Use the function in Exercise 79.

  a. Use this function to predict the online retail sales in the United States for 2018.

  b. Look up the annual online retail sales for the United States for the current year.

  c. Based on your answers for parts **a** and **b**, discuss some possible limitations of using this quadratic function to predict data.

11.6 Further Graphing of Quadratic Functions

OBJECTIVES

1 Write Quadratic Functions in the Form $y = a(x - h)^2 + k$.

2 Derive a Formula for Finding the Vertex of a Parabola.

3 Find the Minimum or Maximum Value of a Quadratic Function.

OBJECTIVE

1 Writing Quadratic Functions in the Form $y = a(x - h)^2 + k$

We know that the graph of a quadratic function is a parabola. If a quadratic function is written in the form

$$f(x) = a(x - h)^2 + k$$

we can easily find the vertex (h, k) and graph the parabola. To write a quadratic function in this form, complete the square. (See Section 11.1 for a review of completing the square.)

EXAMPLE I Graph $f(x) = x^2 - 4x - 12$. Find the vertex and any intercepts.

Solution The graph of this quadratic function is a parabola. To find the vertex of the parabola, we will write the function in the form $y = (x - h)^2 + k$. To do this, we complete the square on the binomial $x^2 - 4x$. To simplify our work, we let $f(x) = y$.

$$y = x^2 - 4x - 12 \quad \text{Let } f(x) = y.$$
$$y + 12 = x^2 - 4x \qquad \text{Add 12 to both sides to get the } x\text{-variable terms alone.}$$

Now we add the square of half of -4 to both sides.

$$\frac{1}{2}(-4) = -2 \quad \text{and} \quad (-2)^2 = 4$$

$$y + 12 + 4 = x^2 - 4x + 4 \qquad \text{Add 4 to both sides.}$$
$$y + 16 = (x - 2)^2 \qquad \text{Factor the trinomial.}$$
$$y = (x - 2)^2 - 16 \quad \text{Subtract 16 from both sides.}$$
$$f(x) = (x - 2)^2 - 16 \quad \text{Replace } y \text{ with } f(x).$$

From this equation, we can see that the vertex of the parabola is $(2, -16)$, a point in quadrant IV, and the axis of symmetry is the line $x = 2$.

Notice that $a = 1$. Since $a > 0$, the parabola opens upward. This parabola opening upward with vertex $(2, -16)$ will have two x-intercepts and one y-intercept. (See the Helpful Hint after this example.)

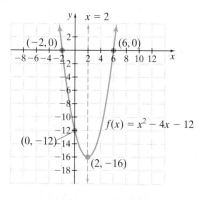

x-intercepts: let y or $f(x) = 0$

$$f(x) = x^2 - 4x - 12$$
$$0 = x^2 - 4x - 12$$
$$0 = (x - 6)(x + 2)$$
$$0 = x - 6 \quad \text{or} \quad 0 = x + 2$$
$$6 = x \qquad\qquad -2 = x$$

y-intercept: let $x = 0$

$$f(x) = x^2 - 4x - 12$$
$$f(0) = 0^2 - 4\cdot 0 - 12$$
$$= -12$$

The two x-intercepts are $(6, 0)$ and $(-2, 0)$. The y-intercept is $(0, -12)$. The sketch of $f(x) = x^2 - 4x - 12$ is shown.

Notice that the axis of symmetry is always halfway between the x-intercepts. For this example, halfway between -2 and 6 is $\dfrac{-2 + 6}{2} = 2$, and the axis of symmetry is $x = 2$.   □

PRACTICE

1   Graph $g(x) = x^2 - 2x - 3$. Find the vertex and any intercepts.   ■

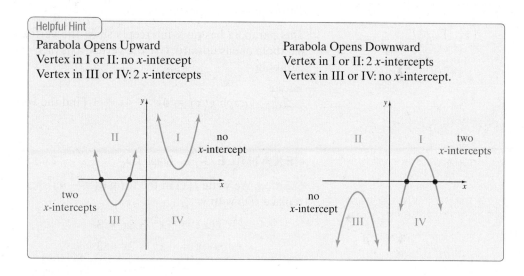

Helpful Hint

Parabola Opens Upward
Vertex in I or II: no x-intercept
Vertex in III or IV: 2 x-intercepts

Parabola Opens Downward
Vertex in I or II: 2 x-intercepts
Vertex in III or IV: no x-intercept.

EXAMPLE 2   Graph $f(x) = 3x^2 + 3x + 1$. Find the vertex and any intercepts.

Solution   Replace $f(x)$ with y and complete the square on x to write the equation in the form $y = a(x - h)^2 + k$.

$$y = 3x^2 + 3x + 1 \quad \text{Replace } f(x) \text{ with } y.$$
$$y - 1 = 3x^2 + 3x \qquad \text{Isolate } x\text{-variable terms.}$$

Factor 3 from the terms $3x^2 + 3x$ so that the coefficient of x^2 is 1.

$$y - 1 = 3(x^2 + x) \quad \text{Factor out 3.}$$

The coefficient of x in the parentheses above is 1. Then $\dfrac{1}{2}(1) = \dfrac{1}{2}$ and $\left(\dfrac{1}{2}\right)^2 = \dfrac{1}{4}$.

Since we are adding $\dfrac{1}{4}$ inside the parentheses, we are really adding $3\left(\dfrac{1}{4}\right)$, so we *must* add $3\left(\dfrac{1}{4}\right)$ to the left side.

(Continued on next page)

$$y - 1 + 3\left(\frac{1}{4}\right) = 3\left(x^2 + x + \frac{1}{4}\right)$$

$$y - \frac{1}{4} = 3\left(x + \frac{1}{2}\right)^2 \qquad \text{Simplify the left side and factor the right side.}$$

$$y = 3\left(x + \frac{1}{2}\right)^2 + \frac{1}{4} \qquad \text{Add } \frac{1}{4} \text{ to both sides.}$$

$$f(x) = 3\left(x + \frac{1}{2}\right)^2 + \frac{1}{4} \qquad \text{Replace } y \text{ with } f(x).$$

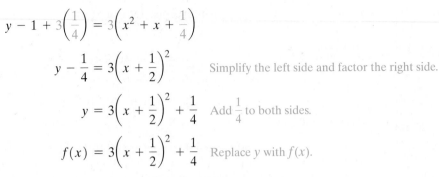

$y = 3x^2 + 3x + 1$

$(0, 1)$

$\left(-\frac{1}{2}, \frac{1}{4}\right)$

$x = -\frac{1}{2}$

Then $a = 3, h = -\frac{1}{2}$, and $k = \frac{1}{4}$. This means that the parabola opens upward with vertex $\left(-\frac{1}{2}, \frac{1}{4}\right)$ and that the axis of symmetry is the line $x = -\frac{1}{2}$.

To find the y-intercept, let $x = 0$. Then

$$f(0) = 3(0)^2 + 3(0) + 1 = 1$$

Thus, the y-intercept is $(0, 1)$.

This parabola has no x-intercepts since the vertex is in the second quadrant and the parabola opens upward. Use the vertex, axis of symmetry, and y-intercept to sketch the parabola. ☐

PRACTICE

2 Graph $g(x) = 4x^2 + 4x + 3$. Find the vertex and any intercepts. ■

EXAMPLE 3 Graph $f(x) = -x^2 - 2x + 3$. Find the vertex and any intercepts.

Solution We write $f(x)$ in the form $a(x - h)^2 + k$ by completing the square. First we replace $f(x)$ with y.

$$f(x) = -x^2 - 2x + 3$$

$$y = -x^2 - 2x + 3$$

$$y - 3 = -x^2 - 2x \qquad \begin{array}{l}\text{Subtract 3 from both sides to get} \\ \text{the } x\text{-variable terms alone.}\end{array}$$

$$y - 3 = -1(x^2 + 2x) \qquad \text{Factor } -1 \text{ from the terms } -x^2 - 2x.$$

The coefficient of x is 2. Then $\frac{1}{2}(2) = 1$ and $1^2 = 1$. We add 1 to the right side inside the parentheses and add $-1(1)$ to the left side.

$$y - 3 - 1(1) = -1(x^2 + 2x + 1)$$

$$y - 4 = -1(x + 1)^2 \qquad \begin{array}{l}\text{Simplify the left side and} \\ \text{factor the right side.}\end{array}$$

$$y = -1(x + 1)^2 + 4 \qquad \text{Add 4 to both sides.}$$

$$f(x) = -1(x + 1)^2 + 4 \qquad \text{Replace } y \text{ with } f(x).$$

> **Helpful Hint**
>
> This can be written as
> $f(x) = -1[x - (-1)]^2 + 4$.
> Notice that the vertex is $(-1, 4)$.

Since $a = -1$, the parabola opens downward with vertex $(-1, 4)$ and axis of symmetry $x = -1$.

To find the y-intercept, we let $x = 0$. Then

$$f(0) = -0^2 - 2(0) + 3 = 3$$

Thus, $(0, 3)$ is the y-intercept.

To find the x-intercepts, we let y or $f(x) = 0$ and solve for x.

$$f(x) = -x^2 - 2x + 3$$

$$0 = -x^2 - 2x + 3 \qquad \text{Let } f(x) = 0.$$

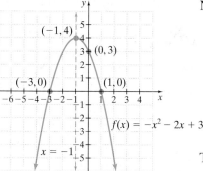

Now we divide both sides by -1 so that the coefficient of x^2 is 1.

$$\frac{0}{-1} = \frac{-x^2}{-1} - \frac{2x}{-1} + \frac{3}{-1} \qquad \text{Divide both sides by } -1.$$

$$0 = x^2 + 2x - 3 \qquad \text{Simplify.}$$

$$0 = (x + 3)(x - 1) \qquad \text{Factor.}$$

$$x + 3 = 0 \quad \text{or} \quad x - 1 = 0 \quad \text{Set each factor equal to 0.}$$

$$x = -3 \qquad\qquad x = 1 \quad \text{Solve.}$$

The x-intercepts are $(-3, 0)$ and $(1, 0)$. Use these points to sketch the parabola. ☐

PRACTICE

3   Graph $g(x) = -x^2 + 5x + 6$. Find the vertex and any intercepts. ■

OBJECTIVE

2   Deriving a Formula for Finding the Vertex ▶

There is also a formula that may be used to find the vertex of a parabola. Now that we have practiced completing the square, we will show that the x-coordinate of the vertex of the graph of $f(x)$ or $y = ax^2 + bx + c$ can be found by the formula $x = \dfrac{-b}{2a}$. To do so, we complete the square on x and write the equation in the form $y = a(x - h)^2 + k$.

First, isolate the x-variable terms by subtracting c from both sides.

$$y = ax^2 + bx + c$$

$$y - c = ax^2 + bx$$

Next, factor a from the terms $ax^2 + bx$.

$$y - c = a\left(x^2 + \frac{b}{a}x\right)$$

Next, add the square of half of $\dfrac{b}{a}$, or $\left(\dfrac{b}{2a}\right)^2 = \dfrac{b^2}{4a^2}$, to the right side inside the parentheses. Because of the factor a, what we really added was $a\left(\dfrac{b^2}{4a^2}\right)$, and this must be added to the left side.

$$y - c + a\left(\frac{b^2}{4a^2}\right) = a\left(x^2 + \frac{b}{a}x + \frac{b^2}{4a^2}\right)$$

$$y - c + \frac{b^2}{4a} = a\left(x + \frac{b}{2a}\right)^2 \qquad \begin{array}{l}\text{Simplify the left side and}\\ \text{factor the right side.}\end{array}$$

$$y = a\left(x + \frac{b}{2a}\right)^2 + c - \frac{b^2}{4a} \qquad \begin{array}{l}\text{Add } c \text{ to both sides and subtract } \dfrac{b^2}{4a}\\ \text{from both sides.}\end{array}$$

Compare this form with $f(x)$ or $y = a(x - h)^2 + k$ and see that h is $\dfrac{-b}{2a}$, which means that the x-coordinate of the vertex of the graph of $f(x) = ax^2 + bx + c$ is $\dfrac{-b}{2a}$.

Vertex Formula

The graph of $f(x) = ax^2 + bx + c$, when $a \neq 0$, is a parabola with vertex

$$\left(\frac{-b}{2a}, f\left(\frac{-b}{2a}\right)\right)$$

Let's use this formula to find the vertex of the parabola we graphed in Example 1.

EXAMPLE 4   Find the vertex of the graph of $f(x) = x^2 - 4x - 12$.

Solution To find the vertex (h, k), notice that for $f(x) = x^2 - 4x - 12$, we have $a = 1, b = -4$, and $c = -12$. Then

$$h = \frac{-b}{2a} = \frac{-(-4)}{2(1)} = 2$$

The x-value of the vertex is 2. To find the corresponding $f(x)$ or y-value, find $f(2)$. Then

$$f(2) = 2^2 - 4(2) - 12 = 4 - 8 - 12 = -16$$

The vertex is $(2, -16)$. These results agree with our findings in Example 1.   ☐

PRACTICE
4   Find the vertex of the graph of $g(x) = x^2 - 2x - 3$.   ■

OBJECTIVE
3   Finding Minimum and Maximum Values ▶

The vertex of a parabola gives us some important information about its corresponding quadratic function. The quadratic function whose graph is a parabola that opens upward has a minimum value, and the quadratic function whose graph is a parabola that opens downward has a maximum value. The $f(x)$ or y-value of the vertex is the minimum or maximum value of the function.

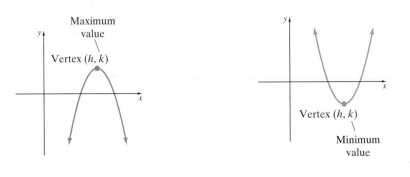

✔ CONCEPT CHECK

Without making any calculations, tell whether the graph of $f(x) = 7 - x - 0.3x^2$ has a maximum value or a minimum value. Explain your reasoning.

EXAMPLE 5   **Finding Maximum Height**

A rock is thrown upward from the ground. Its height in feet above ground after t seconds is given by the function $f(t) = -16t^2 + 20t$. Find the maximum height of the rock and the number of seconds it took for the rock to reach its maximum height.

Solution

1. **UNDERSTAND.** The maximum height of the rock is the largest value of $f(t)$. Since the function $f(t) = -16t^2 + 20t$ is a quadratic function, its graph is a parabola. It opens downward since $-16 < 0$. Thus, the maximum value of $f(t)$ is the $f(t)$ or y-value of the vertex of its graph.

Answer to Concept Check:
$f(x)$ has a maximum value since it opens downward.

2. TRANSLATE. To find the vertex (h, k), notice that for $f(t) = -16t^2 + 20t$, $a = -16, b = 20$, and $c = 0$. We will use these values and the vertex formula

$$\left(\frac{-b}{2a}, f\left(\frac{-b}{2a}\right)\right)$$

3. SOLVE.

$$h = \frac{-b}{2a} = \frac{-20}{-32} = \frac{5}{8}$$

$$f\left(\frac{5}{8}\right) = -16\left(\frac{5}{8}\right)^2 + 20\left(\frac{5}{8}\right)$$

$$= -16\left(\frac{25}{64}\right) + \frac{25}{2}$$

$$= -\frac{25}{4} + \frac{50}{4} = \frac{25}{4}$$

4. INTERPRET. The graph of $f(t)$ is a parabola opening downward with vertex $\left(\frac{5}{8}, \frac{25}{4}\right)$. This means that the rock's maximum height is $\frac{25}{4}$ feet, or $6\frac{1}{4}$ feet, which was reached in $\frac{5}{8}$ second.   □

PRACTICE

5   A ball is tossed upward from the ground. Its height in feet above ground after t seconds is given by the function $h(t) = -16t^2 + 24t$. Find the maximum height of the ball and the number of seconds it took for the ball to reach the maximum height.   ▪

✔ **Vocabulary, Readiness & Video Check**

Fill in each blank.

1. If a quadratic function is in the form $f(x) = a(x - h)^2 + k$, the vertex of its graph is _____.

2. The graph of $f(x) = ax^2 + bx + c, a \neq 0$, is a parabola whose vertex has x-value _____.

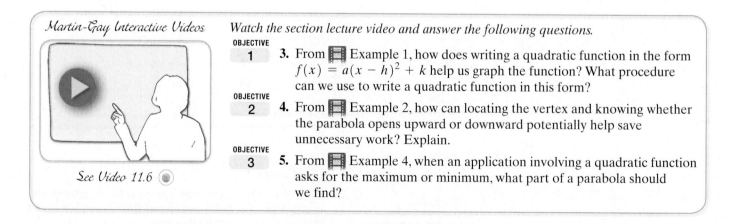

Martin-Gay Interactive Videos

Watch the section lecture video and answer the following questions.

OBJECTIVE 1

3. From ▦ Example 1, how does writing a quadratic function in the form $f(x) = a(x - h)^2 + k$ help us graph the function? What procedure can we use to write a quadratic function in this form?

OBJECTIVE 2

4. From ▦ Example 2, how can locating the vertex and knowing whether the parabola opens upward or downward potentially help save unnecessary work? Explain.

OBJECTIVE 3

5. From ▦ Example 4, when an application involving a quadratic function asks for the maximum or minimum, what part of a parabola should we find?

See Video 11.6 ●

11.6 Exercise Set MyMathLab® ▷

Fill in each blank.

	Parabola Opens	Vertex Location	Number of x-intercept(s)	Number of y-intercept(s)
1.	up	Q I		
2.	up	Q III		
3.	down	Q II		
4.	down	Q IV		
5.	up	x-axis		
6.	down	x-axis		
7.		Q III	0	
8.		Q I	2	
9.		Q IV	2	
10.		Q II	0	

Find the vertex of the graph of each quadratic function. See Examples 1 through 4.

11. $f(x) = x^2 + 8x + 7$

12. $f(x) = x^2 + 6x + 5$

13. $f(x) = -x^2 + 10x + 5$

14. $f(x) = -x^2 - 8x + 2$

15. $f(x) = 5x^2 - 10x + 3$

16. $f(x) = -3x^2 + 6x + 4$

17. $f(x) = -x^2 + x + 1$

18. $f(x) = x^2 - 9x + 8$

Match each function with its graph. See Examples 1 through 4.

19. $f(x) = x^2 - 4x + 3$

20. $f(x) = x^2 + 2x - 3$

21. $f(x) = x^2 - 2x - 3$

22. $f(x) = x^2 + 4x + 3$

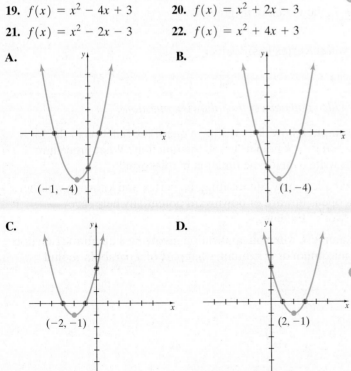

A. (−1, −4)

B. (1, −4)

C. (−2, −1)

D. (2, −1)

MIXED PRACTICE

Find the vertex of the graph of each quadratic function. Determine whether the graph opens upward or downward, find any intercepts, and sketch the graph. See Examples 1 through 4.

23. $f(x) = x^2 + 4x - 5$

24. $f(x) = x^2 + 2x - 3$

▷ **25.** $f(x) = -x^2 + 2x - 1$

26. $f(x) = -x^2 + 4x - 4$

27. $f(x) = x^2 - 4$

28. $f(x) = x^2 - 1$

▷ **29.** $f(x) = 4x^2 + 4x - 3$

30. $f(x) = 2x^2 - x - 3$

31. $f(x) = \frac{1}{2}x^2 + 4x + \frac{15}{2}$

32. $f(x) = \frac{1}{5}x^2 + 2x + \frac{9}{5}$

33. $f(x) = x^2 - 6x + 5$

34. $f(x) = x^2 - 4x + 3$

▷ **35.** $f(x) = x^2 - 4x + 5$

36. $f(x) = x^2 - 6x + 11$

37. $f(x) = 2x^2 + 4x + 5$

38. $f(x) = 3x^2 + 12x + 16$

39. $f(x) = -2x^2 + 12x$

40. $f(x) = -4x^2 + 8x$

41. $f(x) = x^2 + 1$

42. $f(x) = x^2 + 4$

43. $f(x) = x^2 - 2x - 15$

44. $f(x) = x^2 - x - 12$

45. $f(x) = -5x^2 + 5x$

46. $f(x) = 3x^2 - 12x$

47. $f(x) = -x^2 + 2x - 12$

48. $f(x) = -x^2 + 8x - 17$

49. $f(x) = 3x^2 - 12x + 15$

50. $f(x) = 2x^2 - 8x + 11$

51. $f(x) = x^2 + x - 6$

52. $f(x) = x^2 + 3x - 18$

53. $f(x) = -2x^2 - 3x + 35$

54. $f(x) = 3x^2 - 13x - 10$

Solve. See Example 5.

▷ **55.** If a projectile is fired straight upward from the ground with an initial speed of 96 feet per second, then its height h in feet after t seconds is given by the equation

$$h(t) = -16t^2 + 96t$$

Find the maximum height of the projectile.

56. If Rheam Gaspar throws a ball upward with an initial speed of 32 feet per second, then its height h in feet after t seconds is given by the equation

$$h(t) = -16t^2 + 32t$$

Find the maximum height of the ball.

57. The cost C in dollars of manufacturing x bicycles at Holladay's Production Plant is given by the function

$$C(x) = 2x^2 - 800x + 92,000.$$

a. Find the number of bicycles that must be manufactured to minimize the cost.

b. Find the minimum cost.

58. The Utah Ski Club sells calendars to raise money. The profit P, in cents, from selling x calendars is given by the equation $P(x) = 360x - x^2$.

a. Find how many calendars must be sold to maximize profit.

b. Find the maximum profit in dollars.

59. Find two numbers whose sum is 60 and whose product is as large as possible. [*Hint:* Let x and $60 - x$ be the two positive numbers. Their product can be described by the function $f(x) = x(60 - x)$.]

60. Find two numbers whose sum is 11 and whose product is as large as possible. (Use the hint for Exercise 59.)

61. Find two numbers whose difference is 10 and whose product is as small as possible. (Use the hint for Exercise 59.)

62. Find two numbers whose difference is 8 and whose product is as small as possible. (Use the hint for Exercise 59.)

△ 63. The length and width of a rectangle must have a sum of 40. Find the dimensions of the rectangle that will have the maximum area. (Use the hint for Exercise 59.)

△ 64. The length and width of a rectangle must have a sum of 50. Find the dimensions of the rectangle that will have maximum area. (Use the hint for Exercise 59.)

REVIEW AND PREVIEW

Sketch the graph of each function. See Sections 3.2 and 11.5.

65. $f(x) = x^2 + 2$
66. $f(x) = (x - 3)^2$

67. $g(x) = x + 2$
68. $h(x) = x - 3$

69. $f(x) = (x + 5)^2 + 2$
70. $f(x) = 2(x - 3)^2 + 2$

71. $f(x) = 3(x - 4)^2 + 1$
72. $f(x) = (x + 1)^2 + 4$

73. $f(x) = -(x - 4)^2 + \dfrac{3}{2}$
74. $f(x) = -2(x + 7)^2 + \dfrac{1}{2}$

CONCEPT EXTENSIONS

Without calculating, tell whether each graph has a minimum value or a maximum value. See the Concept Check in the section.

75. $f(x) = 2x^2 - 5$

76. $g(x) = -7x^2 + x + 1$

77. $f(x) = 3 - \dfrac{1}{2}x^2$

78. $G(x) = 3 - \dfrac{1}{2}x + 0.8x^2$

Find the vertex of the graph of each quadratic function. Determine whether the graph opens upward or downward, find the y-intercept, approximate the x-intercepts to one decimal place, and sketch the graph.

79. $f(x) = x^2 + 10x + 15$ **80.** $f(x) = x^2 - 6x + 4$

81. $f(x) = 3x^2 - 6x + 7$ **82.** $f(x) = 2x^2 + 4x - 1$

Find the maximum or minimum value of each function. Approximate to two decimal places.

83. $f(x) = 2.3x^2 - 6.1x + 3.2$

84. $f(x) = 7.6x^2 + 9.8x - 2.1$

85. $f(x) = -1.9x^2 + 5.6x - 2.7$

86. $f(x) = -5.2x^2 - 3.8x + 5.1$

87. The projected number of Wi-Fi-enabled cell phones in the United States can be modeled by the quadratic function $c(x) = -0.4x^2 + 21x + 35$, where $c(x)$ is the projected number of Wi-Fi-enabled cell phones in millions and x is the number of years after 2009. (*Source:* Techcrunch)

a. Will this function have a maximum or a minimum? How can you tell?

b. According to this model, in what year will the number of Wi-Fi-enabled cell phones in the United States be at its maximum or minimum?

c. What is the maximum/minimum number of Wi-Fi-enabled cell phones predicted? Round to the nearest whole million.

88. Methane is a gas produced by landfills, natural gas systems, and coal mining that contributes to the greenhouse effect and global warming. Projected methane emissions in the United States can be modeled by the quadratic function

$$f(x) = -0.072x^2 + 1.93x + 173.9$$

where $f(x)$ is the amount of methane produced in million metric tons and x is the number of years after 2000. (*Source:* Based on data from the U.S. Environmental Protection Agency, 2000–2020)

a. According to this model, what will U.S. emissions of methane be in 2018? Round to 2 decimal places.

b. Will this function have a maximum or a minimum? How can you tell?

c. In what year will methane emissions in the United States be at their maximum/minimum? Round to the nearest whole year.

d. What is the level of methane emissions for that year? (Use your rounded answer from part **(c).** Round this answer to 2 decimal places.)

Use a graphing calculator to check each exercise.

89. Exercise 37   **90.** Exercise 38

91. Exercise 47   **92.** Exercise 48

Chapter 11 Vocabulary Check

Fill in each blank with one of the words or phrases listed below.

quadratic formula	quadratic	discriminant	$\pm\sqrt{b}$
completing the square	quadratic inequality	(h, k)	$(0, k)$
$(h, 0)$	$\dfrac{-b}{2a}$		

1. The _____ helps us find the number and type of solutions of a quadratic equation.

2. If $a^2 = b$, then $a = $ _____.

3. The graph of $f(x) = ax^2 + bx + c$, where a is not 0, is a parabola whose vertex has x-value _____.

4. A _____ is an inequality that can be written so that one side is a quadratic expression and the other side is 0.

5. The process of writing a quadratic equation so that one side is a perfect square trinomial is called _____.

6. The graph of $f(x) = x^2 + k$ has vertex _____.

7. The graph of $f(x) = (x - h)^2$ has vertex _____.

8. The graph of $f(x) = (x - h)^2 + k$ has vertex _____.

9. The formula $x = \dfrac{-b \pm \sqrt{b^2 - 4ac}}{2a}$ is called the _____.

10. A _____ equation is one that can be written in the form $ax^2 + bx + c = 0$ where $a, b,$ and c are real numbers and a is not 0.

Chapter 11 Highlights

DEFINITIONS AND CONCEPTS	EXAMPLES
Section 11.1 Solving Quadratic Equations by Completing the Square	
Square Root Property	Solve: $(x + 3)^2 = 14$
If b is a real number and if $a^2 = b$, then $a = \pm\sqrt{b}$.	$x + 3 = \pm\sqrt{14}$
	$x = -3 \pm \sqrt{14}$
To Solve a Quadratic Equation in x by Completing the Square	Solve: $3x^2 - 12x - 18 = 0$
Step 1. If the coefficient of x^2 is not 1, divide both sides of the equation by the coefficient of x^2.	**1.** $x^2 - 4x - 6 = 0$
Step 2. Isolate the variable terms.	**2.** $\qquad x^2 - 4x = 6$
Step 3. Complete the square by adding the square of half of the coefficient of x to both sides.	**3.** $\dfrac{1}{2}(-4) = -2$ and $(-2)^2 = 4$
	$x^2 - 4x + 4 = 6 + 4$
Step 4. Write the resulting trinomial as the square of a binomial.	**4.** $\qquad (x - 2)^2 = 10$
Step 5. Apply the square root property and solve for x.	**5.** $\qquad x - 2 = \pm\sqrt{10}$
	$x = 2 \pm \sqrt{10}$

DEFINITIONS AND CONCEPTS	EXAMPLES

Section 11.2   Solving Quadratic Equations by the Quadratic Formula

A quadratic equation written in the form $ax^2 + bx + c = 0$ has solutions

$$x = \frac{-b \pm \sqrt{b^2 - 4ac}}{2a}$$

Solve: $x^2 - x - 3 = 0$

$$a = 1, b = -1, c = -3$$

$$x = \frac{-(-1) \pm \sqrt{(-1)^2 - 4(1)(-3)}}{2 \cdot 1}$$

$$x = \frac{1 \pm \sqrt{13}}{2}$$

Section 11.3   Solving Equations by Using Quadratic Methods

Substitution is often helpful in solving an equation that contains a repeated variable expression.

Solve: $(2x + 1)^2 - 5(2x + 1) + 6 = 0$

Let $m = 2x + 1$. Then

$$m^2 - 5m + 6 = 0 \qquad \text{Let } m = 2x + 1.$$

$$(m - 3)(m - 2) = 0$$

$$m = 3 \quad \text{or} \quad m = 2$$

$$2x + 1 = 3 \quad \text{or} \quad 2x + 1 = 2 \quad \text{Substitute back.}$$

$$x = 1 \quad \text{or} \quad x = \frac{1}{2}$$

Section 11.4   Nonlinear Inequalities in One Variable

To Solve a Polynomial Inequality

Step 1. Write the inequality in standard form.

Step 2. Solve the related equation.

Step 3. Use solutions from Step 2 to separate the number line into regions.

Step 4. Use test points to determine whether values in each region satisfy the original inequality.

Step 5. Write the solution set as the union of regions whose test point value is a solution.

Solve: $x^2 \geq 6x$

1. $x^2 - 6x \geq 0$

2. $x^2 - 6x = 0$
    $x(x - 6) = 0$
    $x = 0 \quad \text{or} \quad x = 6$

3.
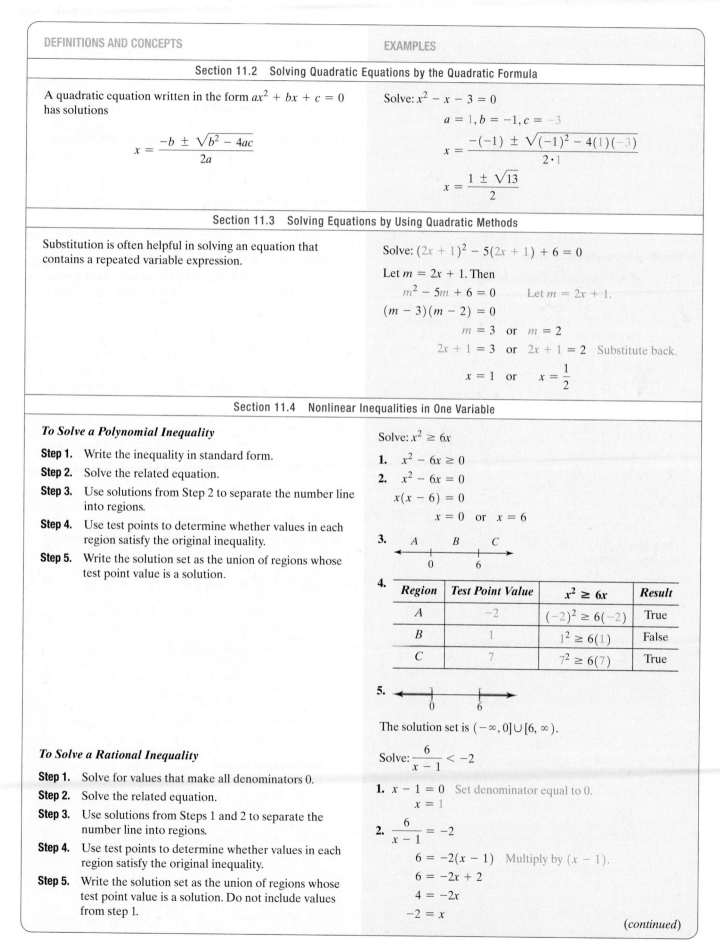

4.

Region	Test Point Value	$x^2 \geq 6x$	Result
A	-2	$(-2)^2 \geq 6(-2)$	True
B	1	$1^2 \geq 6(1)$	False
C	7	$7^2 \geq 6(7)$	True

5.

The solution set is $(-\infty, 0] \cup [6, \infty)$.

To Solve a Rational Inequality

Step 1. Solve for values that make all denominators 0.

Step 2. Solve the related equation.

Step 3. Use solutions from Steps 1 and 2 to separate the number line into regions.

Step 4. Use test points to determine whether values in each region satisfy the original inequality.

Step 5. Write the solution set as the union of regions whose test point value is a solution. Do not include values from step 1.

Solve: $\dfrac{6}{x - 1} < -2$

1. $x - 1 = 0 \quad$ Set denominator equal to 0.
    $x = 1$

2. $\dfrac{6}{x - 1} = -2$

$$6 = -2(x - 1) \quad \text{Multiply by } (x - 1).$$

$$6 = -2x + 2$$

$$4 = -2x$$

$$-2 = x$$

(continued)

DEFINITIONS AND CONCEPTS	EXAMPLES

Section 11.4 Nonlinear Inequalities in One Variable (continued)

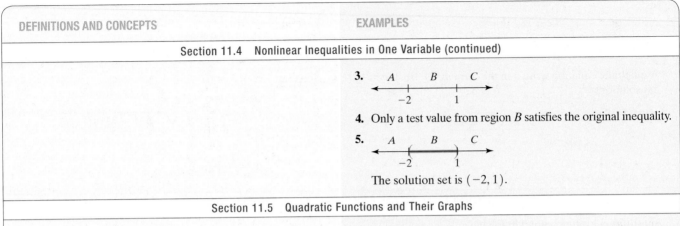

3.

$$-2 \qquad 1$$

4. Only a test value from region B satisfies the original inequality.

5.

$$-2 \qquad 1$$

The solution set is $(-2, 1)$.

Section 11.5 Quadratic Functions and Their Graphs

Graph of a Quadratic Function

The graph of a quadratic function written in the form $f(x) = a(x - h)^2 + k$ is a parabola with vertex (h, k). If $a > 0$, the parabola opens upward; if $a < 0$, the parabola opens downward. The axis of symmetry is the line whose equation is $x = h$.

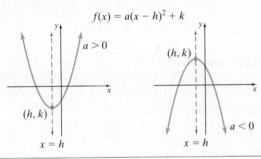

Graph: $g(x) = 3(x - 1)^2 + 4$

The graph is a parabola with vertex $(1, 4)$ and axis of symmetry $x = 1$. Since $a = 3$ is positive, the graph opens upward.

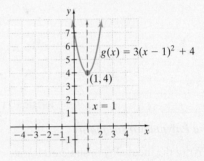

Section 11.6 Further Graphing of Quadratic Functions

The graph of $f(x) = ax^2 + bx + c$, where $a \neq 0$, is a parabola with vertex

$$\left(\frac{-b}{2a}, f\left(\frac{-b}{2a} \right) \right)$$

Graph $f(x) = x^2 - 2x - 8$. Find the vertex and x- and y-intercepts.

$$\frac{-b}{2a} = \frac{-(-2)}{2 \cdot 1} = 1$$
$$f(1) = 1^2 - 2(1) - 8 = -9$$

The vertex is $(1, -9)$.

$$0 = x^2 - 2x - 8$$
$$0 = (x - 4)(x + 2)$$
$$x = 4 \quad \text{or} \quad x = -2$$

The x-intercepts are $(4, 0)$ and $(-2, 0)$.

$$f(0) = 0^2 - 2 \cdot 0 - 8 = -8$$

The y-intercept is $(0, -8)$.

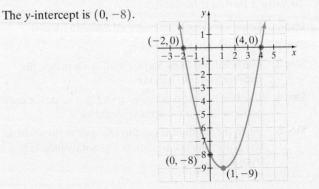

Chapter 11 **Review**

(11.1) *Solve by factoring.*

1. $x^2 - 15x + 14 = 0$

2. $7a^2 = 29a + 30$

Solve by using the square root property.

3. $4m^2 = 196$

4. $(5x - 2)^2 = 2$

Solve by completing the square.

5. $z^2 + 3z + 1 = 0$

6. $(2x + 1)^2 = x$

7. If P dollars are originally invested, the formula $A = P(1 + r)^2$ gives the amount A in an account paying interest rate r compounded annually after 2 years. Find the interest rate r such that $2500 increases to $2717 in 2 years. Round the result to the nearest hundredth of a percent.

△ **8.** Two ships leave a port at the same time and travel at the same speed. One ship is traveling due north and the other due east. In a few hours, the ships are 150 miles apart. How many miles has each ship traveled? Give the exact answer and a one-decimal-place approximation.

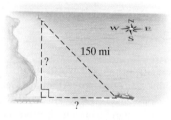

(11.2) *If the discriminant of a quadratic equation has the given value, determine the number and type of solutions of the equation.*

9. -8

10. 48

11. 100

12. 0

Solve by using the quadratic formula.

13. $x^2 - 16x + 64 = 0$

14. $x^2 + 5x = 0$

15. $2x^2 + 3x = 5$

16. $9x^2 + 4 = 2x$

17. $6x^2 + 7 = 5x$

18. $(2x - 3)^2 = x$

19. Cadets graduating from military school usually toss their hats high into the air at the end of the ceremony. One cadet threw his hat so that its distance $d(t)$ in feet above the ground t seconds after it was thrown was $d(t) = -16t^2 + 30t + 6$.
  a. Find the distance above the ground of the hat 1 second after it was thrown.
  b. Find the time it takes the hat to hit the ground. Give the exact time and a one-decimal-place approximation.

△ **20.** The hypotenuse of an isosceles right triangle is 6 centimeters longer than either of the legs. Find the length of the legs.

(11.3) *Solve each equation for the variable.*

21. $x^3 = 27$

22. $y^3 = -64$

23. $\dfrac{5}{x} + \dfrac{6}{x - 2} = 3$

24. $x^4 - 21x^2 - 100 = 0$

25. $x^{2/3} - 6x^{1/3} + 5 = 0$

26. $5(x + 3)^2 - 19(x + 3) = 4$

27. $a^6 - a^2 = a^4 - 1$

28. $y^{-2} + y^{-1} = 20$

29. Two postal workers, Jerome Grant and Tim Bozik, can sort a stack of mail in 5 hours. Working alone, Tim can sort the mail in 1 hour less time than Jerome can. Find the time that each postal worker can sort the mail alone. Round the result to one decimal place.

30. A negative number decreased by its reciprocal is $-\dfrac{24}{5}$. Find the number.

(11.4) *Solve each inequality for x. Write each solution set in interval notation.*

31. $2x^2 - 50 \le 0$

32. $\dfrac{1}{4}x^2 < \dfrac{1}{16}$

33. $(x^2 - 4)(x^2 - 25) \le 0$

34. $(x^2 - 16)(x^2 - 1) > 0$

35. $\dfrac{x - 5}{x - 6} < 0$

36. $\dfrac{(4x + 3)(x - 5)}{x(x + 6)} > 0$

37. $(x + 5)(x - 6)(x + 2) \le 0$

38. $x^3 + 3x^2 - 25x - 75 > 0$

39. $\dfrac{x^2 + 4}{3x} \le 1$

40. $\dfrac{3}{x - 2} > 2$

(11.5) *Sketch the graph of each function. Label the vertex and the axis of symmetry.*

41. $f(x) = x^2 - 4$

42. $g(x) = x^2 + 7$

43. $H(x) = 2x^2$

44. $h(x) = -\dfrac{1}{3}x^2$

45. $F(x) = (x - 1)^2$

46. $G(x) = (x + 5)^2$

47. $f(x) = (x - 4)^2 - 2$

48. $f(x) = -3(x - 1)^2 + 1$

(11.6) *Sketch the graph of each function. Find the vertex and the intercepts.*

49. $f(x) = x^2 + 10x + 25$

50. $f(x) = -x^2 + 6x - 9$

51. $f(x) = 4x^2 - 1$

52. $f(x) = -5x^2 + 5$

53. Find the vertex of the graph of $f(x) = -3x^2 - 5x + 4$. Determine whether the graph opens upward or downward, find the y-intercept, approximate the x-intercepts to one decimal place, and sketch the graph.

54. The function $h(t) = -16t^2 + 120t + 300$ gives the height in feet of a projectile fired from the top of a building after t seconds.
   a. When will the object reach a height of 350 feet? Round your answer to one decimal place.
   b. Explain why part **a** has two answers.

55. Find two numbers whose product is as large as possible, given that their sum is 420.

56. Write an equation of a quadratic function whose graph is a parabola that has vertex $(-3, 7)$. Let the value of a be $-\dfrac{7}{9}$.

MIXED REVIEW

Solve each equation or inequality.

57. $x^2 - x - 30 = 0$

58. $10x^2 = 3x + 4$

59. $9y^2 = 36$

60. $(9n + 1)^2 = 9$

61. $x^2 + x + 7 = 0$

62. $(3x - 4)^2 = 10x$

63. $x^2 + 11 = 0$

64. $x^2 + 7 = 0$

65. $(5a - 2)^2 - a = 0$

66. $\dfrac{7}{8} = \dfrac{8}{x^2}$

67. $x^{2/3} - 6x^{1/3} = -8$

68. $(2x - 3)(4x + 5) \geq 0$

69. $\dfrac{x(x + 5)}{4x - 3} \geq 0$

70. $\dfrac{3}{x - 2} > 2$

71. The busiest airport in the world is the Hartsfield-Jackson International Airport in Atlanta, Georgia. The total amount of passenger traffic through Atlanta during the period 2005 through 2014 can be modeled by the equation $y = -111x^2 + 1960x + 85{,}907$, where y is the number of passengers enplaned and deplaned in thousands, and x is the number of years after 2005. (*Source:* Based on data from Airports Council International)
   a. Estimate the passenger traffic at Atlanta's Hartsfield-Jackson International Airport in 2020.
   b. According to this model, will the passenger traffic at Atlanta's Hartsfield-Jackson International Airport continue to grow? Why or why not?

1c

Chapter 11 Getting Ready for the Test

MULTIPLE CHOICE *For each quadratic equation in Exercises 1 and 2, choose the correct substitution for a, b, and c in the standard form* $ax^2 + bx + c = 0$.

▶ **1.** $x^2 = 8$

   A. $a = 1, b = 0, c = 8$ **B.** $a = 1, b = 8, c = 0$ **C.** $a = 1, b = 0, c = -8$

▶ **2.** $\dfrac{1}{9}x^2 + \dfrac{1}{3} = x$ One correct substitution is $a = \dfrac{1}{9}$, $b = -1$, $c = \dfrac{1}{3}$. Find another.

   A. $a = 1, b = -1, c = 3$ **B.** $a = 1, b = -9, c = 3$ **C.** $a = 1, b = 9, c = 3$ **D.** $a = 1, b = -1, c = 1$.

MULTIPLE CHOICE *Select the correct choice.*

3. $\dfrac{-4 \pm \sqrt{-4}}{2}$ simplifies to

    A. $-2 \pm i$ **B.** $-2 \pm 2i$ **C.** $\pm 4i$ **D.** $-2 \pm i\sqrt{2}$

4. $\dfrac{9 \pm \sqrt{27}}{3}$ simplifies to

    A. $3 \pm \sqrt{27}$ **B.** $3 \pm 3\sqrt{3}$ **C.** $9 \pm \sqrt{3}$ **D.** $3 \pm \sqrt{3}$

5. To solve $2x^2 + 16x = 5$ by completing the square, choose the next correct step.

    A. $x^2 + 8x = 5$ **B.** $x^2 + 8x = \dfrac{5}{2}$ **C.** $2x^2 + 16x + 16 = 5$ **D.** $2x^2 + 16x + 64 = 5$

6. To solve $x^2 - 7x = 5$ by completing the square, choose the next correct step.

    A. $x^2 - 7x + 49 = 5$ **B.** $x^2 - 7x + 49 = 5 + 49$ **C.** $x^2 - 7x + \dfrac{49}{4} = 5$ **D.** $x^2 - 7x + \dfrac{49}{4} = 5 + \dfrac{49}{4}$

7. The solution set of $(x + 5)(x - 1) \le 0$ is $[-5, 1]$. Use this to select the solution set of $\dfrac{x + 5}{x - 1} \le 0$.

    A. $[-5, 1]$ **B.** $(-5, 1]$ **C.** $[-5, 1)$ **D.** $(-5, 1)$

8. Choose the correct description of the graph of $f(x) = -103(x - 20)^2 + 5.6$.

    A. opens up; vertex $(20, 5.6)$ **B.** opens up; vertex $(-20, 5.6)$

    C. opens down; vertex $(20, 5.6)$ **D.** opens down; vertex $(20, -5.6)$

9. Choose the correct description of the graph of $f(x) = 0.5(x + 1)^2 - 3$.

    A. opens up; vertex $(-1, -3)$ **B.** opens up; vertex $(1, -3)$

    C. opens down; vertex $(-1, -3)$ **D.** opens down; vertex $(-3, -1)$

10. Select the vertex of the graph of $f(x) = 3x^2 + 12x - 7$.

    A. $(-2, -7)$ **B.** $(-2, -19)$ **C.** $\left(-\dfrac{1}{2}, -12\dfrac{1}{4}\right)$ **D.** $(-12, 281)$

11. Select the x-intercept(s) of the graph of $f(x) = 2x^2 - x - 10$.

    A. $(0, 0)$ **B.** $(5, 0), (-2, 0)$ **C.** $\left(\dfrac{5}{2}, 0\right), (-2, 0)$ **D.** $\left(-\dfrac{5}{2}, 0\right), (2, 0)$

Chapter 11 Test   MyMathLab°   YouTube™

Solve each equation.

1. $5x^2 - 2x = 7$

2. $(x + 1)^2 = 10$

3. $m^2 - m + 8 = 0$

4. $u^2 - 6u + 2 = 0$

5. $7x^2 + 8x + 1 = 0$

6. $y^2 - 3y = 5$

7. $\dfrac{4}{x + 2} + \dfrac{2x}{x - 2} = \dfrac{6}{x^2 - 4}$

8. $x^5 + 3x^4 = x + 3$

9. $x^6 + 1 = x^4 + x^2$

10. $(x + 1)^2 - 15(x + 1) + 56 = 0$

Solve by completing the square.

11. $x^2 - 6x = -2$

12. $2a^2 + 5 = 4a$

Solve each inequality for x. Write the solution set in interval notation.

13. $2x^2 - 7x > 15$

14. $(x^2 - 16)(x^2 - 25) \ge 0$

15. $\dfrac{5}{x + 3} < 1$

16. $\dfrac{7x - 14}{x^2 - 9} \le 0$

Graph each function. Label the vertex.

17. $f(x) = 3x^2$

18. $G(x) = -2(x - 1)^2 + 5$

Graph each function. Find and label the vertex, y-intercept, and x-intercepts (if any).

19. $h(x) = x^2 - 4x + 4$

20. $F(x) = 2x^2 - 8x + 9$

21. Dave and Sandy Hartranft can paint a room together in 4 hours. Working alone, Dave can paint the room in 2 hours less time than Sandy can. Find how long it takes Sandy to paint the room alone.

22. A stone is thrown upward from a bridge. The stone's height in feet, $s(t)$, above the water t seconds after the stone is thrown is a function given by the equation $s(t) = -16t^2 + 32t + 256$.

   a. Find the maximum height of the stone.

   b. Find the time it takes the stone to hit the water. Round the answer to two decimal places.

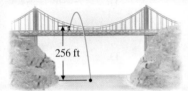

23. Given the diagram shown, approximate to the nearest tenth of a foot how many feet of walking distance a person saves by cutting across the lawn instead of walking on the sidewalk.

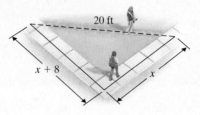

Chapter 11 **Cumulative Review**

1. Find the value of each expression when $x = 2$ and $y = -5$.

   a. $\dfrac{x - y}{12 + x}$ **b.** $x^2 - 3y$

2. Solve: $|3x - 2| = -5$

3. Simplify each expression by combining like terms.

   a. $2x + 3x + 5 + 2$ **b.** $-5a - 3 + a + 2$

   c. $4y - 3y^2$ **d.** $2.3x + 5x - 6$

   e. $-\dfrac{1}{2}b + b$

4. Use the addition method to solve the system.

$$\begin{cases} -6x + y = 5 \\ 4x - 2y = 6 \end{cases}$$

5. Solve the following system of equations by graphing.

$$\begin{cases} 2x + y = 7 \\ 2y = -4x \end{cases}$$

6. Simplify. Use positive exponents to write each answer.

   a. $(a^{-2}bc^3)^{-3}$ **b.** $\left(\dfrac{a^{-4}b^2}{c^3}\right)^{-2}$

   c. $\left(\dfrac{3a^8b^2}{12a^5b^5}\right)^{-2}$

7. Solve the system: $\begin{cases} 7x - 3y = -14 \\ -3x + y = 6 \end{cases}$

8. Multiply.

   a. $(4a - 3)(7a - 2)$

   b. $(2a + b)(3a - 5b)$

9. Simplify each quotient.

   a. $\dfrac{x^5}{x^2}$ **b.** $\dfrac{4^7}{4^3}$ **c.** $\dfrac{(-3)^5}{(-3)^2}$

   d. $\dfrac{s^2}{t^3}$ **e.** $\dfrac{2x^5y^2}{xy}$

10. Factor.

   a. $9x^3 + 27x^2 - 15x$

   b. $2x(3y - 2) - 5(3y - 2)$

   c. $2xy + 6x - y - 3$

11. If $P(x) = 2x^3 - 4x^2 + 5$

   a. Find $P(2)$ by substitution.

   b. Use synthetic division to find the remainder when $P(x)$ is divided by $x - 2$.

12. Factor: $x^2 - 2x - 48$

13. Solve: $(5x - 1)(2x^2 + 15x + 18) = 0$

14. Factor: $2ax^2 - 12axy + 18ay^2$

15. Simplify the rational expression.

$$\dfrac{2x^2}{10x^3 - 2x^2}$$

16. Solve: $2(a^2 + 2) - 8 = -2a(a - 2) - 5$

17. Simplify: $\dfrac{x^{-1} + 2xy^{-1}}{x^{-2} - x^{-2}y^{-1}}$

18. Find the vertex and any intercepts of $f(x) = x^2 + x - 12$.

19. Factor: $4m^4 - 4m^2 + 1$

20. Simplify: $\dfrac{x^2 - 4x + 4}{2 - x}$

21. The square of a number plus three times the number is 70. Find the number.

22. Subtract: $\dfrac{a + 1}{a^2 - 6a + 8} - \dfrac{3}{16 - a^2}$

23. Use the product rule to simplify.

   a. $\sqrt{25x^3}$ **b.** $\sqrt[3]{54x^6y^8}$

   c. $\sqrt[4]{81z^{11}}$

24. Simplify: $\dfrac{(2a)^{-1} + b^{-1}}{a^{-1} + (2b)^{-1}}$

25. Rationalize the denominator of each expression.

a. $\dfrac{2}{\sqrt{5}}$

b. $\dfrac{2\sqrt{16}}{\sqrt{9x}}$

c. $\sqrt[3]{\dfrac{1}{2}}$

26. Divide $x^3 - 3x^2 - 10x + 24$ by $x + 3$.

27. Solve: $\sqrt{2x + 5} + \sqrt{2x} = 3$

28. If $P(x) = 4x^3 - 2x^2 + 3$,

   a. Find $P(-2)$ by substitution.

   b. Use synthetic division to find the remainder when $P(x)$ is divided by $x + 2$.

29. Solve: $\dfrac{x}{2} + \dfrac{8}{3} = \dfrac{1}{6}$

30. Solve: $\dfrac{x + 3}{x^2 + 5x + 6} = \dfrac{3}{2x + 4} - \dfrac{1}{x + 3}$

31. The quotient of a number and 6, minus $\dfrac{5}{3}$, is the quotient of the number and 2. Find the number.

32. Mr. Briley can roof his house in 24 hours. His son can roof the same house in 40 hours. If they work together, how long will it take to roof the house?

33. Suppose that y varies directly as x. If y is 5 when x is 30, find the constant of variation and the direct variation equation.

34. Suppose that y varies inversely as x. If y is 8 when x is 24, find the constant of variation and the inverse variation equation.

35. Simplify. Assume that the variables represent any real number.

   a. $\sqrt{(-3)^2}$ **b.** $\sqrt{x^2}$

   c. $\sqrt[4]{(x - 2)^4}$ **d.** $\sqrt[3]{(-5)^3}$

   e. $\sqrt[5]{(2x - 7)^5}$ **f.** $\sqrt{25x^2}$

   g. $\sqrt{x^2 + 2x + 1}$

36. Simplify. Assume that the variables represent any real number.

   a. $\sqrt{(-2)^2}$

   b. $\sqrt{y^2}$

   c. $\sqrt[4]{(a - 3)^4}$

   d. $\sqrt[3]{(-6)^3}$

   e. $\sqrt[5]{(3x - 1)^5}$

37. Use rational exponents to simplify. Assume that variables represent positive numbers.

   a. $\sqrt[8]{x^4}$

   b. $\sqrt[6]{25}$

   c. $\sqrt[4]{r^2 s^6}$

38. Use rational exponents to simplify. Assume that variables represent positive numbers.

   a. $\sqrt[4]{5^2}$

   b. $\sqrt[12]{x^3}$

   c. $\sqrt[6]{x^2 y^4}$

39. Divide. Write in the form $a + bi$.

   a. $\dfrac{2 + i}{1 - i}$

   b. $\dfrac{7}{3i}$

40. Write each product in the form of $a + bi$.

   a. $3i(5 - 2i)$

   b. $(6 - 5i)^2$

   c. $(\sqrt{3} + 2i)(\sqrt{3} - 2i)$

41. Use the square root property to solve $(x + 1)^2 = 12$.

42. Use the square root property to solve $(y - 1)^2 = 24$.

43. Solve: $x - \sqrt{x} - 6 = 0$

44. Use the quadratic formula to solve $m^2 = 4m + 8$.

Answers to Selected Exercises

CHAPTER 3 GRAPHING

Section 3.1

Practice Exercises

1. a. Oceania/Australia region, 25 million Internet users   **b.** 85 million more Internet users   **2. a.** 70 beats per minute   **b.** 60 beats per minute
c. 5 minutes after lighting   **3.**   **4. a.** $(2008, 79), (2009, 79), (2010, 72), (2011, 73), (2012, 56), (2013, 48), (2014, 46)$

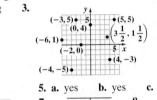

b.

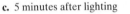

5. a. yes   **b.** yes   **c.** no   **6. a.** $(0, -8)$ **b.** $(6, 4)$ **c.** $(-3, -14)$

7.

	x	y
a.	-2	8
b.	3	-12
c.	0	0

8.

	x	y
a.	-10	-4
b.	0	-2
c.	10	0

9.

x	0	1	2	3	4
y	12,000	10,200	8400	6600	4800

Vocabulary, Readiness & Video Check 3.1

1. x-axis; y-axis   **3.** quadrants; four   **5.** one   **7.** horizontal: top tourist destinations; vertical: number of arrivals (in millions) to these destinations
9. Data occurring in pairs of numbers can be written as ordered pairs, called paired data, and then graphed on a coordinate system.
11. a linear equation in one variable

Exercise Set 3.1

1. China   **3.** France, U.S., Spain, and China   **5.** 53 million   **7.** 82,000   **9.** 2011; 103,000   **11.** 15.8   **13.** from 2008 to 2010

15. 2010 to 2014   **17.** $\left(-1, 4\frac{1}{2}\right)$

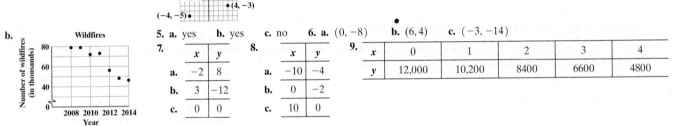

$(1, 5)$ and $(3.7, 2.2)$ are in quadrant I, $\left(-1, 4\frac{1}{2}\right)$ is in quadrant II, $(-5, -2)$ is in quadrant III, $(2, -4)$
and $\left(\frac{1}{2}, -3\right)$ are in quadrant IV, $(-3, 0)$ lies on the x-axis, $(0, -1)$ lies on the y-axis   **19.** $(0, 0)$
21. $(3, 2)$ **23.** $(-2, -2)$ **25.** $(2, -1)$ **27.** $(0, -3)$ **29.** $(1, 3)$ **31.** $(-3, -1)$

33. a. $(2010, 21.0), (2011, 22.4), (2012, 23.9), (2013, 25.0), (2014, 28.0)$ **b.** In the year 2014, the worldwide box office was $28.0 billion.
c.   **d.** The worldwide box office increased every year.   **35. a.** $(0.50, 10), (0.75, 12), (1.00, 15), (1.25, 16), (1.50, 18),$
$(1.50, 19), (1.75, 19), (2.00, 20)$ **b.** When Minh studied 1.25 hours, her quiz score was 16.   **c.**
d. answers may very

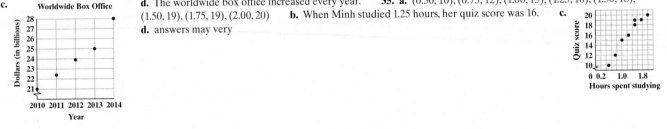

37. a. $(2313, 2), (2085, 1), (2711, 21), (2869, 39), (2920, 42), (4038, 99), (1783, 0), (2493, 9)$ **b.**   **c.** The farther from the equator, the more snowfall.   **39.** yes; no; yes   **41.** yes; yes   **43.** no; yes; yes

45. $(-4, -2), (4, 0)$ **47.** $(-8, -5), (16, 1)$ **49.** $0; 7; -\dfrac{2}{7}$ **51.** 2; 2; 5

53. $0; -3; 2$ **55.** 2; 6; 3   **57.** $-12; 5; -6$ **59.** $\dfrac{5}{7}; \dfrac{5}{2}; -1$ **61.** $0; -5; -2$

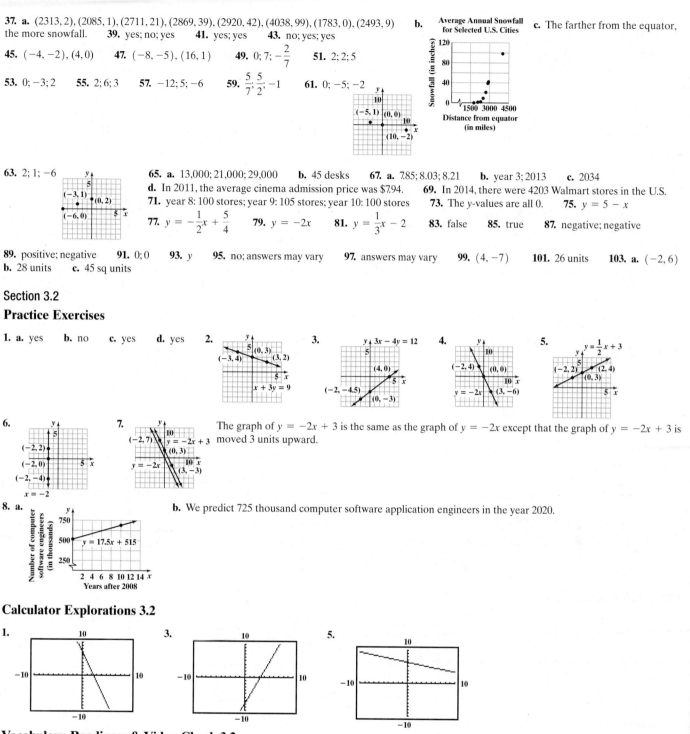

63. $2; 1; -6$ **65. a.** 13,000; 21,000; 29,000   **b.** 45 desks   **67. a.** 7.85; 8.03; 8.21   **b.** year 3; 2013   **c.** 2034   **d.** In 2011, the average cinema admission price was $7.94.   **69.** In 2014, there were 4203 Walmart stores in the U.S.   **71.** year 8: 100 stores; year 9: 105 stores; year 10: 100 stores   **73.** The y-values are all 0.   **75.** $y = 5 - x$ **77.** $y = -\dfrac{1}{2}x + \dfrac{5}{4}$ **79.** $y = -2x$ **81.** $y = \dfrac{1}{3}x - 2$ **83.** false   **85.** true   **87.** negative; negative

89. positive; negative   **91.** 0; 0   **93.** y **95.** no; answers may vary   **97.** answers may vary   **99.** $(4, -7)$ **101.** 26 units   **103. a.** $(-2, 6)$ **b.** 28 units   **c.** 45 sq units

Section 3.2

Practice Exercises

1. a. yes   **b.** no   **c.** yes   **d.** yes   **2.**   **3.**   **4.**   **5.**

6.   **7.**   The graph of $y = -2x + 3$ is the same as the graph of $y = -2x$ except that the graph of $y = -2x + 3$ is moved 3 units upward.

8. a.   **b.** We predict 725 thousand computer software application engineers in the year 2020.

Calculator Explorations 3.2

1.   **3.**   **5.**

Vocabulary, Readiness & Video Check 3.2

1. In the definition, x and y both have an understood power of 1. Example 3 shows an equation where y has a power of 2, so it is not a linear equation in two variables.   **3.** An infinite number of points make up the line and each point corresponds to an ordered pair that is a solution of the linear equation in two variables.

Exercise Set 3.2

1. yes   **3.** yes   **5.** no   **7.** yes

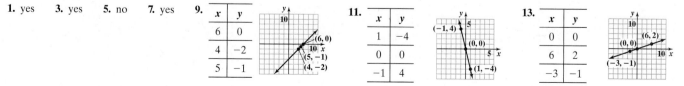

9.

x	y
6	0
4	-2
5	-1

11.

x	y
1	-4
0	0
-1	4

13.

x	y
0	0
6	2
-3	-1

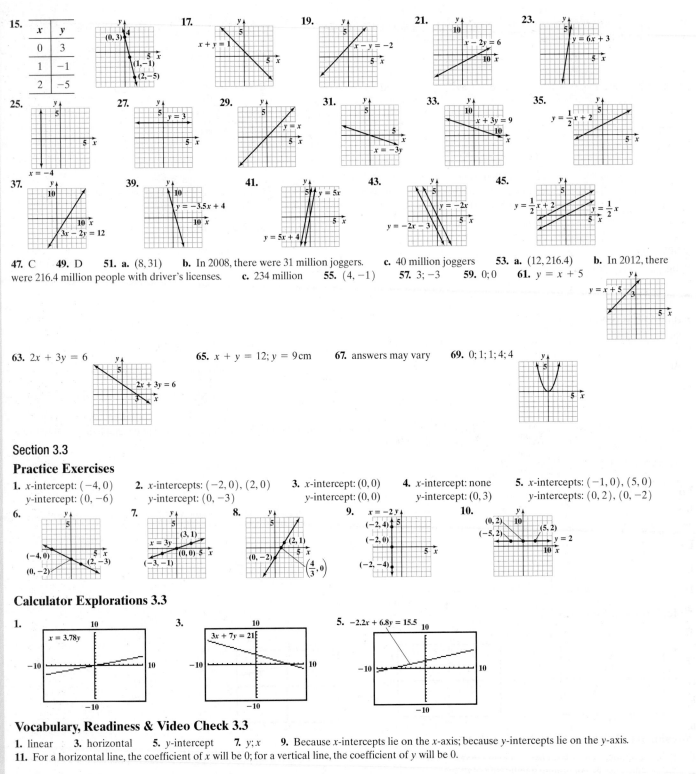

15.

x	y
0	3
1	−1
2	−5

47. C **49.** D **51. a.** $(8, 31)$ **b.** In 2008, there were 31 million joggers. **c.** 40 million joggers **53. a.** $(12, 216.4)$ **b.** In 2012, there were 216.4 million people with driver's licenses. **c.** 234 million **55.** $(4, -1)$ **57.** 3; −3 **59.** 0; 0 **61.** $y = x + 5$

63. $2x + 3y = 6$ **65.** $x + y = 12; y = 9 \, \text{cm}$ **67.** answers may vary **69.** 0; 1; 1; 4; 4

Section 3.3

Practice Exercises

1. x-intercept: $(-4, 0)$ y-intercept: $(0, -6)$ **2.** x-intercepts: $(-2, 0), (2, 0)$ y-intercept: $(0, -3)$ **3.** x-intercept: $(0, 0)$ y-intercept: $(0, 0)$ **4.** x-intercept: none y-intercept: $(0, 3)$ **5.** x-intercepts: $(-1, 0), (5, 0)$ y-intercepts: $(0, 2), (0, -2)$

Calculator Explorations 3.3

Vocabulary, Readiness & Video Check 3.3

1. linear **3.** horizontal **5.** y-intercept **7.** y; x **9.** Because x-intercepts lie on the x-axis; because y-intercepts lie on the y-axis. **11.** For a horizontal line, the coefficient of x will be 0; for a vertical line, the coefficient of y will be 0.

Exercise Set 3.3

1. $(-1, 0); (0, 1)$ **3.** $(-2, 0); (2, 0); (0, -2)$ **5.** $(-2, 0); (1, 0); (3, 0); (0, 3)$ **7.** $(-1, 0); (1, 0); (0, 1); (0, -2)$ **9.** infinite **11.** 0

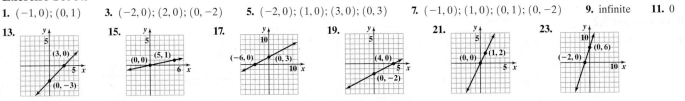

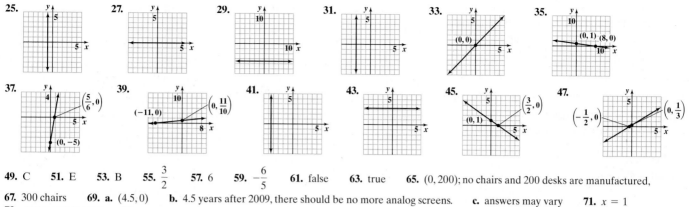

49. C   **51.** E   **53.** B   **55.** $\dfrac{3}{2}$ **57.** 6   **59.** $-\dfrac{6}{5}$ **61.** false   **63.** true   **65.** $(0, 200)$; no chairs and 200 desks are manufactured,

67. 300 chairs   **69. a.** $(4.5, 0)$ **b.** 4.5 years after 2009, there should be no more analog screens.   **c.** answers may vary   **71.** $x = 1$
73. answers may vary   **75.** answers may vary

Section 3.4
Practice Exercises

1. -1 **2.** $\dfrac{1}{3}$ **3.** $m - \dfrac{2}{3}$; y-intercept: $(0, -2)$ **4.** $m = 6$; y-intercept: $(0, -5)$ **5.** $m = -\dfrac{5}{2}$; y-intercept: $(0, 4)$ **6.** $m = 0$

7. slope is undefined   **8. a.** perpendicular   **b.** neither   **c.** parallel   **9.** 25%   **10.** $m = \dfrac{0.75 \text{ dollar}}{1 \text{ pound}}$; The Wash-n-Fold charges \$0.75 per pound of laundry.

Calculator Explorations 3.4

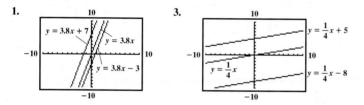

Vocabulary, Readiness & Video Check 3.4

1. slope   **3.** 0   **5.** positive   **7.** $y; x$ **9.** solve the equation for y; the slope is the coefficient of x **11.** slope-intercept form; this form makes the slope easy to see, and you need to compare slopes to determine if two lines are parallel or perpendicular

Exercise Set 3.4

1. -1 **3.** undefined   **5.** $-\dfrac{2}{3}$ **7.** 0   **9.** $m = -\dfrac{4}{3}$ **11.** undefined slope   **13.** $m = \dfrac{5}{2}$ **15.** negative   **17.** undefined   **19.** upward
21. horizontal   **23.** line 1   **25.** line 2   **27.** D   **29.** B   **31.** E   **33.** undefined slope   **35.** $m = 0$ **37.** undefined slope
39. $m = 0$ **41.** $m = 5$ **43.** $m = -0.3$ **45.** $m = -2$ **47.** $m = \dfrac{2}{3}$ **49.** undefined slope   **51.** $m = \dfrac{1}{2}$ **53.** $m = 0$ **55.** $m = -\dfrac{3}{4}$
57. $m = 4$ **59. a.** 1   **b.** -1 **61. a.** $\dfrac{9}{11}$ **b.** $-\dfrac{11}{9}$ **63.** neither   **65.** neither   **67.** parallel   **69.** perpendicular   **71.** $\dfrac{3}{5}$ **73.** 12.5%
75. 40%   **77.** 37%; 35%   **79.** $m = 1.4$ or $\dfrac{1.4}{1}$; every 1 year, there are 1.4 million more U.S. households with computers.   **81.** $m = 0.47$ or $\dfrac{0.47}{1}$; It costs \$0.47 per 1 mile to own and operate a compact car.   **83.** $y = 2x - 14$ **85.** $y = -6x - 11$ **87.** $m = \dfrac{1}{2}$ **89.** answers may vary
91. 2005–2006; 2010–2011   **93.** 2002; 29 mi per gallon   **95.** from 2011 to 2012   **97.** $x = 6$ **99. a.** $(2004, 27{,}000)$; $(2014, 29{,}500)$
b. 250 or $\dfrac{250}{1}$ **c.** For the years 2004 through 2014, the number of organ transplants increased at a rate of 250 per 1 year.   **101.** The slope through $(-3, 0)$ and $(1, 1)$ is $\dfrac{1}{4}$. The slope through $(-3, 0)$ and $(-4, 4)$ is -4. The product of the slopes is -1, so the sides are perpendicular.
103. -0.25 **105.** 0.875   **107.** The line becomes steeper.

Integrated Review

1. $m = 2$ **2.** $m = 0$ **3.** $m = -\dfrac{2}{3}$ **4.** undefined slope   **5.**   **6.** $x + y = 3$ **7.**

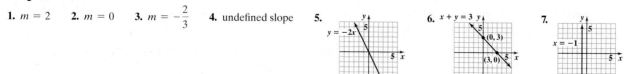

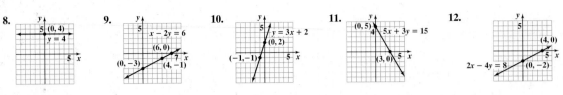

13. parallel   **14.** neither   **15. a.** $(0, 490)$ **b.** In 2002, there were 490 thousand bridges on public roads.   **c.** 4.09 or $\dfrac{4.09}{1}$

d. For the years 2002 through 2013, the number of bridges on public roads increased at a rate of 4.09 thousand per 1 year.   **16. a.** $(4, 43.9)$
b. In 2013, the revenue for online advertising was $43.9 billion.

Section 3.5

Practice Exercises

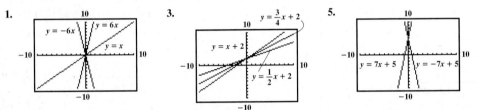

3. $y = \dfrac{1}{2}x + 7$ **4.** $4x - y = 5$ **5.** $5x + 4y = 19$ **6.** $x = 3$ **7.** $y = 3$

8. a. $y = -1500x + 195,000$ **b.** $105,000

Calculator Explorations 3.5

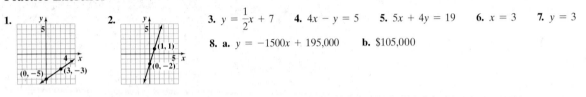

Vocabulary, Readiness & Video Check 3.5

1. slope-intercept; $m; b$ **3.** y-intercept; fraction   **5.** Write the equation with x- and y- terms on one side of the equal sign and a constant on the other side.   **7.** Example 6: $y = -3$; Example 7: $x = -2$

Exercise Set 3.5

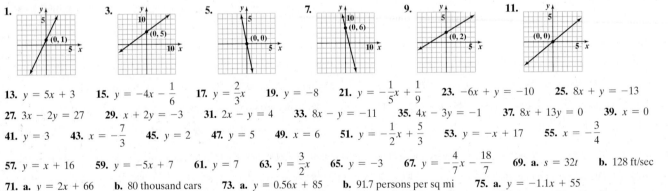

13. $y = 5x + 3$ **15.** $y = -4x - \dfrac{1}{6}$ **17.** $y = \dfrac{2}{3}x$ **19.** $y = -8$ **21.** $y = -\dfrac{1}{5}x + \dfrac{1}{9}$ **23.** $-6x + y = -10$ **25.** $8x + y = -13$
27. $3x - 2y = 27$ **29.** $x + 2y = -3$ **31.** $2x - y = 4$ **33.** $8x - y = -11$ **35.** $4x - 3y = -1$ **37.** $8x + 13y = 0$ **39.** $x = 0$
41. $y = 3$ **43.** $x = -\dfrac{7}{3}$ **45.** $y = 2$ **47.** $y = 5$ **49.** $x = 6$ **51.** $y = -\dfrac{1}{2}x + \dfrac{5}{3}$ **53.** $y = -x + 17$ **55.** $x = -\dfrac{3}{4}$
57. $y = x + 16$ **59.** $y = -5x + 7$ **61.** $y = 7$ **63.** $y = \dfrac{3}{2}x$ **65.** $y = -3$ **67.** $y = -\dfrac{4}{7}x - \dfrac{18}{7}$ **69. a.** $s = 32t$ **b.** 128 ft/sec
71. a. $y = 2x + 66$ **b.** 80 thousand cars   **73. a.** $y = 0.56x + 85$ **b.** 91.7 persons per sq mi   **75. a.** $y = -1.1x + 55$
b. 38.5 million   **77. a.** $S = -1000p + 13,000$ **b.** 9500 Fun Noodles   **79.** -1 **81.** 5   **83.** no   **85.** yes   **87.** point-slope
89. slope-intercept   **91.** horizontal   **93.** answers may vary   **95. a.** $3x - y = -5$ **b.** $x + 3y = 5$ **97. a.** $3x + 2y = -1$ **b.** $2x - 3y = 21$

Section 3.6

Practice Exercises

1. domain: $\{0, 1, 5\}$; range: $\{-2, 0, 3, 4\}$ **2. a.** function   **b.** not a function   **3. a.** not a function   **b.** function   **4. a.** function
b. function   **c.** function   **d.** not a function   **5. a.** function   **b.** function   **c.** function   **d.** not a function   **6. a.** 69°F   **b.** February
c. yes   **7. a.** $h(2) = 9; (2, 9)$ **b.** $h(-5) = 30; (-5, 30)$ **c.** $h(0) = 5; (0, 5)$ **8. a.** domain: $(-\infty, \infty)$ **b.** domain: $(-\infty, 0) \cup (0, \infty)$
9. a. domain: $[-4, 6]$; range: $[-2, 3]$ **b.** domain: $(-\infty, \infty)$; range: $(-\infty, 3]$

Vocabulary, Readiness & Video Check 3.6

1. relation   **3.** range   **5.** vertical   **7.** A relation is a set of ordered pairs and an equation in two variables defines a set of ordered pairs. Therefore, an equation in two variables can also define a relation.   **9.** A vertical line represents one x-value paired with many y-values. A function only allows an x-value paired with exactly one y-value, so if a vertical line intersects a graph more than once, there's an x-value paired with more than one y-value, and we don't have a function.

Exercise Set 3.6

1. $\{-7, 0, 2, 10\}$; $\{-7, 0, 4, 10\}$ **3.** $\{0, 1, 5\}$; $\{-2\}$ **5.** yes   **7.** no   **9.** no   **11.** yes   **13.** yes   **15.** no   **17.** yes   **19.** yes
21. yes   **23.** no   **25.** no   **27.** 9:30 p.m.   **29.** January 1 and December 1   **31.** yes; it passes the vertical line test   **33.** $4.25 per hour
35. 2009   **37.** yes; answers may vary   **39.** $1.80   **41.** more than 5 ounces and less than or equal to 6 ounces   **43.** yes; answers may vary
45. $-9, -5, 1$ **47.** $6, 2, 11$ **49.** $-6, 0, 9$ **51.** $2, 0, 3$ **53.** $5, 0, -20$ **55.** $5, 3, 35$ **57.** $(3, 6)$ **59.** $\left(0, -\dfrac{1}{2}\right)$ **61.** $(-2, 9)$
63. $(-\infty, \infty)$ **65.** all real number except -5 or $(-\infty, -5) \cup (-5, \infty)$ **67.** $(-\infty, \infty)$ **69.** domain: $(-\infty, \infty)$; range: $[-4, \infty)$ **71.** domain:
$(-\infty, \infty)$; range: $(-\infty, \infty)$ **73.** domain: $(-\infty, \infty)$; range: $\{2\}$ **75.** -1 **77.** -1 **79.** $-1, 5$ **81.** $(-2, 1)$ **83.** $(-3, -1)$
85. $f(-5) = 12$ **87.** $(3, -4)$ **89.** $f(5) = 0$ **91. a.** 166.38 cm   **b.** 148.25 cm   **93.** answers may vary   **95.** $f(x) = x + 7$
97. a. 11   **b.** $2a + 7$ **99. a.** 16   **b.** $a^2 + 7$

Chapter 3 Vocabulary Check

1. solution   **2.** y-axis   **3.** linear   **4.** x-intercept   **5.** standard   **6.** y-intercept   **7.** slope-intercept   **8.** point-slope   **9.** y
10. x-axis   **11.** x **12.** slope   **13.** function   **14.** domain   **15.** range   **16.** relation

Chapter 3 Review

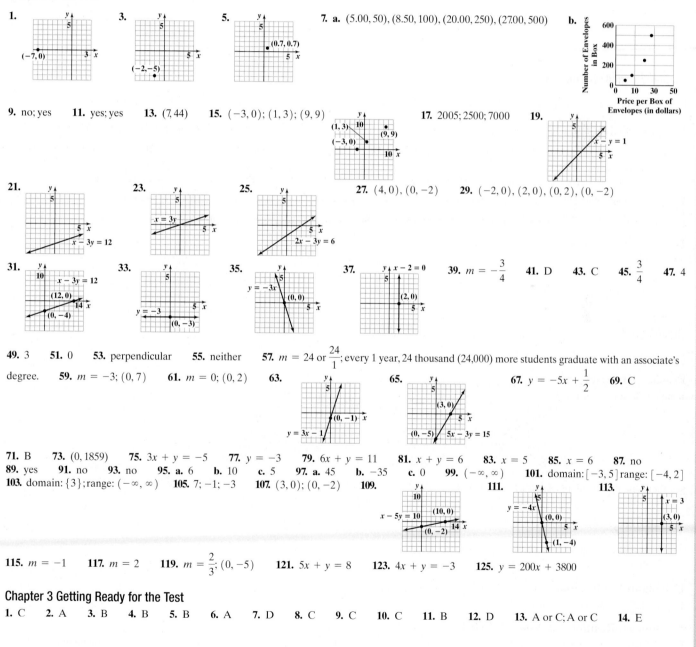

7. a. $(5.00, 50), (8.50, 100), (20.00, 250), (27.00, 500)$

9. no; yes   **11.** yes; yes   **13.** $(7, 44)$ **15.** $(-3, 0)$; $(1, 3)$; $(9, 9)$ **17.** $2005; 2500; 7000$

27. $(4, 0), (0, -2)$ **29.** $(-2, 0), (2, 0), (0, 2), (0, -2)$

39. $m = -\dfrac{3}{4}$ **41.** D   **43.** C   **45.** $\dfrac{3}{4}$ **47.** 4

49. 3   **51.** 0   **53.** perpendicular   **55.** neither   **57.** $m = 24$ or $\dfrac{24}{1}$; every 1 year, 24 thousand (24,000) more students graduate with an associate's
degree.   **59.** $m = -3$; $(0, 7)$ **61.** $m = 0$; $(0, 2)$ **67.** $y = -5x + \dfrac{1}{2}$ **69.** C

71. B   **73.** $(0, 1859)$ **75.** $3x + y = -5$ **77.** $y = -3$ **79.** $6x + y = 11$ **81.** $x + y = 6$ **83.** $x = 5$ **85.** $x = 6$ **87.** no
89. yes   **91.** no   **93.** no   **95. a.** 6   **b.** 10   **c.** 5   **97. a.** 45   **b.** -35 **c.** 0   **99.** $(-\infty, \infty)$ **101.** domain: $[-3, 5]$ range: $[-4, 2]$
103. domain: $\{3\}$; range: $(-\infty, \infty)$ **105.** $7; -1; -3$ **107.** $(3, 0); (0, -2)$

115. $m = -1$ **117.** $m = 2$ **119.** $m = \dfrac{2}{3}$; $(0, -5)$ **121.** $5x + y = 8$ **123.** $4x + y = -3$ **125.** $y = 200x + 3800$

Chapter 3 Getting Ready for the Test

1. C   **2.** A   **3.** B   **4.** B   **5.** B   **6.** A   **7.** D   **8.** C   **9.** C   **10.** C   **11.** B   **12.** D   **13.** A or C; A or C   **14.** E

Chapter 3 Test

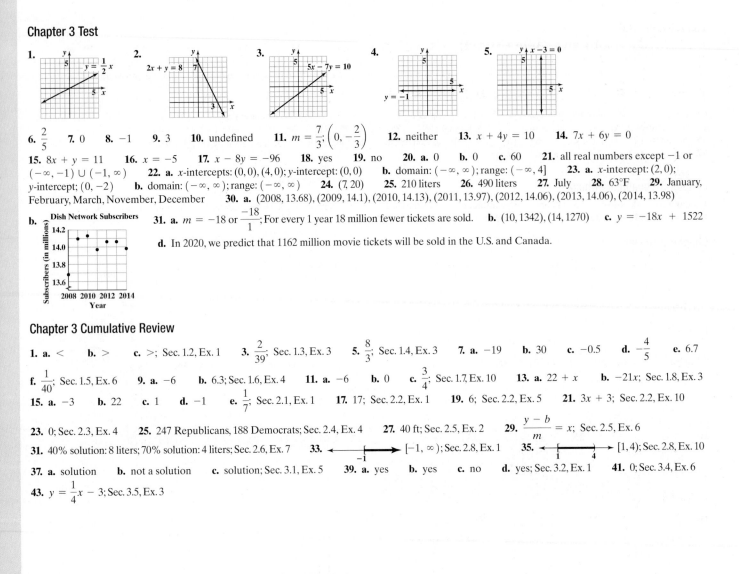

6. $\dfrac{2}{5}$ **7.** 0 **8.** -1 **9.** 3 **10.** undefined **11.** $m = \dfrac{7}{3}; \left(0, -\dfrac{2}{3}\right)$ **12.** neither **13.** $x + 4y = 10$ **14.** $7x + 6y = 0$

15. $8x + y = 11$ **16.** $x = -5$ **17.** $x - 8y = -96$ **18.** yes **19.** no **20. a.** 0 **b.** 0 **c.** 60 **21.** all real numbers except -1 or $(-\infty, -1) \cup (-1, \infty)$ **22. a.** x-intercepts: $(0, 0), (4, 0)$; y-intercept: $(0, 0)$ **b.** domain: $(-\infty, \infty)$; range: $(-\infty, 4]$ **23. a.** x-intercept: $(2, 0)$; y-intercept; $(0, -2)$ **b.** domain: $(-\infty, \infty)$; range: $(-\infty, \infty)$ **24.** $(7, 20)$ **25.** 210 liters **26.** 490 liters **27.** July **28.** 63°F **29.** January, February, March, November, December **30. a.** $(2008, 13.68), (2009, 14.1), (2010, 14.13), (2011, 13.97), (2012, 14.06), (2013, 14.06), (2014, 13.98)$

b. 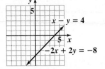 **31. a.** $m = -18$ or $\dfrac{-18}{1}$; For every 1 year 18 million fewer tickets are sold. **b.** $(10, 1342), (14, 1270)$ **c.** $y = -18x + 1522$

d. In 2020, we predict that 1162 million movie tickets will be sold in the U.S. and Canada.

Chapter 3 Cumulative Review

1. a. $<$ **b.** $>$ **c.** $>$; Sec. 1.2, Ex. 1 **3.** $\dfrac{2}{39}$; Sec. 1.3, Ex. 3 **5.** $\dfrac{8}{3}$; Sec. 1.4, Ex. 3 **7. a.** -19 **b.** 30 **c.** -0.5 **d.** $-\dfrac{4}{5}$ **e.** 6.7

f. $\dfrac{1}{40}$; Sec. 1.5, Ex. 6 **9. a.** -6 **b.** 6.3; Sec. 1.6, Ex. 4 **11. a.** -6 **b.** 0 **c.** $\dfrac{3}{4}$; Sec. 1.7, Ex. 10 **13. a.** $22 + x$ **b.** $-21x$; Sec. 1.8, Ex. 3

15. a. -3 **b.** 22 **c.** 1 **d.** -1 **e.** $\dfrac{1}{7}$; Sec. 2.1, Ex. 1 **17.** 17; Sec. 2.2, Ex. 1 **19.** 6; Sec. 2.2, Ex. 5 **21.** $3x + 3$; Sec. 2.2, Ex. 10

23. 0; Sec. 2.3, Ex. 4 **25.** 247 Republicans, 188 Democrats; Sec. 2.4, Ex. 4 **27.** 40 ft; Sec. 2.5, Ex. 2 **29.** $\dfrac{y - b}{m} = x$; Sec. 2.5, Ex. 6

31. 40% solution: 8 liters; 70% solution: 4 liters; Sec. 2.6, Ex. 7 **33.** $[-1, \infty)$; Sec. 2.8, Ex. 1 **35.** $[1, 4)$; Sec. 2.8, Ex. 10

37. a. solution **b.** not a solution **c.** solution; Sec. 3.1, Ex. 5 **39. a.** yes **b.** yes **c.** no **d.** yes; Sec. 3.2, Ex. 1 **41.** 0; Sec. 3.4, Ex. 6

43. $y = \dfrac{1}{4}x - 3$; Sec. 3.5, Ex. 3

CHAPTER 4 SOLVING SYSTEMS OF LINEAR EQUATIONS

Section 4.1

Practice Exercises

1. no **2.** yes **3.** $(8, 5)$ **4.** $(-3, -5)$ **5.** no solution; inconsistent system; $\{\ \}$ or $\varnothing$

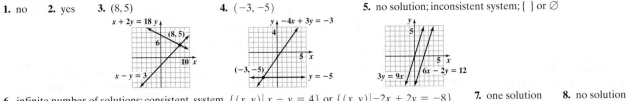

6. infinite number of solutions; consistent, system, $\{(x, y) \mid x - y = 4\}$ or $\{(x, y) \mid -2x + 2y = -8\}$ **7.** one solution **8.** no solution

Calculator Explorations 4.1

1. $(0.37, 0.23)$ **3.** $(0.03, -1.89)$

Vocabulary, Readiness & Video Check 4.1

1. dependent **3.** consistent **5.** inconsistent **7.** The ordered pair must satisfy all equations of the system in order to be a solution of the system, so we must check that the ordered pair is a solution of both equations. **9.** Writing the equations of a system in slope-intercept form lets you see their slope and y-intercept. Different slopes mean one solution; same slope with different y-intercepts means no solution; same slope with same y-intercept means infinite number of solutions.

Exercise Set 4.1

1. one solution, $(-1, 3)$ **3.** infinite number of solutions **5. a.** no **b.** yes **7. a.** yes **b.** no **9. a.** yes **b.** yes

11. a. no **b.** no **13.** **15.** **17.** **19.** **21.**

23. **25.** no solution; { } or ∅ **27.** **29.** **31.** no solution; { } or ∅

33. infinite number of solutions; $\{(x, y) \mid y - 3x = -2\}$ or $\{(x, y) \mid 6x - 2y = 4\}$ **35.** **37.** **39.**

41. infinite number of solutions; $\{(x, y) \mid 6x - y = 4\}$ or $\left\{(x, y) \mid \dfrac{1}{2} y = -2 + 3x\right\}$ **43. a.** intersecting; **b.** one solution **45. a.** parallel; **b.** no solution **47. a.** identical lines; **b.** infinite number of solutions **49. a.** intersecting; **b.** one solution **51. a.** intersecting; **b.** one solution **53. a.** identical lines; **b.** infinite number of solutions **55. a.** parallel; **b.** no solution **57.** 2 **59.** $-\dfrac{2}{5}$ **61.** 2

63. answers may vary; possible answer **65.** answers may vary; possible answer **67.** answers may vary **69.** 2009, 2010

71. 2006, 2007, 2012, 2013, 2014 **73.** answers may vary **75. a.** $(4, 9)$ **b.** **c.** yes **77.** answers may vary

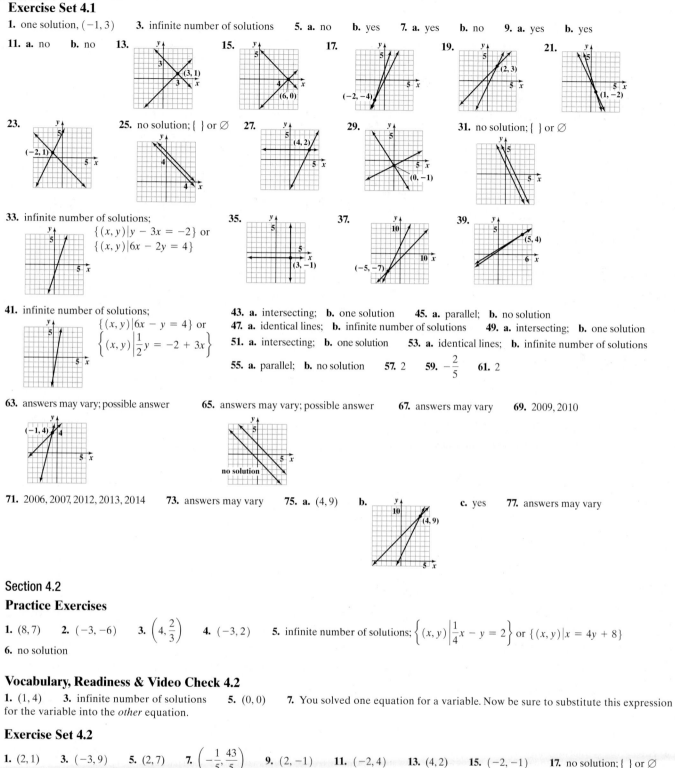

Section 4.2

Practice Exercises

1. $(8, 7)$ **2.** $(-3, -6)$ **3.** $\left(4, \dfrac{2}{3}\right)$ **4.** $(-3, 2)$ **5.** infinite number of solutions; $\left\{(x, y) \mid \dfrac{1}{4} x - y = 2\right\}$ or $\{(x, y) \mid x = 4y + 8\}$
6. no solution

Vocabulary, Readiness & Video Check 4.2

1. $(1, 4)$ **3.** infinite number of solutions **5.** $(0, 0)$ **7.** You solved one equation for a variable. Now be sure to substitute this expression for the variable into the *other* equation.

Exercise Set 4.2

1. $(2, 1)$ **3.** $(-3, 9)$ **5.** $(2, 7)$ **7.** $\left(-\dfrac{1}{5}, \dfrac{43}{5}\right)$ **9.** $(2, -1)$ **11.** $(-2, 4)$ **13.** $(4, 2)$ **15.** $(-2, -1)$ **17.** no solution; { } or ∅

19. $(3, -1)$ **21.** $(3, 5)$ **23.** $\left(\dfrac{2}{3}, -\dfrac{1}{3}\right)$ **25.** $(-1, -4)$ **27.** $(-6, 2)$ **29.** $(2, 1)$ **31.** no solution; { } or ∅ **33.** infinite number of

solutions; $\left\{(x, y) \mid \dfrac{1}{3} x - y = 2\right\}$ or $\{(x, y) \mid x - 3y = 6\}$ **35.** $\left(\dfrac{1}{2}, 2\right)$ **37.** $(1, -3)$ **39.** $-6x - 4y = -12$ **41.** $-12x + 3y = 9$ **43.** $5n$

45. $-15b$ **47.** answers may vary **49.** no; answers may vary **51.** **c**; answers may vary **53. a.** $(13, 492)$ **b.** In $1970 + 13 = 1983$, the number of men and women receiving bachelor's degrees was the same. **c.** answers may vary **55.** $(-2.6, 1.3)$ **57.** $(3.28, 2.11)$

Section 4.3

Practice Exercises

1. $(5, 3)$ **2.** $(3, -4)$ **3.** no solution; { } or $\varnothing$ **4.** infinite number of solutions; $\{(x, y) \mid 4x - 3y = 5\}$ or $\{(x, y) \mid -8x + 6y = -10\}$ **5.** $(2, 2)$
6. $\left(-\dfrac{8}{5}, \dfrac{6}{5}\right)$

Vocabulary, Readiness & Video Check 4.3

1. false   **3.** true   **5.** The multiplication property of equality; be sure to multiply *both* sides of the equation by the number chosen.

Exercise Set 4.3

1. $(1, 2)$ **3.** $(2, -3)$ **5.** $(-2, -5)$ **7.** $(5, -2)$ **9.** $(-7, 5)$ **11.** $(6, 0)$ **13.** no solution; { } or $\varnothing$ **15.** infinite number of solutions;
$\{(x, y) \mid -x + 5y = -1\}$ or $\{(x, y) \mid 3x - 15y = 3\}$ **17.** $\left(2, -\dfrac{1}{2}\right)$ **19.** $(-2, 0)$ **21.** $(1, -1)$ **23.** no solution; { } or $\varnothing$ **25.** $\left(\dfrac{12}{11}, -\dfrac{4}{11}\right)$
27. $\left(\dfrac{3}{2}, 3\right)$ **29.** infinite number of solutiotns; $\left\{(x, y) \,\middle|\, \dfrac{10}{3}x + 4y = -4\right\}$ or $\{(x, y) \mid 5x + 6y = -6\}$ **31.** $(1, 6)$ **33.** $\left(-\dfrac{1}{2}, -2\right)$ **35.** infinite
number of solutions; $\left\{(x, y) \,\middle|\, \dfrac{x}{3} - y = 2\right\}$ or $\left\{(x, y) \,\middle|\, -\dfrac{x}{2} + \dfrac{3y}{2} = -3\right\}$ **37.** $\left(-\dfrac{2}{3}, \dfrac{2}{5}\right)$ **39.** $(2, 4)$ **41.** $(-0.5, 2.5)$ **43.** $(2, 5)$
45. $(-3, 2)$ **47.** $(0, 3)$ **49.** $(5, 7)$ **51.** $\left(\dfrac{1}{3}, 1\right)$ **53.** infinite number of solutions; $\left\{(x, y) \,\middle|\, \dfrac{x + 2}{2} = \dfrac{y + 11}{3}\right\}$ or $\left\{(x, y) \,\middle|\, \dfrac{x}{2} = \left(\dfrac{2y + 16}{6}\right)\right\}$
55. $(-8.9, 10.6)$ **57.** $2x + 6 = x - 3$ **59.** $20 - 3x = 2$ **61.** $4(n + 6) = 2n$ **63.** $2; 6x - 2y = -24$ **65.** **b;** answers may vary
67. answers may vary   **69. a.** $b = 15$ **b.** any real number except 15   **71.** $(-4.2, 9.6)$ **73. a.** $(10, 67)$ or $(10, 68)$
b. In 2022 $(2012 + 10)$, the percent of workers age 20–24 and the percent of workers age 55–64 will be the same.   **c.** 67% or 68% of the workforce for each of these age groups

Integrated Review

1. $(2, 5)$ **2.** $(4, 2)$ **3.** $(5, -2)$ **4.** $(6, -14)$ **5.** $(-3, 2)$ **6.** $(-4, 3)$ **7.** $(0, 3)$ **8.** $(-2, 4)$ **9.** $(5, 7)$ **10.** $(-3, -23)$
11. $\left(\dfrac{1}{3}, 1\right)$ **12.** $\left(-\dfrac{1}{4}, 2\right)$ **13.** no solution; { } or $\varnothing$ **14.** infinite number of solutions; $\{(x, y) \mid -x + 2y = 3\}$ or $\{(x, y) \mid 3x - 6y = -9\}$
15. $(0.5, 3.5)$ **16.** $(-0.75, 1.25)$ **17.** infinite number of solutions; $\{(x, y) \mid x = 3y - 7\}$ or $\{(x, y) \mid 2x - 6y = -14\}$ **18.** no solution; { } or $\varnothing$
19. $(7, -3)$ **20.** $(-1, -3)$ **21.** answers may vary   **22.** answers may vary

Section 4.4

Practice Exercises

1. $(-1, 2, 1)$ **2.** { } or $\varnothing$ **3.** $\left(\dfrac{2}{3}, -\dfrac{1}{2}, 0\right)$ **4.** $\{(x, y, z) \mid 2x + y - 3z = 6\}$ **5.** $(6, 15, -5)$

Vocabulary, Readiness & Video Check 4.4

1. a, b, d   **3.** yes; answers may vary   **5.** Once we have one equation in two variables, we need to get another equation in the *same* two variables, giving us a system of two equations in two variables. We solve this new system to find the value of two variables. We then substitute these values into an original equation to find the value of the third.

Exercise Set 4.4

1. $(-1, 5, 2)$ **3.** $(-2, 5, 1)$ **5.** $(-2, 3, -1)$ **7.** $\{(x, y, z) \mid x - 2y + z = -5\}$ **9.** $\varnothing$ **11.** $(0, 0, 0)$ **13.** $(-3, -35, -7)$
15. $(6, 22, -20)$ **17.** $\varnothing$ **19.** $(3, 2, 2)$ **21.** $\{(x, y, z) \mid x + 2y - 3z = 4\}$ **23.** $(-3, -4, -5)$ **25.** $\left(0, \dfrac{1}{2}, -4\right)$ **27.** $(12, 6, 4)$
29. 15 and 30   **31.** 5   **33.** $-\dfrac{5}{3}$ **35.** answers may vary   **37.** answers may vary   **39.** $(1, 1, -1)$ **41.** $(1, 1, 0, 2)$
43. $(1, -1, 2, 3)$ **45.** answers may vary

Section 4.5

Practice Exercises

1. a. 2017   **b.** yes; answers may vary   **2.** 18, 12   **3.** 17 and 12   **4. a.** Adult: $19   **b.** Child: $6   **c.** No, the regular rates are less than the group rate   **5.** Atlantique: 500 kph; V150: 575 kph   **6.** 0.95 liter of water; 0.05 liter of 99% HCl   **7.** 1500 packages   **8.** $40°, 60°, 80°$

Vocabulary, Readiness & Video Check 4.5

1. Up to now we've been choosing one variable/unknown and translating to one equation. To solve by a system of equations, we'll choose two variables to represent two unknowns and translate to two equations.   **3.** The ordered triple still needs to be interpreted in the context of the application. Each value actually represents the angle measure of a triangle, in degrees.

Exercise Set 4.5

1. c   **3.** b   **5.** a   **7.** $\begin{cases} x + y = 15 \\ x - y = 7 \end{cases}$ **9.** $\begin{cases} x + y = 6500 \\ x = y + 800 \end{cases}$ **11.** 33 and 50   **13.** 10 and 8   **15.** 14 and -3 **17.** Gonzalez: 116; Trout: 111
19. child's ticket: $18; adult's ticket: $29   **21.** quarters: 53; nickels: 27   **23.** McDonald's: $99.50; The Ohio Art Company: $7.50   **25.** daily fee: $32;
mileage charge: $0.25 per mi   **27.** distance downstream = distance upstream = 18 mi; time downstream: 2 hr; time upstream: $4\dfrac{1}{2}$ hr; still water: 6.5 mph;

current: 2.5 mph **29.** still air: 455 mph; wind: 65 mph **31.** $4\frac{1}{2}$ hr **33.** 12% solution: $7\frac{1}{2}$ liters; 4% solution: $4\frac{1}{2}$ liters **35.** \$4.95 beans: 113 lb;

\$2.65 beans: 87 lb **37.** $60°, 30°$ **39.** $20°, 70°$ **41.** number sold at \$9.50: 23; number sold at \$7.50: 67 **43.** $2\frac{1}{4}$ mph and $2\frac{3}{4}$ mph

45. 30%: 50 gal; 60%: 100 gal **47.** length: 42 in.; width: 30 in. **49. a.** answers may vary **b.** 2008 **51. a.** 2012 **b.** answers may vary
53. $x = 75; y = 105$ **55.** 625 units **57.** 3000 units **59.** 1280 units **61. a.** $R(x) = 450x$ **b.** $C(x) = 200x + 6000$ **c.** 24 desks
63. 2 units of Mix A; 3 units of Mix B; 1 unit of Mix C **65.** 5 in.; 7 in.; 7 in.; 10 in. **67.** 18, 13, and 9 **69.** free throws; 703 2-pt field goals;

657 3-pt fields goals; 192 **71.** $x = 60; y = 55; z = 65$ **73.** $(3, \infty)$ **75.** $\left[\frac{1}{2}, \infty\right)$ **77.** a **79.** width: 9 ft; length: 15 ft **81.** $a = 3, b = 4, c = -1$

83. $a = 0.5, b = 24.5, c = 849$; 2015: 1774 thousand students **85.** $(10, 13)$

Chapter 4 Vocabulary Check

1. dependent **2.** system of linear equations **3.** consistent **4.** solution **5.** addition; substitution **6.** inconsistent **7.** independent

Chapter 4 Review

1. a. no **b.** yes **c.** no **3. a.** no **b.** no **c.** yes **5.** **7.** **9.**

11. no solution; $\{ \ \}$ or $\varnothing$ **13.** $(-1, 4)$ **15.** $(3, -2)$ **17.** infinite number of solutions; $\{(x, y) | 4y = 2x + 6\}$ or $\{(x, y) | x - 2y = -3\}$
19. no solution; $\{ \ \}$ or $\varnothing$ **21.** $(-6, 2)$ **23.** $(3, 7)$

25. infinite number of solutions; $\{(x, y) | 2x - 6y = -1\}$ or $\left\{(x, y) \middle| -x + 3y = \frac{1}{2}\right\}$ **27.** $(8, -6)$ **29.** $(2, 0, 2)$ **31.** $\left(-\frac{1}{2}, \frac{3}{4}, 1\right)$ **33.** $\varnothing$
35. $(1, 1, -2)$ **37.** -6 and 22 **39.** current of river: 3.2 mph; speed in still water: 21.1 mph **41.** egg: \$0.40; strip of bacon: \$0.65
43. 17 pennies; 20 nickels; 16 dimes **45.** two sides: 22 cm each; third side: 29 cm

47. **49.** $(3, 2)$ **51.** $\left(1\frac{1}{2}, -3\right)$ **53.** infinite number of solutions; $\{(x, y) | 3x - y = 4\}$ or $\{(x, y) | 4y = 12x - 16\}$ **55.** $(-5, 2)$
57. $(-1, 3, 5)$ **59.** 4 and 8 **61.** 24 nickels and 41 dimes **63.** 28 units, 42 units, 56 units

Chapter 4 Getting Ready for the Test

1. B **2.** C **3.** B **4.** A **5.** D **6.** B **7.** D **8.** C **9.** B **10.** B **11.** A **12.** C

Chapter 4 Test

1. false **2.** false **3.** true **4.** false **5.** no **6.** yes

7. $(-4, 2)$ **8.** $(-4, 1)$ **9.** $\left(\frac{1}{2}, -2\right)$ **10.** $(4, -2)$ **11.** no solution; $\{ \ \}$ or $\varnothing$ **12.** $(4, -5)$ **13.** $(7, 2)$
14. $(5, -2)$ **15.** 78, 46 **16.** 120 cc **17.** Texas: 248 thousand; Missouri: 108 thousand
18. 3 mph; 6 mph **19.** $(-1, -2, 4)$ **20.** $\varnothing$ **21.** $23°, 45°, 112°$

Chapter 4 Cumulative Review

1. a. $<$ **b.** $=$ **c.** $>$; Sec. 1.2, Ex. 6 **3. a.** commutative property of multiplication **b.** associative property of addition
c. identity element for addition **d.** commutative property of multiplication **e.** multiplicative inverse property **f.** additive inverse
property **g.** commutative and associative properties of multiplication; Sec. 1.8, Ex. 6 **5.** $-2x - 1$; Sec. 2.1, Ex. 7 **7.** 8; Sec. 2.2, Ex. 4

9. 6; Sec. 2.2, Ex. 5 **11.** 12; Sec. 2.3, Ex. 3 **13.** 10; Sec. 2.4, Ex. 2 **15.** $x = \dfrac{y - b}{m}$; Sec. 2.5, Ex. 6 **17.** $[2, \infty)$; Sec. 2.8, Ex. 3

19. ; Sec. 3.3, Ex. 7 **21.** $-\dfrac{8}{3}$; Sec. 3.4, Ex. 1 **23.** slope: $\dfrac{3}{4}$; y-intercept: $(0, 6)$; Sec. 3.4, Ex. 3 **25.** slope: $\dfrac{3}{4}$; y-intercept: $(0, -1)$;
Sec. 3.4, Ex. 5 **27.** $y = -2x + 3$; $2x + y = 3$; Sec. 3.5, Ex. 4 **29.** $x = -1$; Sec. 3.5, Ex. 6
31. domain: $\{-1, 0, 3\}$; range: $\{-2, 0, 2, 3\}$; Sec. 3.6, Ex. 1 **33. a.** function **b.** not a function; Sec. 3.6, Ex. 2
35. one solution; Sec. 4.1, Ex. 8 **37.** $\left(6, \dfrac{1}{2}\right)$; Sec. 4.2, Ex. 3 **39.** $(6, 1)$; Sec. 4.3, Ex. 1 **41.** $(-4, 2, -1)$;
Sec. 4.4, Ex. 1 **43.** 7 and 11; Sec. 4.5, Ex. 3

CHAPTER 5 EXPONENTS AND POLYNOMIALS

Section 5.1

Practice Exercises

1. a. 27 **b.** 4 **c.** 64 **d.** -64 **e.** $\dfrac{27}{64}$ **f.** 0.0081 **g.** 75 **2. a.** 243 **b.** $\dfrac{3}{8}$ **3. a.** 3^{10} **b.** y^5 **c.** z^5 **d.** x^{11} **e.** $(-2)^8$

f. $b^3 \cdot t^5$ **4.** $15y^7$ **5. a.** $y^{12}z^4$ **b.** $-7m^5n^{14}$ **6. a.** z^{21} **b.** 4^{18} **c.** $(-2)^{15}$ **7. a.** p^5r^5 **b.** $36b^2$ **c.** $\dfrac{1}{64}x^6y^3$ **d.** $81a^{12}b^{16}c^4$

8. a. $\dfrac{x^5}{y^{10}}$ **b.** $\dfrac{32a^{20}}{b^{15}}$ **9. a.** z^4 **b.** 25 **c.** 64 **d.** $\dfrac{q^5}{t^2}$ **e.** $6x^2y^2$ **10. a.** -1 **b.** 1 **c.** 1 **d.** 1 **e.** 1 **f.** 7 **11. a.** $\dfrac{z^2}{144}$

b. $64x^{18}$ **c.** y^{13} **12. a.** 63 **b.** 2 **c.** $\dfrac{x^6}{9y^8}$ **d.** $-z^{30}$

Vocabulary, Readiness & Video Check 5.1

1. exponent **3.** add **5.** 1 **7.** Example 4 can be written as $-4^2 = -1 \cdot 4^2$, which is similar to Example 7, $4 \cdot 3^2$, and shows why the negative sign should not be considered part of the base when there are no parentheses. **9.** Be careful not to confuse the power rule with the product rule. The power rule involves a power raised to a power (exponents are multiplied), and the product rule involves a product (exponents are added). **11.** the quotient rule

Exercise Set 5.1

1. exponent: 2; base: 3 **3.** exponent: 2; base: 4 **5.** exponent: 2; base: x **7.** 49 **9.** -5 **11.** -16 **13.** 16 **15.** 0.00001 **17.** $\dfrac{1}{81}$

19. 224 **21.** -250 **23.** 4 **25.** 135 **27.** 150 **29.** $\dfrac{32}{5}$ **31.** x^7 **33.** $(-3)^{12}$ **35.** $15y^5$ **37.** $x^{19}y^6$ **39.** $-72m^3n^8$ **41.** $-24z^{20}$

43. $20x^5$ sq ft **45.** x^{36} **47.** p^8q^8 **49.** $8a^{15}$ **51.** $x^{10}y^{15}$ **53.** $49a^4b^{10}c^2$ **55.** $\dfrac{r^9}{s^9}$ **57.** $\dfrac{m^5p^5}{n^5}$ **59.** $\dfrac{4x^2z^2}{y^{10}}$ **61.** $64z^{10}$ sq dm

63. $27y^{12}$ cu ft **65.** x^2 **67.** -64 **69.** p^6q^5 **71.** $\dfrac{y^3}{2}$ **73.** 1 **75.** 1 **77.** -7 **79.** 2 **81.** -81 **83.** $\dfrac{1}{64}$ **85.** b^6 **87.** a^9

89. $-16x^7$ **91.** $a^{11}b^{20}$ **93.** $26m^9n^7$ **95.** z^{40} **97.** $64a^3b^3$ **99.** $36x^2y^2z^6$ **101.** $3x$ **103.** $81x^2y^2$ **105.** 9 **107.** $\dfrac{y^{15}}{8x^{12}}$ **109.** $2x^2y$

111. 2 **113.** $\dfrac{x^{18}}{4y^{22}}$ **115.** $-b^5$ **117.** $2y - 10$ **119.** $-x - 4$ **121.** $-x + 5$ **123.** C **125.** E **127.** answers may vary

129. answers may vary **131.** 343 cu m **133.** volume **135.** answers may vary **137.** answers may vary **139.** x^{9a} **141.** a^{5b} **143.** x^{5a}
145. \$1045.85

Section 5.2

Practice Exercises

1. a. degree 3 **b.** degree 2 **c.** degree 1 **d.** degree 8 **e.** degree 0 **2. a.** trinomial, degree 2 **b.** binomial, degree 1 **c.** none of these, degree 3
3.

Term	Numerical Coefficient	Degree of Term
$-3x^3y^2$	-3	5
$4xy^2$	4	3
$-y^2$	-1	2
$3x$	3	1
-2	-2	0

4. a. 4 **b.** -21 **5.** 114 ft; 66 ft **6. a.** $-2y$ **b.** $z + 5z^3$ **c.** $14x^3$ **d.** $4a^2 - 12$ **e.** $\dfrac{1}{3}x^4 + \dfrac{11}{24}x^3 - x^2$ **7.** $-3x^2 + 5xy + 5y^2$ **8.** $x^2 + 2x + 4 + 5x + 3x^2$; $4x^2 + 7x + 4$ **9. a.** $5y^2 - 3y + 2x - 9$ **b.** $-8a^2b - 3ab^2$ **10.** $7x^3 - 6x + 7$ **11.** $2x^3 - 4x^2 + 4x - 6$ **12.** $7x - 11$ **13. a.** $-5a^2 - ab + 6b^2$ **b.** $3x^2y^2 - 10xy - 4xy^2 + 5 - 6y^2$

Graphing Calculator Explorations 5.2

1. $x^3 - 4x^2 + 7x - 8$ **3.** $-2.1x^2 - 3.2x - 1.7$ **5.** $7.69x^2 - 1.26x + 5.3$

Vocabulary, Readiness & Video Check 5.2

1. binomial **3.** trinomial **5.** constant **7.** The degree of the polynomial is the greatest degree of any of its terms, so we need to find the degree of each term first. **9.** simplifying it

Exercise Set 5.2

1. 1; binomial **3.** 3; none of these **5.** 6; trinomial **7.** 8; binomial **9.** 3 **11.** 2 **13.** 57 **15.** 499 **17.** 1 **19.** $-\dfrac{11}{16}$ **21.** 1134 ft

23. 1006 ft **25.** 2280 thousand **27.** $23x^2$ **29.** $12x^2 - y$ **31.** $7s$ **33.** $-1.1y^2 + 4.8$ **35.** $-\dfrac{7}{12}x^3 + \dfrac{7}{5}x^2 + 6$ **37.** $5a^2 - 9ab + 16b^2$

39. $-3x^2 + 10$ **41.** $-x^2 + 14$ **43.** $-2x + 9$ **45.** $2x^2 + 7x - 16$ **47.** $8t^2 - 4$ **49.** $-2z^2 - 16z + 6$ **51.** $2x^3 - 2x^2 + 7x + 2$
53. $-y^2 - 3y - 1$ **55.** $2x^2 + 11x$ **57.** $-16x^4 + 8x + 9$ **59.** $7x^2 + 14x + 18$ **61.** $3x - 3$ **63.** $7x^2 - 4x + 2$ **65.** $62x^2 + 5$
67. $7x^2 - 2x + 2$ **69.** $12x + 2$ **71.** $4y^2 + 12y + 19$ **73.** $4x^2 + 7x + x^2 + 5x$; $5x^2 + 12x$ **75.** $-2a - b + 1$ **77.** $3x^2 + 5$
79. $6x^2 - 2xy + 19y^2$ **81.** $8r^2s + 16rs - 8 + 7r^2s^2$ **83.** $-5.42x^2 + 7.75x - 19.61$ **85.** $3.7y^4 - 0.7y^3 + 2.2y - 4$ **87.** $6x^2$ **89.** $-12x^8$
91. $200x^3y^2$ **93.** $18x + 44$ **95.** $(x^2 + 7x + 4)$ ft **97.** $(3y^2 + 4y + 11)$ m **99.** 3071 million users **101.** answers may vary
103. answers may vary **105.** B **107.** E **109. a.** $4z$ **b.** $3z^2$ **c.** $-4z$ **d.** $3z^2$; answers may vary **111. a.** m^3 **b.** $3m$ **c.** $-m^3$
d. $-3m$; answers may vary **113.** $3x^{2a} + 2x^a + 0.7$ **115.** $4x^{2y} + 2x^y - 11$ **117.** $4x^2 - 3x + 6$ **119.** $-x^2 - 6x + 10$ **121.** $3x^2 - 12x + 13$
123. a. $2a - 3$ **b.** $-2x - 3$ **c.** $2x + 2h - 3$ **125. a.** $4a$ **b.** $-4x$ **c.** $4x + 4h$ **127.** 2; 2 **129.** 4; 3; 3; 4 **131.** $2x^2 + 4xy$

Section 5.3
Practice Exercises

1. $10y^2$ **2.** $-2z^8$ **3.** $\frac{7}{72}b^9$ **4. a.** $27x^6 + 33x$ **b.** $-12x^5 + 54x^4 - 12x^3$ **5.** $10x^2 + 11x - 6$ **6.** $25x^2 - 30xy + 9y^2$
7. $2y^3 + 5y^2 - 7y + 20$ **8.** $s^3 + 6s^2t + 12st^2 + 8t^3$ **9.** $5x^3 - 23x^2 + 17x - 20$ **10.** $x^5 - 2x^4 + 2x^3 - 3x^2 + 2$
11. $5x^4 - 3x^3 + 11x^2 + 8x - 6$

Vocabulary, Readiness & Video Check 5.3

1. c. distributive   **3. c.** $(5y - 1)(5y - 1)$ **5.** No. The monomials are unlike terms.   **7.** Yes. The parentheses have been removed for the vertical format, but every term in the first polynomial is still distributed to every term in the second polynomial.

Exercise Set 5.3

1. $-28n^{10}$ **3.** $-12.4x^{12}$ **5.** $-\frac{2}{15}y^3$ **7.** $-24x^8$ **9.** $6x^2 + 15x$ **11.** $-2a^2 - 8a$ **13.** $6x^3 - 9x^2 + 12x$ **15.** $-6a^4 + 4a^3 - 6a^2$
17. $-4x^3y + 7x^2y^2 - xy^3 - 3y^4$ **19.** $4x^4 - 3x^3 + \frac{1}{2}x^2$ **21.** $x^2 + 7x + 12$ **23.** $a^2 + 5a - 14$ **25.** $x^2 + \frac{1}{3}x - \frac{2}{9}$ **27.** $12x^4 + 25x^2 + 7$
29. $4y^2 - 16y + 16$ **31.** $12x^2 - 29x + 15$ **33.** $9x^4 + 6x^2 + 1$ **35. a.** $-4y^4$ **b.** $3y^2$ **c.** answers may vary   **37.** $x^3 - 5x^2 + 13x - 14$
39. $x^4 + 5x^3 - 3x^2 - 11x + 20$ **41.** $10a^3 - 27a^2 + 26a - 12$ **43.** $x^3 + 6x^2 + 12x + 8$ **45.** $8y^3 - 36y^2 + 54y - 27$
47. $12x^2 - 64x - 11$ **49.** $10x^3 + 22x^2 - x - 1$ **51.** $2x^4 + 3x^3 - 58x^2 + 4x + 63$ **53.** $8.4y^7$ **55.** $-3x^3 - 6x^2 + 24x$
57. $2x^2 + 39x + 19$ **59.** $x^2 - \frac{2}{7}x - \frac{3}{49}$ **61.** $9y^2 + 30y + 25$ **63.** $a^3 - 2a^2 - 18a + 24$ **65.** $8x^3 - 60x^2 + 150x - 125$
67. $32x^3 + 48x^2 - 6x - 20$ **69.** $6x^4 - 8x^3 - 7x^2 + 22x - 12$ **71.** $(4x^2 - 25)$ sq yd   **73.** $(6x^2 - 4x)$ sq in.
75. $5a + 15a = 20a; 5a - 15a = -10a; 5a \cdot 15a = 75a^2; \frac{5a}{15a} = \frac{1}{3}$ **77.** $-3y^5 + 9y^4$, can't be simplified; $-3y^5 - 9y^4$, can't be simplified;
$-3y^5 \cdot 9y^4 = -27y^9; \frac{-3y^5}{9y^4} = -\frac{y}{3}$ **79. a.** $6x + 12$ **b.** $9x^2 + 36x + 35$; answers may vary   **81.** $13x - 7$ **83.** $30x^2 - 28x + 6$
85. $-7x + 5$ **87.** $x^2 + 3x$ **89.** $x^2 + 5x + 6$ **91.** $11a$ **93.** $25x^2 + 4y^2$ **95. a.** $a^2 - b^2$ **b.** $4x^2 - 9y^2$ **c.** $16x^2 - 49$
d. answers may vary   **97.** $(x^2 + 6x + 5)$ sq units

Section 5.4
Practice Exercises

1. $x^2 - 3x - 10$ **2.** $4x^2 - 13x + 9$ **3.** $9x^2 + 42x - 15$ **4.** $16x^2 - 8x + 1$ **5. a.** $b^2 + 6b + 9$ **b.** $x^2 - 2xy + y^2$
c. $9y^2 + 12y + 4$ **d.** $a^4 - 10a^2b + 25b^2$ **6. a.** $3x^2 - 75$ **b.** $16b^2 - 9$ **c.** $x^2 - \frac{4}{9}$ **d.** $25s^2 - t^2$ **e.** $4y^2 - 9z^4$
7. a. $4x^2 - 21x - 18$ **b.** $49b^2 - 28b + 4$ **c.** $x^2 - 0.16$ **d.** $3x^6 - \frac{9}{7}x^4 + \frac{2}{7}x^2 - \frac{6}{49}$ **e.** $x^3 + 6x^2 + 3x - 2$

Vocabulary, Readiness & Video Check 5.4

1. false   **3.** false   **5.** a binomial times a binomial   **7.** Multiplying gives you four terms, and the two like terms will always subtract out.

Exercise Set 5.4

1. $x^2 + 7x + 12$ **3.** $x^2 + 5x - 50$ **5.** $5x^2 + 4x - 12$ **7.** $20y^2 - 125y + 30$ **9.** $6x^2 + 13x - 5$ **11.** $x^2 + \frac{1}{3}x - \frac{2}{9}$ **13.** $x^2 + 4x + 4$
15. $4x^2 - 4x + 1$ **17.** $9a^2 - 30a + 25$ **19.** $25x^2 + 90x + 81$ **21.** $a^2 - 49$ **23.** $9x^2 - 1$ **25.** $9x^2 - \frac{1}{4}$ **27.** $81x^2 - y^2$
29. $4x^2 - 0.01$ **31.** $a^2 + 9a + 20$ **33.** $a^2 + 14a + 49$ **35.** $12a^2 - a - 1$ **37.** $x^2 - 4$ **39.** $9a^2 + 6a + 1$ **41.** $4x^3 - x^2y^4 + 4xy - y^5$
43. $x^3 - 3x^2 - 17x + 3$ **45.** $4a^2 - 12a + 9$ **47.** $25x^2 - 36z^2$ **49.** $x^{10} - 8x^5 + 15$ **51.** $x^2 - 0.64$ **53.** $a^7 + 11a^4 - 3a^3 - 33$
55. $3x^2 - 12x + 12$ **57.** $6b^2 - b - 35$ **59.** $49p^2 - 64$ **61.** $\frac{1}{9}a^4 - 49$ **63.** $15x^4 - 5x^3 + 10x^2$ **65.** $4r^2 - 9s^2$
67. $9x^2 - 42xy + 49y^2$ **69.** $16x^2 - 25$ **71.** $64x^2 + 64x + 16$ **73.** $a^2 - \frac{1}{4}y^2$ **75.** $\frac{1}{25}x^2 - y^2$ **77.** $3a^3 + 2a^2 + 1$
79. $(2x + 1)(2x + 1)$ sq ft or $(4x^2 + 4x + 1)$ sq ft   **81.** $\frac{5b^5}{7}$ **83.** $-2a^{10}b^5$ **85.** $\frac{2y^8}{3}$ **87.** $\frac{1}{3}$ **89.** 1 **91.** C   **93.** D   **95.** 2; 2
97. $(x^4 - 3x^2 + 1)$ sq m   **99.** $(24x^2 - 32x + 8)$ sq m   **101.** $(x^2 + 10x + 25)$ sq units   **103.** answers may vary   **105.** answers may vary
107. answers may vary   **109.** $x^2 + 2xy + y^2 - 9$ **111.** $a^2 - 6a + 9 - b^2$

Integrated Review

1. $35x^5$ **2.** $32y^9$ **3.** -16 **4.** 16 **5.** $2x^2 - 9x - 5$ **6.** $3x^2 + 13x - 10$ **7.** $3x - 4$ **8.** $4x + 3$ **9.** $7x^6y^2$ **10.** $\frac{10b^6}{7}$
11. $144m^{14}n^{12}$ **12.** $64y^{27}z^{30}$ **13.** $48y^2 - 27$ **14.** $98x^2 - 2$ **15.** $x^{63}y^{45}$ **16.** $27x^{27}$ **17.** $2x^2 - 2x - 6$ **18.** $6x^2 + 13x - 11$
19. $2.5y^2 - 6y - 0.2$ **20.** $8.4x^2 - 6.8x - 5.7$ **21.** $x^2 + 8xy + 16y^2$ **22.** $y^2 - 18yz + 81z^2$ **23.** $2x + 8y$ **24.** $2y - 18z$
25. $7x^2 - 10xy + 4y^2$ **26.** $-a^2 - 3ab + 6b^2$ **27.** $x^3 + 2x^2 - 16x + 3$ **28.** $x^3 - 2x^2 - 5x - 2$ **29.** $6x^5 + 20x^3 - 21x^2 - 70$
30. $20x^7 + 25x^3 - 4x^4 - 5$ **31.** $2x^3 - 19x^2 + 44x - 7$ **32.** $5x^3 + 9x^2 - 17x + 3$ **33.** cannot simplify   **34.** $25x^3y^3$ **35.** $125x^9$
36. $\frac{x^3}{y^3}$ **37.** $2x$ **38.** x^2

Section 5.5

Practice Exercises

1. a. $\dfrac{1}{125}$ **b.** $\dfrac{3}{y^4}$ **c.** $\dfrac{5}{6}$ **d.** $\dfrac{1}{25}$ **e.** $\dfrac{1}{x^5}$ **2. a.** s^5 **b.** 8 **c.** $\dfrac{y^5}{x^7}$ **d.** $\dfrac{9}{64}$ **3. a.** $\dfrac{1}{x^5}$ **b.** $5y^7$ **c.** z^5 **d.** $\dfrac{81}{25}$ **4. a.** $\dfrac{b^{15}}{a^{20}}$

b. x^{10} **c.** $\dfrac{q^2}{25p^{16}}$ **d.** $\dfrac{6y^2}{x^7}$ **e.** $-27x^6y^9$ **5. a.** 7×10^{-6} **b.** 2.07×10^7 **c.** 4.3×10^{-3} **d.** 8.12×10^8 **6. a.** 0.000367

b. 8,954,000 **c.** 0.00002009 **d.** 4054 **7. a.** 4000 **b.** 20,000,000,000

Calculator Explorations 5.5

1. 5.31 EE 3 **3.** 6.6 EE −9 **5.** 1.5×10^{13} **7.** 8.15×10^{19}

Vocabulary, Readiness & Video Check 5.5

1. b. $\dfrac{1}{x^3}$ **3. c.** scientific notation **5.** A negative exponent has nothing to do with the sign of the simplified result. **7.** When you move the decimal point to the left, the sign of the exponent will be positive; when you move the decimal point to the right, the sign of the exponent will be negative.
9. the quotient rule

Exercise Set 5.5

1. $\dfrac{1}{64}$ **3.** $\dfrac{1}{81}$ **5.** $\dfrac{7}{x^3}$ **7.** 32 **9.** −64 **11.** $\dfrac{8}{15}$ **13.** p^3 **15.** $\dfrac{q^4}{p^5}$ **17.** $\dfrac{1}{x^3}$ **19.** z^3 **21.** $\dfrac{4}{9}$ **23.** $-p^4$ **25.** −2 **27.** x^4

29. p^4 **31.** m^{11} **33.** r^6 **35.** $\dfrac{1}{x^{15}y^9}$ **37.** $\dfrac{1}{x^4}$ **39.** $\dfrac{1}{a^2}$ **41.** $4k^3$ **43.** $3m$ **45.** $-\dfrac{4a^5}{b}$ **47.** $-\dfrac{6x^2}{y^3}$ **49.** $\dfrac{a^{30}}{b^{12}}$ **51.** $\dfrac{1}{x^{10}y^6}$

53. $\dfrac{z^2}{4}$ **55.** $\dfrac{1}{32x^5}$ **57.** $\dfrac{49a^4}{b^6}$ **59.** $a^{24}b^8$ **61.** x^9y^{19} **63.** $-\dfrac{y^8}{8x^2}$ **65.** $-\dfrac{6x}{7y^2}$ **67.** $\dfrac{25b^{33}}{a^{16}}$ **69.** 7.8×10^4 **71.** 1.67×10^{-6}

73. 6.35×10^{-3} **75.** 1.16×10^6 **77.** 2×10^9 **79.** 2.4×10^3 **81.** 0.0000000008673 **83.** 0.033 **85.** 20,320 **87.** 700,000,000
89. 9,460,000,000,000 **91.** $\$7.14 \times 10^{11}$ **93.** \$863,000,000,000 **95.** \$47,000 **97.** 0.000036 **99.** 0.0000000000000000028 **101.** 0.0000005
103. 200,000 **105.** $\dfrac{5x^3}{3}$ **107.** $\dfrac{5z^3y^2}{7}$ **109.** $5y - 6 + \dfrac{5}{y}$ **111.** $\dfrac{27}{x^6z^3}$ cu in. **113.** $9a^{13}$ **115.** −5 **117.** answers may vary
119. a. 1.3×10^1 **b.** 4.4×10^7 **c.** 6.1×10^{-2} **121.** answers may vary **123.** a^m **125.** $27y^{6z}$ **127.** −394.5 **129.** 1.3 sec

Section 5.6

Practice Exercises

1. $2t + 1$ **2.** $4x^4 + 5x - \dfrac{3}{x}$ **3.** $3x^3y^3 - 2 + \dfrac{1}{5x}$ **4.** $x + 3$ **5.** $2x + 3 + \dfrac{-10}{2x + 1}$ or $2x + 3 - \dfrac{10}{2x + 1}$ **6.** $3x^2 - 2x + 5 + \dfrac{-13}{3x + 2}$ or

$3x^2 - 2x + 5 - \dfrac{13}{3x + 2}$ **7.** $3x^2 - 2x - 9 + \dfrac{5x + 22}{x^2 + 2}$ **8.** $x^2 - 3x + 9$

Vocabulary, Readiness & Video Check 5.6

1. dividend, quotient, divisor **3.** a^2 **5.** y **7.** the common denominator

Exercise Set 5.6

1. $12x^3 + 3x$ **3.** $4x^3 - 6x^2 + x + 1$ **5.** $5p^2 + 6p$ **7.** $-\dfrac{3}{2x} + 3$ **9.** $-3x^2 + x - \dfrac{4}{x^3}$ **11.** $-1 + \dfrac{3}{2x} - \dfrac{7}{4x^4}$ **13.** $x + 1$ **15.** $2x + 3$

17. $2x + 1 + \dfrac{7}{x - 4}$ **19.** $3a^2 - 3a + 1 + \dfrac{2}{3a + 2}$ **21.** $4x + 3 - \dfrac{2}{2x + 1}$ **23.** $2x^2 + 6x - 5 - \dfrac{2}{x - 2}$ **25.** $x + 6$ **27.** $x^2 + 3x + 9$

29. $-3x + 6 - \dfrac{11}{x + 2}$ **31.** $2b - 1 - \dfrac{6}{2b - 1}$ **33.** $ab - b^2$ **35.** $4x + 9$ **37.** $x + 4xy - \dfrac{y}{2}$ **39.** $2b^2 + b + 2 - \dfrac{12}{b + 4}$

41. $5x - 2 + \dfrac{2}{x + 6}$ **43.** $x^2 - \dfrac{12x}{5} - 1$ **45.** $6x - 1 - \dfrac{1}{x + 3}$ **47.** $6x - 1$ **49.** $-x^3 + 3x^2 - \dfrac{4}{x}$ **51.** $x^2 + 3x + 9$

53. $y^2 + 5y + 10 + \dfrac{24}{y - 2}$ **55.** $-6x - 12 - \dfrac{19}{x - 2}$ **57.** $x^3 - x^2 + x$ **59.** $2a^3 + 2a$ **61.** $2x^3 + 14x^2 - 10x$ **63.** $-3x^2y^3 - 21x^3y^2 - 24xy$
65. $9a^2b^3c + 36ab^2c - 72ab$ **67.** $(3x^3 + x - 4)$ ft **69.** c **71.** answers may vary **73.** $(2x + 5)$ m **75.** $9x^{7a} - 6x^{5a} + 7x^{2a} - 1$

Section 5.7

Practice Exercises

1. $4x^2 + x + 7 + \dfrac{12}{x - 1}$ **2.** $x^3 - 5x + 21 - \dfrac{51}{x + 3}$ **3. a.** −4 **b.** −4 **4.** 15

Vocabulary, Readiness & Video Check 5.7

1. The last number n is the remainder and the other numbers are the coefficients of the variables in the quotient; the degree of the quotient is one less than the degree of the dividend

Exercise Set 5.7

1. $x + 8$ **3.** $x - 1$ **5.** $x^2 - 5x - 23 - \dfrac{41}{x - 2}$ **7.** $4x + 8 + \dfrac{7}{x - 2}$ **9.** 3 **11.** 73 **13.** −8 **15.** $x^2 + \dfrac{2}{x - 3}$ **17.** $6x + 7 + \dfrac{1}{x + 1}$

19. $2x^3 - 3x^2 + x - 4$ **21.** $3x - 9 + \dfrac{12}{x+3}$ **23.** $3x^2 - \dfrac{9}{2}x + \dfrac{7}{4} + \dfrac{47}{8\left(x - \frac{1}{2}\right)}$ **25.** $3x^2 + 3x - 3$ **27.** $3x^2 + 4x - 8 + \dfrac{20}{x+1}$

29. $x^2 + x + 1$ **31.** $2x^2 - 3 - \dfrac{2}{x+6}$ **33.** 1   **35.** -133 **37.** 3   **39.** $-\dfrac{187}{81}$ **41.** $\dfrac{95}{32}$ **43.** answers may vary   **45.** $-\dfrac{5}{6}$ **47.** 54

49. 8   **51.** -32 **53.** 48   **55.** 25   **57.** -2 **59.** yes   **61.** no   **63.** $(x^3 - 5x^2 + 2x - 1)$ cm   **65.** $x^3 + \dfrac{5}{3}x^2 + \dfrac{5}{3}x + \dfrac{8}{3} + \dfrac{8}{3(x-1)}$

67. $(x+3)(x^2+4) = x^3 + 3x^2 + 4x + 12$ **69.** 0   **71.** $x^3 + 2x^2 + 7x + 28$

Chapter 5 Vocabulary Check

1. term   **2.** FOIL   **3.** trinomial   **4.** degree of a polynomial   **5.** binomial   **6.** coefficient   **7.** degree of a term   **8.** monomial
9. polynomials   **10.** distributive

Chapter 5 Review

1. base: 7; exponent: 9   **3.** base: 5; exponent: 4   **5.** 512   **7.** -36 **9.** 1   **11.** y^9 **13.** $-6x^{11}$ **15.** x^8 **17.** $81y^{24}$ **19.** x^5

21. a^4b^3 **23.** $\dfrac{x^3y^4}{4}$ **25.** $40a^{19}$ **27.** 3   **29.** b   **31.** 7   **33.** 8   **35.** 5   **37.** 5   **39.** 4000 ft; 3984 ft; 3856 ft; 3600 ft   **41.** $15a^2 + 4a$

43. $-6a^2b - 3b^2 - q^2$ **45.** $8x^2 + 3x + 6$ **47.** $-7y^2 - 1$ **49.** $4x - 13y$ **51.** 290   **53.** $(6x^2y - 12x + 12)$ cm   **55.** $8a + 28$
57. $-7x^3 - 35x$ **59.** $-6a^4 + 8a^2 - 2a$ **61.** $2x^2 - 12x - 14$ **63.** $x^2 - 18x + 81$ **65.** $4a^2 + 27a - 7$ **67.** $25x^2 + 20x + 4$
69. $x^4 + 7x^3 + 4x^2 + 23x - 35$ **71.** $x^4 + 4x^3 + 4x^2 - 16$ **73.** $x^3 + 21x^2 + 147x + 343$ **75.** $x^2 + 14x + 49$ **77.** $9x^2 - 42x + 49$

79. $25x^2 - 90x + 81$ **81.** $49x^2 - 16$ **83.** $4x^2 - 36$ **85.** $(9x^2 - 6x + 1)$ sq m   **87.** $\dfrac{1}{49}$ **89.** $\dfrac{2}{x^4}$ **91.** 125   **93.** $\dfrac{17}{16}$ **95.** x^8

97. r **99.** c^4 **101.** $\dfrac{1}{x^6y^{13}}$ **103.** a^{11m} **105.** $27x^3y^{6z}$ **107.** 2.7×10^{-4} **109.** 8.08×10^7 **111.** 2.5×10^9 **113.** 867,000

115. 0.00086   **117.** 1,431,280,000,000,000   **119.** 0.016   **121.** $\dfrac{1}{7} + \dfrac{3}{x} + \dfrac{7}{x^2}$ **123.** $a + 1 + \dfrac{6}{a-2}$ **125.** $a^2 + 3a + 8 + \dfrac{22}{a-2}$

127. $2x^3 - x^2 + 2 - \dfrac{1}{2x-1}$ **129.** $\left(5x - 1 + \dfrac{20}{x^2}\right)$ ft   **131.** $3x^2 + 6x + 24 + \dfrac{44}{x-2}$ **133.** $x^4 - x^3 + x^2 - x + 1 - \dfrac{2}{x+1}$

135. $3x^3 + 13x^2 + 51x + 204 + \dfrac{814}{x-4}$ **137.** 3043   **139.** $-\dfrac{1}{8}$ **141.** $\dfrac{2x^6}{3}$ **143.** $\dfrac{x^{16}}{16y^{12}}$ **145.** $11x - 5$ **147.** $5y^2 - 3y - 1$

149. $28x^3 + 12x$ **151.** $x^3 + x^2 - 18x + 18$ **153.** $25x^2 + 40x + 16$ **155.** $4a - 1 + \dfrac{2}{a^2} - \dfrac{5}{2a^3}$ **157.** $2x^2 + 7x + 5 + \dfrac{19}{2x-3}$

Chapter 5 Getting Ready for the Test

1. C   **2.** A   **3.** E   **4.** D   **5.** F   **6.** C   **7.** E   **8.** I   **9.** C   **10.** D   **11.** C   **12.** B   **13.** F   **14.** D   **15.** C

Chapter 5 Test

1. 32   **2.** 81   **3.** -81 **4.** $\dfrac{1}{64}$ **5.** $-15x^{11}$ **6.** y^5 **7.** $\dfrac{1}{r^5}$ **8.** $\dfrac{y^{14}}{x^2}$ **9.** $\dfrac{1}{6xy^8}$ **10.** 5.63×10^5 **11.** 8.63×10^{-5} **12.** 0.0015

13. 62,300   **14.** 0.036   **15. a.** 4, 3; 7, 3; 1, 4; -2, 0   **b.** 4   **16.** $-2x^2 + 12xy + 11$ **17.** $16x^3 + 7x^2 - 3x - 13$ **18.** $-3x^3 + 5x^2 + 4x + 5$

19. $x^3 + 8x^2 + 3x - 5$ **20.** $3x^3 + 22x^2 + 41x + 14$ **21.** $6x^4 - 9x^3 + 21x^2$ **22.** $3x^2 + 16x - 35$ **23.** $9x^2 - \dfrac{1}{25}$ **24.** $16x^2 - 16x + 4$

25. $64x^2 + 48x + 9$ **26.** $x^4 - 81b^2$ **27.** 1001 ft; 985 ft; 857 ft; 601 ft   **28.** $(4x^2 - 9)$ sq in.   **29.** $\dfrac{x}{2y} + 3 - \dfrac{7}{8y}$ **30.** $x + 2$

31. $9x^2 - 6x + 4 - \dfrac{16}{3x+2}$ **32. a.** 960 ft   **b.** 953.44 ft   **33.** $4x^3 - 15x^2 + 45x - 136 + \dfrac{407}{x+3}$ **34.** 91

Chapter 5 Cumulative Review

1. a. true   **b.** true   **c.** false   **d.** true; Sec. 1.2, Ex. 2   **3. a.** $\dfrac{64}{25}$ **b.** $\dfrac{1}{20}$ **c.** $\dfrac{5}{4}$; Sec. 1.3, Ex. 4   **5. a.** 9   **b.** 125   **c.** 16   **d.** 7

e. $\dfrac{9}{49}$; Sec. 1.4, Ex. 1   **7. a.** -10 **b.** -21 **c.** -12; Sec. 1.5, Ex. 3   **9.** -12; Sec. 1.6, Ex. 3   **11. a.** $\dfrac{1}{22}$ **b.** $\dfrac{16}{3}$ **c.** $-\dfrac{1}{10}$

d. $-\dfrac{13}{9}$; Sec. 1.7, Ex. 5   **13. a.** $(5+4)+6$ **b.** $-1 \cdot (2 \cdot 5)$; Sec. 1.8, Ex. 2   **15. a.** $22 + x$ **b.** $-21x$; Sec. 1.8, Ex. 3   **17. a.** $15x + 10$

b. $-2y - 0.6z + 2$ **c.** $-9x - y + 2z - 6$; Sec. 2.1, Ex. 5   **19.** 17; Sec. 2.2, Ex. 1   **21.** 6; Sec. 2.3, Ex. 5   **23.** -10; Sec. 2.4, Ex. 1

25. 10; Sec. 2.4, Ex. 2   **27.** width: 4 ft; length: 10 ft; Sec. 2.5, Ex. 4   **29.** $\dfrac{5F - 160}{9} = C$; Sec. 2.5, Ex. 8   **31.** ←———•———→; Sec. 2.8, Ex. 9

33. a. $(0, 12)$ **b.** $(2, 6)$ **c.** $(-1, 15)$; Sec. 3.1, Ex. 6   **35.** ; Sec. 3.2, Ex. 2   **37.** ; Sec. 3.3, Ex. 9

39. undefined slope; Sec. 3.4, Ex. 7   **41.** $9x^2 - 6x - 1$; Sec. 5.2, Ex. 11   **43.** $-6x^7$; Sec. 5.1, Ex. 4   **45.** $12x^3 - 12x^2 - 9x + 2$; Sec. 5.2, Ex. 10

47. $4x^2 - 4xy + y^2$; Sec. 5.3, Ex. 6   **49.** $3m + 1$; Sec. 5.6, Ex. 1

CHAPTER 6 FACTORING POLYNOMIALS

Section 6.1

Practice Exercises

1. a. 6 **b.** 1 **c.** 4 **2. a.** y^4 **b.** x **3. a.** $5y^2$ **b.** x^2 **c.** a^2b^2 **4. a.** $4(t+3)$ **b.** $y^4(y^4+1)$ **5.** $8b^2(-b^4+2b^2-1)$ or
$-8b^2(b^4-2b^2+1)$ **6.** $5x(x^3-4)$ **7.** $\frac{1}{9}z^3(5z^2+z-2)$ **8.** $4ab^3(2ab-5a^2+3)$ **9.** $(y-2)(8+x)$ **10.** $(p+q)(7xy^3-1)$
11. $(x+3)(y+4)$ **12.** $(5x-3)(8x^2+3)$ **13.** $(2x+3y)(y-1)$ **14.** $(7a+5)(a^2+1)$ **15.** $(y-3)(4x-5)$ **16.** cannot be
factored by grouping **17.** $3(x-a)(y-2a)$

Vocabulary, Readiness & Video Check 6.1

1. factors **3.** least **5.** false **7.** The GCF of a list of numbers is the largest number that is a factor of all numbers in the list. **9.** When factoring
out a GCF, the number of terms in the other factor should have the same number of terms as your original polynomial.

Exercise Set 6.1

1. 4 **3.** 6 **5.** 1 **7.** y^2 **9.** z^7 **11.** xy^2 **13.** 7 **15.** $4y^3$ **17.** $5x^2$ **19.** $3x^3$ **21.** $9x^2y$ **23.** $10a^6b$ **25.** $3(a+2)$
27. $15(2x-1)$ **29.** $x^2(x+5)$ **31.** $2y^3(3y+1)$ **33.** $4(x-2y+1)$ **35.** $3x(2x^2-3x+4)$ **37.** $a^2b^2(a^5b^4-a+b^3-1)$
39. $4(2x^5+4x^4-5x^3+3)$ **41.** $\frac{1}{3}x(x^3+2x^2-4x^4+1)$ **43.** $(x^2+2)(y+3)$ **45.** $(y+4)(z-3)$ **47.** $(z^2-6)(r+1)$
49. $-2(x+7)$ **51.** $-x^5(2-x^2)$ **53.** $-3a^2(a^2-3a+1)$ **55.** $(x+2)(x^2+5)$ **57.** $(x+3)(5+y)$ **59.** $(3x-2)(2x^2+5)$
61. $(5m^2+6n)(m+1)$ **63.** $(y-4)(2+x)$ **65.** $(2x-1)(x^2+4)$ **67.** not factorable by grouping **69.** $(x-2y)(4x-3)$
71. $(5q-4p)(q-1)$ **73.** $x(x^2+1)(2x+5)$ **75.** $2(2y-7)(3x^2-1)$ **77.** $2x(16y-9x)$ **79.** $(x+2)(y-3)$ **81.** $7xy(2x^2+x-1)$
83. $(4x-1)(7x^2+3)$ **85.** $-8x^8y^5(5y+2x)$ **87.** $3(2a+3b^2)(a+b)$ **89.** $x^2+7x+10$ **91.** b^2-3b-4 **93.** 2, 6 **95.** $-1, -8$
97. $-2, 5$ **99.** b **101.** factored **103.** not factored **105.** answers may vary **107.** answers may vary **109. a.** 22% **b.** 70%
c. $0.6(x^2-x+6)$ **111.** $12x^3-2x; 2x(6x^2-1)$ **113.** (n^3-6)units **115.** $(x^n+2)(x^n+3)$ **117.** $(3x^n-5)(x^n+7)$

Section 6.2

Practice Exercises

1. $(x+2)(x+3)$ **2.** $(x-10)(x-7)$ **3.** $(x+7)(x-2)$ **4.** $(p-9)(p+7)$ **5.** prime polynomial **6.** $(x+3y)(x+4y)$
7. $(x^2+12)(x^2+1)$ **8.** $(x-6)(x-8)$ **9.** $4(x-3)(x-3)$ **10.** $3y^2(y-7)(y+1)$

Vocabulary, Readiness & Video Check 6.2

1. true **3.** false **5.** $+5$ **7.** -3 **9.** $+2$ **11.** 15 is positive, so its factors would have to be either both positive or both negative. Since the
factors need to sum to -8, both factors must be negative.

Exercise Set 6.2

1. $(x+6)(x+1)$ **3.** $(y-9)(y-1)$ **5.** $(x-3)(x-3)$ or $(x-3)^2$ **7.** $(x-6)(x+3)$ **9.** $(x+10)(x-7)$ **11.** prime
13. $(x+5y)(x+3y)$ **15.** $(a^2-5)(a^2+3)$ **17.** $(m+13)(m+1)$ **19.** $(t-2)(t+12)$ **21.** $(a-2b)(a-8b)$ **23.** $2(z+8)(z+2)$
25. $2x(x-5)(x-4)$ **27.** $(x-4y)(x+y)$ **29.** $(x+12)(x+3)$ **31.** $(x-2)(x+1)$ **33.** $(r-12)(r-4)$ **35.** $(x+2y)(x-y)$
37. $3(x+5)(x-2)$ **39.** $3(x-18)(x-2)$ **41.** $(x-24)(x+6)$ **43.** prime **45.** $(x-5)(x-3)$ **47.** $6x(x+4)(x+5)$
49. $4y(x^2+x-3)$ **51.** $(x-7)(x+3)$ **53.** $(x+5y)(x+2y)$ **55.** $2(t+8)(t+4)$ **57.** $x(x-6)(x+4)$ **59.** $2t^3(t-4)(t-3)$
61. $5xy(x-8y)(x+3y)$ **63.** $3(m-9)(m-6)$ **65.** $-1(x-11)(x-1)$ **67.** $\frac{1}{2}(y-11)(y+2)$ **69.** $x(xy-4)(xy+5)$
71. $2x^2+11x+5$ **73.** $15y^2-17y+4$ **75.** $9a^2+23ab-12b^2$ **77.** $x^2+5x-24$ **79.** answers may vary
81. $2x^2+28x+66; 2(x+3)(x+11)$ **83.** $-16(t-5)(t+1)$ **85.** $\left(x+\frac{1}{4}\right)\left(x+\frac{1}{4}\right)$ or $\left(x+\frac{1}{4}\right)^2$ **87.** $(x+1)(z-10)(z+7)$
89. $(x^n+10)(x^n-2)$ **91.** 5; 8; 9 **93.** 3; 4 **95.** 8; 16 **97.** 6; 26

Section 6.3

Practice Exercises

1. $(2x+5)(x+3)$ **2.** $(5x-4)(3x-2)$ **3.** $(4x-1)(x+3)$ **4.** $(7x-y)(3x+2y)$ **5.** $(2x^2-7)(x^2+1)$ **6.** $x(3x+2)(x+5)$
7. $-1(4x-3)(2x+1)$ **8.** $(x+7)^2$ **9.** $(2x+9y)(2x+y)$ **10.** $(6n^2-1)^2$ **11.** $3x(2x-7)^2$

Vocabulary, Readiness & Video Check 6.3

1. perfect square trinomial **3.** perfect square trinomial **5.** d **7.** Consider the factors of the first and last terms and the signs of the trinomial.
Continue to check by multiplying until you get the middle term of the trinomial. **9.** The first and last terms are squares, a^2 and b^2, and the middle
term is $2 \cdot a \cdot b$ or $-2 \cdot a \cdot b$.

Exercise Set 6.3

1. $x+4$ **3.** $10x-1$ **5.** $5x-2$ **7.** $(2x+3)(x+5)$ **9.** $(y-1)(8y-9)$ **11.** $(2x+1)(x-5)$ **13.** $(4r-1)(5r+8)$
15. $(10x+1)(x+3)$ **17.** prime **19.** $(3x-5y)(2x-y)$ **21.** $(3m-5)(5m+3)$ **23.** $x(3x+2)(4x+1)$ **25.** $3(7b+5)(b-3)$
27. $(3z+4)(4z-3)$ **29.** $2y^2(3x-10)(x+3)$ **31.** $(2x-7)(2x+3)$ **33.** $-1(x-6)(x+4)$ **35.** $x(4x+3)(x-3)$
37. $(4x-9)(6x-1)$ **39.** $(x+11)^2$ **41.** $(x-8)^2$ **43.** $(4a-3)^2$ **45.** $(x^2+2)^2$ **47.** $2(n-7)^2$ **49.** $(4y+5)^2$

51. $(2x + 11)(x - 9)$ **53.** $(8x + 3)(3x + 4)$ **55.** $(3a + b)(a + 3b)$ **57.** $(x - 4)(x - 5)$ **59.** $(p + 6q)^2$ **61.** $(xy - 5)^2$
63. $b(8a - 3)(5a + 3)$ **65.** $2x(3x + 2)(5x + 3)$ **67.** $2y(3y + 5)(y - 3)$ **69.** $5x^2(2x - y)(x + 3y)$ **71.** $-1(2x - 5)(7x - 2)$
73. $p^2(4p - 5)^2$ **75.** $(3x - 2)(x + 1)$ **77.** $(4x + 9y)(2x - 3y)$ **79.** prime   **81.** $(3x - 4y)^2$ **83.** $(6x - 7)(3x + 2)$
85. $(7t + 1)(t - 4)$ **87.** $(7p + 1)(7p - 2)$ **89.** $m(m + 9)^2$ **91.** prime   **93.** $a(6a^2 + b^2)(a^2 + 6b^2)$ **95.** $x^2 - 4$ **97.** $a^3 + 27$
99. Facebook   **101.** answers may vary   **103.** no   **105.** answers may vary   **107.** $4x^2 + 21x + 5; (4x + 1)(x + 5)$ **109.** $\left(2x + \dfrac{1}{2}\right)^2$
111. $(y - 1)^2(4x^2 + 10x + 25)$ **113.** 8   **115.** $a^2 + 2ab + b^2$ **117.** $2; 14$ **119.** 2   **121.** $-3xy^2(4x - 5)(x + 1)$
123. $(y - 1)^2(2x + 5)^2$ **125.** $(3x^n + 2)(x^n + 5)$ **127.** answers may vary

Section 6.4

Practice Exercises

1. $(5x + 1)(x + 12)$ **2.** $(4x - 5)(3x - 1)$ **3.** $2(5x + 1)(3x - 2)$ **4.** $5m^2(8m - 7)(m + 1)$ **5.** $(4x + 3)^2$

Vocabulary, Readiness & Video Check 6.4

1. a   **3.** b   **5.** This gives us a four-term polynomial, which may be factored by grouping.

Exercise Set 6.4

1. $(x + 3)(x + 2)$ **3.** $(y + 8)(y - 2)$ **5.** $(8x - 5)(x - 3)$ **7.** $(5x^2 - 3)(x^2 + 5)$ **9. a.** $9, 2$ **b.** $9x + 2x$ **c.** $(3x + 1)(2x + 3)$
11. a. $-20, -3$ **b.** $-20x - 3x$ **c.** $(3x - 4)(5x - 1)$ **13.** $(3y + 2)(7y + 1)$ **15.** $(7x - 11)(x + 1)$ **17.** $(5x - 2)(2x - 1)$
19. $(2x - 5)(x - 1)$ **21.** $(2x + 3)^2$ **23.** $(2x + 3)(2x - 7)$ **25.** $(5x - 4)(2x - 3)$ **27.** $x(2x + 3)(x + 5)$
29. $2(8y - 9)(y - 1)$ **31.** $(2x - 3)(3x - 2)$ **33.** $3(3a + 2)(6a - 5)$ **35.** $a(4a + 1)(5a + 8)$ **37.** $3x(4x + 3)(x - 3)$
39. $y(3x + y)(x + y)$ **41.** prime   **43.** $5(x + 5y)^2$ **45.** $6(a + b)(4a - 5b)$ **47.** $p^2(15p + q)(p + 2q)$ **49.** $2(9a^2 - 2)^2$
51. $(7 + x)(5 + x)$ or $(x + 7)(x + 5)$ **53.** $(6 - 5x)(1 - x)$ or $(5x - 6)(x - 1)$ **55.** $x^2 - 4$ **57.** $y^2 + 8y + 16$ **59.** $81z^2 - 25$
61. $x^3 - 27$ **63.** $10x^2 + 45x + 45; 5(2x + 3)(x + 3)$ **65.** $(x^n + 2)(x^n + 3)$ **67.** $(3x^n - 5)(x^n + 7)$ **69.** answers may vary

Section 6.5

Practice Exercises

1. $(x + 9)(x - 9)$ **2. a.** $(3x - 1)(3x + 1)$ **b.** $(6a - 7b)(6a + 7b)$ **c.** $\left(p + \dfrac{5}{6}\right)\left(p - \dfrac{5}{6}\right)$ **3.** $(p^2 - q^5)(p^2 + q^5)$
4. a. $(z^2 + 9)(z + 3)(z - 3)$ **b.** prime polynomial   **5.** $y(6y + 5)(6y - 5)$ **6.** $5(4y^2 + 1)(2y + 1)(2y - 1)$
7. $-1(3x + 10)(3x - 10)$ or $(10 + 3x)(10 - 3x)$ **8.** $(x + 4)(x^2 - 4x + 16)$ **9.** $(x - 5)(x^2 + 5x + 25)$ **10.** $(3y + 1)(9y^2 - 3y + 1)$
11. $4(2x - 5y)(4x^2 + 10xy + 25y^2)$

Graphing Calculator Explorations 6.5

	$x^2 - 2x + 1$	$x^2 - 2x - 1$	$(x - 1)^2$
$x = 5$	16	14	16
$x = -3$	16	14	16
$x = 2.7$	2.89	0.89	2.89
$x = -12.1$	171.61	169.61	171.61
$x = 0$	1	-1	1

Vocabulary, Readiness & Video Check 6.5

1. difference of two cubes   **3.** sum of two cubes   **5.** $(7x)^2$ **7.** $(2y)^3$ **9.** In order to recognize the binomial as a difference of squares and also to identify the terms to use in the special factoring formula.   **11.** First rewrite the original binomial with terms writtten as cubes. Answers will then vary depending on your interpretation.

Exercise Set 6.5

1. $(x + 2)(x - 2)$ **3.** $(9p + 1)(9p - 1)$ **5.** $(5y - 3)(5y + 3)$ **7.** $(11m + 10n)(11m - 10n)$ **9.** $(xy - 1)(xy + 1)$
11. $\left(x - \dfrac{1}{2}\right)\left(x + \dfrac{1}{2}\right)$ **13.** $-1(2r + 1)(2r - 1)$ or $(1 - 2r)(1 + 2r)$ **15.** prime   **17.** $(x - 6)(x + 6)$ or $-1(6 + x)(6 - x)$
19. $(m^2 + 1)(m + 1)(m - 1)$ **21.** $(m^2 + n^9)(m^2 - n^9)$ **23.** $(x + 5)(x^2 - 5x + 25)$ **25.** $(2a - 1)(4a^2 + 2a + 1)$
27. $(m + 3n)(m^2 - 3mn + 9n^2)$ **29.** $5(k + 2)(k^2 - 2k + 4)$ **31.** $(xy - 4)(x^2y^2 + 4xy + 16)$ **33.** $2(5r - 4t)(25r^2 + 20rt + 16t^2)$
35. $(r + 8)(r - 8)$ **37.** $(x + 13y)(x - 13y)$ **39.** $(3 - t)(9 + 3t + t^2)$ **41.** $2(3r + 2)(3r - 2)$ **43.** $x(3y + 2)(3y - 2)$
45. $8(m + 2)(m^2 - 2m + 4)$ **47.** $xy(y - 3z)(y + 3z)$ **49.** $4(3x - 4y)(3x + 4y)$ **51.** $9(4 - 3x)(4 + 3x)$ **53.** $(xy - z^2)(x^2y^2 + xyz^2 + z^4)$
55. $\left(7 - \dfrac{3}{5}m\right)\left(7 + \dfrac{3}{5}m\right)$ **57.** $(t + 7)(t^2 - 7t + 49)$ **59.** $n(n^2 + 49)$ **61.** $x^2(x^2 + 9)(x + 3)(x - 3)$ **63.** $pq(8p + 9q)(8p - 9q)$
65. $xy^2(27xy + 1)$ **67.** $a(5a - 4b)(25a^2 + 20ab + 16b^2)$ **69.** $16x^2(x + 2)(x - 2)$ **71.** 6   **73.** -2 **75.** $\dfrac{1}{5}$
77. $(x + 2 + y)(x + 2 - y)$ **79.** $(a + 4)(a - 4)(b - 4)$ **81.** $(x + 3 + 2y)(x + 3 - 2y)$ **83.** $(x^n + 10)(x^n - 10)$
85. $(x + 6)$ **87.** answers may vary   **89. a.** 2992 ft   **b.** 1536 ft   **c.** 14 sec   **d.** $16(14 - t)(14 + t)$ **91. a.** 2560 ft   **b.** 1920 ft
c. 13 sec   **d.** $16(13 + t)(13 - t)$

Integrated Review
Practice Exercises

1. $(3x - 1)(2x - 3)$ **2.** $(3x + 1)(x - 2)(x + 2)$ **3.** $3(3x - y)(3x + y)$ **4.** $(2a + b)(4a^2 - 2ab + b^2)$ **5.** $6xy^2(5x + 2)(2x - 3)$

Exercise Set

1. $(x + y)^2$ **2.** $(x - y)^2$ **3.** $(a + 12)(a - 1)$ **4.** $(a - 10)(a - 1)$ **5.** $(a + 2)(a - 3)$ **6.** $(a - 1)^2$ **7.** $(x + 1)^2$
8. $(x + 2)(x - 1)$ **9.** $(x + 1)(x + 3)$ **10.** $(x + 3)(x - 2)$ **11.** $(x + 3)(x + 4)$ **12.** $(x + 4)(x - 3)$ **13.** $(x + 4)(x - 1)$
14. $(x - 5)(x - 2)$ **15.** $(x + 5)(x - 3)$ **16.** $(x + 6)(x + 5)$ **17.** $(x - 6)(x + 5)$ **18.** $(x + 8)(x + 3)$ **19.** $2(x + 7)(x - 7)$
20. $3(x + 5)(x - 5)$ **21.** $(x + 3)(x + y)$ **22.** $(y - 7)(3 + x)$ **23.** $(x + 8)(x - 2)$ **24.** $(x - 7)(x + 4)$ **25.** $4x(x + 7)(x - 2)$
26. $6x(x - 5)(x + 4)$ **27.** $2(3x + 4)(2x + 3)$ **28.** $(2a - b)(4a + 5b)$ **29.** $(2a + b)(2a - b)$ **30.** $(4 - 3x)(7 + 2x)$
31. $(5 - 2x)(4 + x)$ **32.** prime   **33.** prime   **34.** $(3y + 5)(2y - 3)$ **35.** $(4x - 5)(x + 1)$ **36.** $y(x + y)(x - y)$ **37.** $4(t^2 + 9)$
38. $(x + 1)(x + y)$ **39.** $(x + 1)(a + 2)$ **40.** $9x(2x^2 - 7x + 1)$ **41.** $4a(3a^2 - 6a + 1)$ **42.** $(x + 16)(x - 2)$ **43.** prime
44. $(4a - 7b)^2$ **45.** $(5p - 7q)^2$ **46.** $(7x + 3y)(x + 3y)$ **47.** $(5 - 2y)(25 + 10y + 4y^2)$ **48.** $(4x + 3)(16x^2 - 12x + 9)$
49. $-(x - 5)(x + 6)$ **50.** $-(x - 2)(x - 4)$ **51.** $(7 - x)(2 + x)$ **52.** $(3 + x)(1 - x)$ **53.** $3x^2y(x + 6)(x - 4)$ **54.** $2xy(x + 5y)(x - y)$
55. $5xy^2(x - 7y)(x - y)$ **56.** $4x^2y(x - 5)(x + 3)$ **57.** $3xy(4x^2 + 81)$ **58.** $2xy^2(3x^2 + 4)$ **59.** $(2 + x)(2 - x)$ **60.** $(3 + y)(3 - y)$
61. $(s + 4)(3r - 1)$ **62.** $(x - 2)(x^2 + 3)$ **63.** $(4x - 3)(x - 2y)$ **64.** $(2x - y)(2x + 7z)$ **65.** $6(x + 2y)(x + y)$
66. $2(x + 4y)(6x - y)$ **67.** $(x + 3)(y + 2)(y - 2)$ **68.** $(y + 3)(y - 3)(x^2 + 3)$ **69.** $(5 + x)(x + y)$ **70.** $(x - y)(7 + y)$
71. $(7t - 1)(2t - 1)$ **72.** prime   **73.** $(3x + 5)(x - 1)$ **74.** $(7x - 2)(x + 3)$ **75.** $(x + 12y)(x - 3y)$ **76.** $(3x - 2y)(x + 4y)$
77. $(1 - 10ab)(1 + 2ab)$ **78.** $(1 + 5ab)(1 - 12ab)$ **79.** $(3 + x)(3 - x)(1 + x)(1 - x)$ **80.** $(3 + x)(3 - x)(2 + x)(2 - x)$
81. $(x + 4)(x - 4)(x^2 + 2)$ **82.** $(x + 5)(x - 5)(x^2 + 3)$ **83.** $(x - 15)(x - 8)$ **84.** $(y + 16)(y + 6)$ **85.** $2x(3x - 2)(x - 4)$
86. $2y(3y + 5)(y - 3)$ **87.** $(3x - 5y)(9x^2 + 15xy + 25y^2)$ **88.** $(6y - z)(36y^2 + 6yz + z^2)$ **89.** $(xy + 2z)(x^2y^2 - 2xyz + 4z^2)$
90. $(3ab + 2)(9a^2b^2 - 6ab + 4)$ **91.** $2xy(1 + 6x)(1 - 6x)$ **92.** $2x(x + 3)(x - 3)$ **93.** $(x + 2)(x - 2)(x + 6)$
94. $(x - 2)(x + 6)(x - 6)$ **95.** $2a^2(3a + 5)$ **96.** $2n(2n - 3)$ **97.** $(a^2 + 2)(a + 2)$ **98.** $(a - b)(1 + x)$ **99.** $(x + 2)(x - 2)(x + 7)$
100. $(a + 3)(a - 3)(a + 5)$ **101.** $(x - y + z)(x - y - z)$ **102.** $(x + 2y + 3)(x + 2y - 3)$ **103.** $(9 + 5x + 1)(9 - 5x - 1)$
104. $(b + 4a + c)(b - 4a - c)$ **105.** answers may vary   **106.** yes; $9(x^2 + 9y^2)$ **107.** a, c   **108.** b, c

Section 6.6
Practice Exercises

1. $-4, 5$ **2.** $-\dfrac{3}{4}, 12$ **3.** $0, \dfrac{6}{7}$ **4.** $-4, 12$ **5.** $\dfrac{4}{3}$ **6.** $-3, \dfrac{2}{3}$ **7.** $-6, 4$ **8.** $-3, 0, 3$ **9.** $\dfrac{2}{3}, \dfrac{3}{2}, 5$ **10.** $-3, 0, 2$
11. The x-intercepts are $(2, 0)$ and $(4, 0)$.

Calculator Explorations 6.6

1. $-0.9, 2.2$ **3.** no real solution   **5.** $-1.8, 2.8$

Vocabulary, Readiness & Video Check 6.6

1. quadratic   **3.** $3, -5$ **5.** One side of the equation must be a factored polynomial and the other side must be zero.   **7.** To find the x-intercepts of any graph in two variables, we let $y = 0$. Doing this with our quadratic equation gives us an equation $= 0$, which we can try to solve by factoring.

Exercise Set 6.6

1. $6, 7$ **3.** $2, -1$ **5.** $-9, -17$ **7.** $0, -6$ **9.** $0, 8$ **11.** $-\dfrac{3}{2}, \dfrac{5}{4}$ **13.** $\dfrac{7}{2}, -\dfrac{2}{7}$ **15.** $\dfrac{1}{2}, -\dfrac{1}{3}$ **17.** $-0.2, -1.5$ **19.** $9, 4$ **21.** $-4, 2$

23. $0, 7$ **25.** $8, -4$ **27.** $4, -4$ **29.** $-3, 12$ **31.** $\dfrac{7}{3}, -2$ **33.** $-5, 5$ **35.** $-2, \dfrac{1}{6}$ **37.** $0, 4, 8$ **39.** $\dfrac{3}{4}$ **41.** $-\dfrac{1}{2}, 0, \dfrac{1}{2}$ **43.** $-\dfrac{3}{8}, 0, \dfrac{1}{2}$

45. $-3, 2$ **47.** $-20, 0$ **49.** $\dfrac{17}{2}$ **51.** $-\dfrac{1}{2}, \dfrac{1}{2}$ **53.** $-\dfrac{3}{2}, -\dfrac{1}{2}, 3$ **55.** $-5, 3$ **57.** $-\dfrac{5}{6}, \dfrac{6}{5}$ **59.** $2, -\dfrac{4}{5}$ **61.** $-\dfrac{4}{3}, 5$ **63.** $-4, 3$

65. $\dfrac{8}{3}, -9, 0$ **67.** -7 **69.** $0, \dfrac{3}{2}$ **71.** $0, 1, -1$ **73.** $-6, \dfrac{4}{3}$ **75.** $\dfrac{6}{7}, 1$ **77.** $\left(-\dfrac{4}{3}, 0\right), (1, 0)$ **79.** $(-2, 0), (5, 0)$ **81.** $(-6, 0), \left(\dfrac{1}{2}, 0\right)$

83. E   **85.** B   **87.** C   **89.** $\dfrac{47}{45}$ **91.** $\dfrac{17}{60}$ **93.** $\dfrac{15}{8}$ **95.** $\dfrac{7}{10}$ **97.** didn't write equation in standard form; should be $x = 4$ or $x = -2$

99. answers may vary; for example $(x - 6)(x + 1) = 0$ **101.** answers may vary; for example, $x^2 - 12x + 35 = 0$ **103. a.** $300; 304; 276; 216;$
$124; 0; -156$ **b.** 5 sec   **c.** 304 ft   **d.**   **105.** $0, \dfrac{1}{2}$ **107.** $0, -15$

$y = -16x^2 + 20x + 300$

Section 6.7
Practice Exercises

1. 2 sec   **2.** There are two numbers. They are -4 and 12.   **3.** base: 35 ft; height: 12 ft   **4.** 7 and 8 or -6 and -5 **5.** leg: 8 units; leg: 15 units; hypotenuse: 17 units

Vocabulary, Readiness & Video Check 6.7

1. In applications, the context of the problem needs to be considered. Each exercise resulted in both a positive and a negative solution, and a negative solution is not appropriate for any of the problems.

Exercise Set 6.7

1. width $= x$; length $= x + 4$ **3.** x and $x + 2$ if x is an odd integer **5.** base $= x$; height $= 4x + 1$ **7.** 11 units **9.** 15 cm, 13 cm, 70 cm, 22 cm **11.** base $= 16$ mi; height $= 6$ mi **13.** 5 sec **15.** width $= 5$ cm; length $= 6$ cm **17.** 54 diagonals **19.** 10 sides **21.** -12 or 11 **23.** 14, 15 **25.** 13 feet **27.** 5 in. **29.** 12 mm, 16 mm, 20 mm **31.** 10 km **33.** 36 ft **35.** 9.5 sec **37.** 20% **39.** length: 15 mi; width: 8 mi **41.** 105 units **43.** 1.8 million **45.** 2.3 million **47.** 2003 **49.** answers may vary **51.** $\frac{4}{7}$ **53.** $\frac{3}{2}$ **55.** $\frac{1}{3}$ **57.** slow boat: 8 mph; fast boat: 15 mph **59.** 13 and 7 **61.** width: 29 m; length: 35 m **63.** answers may vary

Chapter 6 Vocabulary Check

1. quadratic equation **2.** Factoring **3.** greatest common factor **4.** perfect square trinomial **5.** difference of two squares **6.** difference of two cubes **7.** sum of two cubes **8.** 0 **9.** hypotenuse **10.** leg **11.** hypotenuse

Chapter 6 Review

1. $2x - 5$ **3.** $4x(5x + 3)$ **5.** $(2x + 3)(3x - 5)$ **7.** $(x - 1)(3x + 2)$ **9.** $(2a + b)(5a + 7b)$ **11.** $(x + 4)(x + 2)$ **13.** prime **15.** $(x + 6y)(x - 2y)$ **17.** $2(3 - x)(12 + x)$ **19.** $10a(a - 1)(a - 10)$ **21.** $-48, 2$ **23.** $(2x + 1)(x + 6)$ **25.** $(3x + 4y)(2x - y)$ **27.** $5y(2y - 3)(y + 4)$ **29.** $2(3x - 5)^2$ **31.** $(2x + 3)(2x - 3)$ **33.** prime **35.** $(2x + 3)(4x^2 - 6x + 9)$ **37.** $2(3 - xy)(9 + 3xy + x^2y^2)$ **39.** $(4x^2 + 1)(2x + 1)(2x - 1)$ **41.** $-6, 2$ **43.** $-\frac{1}{5}, -3$ **45.** $-4, 6$ **47.** $2, 8$ **49.** $-\frac{2}{7}, \frac{3}{8}$ **51.** $-\frac{2}{5}$ **53.** 3 **55.** $0, -\frac{7}{4}, 3$ **57.** c **59.** 9 units **61.** width: 20 in.; length: 25 in. **63.** 19 and 20 **65. a.** 17.5 sec and 10 sec; The rocket reaches a height of 2800 ft on its way up and on its way back down. **b.** 27.5 sec **67.** $7(x - 9)$ **69.** $\left(m + \frac{2}{5}\right)\left(m - \frac{2}{5}\right)$ **71.** $(y + 2)(x - 1)$ **73.** $3x(x - 9)(x - 1)$ **75.** $2(x + 3)(x - 3)$ **77.** $5(x + 2)^2$ **79.** $2xy(2x - 3y)$ **81.** $3(8x^2 - x - 6)$ **83.** $(x + 3)(x + 2)(x - 2)$ **85.** $5x^2 - 9x - 2$; $(5x + 1)(x - 2)$ **87.** $-\frac{7}{2}, 4$ **89.** $0, -7, -4$ **91.** $0, 16$ **93.** length: 6 in.; width: 2 in. **95.** $28x^2 - \pi x^2$; $x^2(28 - \pi)$

Chapter 6 Getting Ready for the Test

1. B **2.** D **3.** A **4.** A **5.** B **6.** B **7.** B **8.** A **9.** C

Chapter 6 Test

1. $(x + 7)(x + 4)$ **2.** $(7 - m)(7 + m)$ **3.** $(y + 11)^2$ **4.** $(a + 3)(4 - y)$ **5.** prime **6.** $(y - 12)(y + 4)$ **7.** prime **8.** $3x(3x + 1)(x + 4)$ **9.** $(3a - 7)(a + b)$ **10.** $(3x - 2)(x - 1)$ **11.** $(x + 12y)(x + 2y)$ **12.** $5(6 + x)(6 - x)$ **13.** $(6t + 5)(t - 1)$ **14.** $(y + 2)(y - 2)(x - 7)$ **15.** $x(1 + x^2)(1 + x)(1 - x)$ **16.** $-xy(y^2 + x^2)$ **17.** $(4x - 1)(16x^2 + 4x + 1)$ **18.** $8(y - 2)(y^2 + 2y + 4)$ **19.** $-9, 3$ **20.** $-7, 2$ **21.** $-7, 1$ **22.** $0, \frac{3}{2}, -\frac{4}{3}$ **23.** $0, 3, -3$ **24.** $-3, 5$ **25.** $0, \frac{5}{2}$ **26.** 17 ft **27.** 8 and 9 **28.** 7 sec **29.** hypotenuse: 25 cm; legs: 15 cm, 20 cm

Chapter 6 Cumulative Review

1. a. $9 \le 11$ **b.** $8 > 1$ **c.** $3 \ne 4$; Sec. 1.2, Ex. 3 **3. a.** $\frac{6}{7}$ **b.** $\frac{11}{27}$ **c.** $\frac{22}{5}$; Sec. 1.3, Ex. 2 **5.** $\frac{14}{3}$; Sec. 1.4, Ex. 5 **7. a.** -12 **b.** -1; Sec. 1.5, Ex. 7 **9. a.** -32 **b.** -14 **c.** 90; Sec. 1.7, Ex. 1 **11. a.** $4x$ **b.** $11y^2$ **c.** $8x^2 - x$ **d.** $5n^2$; Sec. 2.1, Ex. 3 **13.** 140; Sec. 2.2, Ex. 7 **15.** -11; Sec. 2.2, Ex. 6 **17.** $\frac{16}{3}$; Sec. 2.3, Ex. 2 **19.** shorter: 12 in.; longer: 36 in.; Sec. 2.4, Ex. 3

21.

; Sec. 3.2, Ex. 5 **23.** $m = \frac{3}{4}$; y-intercept: $(0, -1)$; Sec. 3.4, Ex. 5 **25. a.** 250 **b.** 1; Sec. 5.1, Ex. 2 **27. a.** 2 **b.** 5 **c.** 1 **d.** 6 **e.** 0; Sec. 5.2, Ex. 1 **29.** $9x^2 - 6x - 1$; Sec. 5.2, Ex. 11 **31.** $6x^2 - 11x - 10$; Sec. 5.3, Ex. 5 **33.** $9y^2 + 6y + 1$; Sec. 5.4, Ex. 4 **35. a.** $\frac{1}{9}$ **b.** $\frac{2}{x^3}$ **c.** $\frac{3}{4}$ **d.** $\frac{1}{16}$ **e.** $\frac{1}{y^4}$; Sec. 5.5, Ex. 1 **37. a.** 3.67×10^8 **b.** 3.0×10^{-6} **c.** 2.052×10^{10} **d.** 8.5×10^{-4}; Sec. 5.5, Ex. 5 **39.** $x + 4$; Sec. 5.6, Ex. 4 **41. a.** x^3 **b.** y; Sec. 6.1, Ex. 2 **43.** $(x + 3)(x + 4)$; Sec. 6.2, Ex. 1 **45.** $(4x - 1)(2x - 5)$; Sec. 6.3, Ex. 2 **47.** $(5a + 3b)(5a - 3b)$; Sec. 6.5, Ex. 2b **49.** $3, -1$; Sec. 6.6, Ex. 1

CHAPTER 7 RATIONAL EXPRESSIONS

Section 7.1
Practice Exercises

1. a. $\{x \mid x \text{ is a real number}\}$ **b.** $\{x \mid x \text{ is a real number and } x \neq -3\}$ **c.** $\{x \mid x \text{ is a real number and } x \neq 2, x \neq 3\}$ **2. a.** $\dfrac{1}{2z-1}$ **b.** $\dfrac{5x+3}{6x-5}$

3. a. 1   **b.** -1 **4.** $-\dfrac{5(2+x)}{x+3}$ **5. a.** $x^2 - 4x + 16$ **b.** $\dfrac{5}{z-3}$ **6.** $\dfrac{-(x+3)}{6x-11}; \dfrac{-x-3}{6x-11}; \dfrac{x+3}{-(6x-11)}; \dfrac{x+3}{-6x+11}; \dfrac{x+3}{11-6x}$

7. a. \$7.20   **b.** \$3.60

Graphing Calculator Explorations 7.1

1. $\{x \mid x \text{ is a real number and } x \neq -2, x \neq 2\}$ 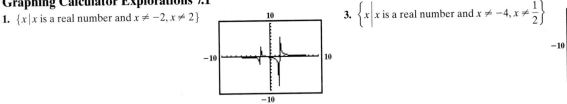   **3.** $\left\{ x \mid x \text{ is a real number and } x \neq -4, x \neq \dfrac{1}{2} \right\}$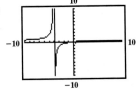

Vocabulary, Readiness & Video Check 7.1

1. rational   **3.** domain   **5.** 1   **7.** $\dfrac{-a}{b}; \dfrac{a}{-b}$ **9.** Rational expressions are fractions and are therefore undefined if the denominator is zero; the domain of a rational function is all real numbers except those that make the denominator of the related rational expression equal to 0. If a denominator contains variables, set it equal to zero and solve.   **11.** We insert parentheses around the numerator or denominator if it has more than one term because the negative sign needs to apply to the entire numerator or denominator.

Exercise Set 7.1

1. $\{x \mid x \text{ is a real number}\}$ **3.** $\{t \mid t \text{ is a real number and } t \neq 0\}$ **5.** $\{x \mid x \text{ is a real number and } x \neq 7\}$ **7.** $\left\{ x \mid x \text{ is a real number and } x \neq \dfrac{1}{3} \right\}$

9. $\{x \mid x \text{ is a real number and } x \neq -2, x \neq 0, x \neq 1\}$ **11.** $\{x \mid x \text{ is a real number and } x \neq 2, x \neq -2\}$ **13.** $\dfrac{-(x-10)}{x+8}; \dfrac{-x+10}{x+8}; \dfrac{x-10}{-(x+8)}; \dfrac{x-10}{-x-8}$

15. $\dfrac{-(5y-3)}{y-12}; \dfrac{-5y+3}{y-12}; \dfrac{5y-3}{-(y-12)}; \dfrac{5y-3}{-y+12}$ **17.** 1   **19.** -1 **21.** $\dfrac{1}{4(x+2)}$ **23.** -5 **25.** $\dfrac{7}{x}$ **27.** $\dfrac{1}{x-9}$ **29.** $5x+1$

31. $\dfrac{x^2}{x-2}$ **33.** $\dfrac{x+2}{2}$ **35.** $-(x+2)$ or $-x-2$ **37.** $\dfrac{11x}{6}$ **39.** $x+y$ **41.** $x^2 - 2x + 4$ **43.** $-x^2 - x - 1$ **45.** $\dfrac{2y+5}{3y+4}$

47. $\dfrac{x-2}{2x^2+1}$ **49.** $\dfrac{1}{3x+5}$ **51.** correct   **53.** correct   **55.** $\dfrac{10}{3}, -8, -\dfrac{7}{3}$ **57.** $-\dfrac{17}{48}, \dfrac{2}{7}, -\dfrac{3}{8}$ **59. a.** \$200 million   **b.** \$500 million

c. \$300 million   **d.** $\{x \mid x \text{ is a real number}\}$ **61.** 400 mg   **63.** $C = 78.125$; medium   **65.** 0.581   **67.** $\dfrac{3}{11}$ **69.** $\dfrac{4}{3}$ **71.** $\dfrac{117}{40}$

73. correct   **75.** incorrect; $\dfrac{1+2}{1+3} = \dfrac{3}{4}$ **77.** no   **79.** yes; 1   **81.** yes; -1 **83.** no; answers may vary   **85.** answers may vary

87. $0, \dfrac{20}{9}, \dfrac{60}{7}, 20, \dfrac{140}{3}, 180, 380, 1980;$

[graph: axes with values 400, 800, 1200, 1600, 2000 on y-axis; 20 40 60 80 100 x]

89. [graph: $y = \dfrac{x^2-16}{x-4}$]

91. [graph: $y = \dfrac{x^2-6x+8}{x-2}$]

Section 7.2
Practice Exercises

1. a. $\dfrac{12a}{5b^2}$ **b.** $-\dfrac{2q}{3}$ **2.** $\dfrac{3}{x+1}$ **3.** $-\dfrac{3x-5}{2x(x+2)}$ **4.** $\dfrac{b^2}{8a^2}$ **5.** $\dfrac{3(x-5)}{4}$ **6.** $\dfrac{2}{x(x-3)}$ **7.** 1   **8. a.** $\dfrac{(y+9)^2}{16x^2}$ **b.** $\dfrac{1}{4x}$

c. $-\dfrac{7(x-2)}{x+4}$ **9.** 2 sq ft   **10.** 504 sq in.   **11.** 549,000 sq ft   **12.** 70.0 miles per hour

Vocabulary, Readiness & Video Check 7.2

1. reciprocals   **3.** $\dfrac{a \cdot d}{b \cdot c}$ or $\dfrac{ad}{bc}$ **5.** $\dfrac{6}{7}$ **7.** fractions; reciprocal   **9.** The units in the unit fraction consist of $\dfrac{\text{units converting to}}{\text{original units}}$.

Exercise Set 7.2

1. $\dfrac{21}{4y}$ **3.** x^4 **5.** $-\dfrac{b^2}{6}$ **7.** $\dfrac{x^2}{10}$ **9.** $\dfrac{1}{3}$ **11.** $\dfrac{m+n}{m-n}$ **13.** $\dfrac{x+5}{x}$ **15.** $\dfrac{(x+2)(x-3)}{(x-4)(x+4)}$ **17.** $\dfrac{2x^4}{3}$ **19.** $\dfrac{12}{y^6}$ **21.** $x(x+4)$

23. $\dfrac{3(x+1)}{x^3(x-1)}$ **25.** m^2-n^2 **27.** $-\dfrac{x+2}{x-3}$ **29.** $\dfrac{x+2}{x-3}$ **31.** $\dfrac{5}{6}$ **33.** $\dfrac{3x}{8}$ **35.** $\dfrac{3}{2}$ **37.** $\dfrac{3x+4y}{2(x+2y)}$ **39.** $\dfrac{2(x+2)}{x-2}$ **41.** $-\dfrac{y(x+2)}{4}$

43. $\dfrac{(a+5)(a+3)}{(a+2)(a+1)}$ **45.** $\dfrac{5}{x}$ **47.** $\dfrac{2(n-8)}{3n-1}$ **49.** $4x^3(x-3)$ **51.** $\dfrac{(a+b)^2}{a-b}$ **53.** $\dfrac{3x+5}{x^2+4}$ **55.** $\dfrac{4}{x-2}$ **57.** $\dfrac{a-b}{6(a^2+ab+b^2)}$

59. 1440 **61.** 5 **63.** 81 **65.** 73 **67.** 56.7 **69.** 1,201,500 sq ft **71.** 270.5 miles/hour **73.** 1 **75.** $-\dfrac{10}{9}$ **77.** $-\dfrac{1}{5}$

79.

81. true **83.** false; $\dfrac{x^2+3x}{20}$ **85.** $\dfrac{2}{9(x-5)}$ sq ft **87.** $\dfrac{x}{2}$ **89.** $\dfrac{5a(2a+b)(3a-2b)}{b^2(a-b)(a+2b)}$ **91.** answers may vary

Section 7.3

Practice Exercises

1. $\dfrac{2a}{b}$ **2.** 1 **3.** $4x-5$ **4. a.** 42 **b.** $45y^3$ **5. a.** $(y-5)(y-4)$ **b.** $a(a+2)$ **6.** $3(2x-1)^2$ **7.** $(x+4)(x+1)(x-4)$

8. $3-x$ or $x-3$ **9. a.** $\dfrac{21x^2y}{35xy^2}$ **b.** $\dfrac{18x}{8x+14}$ **10.** $\dfrac{3x-6}{(x-2)(x+3)(x-5)}$

Vocabulary, Readiness & Video Check 7.3

1. $\dfrac{9}{11}$ **3.** $\dfrac{a+c}{b}$ **5.** $\dfrac{5-(6+x)}{x}$ **7.** We factor denominators into the smallest factors—including coefficients—so we can determine the most number of times each unique factor occurs in any one denominator for the LCD.

Exercise Set 7.3

1. $\dfrac{a+9}{13}$ **3.** $\dfrac{3m}{n}$ **5.** 4 **7.** $\dfrac{y+10}{3+y}$ **9.** $5x+3$ **11.** $\dfrac{4}{a+5}$ **13.** $\dfrac{1}{x-6}$ **15.** $\dfrac{5x+7}{x-3}$ **17.** $x+5$ **19.** 3 **21.** $4x^3$ **23.** $8x(x+2)$ **25.** $(x+3)(x-2)$ **27.** $3(x+6)$ **29.** $5(x-6)^2$ **31.** $6(x+1)^2$ **33.** $x-8$ or $8-x$ **35.** $(x-1)(x+4)(x+3)$ **37.** $(3x+1)(x+1)(x-1)(2x+1)$ **39.** $2x^2(x+4)(x-4)$ **41.** $\dfrac{6x}{4x^2}$ **43.** $\dfrac{24b^2}{12ab^2}$ **45.** $\dfrac{9y}{2y(x+3)}$ **47.** $\dfrac{9ab+2b}{5b(a+2)}$ **49.** $\dfrac{x^2+x}{x(x+4)(x+2)(x+1)}$ **51.** $\dfrac{18y-2}{30x^2-60}$ **53.** $2x$ **55.** $\dfrac{x+3}{2x-1}$ **57.** $x+1$ **59.** $\dfrac{1}{x^2-8}$ **61.** $\dfrac{6(4x+1)}{x(2x+1)}$ **63.** $\dfrac{29}{21}$ **65.** $-\dfrac{7}{12}$ **67.** $\dfrac{7}{30}$ **69.** d **71.** answers may vary **73.** c **75.** b **77.** $-\dfrac{5}{x-2}$ **79.** $\dfrac{7+x}{x-2}$ **81.** $\dfrac{20}{x-2}$ m **83.** answers may vary **85.** 95,304 Earth days **87.** answers may vary **89.** answers may vary

Section 7.4

Practice Exercises

1. a. 0 **b.** $\dfrac{21a+10}{24a^2}$ **2.** $\dfrac{6}{x-5}$ **3.** $\dfrac{13y+3}{5y(y+1)}$ **4.** $\dfrac{13}{x-5}$ **5.** $\dfrac{3b+6}{b+3}$ or $\dfrac{3(b+2)}{b+3}$ **6.** $\dfrac{10-3x^2}{2x(2x+3)}$ **7.** $\dfrac{x(5x+6)}{(x+4)(x+3)(x-3)}$

Vocabulary, Readiness & Video Check 7.4

1. D **3.** A **5.** The problem adds two rational expressions with denominators that are opposites of each other. Recognizing this special case can save you time and effort. If you recognize that one denominator is -1 times the other denominator, you may save time.

Exercise Set 7.4

1. $\dfrac{5}{x}$ **3.** $\dfrac{75a-6b^2}{5b}$ **5.** $\dfrac{6x+5}{2x^2}$ **7.** $\dfrac{11}{x+1}$ **9.** $\dfrac{x-6}{(x-2)(x+2)}$ **11.** $\dfrac{35x-6}{4x(x-2)}$ **13.** $-\dfrac{2}{x-3}$ **15.** 0 **17.** $-\dfrac{1}{x^2-1}$ **19.** $\dfrac{5+2x}{x}$ **21.** $\dfrac{6x-7}{x-2}$ **23.** $-\dfrac{y+4}{y+3}$ **25.** $\dfrac{-5x+14}{4x}$ or $-\dfrac{5x-14}{4x}$ **27.** 2 **29.** $\dfrac{9x^4-4x^2}{21}$ **31.** $\dfrac{x+2}{(x+3)^2}$ **33.** $\dfrac{9b-4}{5b(b-1)}$ **35.** $\dfrac{2+m}{m}$ **37.** $\dfrac{x^2+3x}{(x-7)(x-2)}$ or $\dfrac{x(x+3)}{(x-7)(x-2)}$ **39.** $\dfrac{10}{1-2x}$ **41.** $\dfrac{15x-1}{(x+1)^2(x-1)}$ **43.** $\dfrac{x^2-3x-2}{(x-1)^2(x+1)}$ **45.** $\dfrac{a+2}{2(a+3)}$ **47.** $\dfrac{y(2y+1)}{(2y+3)^2}$ **49.** $\dfrac{x-10}{2(x-2)}$ **51.** $\dfrac{2x+21}{(x+3)^2}$ **53.** $\dfrac{-5x+23}{(x-2)(x-3)}$ **55.** $\dfrac{7}{2(m-10)}$ **57.** $\dfrac{2x^2-2x-46}{(x+1)(x-6)(x-5)}$ or $\dfrac{2(x^2-x-23)}{(x+1)(x-6)(x-5)}$ **59.** $\dfrac{n+4}{4n(n-1)(n-2)}$ **61.** 10 **63.** 2 **65.** $\dfrac{25a}{9(a-2)}$

67. $\dfrac{x + 4}{(x - 2)(x - 1)}$ **69.** $x = \dfrac{2}{3}$ **71.** $x = -\dfrac{1}{2}, x = 1$ **73.** $x = -\dfrac{15}{2}$ **75.** $\dfrac{6x^2 - 5x - 3}{x(x + 1)(x - 1)}$ **77.** $\dfrac{4x^2 - 15x + 6}{(x - 2)^2(x + 2)(x - 3)}$

79. $\dfrac{-2x^2 + 14x + 55}{(x + 2)(x + 7)(x + 3)}$ **81.** $\dfrac{2x - 16}{(x + 4)(x - 4)}$ in.   **83.** $\dfrac{P - G}{P}$ **85.** answers may vary   **87.** $\left(\dfrac{90x - 40}{x}\right)^{\circ}$ **89.** answers may vary

Section 7.5

Practice Exercises

1. -2 **2.** 13 **3.** $-1, 7$ **4.** $-\dfrac{19}{2}$ **5.** No solution   **6.** -8 **7.** $b = \dfrac{ax}{a - x}$

Graphing Calculator Explorations 7.5

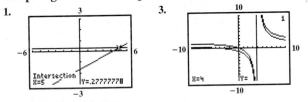

1.   **3.**

Vocabulary, Readiness & Video Check 7.5

1. c   **3.** b   **5.** a   **7.** These equations are solved in very different ways, so you need to determine the next correct move to make. For a linear equation, you first "move" variable terms to one side and numbers to the other; for a quadratic equation, you first set the equation equal to 0.
9. the steps for solving an equation containing rational expressions; as if it's the only variable in the equation

Exercise Set 7.5

1. 30   **3.** 0   **5.** -2 **7.** $-5, 2$ **9.** 5   **11.** 3   **13.** 1   **15.** 5   **17.** no solution   **19.** 4   **21.** -8 **23.** $6, -4$ **25.** 1
27. $3, -4$ **29.** -3 **31.** 0   **33.** -2 **35.** $8, -2$ **37.** no solution   **39.** 3   **41.** $-11, 1$ **43.** $I = \dfrac{E}{R}$ **45.** $B = \dfrac{2U - TE}{T}$
47. $w = \dfrac{Bh^2}{705}$ **49.** $G = \dfrac{V}{N - R}$ **51.** $r = \dfrac{C}{2\pi}$ **53.** $x = \dfrac{3y}{3 + y}$ **55.** $\dfrac{1}{x}$ **57.** $\dfrac{1}{x} + \dfrac{1}{2}$ **59.** $\dfrac{1}{3}$ **61.** $(2, 0), (0, -2)$
63. $(-4, 0), (-2, 0), (3, 0), (0, 4)$ **65.** answers may vary   **67.** $\dfrac{5x + 9}{9x}$ **69.** no solution   **71.** $100°, 80°$ **73.** $22.5°, 67.5°$ **75.** $\dfrac{17}{4}$

Integrated Review

1. expression; $\dfrac{3 + 2x}{3x}$ **2.** expression; $\dfrac{18 + 5a}{6a}$ **3.** equation; 3   **4.** equation; 18   **5.** expression; $\dfrac{x + 1}{x(x - 1)}$ **6.** expression; $\dfrac{3(x + 1)}{x(x - 3)}$
7. equation; no solution   **8.** equation; 1   **9.** expression; 10   **10.** expression; $\dfrac{z}{3(9z - 5)}$ **11.** expression; $\dfrac{5x + 7}{x - 3}$ **12.** expression; $\dfrac{7p + 5}{2p + 7}$
13. equation; 23   **14.** equation; 5   **15.** expression; $\dfrac{25a}{9(a - 2)}$ **16.** expression; $\dfrac{4x + 5}{(x + 1)(x - 1)}$ **17.** expression; $\dfrac{3x^2 + 5x + 3}{(3x - 1)^2}$
18. expression; $\dfrac{2x^2 - 3x - 1}{(2x - 5)^2}$ **19.** expression; $\dfrac{4x - 37}{5x}$ **20.** expression; $\dfrac{29x - 23}{3x}$ **21.** equation; $\dfrac{8}{5}$ **22.** equation; $-\dfrac{7}{3}$
23. answers may vary   **24.** answers may vary

Section 7.6

Practice Exercises

1. 99   **2.** $\dfrac{13}{3}$ **3.** $\$9.03$ **4.** 6   **5.** 15   **6.** $1\dfrac{5}{7}$ hr   **7.** bus: 45 mph; car: 60 mph

Vocabulary, Readiness & Video Check 7.6

1. c   **3.** $\dfrac{1}{x}; \dfrac{1}{x} - 3$ **5.** $z + 5; \dfrac{1}{z + 5}$ **7.** $2y; \dfrac{11}{2y}$ **9.** No. Proportions are actually equations containing rational expressions, so they can also be

solved by using the steps to solve those equations.   **11.** divided by, quotient   **13.** $\dfrac{325}{x + 7} = \dfrac{290}{x}$

Exercise Set 7.6

1. 4   **3.** $\dfrac{50}{9}$ **5.** -3 **7.** $\dfrac{14}{9}$ **9.** 123 lb   **11.** 132 cal   **13.** $y = 21.25$ **15.** $y = 5\dfrac{5}{7}$ ft   **17.** 2   **19.** -3 **21.** $2\dfrac{2}{9}$ hr   **23.** $1\dfrac{1}{2}$ min
25. trip to park rate: r; to park time: $\dfrac{12}{r}$; return trip rate: r; return time: $\dfrac{18}{r} = \dfrac{12}{r} + 1; r = 6$ mph   **27.** 1st portion: 10 mph; cooldown: 8 mph
29. 360 sq ft   **31.** 2   **33.** $\$108.00$ **35.** 20 mph   **37.** $y = 37\dfrac{1}{2}$ ft   **39.** 41 mph; 51 mph   **41.** 5   **43.** 217 mph   **45.** 9 gal
47. 8 mph   **49.** 2.2 mph; 3.3 mph   **51.** 3 hr   **53.** $26\dfrac{2}{3}$ ft   **55.** 216 nuts   **57.** $666\dfrac{2}{3}$ mi   **59.** 20 hr   **61.** car: 70 mph; motorcycle: 60 mph
63. $5\dfrac{1}{4}$ hr   **65.** 8   **67.** first car: 64 mph; second car: 50 mph   **69.** 510 mph   **71.** $x = 5$ **73.** $x = 13.5$ **75.** $-\dfrac{4}{3}$; downward

77. $\dfrac{11}{4}$; upward   **79.** undefined slope; vertical   **81.** 64,000 megawatts   **83.** 35,840,000 people   **85.** yes   **87.** first pump: 28 min; second

pump: 84 min   **89.** none; answers may vary   **91.** answers may vary   **93.** $R = \dfrac{D}{T}$

Section 7.7

Practice Exercises

1. a. $\dfrac{1}{12m}$ **b.** $\dfrac{8x(x+4)}{3(x-4)}$ **c.** $\dfrac{b^2}{a^2}$ **2. a.** $\dfrac{8x(x+4)}{3(x-4)}$ **b.** $\dfrac{b^2}{a^2}$ **3.** $\dfrac{y(3xy+1)}{x^2(1+xy)}$ **4.** $\dfrac{1-6x}{15+6x}$ or $\dfrac{1-6x}{3(5+2x)}$

Vocabulary, Readiness & Video Check 7.7

1. $\dfrac{7}{1+z}$ **3.** $\dfrac{1}{x^2}$ **5.** $\dfrac{2}{x}$ **7.** $\dfrac{1}{9y}$ **9.** a single fraction in the numerator and in the denominator   **11.** Since a negative exponent moves its base from a numerator to a denominator of the expression, a rational expression containing negative exponents can become a complex fraction when rewritten with positive exponents.

Exercise Set 7.7

1. 4   **3.** $\dfrac{7}{13}$ **5.** $\dfrac{4}{x}$ **7.** $\dfrac{9(x-2)}{9x^2+4}$ **9.** $2x+y$ **11.** $\dfrac{2(x+1)}{2x-1}$ **13.** $\dfrac{2x+3}{4-9x}$ **15.** $\dfrac{1}{x^2-2x+4}$ **17.** $\dfrac{x}{5(x-2)}$ **19.** $\dfrac{x-2}{2x-1}$

21. $\dfrac{x}{2-3x}$ **23.** $-\dfrac{y}{x+y}$ **25.** $-\dfrac{2x^3}{y(x-y)}$ **27.** $\dfrac{2x+1}{y}$ **29.** $\dfrac{x-3}{9}$ **31.** $\dfrac{1}{x+2}$ **33.** 2   **35.** $\dfrac{xy^2}{x^2+y^2}$ **37.** $\dfrac{2b^2+3a}{b(b-a)}$

39. $\dfrac{x}{(x+1)(x-1)}$ **41.** $\dfrac{1+a}{1-a}$ **43.** $\dfrac{x(x+6y)}{2y}$ **45.** $\dfrac{5a}{2(a+2)}$ **47.** $xy(5y+2x)$ **49.** $\dfrac{xy}{2x+5y}$ **51.** $\dfrac{x^2y^2}{4}$ **53.** $-9x^3y^4$

55. -9 **57.** a and c   **59.** $\dfrac{770a}{770-s}$ **61.** a, b   **63.** answers may vary   **65.** $\dfrac{1+x}{2+x}$ **67.** $x(x+1)$ **69.** $\dfrac{x-3y}{x+3y}$ **71.** $3a^2+4a+4$

73. a. $\dfrac{1}{a+h}$ **b.** $\dfrac{1}{a}$ **c.** $\dfrac{\dfrac{1}{a+h}-\dfrac{1}{a}}{h}$ **d.** $-\dfrac{1}{a(a+h)}$ **75. a.** $\dfrac{3}{a+h+1}$ **b.** $\dfrac{3}{a+1}$ **c.** $\dfrac{\dfrac{3}{a+h+1}-\dfrac{3}{a+1}}{h}$ **d.** $\dfrac{-3}{(a+h+1)(a+1)}$

Chapter 7 Vocabulary Check

1. rational expression   **2.** complex fraction   **3.** $\dfrac{-a}{b};\dfrac{a}{-b}$ **4.** denominator   **5.** simplifying   **6.** reciprocals   **7.** least common denominator
8. ratio   **9.** proportion   **10.** cross products   **11.** domain

Chapter 7 Review

1. $\{x \mid x \text{ is a real number}\}$ **3.** $\{x \mid x \text{ is a real number and } x \ne 5\}$ **5.** $\{x \mid x \text{ is a real number and } x \ne 0, x \ne 8\}$ **7.** -1 **9.** $\dfrac{1}{x-7}$

11. $\dfrac{x+a}{x-c}$ **13.** $-\dfrac{1}{x^2+4x+16}$ **15.** \$119   **17.** $\dfrac{3x^2}{y}$ **19.** $\dfrac{x-3}{x+2}$ **21.** $\dfrac{x+3}{x-4}$ **23.** $(x-6)(x-3)$ **25.** $\dfrac{1}{2}$ **27.** $-\dfrac{2(2x+3)}{y-2}$

29. $\dfrac{1}{x+2}$ **31.** $\dfrac{2x-10}{3x^2}$ **33.** $14x$ **35.** $\dfrac{10x^2y}{14x^3y}$ **37.** $\dfrac{x^2-3x-10}{(x+2)(x-5)(x+9)}$ **39.** $\dfrac{4y-30x^2}{5x^2y}$ **41.** $\dfrac{-2x-2}{x+3}$ **43.** $\dfrac{x-4}{3x}$

45. $\dfrac{x^2+2x+4}{4x};\dfrac{x+2}{32}$ **47.** 30   **49.** no solution   **51.** $\dfrac{9}{7}$ **53.** $b=\dfrac{4A}{5x^2}$ **55.** 6   **57.** 9   **59.** 675 parts   **61.** 3

63. fast car speed: 30 mph; slow car speed: 20 mph   **65.** $17\dfrac{1}{2}$ hr   **67.** $x=15$ **69.** $-\dfrac{7}{18y}$ **71.** $\dfrac{3y-1}{2y-1}$ **73.** $-\dfrac{x^2+9}{6x}$ **75.** $\dfrac{xy+1}{x}$

77. $\dfrac{1}{2x}$ **79.** $\dfrac{x-4}{x+4}$ **81.** $\dfrac{1}{x-6}$ **83.** $\dfrac{2}{(x+3)(x-2)}$ **85.** $\dfrac{1}{2}$ **87.** 1   **89.** $x=6$ **91.** $\dfrac{3}{10}$ **93.** $\dfrac{1}{y^2-1}$

Chapter 7 Getting Ready for the Test

1. D   **2.** E   **3.** B   **4.** A   **5.** A   **6.** C   **7.** C   **8.** D   **9.** D   **10.** A   **11.** D   **12.** D   **13.** A   **14.** B   **15.** B
16. A   **17.** C   **18.** C   **19.** A   **20.** A

Chapter 7 Test

1. $\{x \mid x \text{ is a real number}, x \ne -1, x \ne -3\}$ **2. a.** \$115   **b.** \$103   **3.** $\dfrac{3}{5}$ **4.** $\dfrac{1}{x+6}$ **5.** $\dfrac{1}{x^2-3x+9}$ **6.** $\dfrac{2m(m+2)}{m-2}$ **7.** $\dfrac{a+2}{a+5}$

8. $-\dfrac{1}{x+y}$ **9.** 15   **10.** $\dfrac{y-2}{4}$ **11.** $\dfrac{19x-6}{2x+5}$ **12.** $\dfrac{3a-4}{(a-3)(a+2)}$ **13.** $\dfrac{3}{x-1}$ **14.** $\dfrac{2(x+5)}{x(y+5)}$ **15.** $\dfrac{x^2+2x+35}{(x+9)(x+2)(x-5)}$

16. $\dfrac{30}{11}$ **17.** -6 **18.** no solution   **19.** $-2,5$ **20.** no solution   **21.** $\dfrac{xz}{2y}$ **22.** $\dfrac{5y^2-1}{y+2}$ **23.** $b-a$ **24.** 18 bulbs   **25.** 5 or 1

26. 30 mph   **27.** $6\dfrac{2}{3}$ hr   **28.** $x=12$

Chapter 7 Cumulative Review

1. a. $\dfrac{15}{x} = 4$ **b.** $12 - 3 = x$ **c.** $4x + 17 \neq 21$ **d.** $3x < 48$; Sec. 1.4, Ex. 9   **3.** amount at 7%: \$12,500; amount at 9%: \$7500; Sec. 2.7, Ex. 4

5.
; Sec. 3.3, Ex. 6   **7. a.** 4^7 **b.** x^{10} **c.** y^4 **d.** y^{12} **e.** $(-5)^{15}$ **f.** a^2b^2; Sec. 5.1, Ex. 3   **9.** $12z + 16$; Sec. 5.2, Ex. 12

11. $27a^3 + 27a^2b + 9ab^2 + b^3$; Sec. 5.3, Ex. 8   **13. a.** $t^2 + 4t + 4$ **b.** $p^2 - 2pq + q^2$ **c.** $4x^2 + 20x + 25$ **d.** $x^4 - 14x^2y + 49y^2$; Sec. 5.4, Ex. 5

15. a. x^3 **b.** 81   **c.** $\dfrac{q^9}{p^4}$ **d.** $\dfrac{32}{125}$; Sec. 5.5, Ex. 2   **17.** $4x^2 - 4x + 6 + \dfrac{-11}{2x + 3}$; Sec. 5.6, Ex. 6   **19. a.** 4   **b.** 1   **c.** 3; Sec. 6.1, Ex. 1

21. $-3a(3a^4 - 6a + 1)$; Sec. 6.1, Ex. 5   **23.** $3(m + 2)(m - 10)$; Sec. 6.2, Ex. 9   **25.** $(3x + 2)(x + 3)$; Sec. 6.3, Ex. 1   **27.** $(x + 6)^2$; Sec. 6.3, Ex. 8

29. prime polynomial; Sec. 6.5, Ex. 4b   **31.** $(x + 2)(x^2 - 2x + 4)$; Sec. 6.5, Ex. 8   **33.** $(2x + 3)(x + 1)(x - 1)$; Ch. 6 Int. Rev., Ex. 2

35. $3(2m + n)(2m - n)$; Ch. 6 Int. Rev., Ex. 3   **37.** $-\dfrac{1}{2}$, 4; Sec. 6.6, Ex. 6   **39.** $(1, 0), (4, 0)$; Sec. 6.6, Ex. 11   **41.** base: 6 m; height: 10 m; Sec. 6.7, Ex. 3

43. $-\dfrac{2(3 + x)}{x + 1}$; Sec. 7.1, Ex. 4   **45.** $\dfrac{2}{x(x + 1)}$; Sec. 7.2, Ex. 6   **47.** $\dfrac{1 + 2x}{2(2 - x)}$; Sec. 7.7, Ex. 4

CHAPTER 9 INEQUALITIES AND ABSOLUTE VALUE

Section 9.1
Practice Exercises

1. $\{1, 3\}$ **2.** $(-\infty, 2)$ **3.** $\{\ \}$ or $\varnothing$ **4.** $(-4, 2)$ **5.** $[-6, 8]$ **6.** $\{1, 2, 3, 4, 5, 6, 7, 9\}$ **7.** $\left(-\infty, \dfrac{3}{8}\right] \cup [3, \infty)$ **8.** $(-\infty, \infty)$

Vocabulary, Readiness & Video Check 9.1

1. compound   **3.** or   **5.** $\cup$ **7.** and   **9.** or

Exercise Set 9.1

1. $\{2, 3, 4, 5, 6, 7\}$ **3.** $\{4, 6\}$ **5.** $\{\ldots, -2, -1, 0, 1, \ldots\}$ **7.** $\{5, 7\}$ **9.** $\{x \mid x \text{ is an odd integer or } x = 2 \text{ or } x = 4\}$ **11.** $\{2, 4\}$
13. $(-3, 1)$ **15.** $\varnothing$ **17.** $(-\infty, -1)$ **19.** $[6, \infty)$ **21.** $(-\infty, -3]$ **23.** $(4, 10)$

25. $(11, 17)$ **27.** $[1, 4]$ **29.** $\left[-3, \dfrac{3}{2}\right]$ **31.** $\left[-\dfrac{7}{3}, 7\right]$ **33.** $(-\infty, 5)$ **35.** $(-\infty, -4] \cup [1, \infty)$

37. $(-\infty, \infty)$ **39.** $[2, \infty)$ **41.** $(-\infty, -4) \cup (-2, \infty)$ **43.** $(-\infty, \infty)$ **45.** $\left(-\dfrac{1}{2}, \dfrac{2}{3}\right)$ **47.** $(-\infty, \infty)$ **49.** $\left[\dfrac{3}{2}, 6\right]$

51. $\left(\dfrac{5}{4}, \dfrac{11}{4}\right)$ **53.** $\varnothing$ **55.** $\left(-\infty, -\dfrac{56}{5}\right) \cup \left(\dfrac{5}{3}, \infty\right)$ **57.** $\left(-5, \dfrac{5}{2}\right)$ **59.** $\left(0, \dfrac{14}{3}\right]$ **61.** $(-\infty, -3]$ **63.** $(-\infty, 1] \cup \left(\dfrac{29}{7}, \infty\right)$ **65.** $\varnothing$

67. $\left[-\dfrac{1}{2}, \dfrac{3}{2}\right)$ **69.** $\left(-\dfrac{4}{3}, \dfrac{7}{3}\right)$ **71.** $(6, 12)$ **73.** -12 **75.** -4 **77.** $-7, 7$ **79.** 0 **81.** 2004, 2005   **83.** answers may vary

85. $(6, \infty)$ **87.** $[3, 7]$ **89.** $(-\infty, -1)$ **91.** $-20.2° \le F \le 95°$ **93.** $67 \le \text{final score} \le 94$

Section 9.2
Practice Exercises

1. $-13, 13$ **2.** $-1, 4$ **3.** $-80, 70$ **4.** $-2, 2$ **5.** 0 **6.** $\{\ \}$ or $\varnothing$ **7.** $\{\ \}$ or $\varnothing$ **8.** $-\dfrac{3}{5}, 5$ **9.** 5

Vocabulary, Readiness & Video Check 9.2

1. C   **3.** B   **5.** D

Exercise Set 9.2

1. $-7, 7$ **3.** $4.2, -4.2$ **5.** $7, -2$ **7.** $8, 4$ **9.** $5, -5$ **11.** $3, -3$ **13.** 0 **15.** $\varnothing$ **17.** $\frac{1}{5}$ **19.** $9, -\frac{1}{2}$ **21.** $-\frac{5}{2}$ **23.** $4, -4$

25. 0 **27.** $\varnothing$ **29.** $0, \frac{14}{3}$ **31.** $2, -2$ **33.** $\varnothing$ **35.** $7, -1$ **37.** $\varnothing$ **39.** $\varnothing$ **41.** $-\frac{1}{8}$ **43.** $\frac{1}{2}, -\frac{5}{6}$ **45.** $2, -\frac{12}{5}$ **47.** $3, -2$

49. $-8, \frac{2}{3}$ **51.** $\varnothing$ **53.** 4 **55.** $13, -8$ **57.** $3, -3$ **59.** $8, -7$ **61.** $2, 3$ **63.** $2, -\frac{10}{3}$ **65.** $\frac{3}{2}$ **67.** $\varnothing$ **69.** 29.1%

71. $33.12°$ **73.** answers may vary   **75.** answers may vary   **77.** $\varnothing$ **79.** $|x| = 5$ **81.** answers may vary   **83.** $|x-1| = 5$ **85.** answers may vary   **87.** $|x| = 6$ **89.** $|x - 2| = |3x - 4|$

Section 9.3
Practice Exercises

1. $(-5, 5)$ **2.** $(-4, 2)$ **3.** $\left[-\frac{2}{3}, 2\right]$ **4.** $\{ \}$ or $\varnothing$ **5.** $\{2\}$

6. $(-\infty, -10] \cup [2, \infty)$ **7.** $(-\infty, \infty)$ **8.** $(-\infty, 0) \cup (12, \infty)$

Vocabulary, Readiness & Video Check 9.3

1. D   **3.** C   **5.** A   **7.** The solution set involves "or" and "or" means "union."

Exercise Set 9.3

1. $[-4, 4]$ **3.** $(1, 5)$ **5.** $(-5, -1)$ **7.** $[-10, 3]$

9. $[-5, 5]$ **11.** $\varnothing$ **13.** $[0, 12]$ **15.** $(-\infty, -3) \cup (3, \infty)$

17. $(-\infty, -24] \cup [4, \infty)$ **19.** $(-\infty, -4) \cup (4, \infty)$ **21.** $(-\infty, \infty)$

23. $\left(-\infty, \frac{2}{3}\right) \cup (2, \infty)$ **25.** $\{0\}$ **27.** $\left(-\infty, -\frac{3}{8}\right) \cup \left(-\frac{3}{8}, \infty\right)$ **29.** $[-2, 2]$

31. $(-\infty, -1) \cup (1, \infty)$ **33.** $(-5, 11)$ **35.** $(-\infty, 4) \cup (6, \infty)$ **37.** $\varnothing$

39. $(-\infty, \infty)$ **41.** $[-2, 9]$ **43.** $(-\infty, -11] \cup [1, \infty)$ **45.** $(-\infty, 0) \cup (0, \infty)$

47. $(-\infty, \infty)$ **49.** $\left[-\frac{1}{2}, 1\right]$ **51.** $(-\infty, -3) \cup (0, \infty)$ **53.** $\varnothing$

55. $\left\{\frac{3}{8}\right\}$ **57.** $\left(-\frac{2}{3}, 0\right)$ **59.** $(-\infty, -12) \cup (0, \infty)$ **61.** $[-1, 8]$

63. $\left[-\frac{23}{8}, \frac{17}{8}\right]$ **65.** $(-2, 5)$ **67.** $5, -2$ **69.** $(-\infty, -7] \cup [17, \infty)$ **71.** $-\frac{9}{4}$ **73.** $(-2, 1)$ **75.** $2, \frac{4}{3}$ **77.** $\varnothing$

79. $\frac{19}{2}, -\frac{17}{2}$ **81.** $\left(-\infty, -\frac{25}{3}\right) \cup \left(\frac{35}{3}, \infty\right)$ **83.** 1960 million; 2130 million; 2290 million   **85.** -1.5 **87.** 0 **89.** $|x| < 7$

91. $|x| \leq 5$ **93.** answers may vary   **95.** $3.45 < x < 3.55$

Integrated Review

1. $(-5, 7)$ **2.** $(-\infty, \infty)$ **3.** $1, \frac{1}{2}$ **4.** $(-3, 2)$ **5.** $(-\infty, -1] \cup [1, \infty)$ **6.** $-18, -\frac{4}{3}$ **7.** $\left[-\frac{2}{3}, 4\right]$

8. $\varnothing$ **9.** $(-\infty, 1]$ **10.** $(-\infty, 0]$ **11.** $[0, 6]$ **12.** $-\frac{3}{2}, 1$ **13.** B   **14.** E   **15.** A   **16.** C   **17.** D

Section 9.4
Practice Exercises

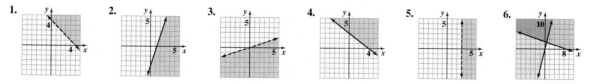

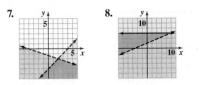

7. **8.**

Vocabulary, Readiness & Video Check 9.4

1. linear inequality in two variables **3.** false **5.** true **7.** yes **9.** yes **11.** We find the boundary line equation by replacing the inequality symbol with =. The points on this line are solutions (line is solid) if the inequality is $\geq$ or $\leq$; they are not solutions (line is dashed) if the inequality is $>$ or $<$.

Exercise Set 9.4

1. no; yes **3.** no; no **5.** no; yes

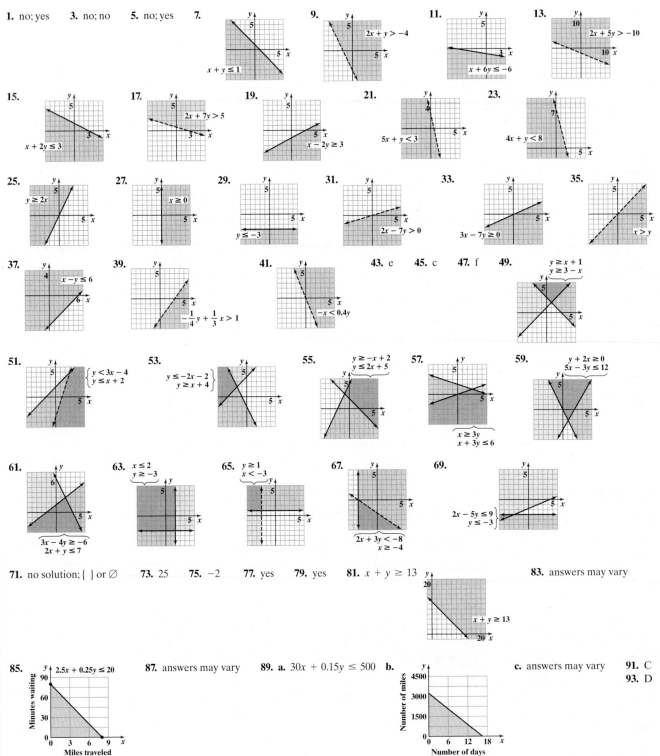

43. e **45.** c **47.** f

71. no solution; { } or $\varnothing$ **73.** 25 **75.** -2 **77.** yes **79.** yes **81.** $x + y \geq 13$

83. answers may vary

85. **87.** answers may vary **89. a.** $30x + 0.15y \leq 500$ **b.** **c.** answers may vary **91.** C **93.** D

95. 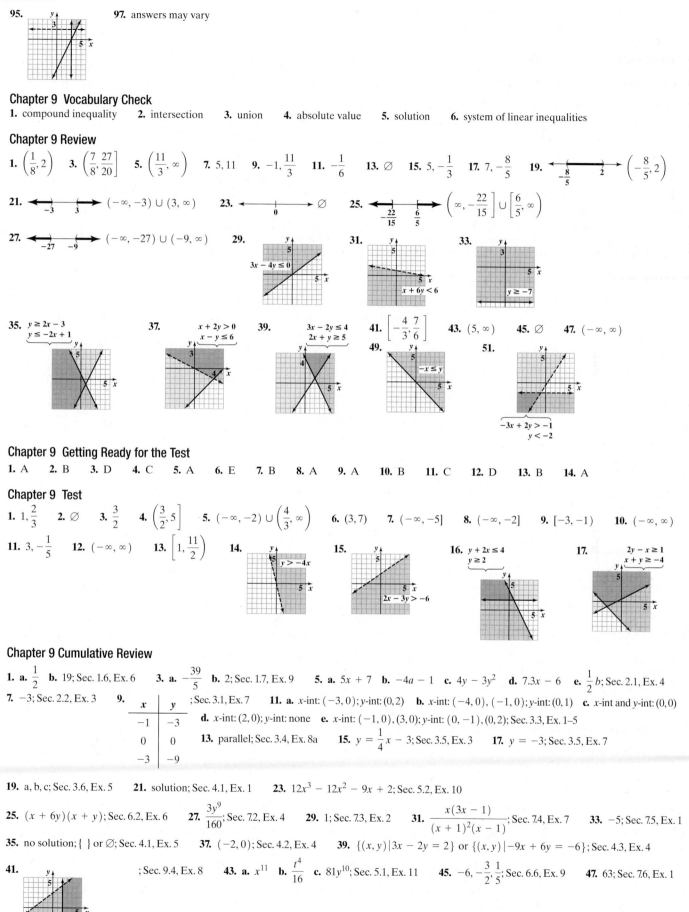   **97.** answers may vary

Chapter 9 Vocabulary Check

1. compound inequality   **2.** intersection   **3.** union   **4.** absolute value   **5.** solution   **6.** system of linear inequalities

Chapter 9 Review

1. $\left(\frac{1}{8}, 2\right)$ **3.** $\left(\frac{7}{8}, \frac{27}{20}\right]$ **5.** $\left(\frac{11}{3}, \infty\right)$ **7.** 5, 11   **9.** $-1, \frac{11}{3}$ **11.** $-\frac{1}{6}$ **13.** $\varnothing$ **15.** $5, -\frac{1}{3}$ **17.** $7, -\frac{8}{5}$ **19.** $\left(-\frac{8}{5}, 2\right)$

21. $(-\infty, -3) \cup (3, \infty)$ **23.** $\varnothing$ **25.** $\left(\infty, -\frac{22}{15}\right] \cup \left[\frac{6}{5}, \infty\right)$

27. $(-\infty, -27) \cup (-9, \infty)$ **29.** $3x - 4y \le 0$ **31.** $x + 6y < 6$ **33.** $y \ge -7$

35. $y \ge 2x - 3$, $y \le -2x + 1$ **37.** $x + 2y > 0$, $x - y \le 6$ **39.** $3x - 2y \le 4$, $2x + y \ge 5$ **41.** $\left[-\frac{4}{3}, \frac{7}{6}\right]$ **43.** $(5, \infty)$ **45.** $\varnothing$ **47.** $(-\infty, \infty)$ **49.** $-x \le y$ **51.** $-3x + 2y > -1$, $y < -2$

Chapter 9 Getting Ready for the Test

1. A   **2.** B   **3.** D   **4.** C   **5.** A   **6.** E   **7.** B   **8.** A   **9.** A   **10.** B   **11.** C   **12.** D   **13.** B   **14.** A

Chapter 9 Test

1. $1, \frac{2}{3}$ **2.** $\varnothing$ **3.** $\frac{3}{2}$ **4.** $\left(\frac{3}{2}, 5\right]$ **5.** $(-\infty, -2) \cup \left(\frac{4}{3}, \infty\right)$ **6.** $(3, 7)$ **7.** $(-\infty, -5]$ **8.** $(-\infty, -2]$ **9.** $[-3, -1)$ **10.** $(-\infty, \infty)$

11. $3, -\frac{1}{5}$ **12.** $(-\infty, \infty)$ **13.** $\left[1, \frac{11}{2}\right)$ **14.** $y > -4x$ **15.** $2x - 3y > -6$ **16.** $y + 2x \le 4$, $y \ge 2$ **17.** $2y - x \ge 1$, $x + y \ge -4$

Chapter 9 Cumulative Review

1. a. $\frac{1}{2}$ **b.** 19; Sec. 1.6, Ex. 6   **3. a.** $-\frac{39}{5}$ **b.** 2; Sec. 1.7, Ex. 9   **5. a.** $5x + 7$ **b.** $-4a - 1$ **c.** $4y - 3y^2$ **d.** $7.3x - 6$ **e.** $\frac{1}{2}b$; Sec. 2.1, Ex. 4

7. -3; Sec. 2.2, Ex. 3   **9.**

x	y
-1	-3
0	0
-3	-9

; Sec. 3.1, Ex. 7   **11. a.** x-int: $(-3, 0)$; y-int: $(0, 2)$ **b.** x-int: $(-4, 0)$, $(-1, 0)$; y-int: $(0, 1)$ **c.** x-int and y-int: $(0, 0)$ **d.** x-int: $(2, 0)$; y-int: none   **e.** x-int: $(-1, 0)$, $(3, 0)$; y-int: $(0, -1)$, $(0, 2)$; Sec. 3.3, Ex. 1–5   **13.** parallel; Sec. 3.4, Ex. 8a   **15.** $y = \frac{1}{4}x - 3$; Sec. 3.5, Ex. 3   **17.** $y = -3$; Sec. 3.5, Ex. 7

19. a, b, c; Sec. 3.6, Ex. 5   **21.** solution; Sec. 4.1, Ex. 1   **23.** $12x^3 - 12x^2 - 9x + 2$; Sec. 5.2, Ex. 10

25. $(x + 6y)(x + y)$; Sec. 6.2, Ex. 6   **27.** $\frac{3y^9}{160}$; Sec. 7.2, Ex. 4   **29.** 1; Sec. 7.3, Ex. 2   **31.** $\frac{x(3x - 1)}{(x + 1)^2(x - 1)}$; Sec. 7.4, Ex. 7   **33.** -5; Sec. 7.5, Ex. 1

35. no solution; $\{\ \}$ or $\varnothing$; Sec. 4.1, Ex. 5   **37.** $(-2, 0)$; Sec. 4.2, Ex. 4   **39.** $\{(x, y)\,|\,3x - 2y = 2\}$ or $\{(x, y)\,|\,-9x + 6y = -6\}$; Sec. 4.3, Ex. 4

41. $\begin{cases} -3x + 4y < 12 \\ x \ge 2 \end{cases}$; Sec. 9.4, Ex. 8   **43. a.** x^{11} **b.** $\frac{t^4}{16}$ **c.** $81y^{10}$; Sec. 5.1, Ex. 11   **45.** $-6, -\frac{3}{2}, \frac{1}{5}$; Sec. 6.6, Ex. 9   **47.** 63; Sec. 7.6, Ex. 1

CHAPTER 10 RATIONAL EXPONENTS, RADICALS, AND COMPLEX NUMBERS

Section 10.1
Practice Exercises

1. a. 7 **b.** 0 **c.** $\frac{4}{9}$ **d.** 0.8 **e.** z^4 **f.** $4b^2$ **g.** -6 **h.** not a real number **2.** 6.708 **3. a.** -1 **b.** 3 **c.** $\frac{3}{4}$ **d.** x^4
e. $-2x$ **4. a.** 10 **b.** -1 **c.** -9 **d.** not a real number **e.** $3x^3$ **5. a.** 4 **b.** $|x^7|$ **c.** $|x+7|$ **d.** -7 **e.** $3x-5$
f. $7|x|$ **g.** $|x+8|$ **6. a.** 4 **b.** 2 **c.** 2 **d.** $\sqrt[3]{-9}$ **7.** **8.**

Vocabulary, Readiness & Video Check 10.1

1. index; radical sign; radicand **3.** is not **5.** $[0,\infty)$ **7.** $(16,4)$ **9.** Divide the index into each exponent in the radicand. **11.** The square root of a negative number is not a real number, but the cube root of a negative number is a real number. **13.** For odd roots, there's only one root/answer whether the radicand is positive or negative, so absolute value bars aren't needed.

Exercise Set 10.1

1. 10 **3.** $\frac{1}{2}$ **5.** 0.01 **7.** -6 **9.** x^5 **11.** $4y^3$ **13.** 2.646 **15.** 6.164 **17.** 14.142 **19.** 4 **21.** $\frac{1}{2}$ **23.** -1 **25.** x^4 **27.** $-3x^3$
29. -2 **31.** not a real number **33.** -2 **35.** x^4 **37.** $2x^2$ **39.** $9x^2$ **41.** $4x^2$ **43.** 8 **45.** -8 **47.** $2|x|$ **49.** x **51.** $|x-5|$
53. $|x+2|$ **55.** -11 **57.** $2x$ **59.** y^6 **61.** $5ab^{10}$ **63.** $-3x^4y^3$ **65.** a^4b **67.** $-2x^2y$ **69.** $\frac{5}{7}$ **71.** $\frac{x^{10}}{2y}$ **73.** $-\frac{z^7}{3x}$ **75.** $\frac{x}{2}$
77. $\sqrt{3}$ **79.** -1 **81.** -3 **83.** $\sqrt{7}$ **85.** $[0,\infty)$; **87.** $[3,\infty)$; 0, 1, 2, 3 **89.** $(-\infty,\infty)$; **91.** $(-\infty,\infty)$; 0, 1, -1, 2, -2

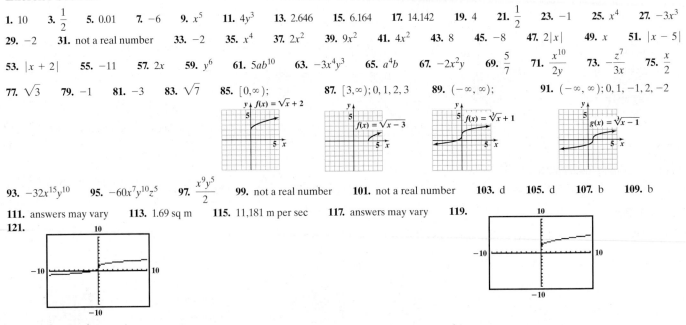

93. $-32x^{15}y^{10}$ **95.** $-60x^7y^{10}z^5$ **97.** $\frac{x^9y^5}{2}$ **99.** not a real number **101.** not a real number **103.** d **105.** d **107.** b **109.** b
111. answers may vary **113.** 1.69 sq m **115.** 11,181 m per sec **117.** answers may vary **119.**
121.

Section 10.2
Practice Exercises

1. a. 6 **b.** 10 **c.** $\sqrt[3]{x}$ **d.** 1 **e.** -8 **f.** $5x^3$ **g.** $3\sqrt[4]{x}$ **2. a.** 64 **b.** -1 **c.** -27 **d.** $\frac{1}{125}$ **e.** $\sqrt[9]{(3x+2)^5}$
3. a. $\frac{1}{27}$ **b.** $\frac{1}{16}$ **4. a.** $y^{10/3}$ **b.** $x^{17/20}$ **c.** $\frac{1}{9}$ **d.** $b^{2/9}$ **e.** $\frac{81}{x^3y^{11/3}}$ **5. a.** $x^{14/15} - x^{13/5}$ **b.** $x + 4x^{1/2} - 12$ **6.** $x^{-1/5}(2 - 7x)$
7. a. $\sqrt[3]{x}$ **b.** $\sqrt{6}$ **c.** $\sqrt[4]{a^2b}$ **8. a.** $\sqrt[12]{x^7}$ **b.** $\sqrt[15]{y^2}$ **c.** $\sqrt[6]{675}$

Vocabulary, Readiness & Video Check 10.2

1. true **3.** true **5.** multiply, c **7.** $-\sqrt[5]{3x}$ **9.** denominator; positive **11.** Write the radical using an equivalent fractional exponent form, simplify the fraction, then write as a radical again.

Exercise Set 10.2

1. 7 **3.** 3 **5.** $\frac{1}{2}$ **7.** 13 **9.** $2\sqrt[3]{m}$ **11.** $3x^2$ **13.** -3 **15.** -2 **17.** 8 **19.** 16 **21.** not a real number **23.** $\sqrt[5]{(2x)^3}$
25. $\sqrt[3]{(7x+2)^2}$ **27.** $\frac{64}{27}$ **29.** $\frac{1}{16}$ **31.** $\frac{1}{16}$ **33.** not a real number **35.** $\frac{1}{x^{1/4}}$ **37.** $a^{2/3}$ **39.** $\frac{5x^{3/4}}{7}$ **41.** $a^{7/3}$ **43.** x **45.** $3^{5/8}$
47. $y^{1/6}$ **49.** $8u^3$ **51.** $-b$ **53.** $\frac{1}{x^2}$ **55.** $27x^{2/3}$ **57.** $\frac{y}{z^{1/6}}$ **59.** $\frac{1}{x^{7/4}}$ **61.** $y - y^{7/6}$ **63.** $x^{5/3} - 2x^{2/3}$ **65.** $4x^{2/3} - 9$
67. $x^{8/3}(1 + x^{2/3})$ **69.** $x^{1/5}(x^{1/5} - 3)$ **71.** $x^{-1/3}(5 + x)$ **73.** $\sqrt{x}$ **75.** $\sqrt[3]{2}$ **77.** $2\sqrt{x}$ **79.** $\sqrt{xy}$ **81.** $\sqrt[3]{a^2b}$ **83.** $\sqrt{x+3}$
85. $\sqrt[15]{y^{11}}$ **87.** $\sqrt[12]{b^5}$ **89.** $\sqrt[24]{x^{23}}$ **91.** $\sqrt{a}$ **93.** $\sqrt[6]{432}$ **95.** $\sqrt[15]{343y^5}$ **97.** $\sqrt[6]{125r^3s^2}$ **99.** $25 \cdot 3$ **101.** $16 \cdot 3$ or $4 \cdot 12$

103. $8 \cdot 2$ **105.** $27 \cdot 2$ **107.** A   **109.** C   **111.** B   **113.** 1509 calories   **115.** 255.8 million   **117.** answers may vary   **119.** $a^{1/3}$

121. $x^{1/5}$ **123.** 1.6818   **125.** 5.6645   **127.** $\dfrac{t^{1/2}}{u^{1/2}}$

Section 10.3

Practice Exercises

1. a. $\sqrt{35}$ **b.** $\sqrt{13z}$ **c.** 5   **d.** $\sqrt[3]{15x^2 y}$ **e.** $\sqrt{\dfrac{5t}{2m}}$ **2. a.** $\dfrac{6}{7}$ **b.** $\dfrac{\sqrt{z}}{4}$ **c.** $\dfrac{5}{2}$ **d.** $\dfrac{\sqrt[4]{5}}{3x^2}$ **3. a.** $7\sqrt{2}$ **b.** $3\sqrt[3]{2}$

c. $\sqrt{35}$ **d.** $3\sqrt[4]{3}$ **4. a.** $6z^3\sqrt{z}$ **b.** $2pq^2\sqrt[3]{4pq}$ **c.** $2x^3\sqrt[4]{x^3}$ **5. a.** 4   **b.** $\dfrac{7}{3}\sqrt{z}$ **c.** $10xy^2\sqrt[3]{x^2}$ **d.** $6x^2 y\sqrt[5]{2y}$

6. $\sqrt{17}$ units ≈ 4.123 units   **7.** $\left(\dfrac{13}{2}, -4\right)$

Vocabulary, Readiness & Video Check 10.3

1. midpoint; point   **3.** distance   **5.** the indexes must be the same   **7.** The power must be 1. Any even power is a perfect square and will leave no factor in the radicand; any higher odd power can have an even power factored from it, leaving one factor remaining in the radicand.   **9.** average; average

Exercise Set 10.3

1. $\sqrt{14}$ **3.** 2   **5.** $\sqrt[3]{36}$ **7.** $\sqrt{6x}$ **9.** $\sqrt{\dfrac{14}{xy}}$ **11.** $\sqrt[4]{20x^3}$ **13.** $\dfrac{\sqrt{6}}{7}$ **15.** $\dfrac{\sqrt{2}}{7}$ **17.** $\dfrac{\sqrt[4]{x^3}}{2}$ **19.** $\dfrac{\sqrt[3]{4}}{3}$ **21.** $\dfrac{\sqrt[4]{8}}{x^2}$

23. $\dfrac{\sqrt[3]{2x}}{3y^4\sqrt[3]{3}}$ **25.** $\dfrac{x\sqrt{y}}{10}$ **27.** $\dfrac{x\sqrt{5}}{2y}$ **29.** $-\dfrac{z^2\sqrt[3]{z}}{3x}$ **31.** $4\sqrt{2}$ **33.** $4\sqrt[3]{3}$ **35.** $25\sqrt{3}$ **37.** $2\sqrt{6}$ **39.** $10x^2\sqrt{x}$ **41.** $2y^2\sqrt[3]{2y}$

43. $a^2 b\sqrt[4]{b^3}$ **45.** $y^2\sqrt{y}$ **47.** $5ab\sqrt{b}$ **49.** $-2x^2\sqrt[5]{y}$ **51.** $x^4\sqrt[3]{50x^2}$ **53.** $-4a^4 b^3\sqrt{2b}$ **55.** $3x^3 y^4\sqrt{xy}$ **57.** $5r^3 s^4$

59. $2x^3 y\sqrt[4]{2y}$ **61.** $\sqrt{2}$ **63.** 2   **65.** 10   **67.** $x^2 y$ **69.** $24m^2$ **71.** $\dfrac{15x\sqrt{2x}}{2}$ or $\dfrac{15x}{2}\sqrt{2x}$ **73.** $2a^2\sqrt[4]{2}$ **75.** $2xy^2\sqrt[5]{x^2}$ **77.** 5 units

79. $\sqrt{41}$ units ≈ 6.403 units   **81.** $\sqrt{10}$ units ≈ 3.162 units   **83.** $\sqrt{5}$ units ≈ 2.236 units   **85.** $\sqrt{192.58}$ units ≈ 13.877 units   **87.** $(4, -2)$

89. $\left(-5, \dfrac{5}{2}\right)$ **91.** $(3, 0)$ **93.** $\left(-\dfrac{1}{2}, \dfrac{1}{2}\right)$ **95.** $\left(\sqrt{2}, \dfrac{\sqrt{5}}{2}\right)$ **97.** $(6.2, -6.65)$ **99.** $14x$ **101.** $2x^2 - 7x - 15$ **103.** y^2

105. $-3x - 15$ **107.** $x^2 - 8x + 16$ **109.** true   **111.** false   **113.** true   **115.** $\dfrac{\sqrt[3]{64}}{\sqrt{64}} = \dfrac{4}{8} = \dfrac{1}{2}$ **117.** x^7 **119.** $a^3 bc^5$ **121.** $z^{10}\sqrt[3]{z^2}$

123. $q^2 r^5 s\sqrt[4]{q^3 r^5}$ **125.** 1.6 m   **127. a.** 20π sq cm   **b.** 211.57 sq ft

Section 10.4

Practice Exercises

1. a. $8\sqrt{17}$ **b.** $-5\sqrt[3]{5z}$ **c.** $3\sqrt{2} + 5\sqrt[3]{2}$ **2. a.** $11\sqrt{6}$ **b.** $-9\sqrt[3]{3}$ **c.** $-2\sqrt{3x}$ **d.** $2\sqrt{10} + 2\sqrt[3]{5}$ **e.** $4x\sqrt[3]{3x}$

3. a. $\dfrac{5\sqrt{7}}{12}$ **b.** $\dfrac{13\sqrt[3]{6y}}{4}$ **4. a.** $2\sqrt{5} + 5\sqrt{3}$ **b.** $2\sqrt{3} + 2\sqrt{2} - \sqrt{30} - 2\sqrt{5}$ **c.** $6z + \sqrt{z} - 12$ **d.** $-6\sqrt{6} + 15$

e. $5x - 9$ **f.** $6\sqrt{x + 2} + x + 11$

Vocabulary, Readiness & Video Check 10.4

1. Unlike   **3.** Like   **5.** $6\sqrt{3}$ **7.** $7\sqrt{x}$ **9.** $8\sqrt[3]{x}$ **11.** Sometimes you can't see that there are like radicals until you simplify, so you may incorrectly think you cannot add or subtract if you don't simplify first.

Exercise Set 10.4

1. $-2\sqrt{2}$ **3.** $10x\sqrt{2x}$ **5.** $17\sqrt{2} - 15\sqrt{5}$ **7.** $-\sqrt[3]{2x}$ **9.** $5b\sqrt{b}$ **11.** $\dfrac{31\sqrt{2}}{15}$ **13.** $\dfrac{\sqrt[3]{11}}{3}$ **15.** $\dfrac{5\sqrt{5x}}{9}$ **17.** $14 + \sqrt{3}$

19. $7 - 3y$ **21.** $6\sqrt{3} - 6\sqrt{2}$ **23.** $-23\sqrt[3]{5}$ **25.** $2a^3 b\sqrt{ab}$ **27.** $20y\sqrt{2y}$ **29.** $2y\sqrt[3]{2x}$ **31.** $6\sqrt[3]{11} - 4\sqrt{11}$ **33.** $3x\sqrt[4]{x^3}$ **35.** $\dfrac{2\sqrt{3}}{3}$

37. $\dfrac{5x\sqrt[3]{x}}{7}$ **39.** $\dfrac{5\sqrt{7}}{2x}$ **41.** $\dfrac{\sqrt[3]{2}}{6}$ **43.** $\dfrac{14x\sqrt[3]{2x}}{9}$ **45.** $15\sqrt{3}$ in.   **47.** $\sqrt{35} + \sqrt{21}$ **49.** $7 - 2\sqrt{10}$ **51.** $3\sqrt{x} - x\sqrt{3}$

53. $6x - 13\sqrt{x} - 5$ **55.** $\sqrt[3]{a^2} + \sqrt[3]{a} - 20$ **57.** $6\sqrt{2} - 12$ **59.** $2 + 2x\sqrt{3}$ **61.** $-16 - \sqrt{35}$ **63.** $x - y^2$ **65.** $3 + 2x\sqrt{3} + x^2$

67. $23x - 5x\sqrt{15}$ **69.** $2\sqrt[3]{2} - \sqrt[3]{4}$ **71.** $x + 1$ **73.** $x + 24 + 10\sqrt{x - 1}$ **75.** $2x + 6 - 2\sqrt{2x + 5}$ **77.** $x - 7$ **79.** $\dfrac{7}{x + y}$

81. $2a - 3$ **83.** $\dfrac{-2 + \sqrt{3}}{3}$ **85.** $22\sqrt{5}$ ft; 150 sq ft   **87. a.** $2\sqrt{3}$ **b.** 3   **c.** answers may vary   **89.** $2\sqrt{6} - 2\sqrt{2} - 2\sqrt{3} + 6$

91. answers may vary

Section 10.5

Practice Exercises

1. a. $\dfrac{5\sqrt{3}}{3}$ **b.** $\dfrac{15\sqrt{x}}{2x}$ **c.** $\dfrac{\sqrt[3]{6}}{3}$ **2.** $\dfrac{\sqrt{15yz}}{5y}$ **3.** $\dfrac{\sqrt[3]{z^2x^2}}{3x^2}$ **4. a.** $\dfrac{5(3\sqrt{5}-2)}{41}$ **b.** $\dfrac{\sqrt{6}+\sqrt{10}+5\sqrt{3}+5\sqrt{5}}{-2}$ **c.** $\dfrac{6x-3\sqrt{xy}}{4x-y}$

5. $\dfrac{2}{\sqrt{10}}$ **6.** $\dfrac{5b}{\sqrt[3]{50ab^2}}$ **7.** $\dfrac{x-9}{4(\sqrt{x}+3)}$

Vocabulary, Readiness & Video Check 10.5

1. conjugate   **3.** rationalizing the numerator   **5.** To write an equivalent expression without a radical in the denominator.   **7.** No, except for the fact you're working with numerators, the process is the same.

Exercise Set 10.5

1. $\dfrac{\sqrt{14}}{7}$ **3.** $\dfrac{\sqrt{5}}{5}$ **5.** $\dfrac{2\sqrt{x}}{x}$ **7.** $\dfrac{4\sqrt[3]{9}}{3}$ **9.** $\dfrac{3\sqrt{2x}}{4x}$ **11.** $\dfrac{3\sqrt[3]{2x}}{2x}$ **13.** $\dfrac{3\sqrt{3a}}{a}$ **15.** $\dfrac{3\sqrt[3]{4}}{2}$ **17.** $\dfrac{2\sqrt{21}}{7}$ **19.** $\dfrac{\sqrt{10xy}}{5y}$ **21.** $\dfrac{\sqrt[3]{75}}{5}$

23. $\dfrac{\sqrt{6x}}{10}$ **25.** $\dfrac{\sqrt{3z}}{6z}$ **27.** $\dfrac{\sqrt[3]{6xy^2}}{3x}$ **29.** $\dfrac{3\sqrt[4]{2}}{2}$ **31.** $\dfrac{2\sqrt[4]{9x}}{3x^2}$ **33.** $\dfrac{5\sqrt[3]{4ab^4}}{2ab^3}$ **35.** $\sqrt{2}-x$ **37.** $5+\sqrt{a}$ **39.** $-7\sqrt{5}-8\sqrt{x}$

41. $-2(2+\sqrt{7})$ **43.** $\dfrac{7(3+\sqrt{x})}{9-x}$ **45.** $-5+2\sqrt{6}$ **47.** $\dfrac{2a+2\sqrt{a}+\sqrt{ab}+\sqrt{b}}{4a-b}$ **49.** $-\dfrac{8(1-\sqrt{10})}{9}$ **51.** $\dfrac{x-\sqrt{xy}}{x-y}$

53. $\dfrac{5+3\sqrt{2}}{7}$ **55.** $\dfrac{5}{\sqrt{15}}$ **57.** $\dfrac{6}{\sqrt{10}}$ **59.** $\dfrac{2x}{7\sqrt{x}}$ **61.** $\dfrac{5y}{\sqrt[3]{100xy}}$ **63.** $\dfrac{2}{\sqrt{10}}$ **65.** $\dfrac{2x}{11\sqrt{2x}}$ **67.** $\dfrac{7}{2\sqrt[3]{49}}$ **69.** $\dfrac{3x^2}{10\sqrt[3]{9x}}$ **71.** $\dfrac{6x^2y^3}{\sqrt{6z}}$

73. $\dfrac{-7}{12+6\sqrt{11}}$ **75.** $\dfrac{3}{10+5\sqrt{7}}$ **77.** $\dfrac{x-9}{x-3\sqrt{x}}$ **79.** $\dfrac{1}{3+2\sqrt{2}}$ **81.** $\dfrac{x-1}{x-2\sqrt{x}+1}$ **83.** 5 **85.** $-\dfrac{1}{2},6$ **87.** 2, 6 **89.** $r=\dfrac{\sqrt{A\pi}}{2\pi}$

91. a. $\dfrac{y\sqrt{15xy}}{6x^2}$ **b.** $\dfrac{y\sqrt{15xy}}{6x^2}$ **c.** answers may vary **93.** $\sqrt[3]{25}$ **95.** answers may vary **97.** answers may vary

Integrated Review

1. 9 **2.** -2 **3.** $\dfrac{1}{2}$ **4.** x^3 **5.** y^3 **6.** $2y^5$ **7.** $-2y$ **8.** $3b^3$ **9.** 6 **10.** $\sqrt[4]{3y}$ **11.** $\dfrac{1}{16}$ **12.** $\sqrt[5]{(x+1)^3}$ **13.** y

14. $16x^{1/2}$ **15.** $x^{5/4}$ **16.** $4^{11/15}$ **17.** $2x^2$ **18.** $\sqrt[4]{a^3b^2}$ **19.** $\sqrt[4]{x^3}$ **20.** $\sqrt[6]{500}$ **21.** $2\sqrt{10}$ **22.** $2xy^2\sqrt[4]{x^3y^2}$ **23.** $3x\sqrt[3]{2x}$

24. $-2b^2\sqrt[5]{2}$ **25.** $\sqrt{5x}$ **26.** $4x$ **27.** $7y^2\sqrt{y}$ **28.** $2a^2\sqrt[4]{3}$ **29.** $2\sqrt{5}-5\sqrt{3}+5\sqrt{7}$ **30.** $y\sqrt[3]{2y}$ **31.** $\sqrt{15}-\sqrt{6}$ **32.** $10+2\sqrt{21}$

33. $4x^2-5$ **34.** $x+2-2\sqrt{x+1}$ **35.** $\dfrac{\sqrt{21}}{3}$ **36.** $\dfrac{5\sqrt[3]{4x}}{2x}$ **37.** $\dfrac{13-3\sqrt{21}}{5}$ **38.** $\dfrac{7}{\sqrt{21}}$ **39.** $\dfrac{3y}{\sqrt[3]{33y^2}}$ **40.** $\dfrac{x-4}{x+2\sqrt{x}}$

Section 10.6

Practice Exercises

1. 18 **2.** $\dfrac{1}{4},\dfrac{3}{4}$ **3.** 10 **4.** 9 **5.** $\dfrac{3}{25}$ **6.** $6\sqrt{3}$ m **7.** $\sqrt{193}$ in. ≈ 13.89 in.

Graphing Calculator Explorations 10.6

1. 3.19 **3.** $\varnothing$ **5.** 3.23

Vocabulary, Readiness & Video Check 10.6

1. extraneous solution   **3.** $x^2-10x+25$ **5.** Applying the power rule can result in an equation with more solutions than the original equation, so you need to check all proposed solutions in the original equation.   **7.** Our answer is either a positive square root of a value or a negative square root of a value. We're looking for a length, which must be positive, so our answer must be the positive square root.

Exercise Set 10.6

1. 8 **3.** 7 **5.** $\varnothing$ **7.** 7 **9.** 6 **11.** $-\dfrac{9}{2}$ **13.** 29 **15.** 4 **17.** -4 **19.** $\varnothing$ **21.** 7 **23.** 9 **25.** 50 **27.** $\varnothing$

29. $\dfrac{15}{4}$ **31.** 13 **33.** 5 **35.** -12 **37.** 9 **39.** -3 **41.** 1 **43.** 1 **45.** $\dfrac{1}{2}$ **47.** 0, 4 **49.** $\dfrac{37}{4}$ **51.** $3\sqrt{5}$ ft

53. $2\sqrt{10}$ m **55.** $2\sqrt{131}$ m ≈ 22.9 m **57.** $\sqrt{100.84}$ mm ≈ 10.0 mm **59.** 17 ft **61.** 13 ft **63.** 14,657,415 sq mi **65.** 100 ft

67. 100 **69.** $\dfrac{\pi}{2}$ sec ≈ 1.57 sec **71.** 12.97 ft **73.** answers may vary **75.** $15\sqrt{3}$ sq mi ≈ 25.98 sq mi **77.** answers may vary

79. 0.51 km **81.** function **83.** function **85.** not a function **87.** $\dfrac{x}{4x+3}$ **89.** $-\dfrac{4z+2}{3z}$

91. $\sqrt{5x-1}+4=7$ **93.** 1   **95. a.–b.** answers may vary   **97.** $-1, 0, 8, 9$ **99.** $-1, 4$
$\quad\quad\sqrt{5x-1}=3$
$\quad\;(\sqrt{5x-1})^2=3^2$
$\quad\quad\quad 5x-1=9$
$\quad\quad\quad\quad 5x=10$
$\quad\quad\quad\quad\; x=2$

Section 10.7

Practice Exercises

1. a. $2i$ **b.** $i\sqrt{7}$ **c.** $-3i\sqrt{2}$ **2. a.** $-\sqrt{30}$ **b.** -3 **c.** $25i$ **d.** $3i$ **3. a.** $-1 - 4i$ **b.** $-3 + 5i$ **c.** $3 - 2i$

4. a. $20 + 0i$ **b.** $-5 + 10i$ **c.** $15 + 16i$ **d.** $8 - 6i$ **e.** $85 + 0i$ **5. a.** $\dfrac{11}{10} - \dfrac{7}{10}i$ **b.** $0 - \dfrac{5}{2}i$ **6. a.** i **b.** 1 **c.** -1 **d.** 1

Vocabulary, Readiness & Video Check 10.7

1. complex **3.** -1 **5.** real **7.** The product rule for radicals; you need to first simplify each separate radical and have nonnegative radicands before applying the product rule. **9.** The fact that $i^2 = -1$. **11.** $i, i^2 = -1, i^3 = -i, i^4 = 1$

Exercise Set 10.7

1. $9i$ **3.** $i\sqrt{7}$ **5.** -4 **7.** $8i$ **9.** $2i\sqrt{6}$ **11.** $-6i$ **13.** $24i\sqrt{7}$ **15.** $-3\sqrt{6}$ **17.** $-\sqrt{14}$ **19.** $-5\sqrt{2}$ **21.** $4i$ **23.** $i\sqrt{3}$

25. $2\sqrt{2}$ **27.** $6 - 4i$ **29.** $-2 + 6i$ **31.** $-2 - 4i$ **33.** $-40 + 0i$ **35.** $18 + 12i$ **37.** $7 + 0i$ **39.** $12 - 16i$ **41.** $0 - 4i$

43. $\dfrac{28}{25} - \dfrac{21}{25}i$ **45.** $4 + i$ **47.** $\dfrac{17}{13} + \dfrac{7}{13}i$ **49.** $63 + 0i$ **51.** $2 - i$ **53.** $27 + 3i$ **55.** $-\dfrac{5}{2} - 2i$ **57.** $18 + 13i$ **59.** $20 + 0i$

61. $10 + 0i$ **63.** $2 + 0i$ **65.** $-5 + \dfrac{16}{3}i$ **67.** $17 + 144i$ **69.** $\dfrac{3}{5} - \dfrac{1}{5}i$ **71.** $5 - 10i$ **73.** $\dfrac{1}{5} - \dfrac{8}{5}i$ **75.** $8 - i$ **77.** $7 + 0i$

79. $12 - 16i$ **81.** 1 **83.** i **85.** $-i$ **87.** -1 **89.** -64 **91.** $-243i$ **93.** $40°$ **95.** $x^2 - 5x - 2 - \dfrac{6}{x - 1}$ **97.** 5 people

99. 14 people **101.** 16.7% **103.** $-1 - i$ **105.** $0 + 0i$ **107.** $2 + 3i$ **109.** $2 + i\sqrt{2}$ **111.** $\dfrac{1}{2} - \dfrac{\sqrt{3}}{2}i$ **113.** answers may vary

115. $6 - 3i\sqrt{3}$ **117.** yes

Chapter 10 Vocabulary Check

1. conjugate **2.** principal square root **3.** rationalizing **4.** imaginary unit **5.** cube root **6.** index; radicand **7.** like radicals
8. complex number **9.** distance **10.** midpoint

Chapter 10 Review

1. 9 **3.** -2 **5.** $-\dfrac{1}{7}$ **7.** -6 **9.** $-a^2 b^3$ **11.** $2ab^2$ **13.** $\dfrac{x^6}{6y}$ **15.** $|-x|$ **17.** -27 **19.** $-x$ **21.** $2|2y + z|$ **23.** y **25. a.** $3, 6$

b. $[0, \infty)$ **c.**

27. $\dfrac{1}{3}$ **29.** $-\dfrac{1}{3}$ **31.** -27 **33.** not a real number **35.** $\dfrac{9}{4}$ **37.** $x^{2/3}$ **39.** $\sqrt[5]{y^4}$ **41.** $\dfrac{1}{\sqrt[3]{x + 2}}$

43. $a^{13/6}$ **45.** $\dfrac{1}{a^{9/2}}$ **47.** $a^4 b^6$ **49.** $\dfrac{b^{5/6}}{49a^{1/4}c^{5/3}}$ **51.** 4.472 **53.** 5.191 **55.** -26.246 **57.** $\sqrt[6]{1372}$

59. $2\sqrt{6}$ **61.** $2x$ **63.** $2\sqrt{15}$ **65.** $3\sqrt[3]{6}$ **67.** $6x^3\sqrt{x}$ **69.** $\dfrac{p^8\sqrt{p}}{11}$ **71.** $\dfrac{y\sqrt[4]{xy^2}}{3}$

73. $\dfrac{5}{\sqrt{\pi}}$ m or $\dfrac{5\sqrt{\pi}}{\pi}$ m **75.** $\sqrt{197}$ units ≈ 14.036 units **77.** $\sqrt{73}$ units ≈ 8.544 units **79.** $2\sqrt{11}$ units ≈ 6.633 units **81.** $(-5, 5)$

83. $\left(-\dfrac{11}{2}, -2\right)$ **85.** $\left(\dfrac{1}{4}, -\dfrac{2}{7}\right)$ **87.** $-2\sqrt{5}$ **89.** $9\sqrt[3]{2}$ **91.** $\dfrac{15 + 2\sqrt{3}}{6}$ **93.** $17\sqrt{2} - 15\sqrt{5}$ **95.** 6 **97.** $-8\sqrt{5}$

99. $a - 9$ **101.** $\sqrt[3]{25x^2} - 81$ **103.** $\dfrac{3\sqrt{7}}{7}$ **105.** $\dfrac{5\sqrt[3]{2}}{2}$ **107.** $\dfrac{x^2 y^2 \sqrt[3]{15yz}}{z}$ **109.** $\dfrac{3\sqrt{y} + 6}{y - 4}$ **111.** $\dfrac{11}{3\sqrt{11}}$ **113.** $\dfrac{3}{7\sqrt[3]{3}}$ **115.** $\dfrac{xy}{\sqrt[3]{10x^2 yz}}$

117. 32 **119.** 35 **121.** 9 **123.** $3\sqrt{2}$ cm **125.** 51.2 ft **127.** $0 + 2i\sqrt{2}$ **129.** $0 + 6i$ **131.** $15 - 4i$ **133.** -64

135. $-12 - 18i$ **137.** $-5 - 12i$ **139.** $\dfrac{3}{2} - i$ **141.** x **143.** -10 **145.** $\dfrac{y^5}{2x^3}$ **147.** $\dfrac{1}{8}$ **149.** $\dfrac{1}{x^{13/2}}$ **151.** $\dfrac{n\sqrt{3n}}{11m^5}$

153. $4x - 20\sqrt{x} + 25$ **155.** $(4, 16)$ **157.** $\dfrac{2\sqrt{x} - 6}{x - 9}$ **159.** 5

Chapter 10 Getting Ready for the Test

1. D **2.** B **3.** A **4.** B **5.** A **6.** A **7.** A **8.** C **9.** B **10.** B **11.** B **12.** A **13.** A **14.** B **15.** B
16. B **17.** D **18.** C **19.** B **20.** D **21.** A

Chapter 10 Test

1. $6\sqrt{6}$ **2.** $-x^{16}$ **3.** $\dfrac{1}{5}$ **4.** 5 **5.** $\dfrac{4x^2}{9}$ **6.** $-a^6 b^3$ **7.** $\dfrac{8a^{1/3}c^{2/3}}{b^{5/12}}$ **8.** $a^{7/12} - a^{7/3}$ **9.** $|4xy|$ or $4|xy|$ **10.** -27 **11.** $\dfrac{3\sqrt{y}}{y}$

12. $\dfrac{8 - 6\sqrt{x} + x}{8 - 2x}$ **13.** $\dfrac{\sqrt[3]{b^2}}{b}$ **14.** $\dfrac{6 - x^2}{8(\sqrt{6} - x)}$ **15.** $-x\sqrt{5x}$ **16.** $4\sqrt{3} - \sqrt{6}$ **17.** $x + 2\sqrt{x} + 1$ **18.** $\sqrt{6} + \sqrt{2} - 4\sqrt{3} - 4$

19. -20 **20.** 23.685 **21.** 0.019 **22.** $2, 3$ **23.** $\varnothing$ **24.** 6 **25.** $0 + i\sqrt{2}$ **26.** $0 - 2i\sqrt{2}$ **27.** $0 - 3i$ **28.** $40 + 0i$ **29.** $7 + 24i$

30. $-\dfrac{3}{2} + \dfrac{5}{2}i$ **31.** $\dfrac{5\sqrt{2}}{2}$ **32.** $[-2, \infty)$; 0, 1, 2, 3;   **33.** $2\sqrt{26}$ units   **34.** $\sqrt{95}$ units   **35.** $\left(-4, \dfrac{7}{2}\right)$ **36.** $\left(-\dfrac{1}{2}, \dfrac{3}{10}\right)$

37. 27 mph   **38.** 360 ft

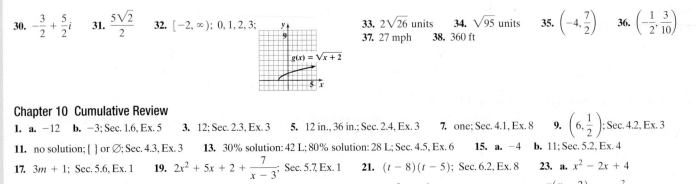

Chapter 10 Cumulative Review

1. a. -12 **b.** -3; Sec. 1.6, Ex. 5   **3.** 12; Sec. 2.3, Ex. 3   **5.** 12 in., 36 in.; Sec. 2.4, Ex. 3   **7.** one; Sec. 4.1, Ex. 8   **9.** $\left(6, \dfrac{1}{2}\right)$; Sec. 4.2, Ex. 3

11. no solution; { } or $\varnothing$; Sec. 4.3, Ex. 3   **13.** 30% solution: 42 L; 80% solution: 28 L; Sec. 4.5, Ex. 6   **15. a.** -4 **b.** 11; Sec. 5.2, Ex. 4

17. $3m + 1$; Sec. 5.6, Ex. 1   **19.** $2x^2 + 5x + 2 + \dfrac{7}{x-3}$; Sec. 5.7, Ex. 1   **21.** $(t-8)(t-5)$; Sec. 6.2, Ex. 8   **23. a.** $x^2 - 2x + 4$

b. $\dfrac{2}{y-5}$; Sec. 7.1, Ex. 5   **25.** 4; Sec. 9.2, Ex. 9   **27.** $3x - 5$; Sec. 7.3, Ex. 3   **29.** $\dfrac{2m+1}{m+1}$; Sec. 7.4, Ex. 5   **31. a.** $\dfrac{x(x-2)}{2(x+2)}$ **b.** $\dfrac{x^2}{y^2}$; Sec. 7.7, Ex. 2

33. $\left[-2, \dfrac{8}{5}\right]$; Sec. 9.3, Ex. 3   **35.** 15 yd; Sec. 7.6, Ex. 4   **37. a.** 1   **b.** -4 **c.** $\dfrac{2}{5}$ **d.** x^2 **e.** $-3x^5$; Sec. 10.1, Ex. 3   **39. a.** $\dfrac{1}{8}$ **b.** $\dfrac{1}{9}$; Sec. 10.2, Ex. 3

41. $\dfrac{x-4}{5(\sqrt{x}-2)}$; Sec. 10.5, Ex. 7   **43.** constant of variation: 15, $u = \dfrac{15}{w}$; Sec. 8.4, Ex. 3

CHAPTER 11 QUADRATIC EQUATIONS AND FUNCTIONS

Section 11.1

Practice Exercises

1. $-4\sqrt{2}, 4\sqrt{2}$ **2.** $-\sqrt{10}, \sqrt{10}$ **3.** $-3 - 2\sqrt{5}, -3 + 2\sqrt{5}$ **4.** $\dfrac{2+3i}{5}, \dfrac{2-3i}{5}$ **5.** $-2 - \sqrt{7}, -2 + \sqrt{7}$ **6.** $\dfrac{3-\sqrt{5}}{2}, \dfrac{3+\sqrt{5}}{2}$

7. $\dfrac{6-\sqrt{33}}{3}, \dfrac{6+\sqrt{33}}{3}$ **8.** $\dfrac{5-i\sqrt{31}}{4}, \dfrac{5+i\sqrt{31}}{4}$ **9.** 6%

Graphing Calculator Explorations 11.1

1. $-1.27, 6.27$ **3.** $-1.10, 0.90$ **5.** no real solutions

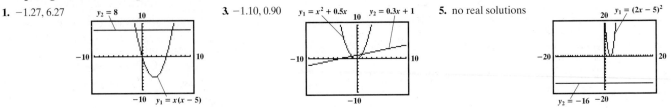

Vocabulary, Readiness & Video Check 11.1

1. $\pm\sqrt{b}$ **3.** completing the square   **5.** 9   **7.** We need a quantity squared by itself on one side of the equation. The only quantity squared is x, so we need to divide both sides by 2 before applying the square root property.   **9.** We're looking for an interest rate, so a negative value does not make sense.

Exercise Set 11.1

1. $-4, 4$ **3.** $-\sqrt{7}, \sqrt{7}$ **5.** $-3\sqrt{2}, 3\sqrt{2}$ **7.** $-\sqrt{10}, \sqrt{10}$ **9.** $-8, -2$ **11.** $6 - 3\sqrt{2}, 6 + 3\sqrt{2}$ **13.** $\dfrac{3-2\sqrt{2}}{2}, \dfrac{3+2\sqrt{2}}{2}$

15. $-3i, 3i$ **17.** $-\sqrt{6}, \sqrt{6}$ **19.** $-2i\sqrt{2}, 2i\sqrt{2}$ **21.** $\dfrac{1-4i}{3}, \dfrac{1+4i}{3}$ **23.** $-7 - \sqrt{5}, -7 + \sqrt{5}$ **25.** $-3 - 2i\sqrt{2}, -3 + 2i\sqrt{2}$

27. $x^2 + 16x + 64 = (x+8)^2$ **29.** $z^2 - 12z + 36 = (z-6)^2$ **31.** $p^2 + 9p + \dfrac{81}{4} = \left(p + \dfrac{9}{2}\right)^2$ **33.** $x^2 + x + \dfrac{1}{4} = \left(x + \dfrac{1}{2}\right)^2$

35. $-5, -3$ **37.** $-3 - \sqrt{7}, -3 + \sqrt{7}$ **39.** $\dfrac{-1-\sqrt{5}}{2}, \dfrac{-1+\sqrt{5}}{2}$ **41.** $-1 - \sqrt{6}, -1 + \sqrt{6}$ **43.** $\dfrac{-1-\sqrt{29}}{2}, \dfrac{-1+\sqrt{29}}{2}$

45. $\dfrac{6-\sqrt{30}}{3}, \dfrac{6+\sqrt{30}}{3}$ **47.** $\dfrac{3-\sqrt{11}}{2}, \dfrac{3+\sqrt{11}}{2}$ **49.** $-4, \dfrac{1}{2}$ **51.** $-4 - \sqrt{15}, -4 + \sqrt{15}$ **53.** $\dfrac{-3-\sqrt{21}}{3}, \dfrac{-3+\sqrt{21}}{3}$ **55.** $-1, \dfrac{5}{2}$

57. $-1 - i, -1 + i$ **59.** $3 - \sqrt{17}, 3 + \sqrt{17}$ **61.** $-2 - i\sqrt{2}, -2 + i\sqrt{2}$ **63.** $\dfrac{-15-7\sqrt{5}}{10}, \dfrac{-15+7\sqrt{5}}{10}$ **65.** $\dfrac{1-i\sqrt{47}}{4}, \dfrac{1+i\sqrt{47}}{4}$

67. $-5 - i\sqrt{3}, -5 + i\sqrt{3}$ **69.** $-4, 1$ **71.** $\dfrac{2-i\sqrt{2}}{2}, \dfrac{2+i\sqrt{2}}{2}$ **73.** $\dfrac{-3-\sqrt{69}}{6}, \dfrac{-3+\sqrt{69}}{6}$ **75.** 20%   **77.** 4%   **79.** 9.63 sec

81. 6.17 sec   **83.** 15 ft by 15 ft   **85.** $10\sqrt{2}$ cm   **87.** -1 **89.** $3 + 2\sqrt{5}$ **91.** $\dfrac{1-3\sqrt{2}}{2}$ **93.** $2\sqrt{6}$ **95.** 5   **97.** complex, but not

real numbers   **99.** real numbers   **101.** complex, but not real numbers   **103.** $-8x, 8x$ **105.** $-5z, 5z$ **107.** answers may vary   **109.** compound; answers may vary   **111.** 6 thousand scissors

Section 11.2
Practice Exercises

1. $2, -\dfrac{1}{3}$ **2.** $\dfrac{4 - \sqrt{22}}{3}, \dfrac{4 + \sqrt{22}}{3}$ **3.** $1 - \sqrt{17}, 1 + \sqrt{17}$ **4.** $\dfrac{-1 - i\sqrt{15}}{4}, \dfrac{1 + i\sqrt{15}}{4}$ **5. a.** one real solution   **b.** two real solutions
c. two complex but not real solutions   **6.** 6 ft   **7.** 2.4 sec

Vocabulary, Readiness & Video Check 11.2

1. $x = \dfrac{-b \pm \sqrt{b^2 - 4ac}}{2a}$ **3.** $-5; -7$ **5.** $1; 0$ **7. a.** Yes, in order to make sure we have correct values for $a, b,$ and c.   **b.** No; clearing
fractions makes the work less tedious, but it's not a necessary step.   **9.** With applications, we need to make sure we answer the question(s) asked.
Here we're asked how much distance is saved, so once the dimensions of the triangle are known, further calculations are needed to answer this question
and solve the problem.

Exercise Set 11.2

1. $-6, 1$ **3.** $-\dfrac{3}{5}, 1$ **5.** 3   **7.** $\dfrac{-7 - \sqrt{33}}{2}, \dfrac{-7 + \sqrt{33}}{2}$ **9.** $\dfrac{1 - \sqrt{57}}{8}, \dfrac{1 + \sqrt{57}}{8}$ **11.** $\dfrac{7 - \sqrt{85}}{6}, \dfrac{7 + \sqrt{85}}{6}$ **13.** $1 - \sqrt{3}, 1 + \sqrt{3}$
15. $-\dfrac{3}{2}, 1$ **17.** $\dfrac{3 - \sqrt{11}}{2}, \dfrac{3 + \sqrt{11}}{2}$ **19.** $\dfrac{-5 - \sqrt{17}}{2}, \dfrac{-5 + \sqrt{17}}{2}$ **21.** $\dfrac{5}{2}, 1$ **23.** $-3 - 2i, -3 + 2i$ **25.** $-2 - \sqrt{11}, -2 + \sqrt{11}$
27. $\dfrac{3 - i\sqrt{87}}{8}, \dfrac{3 + i\sqrt{87}}{8}$ **29.** $\dfrac{3 - \sqrt{29}}{2}, \dfrac{3 + \sqrt{29}}{2}$ **31.** $\dfrac{-5 - i\sqrt{5}}{10}, \dfrac{-5 + i\sqrt{5}}{10}$ **33.** $\dfrac{-1 - \sqrt{19}}{6}, \dfrac{-1 + \sqrt{19}}{6}$
35. $\dfrac{-1 - i\sqrt{23}}{4}, \dfrac{-1 + i\sqrt{23}}{4}$ **37.** 1   **39.** $3 - \sqrt{5}, 3 + \sqrt{5}$ **41.** two real solutions   **43.** one real solution   **45.** two real solutions
47. two complex but not real solutions   **49.** two real solutions   **51.** 14 ft   **53.** $(2 + 2\sqrt{2})$ cm, $(2 + 2\sqrt{2})$ cm, $(4 + 2\sqrt{2})$ cm
55. width: $(-5 + 5\sqrt{17})$ ft; length: $(5 + 5\sqrt{17})$ ft   **57. a.** $50\sqrt{2}$ m   **b.** 5000 sq m   **59.** 37.4 ft by 38.5 ft   **61.** base: $(2 + 2\sqrt{43})$ cm; height:
$(-1 + \sqrt{43})$ cm   **63.** 8.9 sec   **65.** 2.8 sec   **67.** $\dfrac{11}{5}$ **69.** 15   **71.** $(x^2 + 5)(x + 2)(x - 2)$ **73.** $(z + 3)(z - 3)(z + 2)(z - 2)$
75. b   **77.** answers may vary   **79.** 0.6, 2.4   **81.** Sunday to Monday   **83.** Wednesday   **85.** $f(4) = 32$; yes   **87. a.** 3129 million
b. 2019   **89. a.** \$679.8 billion   **b.** 2001   **c.** 2027   **91.** answers may vary   **93.** $\dfrac{\sqrt{3}}{3}$ **95.** $\dfrac{-\sqrt{2} - i\sqrt{2}}{2}, \dfrac{-\sqrt{2} + i\sqrt{2}}{2}$
97. $\dfrac{\sqrt{3} - \sqrt{11}}{4}, \dfrac{\sqrt{3} + \sqrt{11}}{4}$ **99.** 8.9 sec: 1200   2.8 sec: 200   **101.** two real solutions

Section 11.3
Practice Exercises

1. 8   **2.** $\dfrac{5 \pm \sqrt{137}}{8}$ **3.** $4, -4, 3i, -3i$ **4.** $1, -3$ **5.** $1, 64$ **6.** Katy: $\dfrac{7 + \sqrt{65}}{2} \approx 7.5$ hr; Steve: $\dfrac{9 + \sqrt{65}}{2} \approx 8.5$ hr
7. to Shanghai: 40 km/hr; to Ningbo: 90 km/hr

Vocabulary, Readiness & Video Check 11.3

1. The values we get for the substituted variable are *not* our final answers. Remember to always substitute back to the original variable and solve for it if
necessary.

Exercise Set 11.3

1. 2   **3.** 16   **5.** 1, 4   **7.** $3 - \sqrt{7}, 3 + \sqrt{7}$ **9.** $\dfrac{3 - \sqrt{57}}{4}, \dfrac{3 + \sqrt{57}}{4}$ **11.** $\dfrac{1 - \sqrt{29}}{2}, \dfrac{1 + \sqrt{29}}{2}$ **13.** $-2, 2, -2i, 2i$
15. $-\dfrac{1}{2}, \dfrac{1}{2}, -i\sqrt{3}, i\sqrt{3}$ **17.** $-3, 3, -2, 2$ **19.** $125, -8$ **21.** $-\dfrac{4}{5}, 0$ **23.** $-\dfrac{1}{8}, 27$ **25.** $-\dfrac{2}{3}, \dfrac{4}{3}$ **27.** $-\dfrac{1}{125}, \dfrac{1}{8}$ **29.** $-\sqrt{2}, \sqrt{2}, -\sqrt{3}, \sqrt{3}$
31. $\dfrac{-9 - \sqrt{201}}{6}, \dfrac{-9 + \sqrt{201}}{6}$ **33.** 2, 3   **35.** 3   **37.** 27, 125   **39.** $1, -3i, 3i$ **41.** $\dfrac{1}{8}, -8$ **43.** $-\dfrac{1}{2}, \dfrac{1}{3}$ **45.** 4   **47.** -3
49. $-\sqrt{5}, \sqrt{5}, -2i, 2i$ **51.** $-3, \dfrac{3 - 3i\sqrt{3}}{2}, \dfrac{3 + 3i\sqrt{3}}{2}$ **53.** 6, 12   **55.** $-\dfrac{1}{3}, \dfrac{1}{3}, -\dfrac{i\sqrt{6}}{3}, \dfrac{i\sqrt{6}}{3}$ **57.** 5   **59.** 55 mph: 66 mph
61. 5 mph, then 4 mph   **63.** inlet pipe: 15.5 hr; hose: 16.5 hr   **65.** 8.5 hr   **67.** 12 or -8 **69. a.** $(x - 6)$ in.   **b.** $300 = (x - 6) \cdot (x - 6) \cdot 3$
c. 16 in. by 16 in.   **71.** 22 feet   **73.** $(-\infty, 3]$ **75.** $(-5, \infty)$ **77.** domain: $(-\infty, \infty)$; range: $(-\infty, \infty)$; function   **79.** domain: $(-\infty, \infty)$;
range: $[-1, \infty)$; function   **81.** $1, -3i, 3i$ **83.** $-\dfrac{1}{2}, \dfrac{1}{3}$ **85.** $-3, \dfrac{3 - 3i\sqrt{3}}{2}, \dfrac{3 + 3i\sqrt{3}}{2}$ **87.** answers may vary   **89. a.** approximately 164.37 mph
b. 54.754 sec/lap   **c.** 55.947 sec/lap   **d.** 160.87 mph

Integrated Review

1. $-\sqrt{10}, \sqrt{10}$ **2.** $-\sqrt{14}, \sqrt{14}$ **3.** $1 - 2\sqrt{2}, 1 + 2\sqrt{2}$ **4.** $-5 - 2\sqrt{3}, -5 + 2\sqrt{3}$ **5.** $-1 - \sqrt{13}, -1 + \sqrt{13}$ **6.** $1, 11$

7. $\dfrac{-3 - \sqrt{69}}{6}, \dfrac{-3 + \sqrt{69}}{6}$ **8.** $\dfrac{-2 - \sqrt{5}}{4}, \dfrac{-2 + \sqrt{5}}{4}$ **9.** $\dfrac{2 - \sqrt{2}}{2}, \dfrac{2 + \sqrt{2}}{2}$ **10.** $-3 - \sqrt{5}, -3 + \sqrt{5}$ **11.** $-2 - i\sqrt{3}, -2 + i\sqrt{3}$

12. $\dfrac{-1 - i\sqrt{11}}{2}, \dfrac{-1 + i\sqrt{11}}{2}$ **13.** $\dfrac{-3 - i\sqrt{15}}{2}, \dfrac{-3 + i\sqrt{15}}{2}$ **14.** $-3i, 3i$ **15.** $-17, 0$ **16.** $\dfrac{1 - \sqrt{13}}{4}, \dfrac{1 + \sqrt{13}}{4}$ **17.** $2 - 3\sqrt{3}, 2 + 3\sqrt{3}$

18. $2 - \sqrt{3}, 2 + \sqrt{3}$ **19.** $-2, \dfrac{4}{3}$ **20.** $\dfrac{-5 - \sqrt{17}}{4}, \dfrac{-5 + \sqrt{17}}{4}$ **21.** $1 - \sqrt{6}, 1 + \sqrt{6}$ **22.** $-\sqrt{31}, \sqrt{31}$ **23.** $-\sqrt{11}, \sqrt{11}$

24. $-i\sqrt{11}, i\sqrt{11}$ **25.** $-11, 6$ **26.** $\dfrac{-3 - \sqrt{19}}{5}, \dfrac{-3 + \sqrt{19}}{5}$ **27.** $\dfrac{-3 - \sqrt{17}}{4}, \dfrac{-3 + \sqrt{17}}{4}$ **28.** 4 **29.** $\dfrac{-1 - \sqrt{17}}{8}, \dfrac{-1 + \sqrt{17}}{8}$

30. $10\sqrt{2}\,\text{ft} \approx 14.1\,\text{ft}$ **31.** Jack: 9.1 hr; Lucy: 7.1 hr **32.** 5 mph during the first part, then 6 mph

Section 11.4
Practice Exercises

1. $(-\infty, -3) \cup (4, \infty)$ **2.** $[0, 8]$ **3.** $(-\infty, -3] \cup [-1, 2]$ **4.** $(-4, 5]$ **5.** $(-\infty, -3) \cup \left(-\dfrac{8}{5}, \infty\right)$

Vocabulary, Readiness & Video Check 11.4

1. $[-7, 3)$ **3.** $(-\infty, 0]$ **5.** $(-\infty, -12) \cup [-10, \infty)$ **7.** We use the solutions of the related equation to divide the number line into regions that either entirely are or entirely are not solution regions; the solutions of the related equation are solutions of the inequality only if the inequality symbol is $\le$ or $\ge$.

Exercise Set 11.4

1. $(-\infty, -5) \cup (-1, \infty)$ **3.** $[-4, 3]$ **5.** $[2, 5]$ **7.** $\left(-5, -\dfrac{1}{3}\right)$ **9.** $(2, 4) \cup (6, \infty)$ **11.** $(-\infty, -4] \cup [0, 1]$

13. $(-\infty, -3) \cup (-2, 2) \cup (3, \infty)$ **15.** $(-7, 2)$ **17.** $(-1, \infty)$ **19.** $(-\infty, -1] \cup (4, \infty)$ **21.** $(-\infty, 2) \cup \left(\dfrac{11}{4}, \infty\right)$ **23.** $(0, 2] \cup [3, \infty)$

25. $(-\infty, 3)$ **27.** $\left[-\dfrac{5}{4}, \dfrac{3}{2}\right]$ **29.** $(-\infty, 0) \cup (1, \infty)$ **31.** $(-\infty, -4] \cup [4, 6]$ **33.** $\left(-\infty, -\dfrac{2}{3}\right] \cup \left[\dfrac{3}{2}, \infty\right)$

35. $\left(-4, -\dfrac{3}{2}\right) \cup \left(\dfrac{3}{2}, \infty\right)$ **37.** $(-\infty, -5] \cup [-1, 1] \cup [5, \infty)$ **39.** $\left(-\infty, -\dfrac{5}{3}\right) \cup \left(\dfrac{7}{2}, \infty\right)$ **41.** $(0, 10)$ **43.** $(-\infty, -4) \cup [5, \infty)$

45. $(-\infty, -6] \cup (-1, 0] \cup (7, \infty)$ **47.** $(-\infty, 1) \cup (2, \infty)$ **49.** $(-\infty, -8] \cup (-4, \infty)$ **51.** $(-\infty, 0] \cup \left(5, \dfrac{11}{2}\right]$ **53.** $(0, \infty)$

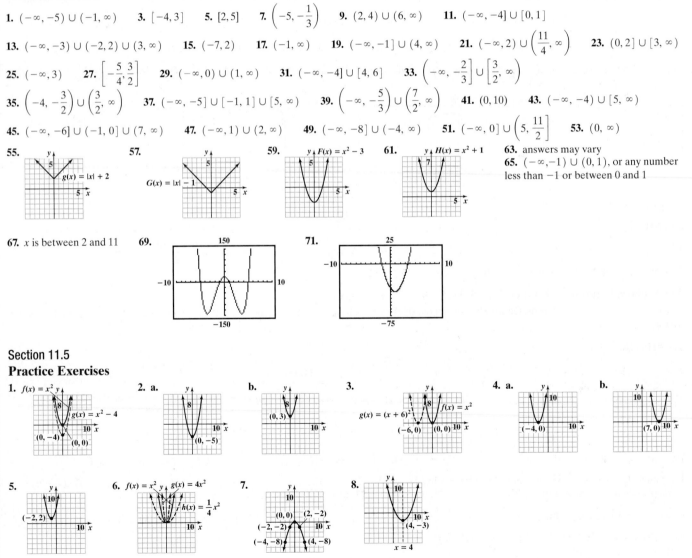

55. **57.** **59.** **61.** **63.** answers may vary
65. $(-\infty, -1) \cup (0, 1)$, or any number less than -1 or between 0 and 1

67. x is between 2 and 11 **69.** **71.**

Section 11.5
Practice Exercises

1. $f(x) = x^2$; $g(x) = x^2 - 4$ **2. a.** **b.** $(0, 3)$; $(0, -5)$ **3.** $g(x) = (x + 6)^2$; $f(x) = x^2$ **4. a.** $(-4, 0)$ **b.** $(7, 0)$

5. $(-2, 2)$ **6.** $f(x) = x^2$; $g(x) = 4x^2$; $h(x) = \dfrac{1}{4}x^2$ **7.** **8.**

Graphing Calculator Explorations 11.5

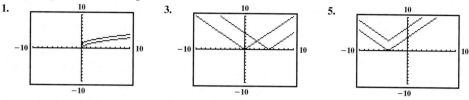

1. **3.** **5.**

Vocabulary, Readiness & Video Check 11.5

1. quadratic **3.** upward **5.** lowest **7.** $(0, 0)$ **9.** $(2, 0)$ **11.** $(0, 3)$ **13.** $(-1, 5)$ **15.** Graphs of the form $f(x) = x^2 + k$ shift up or down the y-axis k units from $y = x^2$; the y-intercept. **17.** The vertex, (h, k), and the axis of symmetry, $x = h$; the basic shape of $y = x^2$ does not change. **19.** the coordinates of the vertex, whether the graph opens upward or downward, whether the graph is narrower or wider than $y = x^2$, and the graph's axis of symmetry

Exercise Set 11.5

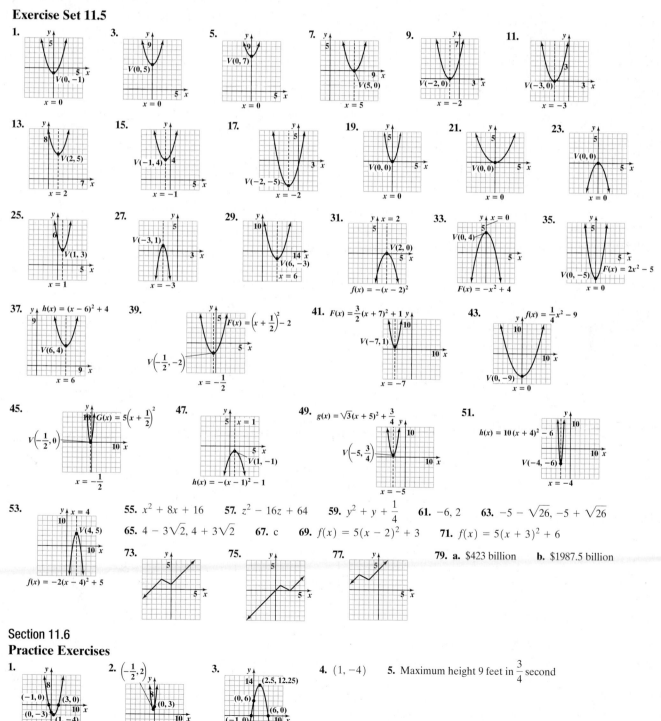

55. $x^2 + 8x + 16$ **57.** $z^2 - 16z + 64$ **59.** $y^2 + y + \dfrac{1}{4}$ **61.** $-6, 2$ **63.** $-5 - \sqrt{26}, -5 + \sqrt{26}$

65. $4 - 3\sqrt{2}, 4 + 3\sqrt{2}$ **67.** c **69.** $f(x) = 5(x - 2)^2 + 3$ **71.** $f(x) = 5(x + 3)^2 + 6$

79. a. $423 billion **b.** $1987.5 billion

Section 11.6
Practice Exercises

4. $(1, -4)$ **5.** Maximum height 9 feet in $\dfrac{3}{4}$ second

Vocabulary, Readiness & Video Check 11.6

1. (h, k) **3.** We can immediately identify the vertex (h, k), whether the parabola opens upward or downward, and know its axis of symmetry; completing the square.   **5.** the vertex

Exercise Set 11.6

1. $0; 1$ **3.** $2; 1$ **5.** $1; 1$ **7.** down   **9.** up   **11.** $(-4, -9)$ **13.** $(5, 30)$ **15.** $(1, -2)$ **17.** $\left(\dfrac{1}{2}, \dfrac{5}{4}\right)$ **19.** D   **21.** B

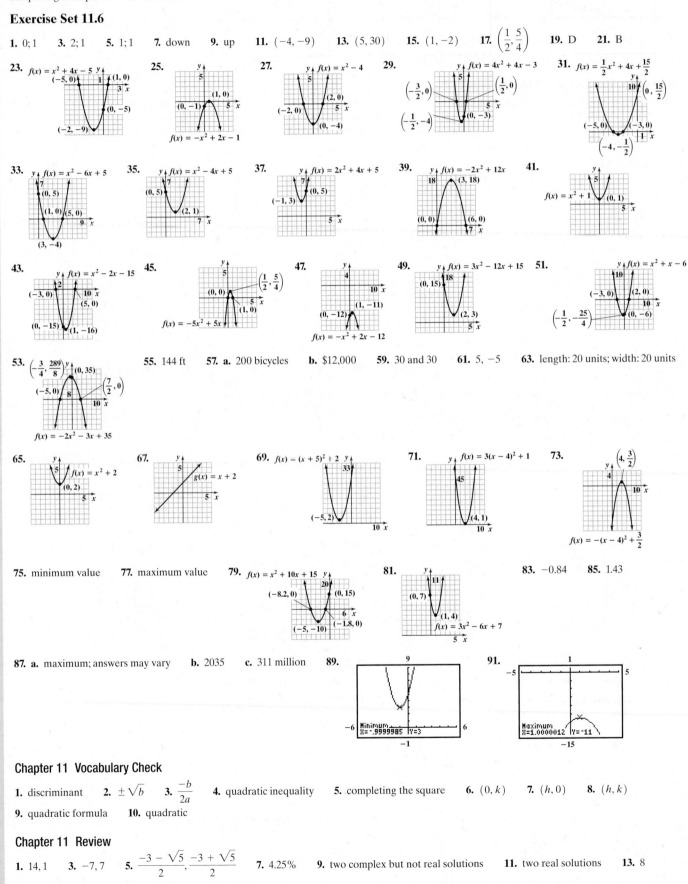

53. $\left(-\dfrac{3}{4}, \dfrac{289}{8}\right)$ **55.** 144 ft   **57. a.** 200 bicycles   **b.** \$12,000   **59.** 30 and 30   **61.** $5, -5$ **63.** length: 20 units; width: 20 units

75. minimum value   **77.** maximum value

83. -0.84 **85.** 1.43

87. a. maximum; answers may vary   **b.** 2035   **c.** 311 million   **89.**   **91.**

Chapter 11 Vocabulary Check

1. discriminant   **2.** $\pm\sqrt{b}$ **3.** $\dfrac{-b}{2a}$ **4.** quadratic inequality   **5.** completing the square   **6.** $(0, k)$ **7.** $(h, 0)$ **8.** (h, k) **9.** quadratic formula   **10.** quadratic

Chapter 11 Review

1. $14, 1$ **3.** $-7, 7$ **5.** $\dfrac{-3 - \sqrt{5}}{2}, \dfrac{-3 + \sqrt{5}}{2}$ **7.** 4.25% **9.** two complex but not real solutions   **11.** two real solutions   **13.** 8

15. $-\dfrac{5}{2}, 1$ **17.** $\dfrac{5 - i\sqrt{143}}{12}, \dfrac{5 + i\sqrt{143}}{12}$ **19. a.** 20 ft   **b.** $\dfrac{15 + \sqrt{321}}{16}$ sec; 2.1 sec   **21.** $3, \dfrac{-3 - 3i\sqrt{3}}{2}, \dfrac{-3 + 3i\sqrt{3}}{2}$ **23.** $\dfrac{2}{3}, 5$ **25.** $1, 125$

27. $-1, 1, -i, i$ **29.** Jerome: 10.5 hr; Tim: 9.5 hr   **31.** $[-5, 5]$ **33.** $[-5, -2] \cup [2, 5]$ **35.** $(5, 6)$ **37.** $(-\infty, -5] \cup [-2, 6]$ **39.** $(-\infty, 0)$

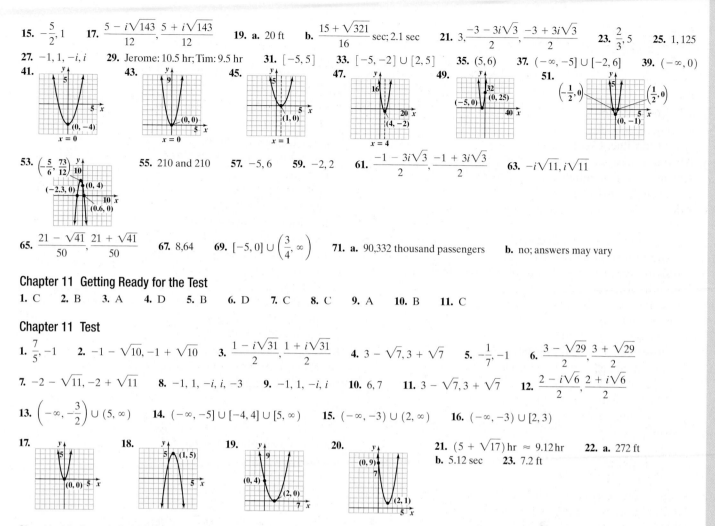

41.   **43.**   **45.**   **47.**   **49.**   **51.**

53. $\left(-\dfrac{5}{6}, \dfrac{73}{12}\right)$ **55.** 210 and 210   **57.** $-5, 6$ **59.** $-2, 2$ **61.** $\dfrac{-1 - 3i\sqrt{3}}{2}, \dfrac{-1 + 3i\sqrt{3}}{2}$ **63.** $-i\sqrt{11}, i\sqrt{11}$

65. $\dfrac{21 - \sqrt{41}}{50}, \dfrac{21 + \sqrt{41}}{50}$ **67.** 8, 64   **69.** $[-5, 0] \cup \left(\dfrac{3}{4}, \infty\right)$ **71. a.** 90,332 thousand passengers   **b.** no; answers may vary

Chapter 11 Getting Ready for the Test

1. C   **2.** B   **3.** A   **4.** D   **5.** B   **6.** D   **7.** C   **8.** C   **9.** A   **10.** B   **11.** C

Chapter 11 Test

1. $\dfrac{7}{5}, -1$ **2.** $-1 - \sqrt{10}, -1 + \sqrt{10}$ **3.** $\dfrac{1 - i\sqrt{31}}{2}, \dfrac{1 + i\sqrt{31}}{2}$ **4.** $3 - \sqrt{7}, 3 + \sqrt{7}$ **5.** $-\dfrac{1}{7}, -1$ **6.** $\dfrac{3 - \sqrt{29}}{2}, \dfrac{3 + \sqrt{29}}{2}$

7. $-2 - \sqrt{11}, -2 + \sqrt{11}$ **8.** $-1, 1, -i, i, -3$ **9.** $-1, 1, -i, i$ **10.** $6, 7$ **11.** $3 - \sqrt{7}, 3 + \sqrt{7}$ **12.** $\dfrac{2 - i\sqrt{6}}{2}, \dfrac{2 + i\sqrt{6}}{2}$

13. $\left(-\infty, -\dfrac{3}{2}\right) \cup (5, \infty)$ **14.** $(-\infty, -5] \cup [-4, 4] \cup [5, \infty)$ **15.** $(-\infty, -3) \cup (2, \infty)$ **16.** $(-\infty, -3) \cup [2, 3)$

17.   **18.**   **19.**   **20.**   **21.** $(5 + \sqrt{17})$ hr ≈ 9.12 hr   **22. a.** 272 ft   **b.** 5.12 sec   **23.** 7.2 ft

Chapter 11 Cumulative Review

1. a. $\dfrac{1}{2}$ **b.** 19; Sec. 1.6, Ex. 6   **3. a.** $5x + 7$ **b.** $-4a - 1$ **c.** $4y - 3y^2$ **d.** $7.3x - 6$ **e.** $\dfrac{1}{2}b$; Sec. 2.1, Ex. 4   **5.** no solution; $\{\ \}$ or $\varnothing$; Sec. 4.1, Ex. 5

7. $(-2, 0)$; Sec. 4.2, Ex. 4   **9. a.** x^3 **b.** 256   **c.** -27 **d.** cannot be simplified   **e.** $2x^4y$; Sec. 5.1, Ex. 9   **11. a.** 5   **b.** 5; Sec. 5.7, Ex. 3

13. $-6, -\dfrac{3}{2}, \dfrac{1}{5}$; Sec. 6.6, Ex. 9   **15.** $\dfrac{1}{5x - 1}$; Sec. 7.1, Ex. 2a   **17.** $\dfrac{xy + 2x^3}{y - 1}$; Sec. 7.7, Ex. 3   **19.** $(2m^2 - 1)^2$; Sec. 6.3, Ex. 10   **21.** -10 and 7; Sec.

6.7, Ex. 2   **23. a.** $5x\sqrt{x}$ **b.** $3x^2y^2\sqrt[3]{2y^2}$ **c.** $3z^2\sqrt[4]{z^3}$; Sec. 10.3, Ex. 4   **25. a.** $\dfrac{2\sqrt{5}}{5}$ **b.** $\dfrac{8\sqrt{x}}{3x}$ **c.** $\dfrac{\sqrt[3]{4}}{2}$; Sec. 10.5, Ex. 1   **27.** $\dfrac{2}{9}$; Sec. 10.6, Ex. 5

29. -5; Sec. 7.5, Ex. 1   **31.** -5; Sec. 7.6, Ex. 5   **33.** $k = \dfrac{1}{6}; y = \dfrac{1}{6}x$; Sec. 8.4, Ex. 1   **35. a.** 3   **b.** $|x|$ **c.** $|x - 2|$ **d.** -5 **e.** $2x - 7$

f. $5|x|$ **g.** $|x + 1|$; Sec. 10.1, Ex. 5   **37. a.** $\sqrt{x}$ **b.** $\sqrt[3]{5}$ **c.** $\sqrt{rs^3}$; Sec. 10.2, Ex. 7   **39. a.** $\dfrac{1}{2} + \dfrac{3}{2}i$ **b.** $0 - \dfrac{7}{3}i$; Sec. 10.7, Ex. 5

41. $-1 + 2\sqrt{3}, -1 - 2\sqrt{3}$; Sec. 11.1, Ex. 3   **43.** 9; Sec. 11.3, Ex. 1

Index

A

$a^{-m/n}$, 606–607, 651
$a^{1/2}$, 605, 651
Absolute value, 13–14, 70, 567
Absolute value equations, 567–570, 588–589
Absolute value inequalities, 572–576, 589
Acute angles, 908
Addends, 36–37, 52
Addition
  associative property of, 62–63, 72
  commutative property of, 62, 72
  distributive property of multiplication over, 63–65, 73
  identity for, 65–66, 73
  of complex numbers, 645, 653
  of decimals, 861
  of fractions, 20–22, 70
  of functions, 723–724, 726, 780
  of polynomials, 327–329, 330, 370
  of radicals, 620–622, 652
  of rational expressions, 464–468, 472–475, 507–508
  of real numbers, 36–40, 45–46, 71–72
  problem solving using, 39–40
  words/phrases for, 31
Addition method, for solving systems of linear equations, 268–272, 302
Addition property of equality, 87–90, 91–92, 160
Addition property of inequality, 148–149, 163
Additive inverses, 40–41, 65, 66, 72
Adjacent angles, 909
Algebra of functions, 723–724, 780
Algebraic expressions
  defined, 29, 71
  evaluation of, 29–30, 46–47, 57–58, 71
  simplifying, 79–83, 159, 868–870
  translation of phrases into, 31–32
  words/phrases written as, 83, 92–93, 868–870
All real numbers, notation for, 102
Alternate interior angles, 909
$a^{m/n}$, 605–606, 651
Angles, 48, 908, 909
Applications. *See* Applications index; Problem solving
Approximation
  decimal, 597
  of common logarithms, 767
  of natural logarithms, 769
  of square roots, 597
Area, 117
Arithmetic sequences, 829–832, 842–843, 854, 855
Array of signs, 902
Associative properties of addition/multiplication, 62–63, 72
Asymptotes, 803
$ax^2 + bx + c$, 394–400, 402–406, 437
Axis of symmetry, 698–703, 716

B

Balancing scales, 87
Bar graphs, 172
Bases, exponential, 26, 54, 71, 311, 313
Binomial theorem, 851–852, 855
Binomials
  defined, 322–323, 369
  expansion of, 849–852
  factorials and, 850–851, 855
  factoring, 407–411, 437
  FOIL method for, 341–343, 370
  formula for, 851
  nth terms of, 852
  Pascal's triangle for, 849–850
  squaring, 342–343, 370
Boundary lines, 579–582
Boyle's law, 545
Brackets, in order of operations, 29, 45
Broken-line graphs, 173

C

Calculators. *See* Graphing calculators
Cartesian coordinate system, 878
Center
  of circles, 794, 795–796
  of ellipses, 800, 801
  of hyperbolas, 802, 804
Central tendency, measures of, 906–907
Change of base formula, 771
Circles
  center of, 794, 795–796
  graphing, 794–795, 797, 807, 818
  radius of, 794, 795–796
  standard form of, 794, 807
  writing equations of, 796
Coefficients, 79, 159, 322, 369
Columns, of matrices, 894
Combined variation, problem solving with, 546–548, 553
Combining like terms, 80–81, 159
Common denominators, 464–465, 507. *See also* Least common denominators (LCDs)
Common difference, 829, 854
Common factors, 18–19, 449. *See also* Greatest common factor (GCF)
Common logarithms, 767–769, 782
Common ratio, 832, 855
Common terms, 449
Commutative properties of addition/ multiplication, 62, 72
Complementary angles, 48, 908
Completing the square, 663–665, 714
Complex conjugates, 646, 654

Complex fractions
   defined, 499
   least common denominators of, 501–502, 865
   simplifying, 499–503, 509
Complex number system, 643
Complex numbers, 643–648, 653–654
Composite functions, 724–726, 780
Composite numbers, 18
Compound inequalities
   compact form of, 561, 562
   defined, 560, 588
   intersection of two sets of, 560, 588
   solving, 152–154, 164, 560–564, 588
   union of two sets of, 563, 588
Compound interest formula, 666
Congruent triangles, 910–911
Conic sections. *See also* Parabolas
   circles, 794–797, 807, 818
   defined, 791
   ellipses, 800–802, 804, 807, 818
   hyperbolas, 802–804, 807, 818–819
Conjugates
   complex, 646, 654
   defined, 628, 652
   rationalizing denominators and numerators using, 628–629, 630
Consecutive integers
   algebraic expressions with, 93, 868
   problem solving for, 110–111, 429–430
Consistent systems of linear equations, 255, 256, 257, 276, 301
Constant of proportionality, 542, 544, 546
Constant of variation, 542, 544, 546
Constants
   defined, 322
   degree of, 323
   terms, 322, 421
Conversions
   measurements, 460–461
   temperature, 117, 119–120
Coordinate plane, 174–175, 241–242, 878
Coplanar lines, 909
Corner points, 583
Corresponding angles, 909
Cramer's rule, 899, 900–901, 903–904
Cross products, 487–488, 508
Cube roots
   defined, 597, 651
   finding, 597–598
   graphing, 600–601
   of perfect cube, 614
   of real numbers, 597, 651
   simplifying, 614–615
Cubes
   factoring sum or difference of, 410–411
   negative, 598
   perfect, 614, 630

D

Decimal approximations, 597

Decimals
   addition of, 861
   division of, 861
   in linear equations, 100–101
   multiplication of, 54, 861
   rational and irrational numbers written as, 11
   subtraction of, 861
   table of, 863
Denominators. *See also* Least common denominators (LCDs)
   common, 464–465
   defined, 17, 70
   of rational expressions, 464–468, 472–475, 507–508
   rationalizing, 626–629, 652
   unlike, 472–475, 507–508
Dependent equations, 256, 257, 276, 301
Dependent variables, 234
Descending powers, of polynomials, 322
Determinants, solving equations with, 899–904
Diameter, of circles, 794
Difference of squares, 343, 407–409
Difference, common, 829
Direct translation problems, 106–107
Direct variation, problem solving with, 542–544, 553
Discount problems, 131
Discriminants, 674–675
Distance formula, 117, 140, 492, 616–618, 651
Distance problems, 140–142, 492–494, 616–618
Distributive property
   for multiplying polynomials, 335–336
   for parenthesis removal, 81–82, 89, 159
   in combining like terms, 80
   of multiplication over addition, 63–65, 73
Dividends, 56, 358
Division
   by zero, 56
   long, 358–361
   of complex numbers, 646–647, 654
   of decimals, 861
   of fractions, 20, 55–57, 70
   of functions, 723–724, 780
   of polynomials, 357–361, 364–366, 371
   of rational expressions, 457–459, 507
   of real numbers, 55–57, 72
   problem solving using, 58
   symbol for, 56
   synthetic, 364–366, 371
   words/phrases for, 31
Divisors, 56, 360
Domain, 230, 235–236, 244, 445–446, 451

E

Elements
   of matrices, 894
   of sets, 8, 69
Elimination method
   for linear equations, 268–272, 277–280, 303
   for nonlinear equations, 810–811
Ellipses, 800–802, 804, 807, 818
Equal symbol, 8, 30, 70

Equality
    addition property of, 87–90, 91–92, 160
    logarithmic property of, 773, 782
    multiplication property of, 90–92, 160
    words/phrases for, 31
Equations. *See also* Linear equations in one variable; Linear
        equations in two variables; Quadratic equations;
        Rational equations; Systems of linear equations
    absolute value, 567–570, 588–589
    defined, 30, 71, 87
    dependent, 256, 257, 276, 301
    determinants for solving, 899–904
    equivalent, 87, 160
    false, 101
    graphs and graphing utilities for, 187, 202, 891–892
    in point-slope form, 222–223, 244, 518
    independent, 256, 257, 301
    matrices for solving, 894–898
    no solutions to, 101
    nonlinear systems of, 808–811, 819
    of circles, 796
    of exponential functions, 741–742, 773–774
    of inverse functions, 732–734
    of lines, 220–225
    of logarithmic functions, 755–756, 774–775
    ordered pairs as solution to, 177–181, 188–193, 229, 230, 242
    ordered triples as solution to, 276, 302
    percent, 129–130
    radical, 633–636
    slope-intercept form for graphing/writing,
        220–223, 244, 518
    solutions to, 30–31, 71, 87, 97–102, 160, 177–178
    steps to solve, 927–928
    translating sentences into, 32
    variables, solving for, 122
    with rational expressions, 478–482, 508, 885–886
Equivalent equations, 87, 160
Equivalent fractions, 21, 70
Estimation. *See* Approximation
Exam preparation, 5, 916–917, 918, 922
Expanding process for finding determinants, 902
Expansion of binomials, 849–852
Exponential decay, 749–750, 781
Exponential expressions
    bases of, 26, 54, 71, 311, 313
    defined, 311
    evaluating, 26–27, 28, 311–312
    multiplying, 54
    on calculators, 33
    radical, 609
    simplifying, 313, 318–319, 350–351
Exponential functions, 739–745
    defined, 739, 781
    graphing, 739–741, 744–745
    modeling exponential growth and decay, 748–750, 781
    problem solving with, 742–744, 775–776
    solving, 741–742, 773–774
Exponential growth, 748–749, 781
Exponential notation, 26, 311

Exponents
    defined, 26, 71, 311, 369
    negative, 348–350, 370, 502–503
    power rule for, 314–316, 369, 633
    product rule for, 312–314, 369
    quotient rule for, 316–318, 348, 369
    rational, 605–609, 651
    summary of rules for, 350, 607, 651
    zero as, 318, 369
Expressions. *See* Algebraic expressions; Exponential
        expressions; Radical expressions; Rational expressions
Exterior angles, 909
Extraneous solutions, 633

F
Factored form, 379, 381
Factorials, 850–851, 855
Factoring
    binomials, 407–411, 437
    by grouping method, 383–385, 402–406, 436, 437
    defined, 379, 436
    difference of two squares, 407–409
    perfect square trinomials, 398–400, 437
    polynomials, 882–884
    quadratic equations, 418–422, 438
    strategies for, 414–416, 437–438, 882–884
    sum or difference of two cubes, 410–411
    trinomials of form $ax^2 + bx + c$, 394–400, 402–406, 437
    trinomials of form $x^2 + bx + c$, 387–391, 436
Factoring out, 379, 381–383, 391, 398
Factors. *See also* Greatest common factor (GCF)
    common, 18–19, 449
    defined, 17, 70, 379
    zero as, 53
False equations, 101
Finite sequences, 825, 854
Finite series, 837
Focus
    of ellipses, 800
    of hyperbolas, 802
FOIL method, 341–343, 370
Formulas
    area, 117
    binomial, 851
    change of base, 771
    defined, 117, 161
    discount, 131
    distance, 117, 140, 492, 616–618, 651
    for problem solving, 117–123, 161
    interest, 117, 666
    mark-up, 131
    midpoint, 616, 617–618, 652
    perimeter, 117
    Pythagorean theorem, 430, 637, 912
    quadratic, 671–674, 715
    temperature conversion, 117
    variables in, 121–123, 161
    vertex, 709–710
    volume, 117

Fourth roots, 614–615
Fraction bars, 17, 27, 28
Fractions
    addition of, 20–22, 70
    complex, 499–503, 509
    defined, 17, 70
    division of, 20, 55–57, 70
    equivalent, 21, 70
    fundamental principle of, 18
    improper, 22
    in linear equations, 99–100
    in lowest terms, 17, 70
    multiplication of, 19–20, 54, 70, 455
    reciprocal of, 20, 70
    simplified, 17, 70
    subtraction of, 20–22, 70
    table of, 863
    unit, 460, 461
Functions
    addition of, 723–724, 726, 780
    algebra of, 723–724, 780
    composite, 724–726, 780
    defined, 230, 244
    division of, 723–724, 780
    domain of, 230, 235–236, 244, 445–446, 451
    exponential (*See* Exponential functions)
    graphing, 231, 233–234
    horizontal line test for, 730–731, 780
    identifying, 230–231
    inverse, 731–735, 780
    linear, 232, 517–521, 535–536, 552
    linear equations as, 232
    logarithmic (*See* Logarithmic functions)
    multiplication of, 723–724, 780
    nonlinear, 528–530, 536, 553
    notation for, 234–236, 244, 324–325, 369, 518–519,
        525–528
    one-to-one, 728–729, 731, 735, 780
    piecewise-defined, 534–535, 553
    radical, 600, 651
    range of, 230, 236, 244
    relations as, 230–231
    subtraction of, 723–724, 780
    vertical line test for, 231–234, 244, 517
Fundamental principle of fractions, 18
Fundamental principle of rational
    expressions, 447

G
Gaussian Mirror/Lens Formula, 444
General terms, 825–827, 830, 833, 854, 855
Geometric sequences, 832–834, 844–846, 855
Geometry. *See also* Lines; Triangles
    angles, 48, 909
    area, 117
    defined, 908
    plane figures, 908–909
    polygons, 910
    volume, 117

Graphing calculators
    addition of functions on, 726
    circles on, 797
    domain of rational functions on, 451
    ellipses on, 804
    equations containing rational expressions on, 482
    exponential expressions on, 33
    expression evaluation on, 411
    features of, 193
    for linear equation solutions, 102
    for sketching graphs of multiple equations on
        same axes, 213–214, 530
    for solving equations, 187, 202, 891–892
    interest on, 776–777
    interpreting window settings on, 889–890
    inverse functions on, 735
    linear functions on, 521
    negative numbers on, 58–59
    order of operations on, 33
    patterns on, 225–226
    polynomial addition and subtraction on, 330
    quadratic equations on, 423–424, 667–668, 704
    radical equations on, 638
    real number operations with, 59
    scientific notation on, 354
    square viewing windows on, 891–892
    systems of linear equations on, 258
    TRACE feature, 744–745
    viewing windows of, 889–892
Graphing notation, 148
Graphs and graphing. *See also* Graphing calculators
    bar, 172
    circles, 794–795, 797, 807, 818
    ellipses, 800–802, 807, 818
    exponential functions, 739–741, 744–745
    for systems of linear equations, 254–257
    for systems of linear inequalities, 583–584, 590
    functions, 231, 233–234
    horizontal and vertical lines, 200–201
    hyperbolas, 802–804, 807, 818–819
    inverse functions, 734
    line, 173
    linear equations in two variables, 187–193, 198–200,
        879–881
    linear functions, 517–518, 535–536, 552
    linear inequalities, 148, 149, 150, 151–152,
        579–582, 589
    logarithmic functions, 756–758
    nonlinear functions, 528–530, 536, 553
    nonlinear inequalities, 813–816, 819
    ordered pairs on, 174–181, 241, 877–879
    paired data, 176–177
    parabolas, 698–703, 706–709, 716, 791–794, 807,
        817–818
    piecewise-defined functions, 534–535, 553
    quadratic equations, 423, 698–703, 706–709, 716
    reading, 172–173, 241
    reflecting, 539–540, 553
    relations, 231

Graphs and graphing (*continued*)
   slope-intercept form and, 208, 220–221
   square and cube root functions, 536–537, 600–601
   vertical and horizontal shifting on, 537–539, 553
Greatest common factor (GCF)
   defined, 379
   factoring out, 381–383, 391, 398, 436
   finding, 379–381
Grouping method
   defined, 402
   factoring by, 383–385, 402–406, 436, 437
Grouping symbols, 27–29

H

Half-life, 750
Half-planes, 579–582
Hooke's law, 543–544
Horizontal axis (*x*-axis), 174, 241, 539
Horizontal line test, 730–731, 780
Horizontal lines
   equations of, 224
   graphing, 200–201
   on coordinate plane, 201
   slope of, 209–210, 225, 243, 518
Horizontal shifting, 538–539, 553
Hyperbolas, 802–804, 807, 818–819
Hypotenuse, 430, 912

I

Identities
   for addition, 65–66, 73
   for multiplication, 65–66, 73
   of linear equations, 101, 102
Identity properties, 65–66, 73
Imaginary numbers, 643, 644, 647–648
Imaginary units, 643, 644, 647–648
Improper fractions, 22
Inconsistent systems of linear equations, 255, 256, 257, 276, 301
Independent equations, 256, 257, 301
Independent variables, 234
Index, 598, 599, 605, 837
Inequalities
   absolute value, 572–576, 589
   addition property of, 148–149, 163
   compound, 152–154, 164, 560–564
   linear (*See* Linear inequalities)
   multiplication property of, 149–150, 163
   nonlinear, 691–695, 715–716, 813–816, 819
   on number line, 148
   ordered pairs as solution to, 578
   polynomial, 691–694, 715
   quadratic, 691
   rational, 694–695, 715–716
   simple, 152
   solutions of, 147–148, 929
Inequality symbols, 8–9, 70, 147, 149
Infinite sequences, 825, 845–846, 854
Infinite series, 837

Integers
   consecutive, 93, 110–111, 429–430, 868
   defined, 10, 69
   greatest common factor of list of, 379–380, 436
   negative, 10
   on number lines, 10–11
   positive, 10
   quotient of, 11
Intercepts. *See also x*-intercepts*; y*-intercepts
   defined, 242
   for graphing linear equations, 198–200
   identifying, 197–198
Interest problems, 117, 143–144, 666–667
Interior angles, 909
Intersecting lines, 909
Intersection of two sets, 560, 588
Interval notation, 148, 149, 153–154, 561, 562
Inverse functions, 731–735, 780
Inverse variation, problem solving with, 544–545, 553
Inverses
   additive, 40–41, 65, 66, 72
   multiplicative, 55, 66, 73
Irrational numbers, 11, 69, 597

J

Joint variation, problem solving with, 545–546, 553

L

Least common denominators (LCDs)
   defined, 21–22, 466
   of complex fractions, 501–502, 865
   of rational expressions, 466–468, 472–475, 507
Legs, of right triangles, 430, 912
Like radicals, 620, 652
Like terms, 79–81, 159, 325–326
Line graphs, 173
Linear equations in one variable
   decimals in, 100–101
   fractions in, 99–100
   infinite solutions to, 101
   no solutions to, 101
   on calculators, 102
   solving, 97–102, 160, 177–178, 865–867
   writing, 87
Linear equations in two variables
   as functions, 232
   defined, 187
   forms of, 225
   graphing, 187–193, 198–200, 879–881
   identifying, 187–188
   point-slope form of, 222–223, 225, 244
   problem solving with, 283–291
   slope-intercept form of, 208, 220–223, 225, 244
   solutions of, 177–178
   standard form of, 187, 225, 242
Linear equations in three variables
   problem solving with, 293–294
   solving systems of, 276–280, 302–303

Linear functions, 517–521
  graphing, 517–518, 535–536, 552
  linear equations as, 232
  of parallel and perpendicular lines, 520–521
  on graphing calculators, 521
  writing, 518–519, 552
Linear inequalities
  addition property of inequality and, 148–149, 163
  applications of, 154–155
  compound, 152–154, 164
  graphing solutions to, 148, 149, 150, 151–152,
    579–582, 589
  in one variable, 147, 151, 163
  in two variables, 578–582, 589
  multiplication property of inequality and, 149–150, 163
  solving, 147–155, 163–164, 582–584
  systems of, 582–584, 590
Lines
  boundary, 579–582
  coplanar, 909
  equations of, 220–225
  horizontal, 200–201, 209–210, 224, 225, 243, 518
  intersecting, 909
  parallel, 204, 210–212, 225, 243, 520–521, 909, 910
  perpendicular, 210–212, 225, 243, 520–521, 909
  slope of, 205–212, 243–244
  transversals, 909, 910
  vertical, 200–201, 209–210, 223, 225, 243
Logarithmic functions
  change of base formula for, 771
  common, 767–769, 782
  defined, 753, 756, 781, 782
  equality property of, 773, 782
  graphing, 756–758
  natural, 767, 769–770, 782
  notation for, 752–754
  power property of, 762, 764, 782
  problem solving with, 775–776
  product property of, 760–761, 762–764, 782
  properties of, 756, 760–764, 781, 782
  quotient property of, 761–762, 763, 764, 782
  solving, 755–756, 774–775
Logarithmic notation, 752–754
Long division, 358–361
Lowest terms
  of fractions, 17, 70
  of rational expressions, 447

M
Mark-up problems, 131
Mathematical statements, 8, 9–10
Mathematics class
  exam preparation in, 5, 916–917, 918, 922
  help in, 5, 922, 924
  homework assignments for, 920–922
  organizational skills for, 2, 918–919, 921
  positive attitude in, 2, 916
  preparation for, 2
  study skills builders for, 915–924
    textbook use in, 3–4, 923–924
    time management in, 6
    tips for success in, 2–6
Matrices
  solving equations with, 894–898
  square, 899
Mean, 906, 907
Measurement conversions, 460–461
Measures of central tendency, 906–907
Median, 906–907
Members, of sets, 8
Midpoint
  formula for, 616, 617–618, 652
  of diameter, 794
Minor, of determinants, 902
Mixed numbers, 22–23
Mixture problems, 133–134, 162
Mode, 906–907
Money problems, 142–143
Monomials, 322–323, 357–358, 369
Multiplication. *See also* Products
  associative property of, 62–63, 72
  commutative property of, 62, 72
  distributive property for polynomials,
    335–336
  distributive property over addition, 63–65, 73
  FOIL method of, 341–343, 370
  identity for, 65–66, 73
  of complex numbers, 645–646, 653
  of decimals, 861
  of exponential expressions, 54
  of fractions, 19–20, 54, 70, 455
  of functions, 723–724, 780
  of polynomials, 334–337, 341–345, 370
  of radicals, 623, 652
  of rational expressions, 455–457, 459, 507
  of real numbers, 52–54, 56, 72
  of sum and difference of two terms, 343–344, 370
  problem solving using, 58
  squaring, 342–343, 370
  symbol for, 17
  words/phrases for, 31
Multiplication property of equality, 90–92, 160
Multiplication property of inequality, 149–150, 163
Multiplicative inverses, 55, 66, 73

N
Natural logarithms, 767, 769–770, 782
Natural numbers, 8, 69
Negative exponents, 348–350, 370, 502–503
Negative infinity, 148
Negative integers, 10
Negative numbers
  cube root of, 598
  defined, 12
  on calculators, 58–59
Negative reciprocals, 211, 243
Negative square roots, 596, 598, 650
No solution, notation for, 101

Nonlinear functions, graphing, 528–530, 536, 553
Nonlinear inequalities
    graphing, 813–816, 819
    in one variable, 691–695, 715–716
    systems of, 814–816, 819
Nonlinear systems of equations, 808–811, 819
Notation. *See* Symbols/notation
nth roots, 598–599
nth terms of binomials, 852
Number lines
    defined, 70
    drawing, 8
    inequalities on, 148
    integers on, 10–11
    real numbers on, 11–12, 36–37
Numbers. *See also* Integers; Ordered pairs; Real
        numbers
    complex, 643–648, 653–654
    composite, 18
    imaginary, 643, 644, 647–648
    in scientific notation, 350–354
    irrational, 11, 69, 597
    mixed, 22–23
    natural, 8, 69
    negative, 12, 58–59, 598
    opposite of, 40–41
    positive, 12
    prime, 17–18
    rational, 11, 69, 445
    signed, 12
    unknown, 106–111, 285–286, 427–428, 490–491,
        870–871
    whole, 8, 10, 69
Numerators, 17, 70, 629–630
Numerical coefficients, 79, 159, 322, 369

O
Obtuse angles, 908
One-to-one functions, 728–729, 731, 735, 780
Opposites, 40–41, 65, 72
Order of operations
    in expression evaluation, 27–29, 45, 71
    on calculators, 33
Order property for real numbers, 13, 70
Ordered pairs
    as equation solutions, 177–181, 188–193,
        229, 230, 242
    as inequality solutions, 578
    data represented as, 176–177
    defined, 174
    in system of linear equations, 253
    on graphs, 174–181, 241, 877–879
    plotting, 174, 188–193, 241
Ordered triples
    as equation solutions, 276, 302
    in system of linear equations, 276, 302
Organizational skills, 2, 918–919, 921
Origin, on coordinate plane, 174, 241

P
Paired data, 176–177. *See also* Ordered pairs
Parabolas. *See also* Quadratic equations
    defined, 423, 536
    graphing, 698–703, 706–709, 716, 791–794, 807, 817–818
    standard form of, 791, 807
    vertex of, 698–703, 706–710, 716
Parallel lines
    cut by transversals, 910
    defined, 204, 210, 909
    finding equations of, 520–521
    slope of, 210–212, 225, 243
Parentheses
    distributive property in removal of, 81–82, 89, 159
    for replacement values, 47
    in multiplication of exponential expressions, 54
    in order of operations, 27, 28, 29, 45
Partial sums, 838–839, 842–846, 855
Pascal's triangle, 849–850
Percent problems, 129–133
    discount and mark-up, 131
    increase and decrease, 132–133, 872
    solving equations for, 129–130
    strategies to solve, 162
Percent table, 863, 871
Perfect cubes, 614, 630
Perfect square trinomials, 398–400, 406, 437
Perfect squares, 597, 614
Perimeter, formula for, 117
Perpendicular lines
    defined, 210–211, 909
    finding equations of, 520–521
    slope of, 210–212, 225, 243
Phrases. *See* Words/phrases
Piecewise-defined functions, 534–535, 553
Pixels, 889
Plane figures, 908–909
Point-slope form, 222–225, 244, 518
Polygons, 910
Polynomials. *See also* Binomials; Factoring; Trinomials
    adding, 327–329, 330, 370
    combining like terms of, 325–326
    defined, 322, 369
    degree of, 323–324, 369
    descending powers of, 322
    dividing, 357–361, 364–366, 371
    evaluating, 325
    factoring strategies for, 882–884
    FOIL method for, 341–343, 370
    function notation for, 324–325, 369
    inequalities, 691–694, 715
    monomials, 322–323, 357–358, 369
    multiplying, 334–337, 341–345, 370
    operations on, 881–882
    prime, 390
    quotients of, 445
    simplifying, 325–327
    squaring, 342–343, 370

subtracting, 328–329, 330, 370
types of, 322–323
Positive attitude, 2, 916
Positive integers, 10
Positive numbers, 12
Positive square roots, 519, 528, 650
Power property, of logarithmic functions, 762, 764, 782
Power rule, for exponents, 314–316, 369, 633
Power, in exponential expressions, 311
Price problems, 287–288
Prime factorization, 18
Prime numbers, 17–18
Prime polynomials, 390
Principal square roots, 528, 596, 650
Problem solving. *See also* Applications index
  combined variation and, 546–548, 553
  direct variation and, 542–544, 553
  distance problems, 140–142, 492–494, 616–618
  for consecutive integer problems, 110–111
  for direct translation problems, 106–107
  for unknown numbers, 106–111, 285–286, 427–428, 490–491, 870–871
  formulas for, 117–123, 161
  general strategy for, 106, 128, 140, 161, 163, 284
  interest problems, 117, 143–144, 666–667
  inverse variation and, 544–545, 553
  joint variation and, 545–546, 553
  mixture problems, 133–134, 162
  money problems, 142–143
  percent problems, 129–133, 162
  proportions for, 488–490, 508–509
  radical equations and, 633–638, 653
  steps for, 870–872
  variation and, 542–548, 553
  with addition, 39–40
  with division, 58
  with exponential functions, 742–744, 775–776
  with inequalities, 154–155
  with linear equations in two variables, 283–291
  with linear equations in three variables, 293–294
  with logarithmic functions, 775–776
  with multiplication, 58
  with point-slope form, 224–225
  with Pythagorean theorem, 430–431, 636–638, 913
  with quadratic equations, 426–431, 438–439, 666–667, 675–677, 684–686
  with rational equations, 490–491
  with rational functions, 450–451
  with sequences, 827
  with subtraction, 47
  with systems of linear equations, 283–294, 303–304
  work problems, 491–492
Product rule
  for exponents, 312–314, 369
  for radicals, 612, 614–615
  for square roots, 612
Products. *See also* Multiplication
  cross, 487–488, 508

defined, 17, 70
  logarithmic property of, 760–761, 762–764, 782
  power rule for, 315, 369
  special, 341–345, 370
  zero involved in, 53, 72
Proportionality, constant of, 542, 544, 546
Proportions
  defined, 486, 508
  for problem solving, 488–490, 508–509
  rational equations and, 487–488
  solving, 486–488
Pure imaginary numbers, 644
Pythagorean theorem
  distance formula and, 616–618
  formula for, 430, 637, 912
  problem solving with, 430–431, 636–638, 913

Q
Quadrants, on coordinate plane, 174
Quadratic equations. *See also* Parabolas
  completing the square to solve, 663–665, 714
  defined, 417, 661
  discriminant and, 674–675
  factoring to solve, 418–422, 438
  graphs of, 423, 698–703, 706–709, 716
  in two variables, 423
  minimum and maximum values, 710–711
  on graphing calculators, 423–424, 667–668, 704
  problem solving with, 426–431, 438–439, 666–667, 675–677, 684–686
  quadratic formula to solve, 671–674, 715
  solving, 661–665, 671–674, 681–684, 714–715, 865–867
  square root property to solve, 661–662, 671, 714
  standard form of, 417, 671, 672
  with degree greater than two, 421–422
  x-intercepts of graph of, 423
  zero factor property to solve, 418–420
Quadratic formula, 671–674, 715
Quadratic inequalities, 691
Quotient rule
  for exponents, 316–318, 348, 369
  for radicals, 613, 614, 615–616
  for square roots, 613
Quotients
  logarithmic property of, 761–762, 763, 764, 782
  of integers, 11
  of polynomials, 445
  of real numbers, 55–56, 72
  power rule for, 316, 369
  zero involved in, 56, 72

R
Radical equations
  on graphing calculators, 638
  power rule for, 633
  problem solving and, 633–638, 653
  solving, 633–636

Radical expressions
  defined, 596
  rationalizing denominators and numerators of,
    626–630, 652–653
  simplifying, 609, 612–616, 651–652
Radical functions, 600, 651
Radical sign, 596
Radicals. *See also* Roots; Square roots
  adding, 620–622, 652
  like, 620, 652
  multiplying, 623, 652
  product rule for, 612, 614–615
  quotient rule for, 613, 614, 615–616
  simplifying, 599–600, 609, 612–616, 651–652
  subtracting, 620–622, 652
  variables in, 599–600, 615–616
Radicands
  defined, 596
  perfect fourth powers of, 614
  perfect square, 597
Radius, of circles, 794, 795–796
Range, 230, 236, 244
Rate of change, 212–213, 243
Rational equations
  problem solving with, 490–491, 508–509
  proportions and, 487–488
  solving number problems modeled by, 490–491
Rational exponents, 605–609, 651
Rational expressions
  adding, 464–468, 472–475, 507–508
  common denominator of, 464–465, 507
  complex, 499–503
  defined, 445, 506
  dividing, 457–459, 507
  equations containing, 478–482, 508, 885–886
  evaluating, 445
  fundamental principle of, 447
  in lowest terms, 447
  least common denominators of, 466–468, 472–475, 507
  multiplying, 455–457, 459, 507
  operations on, 885–886
  simplifying, 446–450, 506
  subtracting, 464–468, 472–475, 507–508
  undefined, 445
  unlike denominators of, 472–475, 507–508
  writing equivalent forms of, 450, 468–469
Rational functions
  defined, 445, 506
  domain of, 445–446, 451
  problem solving with, 450–451
Rational inequalities, 694–695, 715–716
Rational numbers, 11, 69, 445
Rationalizing denominators, 626–629, 652
Rationalizing numerators, 629–630, 653
Ratios, 486, 508, 832
Real numbers
  absolute value of, 13–14, 70, 567
  addition of, 36–40, 45–46, 71–72

  cube root of, 597, 651
  defined, 11, 69
  division of, 55–57, 72
  multiplication of, 52–54, 56, 72
  negative, 12
  on calculators, 59
  on number lines, 11–12, 36–37
  order property for, 13, 70
  positive, 12
  properties of, 62–66, 72–73
  subtraction of, 44–47, 72
Reciprocals. *See also* Multiplicative inverses
  defined, 20, 66, 70, 73
  finding, 55
  inversely proportional, 544
  negative, 211, 243
Rectangular coordinate system, 174–175, 241–242, 878
Reflecting graphs, 539–540, 553
Relations
  as functions, 230–231
  defined, 230, 244
  graphs of, 231
Remainder theorem, 366, 371
Right angles, 908
Right triangles, 430, 912–913
Rise, 205
Roots. *See also* Cube roots; Radicals; Square roots
  fourth, 614–615
  *n*th, 598–599
Rounding. *See* Approximation
Row operations, 894
Row, of matrices, 894
Run, 205

S
Scales, balancing, 87
Scatter diagrams, 176–177
Scientific calculators. *See* Graphing calculators
Scientific notation
  converting to standard form, 352–353
  defined, 351
  on calculators, 354
  performing operations with, 353
  writing numbers in, 351–352, 371
Sequences. *See also* Series
  arithmetic, 829–832, 842–843, 854, 855
  defined, 825
  Fibonacci, 824, 829
  finding general terms of, 826–827
  finite, 825, 854
  geometric, 832–834, 844–846, 855
  infinite, 825, 845–846, 854
  notation for, 825, 854
  problem solving with, 827
  writing terms of, 825–826
Series. *See also* Sequences
  defined, 837, 855
  finite, 837

infinite, 837
    partial sums of, 838–839, 842–846, 855
    summation notation for identifying, 837–838
Sets
    defined, 8, 69
    identifying, 10–12
    of integers, 10, 69
    of irrational numbers, 11, 69
    of natural numbers, 8, 69
    of rational numbers, 11, 69
    of real numbers, 11, 69
    of whole numbers, 8, 69
Sigma, 837
Signed numbers, 12
Similar triangles, 489–490, 911–912
Simple inequalities, 152
Simple interest formula, 117, 143, 666
Simplification
    of algebraic expressions, 79–83, 159, 868–870
    of complex fractions, 499–503, 509
    of cube roots, 614–615
    of exponential expressions, 313, 318–319, 350–351
    of fractions, 17, 70
    of negative exponents, 348–350, 502–503
    of polynomials, 325–327
    of radicals, 599–600, 609, 612–616, 651–652
    of rational exponent expressions, 607–608
    of rational expressions, 446–450, 506
    review of, 925–926
Slope
    as rate of change, 212–213, 243
    defined, 205
    of horizontal and vertical lines, 209–210, 225, 243, 518
    of parallel and perpendicular lines, 210–212, 225, 243
    overview, 210
    point-slope form, 222–225, 244, 518
    strategies for finding, 205–212
    undefined, 209, 210
Slope-intercept form
    defined, 208, 220
    of linear equations in two variables, 208, 220–223, 225, 244
    to graph equations, 220–221
    to write equations, 221–223, 244, 518
Solutions
    extraneous, 633
    of absolute value equations, 567–570, 588–589
    of absolute value inequalities, 572–576, 589
    of compound inequalities, 152–154, 164, 560–564, 588
    of equations, 30–31, 71, 87, 97–102, 160, 177–178
    of exponential function equations, 741–742, 773–774
    of inequalities, 147–148, 929
    of linear equations in one variable, 97–102, 160, 177–178, 865–867
    of linear equations in two variables, 177–178
    of linear equations in three variables, 276–280, 302–303
    of linear inequalities, 147–155, 163–164, 582–584
    of logarithmic function equations, 755–756, 774–775
    of nonlinear systems of equations, 808–811, 819

    of quadratic equations, 661–665, 671–674, 681–684, 714–715, 865–867
    of radical equations, 633–636
    of systems of linear equations, 253, 301
    ordered pairs as, 177–181, 188–193, 229, 230, 242, 578
    ordered triples as, 276, 302
Special products
    defined, 342
    FOIL method for, 341–343, 370
    squaring binomials, 342–343, 370
    use of, 344–345
Square matrices, 899
Square root property, 661–662, 671, 714
Square roots. See also Radicals
    approximating, 597
    defined, 596
    finding, 528, 596–597
    graphing, 536–537, 600–601
    negative, 596, 598, 650
    positive, 528, 619, 650
    product rule for, 612
    quotient rule for, 613
    symbol for, 596
Squares
    completing the square, 663–665, 714
    difference of, 343, 407–409
    factoring difference of, 407–409
    of binomials, 342–343, 370
    perfect, 597, 614
Standard form
    of circles, 794, 807
    of ellipses, 800, 807
    of hyperbolas, 803, 807
    of linear equations, 187, 225, 242, 879
    of parabolas, 791, 807
    of quadratic equations, 417, 671, 672
    of quadratic inequalities, 691
    scientific notation converted to, 352–353
Standard window, in graphing utilities, 193
Straight angles, 908
Study groups, 2, 5
Study skills builders, 915–924
Substitution method
    for linear equations, 261–266, 277, 280, 302
    for nonlinear equations, 808–810
Subtraction
    of complex numbers, 645, 653
    of decimals, 861
    of fractions, 20–22, 70
    of functions, 723–724, 780
    of mixed numbers, 23
    of polynomials, 328–329, 330, 370
    of radicals, 620–622, 652
    of rational expressions, 464–468, 472–475, 507–508
    of real numbers, 44–47, 72
    problem solving using, 47
    words/phrases for, 31, 32
Sum and difference of two terms, multiplying, 343–344, 370

Sum or difference of two cubes, factoring, 410–411
Summation notation, 837–838, 855
Supplementary angles, 48, 908
Symbols/notations. *See also* Scientific notation; Variables; Words/phrases
  additive inverse, 41, 72
  all real numbers, 102
  angles, 909
  division, 56
  equal symbol, 8, 30, 70
  exponential, 26, 311
  for multiplication, 17
  for polynomials, 324–325, 369
  for sequences, 825, 854
  function, 234–236, 244, 324–325, 369, 518–519, 525–528
  graphing, 148
  grouping, 27–29
  in order of operations, 27–29
  inequality symbols, 8–9, 70, 147, 149
  interval, 148, 149, 153–154, 561, 562
  logarithmic, 752–754
  negative infinity, 148
  no solution, 101
  nth root, 598–599
  radical sign, 596
  summation, 837–838, 855
Symmetry, axis of, 698–703, 716
Synthetic division, 364–366, 371
Systems of linear equations, 253–294
  addition method for solving, 268–272, 302
  consistent, 255, 256, 257, 276, 301
  defined, 253
  determinants for solving, 900–902, 903–904
  elimination method for solving, 268–272, 277–280, 303
  graphing to solve, 254–257
  in three variables, 276–280, 302–303
  inconsistent, 255, 256, 257, 276, 301
  nongraph solutions to, 257–258
  on graphing calculators, 258
  problem solving with, 283–294, 303–304
  solutions of, 253, 301
  substitution method for solving, 261–266, 277, 280, 302
Systems of linear inequalities, 582–584, 590
Systems of nonlinear equations, 808–811, 819
Systems of nonlinear inequalities, 814–816, 819

T

Table of values, 179–181
Temperature conversion, 117, 119–120
Terms
  common, 449
  constant, 322, 421
  defined, 79, 322, 369
  degree of, 323–324, 369
  general, 825–827, 830, 833, 854, 855
  greatest common factor of list of, 380–381, 436
  like, 79–81, 159, 325–326
  nth terms of binomials, 852

  of infinite geometric sequences, 845
  of sequences, 825–827
  unlike, 79–80, 159, 325
Test preparation. *See* Exam preparation
Time management, 6
Transversals, 909, 910
Triangles
  congruent, 910–911
  defined, 910
  dimensions of, 430–431
  Pascal's, 849–850
  right, 430, 912–913
  similar, 489–490, 911–912
Trinomials
  defined, 322–323, 369
  of form $ax^2 + bx + c$, 394–400, 402–406, 437
  of form $x^2 + bx + c$, 387–391, 436, 663–665
  perfect square, 398–400, 406, 437
Tutoring services, 3, 5

U

Undefined expressions, 445
Undefined slope, 209, 210
Union of two sets, 563, 588
Unit fractions, 460, 461
Unknown numbers, 106–111, 285–286, 427–428, 490–491, 870–871
Unlike denominators, 472–475, 507–508
Unlike terms, 79–80, 159, 325

V

Variables
  defined, 29, 71
  dependent, 234
  in formulas, 121–123, 161
  independent, 234
  radicals containing, 599–600, 615–616
Variation
  combined, 546–548, 553
  constant of, 542, 544, 546
  direct, 542–544, 553
  inverse, 544–545, 553
  joint, 545–546, 553
  problem solving and, 542–548, 553
Vertex, 698–703, 706–710, 716
Vertex formula, 709–710
Vertical angles, 909
Vertical axis (y-axis), 174, 241, 698, 699, 702
Vertical format, for multiplying polynomials, 337
Vertical line test, 231–234, 244, 517
Vertical lines
  equations of, 223
  graphing, 200–201
  on coordinate plane, 201
  slope of, 209–210, 225, 243
Vertical shifting, 537–538, 553
Viewing windows, 889–892
Volume, 117

W

Whole numbers, 8, 10, 69
Window, in graphing utilities, 193
Words/phrases. *See also* Symbols/notations
    translating into algebraic expressions, 31–32
    writing as algebraic expressions, 83, 92–93, 868–870
Work problems, 491–492

X

x-axis, 174, 241, 539
x-coordinates, 174, 709, 878
x-intercepts
    defined, 197, 242, 880
    finding and plotting, 198–200, 243
    of quadratic equation graphs, 423, 706–707
$x^2 + bx + c$, 387–391, 436, 663–665

Y

y-axis, 174, 241, 698, 699, 702
y-coordinates, 174, 878
y-intercepts
    defined, 197, 242, 880
    finding and plotting, 198–200, 243
    of quadratic equation graphs, 706–707
    slope-intercept form and, 208

Z

Zero
    as exponent, 318, 369
    as identity element for addition, 65
    products involving, 53, 72
    quotients involving, 56, 72
Zero factor property, 418–420, 661